etrical Patterns and Designs by Spyros Horemis, Dover Publications Inc.

Terry Sincich
son Education, Inc.
ll
v Jersey 07458

United States of America

6 5 4 3 2 1

6

Pearson
Custom Publishing
is a division of

PEARSON

www.pearsonhighered.com

ISBN 10: 0-555-00648-4
ISBN 13: 978-0-555-00648-1

APPLET CORRELATION

Applet	Concept Illustrated	Description	Applet Exercise Number and Page
Sample from a population	This applet illustrates the concept that a sample should be representative of the population from which it is drawn. It may be used to assess how well a sample represents the population and the role that sample size plays in this process.	This applet pro... population. The user may specify the sample size and the shape of the population distribution. The applet reports the mean, median, and standard deviation of the sample and creates a plot of the sample.	**4.4**, p. 208; **5.1**, p. 231; **5.3**, p. 247
Sampling distributions	This applet illustrates the concept that the mean and standard deviation of the distribution of sample means are unbiased estimators of the mean and standard deviation of the population distribution. It may be used to compare the means and standard deviations of the distributions and to assess the effect of sample size. It can also be used to study sample proportions.	This applet simulates repeatedly choosing samples of a fixed size n from a population. The user may specify the size of the sample, the number of samples to be chosen, and the shape of the population distribution. The applet reports the means, medians, and standard deviations of both the sample means and the sample medians and also creates plots for both.	**6.1**, p. 295; **6.2**, p. 296
Random numbers	This applet illustrates the concept of randomness. It may be used to simulate selecting a random sample from a population by first assigning a unique integer to each experimental unit and then using the random numbers generated by the applet to determine the experimental units that will be included in the sample.	This applet generates random numbers from a range of integers specified by the user.	**1.1**, p. 18; **1.2**, p. 19; **3.6**, p. 172; **4.1**, p. 187; **5.2**, p. 231
Long run probability demonstrations:			
Simulating the probability of rolling a 6	This applet illustrates the concept that theoretical probabilities are long run experimental probabilities. It can be used to investigate the relationship between the theoretical and experimental probabilities of rolling a 6 as the number of times the die is rolled increases.	This applet simulates rolling a fair die. The user specifies the number of rolls. The applet reports the outcome of each roll and creates a frequency histogram for the outcomes. It also calculates and plots the proportion of 6s rolled during the simulation.	**3.1**, p. 124; **3.3**, p. 135; **3.4**, p. 135; **3.5**, p. 149
Simulating the probability of rolling a 3 or 4	This applet illustrates the concept that theoretical probabilities are long run experimental probabilities. It can be used to investigate the relationship between the theoretical and experimental probabilities of rolling a 3 or a 4 as the number of times the die is rolled increases.	This applet simulates rolling a fair die. The user specifies the number of rolls. The applet reports the outcome of each roll and creates a frequency histogram for the outcomes. It also calculates and plots the proportion of 3s and 4s rolled during the simulation.	**3.3**, p. 135; **3.4**, p. 135
Simulating the probability of a head with a fair coin	This applet illustrates the concept that theoretical probabilities are long run experimental probabilities. It can be used to investigate the relationship between the theoretical and experimental probabilities of getting heads as the number of times the coin is flipped increases.	This applet simulates flipping a fair coin. The user specifies the number of flips. The applet reports the outcome of each flip and creates a bar graph for the outcomes. It also calculates and plots the proportion of heads rolled during the simulation.	**3.2**, p. 124; **4.2**, p. 187
Simulating the probability of a head with an unfair coin $(P(H) = .02)$	This applet illustrates the concept that theoretical probabilities are long run experimental probabilities. It can be used to investigate the relationship between the theoretical and experimental probabilities of getting heads as the number of times an unfair coin is flipped increases.	This applet simulates flipping a coin where heads is less likely to occur than tails. The user specifies the number of flips. The applet reports the outcome of each flip and creates a bar graph for the outcomes. It also calculates and plots the proportion of heads rolled during the simulation.	**4.3**, p. 208
Simulating the probability of a head with an unfair coin $(P(H) = .08)$	This applet illustrates the concept that theoretical probabilities are long run experimental probabilities. It can be used to investigate the relationship between the theoretical and experimental probabilities of getting heads as the number of times an unfair coin is flipped increases.	This applet simulates flipping a coin where heads is more likely to occur than tails. The user specifies the number of flips. The applet reports the outcome of each flip and creates a bar graph for the outcomes. It also calculates and plots the proportion of heads rolled during the simulation.	**4.3**, p. 208
Simulating the stock market	This applet illustrates the concept that theoretical probabilities are long run experimental probabilities.	This applet simulates fluctuation in the stock market, where on any given day going up is equally likely as going down. The user specifies the number of days. The applet reports whether the stock market goes up or down each day and creates a bar graph for the outcomes. It also calculates and plots the proportion of days that the stock market goes up during the simulation.	**4.5**, p. 208

Applet	Concept Illustrated	Description	Applet Exercise Number and Page
Mean versus median	This applet illustrates the concept that the mean and the median of a data set respond differently to changes in the data. It can be used to investigate how skewness and outliers affect measures of central tendency.	This applet is designed to allow the user to visualize the relationship between the mean and median of a data set. The user may easily add and delete data points. The applet automatically updates the mean and median for each change in the data.	**2.1**, p. 34; **2.2**, p. 34; **2.3**, p. 34
Standard deviation	This applet illustrates the concept that standard deviation measures the spread of a data set. It can be used to investigate how the shape and spread of a distribution affect the standard deviation.	This applet is designed to allow the user to visualize the relationship between the mean and standard deviation of a data set. The user may easily add and delete data points. The applet automatically updates the mean and standard deviation for each change in the data.	**2.4**, p. 42; **2.5**, p. 42; **2.6**, p. 42; **2.7**, p. 63
Confidence intervals for a proportion	This applet illustrates the concept that not all confidence intervals contain the population proportion. It can be used to investigate the meaning of 95% and 99% confidence.	This applet generates confidence intervals for a population proportion. The user specifies the population proportion and the sample size. The applet simulates selecting 100 random samples from the population and finds the 95% and 99% confidence intervals for each sample. The confidence intervals are plotted and the number and proportion containing the true proportion are reported.	**7.5**, p. 331; **7.6**, p. 331
Confidence intervals for a mean (the impact of confidence level)	This applet illustrates the concept that not all confidence intervals contain the population mean. It can be used to investigate the meaning of 95% and 99% confidence.	This applet generates confidence intervals for a population mean. The user specifies the sample size, the shape of the distribution, the population mean, and the population standard deviation. The applet simulates selecting 100 random samples from the population and finds the 95% and 99% confidence intervals for each sample. The confidence intervals are plotted and the number and proportion containing the true mean are reported.	**7.1**, p. 313; **7.2**, p. 313
Confidence intervals for a mean (the impact of not knowing the standard deviation)	This applet illustrates the concept that confidence intervals obtained using the sample standard deviation are different from those obtained using the population standard deviation. It can be used to investigate the effect of not knowing the population standard deviation.	This applet generates confidence intervals for a population mean. The user specifies the sample size, the shape of the distribution, the population mean, and the population standard deviation. The applet simulates selecting 100 random samples from the population and finds the 95% z-interval and 95% t-interval for each sample. The confidence intervals are plotted and the number and proportion containing the true mean are reported.	**7.3**, p. 323; **7.4**, p. 323
Hypotheses tests for a proportion	This applet illustrates the concept that not all tests of hypotheses lead correctly to either rejecting or failing to reject the null hypothesis. It can be used to investigate the relationship between the level of confidence and the probabilities of making Type I and Type II errors.	This applet performs hypotheses tests for a population proportion. The user specifies the population proportion, the sample size, and the null and alternative hypotheses. The applet simulates selecting 100 random samples from the population and calculates and plots the z statistic and p-value for each sample. The applet reports the number and proportion of times the null hypothesis is rejected at both the .05 level and the .01 level.	**8.5**; p. 384; **8.6**; p. 384
Hypotheses tests for a mean	This applet illustrates the concept that not all tests of hypotheses lead correctly to either rejecting or failing to reject the null hypothesis. It can be used to investigate the relationship between the level of confidence and the probabilities of making Type I and Type II errors.	This applet performs hypotheses tests for a population mean. The user specifies the shape of the population distribution, the population mean and standard deviation, the sample size, and the null and alternative hypotheses. The applet simulates selecting 100 random samples from the population and calculates and plots the t statistic and p-value for each sample. The applet reports the number and proportion of times the null hypotheses is rejected at both the .05 level and the .01 level.	**8.1**, p. 357; **8.2**; p. 363; **8.3**; p. 363; **8.4**; p. 363
Correlation by eye	This applet illustrates the concept that the correlation coefficient measures the strength of a linear relationship between two variables. It helps the user learn to assess the strength of a linear relationship from a scattergram.	This applet computes the correlation coefficient r for a set of bivariate data plotted on a scattergram. The user can easily add or delete points and guess the value of r. The applet then compares the guess to its calculated value.	**11.2**, p. 599
Regression by eye	This applet illustrates the concept that the least squares regression line has a smaller SSE than any other line that might approximate a set of bivariate data. It helps the user learn to approximate the location of a regression line on a scattergram.	This applet computes the least squares regression line for a set of bivariate data plotted on a scattergram. The user can easily add or delete points and guess the location of the regression line by manipulating a line provided on the scattergram. The applet will then plot the least squares line. It displays the equations and the SSEs for both lines.	**11.1**, p. 573

STATISTI

James T. McClave • Terry S

Statistical Methods II — STA

Custom Edition for The University of Central Florida

Taken from:

Statistics, Eleventh Edition
by James T. McClave and Terry Sincich

Custom Publishing

New York   Boston   San Francisco
London   Toronto   Sydney   Tokyo   Singapore   Madrid
Mexico City   Munich   Paris   Cape Town   Hong Kong   Montreal

Preface

This 11th edition of *Statistics* is an introductory text emphasizing inference, with extensive coverage of data collection and analysis as needed to evaluate the reported results of statistical studies and make good decisions. As in earlier editions, the text stresses the development of statistical thinking, the assessment of credibility, and the value of the inferences made from data, both by those who consume and those who produce them. The book assumes a mathematical background of basic algebra.

The text incorporates the following features, developed from the American Statistical Association's Guidelines for Assessment and Instruction in Statistics Education (GAISE) Project:

- Emphasize statistical literacy and develop statistical thinking.
- Use real data in applications.
- Use technology for developing conceptual understanding and analyzing data.
- Foster active learning in the classroom.
- Stress conceptual understanding rather than mere knowledge of procedures.

A briefer version of the book, *A First Course in Statistics*, is available for single-semester courses that include minimal coverage of regression analysis, analysis of variance, and categorical data analysis.

NEW IN THE 11TH EDITION

- ***Over 1,200 Exercises, with Revisions and Updates to 30%*** Many new and updated exercises, based on contemporary studies and real data, have been added. Most of these exercises foster and promote critical thinking skills. In addition to "Learning the Mechanics" exercises, "Applied Exercises" are categorized into "Basic," "Intermediate," and "Advanced" at the end of each section.
- ***New Visual End-of-Chapter Summaries*** Flow graphs for selecting the appropriate statistical method, as well as boxed notes with key words, formulas, definitions, lists, and key concepts, are now provided at the end of each chapter. This graphical presentation is especially helpful to those students who are visual learners. It aids students by summarizing and reinforcing the important points from the chapter.
- ***"Hands-On" Activities for Students*** In each chapter, students are provided with several opportunities to participate in hands-on classroom activities, ranging from real data collection to formal statistical analysis. These powerful optional activities, based on the key concepts and procedures covered in the chapter, can be performed by students individually or as a class.
- ***Applet Exercises*** The text is accompanied by a CD containing applets (short JAVA computer programs). These point-and-click applets allow students to easily run simulations that demonstrate some of the more difficult statistical concepts (e.g., sampling distributions and confidence levels). Each chapter contains several optional applet exercises in the exercise sets. They are denoted with the following Applet icon: APPLET
- ***New Statistics in Action Cases*** Several new *Statistics in Action* cases have been added, each centering on a contemporary, controversial, or high-profile issue and the accompanying data. For example, we explore whether homework assigned to family members is really effective (Chapter 9), and we explore the relationship between how often and how much college students drink alcohol (Chapter 13).
- ***Nonparametrics Chapter on the CD That Accompanies the Text*** In accordance with the recommendations of reviewers and current users of the text, *Chapter 14*

(Nonparametric Statistics) is now available on a CD that accompanies the text or online at the Prentice Hall text website, www.prenhall.com/statistics. (Click on "Introductory Statistics" and then click on the listing for this textbook.)

- *Data files and Applets* The accompanying CD contains files for all of the data sets marked with a CD icon in the text. These include data sets for text examples, exercises, and *Statistics in Action* cases. All data files are saved in four different formats: MINITAB, SAS, SPSS, and ASCII (for easy importing into other statistical software packages). The CD also contains the applets used to illustrate statistical concepts.

Content-Specific Changes to This Edition

- *Chapter 11 (Simple Linear Regression)* Several sections from the previous edition have been combined and streamlined to shorten the chapter. The section on estimating σ^2 is now included in Section 11.3 ("Model Assumptions"), while the sections on the coefficients of correlation and determination are combined into a single section (Section 11.5).
- *Chapter 12 (Multiple Regression and Model Building)* Two sections from the previous edition have been reorganized: Section 12.2 now presents tests on the individual model parameters, as well as interpretations of their values; Section 12.3 discusses how to make inferences about the overall utility of the multiple-regression model.

TRADITIONAL STRENGTHS

We have maintained the pedagogical features of *Statistics* that we believe make it unique among introductory statistics texts. These features, which assist the student in achieving an overview of statistics and an understanding of its relevance to everyday life, are as follows:

- *Use Examples as a Teaching Device* Almost all new ideas are introduced and illustrated by a collection of over 125 data-based applications and examples. We believe that students understand definitions, generalizations, and theoretical concepts better after seeing an application. All examples have three components: (1) "Problem"; (2) "Solution"; and (3) "Look Back." This step-by-step process provides students with a defined structure by which to approach problems and enhances their problem-solving skills. The "Look Back" feature often gives helpful hints to apply in solving the problem and/or provides a further reflection or insight into the concept or procedure that is covered.
- *Now Work* A "Now Work" exercise follows each example. "Now Work" directs the student to an end-of-section exercise that is similar in style and concept to the text example. This gives students the opportunity to test and confirm their understanding.
- *Statistics in Action* Each chapter begins with a case study on an actual contemporary, controversial, or high-profile issue. Relevant research questions and data from the study are presented, and the proper analysis is demonstrated in short "Statistics in Action Revisited" sections throughout the chapter. These case studies motivate students to critically evaluate the findings and think through the statistical issues involved.
- *Real-Data Exercises* The text includes more than 1,200 exercises based on applications in a variety of disciplines and research areas. All the applied exercises employ the use of current real data extracted from a wide variety of current publications (e.g., newspapers, magazines, journals, and the Internet). Some students have difficulty learning the mechanics of statistical techniques when all problems are couched in terms of realistic applications. For this reason, all exercise sections are divided into five parts:

  Understanding the Principles These are short-answer exercises on definitions, concepts, and assumptions.

Learning the Mechanics Designed as straightforward applications of new concepts, these exercises allow students to test their ability to comprehend a mathematical concept or a definition.

Applying the Concepts—Basic Based on applications taken from a wide variety of journals, newspapers, and other sources, these short exercises help the student to begin developing the skills necessary to diagnose and analyze real-world problems.

Applying the Concepts—Intermediate Based on more detailed real-world applications, these exercises require the student to apply critical thinking and knowledge of the technique presented in the section.

Applying the Concepts—Advanced These more challenging real-data exercises require students to utilize their critical thinking skills.

- *Critical Thinking Challenges* At the end of the "Chapter Supplementary Exercises," students are asked to apply their critical thinking skills to solve one or two challenging real-life problems. These exercises expose students to real-world problems with solutions that are derived from careful, logical thought and selection of the appropriate statistical analysis tool

- *Exploring Data with Statistical Computer Software and the Graphing Calculator* Each statistical analysis method presented is demonstrated with the use of output from three leading Windows-based statistical software packages: SPSS, MINITAB, and SAS. In addition, output and keystroke instructions for the TI-84/ TI-83 Graphing Calculator are covered in optional boxes that are easy to locate throughout the text.

- *Statistical Software Printouts* These appear throughout the text in examples and exercises and include MINITAB, as well as SPSS and SAS printouts. Students are exposed to the computer printouts they will encounter in today's high tech world.

- *"Using Technology" Tutorials* MINITAB Software Tutorials appear at the end of each chapter and include point-and-click instructions (with screen shots) for using MINITAB. These tutorials are easily located and provide students with useful information on how to best use and maximize MINITAB statistical software.

- *Profiles of Statisticians in History* **(Biography)** Boxes featuring famous statisticians give a brief description of their achievements. With these profiles, students will develop an appreciation of each statistician's efforts and of the discipline of statistics as a whole.

FLEXIBILITY IN COVERAGE

The text is written to allow the instructor flexibility in coverage of topics through sections marked "optional" in relevant chapters. Suggestions for covering two topics, probability and regression, are as follows:

- *Probability and Counting Rules* One of the most troublesome aspects of an introductory business statistics course is the study of probability. Probability poses a challenge for instructors because they must decide on the level of presentation, and students find it a difficult subject to comprehend. We believe that one cause of these problems is the mixture of probability and counting rules that occurs in most introductory texts. Consequently, we have included the counting rules (with examples) in an appendix (Appendix A) rather than in the chapter (Chapter 3). Thus, the instructor can control the level of coverage of probability.

- *Multiple Regression and Model Building* This topic represents one of the most useful statistical tools for the solution of applied problems. Although an entire text could be devoted to regression modeling, we feel that we have presented coverage that is understandable, usable, and much more comprehensive that the presentations in other introductory statistics texts. We devote two full chapters to discussing the major types of inferences that can be derived from a regression analysis, showing how these results appear in the output from statistical software and, most important, selecting multiple-regression models to be used in an analysis. Thus, the instructor has the choice of a one-chapter coverage of simple linear regression (Chapter 11), a two-chapter treatment of simple and multiple regression (excluding the optional sections in Chapter 12 on model building), or complete coverage of regression analysis, including model building and regression diagnostics. This extensive coverage of such useful statistical tools will provide added evidence to the student of the relevance of statistics to real-world business problems.

- *Role of Calculus in Various Derivations* Although the text is designed for students who lack a calculus background, **footnotes** explain the role of calculus in various derivations. Footnotes are also used to inform the student about some of the theory underlying certain methods of analysis. The footnotes allow additional flexibility in the mathematical and theoretical level at which the material is presented.

ACKNOWLEDGMENTS

This book reflects the efforts of a great many people over a number of years. First, we would like to thank the following professors, whose reviews and comments on this and previous editions have contributed to the eleventh edition:

Bill Adamson, South Dakota State; Ibrahim Ahmad, Northern Illinois University; Roddy Akbari, Guilford Technical Community College; David Atkinson, Olivet Nazarene University; Mary Sue Beersman, Northeast Missouri State University; William H. Beyer, University of Akron; Marvin Bishop, Manhattan College; Patricia M. Buchanan, Pennsylvania State University; Dean S. Burbank, Gulf Coast Community College; Ann Cascarelle, St. Petersburg College; Kathryn Chaloner, University of Minnesota; Hanfeng Chen, Bowling Green State University; Gerardo Chin-Leo, The Everygreen State College; Linda Brant Collins, Iowa State University; Brant Deppa, Winona State University; John Dirkse, California State University—Bakersfield; N.B. Ebrahimi, Northern Illinois University; John Egenolf, University of Alaska—Anchorage; Dale Everson, University of Idaho; Christine Franklin, University of Georgia; Khadiga Gamgoum, Northern Virginia CC; Rudy Gideon, University of Montana; Victoria Marie Gribshaw, Seton Hill College; Larry Griffey, Florida Community College; David Groggel, Miami University at Oxford; Sneh Gulati, Florida International University; John E. Groves, California Polytechnic State University—San Luis Obispo; Dale K. Hathaway, Olivet Nazarene University; Shu-ping Hodgson, Central Michigan University; Jean L. Holton, Virginia Commonwealth University; Soon Hong, Grand Valley; Ina Parks S. Howell, Florida International University; Gary Itzkowitz, Rowan College of New Jersey; John H. Kellermeier, State University College at Plattsburgh; Golan Kibria, Florida International University; Timothy J. Killeen, University of Connecticut; William G. Koellner, Montclair State University; James R. Lackritz, San Diego State University; Diane Lambert, AT&T/Bell Laboratories; Edwin G. Landauer, Clackamas Community College; James Lang, Valencia Junior College; Glenn Larson, University of Regina; John J. Lefante, Jr., University of South Alabama; Pi-Erh Lin, Florida State University; R. Bruce Lind, University of Puget Sound; Rhonda Magel, North Dakota State University; Linda C. Malone, University of Central Florida; Allen E. Martin, California State University—Los Angeles; Rick Martinez, Foothill College; Brenda Masters, Oklahoma State University; Leslie Matekaitis, Cal Genetics; E. Donice McCune, Stephen F. Austin State University; Mark M. Meerschaert, University of Nevada—Reno; Greg Miller, Steven F. Austin State University; Satya Narayan Mishra, University of South Alabama; Kazemi Mohammed, UNC–Charlotte; Christopher Morrell, Loyola College in Maryland; Mir Mortazavi, Eastern New Mexico University; A. Mukherjea, University of South Florida; Steve Nimmo, Morningside College (Iowa); Susan Nolan, Seton Hall University; Thomas O'Gorman, Northern Illinois University; Bernard Ostle, University of Central Florida; William B. Owen, Central Washington University; Won J. Park, Wright State University;

John J. Peterson, Smith Kline & French Laboratories; Ronald Pierce, Eastern Kentucky University; Betty Rehfuss, North Dakota State University—Bottineau; Andrew Rosalsky, University of Florida; C. Bradley Russell, Clemson University; Rita Schillaber, University of Alberta; James R. Schott, University of Central Florida; Susan C. Schott, University of Central Florida; George Schultz, St. Petersburg Junior College; Carl James Schwarz, University of Manitoba; Mike Seyfried, Shippensburg University; Arvind K. Shah, University of South Alabama; Lewis Shoemaker, Millersville University; Sean Simpson, Westchester CC; Charles W. Sinclair, Portland State University; Robert K. Smidt, California Polytechnic State University—San Luis Obispo; Vasanth B. Solomon, Drake University; W. Robert Stephenson, Iowa State University; Thaddeus Tarpey, Wright State University; Kathy Taylor, Clackamas Community College; Barbara Treadwell, Western Michigan University; Dan Voss, Wright State University; Augustin Vukov, University of Toronto; Dennis D. Wackerly, University of Florida; Barbara Wainwright, Salisbury University; Matthew Wood, University of Missouri—Columbia.

REVIEWERS INVOLVED WITH THE 11TH EDITION OF *STATISTICS*

Dwight Galster, South Dakota State University
Geoffrey Exoo, Indiana State University
Yvonne Chueh, Central Washington University
Georgiana Baker, University of South Carolina
Mohammad Kazemi, University of North Carolina–Charlotte
John Holcomb, Cleveland State University
Mary Ehlers, Seattle University
Barbara Wainwright, Salisbury University
Rasul Khan, Cleveland State University
Jan Case, Jacksonville State University

OTHER CONTRIBUTORS

Special thanks are due to our ancillary authors, Nancy Boudreau and Mark Dummeldinger, who have worked with us for many years. C. Brad Davis provided the excellent student activities and applet exercises, while accuracy checker Sarah Streett helped us to ensure a highly accurate, clean text. Finally, the Prentice Hall staff of Petra Recter, Joanne Wendelken, Michael Bell, Dawn Murrin, Raegan Heerema, Bayani DeLeon, Thomas Benfatti, and Wayne Parkins helped greatly with all phases of the text development, production, and marketing efforts.

STUDENT RESOURCES

- **Student Solutions Manual**

  Includes complete worked-out solutions to the odd-numbered text exercises.

- **Technology Manual**

  Provides tutorial instruction and worked-out examples for the TI-84 Calculator, Excel, and MINITAB 14. Includes a CD with PHStat (Excel Plug-in).

MyStatLab™

MyStatLab (part of the MyMathLab® and MathXL® product family) is a text-specific, easily customized online course that integrates interactive multimedia instruction with textbook content. Powered by CourseCompass™ (Pearson Education's online teaching and learning environment) and MathXL (our online homework, tutorial, and assessment system), MyStatLab gives you the tools you need to deliver all or a portion of your course online, whether your students are in a lab setting or working from home. MyStatLab provides a rich and flexible set of course materials, featuring free-response tutorial exercises for unlimited practice and mastery. Students can also use online tools, such as video lectures and a multimedia textbook, to independently improve their understanding and performance. Instructors can use MyStatLab's homework and test managers to select and assign online exercises correlated directly to the textbook, and they can also create and assign their own online exercises and import TestGen® tests for added flexibility. MyStatLab's online gradebook—designed specifically for mathematics and statistics—automatically tracks students' homework and test results and gives the instructor control over how to calculate final grades. Instructor's can also add offline (paper-and-pencil) grades to the gradebook. MyStatLab is available to qualified adopters. For more information, contact your Pearson sales representative.

MathXL®

Math XL® for Statistics is a powerful online homework, tutorial, and assessment system that accompanies Pearson Education's textbooks in statistics. With MathXL for Statistics, instructors can create, edit, and assign online homework and tests using algorithmically generated exercises correlated at the objective level to the textbook. They can also create and assign their own online exercises and import TestGen tests for added flexibility. All student work is tracked in MathXL's online gradebook. Students can take chapter tests in MathXL and receive personalized study plans based on their test results. The study plan diagnoses weaknesses and links students directly to tutorial exercises for the objectives they need to study and retest. MathXL for Statistics is available to qualified adopters. For more information, visit our website at www.mathxl.com, or contact your Pearson sales representative.

Applications Index

Statistics

Inferences Based on a Single Sample

Estimation with Confidence Intervals

CONTENTS

STATISTICS IN ACTION

Speed—Can a High School Football Player Improve His Sprint Time?

USING TECHNOLOGY

Confidence Intervals with MINITAB

WHERE WE'VE BEEN

- Learned that populations are characterized by numerical descriptive measures—called *parameters*

- Found that decisions about population parameters are based on *statistics* computed from the sample

- Discovered that *inferences* about parameters are subject to uncertainty and that this uncertainty is reflected in the *sampling distribution* of a statistic

WHERE WE'RE GOING

- Estimate a population parameter (means or proportion) on the basis of a large sample selected from the population

- Use the sampling distribution of a statistic to form a confidence interval for the population parameter

- Show how to select the proper sample size for estimating a population parameter

STATISTICS IN ACTION

Speed—Can a High School Football Player Improve His Sprint Time?

The game of football requires both skill and speed. Consider that one of the key "statistics" for National Football League (NFL) coaches in evaluating college players for the NFL draft is a player's 40-yard sprint time. There are a plethora of drills available to football coaches that have been successfully used to aid a player's skill development. However, many coaches are under the impression that "you can't teach speed." Michael Gray and Jessica Sauerbeck, researchers at Northern Kentucky University, designed and tested a speed training program for junior varsity and varsity high school football players (The Sport Journal, Winter 2004).

The training program was carried out over a five-week period and incorporated a number of speed improvement drills, including 50-yard sprints run at varying speeds, high-knee running sprints, butt-kick sprints, "crazy legs" straddle runs, quick-feet drills, jumping, power skipping, and all-out sprinting. A sample of 38 high school athletes participated in the study. Each participant was timed in a 40-yard sprint prior to the start of the program and timed again after completing the program. The decrease in times (measured in seconds) was recorded for each athlete. These data, saved in the **SPRINT** file, are shown in Table SIA7.1. [*Note*: A negative decrease implies that the athlete's time after completion of the program was higher than his time prior to training.] The goal of the research is to demonstrate that the training program is effective in improving 40-yard sprint times.

In this chapter, several Statistics in Action Revisited examples demonstrate how confidence intervals can be used to evaluate the effectiveness of the speed training program.

Statistics in Action Revisited

- Estimating the Mean Decrease in Sprint Time (p. 311)
- Estimating the Proportion of Sprinters Who Improve after Speed Training (p. 330)
- Determining the Number of Athletes to Participate in the Training Program (p. 337)

 SPRINT

TABLE SIA7.1 Decrease in 40-Yard Sprint Times for 38 Football Players

−.01	.10	.10	.24	.25	.05	.28	.25	.20	.14
.32	.34	.30	.09	.05	0.00	.04	.17	0.00	.21
.15	.30	.02	.12	.14	.10	.08	.50	.36	.10
.01	.90	.34	.38	.44	.08	0.00	0.00		

Source: Gray, M., and Sauerbeck, J. A. "Speed training program for high school football players," *The Sport Journal*, Vol. 7, No. 1, Winter 2004 (Table 2).

7.1 Identifying the Target Parameter

In this chapter, our goal is to estimate the value of an unknown population parameter, such as a population mean or a proportion from a binomial population. For example, we might want to know the mean gas mileage for a new car model, the average expected life of a flat-screen computer monitor, or the proportion of Iraq War veterans with post-traumatic stress syndrome.

You'll see that different techniques are used for estimating a mean or proportion, depending on whether a sample contains a large or small number of measurements. Nevertheless, our objectives remain the same: We want to use the sample information to estimate the population parameter of interest (called the *target parameter*) and to assess the reliability of the estimate.

> ### Definition 7.1
> The unknown population parameter (e.g., mean or proportion) that we are interested in estimating is called the **target parameter.**

Often, there are one or more key words in the statement of the problem that indicate the appropriate target parameter. Some key words associated with the two parameters covered in this section are listed in the following box:

Determining the Target Parameter

Parameter	Key Words or Phrases	Type of Data
μ	Mean; average	Quantitative
p	Proportion; percentage; fraction; rate	Qualitative

For the examples given in the first paragraph of this section, the words *mean* in "mean gas mileage" and *average* in "average life expectancy" imply that the target parameter is the population mean μ. The word *proportion* in "proportion of Iraq War veterans with post-traumatic stress syndrome" indicates that the target parameter is the binomial proportion p.

In addition to key words and phrases, the type of data (quantitative or qualitative) collected is indicative of the target parameter. With quantitative data, you are likely to be estimating the mean of the data. With qualitative data with two outcomes (success or failure), the binomial proportion of successes is likely to be the parameter of interest.

We consider a method of estimating a population mean on the basis of a large sample in Section 7.2 and a small sample in Section 7.3. Estimating a population proportion is presented in Section 7.4. Finally, we show how to determine the sample sizes necessary for reliable estimates of the target parameters in Section 7.5.

7.2 Large-Sample Confidence Interval for a Population Mean

Suppose a large hospital wants to estimate the average length of time patients remain in the hospital. Hence, the hospital's target parameter is the population mean μ. To accomplish this objective, the hospital administrators plan to randomly sample 100 of all previous patients' records and to use the sample mean $\bar{x}$ of the lengths of stay to estimate μ, the mean of *all* patients' visits. The sample mean $\bar{x}$ represents a *point estimator* of the population mean μ (Definition 6.4). How can we assess the accuracy of this large-sample point estimator?

According to the central limit theorem, the sampling distribution of the sample mean is approximately normal for large samples, as shown in Figure 7.1.

Let us calculate the interval

$$\bar{x} \pm 2\sigma_{\bar{x}} = \bar{x} \pm \frac{2\sigma}{\sqrt{n}}$$

That is, we form an interval four standard deviations wide—from two standard deviations below the sample mean to two standard deviations above the mean. Prior to drawing the sample, what are the chances that this interval will enclose μ, the population mean?

To answer this question, refer to Figure 7.1. If the 100 measurements yield a value of $\bar{x}$ that falls between the two lines on either side of μ

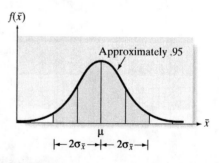

FIGURE 7.1

Sampling distribution of $\bar{x}$

(i.e., within two standard deviations of μ), then the interval $\bar{x} \pm 2\sigma_{\bar{x}}$ will contain μ; if $\bar{x}$ falls outside these boundaries, the interval $\bar{x} \pm 2\sigma_{\bar{x}}$ will not contain μ. Since the area under the normal curve (the sampling distribution of $\bar{x}$) between these boundaries is about .95 (more precisely, from Table IV in Appendix A, the area is .9544), the interval $\bar{x} \pm 2\sigma_{\bar{x}}$ will contain μ with a probability approximately equal to .95.

For instance, consider the lengths of time spent in the hospital for 100 patients, shown in Table 7.1. A SAS printout of summary statistics for the sample of 100 lengths of stay is shown in Figure 7.2.

From the top of the printout, we find that $\bar{x} = 4.53$ days and $s = 3.68$ days. To achieve our objective, we must construct the interval

$$\bar{x} \pm 2\sigma_{\bar{x}} = 4.53 \pm 2\frac{\sigma}{\sqrt{100}}$$

But now we face a problem. You can see that without knowing the standard deviation σ of the original population—that is, the standard deviation of the lengths of stay of *all* patients—we cannot calculate this interval. However, since we have a large sample ($n = 100$ measurements), we can approximate the interval by using the sample standard deviation s to approximate σ. Thus,

$$\bar{x} \pm 2\frac{\sigma}{\sqrt{100}} \approx \bar{x} \pm 2\frac{s}{\sqrt{100}} = 4.53 \pm 2\left(\frac{3.68}{10}\right) = 4.53 \pm .74$$

That is, we estimate that the mean length of stay in the hospital for all patients falls into the interval from 3.79 to 5.27 days. (This interval is highlighted at the bottom of the SAS printout in Figure 7.2. Differences are due to rounding.)

HOSPLOS

TABLE 7.1 Lengths of Stay (in Days) for 100 Patients

2	3	8	6	4	4	6	4	2	5
8	10	4	4	4	2	1	3	2	10
1	3	2	3	4	3	5	2	4	1
2	9	1	7	17	9	9	9	4	4
1	1	1	3	1	6	3	3	2	5
1	3	3	14	2	3	9	6	6	3
5	1	4	6	11	22	1	9	6	5
2	2	5	4	3	6	1	5	1	6
17	1	2	4	5	4	4	3	2	3
3	5	2	3	3	2	10	2	4	2

```
Sample Statistics for LOS

      N           Mean          Std. Dev.       Std. Error
----------------------------------------------------------
     100          4.53            3.68             0.37

Hypothesis Test

    Null hypothesis:    Mean of LOS  =  0
    Alternative:        Mean of LOS ^= 0

         t Statistic       Df       Prob > t
    -------------------------------------------
           12.318          99         <.0001

95 % Confidence Interval for the Mean

        Lower Limit:                3.80
        Upper Limit:                5.26
```

FIGURE 7.2

SAS printout with summary statistics and 95% confidence interval for data on 100 hospital stays

Can we be sure that μ, the true mean, is in the interval from 3.79 to 5.27? We cannot be certain, but we can be reasonably confident that it is. This confidence is derived from the knowledge that if we were to draw repeated random samples of 100 measurements from this population and form the interval $\bar{x} \pm 2\sigma_{\bar{x}}$ each time, approximately 95% of the intervals would contain μ. We have no way of knowing (without looking at all the patients' records) whether our sample interval is one of the 95% that contain μ or one of the 5% that do not, but the odds certainly favor its containing μ. Consequently, the interval from 3.79 to 5.27 provides a reliable estimate of the mean length of patient stay in the hospital.

The formula that tells us how to calculate an interval estimate on the basis of sample data is called an *interval estimator* or *confidence interval*. The probability, .95, that measures the confidence we can place in the interval estimate is called a *confidence coefficient*. The percentage, 95%, is called the *confidence level* for the interval estimate. It is not usually possible to assess precisely the reliability of point estimators, because they are single points rather than intervals. So, since we prefer to use estimators for which a measure of reliability can be calculated, we will generally use interval estimators.

Definition 7.2

An **interval estimator** (or **confidence interval**) is a formula that tells us how to use sample data to calculate an interval that estimates a population parameter.

Definition 7.3

The **confidence coefficient** is the probability that an interval estimator encloses the population parameter—that is, the relative frequency with which the interval estimator encloses the population parameter when the estimator is used repeatedly a very large number of times. The **confidence level** is the confidence coefficient expressed as a percentage.

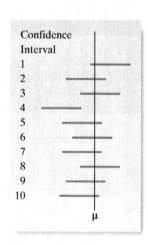

FIGURE 7.3

Confidence intervals for μ: 10 samples

Now we have seen how an interval can be used to estimate a population mean. When we use an interval estimator, we can usually calculate the probability that the estimation *process* will result in an interval that contains the true value of the population mean. That is, the probability that the interval contains the parameter in repeated usage is usually known. Figure 7.3 shows what happens when 10 different samples are drawn from a population and a confidence interval for μ is calculated from each. The location of μ is indicated by the vertical line in the figure. Ten confidence intervals, each based on one of 10 samples, are shown as horizontal line segments. Note that the confidence intervals move from sample to sample, sometimes containing μ and other times missing μ. *If our confidence level is 95%, then in the long run, 95% of our sample confidence intervals will contain μ.*

Suppose you wish to choose a confidence coefficient other than .95. Notice in Figure 7.1 that the confidence coefficient .95 is equal to the total area under the sampling distribution, less .05 of the area, which is divided equally between the two tails. Using this idea, we can construct a confidence interval with any desired confidence coefficient by increasing or decreasing the area (call it α) assigned to the tails of the sampling distribution. (See Figure 7.4.) For example, if we place the area $\alpha/2$ in each tail and if $z_{\alpha/2}$ is the z value such that $\alpha/2$ will lie to its right, then the confidence interval with confidence coefficient is $(1 - \alpha)$ is

$$\bar{x} \pm z_{\alpha/2}\sigma_{\bar{x}}$$

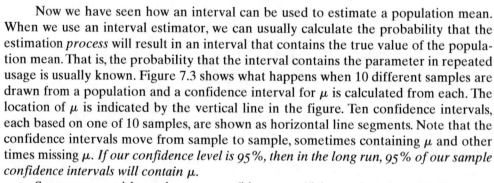

FIGURE 7.4

Locating $z_{\alpha/2}$ on the standard normal curve

Biography

JERZY NEYMAN (1894–1981)— Speaking Statistics with a Polish Accent

Polish-born Jerzy Neyman was educated at the University of Kharkov (Russia) in elementary mathematics, but taught himself graduate mathematics by studying journal articles on the subject. After receiving his doctorate in 1924 from the University of Warsaw (Poland), Neyman accepted a position at University College (London). There, he developed a friendship with Egon Pearson; Neyman and Pearson together developed the theory of hypothesis testing (Chapter 8). In a 1934 talk to the Royal Statistical Society, Neyman first pro-

posed the idea of interval estimation, which he called "confidence intervals." (It is interesting that Neyman rarely receives credit in textbooks as the originator of the confidence interval procedure.) In 1938, he emigrated to the United States and went to the University of California at Berkeley, where he built one of the strongest statistics departments in the country. Jerzy Neyman is considered one of the great founders of modern statistics. He was a superb teacher and innovative researcher who loved his students, always sharing his ideas with them. Neyman's influence on those he met is best expressed by a quote from prominent statistician David Salsburg: "We have all learned to speak statistics with a Polish accent."

Definition 7.4

The value z_α is defined as the value of the standard normal random variable z such that the area α will lie to its right. In other words, $P(z > z_\alpha) = \alpha$.

To illustrate, for a confidence coefficient of .90, we have $(1 - \alpha) = .90$, $\alpha = .10$, and $\alpha/2 = .05$; $z_{.05}$ is the z value that locates area .05 in the upper tail of the sampling distribution. Recall that Table IV in Appendix A gives the areas between the mean and a specified z-value. Since the total area to the right of the mean is .5, we find that $z_{.05}$ will be the z value corresponding to an area of $.5 - .05 = .45$ to the right of the mean. (See Figure 7.5.) This z value is $z_{.05} = 1.645$.

Confidence coefficients used in practice usually range from .90 to .99. The most commonly used confidence coefficients with corresponding values of α and $z_{\alpha/2}$ are shown in Table 7.2.

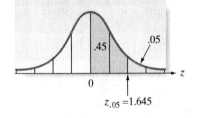

FIGURE 7.5
The z value ($z_{.05}$) corresponding to an area equal to .05 in the upper tail of the z-distribution

TABLE 7.2   Commonly Used Values of $z\alpha_{/2}$

Confidence Level $100(1 - \alpha)$	α	$\alpha/2$	$z_{\alpha/2}$
90%	.10	.05	1.645
95%	.05	.025	1.96
99%	.01	.005	2.575

Now Work Exercise 7.7

Large-Sample $100(1 - \alpha)\%$ Confidence Interval for μ

The large-sample $100(1 - \alpha)\%$ confidence interval for μ is

$$\bar{x} \pm z_{\alpha/2}\sigma_{\bar{x}} = \bar{x} \pm z_{\alpha/2}\frac{\sigma}{\sqrt{n}}$$

where $z_{\alpha/2}$ is the z value with an area $\alpha/2$ to its right (see Figure 7.4) and $\sigma_{\bar{x}} = \sigma/\sqrt{n}$. The parameter σ is the standard deviation of the sampled population and n is the sample size.

Note: When σ is unknown (as is almost always the case) and n is large (say, $n \geq 30$), the confidence interval is approximately equal to

$$\bar{x} \pm z_{\alpha/2}\left(\frac{s}{\sqrt{n}}\right)$$

where s is the sample standard deviation.

> **Conditions Required for a Valid Large-Sample Confidence Interval for μ**
>
> 1. A random sample is selected from the target population.
> 2. The sample size n is large (i.e., $n \geq 30$). (Due to the central limit theorem, this condition guarantees that the sampling distribution of $\bar{x}$ is approximately normal.)

EXAMPLE 7.1

A LARGE-SAMPLE CONFIDENCE INTERVAL FOR μ—Mean Number of unoccupied Seats per Flight

⊙ AIRNOSHOWS

Problem Unoccupied seats on flights cause airlines to lose revenue. Suppose a large airline wants to estimate its average number of unoccupied seats per flight over the past year. To accomplish this, the records of 225 flights are randomly selected, and the number of unoccupied seats is noted for each of the sampled flights. (The data are saved in the **AIRNOSHOWS** file.) Descriptive statistics for the data are displayed in the MINITAB printout of Figure 7.6.

Estimate μ, the mean number of unoccupied seats per flight during the past year, using a 90% confidence interval.

Solution The general form of the 90% confidence interval for a population mean is

$$\bar{x} \pm z_{\alpha/2}\sigma_{\bar{x}} = \bar{x} \pm z_{.05}\sigma_{\bar{x}} = \bar{x} \pm 1.645\left(\frac{\sigma}{\sqrt{n}}\right)$$

From Figure 7.6, we find (after rounding) that $\bar{x} = 11.6$. Since we do not know the value of σ (the standard deviation of the number of unoccupied seats per flight for all flights of the year), we use our best approximation—the sample standard deviation, $s = 4.1$ shown on the MINITAB printout. Then the 90% confidence interval is approximately

$$11.6 \pm 1.645\left(\frac{4.1}{\sqrt{225}}\right) = 11.6 \pm .45$$

or from 11.15 to 12.05. That is, at the 90% confidence level, we estimate the mean number of unoccupied seats per flight to be between 11.15 and 12.05 during the sampled year. This result is verified (except for rounding) on the right side of the MINITAB printout in Figure 7.6.

FIGURE 7.6

MINITAB printout with descriptive statistics and 90% confidence interval for Example 7.1

Variable	N	Mean	StDev	SE Mean	90% CI
NOSHOWS	225	11.5956	4.1026	0.2735	(11.1438, 12.0473)

Look Back We stress that the confidence level for this example, 90%, refers to the procedure used. If we were to apply that procedure repeatedly to different samples, approximately 90% of the intervals would contain μ. Although we do not know for sure whether this particular interval (11.15, 12.05) is one of the 90% that contain μ or one of the 10% that do not, our knowledge of probability gives us "confidence" that the interval contains μ.

Now Work Exercise 7.11

The interpretation of confidence intervals for a population mean is summarized in the next box.

> **Interpretation of a Confidence Interval for a Population Mean**
>
> When we form a $100(1 - \alpha)\%$ confidence interval for μ, we usually express our confidence in the interval with a statement such as "We can be $100(1 - \alpha)\%$ confident that μ lies between the lower and upper bounds of the confidence interval," where, for a particular application, we substitute the appropriate numerical values for the level of

(continued)

confidence and for the lower and upper bounds. *The statement reflects our confidence in the estimation process, rather than in the particular interval that is calculated from the sample data.* We know that repeated application of the same procedure will result in different lower and upper bounds on the interval. Furthermore, we know that $100(1 - \alpha)\%$ of the resulting intervals will contain μ. There is (usually) no way to determine whether any particular interval is one of those which contain μ or one of those which do not. However, unlike point estimators, confidence intervals have some measure of reliability—the confidence coefficient—associated with them. For that reason, they are generally preferred to point estimators.

Sometimes, the estimation procedure yields a confidence interval that is too wide for our purposes. In this case, we will want to reduce the width of the interval to obtain a more precise estimate of μ. One way to accomplish that is to decrease the confidence coefficient, $1 - \alpha$. For example, consider the problem of estimating the mean length of stay, μ for hospital patients. Recall that for a sample of 100 patients, $\bar{x} = 4.53$ days and $s = 3.68$ days. A 90% confidence interval for μ is

$$\bar{x} \pm 1.645(\sigma/\sqrt{n}) \approx 4.53 \pm (1.645)(3.68)/\sqrt{100} = 4.53 \pm .61$$

or (3.92, 5.14). You can see that this interval is narrower than the previously calculated 95% confidence interval, (3.79, 5.27). Unfortunately, we also have "less confidence" in the 90% confidence interval. An alternative method used to decrease the width of an interval without sacrificing "confidence" is to increase the sample size n. We demonstrate this method in Section 7.5.

STATISTICS IN ACTION REVISITED

Estimating the Mean Decrease in Sprint Time

Refer to the speed training program for junior varsity and varsity high school football players described on p. 305. Recall that the five-week training program incorporated a number of speed improvement drills for a sample of 38 high school athletes. The time in a 40-yard sprint run both before and after the training program was recorded for each athlete, and the decreases in time (measured in seconds) were saved in the **SPRINT** file (Table SIA7.1). Is the training program really effective in improving 40-yard sprint times?

One way to answer this question is to form a confidence interval for the true mean decrease in sprint time for all athletes who participate in the speed training program. If the true decrease is positive (i.e., if the "before" mean time is greater than the "after" mean time), then we conclude that the train-

ing program is effective. Since the sample size is large ($n = 38$), we can apply the large-sample methodology of this section.

The data are stored as a MINITAB worksheet and the software used to find a large-sample 95% confidence interval for the population mean decrease in sprint times. The MINITAB printout is displayed in Figure SIA7.1.

The interval, highlighted on the printout, is (.128, .247). Note that the entire interval falls above 0. Consequently, we are 95% confident that the true mean decrease in sprint times is positive. It appears that the speed training program is, in fact, effective in improving the average 40-yard sprint times of high school athletes. Note, however, that the mean decrease in time ranges from a minimum of .128 second to a maximum of .247 second. Although this decrease might be deemed critically important to world-class sprinters, it would probably be unnoticeable to high school football players.

Variable	N	Mean	StDev	SE Mean	95% CI
DecrTime	38	0.187895	0.181423	0.029431	(0.128262, 0.247527)

FIGURE SIA7.1

MINITAB confidence interval for speed training study

Confidence Interval for a Population Mean (known σ or $n \geq 30$)

Using the TI-84/TI-83 Graphing Calculator

Creating a Confidence Interval for a Population Mean

Step 1   *Enter the data. (Skip to Step 2 if you have summary statistics, not raw data.)*

Press **STAT** and select **1:Edit**.
Note: If the list already contains data, clear the old data. Use the up **ARROW** to highlight '**L1**'.
Press **CLEAR ENTER**.
Use the **ARROW** and **ENTER** keys to enter the data set into **L1**.

Step 2   *Access the Statistical Tests Menu*

Press **STAT**.
Arrow right to **TESTS**.
Arrow down to **Zinterval**.
Press **ENTER**.

```
EDIT CALC TESTS
1:Z-Test…
2:T-Test…
3:2-SampZTest…
4:2-SampTTest…
5:1-PropZTest…
6:2-PropZTest…
7↓ZInterval…
```

Step 3   *Choose "**Data**" or "**Stats**". ("Data" is selected when you have entered the raw data into a List. "Stats" is selected when you are given only the mean, standard deviation, and sample size.)*

Press **ENTER**.
If you selected "Data", enter a value for σ. (The best approximation is s, the sample standard deviation.)
Set **List** to **L1**.
Set **Freq** to **1**.
Set **C-Level** to the confidence level.
Arrow down to "**Calculate**".
Press **ENTER**.

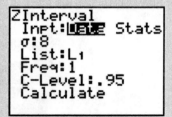

If you selected "Stats", enter a value for σ. (The best approximation is s, the sample standard deviation.)
Enter the sample mean and sample size.
Set **C-Level** to the confidence level.
Arrow down to "**Calculate**".
Press **ENTER**.
(The screen at the right is set up for an example with a standard deviation of 20, a mean of 200, and a sample size of 40.)
The confidence interval will be displayed along with the sample mean and the sample size.

Example   Use the the following information to compute a 90% confidence interval for the mean number of unoccupied seats per flight:

$$\bar{x} = 11.6 \text{ seats}, \qquad s = 4.1 \text{ seats}, \qquad n = 225 \text{ flights}$$

As you can see from the screen, our 90% confidence interval is (11.5, 12.05): You will also notice that the output displays the sample mean and sample size.

```
ZInterval
(11.15,12.05)
x̄=11.6
n=225
```

Exercises 7.1–7.24

Understanding the Principles

7.1 Define the target parameter.

7.2 What is the confidence coefficient in a 90% confidence interval for μ?

7.3 Explain the difference between an interval estimator and a point estimator for μ.

7.4 Explain what is meant by the statement "We are 95% confident that an interval estimate contains μ."

7.5 Will a large-sample confidence interval be valid if the population from which the sample is taken is not normally distributed? Explain.

7.6 What conditions are required to form a valid large-sample confidence interval for μ?

Learning the Mechanics

7.7 Find $z_{\alpha/2}$ for each of the following:
NW **a.** $\alpha = .10$ **b.** $\alpha = .01$
c. $\alpha = .05$ **d.** $\alpha = .20$

7.8 What is the confidence level of each of the following confidence intervals for μ?

a. $\bar{x} \pm 1.96\left(\dfrac{\sigma}{\sqrt{n}}\right)$

b. $\bar{x} \pm 1.645\left(\dfrac{\sigma}{\sqrt{n}}\right)$

c. $\bar{x} \pm 2.575\left(\dfrac{\sigma}{\sqrt{n}}\right)$

d. $\bar{x} \pm 1.28\left(\dfrac{\sigma}{\sqrt{n}}\right)$

e. $\bar{x} \pm .99\left(\dfrac{\sigma}{\sqrt{n}}\right)$

7.9 A random sample of n measurements was selected from a population with unknown mean μ and standard deviation σ. Calculate a 95% confidence interval for μ for each of the following situations:
a. $n = 75$, $\bar{x} = 28$, $s^2 = 12$
b. $n = 200$, $\bar{x} = 102$, $s^2 = 22$
c. $n = 100$, $\bar{x} = 15$, $s = .3$
d. $n = 100$, $\bar{x} = 4.05$, $s = .83$
e. Is the assumption that the underlying population of measurements is normally distributed necessary to ensure the validity of the confidence intervals in parts **a–d**? Explain.

7.10 A random sample of 90 observations produced a mean $\bar{x} = 25.9$ and a standard deviation $s = 2.7$.
a. Find a 95% confidence interval for the population mean μ.
b. Find a 90% confidence interval for μ.
c. Find a 99% confidence interval for μ.

7.11 A random sample of 100 observations from a normally distributed population possesses a mean equal to 83.2 and a standard deviation equal to 6.4.
NW
a. Find a 95% confidence interval for μ.
b. What do you mean when you say that a confidence coefficient is .95?
c. Find a 99% confidence interval for μ.
d. What happens to the width of a confidence interval as the value of the confidence coefficient is increased while the sample size is held fixed?

e. Would your confidence intervals of parts **a** and **c** be valid if the distribution of the original population were not normal? Explain.

7.12 The mean and standard deviation of a random sample of n measurements are equal to 33.9 and 3.3, respectively.
a. Find a 95% confidence interval for μ if $n = 100$.
b. Find a 95% confidence interval for μ if $n = 400$.
c. Find the widths of the confidence intervals you calculated in parts **a** and **b**. What is the effect on the width of a confidence interval of quadrupling the sample size while holding the confidence coefficient fixed?

APPLET Applet Exercise 7.1

Use the applet entitled *Confidence Intervals for a Mean (the impact of confidence level)* to investigate the situation in Exercise 7.11 further. For this exercise, assume that $\mu = 83.2$ is the population mean and $\sigma = 6.4$ is the population standard deviation.
a. Using $n = 100$ and the normal distribution with mean and standard deviation as just given, run the applet one time. How many of the 95% confidence intervals contain the mean? How many would you expect to contain the mean? How many of the 99% confidence intervals contain the mean? How many would you expect to contain the mean?
b. Which confidence level has a greater frequency of intervals that contain the mean? Is this result what you would expect? Explain.
c. Without clearing, run the applet several more times. What happens to the proportion of 95% confidence intervals that contain the mean as you run the applet more and more? What happens to the proportion of 99% confidence intervals that contain the mean as you run the applet more and more? Interpret these results in terms of the meanings of the 95% confidence interval and the 99% confidence interval.
d. Change the distribution to *right skewed*, clear, and run the applet several more times. Do you get the same results as in part **c**? Would you change your answer to part **e** of Exercise 7.11? Explain.

APPLET Applet Exercise 7.2

Use the applet entitled *Confidence Intervals for a Mean (the impact of confidence level)* to investigate the effect of the sample size on the proportion of confidence intervals that contain the mean when the underlying distribution is skewed. Set the distribution to *right skewed*, the mean to 10, and the standard deviation to 1.
a. Using $n = 30$, run the applet several times without clearing. What happens to the proportion of 95% confidence intervals that contain the mean as you run the applet more and more? What happens to the proportion of 99% confidence intervals that contain the mean as you run the applet more and more? Do the proportions seem to be approaching the values that you would expect?
b. Clear and run the applet several times, using $n = 100$. What happens to the proportions of 95% confidence intervals and 99% confidence intervals that contain the mean this time? How do these results compare with your results in part **a**?
c. Clear and run the applet several times, using $n = 1000$. How do the results compare with your results in parts **a** and **b**?

d. Describe the effect of sample size on the likelihood that a confidence interval contains the mean for a skewed distribution.

Applying the Concepts—Basic

7.13 Latex allergy in health-care workers. Health-care workers who use latex gloves with glove powder on a daily basis are particularly susceptible to developing a latex allergy. Symptoms of a latex allergy include conjunctivitis, hand eczema, nasal congestion, a skin rash, and shortness of breath. Each in a sample of 46 hospital employees who were diagnosed with latex allergy based on a skin-prick test reported on their exposure to latex gloves. (*Current Allergy & Clinical Immunology*, March 2004.) Summary statistics for the number of latex gloves used per week are $\bar{x} = 19.3$ and $s = 11.9$.
  a. Give a point estimate for the average number of latex gloves used per week by all health-care workers with a latex allergy.
  b. Form a 95% confidence interval for the average number of latex gloves used per week by all health-care workers with a latex allergy.
  c. Give a practical interpretation of the interval you found in part **b**.
  d. Give the conditions required for the interval in part **b** to be valid.

7.14 Personal networks of older adults. In sociology, a personal network is defined as the people with whom you make frequent contact. The Living Arrangements and Social Networks of Older Adults (LSN) research program used a stratified random sample of men and women born between 1908 and 1937 to gauge the size of the personal network of older adults. Each adult in the sample was asked to "please name the people (e.g., in your neighborhood) you have frequent contact with and who are also important to you." Based on the number of people named, the personal network size for each adult was determined. The responses of 2,819 adults in the LSN sample yielded the following statistics on network size: $\bar{x} = 14.6$; $s = 9.8$. (*Sociological Methods & Research*, August 2001.)
  a. Give a point estimate for the mean personal network size of all older adults.
  b. Form a 95% confidence interval for the mean personal network size of all older adults.
  c. Give a practical interpretation of the interval you found in part **b**.
  d. Give the conditions required for the interval in part **b** to be valid.

PONDICE

7.15 Albedo of ice melt ponds. Refer to the National Snow and Ice Data Center (NSIDC) collection of data on the albedo, depth, and physical characteristics of ice-melt ponds in the Canadian Arctic, presented in Exercise 2.11 (p. 35). Albedo is the ratio of the light reflected by the ice to that received by it. (High albedo values give a white appearance to the ice.) Visible albedo values were recorded for a sample of 504 ice-melt ponds located in the Barrow Strait in the Canadian Arctic; these data are saved in the **PONDICE** file.
  a. Find a 90% confidence interval for the true mean visible albedo value of all Canadian Arctic ice ponds.
  b. Give both a practical and a theoretical interpretation of the interval.

c. Recall from Exercise 2.11 that the type of ice for each pond was classified as first-year ice, multiyear ice, or landfast ice. Find 90% confidence intervals for the mean visible albedo for each of the three types of ice. Interpret the intervals.

NZBIRDS

7.16 Extinct New Zealand birds. Refer to the *Evolutionary Ecology Research* (July 2003) study of the patterns of extinction in the New Zealand bird population, presented in Exercise 2.96 (p. 73). Suppose you are interested in estimating the mean egg length (in millimeters) for the New Zealand bird population.
  a. What is the target parameter?
  b. Recall that the egg lengths for 132 bird species are saved in the **NZBIRDS** file. Obtain a random sample of 50 egg lengths from the data set.
  c. Find the mean and standard deviation of the 50 egg lengths you obtained in part **b**.
  d. Use the information from part **c** to form a 99% confidence interval for the true mean egg length of a bird species found in New Zealand.
  e. Give a practical interpretation of the interval you found in part **d**.

Applying the Concepts—Intermediate

PERAGGR

7.17 Personality and aggressive behavior. How does personality impact aggressive behavior? A team of university psychologists conducted a review of studies that examined the relationship between personality and aggressive behavior (*Psychological Bulletin*, Vol. 132, 2006). One variable of interest to the researchers was the difference between the aggressive behavior level of individuals in the study who scored high on a personality test and those who scored low on the test. This variable, standardized to be between -7 and 7, was called "effect size". (A large positive effect size indicates that those who score high on the personality test are more aggressive than those who score low.) The researchers collected the effect sizes for a sample of $n = 109$ studies published in psychology journals. This data is saved in the **PERAGGR** file. A dot plot and summary statistics for effect size are shown in the MINITAB printouts at the bottom of p. 315. Of interest to the researchers is the true mean effect size μ for all psychological studies of personality and aggressive behavior.
  a. Identify the parameter of interest to the researchers.
  b. Examine the dot plot. Does effect size have a normal distribution? Explain why your answer is irrelevant to the subsequent analysis.
  c. Locate a 95% confidence interval for μ on the accompanying printout. Interpret the result.
  d. If the true mean effect size exceeds 0, then the researchers will conclude that in the population, those who score high on a personality test are more aggressive than those who score low. Can the researchers draw this conclusion? Explain.

7.18 Sentence complexity study. Refer to the *Applied Psycholinguistics* (June 1998) study of language skills of low-income children, presented in Exercise 2.98 (p. 74). Each in a sample of 65 low-income children was administered the Communicative Development Inventory (CDI) exam. The

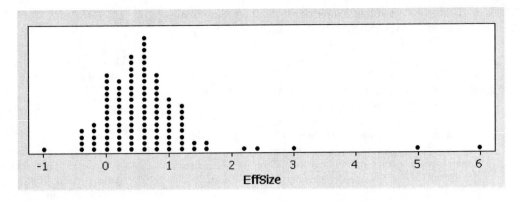

MINITAB Output for
Exercise 7.17

Variable	N	Mean	StDev	SE Mean	95% CI
EffSize	109	0.6477	0.8906	0.0853	(0.4786, 0.8167)

sentence complexity scores had a mean of 7.62 and a standard deviation of 8.91.

a. Construct a 90% confidence interval for the mean sentence complexity score of all low-income children.

b. Interpret the interval you found in part **a** in the words of the problem.

c. Suppose we know that the true mean sentence complexity score of middle-income children is 15.55. Is there evidence that the true mean for low-income children differs from 15.55? Explain.

7.19 Colored string preferred by chickens. Animal behaviorists have discovered that the more domestic chickens peck at objects placed in their environment, the healthier the chickens seem to be. White string has been found to be a particularly attractive pecking stimulus. In one experiment, 72 chickens were exposed to a string stimulus. Instead of white string, blue-colored string was used. The number of pecks each chicken took at the blue string over a specified interval of time was recorded. Summary statistics for the 72 chickens were $\bar{x} = 1.13$ pecks and $s = 2.21$ pecks. (*Applied Animal Behaviour Science*, October 2000.)

a. Use a 99% confidence interval to estimate the population mean number of pecks made by chickens pecking at blue string. Interpret the result.

b. Previous research has shown that $\mu = 7.5$ pecks if chickens are exposed to white string. Based on the results you found in part **a**, is there evidence that chickens are more apt to peck at white string than blue string? Explain.

7.20 Velocity of light from galaxies. Refer to *The Astronomical Journal* (July 1995) study of the velocity of light emitted from a galaxy in the universe, presented in Exercise 2.100 (p. 74). A sample of 103 galaxies located in the galaxy cluster A2142 had a mean velocity of $\bar{x} = 27,117$ kilometers per second (km/s) and a standard deviation of $s = 1,280$ km/s. Suppose your goal is to make an inference about the population mean light velocity of galaxies in cluster A2142.

a. In part **b** of Exercise 2.100, you constructed an interval that captured approximately 95% of the galaxy velocities in the cluster. Explain why that interval is inappropriate for the inference you are asked to make here.

b. Construct a 95% confidence interval for the mean light velocity emitted from all galaxies in cluster A2142. Interpret the result.

7.21 Improving SAT scores. Refer to the *Chance* (Winter 2001) and National Education Longitudinal Survey (NELS) study

of 265 students who paid a private tutor to help them improve their SAT scores, presented in Exercise 2.101 (p. 74). The changes in both the SAT-Mathematics and SAT-Verbal scores for these students are reproduced in the following table:

	SAT-Math	SAT-Verbal
Mean change in score	19	7
Standard deviation of score changes	65	49

a. Construct and interpret a 95% confidence interval for the population mean change in SAT-Mathematics score for students who pay a private tutor.

b. Repeat part **a** for the population mean change in SAT-Verbal score.

c. Suppose the true population mean change in score on one of the SAT tests for all students who paid a private tutor is 15. Which of the two tests, SAT-Mathematics or SAT-Verbal, is most likely to have this mean change? Explain.

7.22 Attention time given to twins. Psychologists have found that twins, in their early years, tend to have lower IQs and pick up language more slowly than nontwins. (*Wisconsin Twin Research Newsletter*, Winter 2004). The slower intellectual growth of most twins may be caused by benign parental neglect. Suppose it is desired to estimate the mean attention time given to twins per week by their parents. A sample of 50 sets of $2\frac{1}{2}$-year-old twin boys is taken, and at the end of 1 week, the attention time given to each pair is recorded. The data (in hours) are listed in the following table:

ATTIMES

20.7	16.7	22.5	12.1	2.9
23.5	6.4	1.3	39.6	35.6
10.9	7.1	46.0	23.4	29.4
44.1	13.8	24.3	9.3	3.4
15.7	46.6	10.6	6.7	5.4
14.0	20.7	48.2	7.7	22.2
20.3	34.0	44.5	23.8	20.0
43.1	14.3	21.9	17.5	9.6
36.4	0.8	1.1	19.3	14.6
32.5	19.1	36.9	27.9	14.0

Find a 90% confidence interval for the mean attention time given to all twin boys by their parents. Interpret the confidence interval.

Applying the Concepts—Advanced

7.23 Study of undergraduate problem drinking. In *Alcohol & Alcoholism* (Jan/Feb. 2007), psychologists at the University of Pennsylvania compared the levels of alcohol consumption of male and female freshman students. Each student was asked to estimate the amount of alcohol (beer, wine, or liquor) they consume in a typical week. Summary statistics for 128 males and 184 females are provided in the accompanying table.

a. For each gender, find a 95% confidence interval for mean weekly alcohol consumption.

b. Prior to sampling, what is the probability that at least one of the two confidence intervals will not contain the population mean it estimates. Assume that the two intervals are independent.

c. Based on the two confidence intervals, what inference can you make about which gender consumes the most alcohol, on average, per week? (*Caution:* In Chapter 9, we will learn about a more valid method of comparing population means.)

	Males	Females
Sample size, n	128	184
Mean (ounces), $\bar{x}$	16.79	10.79
Standard deviation, s	13.57	11.53

Source: Leeman, R. F., Fenton, M., & Volpicelli, J.R. "Impaired control and undergraduate problem drinking," *Alcohol & Alcoholism*, Vol. 42, No. 1, Jan/Feb. 2007 (Table 1).

7.24 Study of cockroach growth. According to scientists, the cockroach has had 300 million years to develop a resistance to destruction. In a study conducted by researchers for S. C. Johnson & Son, Inc. (manufacturers of Raid® and Off®), 5,000 roaches (the expected number in a roach-infested house) were released in the Raid test kitchen. One week later, the kitchen was fumigated and 16,298 dead roaches were counted, a gain of 11,298 roaches for the 1-week period. Assume that none of the original roaches died during the 1-week period and that the standard deviation of x, the number of roaches produced per roach in a 1-week period, is 1.5. Use the number of roaches produced by the sample of 5,000 roaches to find a 95% confidence interval for the mean number of roaches produced per week for each roach in a typical roach-infested house.

7.3 Small-Sample Confidence Interval for a Population Mean

Federal legislation requires pharmaceutical companies to perform extensive tests on new drugs before they can be marketed. Initially, a new drug is tested on animals. If the drug is deemed safe after this first phase of testing, the pharmaceutical company is then permitted to begin human testing on a limited basis. During this second phase, inferences must be made about the safety of the drug on the basis of information obtained from very small samples.

Suppose a pharmaceutical company must estimate the average increase in blood pressure of patients who take a certain new drug. Assume that only six patients (randomly selected from the population of all patients) can be used in the initial phase of human testing. The use of a *small sample* in making an inference about μ presents two immediate problems when we attempt to use the standard normal z as a test statistic.

Problem 1   The shape of the sampling distribution of the sample mean $\bar{x}$ (and the z-statistic) now depends on the shape of the population that is sampled. We can no longer assume that the sampling distribution of $\bar{x}$ is approximately normal, because the central limit theorem ensures normality only for samples that are sufficiently large.

Solution to Problem 1   The sampling distribution of $\bar{x}$ (and z) is exactly normal even for relatively small samples if the sampled population is normal. It is approximately normal if the sampled population is approximately normal.

Problem 2   The population standard deviation σ is almost always unknown. Although it is still true that $\sigma_{\bar{x}} = \sigma/\sqrt{n}$, the sample standard deviation s may provide a poor approximation for σ when the sample size is small.

Solution to Problem 2   Instead of using the standard normal statistic

$$z = \frac{\bar{x} - \mu}{\sigma_{\bar{x}}} = \frac{\bar{x} - \mu}{\sigma/\sqrt{n}}$$

which requires knowledge of, or a good approximation to, σ, we define and use the statistic

$$t = \frac{\bar{x} - \mu}{s/\sqrt{n}}$$

in which the sample standard deviation s replaces the population standard deviation σ.

Biography

WILLIAM S. GOSSET (1876–1937)— Student's *t*-Distribution

At the age of 23, William Gosset earned a degree in chemistry and mathematics at prestigious Oxford University. He was immediately hired by the Guinness Brewing Company in Dublin, Ireland, for his expertise in chemistry. However, Gosset's mathematical skills allowed him to solve numerous practical problems associated with brewing beer. For example, Gosset applied the Poisson distribution to model the number of yeast cells per unit volume in the fermentation process. His most important discovery was the *t*-distribution in 1908. Since most applied researchers worked with small samples, Gosset was interested in the behavior of the mean in the case of small samples. He tediously took numerous small sets of numbers, calculated the mean and standard deviation of each, obtained their *t*-ratio, and plotted the results on graph paper. The shape of the distribution was always the same: the *t*-distribution. Under company policy, employees were forbidden to publish their research results, so Gosset used the pen name *Student* to publish a paper on the subject. Hence, the distribution has been called Student's *t*-distribution.

If we are sampling from a normal distribution, the **t-statistic** has a sampling distribution very much like that of the *z*-statistic: mound shaped, symmetric, and with mean 0. The primary difference between the sampling distributions of *t* and *z* is that the *t*-statistic is more variable than the *z*, a property that follows intuitively when you realize that *t* contains two random quantities ($\bar{x}$ and s), whereas *z* contains only one ($\bar{x}$).

The actual amount of variability in the sampling distribution of *t* depends on the sample size *n*. A convenient way of expressing this dependence is to say that the *t* statistic has $(n-1)$ **degrees of freedom (df).*** Recall that the quantity $(n-1)$ is the divisor that appears in the formula for s^2. This number plays a key role in the sampling distribution of s^2 and appears in discussions of other statistics in later chapters. In particular, the smaller the number of degrees of freedom associated with the *t*-statistic, the more variable will be its sampling distribution.

In Figure 7.7, we show both the sampling distribution of *z* and the sampling distribution of a *t*-statistic with 4 df. You can see that the increased variability of the *t*-statistic means that the *t*-value, t_α, that locates an area α in the upper tail of the *t*-distribution is larger than the corresponding value, z_α. For any given value of α the *t*-value, t_α, increases as the number of degrees of freedom (df) decreases. Values of *t* that will be used in forming small-sample confidence intervals of μ are given in Table VI of Appendix A. A partial reproduction of this table is shown in Table 7.3.

Note that t_α values are listed for various degrees of freedom, where α refers to the tail area under the *t*-distribution to the right of t_α. For example, if we want the *t*-value with an area of .025 to its right and 4 df, we look in the table under the column $t_{.025}$ for the entry in the row corresponding to 4 df. This entry is $t_{.025} = 2.776$, as shown in Figure 7.8. The corresponding standard normal *z*-score is $z_{.025} = 1.96$.

Note that the last row of Table VI, where df = ∞ (infinity), contains the standard normal *z*-values. This follows from the fact that as the sample size *n* grows very large, *s* becomes closer to σ and thus *t* becomes closer in distribution to *z*. In fact, when df = 29, there is little difference between corresponding tabulated values of *z* and *t*. Thus, we choose

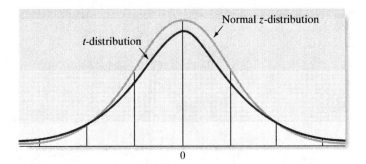

FIGURE 7.7

Standard normal (z) distribution and *t*-distribution with 4 df

---

*Since degrees of freedom are related to the sample size *n*, it is helpful to think of the number of degrees of freedom as the amount of information in the sample available for estimating the target parameter.

TABLE 7.3 Reproduction of Part of Table VI in Appendix A

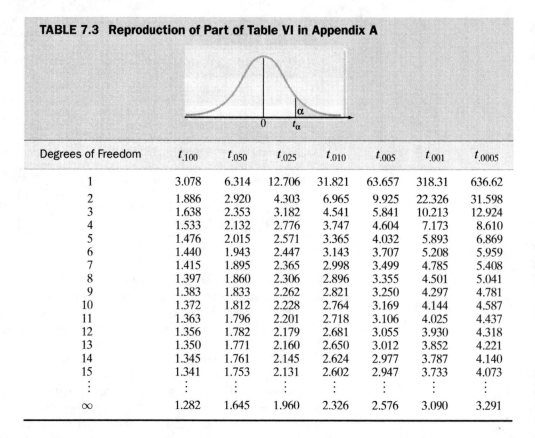

Degrees of Freedom	$t_{.100}$	$t_{.050}$	$t_{.025}$	$t_{.010}$	$t_{.005}$	$t_{.001}$	$t_{.0005}$
1	3.078	6.314	12.706	31.821	63.657	318.31	636.62
2	1.886	2.920	4.303	6.965	9.925	22.326	31.598
3	1.638	2.353	3.182	4.541	5.841	10.213	12.924
4	1.533	2.132	2.776	3.747	4.604	7.173	8.610
5	1.476	2.015	2.571	3.365	4.032	5.893	6.869
6	1.440	1.943	2.447	3.143	3.707	5.208	5.959
7	1.415	1.895	2.365	2.998	3.499	4.785	5.408
8	1.397	1.860	2.306	2.896	3.355	4.501	5.041
9	1.383	1.833	2.262	2.821	3.250	4.297	4.781
10	1.372	1.812	2.228	2.764	3.169	4.144	4.587
11	1.363	1.796	2.201	2.718	3.106	4.025	4.437
12	1.356	1.782	2.179	2.681	3.055	3.930	4.318
13	1.350	1.771	2.160	2.650	3.012	3.852	4.221
14	1.345	1.761	2.145	2.624	2.977	3.787	4.140
15	1.341	1.753	2.131	2.602	2.947	3.733	4.073
⋮	⋮	⋮	⋮	⋮	⋮	⋮	⋮
∞	1.282	1.645	1.960	2.326	2.576	3.090	3.291

the arbitrary cutoff of $n = 30$ (df $= 29$) to distinguish between large-sample and small-sample inferential techniques.

Returning to the example of testing a new drug, suppose that the six test patients have the blood pressure increases (measured in points) shown in Table 7.4. How can we use this information to construct a 95% confidence interval for μ, the mean increase in blood pressure associated with the new drug for all patients in the population?

First, we know that we are dealing with a sample too small to assume, by the central limit theorem, that the sample mean $\bar{x}$ is approximately normally distributed. That is, we do not get the normal distribution of $\bar{x}$ "automatically" from the central limit theorem when the sample size is small. Instead, we must assume that the measured variable, in this case the increase in blood pressure, is normally distributed in order for the distribution of $\bar{x}$ to be normal.

Second, unless we are fortunate enough to know the population standard deviation σ, which in this case represents the standard deviation of *all* the patients' increases in blood pressure when they take the new drug, we cannot use the standard normal z-statistic to form our confidence interval for μ. Instead, we must use the t-distribution, with $(n - 1)$ degrees of freedom.

In this case, $n - 1 = 5$ df, and the t-value is found in Table 7.3 to be

$$t_{.025} = 2.571 \text{ with 5 df}$$

BPINCR

TABLE 7.4 Blood Pressure Increases (Points) for Six Patients

1.7	3.0	.8	3.4	2.7	2.1

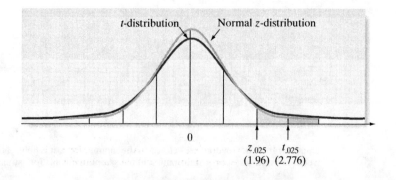

FIGURE 7.8
The $t_{.025}$ value in a t-distribution with 4 df, and the corresponding $z_{.025}$ value

Descriptives

			Statistic	Std. Error
BPINCR	Mean		2.283	.3877
	95% Confidence Interval for Mean	Lower Bound	1.287	
		Upper Bound	3.280	
	5% Trimmed Mean		2.304	
	Median		2.400	
	Variance		.902	
	Std. Deviation		.9496	
	Minimum		.8	
	Maximum		3.4	
	Range		2.6	
	Interquartile Range		1.6	
	Skewness		-.573	.845
	Kurtosis		-.389	1.741

FIGURE 7.9

SPSS confidence interval for mean blood pressure increase

Recall that the large-sample confidence interval would have been of the form

$$\bar{x} \pm z_{\alpha/2}\sigma_{\bar{x}} = \bar{x} \pm z_{\alpha/2}\frac{\sigma}{\sqrt{n}} = \bar{x} \pm z_{.025}\frac{\sigma}{\sqrt{n}}$$

where 95% is the desired confidence level. To form the interval for a small sample from *a normal distribution, we simply substitute t for z and s for σ in the preceding formula, yielding*

$$\bar{x} \pm t_{\alpha/2}\frac{s}{\sqrt{n}}$$

An SPSS printout showing descriptive statistics for the six blood pressure increases is displayed in Figure 7.9. Note that $\bar{x} = 2.283$ and $s = .950$. Substituting these numerical values into the confidence interval formula, we get

$$2.283 \pm (2.571)\left(\frac{.950}{\sqrt{6}}\right) = 2.283 \pm .997$$

or 1.286 to 3.280 points. Note that this interval agrees (except for rounding) with the confidence interval highlighted on the SPSS printout in Figure 7.9.

We interpret the interval as follows: We can be 95% confident that the mean increase in blood pressure associated with taking this new drug is between 1.286 and 3.28 points. As with our large-sample interval estimates, our confidence is in the *process*, not in this particular interval. We know that if we were to repeatedly use this estimation procedure, 95% of the confidence intervals produced would contain the true mean μ, *assuming that the probability distribution of changes in blood pressure from which our sample was selected is normal*. The latter assumption is necessary for the small-sample interval to be valid.

What price did we pay for having to utilize a small sample to make the inference? First, we had to assume that the underlying population is normally distributed, and if the assumption is invalid, our interval might also be invalid.* Second, we had to form the interval by using a *t* value of 2.571 rather than a *z* value of 1.96, resulting in a wider interval to achieve the same 95% level of confidence. If the interval from 1.286 to 3.28 is too wide to be of much use, we know how to remedy the situation: Increase the number of patients sampled in order to decrease the width of the interval (on average).

Now Work Exercise 7.27

---

*By *invalid*, we mean that the probability that the procedure will yield an interval that contains μ is not equal to $(1 - \alpha)$. Generally, if the underlying population is approximately normal, the confidence coefficient will approximate the probability that the interval contains μ.

The procedure for forming a small-sample confidence interval is summarized in the accompanying boxes.

Small-Sample Confidence Interval* for μ

The small-sample confidence interval for μ is

$$\bar{x} \pm t_{\alpha/2}\left(\frac{s}{\sqrt{n}}\right)$$

where $t_{\alpha/2}$ is based on $(n-1)$ degrees of freedom.

Conditions Required for a Valid Small-Sample Confidence Interval for μ

1. A random sample is selected from the target population.
2. The population has a relative frequency distribution that is approximately normal.

EXAMPLE 7.2
A SMALL-SAMPLE CONFIDENCE INTERVAL FOR μ—Destructive Sampling

Problem Some quality control experiments require *destructive sampling* (i.e., the test to determine whether the item is defective destroys the item) in order to measure a particular characteristic of the product. The cost of destructive sampling often dictates small samples. Suppose a manufacturer of printers for personal computers wishes to estimate the mean number of characters printed before the printhead fails. The printer manufacturer tests $n = 15$ printheads and records the number of characters printed until failure for each. These 15 measurements (in millions of characters) are listed in Table 7.5, followed by a MINITAB summary statistics printout in Figure 7.10.

a. Form a 99% confidence interval for the mean number of characters printed before the printhead fails. Interpret the result.

b. What assumption is required for the interval you found in part **a** to be valid? Is that assumption reasonably satisfied?

 PRINTHEAD

TABLE 7.5 Number of Characters (in Millions) for $n = 15$ Printhead Tests

| 1.13 | 1.55 | 1.43 | .92 | 1.25 | 1.36 | 1.32 | .85 | 1.07 | 1.48 | 1.20 | 1.33 | 1.18 | 1.22 | 1.29 |

Variable	N	Mean	StDev	SE Mean	99% CI
NUMCHAR	15	1.23867	0.19316	0.04987	(1.09020, 1.38714)

FIGURE 7.10
MINITAB printout with descriptive statistics and 99% confidence interval for Example 7.2

Solution

a. For this small sample ($n = 15$), we use the *t*-statistic to form the confidence interval. We use a confidence coefficient of .99 and $n - 1 = 14$ degrees of freedom to find $t_{\alpha/2}$ in Table VI:

$$t_{\alpha/2} = t_{.005} = 2.977$$

[*Note:* The small sample forces us to extend the interval almost three standard deviations (of $\bar{x}$) on each side of the sample mean in order to form the 99% confidence interval.] From the MINITAB printout shown in Figure 7.10, we find that $\bar{x} = 1.24$

---

*The procedure given in the box assumes that the population standard deviation σ is unknown, which is almost always the case. If σ is known, we can form the small-sample confidence interval just as we would a large-sample confidence interval, using a standard normal z-value instead of t. However, we must still assume that the underlying population is approximately normal.

and $s = .19$. Substituting these (rounded) values into the confidence interval formula, we obtain

$$\bar{x} \pm t_{.005}\left(\frac{s}{\sqrt{n}}\right) = 1.24 \pm 2.977\left(\frac{.19}{\sqrt{15}}\right)$$

$$= 1.24 \pm .15 \quad \text{or} \quad (1.09, 1.39)$$

This interval is highlighted in Figure 7.10.

   Our interpretation is as follows: The manufacturer can be 99% confident that the printhead has a mean life of between 1.09 and 1.39 million characters. If the manufacturer were to advertise that the mean life of its printheads is (at least) 1 million characters, the interval would support such a claim. Our confidence is derived from the fact that 99% of the intervals formed in repeated applications of this procedure will contain μ.

b. Since n is small, we must assume that the number of characters printed before the printhead fails is a random variable from a normal distribution. That is, we assume that the population from which the sample of 15 measurements is selected is distributed normally. One way to check this assumption is to graph the distribution of data in Table 7.5. If the sample data are approximately normally distributed, then the population from which the sample is selected is very likely to be normal. A MINITAB stem-and-leaf plot for the sample data is displayed in Figure 7.11. The distribution is mound shaped and nearly symmetric. Therefore, the assumption of normality appears to be reasonably satisfied.

Stem-and-Leaf Display: NUMBER

```
Stem-and-leaf of NUMBER   N  = 15
Leaf Unit = 0.010


   1     8    5
   2     9    2
   3    10    7
   5    11    38
  (4)   12    0259
   6    13    236
   3    14    38
   1    15    5
```

FIGURE 7.11

MINITAB stem-and-leaf display of data in Table 7.4

Look Back Other checks for normality, such as a normal probability plot and the ratio IQR/s, may also be used to verify the normality condition.

Now Work Exercise 7.35

   We have emphasized throughout this section that an assumption that the population is approximately normally distributed is necessary for making small-sample inferences about μ when the t-statistic is used. Although many phenomena do have approximately normal distributions, it is also true that many random phenomena have distributions that are not normal or even mound shaped. Empirical evidence acquired over the years has shown that the t-distribution is rather insensitive to moderate departures from normality. That is, the use of the t-statistic when sampling from slightly skewed mound-shaped populations generally produces credible results; however, for cases in which the distribution is distinctly nonnormal, we must either take a large sample or use a *nonparametric method* (the topic of Chapter 14).

What Do You Do When the Population Relative Frequency Distribution Departs Greatly from Normality?

Answer: Use the nonparametric statistical methods of Chapter 14.

Confidence Interval for a Population Mean ($n < 30$)

Using the TI-84/TI-83 Graphing Calculator

Creating a Confidence Interval for a Population Mean

Step 1   *Enter the data. (Skip to Step 2 if you have summary statistics, not raw data.)*

Press **STAT** and select **1:Edit**.
Note: If the list already contains data, clear the old data. Use the up ARROW to highlight "L1".
Press **CLEAR ENTER**.
Use the **ARROW** and **ENTER** keys to enter the data set into **L1**.

```
EDIT CALC TESTS
2↑T-Test…
3:2-SampZTest…
4:2-SampTTest…
5:1-PropZTest…
6:2-PropZTest…
7:ZInterval…
8↓TInterval…
```

Step 2   *Access the Statistical Tests Menu*

Press **STAT**.
Arrow right to **TESTS**.
Arrow down to **Tinterval**.
Press **ENTER**.

Step 3   *Choose "**Data**" or "**Stats**" ("Data" is selected when you have entered the raw data into a List. "Stats" is selected when you are given only the mean, standard deviation, and sample size.)*

Press **ENTER**.
If you selected "Data", set **List** to **L1**.
Set **Freq** to **1**.
Set **C-Level** to the confidence level.
Arrow down to "**Calculate**".
Press **ENTER**.

If you selected "Stats", enter the mean, standard deviation, and sample size.
Set **C-Level** to the confidence level.
Arrow down to "**Calculate**".
Press **ENTER**.
(The screen below is set up for an example with a mean of 100 and a standard deviation of 10.)
The confidence interval will be displayed with the mean, standard deviation, and sample size.

```
TInterval
 Inpt:DATA Stats
 List:L₁
 Freq:1
 C-Level:.95
 Calculate
```

```
TInterval
 Inpt:Data Stats
 x̄:100
 Sx:10
 n:19
 C-Level:.99
 Calculate
```

```
TInterval
 (1.0902,1.3871)
 x̄=1.238666667
 Sx=.1931641296
 n=15
 ■
```

Example   Compute a 99% confidence interval for the mean, using the 15 pieces of data given in Example 7.2:

1.13	1.55	1.43	0.92	1.25
1.36	1.32	0.85	1.07	1.48
1.20	1.33	1.18	1.22	1.29

As you can see from the screen, our 99% confidence interval is **(1.0902, 1.3871)**.
You will also notice that the output displays the mean, standard deviation, and sample size.

Exercises 7.25–7.43

Understanding the Principles

7.25 State the two problems (and corresponding solutions) that arise with using a small sample to estimate μ.

7.26 Compare the shapes of the z- and t-distributions.

7.27 Explain the differences in the sampling distributions of $\bar{x}$ for large and small samples under the following assumptions:
a. The variable of interest, x, is normally distributed.
b. Nothing is known about the distribution of the variable x.

APPLET **Applet Exercise 7.3**

Use the applet entitled *Confidence Intervals for a Mean (the impact of not knowing the standard deviation)* to compare proportions of z-intervals and t-intervals that contain the mean for a population that is normally distributed.

    a. Using $n = 5$ and the normal distribution with mean 50 and standard deviation 10, run the applet several times. How do the proportions of z-intervals and t-intervals that contain the mean compare?

    b. Repeart part **a** first for $n = 10$ and then for $n = 20$. Compare your results with those you obtained in part **a**.

    c. Describe any patterns you observe between the proportion of z-intervals that contain the mean and the proportion of t-intervals that contain the mean as the sample size increases.

APPLET **Applet Exercise 7.4**

Use the applet entitled *Confidence Intervals for a Mean (the impact of not knowing the standard deviation)* to compare proportions of z-intervals and t-intervals that contain the mean for a population with a skewed distribution.

    a. Using $n = 5$ and the right-skewed distribution with mean 50 and standard deviation 10, run the applet several times. How do the proportions of z-intervals and t-intervals that contain the mean compare?

    b. Repeat part **a** first for $n = 10$ and then for $n = 20$. Compare your results with those you obtained in part **a**.

    c. Describe any patterns you observe between the proportion of z-intervals that contain the mean and the proportion of t-intervals that contain the mean as the sample size increases.

    d. How does the skewness of the underlying distribution affect the proportions of z-intervals and t-intervals that contain the mean?

Learning the Mechanics

7.28 Suppose you have selected a random sample of $n = 7$ measurements from a normal distribution. Compare the standard normal z-values with the corresponding t-values if you were forming the following confidence intervals:

    a. 80% confidence interval

    b. 90% confidence interval

    c. 95% confidence interval

    d. 98% confidence interval

    e. 99% confidence interval

    f. Use the table values you obtained in parts **a–e** to sketch the z- and t-distributions. What are the similarities and differences?

7.29 Let t_0 be a specific value of t. Use Table VI in Appendix A to find t_0 values such that the following statements are true:

    a. $P(t \geq t_0) = .025$, where df $= 10$

    b. $P(t \geq t_0) = .01$, where df $= 17$

    c. $P(t \leq t_0) = .005$, where df $= 6$

    d. $P(t \leq t_0) = .05$, where df $= 13$

7.30 Let t_0 be a particular value of t. Use Table VI of Appendix A to find t_0 values such that the following statements are true:

    a. $P(-t_0 < t < t_0) = .95$, where df $= 16$

    b. $P(t \leq -t_0 \text{ or } t \geq t_0) = .05$, where df $= 16$

    c. $P(t \leq t_0) = .05$, where df $= 16$

    d. $P(t \leq -t_0 \text{ or } t \geq t_0) = .10$, where df $= 12$

    e. $P(t \leq -t_0 \text{ or } t \geq t_0) = .01$, where df $= 8$

7.31 The following random sample was selected from a normal distribution: 4, 6, 3, 5, 9, 3.

    a. Construct a 90% confidence interval for the population mean μ.

    b. Construct a 95% confidence interval for the population mean μ.

    c. Construct a 99% confidence interval for the population mean μ.

    d. Assume that the sample mean $\bar{x}$ and sample standard deviation s remain exactly the same as those you just calculated, but that they are based on a sample of $n = 25$ observations rather than $n = 6$ observations. Repeat parts **a–c**. What is the effect of increasing the sample size on the width of the confidence intervals?

7.32 The following sample of 16 measurements was selected from a population that is approximately normally distributed:

⚙ **LM7_32**

91	80	99	110	95	106	78	121	106	100
97	82	100	83	115	104				

    a. Construct an 80% confidence interval for the population mean.

    b. Construct a 95% confidence interval for the population mean, and compare the width of this interval with that of part **a**.

    c. Carefully interpret each of the confidence intervals, and explain why the 80% confidence interval is narrower.

Applying the Concepts—Basic

7.33 Al Qaeda attacks on the United States. Refer to the *Studies in Conflict & Terrorism* (Vol. 29, 2006) analysis of recent incidents involving suicide terrorist attacks, presented in Exercise 2.30 (p. 46). Data on the number of individual suicide bombings or attacks for each in a sample of 21 incidents involving an attack against the United States by the Al Qaeda terrorist group are reproduced in the accompanying table.

    a. Find the mean and standard deviation of the sample data.

    b. Describe the population from which the sample is selected.

    c. Use the information from part **a** to find a 90% confidence interval for the mean μ of the population.

    d. Give a practical interpretation of the result you obtained in part **c**.

    e. In repeatedly sampling, where intervals similar to the one computed in part **c** are generated, what proportion of the intervals will enclose the true value of μ?

⚙ **ALQAEDA**

1	1	2	1	2	4	1	1	1	1	2	3	4	5	1	1	1	2	2	2	1

Source: Moghadam, A. "Suicide terrorism, occupation, and the globalization of martyrdom: A critique of *Dying to Win*," *Studies in Conflict & Terrorism*, Vol. 29, No. 8, 2006 (Table 3).

7.34 Assessing the bending strength of a wooden roof. The white wood material used for the roof of an ancient Japanese temple is imported from Northern Europe. The wooden roof must withstand as much as 100 centimeters of snow in the winter. Architects at Tohoku University (in Japan) conducted a study to estimate the mean bending strength of the white wood roof (*Journal of the International Association for*

MINITAB Output for Exercise 7.35

Variable	N	Mean	StDev	SE Mean	95% CI
CESIUM	9	0.009027	0.004854	0.001618	(0.005296, 0.012759)

Shell and Spatial Structures, Aug. 2004). A sample of 25 pieces of the imported wood was tested and yielded the following statistics on breaking strength (in MPa): $\bar{x} = 75.4$, $s = 10.9$. Estimate the true mean breaking strength of the white wood with a 90% confidence interval. Interpret the result.

LICHEN

7.35 Radioactive lichen. Refer to the Lichen Radionuclide Baseline Research project at the University of Alaska, presented in Exercise 2.34 (p. 47). Recall that the researchers collected 9 lichen specimens and measured the amount (in microcuries per milliliter) of the radioactive element cesium-137 for each. (The natural logarithms of the data values are saved in the **LICHEN** file.) A MINITAB printout with summary statistics for the actual data is shown above.

a. Give a point estimate for the mean amount of cesium in lichen specimens collected in Alaska.

b. Give the *t*-value used in a small-sample 95% confidence interval for the true mean amount of cesium in Alaskan lichen specimens.

c. Use the result you obtained in part **b** and the values of $\bar{x}$ and *s* shown on the MINITAB printout to form a 95% confidence interval for the true mean amount of cesium in Alaskan lichen specimens.

d. Check the interval you found in part **c** with the 95% confidence interval shown on the MINITAB printout.

e. Give a practical interpretation for the interval you obtained in part **c**.

GOBIANTS

7.36 Rainfall and desert ants. Refer to the *Journal of Biogeography* (December 2003) study of ants and their habitat in the desert of Central Asia, presented in Exercise 2.66 (p. 60). Recall that botanists randomly selected five sites in the Dry Steppe region and six sites in the Gobi Desert where ants were observed. One of the variables of interest is the annual rainfall (in millimeters) at each site. (The data are saved in the **GOBIANTS** file.) Summary statistics for the annual rainfall at each site are provided in the SAS printout below.

a. Give a point estimate for the average annual rainfall amount at ant sites in the Dry Steppe region of Central Asia.

b. Give the *t*-value used in a small-sample 90% confidence interval for the true average annual rainfall amount at ant sites in the Dry Steppe region.

c. Use the result you obtained in part **b** and the values of $\bar{x}$ and *s* shown on the SAS printout to form a 90% confidence interval for the target parameter.

d. Give a practical interpretation for the interval you found in part **c**.

e. Use the data in the **GOBIANTS** file to check the validity of the confidence interval you found in part **c**.

f. Repeat parts **a–e** for the Gobi Desert region of Central Asia.

7.37 Oven cooking study. A group of Harvard University School of Public Health researchers studied the impact of cooking on the size of indoor air particles. (*Environmental Science & Technology,* September 1, 2000.) The decay rate (measured in μm/hour) for fine particles produced from oven cooking or toasting was recorded on six randomly selected days. The six measurements obtained are as follows:

DECAY

.95	.83	1.20	.89	1.45	1.12

Source: Abt, E., et al. "Relative contribution of outdoor and indoor particle sources to indoor concentrations." *Environmental Science & Technology,* Vol. 34, No. 17, Sept. 1, 2000 (Table 3).

a. Find and interpret a 95% confidence interval for the true average decay rate of fine particles produced from oven cooking or toasting.

b. Explain what the phrase "95% confident" implies in the interpretation of part **a**.

c. What must be true about the distribution of the population of decay rates for the inference you made in part **a** to be valid?

Applying the Concepts—Intermediate

7.38 Studies on treating Alzheimer's disease. Alzheimer's disease is a progressive disease of the brain. Much research has been conducted on how to treat Alzheimer's. The journal *eCAM* (November 2006) published an article that critiqued the quality of the methodology used in studies on Alzheimer treatment. For each in a sample of 13 studies, the quality of the methodology was measured on the Wong scale, with scores ranging from 9 (low quality) to 27 (high quality). The data are shown in the table on p. 325. Estimate, with a 99% confidence interval, the mean quality μ of all studies on the treatment of Alzheimer's disease. Interpret the result.

SAS Output for Exercise 7.36

The MEANS Procedure

Analysis Variable : RAIN

REGION	N Obs	Mean	Std Dev
DryStepp	5	183.4000000	20.6470337
Gobi	6	110.0000000	15.9749804

TREATAD

22	21	18	19	20	15	19	20	15	20	17	20	21

Source: Chiappelli, F., et al. "Evidence-based research in complementary and alternative medicine III: Treatment of patients with Alzheimer's disease," *eCAM*, Vol. 3, No. 4, Nov. 2006 (Table 1).

7.39 Reproduction of bacteria-infected spider mites. Zoologists in Japan investigated the reproductive traits of spider mites with a bacteria infection. (*Heredity*, Jan. 2007.) Male and female pairs of infected spider mites were mated in a laboratory and the number of eggs produced by each female recorded. Summary statistics for several samples are provided in the accompanying table. Note that, in some samples, one or both infected spider mites were treated with antibiotic prior to mating.
  a. For each type of female–male pair, construct and interpret a 90% confidence interval for the population mean number of eggs produced by the female spider mite.
  b. Identify the type of female–male pair that appears to produce the highest mean number of eggs.

Female–Male Pairs	Sample Size	Mean # of Eggs	Standard Deviation
Both untreated	29	20.9	3.34
Male treated	23	20.3	3.50
Female treated	18	22.9	4.37
Both treated	21	18.6	2.11

Source: Gotoh, T., Noda, H., & Ito, S. "*Cardinium* symbionts cause cytoplasmic incompatibility in spider mites," *Heredity*, Vol. 98, No. 1, Jan. 2007 (Table 2).

7.40 Minimizing tractor skidding distance. In planning for a new forest road to be used for tree harvesting, planners must select the location that will minimize tractor skidding distance. In the *Journal of Forest Engineering* (July 1999), researchers wanted to estimate the true mean skidding distance along a new road in a European forest. The skidding distances (in meters) were measured at 20 randomly selected road sites. These values are given in the accompanying table.
  a. Estimate, with a 95% confidence interval, the true mean skidding distance of the road.
  b. Give a practical interpretation of the interval you found in part **a**.
  c. What conditions are required for the inference you made in part **b** to be valid? Are these conditions reasonably satisfied?
  d. A logger working on the road claims that the mean skidding distance is at least 425 meters. Do you agree?

SKIDDING

488	350	457	199	285	409	435	574	439	546
385	295	184	261	273	400	311	312	141	425

Source: Tujek, J., & Pacola, E. "Algorithms for skidding distance modeling on a raster Digital Terrain Model," *Journal of Forest Engineering*, Vol. 10, No. 1, July 1999 (Table 1).

7.41 Research on brain specimens. In Exercise 2.37 (p. 48), you learned that the postmortem interval (PMI) is the elapsed time between death and the performance of an autopsy on the cadaver. *Brain and Language* (June 1995) reported on the PMIs of 22 randomly selected human brain specimens obtained at autopsy. The data are reproduced in the following table:

BRAINPMI

5.5	14.5	6.0	5.5	5.3	5.8	11.0	6.4
7.0	14.5	10.4	4.6	4.3	7.2	10.5	6.5
3.3	7.0	4.1	6.2	10.4	4.9		

Source: Hayes, T. L., and Lewis, D. A. "Anatomical specialization of the anterior motor speech area: Hemispheric differences in magnopyramidal neurons," *Brain and Language*, Vol. 49, No. 3, June 1995, p. 292 (Table 1).

  a. Construct a 95% confidence interval for the true mean PMI of human brain specimens obtained at autopsy.
  b. Interpret the interval you found in part **a**.
  c. What assumption is required for the interval from part **a** to be valid? Is this assumption satisfied? Explain.
  d. What is meant by the phrase "95% confidence"?

7.42 Eating disorders in females. The "fear of negative evaluation" (FNE) scores for 11 bulimic female students and 14 normal female students, first presented in Exercise 2.38 (p. 48) are reproduced at the bottom of the page. (Recall that the higher the score, the greater is the FNE.)
  a. Construct a 95% confidence interval for the mean FNE score of the population of bulimic female students. Interpret the result.
  b. Construct a 95% confidence interval for the mean FNE score of the population of normal female students. Interpret the result.
  c. What assumptions are required for the intervals of parts **a** and **b** to be statistically valid? Are these assumptions reasonably satisfied? Explain.

Applying the Concepts—Advanced

7.43 Study on waking sleepers early. Scientists have discovered increased levels of the hormone adrenocorticotropin in people just before they awake from sleeping (*Nature*, January 7, 1999). In the study described, 15 subjects were monitored during their sleep after being told that they would be woken at a particular time. One hour prior to the designated wake-up time, the adrenocorticotropin level (pg/mL) was measured in each, with the following results:

$$\bar{x} = 37.3 \qquad s = 13.9$$

  a. Use a 95% confidence interval to estimate the true mean adrenocorticotropin level of sleepers one hour prior to waking.
  b. Interpret the interval you found in part **a** in the words of the problem.
  c. The researchers also found that if the subjects were woken three hours earlier than they anticipated, the average

BULIMIA

Bulimic students	21	13	10	20	25	19	16	21	24	13	14			
Normal students	13	6	16	13	8	19	23	18	11	19	7	10	15	20

Source: Randles, R. H. "On neutral responses (zeros) in the sign test and ties in the Wilcoxon–Mann–Whitney Test." *The American Statistician*, Vol. 55, No. 2, May 2001 (Figure 3).

adrenocorticotropin level was 25.5 pg/mL. Assume that $\mu = 25.5$ for all sleepers who are woken three hours earlier than expected. Use the interval from part **a** to make an inference about the mean adrenocorticotropin level of sleepers under two conditions: one hour before the anticipated wake-up time and three hours before the anticipated wake-up time.

7.4 Large-Sample Confidence Interval for a Population Proportion

The number of public-opinion polls has grown at an astounding rate in recent years. Almost daily, the news media report the results of some poll. Pollsters regularly determine the percentage of people in favor of the president's welfare-reform program, the fraction of voters in favor of a certain candidate, the fraction of customers who favor a particular brand of wine, and the proportion of people who smoke cigarettes. In each case, we are interested in estimating the percentage (or proportion) of some group with a certain characteristic. In this section, we consider methods for making inferences about population proportions when the sample is large.

EXAMPLE 7.3
ESTIMATING A POPULATION PROPORTION—
Fraction Who Trust the President

Problem Public-opinion polls are conducted regularly to estimate the fraction of U.S. citizens who trust the president. Suppose 1,000 people are randomly chosen and 637 answer that they trust the president. How would you estimate the true fraction of *all* U.S. citizens who trust the president?

Solution What we have really asked is how you would estimate the probability p of success in a binomial experiment in which p is the probability that a person chosen trusts the president. One logical method of estimating p for the population is to use the proportion of successes in the sample. That is, we can estimate p by calculating

$$\hat{p} = \frac{\text{Number of people sampled who trust the president}}{\text{Number of people sampled}}$$

where $\hat{p}$ is read "p hat." Thus, in this case,

$$\hat{p} = \frac{637}{1,000} = .637$$

Look Back To determine the reliability of the estimator $\hat{p}$, we need to know its sampling distribution. That is, if we were to draw samples of 1,000 people over and over again, each time calculating a new estimate $\hat{p}$, what would be the frequency distribution of all the $\hat{p}$-values? The answer lies in viewing $\hat{p}$ as the average, or mean, number of successes per trial over the n trials. If each success is assigned a value equal to 1 and each failure is assigned a value of 0, then the sum of all n sample observations is x, the total number of successes, and $\hat{p} = x/n$ is the average, or mean, number of successes per trial in the n trials. The central limit theorem tells us that the relative frequency distribution of the sample mean for any population is approximately normal for sufficiently large samples.

Now Work Exercise 7.51a

The repeated sampling distribution of $\hat{p}$ has the characteristics listed in the next box and shown in Figure 7.12.

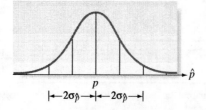

FIGURE 7.12
Sampling distribution of $\hat{p}$

Sampling Distribution of $\hat{p}$

1. The mean of the sampling distribution of $\hat{p}$ is p; that is, $\hat{p}$ is an unbiased estimator of p.
2. The standard deviation of the sampling distribution of $\hat{p}$ is $\sqrt{pq/n}$; that is, $\sigma_p = \sqrt{pq/n}$, where $q = 1 - p$.
3. For large samples, the sampling distribution of $\hat{p}$ is approximately normal. A sample size is considered large if the interval $\hat{p} \pm 3\sigma_{\hat{p}}$ does not include 0 or 1. [*Note:* This requirement is almost equivalent to that given in Section 5.5 for approximating a binomial distribution with a normal one. The difference is that we assumed p to be known in Section 5.5; now we are trying to make inferences about an unknown p, so we use $\hat{p}$ to estimate p in checking the adequacy of the normal approximation.]

The fact that $\hat{p}$ is a "sample mean fraction of successes" allows us to form confidence intervals about p in a manner that is completely analogous to that used for large-sample estimation of μ.

Large-Sample Confidence Interval for p

The large-sample confidence interval for p is

$$\hat{p} \pm z_{\alpha/2}\sigma_{\hat{p}} = \hat{p} \pm z_{\alpha/2}\sqrt{\frac{pq}{n}} \approx \hat{p} \pm z_{\alpha/2}\sqrt{\frac{\hat{p}\hat{q}}{n}}$$

where $\hat{p} = \dfrac{x}{n}$ and $\hat{q} = 1 - \hat{p}$

Note: When n is large, $\hat{p}$ can approximate the value of p in the formula for $\sigma_{\hat{p}}$.

Conditions Required for a Valid Large-Sample Confidence Interval for p

1. A random sample is selected from the target population.
2. The sample size n is large. (This condition will be satisfied if both $n\hat{p} \geq 15$ and $n\hat{q} \geq 15$. Note that $n\hat{p}$ and $n\hat{q}$ are simply the number of successes and number of failures, respectively, in the sample.

Thus, if 637 of 1,000 U.S. citizens say they trust the president, a 95% confidence interval for the proportion of *all* U.S. citizens who trust the president is

$$\hat{p} \pm z_{\alpha/2}\sigma_{\hat{p}} = .637 \pm 1.96\sqrt{\frac{pq}{1,000}}$$

where $q = 1 - p$. Just as we needed an approximation for σ in calculating a large-sample confidence interval for μ, we now need an approximation for p. As Table 7.6 shows, the approximation for p does not have to be especially accurate, because the value of $\sqrt{pq}$ needed for the confidence interval is relatively insensitive to changes in p. Therefore, we can use $\hat{p}$ to approximate p. Keeping in mind that $\hat{q} = 1 - \hat{p}$, we substitute these values into the formula for the confidence interval:

$$\hat{p} \pm 1.96\sqrt{pq/1,000} \approx \hat{p} \pm 1.96\sqrt{\hat{p}\hat{q}/1,000}$$

$$= .637 \pm 1.96\sqrt{(.637)(.363)/1,000} = .637 \pm .030$$

$$= (.607, .667)$$

TABLE 7.6 Values of pq for Several Different Values of p		
P	pq	$\sqrt{pq}$
.5	.25	.50
.6 or .4	.24	.49
.7 or .3	.21	.46
.8 or .2	.16	.40
.9 or .1	.09	.30

Then we can be 95% confident that the interval from 60.7% to 66.7% contains the true percentage of *all* U.S. citizens who trust the president. That is, in repeated constructions of confidence intervals, approximately 95% of all samples would produce confidence intervals that enclose p. Note that the guidelines for interpreting a confidence interval about μ also apply to interpreting a confidence interval for p, because p is the "population mean fraction of successes" in a binomial experiment.

EXAMPLE 7.4

A LARGE-SAMPLE CONFIDENCE INTERVAL FOR p—Proportion Optimistic about the Economy

Problem Many public polling agencies conduct surveys to determine the current consumer sentiment concerning the state of the economy. For example, the Bureau of Economic and Business Research (BEBR) at the University of Florida conducts quarterly surveys to gauge consumer sentiment in the Sunshine State. Suppose that BEBR randomly samples 484 consumers and finds that 257 are optimistic about the state of the economy. Use a 90% confidence interval to estimate the proportion of all consumers in Florida who are optimistic about the state of the economy. Based on the confidence interval, can BEBR infer that the majority of Florida consumers are optimistic about the economy?

Solution The number x of the 484 sampled consumers who are optimistic about the Florida economy is a binomial random variable if we can assume that the sample was randomly selected from the population of Florida consumers and that the poll was conducted identically for each consumer sampled.

The point estimate of the proportion of Florida consumers who are optimistic about the economy is

$$\hat{p} = \frac{x}{n} = \frac{257}{484} = .531$$

We first check to be sure that the sample size is sufficiently large that the normal distribution provides a reasonable approximation to the sampling distribution of $\hat{p}$. We require the number of successes in the sample, $n\hat{p}$, and the number of failures, $n\hat{q}$, both to be at least 15. Since the number of successes is $n\hat{p} = 257$ and the number of failures is $n\hat{q} = 227$, we may conclude that the normal approximation is reasonable.

We now proceed to form the 90% confidence interval for p, the true proportion of Florida consumers who are optimistic about the state of the economy:

$$\hat{p} \pm z_{\alpha/2}\sigma_{\hat{p}} = \hat{p} \pm z_{\alpha/2}\sqrt{\frac{pq}{n}} \approx \hat{p} \pm z_{\alpha/2}\sqrt{\frac{\hat{p}\hat{q}}{n}}$$

$$= .531 \pm 1.645\sqrt{\frac{(.531)(.469)}{484}} = .531 \pm .037 = (.494, .568)$$

(This interval is also shown on the MINITAB printout of Figure 7.13.) Thus, we can be 90% confident that the proportion of all Florida consumers who are confident about the economy is between .494 and .568. As always, our confidence stems from the fact that 90% of all similarly formed intervals will contain the true proportion p and not from any knowledge about whether this particular interval does.

FIGURE 7.13

Portion of MINITAB printout with 90% confidence interval for p

```
Sample    X     N   Sample p          90% CI
1        257   484  0.530992    (0.493681, 0.568303)
```

Can we conclude on the basis of this interval that the majority of Florida consumers are optimistic about the economy? If we wished to use this interval to infer that a majority is optimistic, the interval would have to support the inference that p exceeds .5—that is, that more than 50% of Florida consumers are optimistic about the economy. Note that the interval contains some values below .5 (as low as .494) as well as some above .5 (as high as .568). Therefore, we cannot conclude on the basis of this 90% confidence interval that the true value of p exceeds .5.

Look Back If the entire confidence interval fell above .5 (e.g., an interval from .52 to .54), then we could conclude (with 90% confidence) that the true proportion of consumers who are optimistic exceeds .5.

Now Work Exercise 7.51b–c

Caution

Unless n is extremely large, the large-sample procedure presented in this section performs poorly when p is near 0 or 1. For example, suppose you want to estimate the proportion of people who die from a bee sting. This proportion is likely to be near 0 (say, $p \approx .001$). Confidence intervals for p based on a sample of size $n = 50$ will probably be misleading.

To overcome this potential problem, an *extremely* large sample size is required. Since the value of n required to satisfy "extremely large" is difficult to determine, statisticians (see Agresti & Coull, 1998) have proposed an alternative method, based on the Wilson (1927) point estimator of p. **Wilson's adjustment for estimating p** is outlined in the next box. Researchers have shown that this confidence interval works well for any p, even when the sample size n is very small.

Adjusted $(1 - \alpha)$ 100% Confidence Interval for a Population Proportion p

An adjusted confidence interval for p is

$$\widetilde{p} \pm z_{\alpha/2}\sqrt{\frac{\widetilde{p}(1 - \widetilde{p})}{n + 4}}$$

where $\widetilde{p} = \dfrac{x + 2}{n + 4}$ is the adjusted sample proportion of observations with the characteristic of interest, x is the number of successes in the sample, and n is the sample size.

EXAMPLE 7.5

USING THE ADJUSTED CONFIDENCE INTERVAL PROCEDURE— Proportion Who Are Victims of a Violent Crime

Problem According to *True Odds: How Risk Affects Your Everyday Life* (Walsh, 1997), the probability of being the victim of a violent crime is less than .01. Suppose that, in a random sample of 200 Americans, 3 were victims of a violent crime. Use a 95% confidence interval to estimate the true proportion of Americans who were victims of a violent crime.

Solution Let p represent the true proportion of Americans who were victims of a violent crime. Since p is near 0, an "extremely large" sample is required to estimate its value by the usual large-sample method. Since we are unsure whether the sample size of 200 is large enough, we will apply Wilson's adjustment outlined in the box.

The number of "successes" (i.e., number of victims of a violent crime) in the sample is $x = 3$. Therefore, the adjusted sample proportion is

$$\widetilde{p} = \frac{x + 2}{n + 4} = \frac{3 + 2}{200 + 4} = \frac{5}{204} = .025$$

Note that this adjusted sample proportion is obtained by adding a total of four observations—two "successes" and two "failures"—to the sample data. Substituting $\widetilde{p} = .025$ into the equation for a 95% confidence interval, we obtain

$$\widetilde{p} \pm 1.96\sqrt{\frac{\widetilde{p}(1 - \widetilde{p})}{n + 4}} = .025 \pm 1.96\sqrt{\frac{(.025)(.975)}{204}}$$
$$= .025 \pm .021$$

or (.004, .046). Consequently, we are 95% confident that the true proportion of Americans who are victims of a violent crime falls between .004 and .046.

STATISTICS IN ACTION REVISITED

Estimating the Proportion of Sprinters Who Improve after Speed Training

In the previous Statistics in Action Revisited (p. 331), we discovered that a training program was effective in improving a high school athlete's speed in a 40-yard sprint. This inference was made by measuring the difference between an athlete's sprint time before and after the training program and then forming a confidence interval for the mean difference in times.

Another approach to the problem is to determine (on the basis of the before and after sprint times) whether each athlete improved his or her speed and measure this improvement qualitatively. Thus, each participating athlete's sprint performance will be classified as "Improved" (if the after time is less than the before time) or "Not Improved" (if the after time is greater than or the same as the before time). Now, the variable of interest is qualitative in nature, with two possible outcomes and our goal is to estimate p, the true proportion of all high school athletes who attain improved sprint times after participating in the speed training program.

If you examine the data for the 38 sampled athletes (saved in the **SPRINT** file and listed in Table SIA7.1, p. 305), you will find that 33 of the high school athletes had an "Improved" time in the 40-yard sprint. Thus, our estimate of p is

$$\hat{p} = 33/38 = .868$$

A 95% confidence interval for p can be obtained with the use of the confidence interval formula or with statistical software. A MINITAB printout of the analysis is displayed in Figure SIA7.2. The 95% confidence interval, highlighted on the printout, is (0.761, .976). Thus, we are 95% confident that anywhere from 76% to 97% of the athletes that participate in the speed training program will improve their 40-yard sprint time. These results present a strong case for claiming that the training program is effective in improving sprint speed. [*Note:* The MINITAB confidence interval in Figure SIA7.2 is based on a normal approximation that requires a "large" sample. A sample size of $n = 38$ athletes, although not small, may not be large enough for the sampling distribution of $\hat{p}$ to be normally distributed; thus, the interval may be inaccurate (as stated at the bottom of the MINITAB printout). To arrive at a more reliable estimate of the true proportion of improved sprint times, we may need a larger number of athletes to participate in the speed training program. In the next Statistics in Action Revisited (p. 337), we show how large a sample needs to be selected.]

Test and CI for One Proportion: Status

```
Test of p = 0.5 vs p not = 0.5

Event = Improve


Variable   X   N   Sample p        95% CI         Z-Value  P-Value
Status     33  38  0.868421  (0.760944, 0.975898)   4.54    0.000


* NOTE * The normal approximation may be inaccurate for small samples.
```

FIGURE SIA7.2
MINITAB confidence interval for proportion of improved sprint times

Confidence Interval for a Population Proportion (Large-Sample Case)

Using the TI-84/TI-83 Graphing Calculator

Creating a Confidence Interval for a Population Proportion

Step 1   *Access the Statistical Tests Menu.*
  Press **STAT**.
  Arrow right to **TESTS**.
  Arrow down to **1-PropZInt**.
  Press **ENTER**.

Step 2   *Enter the values for **x, n,** and **C-Level**,*
  Where **x** = number of successes,
  n = sample size, and
  C-Level = level of confidence.
  Arrow down to "**Calculate**".
  Press **ENTER**.

Example   Suppose that 1,100 U.S. citizens are randomly chosen and 532 answer that they favor a flat income tax rate. Use a 95% confidence interval to estimate the true proportion of citizens who favor a flat income tax rate. Here, $x = 532$, $n = 1,100$, and C-Level = .95.

The screens for this example are as follows:

   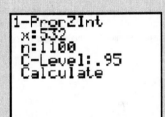

Thus a 95% confidence interval for the true percentage of all U.S. citizens who favor a flat income tax rate is the interval from 45.4% to 51.3%.

Exercises 7.44–7.61

Understanding the Principles

7.44 Describe the sampling distribution of $\hat{p}$ on the basis of large samples of size n. That is, give the mean, the standard deviation, and the (approximate) shape of the distribution of $\hat{p}$ when large samples of size n are (repeatedly) selected from the binomial distribution with probability p of success.

7.45 Explain the meaning of the phrase "$\hat{p}$ is an unbiased estimator of p."

7.46 If p is near 0 or 1, how large a sample is needed to employ the large-sample confidence interval procedure?

APPLET **Applet Exercise 7.5**

Use the applet entitled *Confidence Intervals for a Proportion* to investigate the effect of the value of p on the number of confidence intervals that contain the population proportion p for a fixed sample size. For this exercise, use sample size $n = 10$.

a. Run the applet several times without clearing for $p = .1$. What proportion of the 95% confidence intervals contain p? What proportion of the 99% confidence intervals contain p? Do the results surprise you? Explain.

b. Repeat part **a** for each value of p: $p = .2$, $p = .3$, $p = .4$. $p = .5$, $p = .6$, $p = .7$, $p = .8$, and $p = .9$.

c. Which value of p yields the greatest proportion of each type of interval that contain p?

d. Based on your results, what values of p will yield more reliable confidence intervals for a fixed sample size n? Explain.

APPLET **Applet Exercise 7.6**

Use the applet entitled *Confidence Intervals for a Proportion* to investigate the effect of the sample size on the number of confidence intervals that contain the population proportion p for a value of p close to 0 or 1.

a. Run the applet several times without clearing for $p = .5$ and $n = 50$. Record the proportion of the 99% confidence intervals containing p.

b. Now set $p = .1$ and run the applet several times without clearing for $n = 50$. How does the proportion of the 99% confidence intervals containing p compare with that in part **a**?

c. Repeat part **b**, keeping $p = .1$ and increasing the sample size by 50 until you find a sample size that yields a similar proportion of the 99% confidence intervals containing p as that in part **a**.

d. Based on your results, describe how the value of p affects the sample size needed to guarantee a certain level of confidence.

Learning the Mechanics

7.47 A random sample of size $n = 196$ yielded $\hat{p} = .64$.
   a. Is the sample size large enough to use the methods of this section to construct a confidence interval for p? Explain.
   b. Construct a 95% confidence interval for p.
   c. Interpret the 95% confidence interval.
   d. Explain what is meant by the phrase "95% confidence interval."

7.48 A random sample of size $n = 144$ yielded $\hat{p} = .76$.
   a. Is the sample size large enough to use the methods of this section to construct a confidence interval for p? Explain.
   b. Construct a 90% confidence interval for p.
   c. What assumption is necessary to ensure the validity of this confidence interval?

7.49 For the binomial sample information summarized in each part, indicate whether the sample size is large enough to use the methods of this chapter to construct a confidence interval for p.
   a. $n = 500, \hat{p} = .05$
   b. $n = 100, \hat{p} = .05$
   c. $n = 10, \hat{p} = .5$
   d. $n = 10, \hat{p} = .3$

7.50 A random sample of 50 consumers taste-tested a new snack food. Their responses were coded (0: do not like; 1: like; 2: indifferent) and recorded as follows:

SNACK

1	0	0	1	2	0	1	1	0	0
0	1	0	2	0	2	2	0	0	1
1	0	0	0	0	1	0	2	0	0
0	1	0	0	1	0	0	1	0	1
0	2	0	0	1	1	0	0	0	1

   a. Use an 80% confidence interval to estimate the proportion of consumers who like the snack food.
   b. Provide a statistical interpretation for the confidence interval you constructed in part **a**.

Applying the Concepts—Basic

7.51 **National Firearms Survey.** Refer to the Harvard School of Public Health survey to determine the size and composition of privately held firearm stock in the United States, presented in Exercise 2.6 (p. 34). Recall that, in a representative household telephone survey of 2,770 adults, 26% reported that they own at least one gun. (*Injury Prevention*, Jan. 2007.) The researchers want to estimate the true percentage of adults in the United States that own at least one gun.
   a. Identify the population of interest to the researchers.
   b. Identify the parameter of interest to the researchers.
   c. Compute an estimate of the population parameter.

d. Form a 99% confidence interval around the estimate.
   e. Interpret the confidence interval practically.
   f. Explain the meaning of the phrase "99% confident."

7.52 **Are you really being served red snapper?** Refer to the *Nature* (July 15, 2004) study of fish specimens labeled "red snapper," presented in Exercise 3.79 (p. 150). Recall that federal law prohibits restaurants from serving a cheaper look-alike variety of fish (e.g., vermillion snapper or lane snapper) to customers who order red snapper. In an effort to estimate the true proportion of fillets that are really red snapper, a team of University of North Carolina (UNC) researchers analyzed the meat from each in a sample of 22 "red snapper" fish fillets purchased from vendors across the United States. DNA tests revealed that 17 of the 22 fillets (or 77%) were not red snapper, but the cheaper look-alike variety of fish.
   a. Identify the parameter of interest to the UNC researchers.
   b. Explain why a large-sample confidence interval is inappropriate to apply in this study.
   c. Use Wilson's adjustment to construct a 95% confidence interval for the parameter of interest.
   d. Give a practical interpretation of the confidence interval.

7.53 **What we do when we are sick at home.** *USA Today* (Feb. 15, 2007) reported on the results of an opinion poll in which adults were asked what one thing they are most likely to do when they are home sick with a cold or the flu. In the survey, 63% said that they are most likely to sleep and 18% said that they would watch television. Although the sample size was not reported, typically opinion polls include approximately 1,000 randomly selected respondents.
   a. Assuming a sample size of 1,000 for this poll, construct a 95% confidence interval for the true percentage of all adults who would choose to sleep when they are at home sick.
   b. If the true percentage of adults who would choose to sleep when they are at home sick is 70%, would you be surprised? Explain.

7.54 **Scary-movie study.** According to a University of Michigan study, many adults have experienced lingering "fright" effects from a scary movie or TV show they saw as a teenager. (*Tampa Tribune*, March 10, 1999.) In a survey of 150 college students, 39 said they still experience "residual anxiety" from a scary TV show or movie.
   a. Give a point estimate $\hat{p}$ for the true proportion of college students who experience "residual anxiety" from a scary TV show or movie.
   b. Find a 95% confidence interval for p.
   c. Interpret the interval you found in part **b**.

7.55 **Ancient Greek pottery.** Refer to the *Chance* (Fall 2000) study of 837 pieces of pottery found at the ancient Greek settlement at Phylakopi, presented in Exercise 2.12 (p. 35). Of the 837 pieces, 183 were painted with either a curvilinear, geometric, or naturalistic decoration. Find a 90% confidence interval for the population proportion of all pottery artifacts at Phylakopi that are painted. Interpret the resulting interval.

Applying the Concepts—Intermediate

PONDICE

7.56 **Characteristics of ice-melt ponds.** Refer to the University of Colorado study of ice-melt ponds in the Canadian Arctic, presented in Exercise 2.11 (p. 35). Environmental engineers are using data collected by the National Snow and Ice Data Center to learn how climate affects the sea ice. Data on 504 ice melt ponds are saved in the **PONDICE** file. Of these 504 melt ponds, 88 were classified as having "first-year ice." Recall that the researchers estimated that about 17% of melt ponds in the Canadian Arctic have first-year ice. Use the methodology of this chapter to estimate, with 90% confidence, the percentage of all ice-melt ponds in the Canadian Arctic that have first-year ice. Give a practical interpretation of the results.

BIBLE

7.57 Do you believe in the Bible? Refer to the National Opinion Research Center's General Social Survey (GSS), presented in Exercise 2.17 (p. 36). Data on the approximately 2,800 Americans who participated in the 2004 GSS are saved in the **BIBLE** file. Recall that one question in the survey asked about a person's belief in the Bible. Suppose you want to estimate the proportion of all Americans who believe that the Bible is the actual word of God and is to be taken literally. (*Note:* The variable "Bible1" contains the responses to this question.)

a. Use a 95% confidence interval to estimate the proportion of interest.

b. Give a practical interpretation of the interval you used in part **a**.

c. Discuss how the survey methodology can affect the validity of the results.

7.58 Exercise workout dropouts. Researchers at the University of Florida's Department of Exercise and Sport Sciences conducted a study of variety in exercise workouts. (*Journal of Sport Behavior*, 2001.) A sample of 120 men and women were randomly divided into three groups, with 40 people per group. Group 1 members varied their exercise routine in workouts, group 2 members performed the same exercise at each workout, and group 3 members had no set schedule or regulations for their workouts.

a. By the end of the study, 15 people had dropped out of the first exercise group. Estimate the dropout rate for exercisers who vary their routine in workouts. Use a 90% confidence interval and interpret the result.

b. By the end of the study, 23 people had dropped out of the third exercise group. Estimate the dropout rate for exercisers who have no set schedule for their workouts. Use a 90% confidence interval and interpret the result.

7.59 Whistling dolphins. In Exercise 2.177 (p. 104) you learned about the signature whistles of bottlenose dolphins. Marine scientists categorize signature whistles by type—type a, type b, type c, etc. In one study of a sample of 185 whistles emitted from bottlenose dolphins in captivity, 97 were categorized as type a whistles (*Ethology*, July 1995).

a. Estimate the true proportion of bottlenose dolphin signature whistles that are type a whistles. Use a 99% confidence interval.

b. Interpret the interval you used in part **a**.

7.60 Studies on treating Alzheimer's disease. Refer to the journal *eCAM* (November 2006) assessment of the quality of the methodology used in studies of the treatment for Alzheimer's disease, presented in Exercise 7.38 (p. 324). Data on the quality of the methodology (using the Wong scale) for each in a sample of 13 studies are reproduced in the accompanying table. According to the researchers, a study with a Wong score below 18 used a methodology that "fails to support the author's conclusions" about the treatment of Alzheimer's. Use Wilson's adjustment to estimate the proportion of all studies on the treatment of Alzheimer's disease with a Wong score below 18. Construct a 99% confidence interval around the estimate and interpret the result.

TREATAD

22	21	18	19	20	15	19	20	15	20	17	20	21

Source: Chiappelli, F., et al. "Evidence-based research in complementary and alternative medicine III: Treatment of patients with Alzheimer's disease", *eCAM*, Vol. 3, No. 4, Nov. 2006 (Table 1).

Applying the Concepts—Advanced

7.61 Latex allergy in health-care workers. Refer to the *Current Allergy & Clinical Immunology* (March 2004) study of health-care workers who use latex gloves, Presented in Exercise 7.13 (p. 314). In addition to the 46 hospital employees who were diagnosed with a latex allergy on the basis of a skin-prick test, another 37 health-care workers were diagnosed with the allergy by means of a latex-specific serum test. Of these 83 workers with a confirmed latex allergy, only 36 suspected that they had the allergy when they were asked about it on a questionnaire. Make a statement about the likelihood that a health-care worker with a latex allergy suspects that he or she actually has the allergy. Attach a measure of reliability to your inference.

7.5 Determining the Sample Size

Recall from Section 1.5 that one way to collect the relevant data for a study used to make inferences about a population is to implement a designed (planned) experiment. Perhaps the most important design decision faced by the analyst is to determine the size of the sample. We show in this section that the appropriate sample size for making an inference about a population mean or proportion depends on the desired reliability.

Estimating a Population Mean

Consider the example from Section 7.2 in which we estimated the mean length of stay for patients in a large hospital. A sample of 100 patients' records produced the 95% confidence interval $\bar{x} \pm 2\sigma_{\bar{x}} \approx 4.53 \pm .74$. Consequently, our estimate $\bar{x}$ was within .74 day of the true mean length of stay, μ, for all the hospital's patients at the 95% confidence level. That is, the 95% confidence interval for μ was 2(.74) = 1.48 days wide when 100 accounts were sampled. This is illustrated in Figure 7.14a.

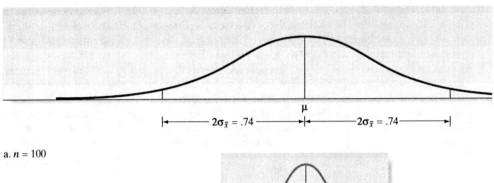

a. $n = 100$

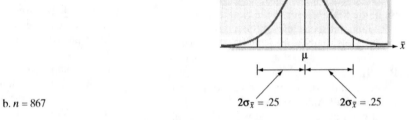

FIGURE 7.14

Relationship between sample size and width of confidence interval: hospital-stay example

b. $n = 867$

Now suppose we want to estimate μ to within .25 day with 95% confidence. That is, we want to narrow the width of the confidence interval from 1.48 days to .50 day, as shown in Figure 7.14b. How much will the sample size have to be increased to accomplish this? If we want the estimator $\bar{x}$ to be within .25 day of μ, then we must have

$$2\sigma_{\bar{x}} = .25 \qquad \text{or, equivalently,} \qquad 2\left(\frac{\sigma}{\sqrt{n}}\right) = .25$$

Note that we are using $\sigma_{\bar{x}} = \dfrac{\sigma}{\sqrt{n}}$ in the formula, since we are dealing with the sampling distribution of $\bar{x}$ (the estimator of μ).

The necessary sample size is obtained by solving this equation for n. To do that, we need an approximation of σ. We have an approximation from the initial sample of 100 patients' records—namely, the sample standard deviation $s = 3.68$. Thus,

$$2\left(\frac{\sigma}{\sqrt{n}}\right) \approx 2\left(\frac{s}{\sqrt{n}}\right) = 2\left(\frac{3.68}{\sqrt{n}}\right) = .25$$

$$\sqrt{n} = \frac{2(3.68)}{.25} = 29.44$$

$$n = (29.44)^2 = 866.71 \approx 867$$

Approximately 867 patients' records will have to be sampled to estimate the mean length of stay, μ, to within .25 day with (approximately) 95% confidence. The confidence interval resulting from a sample of this size will be approximately .50 day wide. (See Figure 7.14b.)

In general, we express the reliability associated with a confidence interval for the population mean μ by specifying the **sampling error** within which we want to estimate μ with $100(1 - \alpha)\%$ confidence. The sampling error (denoted SE) is then equal to the half-width of the confidence interval, as shown in Figure 7.15.

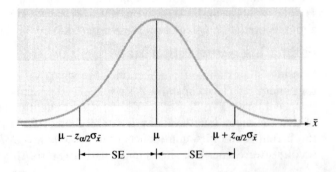

FIGURE 7.15

Specifying the sampling error SE as the half-width of a confidence interval

The procedure for finding the sample size necessary to estimate μ with a specific sampling error is given in the following box:

Determination of Sample Size for $100(1 - \alpha)\%$ Confidence Intervals for μ

In order to estimate μ with a sampling error SE and with $100(1 - \alpha)\%$ confidence, the required sample size is found as follows:

$$z_{\alpha/2}\left(\frac{\sigma}{\sqrt{n}}\right) = \text{SE}$$

The solution for n is given by the equation

$$n = \frac{(z_{\alpha/2})^2\sigma^2}{(\text{SE})^2}$$

The value of σ is usually unknown. It can be estimated by the standard deviation s from a previous sample. Alternatively, we may approximate the range R of observations in the population and (conservatively) estimate $\sigma \approx R/4$. In any case, you should round the value of n obtained *upward* to ensure that the sample size will be sufficient to achieve the specified reliability.

EXAMPLE 7.6

SAMPLE SIZE FOR ESTIMATING μ—
Mean Inflation Pressure of Footballs

Problem Suppose the manufacturer of official NFL footballs uses a machine to inflate the new balls to a pressure of 13.5 pounds. When the machine is properly calibrated, the mean inflation pressure is 13.5 pounds, but uncontrollable factors cause the pressures of individual footballs to vary randomly from about 13.3 to 13.7 pounds. For quality control purposes, the manufacturer wishes to estimate the mean inflation pressure to within .025 pound of its true value with a 99% confidence interval. What sample size should be specified for the experiment?

Solution We desire a 99% confidence interval that estimates μ with a sampling error of SE = .025 pound. For a 99% confidence interval, we have $z_{\alpha/2} = z_{.005} = 2.575$. To estimate σ, we note that the range of observations is $R = 13.7 - 13.3 = .4$ and we use $\sigma \approx R/4 = .1$. Next, we employ the formula derived in the box to find the sample size n:

$$n = \frac{(z_{\alpha/2})^2\sigma^2}{(\text{SE})^2} \approx \frac{(2.575)^2(.1)^2}{(.025)^2} = 106.09$$

We round this up to $n = 107$. Realizing that σ was approximated by $R/4$, we might even advise that the sample size be specified as $n = 110$ to be more certain of attaining the objective of a 99% confidence interval with a sampling error of .025 pound or less.

Look Back To determine the value of the sampling error SE, look for the value that follows the key words "estimate μ to within. . . ."

Now Work Exercise 7.75

Sometimes the formula will lead to a solution that indicates a small sample size is sufficient to achieve the confidence interval goal. Unfortunately, the procedures and assumptions for small samples differ from those for large samples, as we discovered in Section 7.3. Therefore, if the formulas yield a small sample size, one simple strategy is to select a sample size $n = 30$.

Estimating a Population Proportion

The method just outlined is easily applied to a population proportion p. For example, in Section 7.4 a pollster used a sample of 1,000 U.S. citizens to calculate a 95% confidence interval for the proportion who trust the president, obtaining the interval

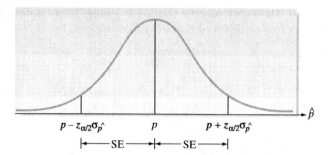

FIGURE 7.16

Specifying the sampling error SE of a confidence interval for a population proportion p

.637 $\pm$ .03. Suppose the pollster wishes to estimate more precisely the proportion who trust the president, say, to within .015 with a 95% confidence interval.

The pollster wants a confidence interval for p with a sampling error SE = .015. The sample size required to generate such an interval is found by solving the following equation for n:

$$z_{\alpha/2}\sigma_{\hat{p}} = SE \qquad \text{or} \qquad z_{\alpha/2}\sqrt{\frac{pq}{n}} = .015 \qquad \text{(see Figure 7.16)}$$

Since a 95% confidence interval is desired, the appropriate z value is $z_{\alpha/2} = z_{.025} = 1.96$. We must approximate the value of the product pq before we can solve the equation for n. As shown in Table 7.6 (p. 328), the closer the values of p and q to .5, the larger is the product pq. Thus, to find a conservatively large sample size that will generate a confidence interval with the specified reliability, we generally choose an approximation of p close to .5. In the case of the proportion of U.S. citizens who trust the president, however, we have an initial sample estimate of $\hat{p} = .637$. A conservatively large estimate of pq can therefore be obtained by using, say, $p = .60$. We now substitute into the equation and solve for n:

$$1.96\sqrt{\frac{(.60)(.40)}{n}} = .015$$

$$n = \frac{(1.96)^2(.60)(.40)}{(.015)^2} = 4,097.7 \approx 4,098$$

The pollster must sample about 4,098 U.S. citizens to estimate the percentage who trust the president with a confidence interval of width .03.

The procedure for finding the sample size necessary to estimate a population proportion p with a specified sampling error SE is given in the following box:

Determination of Sample Size for $100(1 - \alpha)$% Confidence Interval for p

In order to estimate a binomial probability p with sampling error SE and with $100(1 - \alpha)$% confidence, the required sample size is found by solving the following equation for n:

$$z_{\alpha/2}\sqrt{\frac{pq}{n}} = SE$$

The solution for n can be written as follows:

$$n = \frac{(z_{\alpha/2})^2(pq)}{(SE)^2}$$

Since the value of the product pq is unknown, it can be estimated by the sample fraction of successes, $\hat{p}$, from a previous sample. Remember (Table 7.6) that the value of pq is at its maximum when p equals .5, so you can obtain conservatively large values of n by approximating p by .5 or values close to .5. In any case, you should round the value of n obtained *upward* to ensure that the sample size will be sufficient to achieve the specified reliability.

EXAMPLE 7.7

SAMPLE SIZE FOR ESTIMATING *p* — Fraction of Defective Cell Phones

Problem Suppose a large telephone manufacturer that entered the postregulation market quickly has an initial problem with excessive customer complaints and consequent returns of the phones for repair or replacement. The manufacturer wants to estimate the magnitude of the problem in order to design a quality control program. How many telephones should be sampled and checked in order to estimate the fraction defective, *p*, to within .01 with 90% confidence?

Solution In order to estimate *p* to within .01 of its true value, we set the half-width of the confidence interval equal to SE = .01, as shown in Figure 7.17.

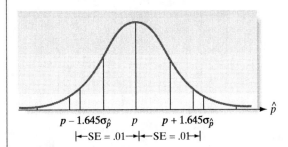

FIGURE 7.17

Specified reliability for estimate of fraction defective in Example 7.7

The equation for the sample size *n* requires an estimate of the product *pq*. We could most conservatively estimate *pq* = .25 (i.e., use *p* = .5), but this estimate may be too conservative. By contrasts, a value of .1, corresponding to 10% defective, will probably be conservatively large for this application. The solution is therefore

$$n = \frac{(z_{\alpha/2})^2(pq)}{(SE)^2} = \frac{(1.645)^2(.1)(.9)}{(.01)^2} = 2{,}435.4 \approx 2{,}436$$

Thus, the manufacturer should sample 2,436 telephones in order to estimate the fraction defective, *p*, to within .01 with 90% confidence.

Look Back Remember that this answer depends on our approximation of *pq*, for which we used .09. If the fraction defective is closer to .05 than .10, we can use a sample of 1,286 telephones (check this) to estimate *p* to within .01 with 90% confidence.

Now Work Exercise 7.74

The cost of sampling will also play an important role in the final determination of the sample size to be selected to estimate either μ or *p*. Although more complex formulas can be derived to balance the reliability and cost considerations, we will solve for the necessary sample size and note that the sampling budget may be a limiting factor. (Consult the references on page 346 for a more complete treatment of this problem.)

STATISTICS IN ACTION REVISITED

Determining the Number of Athletes Required to Participate in the Training Program for a Valid Estimate of *p*

In the previous Statistics in Action applications in this chapter, we used confidence intervals (1) to estimate μ, the population mean decrease in sprint time for athletes who participate in the speed training program (p. 311), and (2) to esti- mate *p*, the population proportion of athletes who improve their sprint times after participating in the speed training program (p. 330). The confidence interval for *p* was fairly wide due to the relatively small number of athletes ($n = 38$) who participated in the program. In order to find a valid, narrower confidence interval for

(continued)

the true proportion, the researchers would need to include more athletes in the study.

How many high school athletes should be sampled to estimate p to within, say, .03 with 95% confidence? Here, we have the sampling error SE = .03 and $z_{.025}$ = 1.96 (since, for a 95% confidence interval, α = .05 and $\alpha/2$ = .025). From our analysis on page 330, the estimated proportion is $\hat{p}$ = .87. Substituting these values into the formula given in the box on page 336, we obtain

$$n = \frac{(z_{.025})^2(\hat{p})(1 - \hat{p})}{(SE)^2} = \frac{(1.96)^2(.87)(.13)}{(.03)^2} = 482.76$$

Consequently, the researchers would have to include 483 high school athletes in the training program in order to find a valid 95% confidence interval for p to within 3% of its true value.

Running the training program with this large number of athletes, however, may be impractical. To reduce the size of the sample, the researchers could choose to increase the sampling error (i.e., the width) of the confidence interval for p or decrease the confidence level $(1 - \alpha)$. However, since both large- and small-sample confidence intervals are available for estimating μ, the researchers can rely on the inference made from the confidence interval for the mean decrease in sprint time (p. 311).

Exercises 7.62–7.82

Understanding the Principles

7.62 How does the sampling error SE compare with the width of a confidence interval?

7.63 **True or false.** For a specified sampling error SE, increasing the confidence level $(1 - \alpha)$ will lead to a larger n in determining the sample size.

7.64 **True or false.** For a fixed confidence level $(1 - \alpha)$, increasing the sampling error SE will lead to a smaller n in determining the sample size.

Learning the Mechanics

7.65 If you wish to estimate a population mean to within .2 with a 95% confidence interval and you know from previous sampling that σ^2 is approximately equal to 5.4, how many observations would you have to include in your sample?

7.66 If nothing is known about p, .5 can be substituted for p in the sample-size formula for a population proportion. But when this is done, the resulting sample size may be larger than needed. Under what circumstances will using p = .5 in the sample-size formula yield a sample size larger than is needed to construct a confidence interval for p with a specified bound and a specified confidence level?

7.67 Suppose you wish to estimate a population mean correct to within .15 with a confidence level of .90. You do not know σ^2, but you know that the observations will range in value between 31 and 39.

a. Find the approximate sample size that will produce the desired accuracy of the estimate. You wish to be conservative to ensure that the sample size will be ample for achieving the desired accuracy of the estimate. [*Hint:* Using your knowledge of data variation from Section 2.5, assume that the range of the observations will equal 4σ.]

b. Calculate the approximate sample size, making the less conservative assumption that the range of the observations is equal to 6σ.

7.68 In each case, find the approximate sample size required to construct a 95% confidence interval for p that has sampling error SE = .06.

a. Assume that p is near .3.

b. Assume that you have no prior knowledge about p, but you wish to be certain that your sample is large enough to achieve the specified accuracy for the estimate.

7.69 The following is a 90% confidence interval for p: (.26, .54). How large was the sample used to construct this interval?

7.70 It costs you $10 to draw a sample of size n = 1 and measure the attribute of interest. You have a budget of $1,200.

a. Do you have sufficient funds to estimate the population mean for the attribute of interest with a 95% confidence interval 4 units in width? Assume that σ = 12.

b. If a 90% confidence level were used, would your answer to part **a** change? Explain.

7.71 Suppose you wish to estimate the mean of a normal population with a 95% confidence interval and you know from prior information that $\sigma^2 \approx 1$.

a. To see the effect of the sample size on the width of the confidence interval, calculate the width of the confidence interval for n = 16, 25, 49, 100, and 400.

b. Plot the width as a function of sample size n on graph paper. Connect the points by a smooth curve, and note how the width decreases as n increases.

Applying the Concepts—Basic

7.72 **Radioactive lichen.** Refer to the Alaskan Lichen Radionuclide Baseline Research study, presented in Exercise 7.35 (p. 324). In a sample of n = 9 lichen specimens, the researchers found the mean and standard deviation of the amount of the radioactive element, cesium-137, that was present to be .009 and .005 microcurie per milliliter, respectively. Suppose the researchers want to increase the sample size in order to estimate the mean μ to within .001 microcurie per milliliter of its true value, using a 95% confidence interval.

a. What is the confidence level desired by the researchers?

b. What is the sampling error desired by the researchers?

c. Compute the sample size necessary to obtain the desired estimate.

7.73 **Scanning errors at Wal-Mart.** Refer to the National Institute for Standards and Technology (NIST) study of the accuracy of checkout scanners at Wal-Mart stores in California, presented in Exercise 3.48 (p. 135). NIST sets standards so that no more than 2 of every 100 items scanned through an electronic checkout scanner can have an inaccurate price. Recall that in a sample of 60 Wal-Mart stores, 52 violated the NIST scanner accuracy standard. (*Tampa Tribune*, Nov. 22, 2005.) Suppose you want to estimate the true proportion of Wal-Mart stores in California that violate the NIST standard.

a. Explain why the large-sample methodology of Section 7.4 is inappropriate for this study.

b. Determine the number of Wal-Mart stores that must be sampled in order to estimate the true proportion to within .05 with 90% confidence, using the large-sample method.

7.74 Aluminum cans contaminated by fire. A gigantic warehouse located in Tampa, Florida, stores approximately 60 million empty aluminum beer and soda cans. Recently, a fire occurred at the warehouse. The smoke from the fire contaminated many of the cans with blackspot, rendering them unusable. A University of South Florida statistician was hired by the insurance company to estimate p, the true proportion of cans in the warehouse that were contaminated by the fire. How many aluminum cans should be randomly sampled to estimate the true proportion to within .02 with 90% confidence?

7.75 Assessing the bending strength of a wooden roof. Refer to the *Journal of the International Association for Shell and Spatial Structures* (Aug. 2004) study to estimate the mean bending strength of imported white wood used on the roof of an ancient Japanese temple, presented in Exercise 7.34 (p. 323). Suppose you want to estimate the true mean breaking strength of the white wood to within 4 MPa, using a 90% confidence interval. How many pieces of the imported wood need to be tested? Recall that the sample standard deviation of the breaking strengths found in the study was 10.9 Mpa.

Applying the Concepts—Intermediate

7.76 Training zoo animals. Refer to Exercise 2.63 (p. 60) and the *Teaching of Psychology* (May 1998) study in which students assisted in the training of zoo animals. A sample of 15 psychology students rated "The Training Game" as a "great" method of understanding the animal's perspective during training on a 7–1 point scale (where 1 = strongly disagree and 7 = strongly agree). The mean response was 5.87, with a standard deviation of 1.51.

a. Construct a 95% confidence interval for the true mean response of the students.

b. Suppose you want to reduce the width of the 95% confidence interval to half the size obtained in part **a**. How many students are required in the sample in order to obtain the desired confidence interval width?

7.77 Bacteria in bottled water. Is the bottled water you drink safe? According to an article in *U.S. News & World Report* (April 12, 1999), the Natural Resources Defense Council warns that the bottled water you are drinking may contain more bacteria and other potentially carcinogenic chemicals than are allowed by state and federal regulations. Of the more than 1,000 bottles studied, nearly one-third exceeded government levels. Suppose that the Natural Resources Defense Council wants an updated estimate of the population proportion of bottled water that violates at least one government standard. Determine the sample size (number of bot-

tles) needed to estimate this proportion to within ± 0.01 with 99% confidence.

7.78 Asthma drug study. The chemical benzalkonium chloride (BAC) is an antibacterial agent that is added to some asthma medications to prevent contamination. Researchers at the University of Florida College of Pharmacy have discovered that adding BAC to asthma drugs can cause airway constriction in patients. In a sample of 18 asthmatic patients, each of whom received a heavy dose of BAC, 10 experienced a significant drop in breathing capacity (*Journal of Allergy and Clinical Immunology*, January 2001.) Based on this information, a 95% confidence interval for the true percentage of asthmatic patients who experience breathing difficulties after taking BAC is (.326, .785).

a. Why might the confidence interval lead to an erroneous inference?

b. How many asthma patients must be included in the study in order to estimate the true percentage who experience a significant drop in breathing capacity to within 4% with a 95% confidence interval?

7.79 Oven cooking study. Refer to Exercise 7.37 (p. 324). Suppose that we want to estimate the average decay rate of fine particles produced from oven cooking or toasting to within .04 with 95% confidence. How large a sample should be selected?

7.80 Caffeine content of coffee. According to a Food and Drug Administration (FDA) study, a cup of coffee contains an average of 115 milligrams (mg) of caffeine, with the amount per cup ranging from 60 to 180 mg. Suppose you want to repeat the FDA experiment in order to obtain an estimate of the mean caffeine content in a cup of coffee correct to within 5 mg with 95% confidence. How many cups of coffee would have to be included in your sample?

7.81 USGA golf ball tests. The United States Golf Association (USGA) tests all new brands of golf balls to ensure that they meet USGA specifications. One test conducted is intended to measure the average distance traveled when the ball is hit by a machine called "Iron Byron." Suppose the USGA wishes to estimate the mean distance for a new brand to within 1 yard with 90% confidence. Assume that past tests have indicated that the standard deviation of the distances Iron Byron hits golf balls is approximately 10 yards. How many golf balls should be hit by Iron Byron to achieve the desired accuracy in estimating the mean?

Applying the Concepts—Advanced

7.82 It costs more to produce defective items—since they must be scrapped or reworked—than it does to produce nondefective items. This simple fact suggests that manufacturers should ensure the quality of their products by perfecting their production processes instead of depending on inspection of finished products (Deming, 1986). In order to better understand a particular metal stamping process, a manufacturer wishes to estimate the mean length of items produced by the process during the past 24 hours.

a. How many parts should be sampled in order to estimate the population mean to within .1 millimeter (mm) with 90% confidence? Previous studies of this machine have indicated that the standard deviation of lengths produced by the stamping operation is about 2 mm.

b. Time permits the use of a sample size no larger than 100. If a 90% confidence interval for is constructed with $n = 100$, will it be wider or narrower than would have been obtained using the sample size determined in part **a**? Explain.

c. If management requires that μ be estimated to within .1 mm and that a sample size of no more than 100 be used, what is (approximately) the maximum confidence level that could be attained for a confidence interval that meets management's specifications?

KEY TERMS

Confidence coefficient   308
Confidence interval   308
Confidence level   308

Degrees of freedom   317
Interval estimator   308
Sampling error   334

Target parameter   306
t-statistic   317
Wilson adjustment for estimating p 329

GUIDE TO FORMING A CONFIDENCE INTERVAL

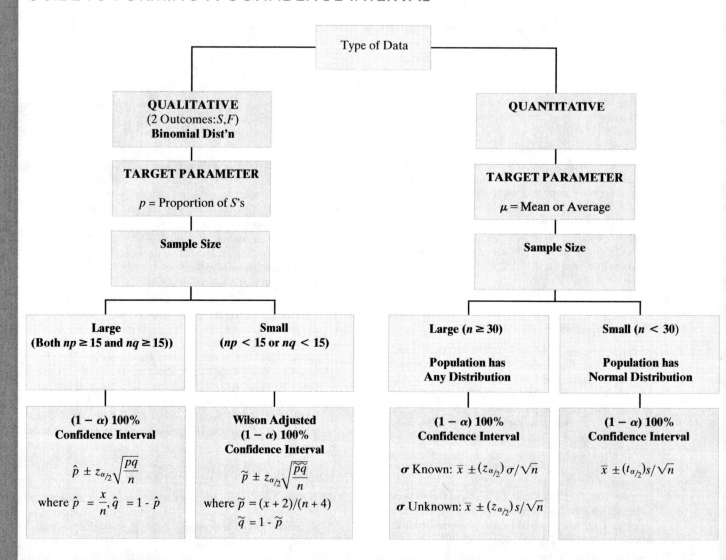

CHAPTER NOTES

Population Parameters, Estimators, & Standard Errors

Parameter (θ)	Estimator ($\hat{\theta}$)	Standard Error of Estimator ($\hat{\sigma}_{\hat{\theta}}$)	Estimated Std. Error ($\hat{\sigma}_{\hat{\theta}}$)
Mean, μ	$\bar{x}$	$\sigma/\sqrt{n}$	$s/\sqrt{n}$
Proportion, p	$\hat{p}$	$\sqrt{pq/n}$	$\sqrt{\hat{p}\hat{q}/n}$

Key Symbols

θ	General population parameter (theta)
μ	Population mean
σ	Population standard deviation
p	Population proportion; P (Success) in binomial trial
q	$1 - p$
$\bar{x}$	Sample mean (estimator of μ)
$\hat{p}$	Sample proportion (estimator of p)
$\mu_{\bar{x}}$	Mean of the population sampling distribution of $\bar{x}$
$\sigma_{\bar{x}}$	Standard deviation of the sampling distribution of $\bar{x}$
$\sigma_{\hat{p}}$	Standard deviation of the sampling distribution of $\hat{p}$
SE	Sampling error in estimation
α	$(1 - \alpha)$ represents the confidence coefficient
$z_{\alpha/2}$	z-value used in a $100(1 - \alpha)\%$ large-sample confidence interval
$t_{\alpha/2}$	Student's t-value used in a $100(1 - \alpha)\%$ small-sample confidence interval

Confidence Interval: An interval that encloses an unknown population parameter with a certain level of confidence, $(1 - \alpha)$

Confidence Coefficient: The probability $(1 - \alpha)$ that a randomly selected confidence interval encloses the true value of the population parameter.

Determining the Sample Size n:

Estimating μ: $n = (z_{\alpha/2})^2 (\sigma^2)/(SE)^2$

Estimating p: $n = (z_{\alpha/2})^2 (pq)/(SE)^2$

Key Words for Identifying the Target Parameter:

μ—Mean, Average

p—Proportion, Fraction, Percentage, Rate, Probability

Commonly Used z-values for a Large-Sample Confidence Interval:

90% CI:	$(1 - \alpha) = .10$	$z_{.05} = 1.645$
95% CI:	$(1 - \alpha) = .05$	$z_{.025} = 1.96$
99% CI:	$(1 - \alpha) = .01$	$z_{.005} = 2.575$

Illustrating the Notion of "95% Confidence"

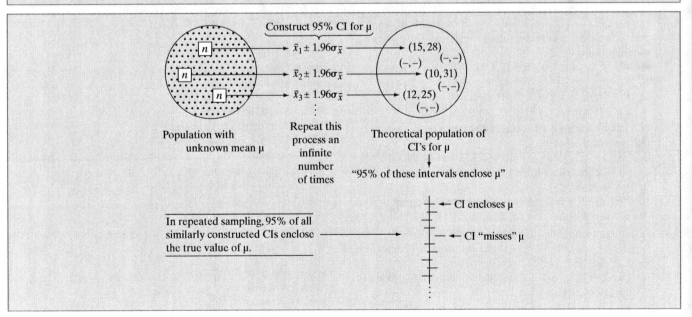

SUPPLEMENTARY EXERCISES 7.83–7.113

Note: List the assumptions necessary for the valid implementation of the statistical procedures you use in solving all these exercises.

Understanding the Principles

7.83 For each of the following, identify the target parameter as μ or p.

  a. Average score on the SAT

  b. Mean time waiting at a supermarket checkout lane

  c. Proportion of voters in favor of legalizing marijuana

  d. Percentage of NFL players who have ever made the Pro Bowl

  e. Dropout rate of American college students

7.84 Interpret the phrase "95% confident" in the following statement: "We are 95% confident that the proportion of all PCs with a computer virus falls between .12 and .18."

7.85 In each of the following instances, determine whether you would use a z- or t-statistic (or neither) to form a 95% confidence interval; then look up the appropriate z or t value.

  a. Random sample of size $n = 21$ from a normal distribution with unknown mean μ and standard deviation σ

  b. Random sample of size $n = 175$ from a normal distribution with unknown mean μ and standard deviation σ

  c. Random sample of size $n = 12$ from a normal distribution with unknown mean and standard deviation $\sigma = 5$

  d. Random sample of size $n = 65$ from a distribution about which nothing is known

  e. Random sample of size $n = 8$ from a distribution about which nothing is known

Learning the Mechanics

7.86 Let represent a particular value of t from Table VI of Appendix A. Find the table values such that the following statements are true:

  a. $P(t \leq t_0) = .05$, where df $= 17$

  b. $P(t \geq t_0) = .005$, where df $= 14$

  c. $P(t \leq -t_0 \text{ or } t \geq t_0) = .10$, where df $= 6$

  d. $P(t \leq -t_0 \text{ or } t \geq t_0) = .01$, where df $= 22$

7.87 In a random sample of 400 measurements, 227 possess the characteristic of interest, A.

  a. Use a 95% confidence interval to estimate the true proportion p of measurements in the population with characteristic A.

  b. How large a sample would be needed to estimate p to within .02 with 95% confidence?

7.88 A random sample of 225 measurements is selected from a population, and the sample mean and standard deviation are $\bar{x} = 32.5$ and $s = 30.0$, respectively.

  a. Use a 99% confidence interval to estimate the mean of the population, μ.

  b. How large a sample would be needed to estimate μ to within .5 with 99% confidence?

  c. What is meant by the phrase "99% confidence" as it is used in this exercise?

Applying the Concepts—Basic

7.89 **CDC health survey.** The Centers for Disease Control and Prevention (CDCP) in Atlanta, Georgia, conduct an annual survey of the general health of the U.S. population as part of their Behavioral Risk Factor Surveillance System. Using random-digit dialing, the CDCP telephones U.S. citizens over 18 years of age and asks them the following four questions:

  (1) Is your health generally excellent, very good, good, fair, or poor?

  (2) How many days during the previous 30 days was your physical health not good because of injury or illness?

  (3) How many days during the previous 30 days was your mental health not good because of stress, depression, or emotional problems?

  (4) How many days during the previous 30 days did your physical or mental health prevent you from performing your usual activities?

Identify the parameter of interest.

7.90 **Tax-exempt charities.** Donations to tax-exempt organizations such as the Red Cross, the Salvation Army, the YMCA, and the American Cancer Society not only go to the stated charitable purpose, but are used to cover fundraising expenses and overhead. The accompanying table lists the charitable commitment (i.e., the percentage of expenses that goes toward the stated charitable purpose) for a sample of 30 charities.

CHARITY

Organization	Charitable Commitment
American Cancer Society	62%
American National Red Cross	91
Big Brothers Big Sisters of America	77
Boy Scouts of America National Council	81
Boys & Girls Clubs of America	81
CARE	91
Covenant House	15
Disabled American Veterans	65
Ducks Unlimited	78
Feed The Children	90
Girl Scouts of the USA	83
Goodwill Industries International	89
Habitat for Humanity International	81
Mayo Foundation	26
Mothers Against Drunk Drivers	71
Multiple Sclerosis Association of America	56
Museum of Modern Art	79
Nature Conservancy	77
Paralyzed Veterans of America	50
Planned Parenthood Federation	81
Salvation Army	84
Shriners Hospital for Children	95
Smithsonian Institution	87
Special Olympics	72
Trust for Public Land	88
United Jewish Appeal/Federation—NY	75
United States Olympic Committee	78
United Way of New York City	85
WGBH Educational Foundation	81
YMCA of the USA	80

Source: "Look Before You Give," *Forbes*, Dec. 27, 1999, pp. 206–216.

a. Give a point estimate for the mean charitable commitment of tax-exempt organizations.

b. Construct a 98% confidence interval for the mean charitable commitment.

c. What assumption(s) must hold for the method of estimation used in part **b** to be appropriate?

d. Why is the confidence interval of part **b** a better estimator of the mean charitable commitment than the point estimator of part **a**?

7.91 Cell phone use by drivers. In a July 2001 research note, the U.S. Department of Transportation reported the results of the *National Occupant Protection Use Survey*. One focus of the survey was to determine the level of cell phone use by drivers while they are in the act of driving a motor passenger vehicle. Data collected by observers at randomly selected intersections across the country revealed that in a sample of 1,165 drivers, 35 were using their cell phone.

a. Give a point estimate of p, the true driver cell phone use rate (i.e., the true proportion of drivers who are using a cell phone while driving).

b. Compute a 95% confidence interval for p.

c. Give a practical interpretation of the interval you found in part **b**.

7.92 "Made in the USA" survey. Refer to Exercise 2.13 (p. 36) and the *Journal of Global Business* (Spring 2002) survey to determine what "Made in the USA" means to consumers. Recall that 106 shoppers at a shopping mall in Muncie, Indiana, responded to the question " 'Made in the USA' means what percentage of U.S. labor and materials?" Sixty-four shoppers answered "100%."

a. Define the population of interest in the survey.

b. What is the characteristic of interest in the population?

c. Use a 90% confidence interval to estimate the true proportion of consumers who believe that "Made in the USA" means 100% U.S. labor and materials.

d. Give a practical interpretation of the interval you used in part **c**.

e. Explain what the phrase "90% confidence" means for this interval.

7.93 "Made in the USA" survey (cont'd). Refer to Exercise 7.92. Suppose the researchers want to increase the sample size in order to estimate the true proportion p to within .05 of its true value with a 90% confidence interval.

a. What is the confidence level desired by the researchers?

b. What is the sampling error desired by the researchers?

c. Compute the sample size necessary to obtain the desired estimate.

7.94 Water pollution testing. The EPA wants to test a randomly selected sample of n water specimens and estimate μ, the mean daily rate of pollution produced by a mining operation. If the EPA wants a 95% confidence interval estimate with a sampling error of 1 milligram per liter (mg/L), how many water specimens are required in the sample? Assume that prior knowledge indicates that pollution readings in water samples taken during a day are approximately normally distributed with a standard deviation equal to 5 (mg/L).

7.95 Crop weights of pigeons. The *Australian Journal of Zoology* (Vol. 43, 1995) reported on a study of the diets and water requirements of spinifex pigeons. Sixteen pigeons were captured in the desert and the crop (i.e., stomach) contents of each examined. The accompanying table reports the weight (in grams) of dry seed in the crop of each pigeon. Find a 99% confidence interval for the average weight of dry seeds in the crops of spinifex pigeons inhabiting the Western Australian desert. Interpret the result.

PIGEONS

.457	3.751	.238	2.967	2.509	1.384	1.454	.818
.335	1.436	1.603	1.309	.201	.530	2.144	.834

Source: Excerpted from Williams, J. B., Bradshaw, D., and Schmidt, L. "Field metabolism and water requirements of spinifex pigeons *(Geophaps plumifera)* in Western Australia," *Australian Journal of Zoology*, Vol. 43, No. 1, 1995, p. 7 (Table 2).

7.96 Ammonia in car exhaust. Refer to the *Environmental Science & Technology* (September 1, 2000) study on the ammonia levels near the exit ramp of a San Francisco highway tunnel, presented in Exercise 2.59 (p. 59). The ammonia concentration (parts per million) data for eight randomly selected days during the afternoon drive time are reproduced in the accompanying table. Find a 99% confidence interval for the population mean daily ammonia level in air in the tunnel. Interpret your result.

AMMONIA

1.53	1.50	1.37	1.51	1.55	1.42	1.41	1.48

7.97 Homeless in the United States. The *American Journal of Orthopsychiatry* (July 1995) published an article on the prevalence of homelessness in the United States. A sample of 487 U.S. adults were asked to respond to the question "Was there ever a time in your life when you did not have a place to live?" A 95% confidence interval for the true proportion who were or are homeless, based on the survey data, was determined to be (.045, .091). Interpret the result fully.

Applying the Concepts—Intermediate

7.98 Hearing loss study. Patients with normal hearing in one ear and unaided sensorineural hearing loss in the other are characterized as suffering from unilateral hearing loss. In a study reported in the *American Journal of Audiology* (March 1995), eight patients with unilateral hearing loss were fitted with a special wireless hearing aid in the "bad" ear. The absolute sound pressure level (SPL) was then measured near the eardrum of the ear when noise was produced at a frequency of 500 hertz. The SPLs of the eight patients, recorded in decibels, are as follows:

SOUND

73.0	80.1	82.8	76.8	73.5	74.3	76.0	68.1

Construct and interpret a 90% confidence interval for the true mean SPL of patients with unilateral hearing loss when noise is produced at a frequency of 500 hertz.

7.99 Brown-bag lunches at work. In a study reported in *The Wall Street Journal* (April 4, 1999), the Tupperware Corporation surveyed 1,007 U.S. workers. Of the people surveyed, 665 indicated that they take their lunch to work with them. Of these 665 taking their lunch, 200 reported that they take it in brown bags.

a. Find a 95% confidence interval estimate of the population proportion of U.S. workers who take their lunch to work with them. Interpret the interval.

b. Consider the population of U.S. workers who take their lunch to work with them. Find a 95% confidence interval estimate of the population proportion who take brown-bag lunches. Interpret the interval.

7.100 Role importance for the elderly. Refer to the *Psychology and Aging* (December 2000) study of the roles that elderly people feel are the most important to them, presented in Exercise 2.10 (p. 35). Recall that in a national sample of 1,102 adults 65 years or older, 424 identified "spouse" as their most salient role. Use a 95% confidence interval to estimate the true percentage of adults 65 years or older who feel that being a spouse is their most salient role. Give a practical interpretation of this interval.

7.101 Inbreeding of tropical wasps. Tropical swarm-founding wasps rely on female workers to raise their offspring. One possible explanation for this strange behavior is inbreeding, which increases relatedness among the wasps, presumably making it easier for the workers to pick out their closest relatives as propagators of their own genetic material. To test this theory, 197 swarm-founding wasps were captured in Venezuela, frozen at $-70°C$, and then subjected to a series of genetic tests (*Science*, November 1988). The data were used to generate an inbreeding coefficient x for each wasp specimen, with the following results: $\bar{x} = .044$ and $s = .884$.

a. Construct a 99% confidence interval for the mean inbreeding coefficient of this species of wasp.

b. A coefficient of 0 implies that the wasp has no tendency to inbreed. Use the confidence interval you constructed in part **a** to make an inference about the tendency for this species of wasp to inbreed.

OILSPILL

7.102 Tanker oil spills. Refer to the *Marine Technology* (January 1995) study of the causes of 50 recent major oil spills from tankers and carriers, presented in Exercise 2.186 (p. 106). The data are stored in the **OILSPILL** file.

a. Give a point estimate for the proportion of major oil spills that are caused by hull failure.

b. Form a 95% confidence interval for the estimate you found in part **a**. Interpret the result.

7.103 Time to solve a math programming problem. *IEEE Transactions* (June 1990) presented a hybrid algorithm for solving a polynomial zero–one mathematical programming problem. The algorithm incorporates a mixture of pseudo-

MATHCPU

.045	1.055	.136	1.894	.379	.136	.336	.258	1.070
.506	.088	.242	1.639	.912	.412	.361	8.788	.579
1.267	.567	.182	.036	.394	.209	.445	.179	.118
.333	.554	.258	.182	.070	3.985	.670	3.888	.136
.091	.600	.291	.327	.130	.145	4.170	.227	.064
.194	.209	.258	3.046	.045	.049	.079		

Source: Snyder, W. S., and Chrissis, J. W. "A hybrid algorithm for solving zero-one mathematical programming problems," *IEEE Transactions*, Vol. 22, No. 2, June 1990, p. 166 (Table 1).

Boolean concepts and time-proven implicit enumeration procedures. Fifty-two random problems were solved by the hybrid algorithm; the times to solution (CPU time in seconds) are listed in the accompanying table.

a. Estimate, with 95% confidence, the mean solution time for the hybrid algorithm. Interpret the result.

b. How many problems must be solved to estimate the mean μ to within .25 second with 95% confidence?

7.104 Psychological study of participation and satisfaction. The relationship between an employee's participation in the performance appraisal process and his or her subsequent reactions toward the appraisal was investigated in the *Journal of Applied Psychology* (August 1998). In Chapter 11, we will discuss a quantitative measure of the relationship between two variables, called the coefficient of correlation, r. The researchers obtained r for a sample of 34 studies that examined the relationship between participation in the appraisal and subsequent satisfaction with the appraisal. These correlations are listed in the accompanying table. (Values of r near $+1$ reflect a strong positive relationship between the variables.) Find a 95% confidence interval for the mean of the data, and interpret it in the words of the problem.

CORR34

.50	.58	.71	.46	.63	.66	.31	.35	.51	.06	.35	.19
.40	.63	.43	.16	$-.08$	.51	.59	.43	.30	.69	.25	.20
.39	.20	.51	.68	.74	.65	.34	.45	.31	.27		

Source: Cawley, B. D., Keeping, L. M., and Levy, P. E. "Participation in the performance appraisal process and employee reactions: A meta-analytic review of field investigations." *Journal of Applied Psychology*, Vol. 83, No. 4, Aug. 1998, pp. 632–633 (Appendix).

SUICIDE

7.105 Jail suicide study. In Exercise 2.187 (p. 107) you considered data on suicides in correctional facilities. The data were published in the *American Journal of Psychiatry* (July 1995). The researchers wanted to know what factors increase the risk of suicide by those incarcerated in urban jails. The data on 37 suicides that occurred in Wayne County Jail, Detroit, Michigan, are saved in the **SUICIDE** file. Answer each of the questions that follow, using a 95% confidence interval for the target parameter implied in the question. Interpret each confidence interval fully.

a. What proportion of suicides at the jail are committed by inmates charged with murder or manslaughter?

b. What proportion of suicides at the jail are committed at night?

c. What is the average length of time an inmate is in jail before committing suicide?

d. What percentage of suicides are committed by white inmates?

7.106 Recommendation letters for professors. Refer to the *American Psychologist* (July 1995) study of applications for university positions in experimental psychology, presented in Exercise 2.62 (p. 59). One of the objectives of the analysis was to identify problems and errors (e.g., not submitting at least three letters of recommendation) in the application packages. In a sample of 148 applications for the positions, 30 failed to provide *any* letters of recommendation. Estimate, with 90% confidence, the true fraction of applicants for a university position in experimental psychology that fail to provide letters of recommendation. Interpret the result.

7.107 Salmonella in ice cream bars. Recently, a case of salmonella (bacterial) poisoning was traced to a particular brand of ice cream bar, and the manufacturer removed the bars from the market. Despite this response, many consumers refused to purchase *any* brand of ice cream bars for some time after the event (McClave, personal correspondence). One manufacturer conducted a survey of consumers 6 months after the poisoning. A sample of 244 ice cream bar consumers was contacted, and 23 indicated that they would not purchase ice cream bars because of the potential for food poisoning.

   a. What is the point estimate of the true fraction of the entire market who refuse to purchase bars 6 months after the poisoning?

   b. Is the sample size large enough to use the normal approximation for the sampling distribution of the estimator of the binomial probability? Justify your response.

   c. Construct a 95% confidence interval for the true proportion of the market who still refuse to purchase ice cream bars 6 months after the event.

   d. Interpret both the point estimate and confidence interval in terms of this application.

7.108 Salmonella in ice cream bars (cont'd). Refer to Exercise 7.107. Suppose it is now 1 year after the poisoning was traced to ice cream bars. The manufacturer wishes to estimate the proportion who still will not purchase bars to within .02, using a 95% confidence interval. How many consumers should be sampled?

7.109 Removing a soil contaminant. A common hazardous compound found in contaminated soil is benzo(a)pyrene [B(a)p]. An experiment was conducted to determine the effectiveness of a method designed to remove B(a)p from soil. (*Journal of Hazardous Materials*, June 1995.) Three soil specimens contaminated with a known amount of B(a)p were treated with a toxin that inhibits microbial growth. After 95 days of incubation, the percentage of B(a)p removed from each soil specimen was measured. The experiment produced the following summary statistics: $\bar{x} = 49.3$ and $s = 1.5$.

   a. Use a 99% confidence interval to estimate the mean percentage of B(a)p removed from a soil specimen in which the toxin was used.

   b. Interpret the interval in terms of this application.

   c. What assumption is necessary to ensure the validity of this confidence interval?

   d. How many soil specimens must be sampled to estimate the mean percentage removed to within .5, using a 99% confidence interval?

7.110 Material safety data sheets. For over 20 years, the Occupational Safety & Health Administration has required companies that handle hazardous chemicals to complete material safety data sheets (MSDSs). These sheets have been criticized for being too hard to understand and complete by workers. Although improvements were implemented in 1990, a recent study of 150 MSDSs revealed that only 11% were completed satisfactorily. (*Chemical & Engineering News*, Feb. 7, 2005.) Find an interval that contains the true proportion of all MSDSs that are completed satisfactorily, with 95% confidence. Would it surprise you if the true proportion was as high as 20%? Explain.

Applying the Concepts—Advanced

7.111 IMA salary survey. Each year, *Management Accounting* reports the results of a salary survey of the members of the Institute of Management Accountants (IMA). One year, the 2,112 members responding had a salary distribution with a 20th percentile of $35,100, a median of $50,000, and an 80th percentile of $73,000.

   a. Use this information to determine the minimum sample size that could be used in next year's survey to estimate the mean salary of IMA members to within $2,000 with 98% confidence. [*Hint*: To estimate s, first apply Chebyshev's theorem to find k such that at least 60% of the data fall within k standard deviations of μ. Then find $s \approx$ (80th percentile −20th percentile)$/k$.]

   b. Explain how you estimated the standard deviation required for the calculation of the sample size.

   c. List any assumptions you make.

7.112 Air bags pose danger for children. By law, all new cars must be equipped with both driver-side and passenger-side safety air bags. There is concern, however, over whether air bags pose a danger for children sitting on the passenger side. In a National Highway Traffic Safety Administration (NHTSA) study of 55 people killed by the explosive force of air bags, 35 were children seated on the front-passenger side. (*Wall Street Journal*, January 22, 1997.) This study led some car owners with the information from children to disconnect the passenger-side air bag.

   a. Use the study to estimate the risk of an air bag fatality on a child seated on the front passenger seat.

   b. NHTSA investigators determined that 24 of 35 children killed by the air bags were not wearing seat belts or were improperly restrained. How does this information affect your assessment of the risk of an air bag fatality?

Critical Thinking Challenge

7.113 Scallops, sampling, and the law. In *Interfaces* (March–April 1995), the case involved a ship that fishes for scallops off the coast of New England. In order to protect baby scallops from being harvested, the U.S. Fisheries and Wildlife Service requires that "the average meat per scallop weigh at least $\frac{1}{36}$ of a pound." The ship was accused of violating this weight standard. Bennett lays out the scenario:

The vessel arrived at a Massachusetts port with 11,000 bags of scallops, from which the harbormaster randomly selected 18 bags for weighing. From each such bag, his agents took a large scoopful of scallops; then, to estimate the bag's average meat per scallop, they divided the total weight of meat in the scoopful by the number of scallops it contained. Based on the 18 [numbers] thus generated, the harbormaster estimated that each of the ship's scallops possessed an average $\frac{1}{39}$ of a pound of meat (that is, they were about seven percent lighter than the minimum requirement). Viewing this outcome as conclusive evidence that the weight standard had been violated, federal authorities at once confiscated 95 percent of the catch (which they then sold at *auction). The fishing voyage was thus transformed into a financial catastrophe for its participants.*

The actual scallop weight measurements for each of the 18 sampled bags are listed in the accompanying table. For ease of exposition, Bennett expressed each number as a multiple of $\frac{1}{36}$ of a pound, the minimum permissible average weight per scallop. Consequently, numbers below 1 indicate individual bags that do not meet the standard.

The ship's owner filed a lawsuit against the federal government, declaring that his vessel had fully complied with the weight standard. A Boston law firm was hired to represent the owner in legal proceedings and Bennett was retained by the firm to provide statistical litigation support and, if necessary, expert witness testimony.

a. Recall that the harbormaster sampled only 18 of the ship's 11,000 bags of scallops. One of the questions the lawyers asked Bennett was "Can a reliable estimate of the mean weight of all the scallops be ob-

tained from a sample of size 18?" Give your opinion on this issue.

b. As stated in the article, the government's decision rule is to confiscate a catch if the sample mean weight of the scallops is less than $\frac{1}{36}$ of a pound. Do you see any flaws in this rule?

c. Develop your own procedure for determining whether a ship is in violation of the minimum-weight restriction. Apply your rule to the data. Draw a conclusion about the ship in question.

SCALLOPS

.93	.88	.85	.91	.91	.84	.90	.98	.88
.89	.98	.87	.91	.92	.99	1.14	1.06	.93

Source: Bennett, A. "Misapplications review: Jail terms." *Interfaces,* Vol. 25, No. 2, Mar.–Apr. 1995, p. 20.

SUMMARY ACTIVITY: Conducting a Pilot Study

Choose a population pertinent to your major area of interest—a population that has an unknown mean or, if the population is binomial, that has an unknown probability of success. For example, a marketing major may be interested in the proportion of consumers who prefer a certain product. A sociology major may be interested in estimating the proportion of people in a certain socioeconomic group or the mean income of people living in a particular part of a city. A political science major may wish to estimate the proportion of an electorate in favor of a certain candidate, a certain amendment, or a certain presidential policy. A pre-med student might want to find the average length of time patients stay in the hospital or the average number of people treated daily in the emergency

room. We could continue with examples, but the point should be clear: Choose something of interest to you.

Define the parameter you want to estimate and conduct a *pilot study* to obtain an initial estimate of the parameter of interest and, more importantly, an estimate of the variability associated with the estimator. A pilot study is a small experiment (perhaps 20 to 30 observations) used to gain some information about the population of interest. The purpose of the study is to help plan more elaborate future experiments. Using the results of your pilot study, determine the sample size necessary to estimate the parameter to within a reasonable bound (of your choice) with a 95% confidence interval.

REFERENCES

Agresti, A., and Coull, B. A. "Approximate is better than 'exact' for interval estimation of binomial proportions." *The American Statistician,* Vol. 52, No. 2, May 1998, pp. 119–126.

Cochran, W. G. *Sampling Techniques,* 3d ed. New York: Wiley, 1977.

Freedman, D., Pisani, R., and Purves, R. *Statistics.* New York: Norton, 1978.

Kish, L. *Survey Sampling.* New York: Wiley, 1965.

Mendenhall, W., Beaver, R. J., and Beaver, B. *Introduction to Probability and Statistics,* 11th ed. North Scituate, MA: Duxbury, 2002.

Wilson, E. G. "Probable inference, the law of succession, and statistical inference." *Journal of the American Statistical Association,* Vol. 22, 1927, pp. 209–212.

Using Technology

Confidence Intervals with MINITAB

MINITAB can be used to obtain one-sample confidence intervals for both a population mean and a population proportion. To use a previously created sample data set to generate a confidence interval for the mean, first access the MINITAB data worksheet. Next, click on the "Stat" button on the MINITAB menu bar, and then click on "Basic Statistics" and "1-sample t," as shown in Figure 7.M.1. The resulting dialog box appears as shown in Figure 7.M.2. Click on "Samples in Columns," and then specify the quantitative variable of interest in the open box. Now click on the "Options" button at the bottom of the dialog box, and specify the confidence level in the resulting dialog box as shown in Figure 7.M.3. Click "OK" to return to the "1-Sample t" dialog box, and then click "OK" again to produce the confidence interval.

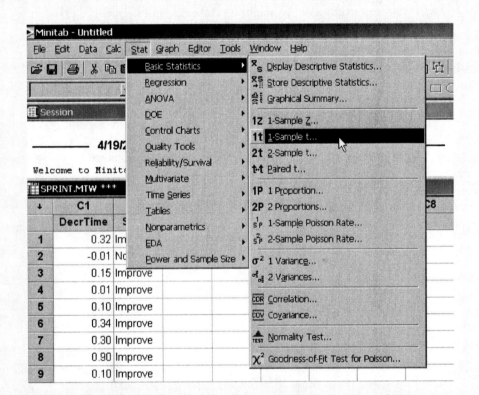

FIGURE 7.M.1
MINITAB menu options for a confidence interval for μ

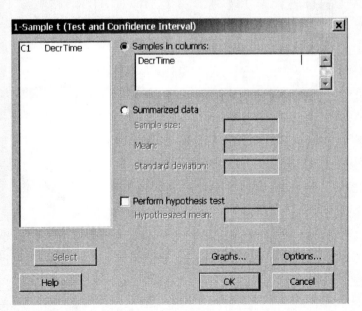

FIGURE 7.M.2
MINITAB one-sample t dialog box

(continued)

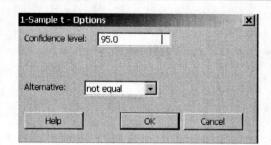

FIGURE 7.M.3
MINITAB one-sample
t options

If you want to produce a confidence interval for the mean from summary information (e.g., the sample mean, sample standard deviation, and sample size), then click on "Summarized data" in the "1-Sample t" dialog box as shown in Figure 7.M.4. Enter the values of the summary statistics, and then click "OK."

[*Important Note*: The MINITAB 1-Sample t procedure uses the *t*-statistic to generate the confidence interval. When the sample size *n* is small, this is the appropriate method. When the sample size *n* is large, the *t*-value will be approximately equal to the large-sample *z*-value and the resulting interval will still be valid. If you have a large sample and you know the value of the population standard deviation σ (which is rarely the case), then select "1-Sample Z" from the "Basic Statistics" menu options (see Figure 7.M.1) and make the appropriate selections.]

To use a previously created sample data set to generate a confidence interval for a population proportion, first access the MINITAB data worksheet. Next, click on the "Stat" button on the MINITAB menu bar, and then click on "Basic Statistics" and "1 Proportion". (See Figure 7.M.1.) The resulting dialog box appears as shown in Figure 7.M.5. Click on "Sam-

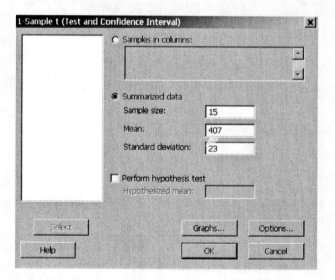

FIGURE 7.M.4
MINITAB one-sample
t dialog box with summary
statistics

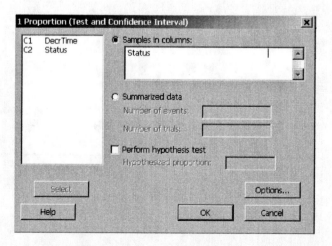

FIGURE 7.M.5
MINITAB one-sample
proportion dialog box

ples in columns," and then specify the qualitative variable of interest in the open box. Now click on the "Options" button at the bottom of the dialog box, and specify the confidence level in the resulting dialog box as shown in Figure 7.M.6. Also, check the "Use test and interval based on normal distribution" box at the bottom. Click "OK" to return to the "1 Proportion" dialog box, and then click "OK" again to produce the confidence interval.

If you want to produce a confidence interval for a proportion from summary information (e.g., the number of success- es and the sample size), then click on "Summarized data" in the "1 Proportion" dialog box. (See Figure 7.M.5.) Enter the value for the number of trials (i.e., the sample size) and the number of events (i.e., the number of successes), and then click "OK."

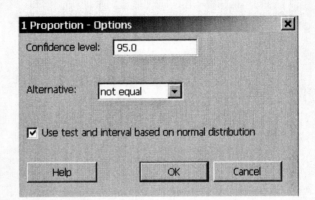

FIGURE 7.M.6
MINITAB one-sample
proportion options

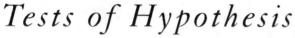

CHAPTER 8

Inferences Based on a Single Sample

Tests of Hypothesis

STATISTICS IN ACTION

Diary of a KLEENEX® User—How Many Tissues in a Box?

USING TECHNOLOGY

Tests of Hypothesis with MINITAB

WHERE WE'VE BEEN

■ Used sample information to provide a *point estimate* of a population parameter

■ Used the sampling distribution of a statistic to assess the reliability of an estimate through a *confidence interval*

WHERE WE'RE GOING

■ Test a specific value of a population parameter (mean or proportion)—called a *test of hypothesis*

■ Provide a measure of reliability for the hypothesis test—called the *significance level* of the test

STATISTICS IN ACTION

Diary of a KLEENEX® User—How Many Tissues in a Box?

In 1924, Kimberly-Clark Corporation invented a facial tissue for removing cold cream and began marketing it as KLEENEX® brand tissues. Today, KLEENEX® is recognized as the top-selling brand of tissue in the world. A wide variety of KLEENEX® products is available, ranging from extra-large tissues to tissues with lotion. Over the past 80 years, Kimberly-Clark Corporation has packaged the tissues in boxes of different sizes and shapes and varied the number of tissues packaged in each box. For example, currently a family-size box contains 144 two-ply tissues, a cold-care box contains 70 tissues (coated with lotion), and a convenience pocket pack contains 15 miniature tissues.

How does Kimberly-Clark Corp. decide how many tissues to put in each box? According to the *Wall Street Journal*, marketing experts at the company use the results of a survey of KLEENEX® customers to help determine how many tissues are packed in a box. In the mid-1980s, when Kimberly-Clark Corp. developed the cold-care box, designed especially for people who have a cold, the company conducted their initial survey of customers for this purpose. Hun-

dreds of customers were asked to keep count of their KLEENEX® use in diaries. According to the *Wall Street Journal* report, the survey results left "little doubt that the company should put 60 tissues in each box." The number 60 was "the average number of times people blow their nose during a cold." (*Note:* In 2000, the company increased the number of tissues packaged in a cold-care box to 70.)

From summary information provided in the *Wall Street Journal* (September 21, 1984) article, we constructed a data set that represents the results of a survey similar to the one just described. In the data file named **TISSUES,** we recorded the number of tissues used by each of 250 consumers during a period when they had a cold. We apply the hypothesis-testing methodology presented in this chapter to that data set in several Statistics in Action Revisited examples.

Statistics in Action Revisited

- Identifying the Key Elements of a Hypothesis Test Relevant to the KLEENEX® Survey (p. 357)

- Testing a Population Mean in the KLEENEX® Survey (p. 371)

- Testing a Population Proportion in the KLEENEX® Survey (p. 383)

S uppose you wanted to determine whether the mean level of a driver's blood alcohol exceeds the legal limit after two drinks, or whether the majority of registered voters approve of the president's performance. In both cases, you are interested in making an inference about how the value of a parameter relates to a specific numerical value. Is it less than, equal to, or greater than the specified number? This type of inference, called a **test of hypothesis,** is the subject of this chapter.

We introduce the elements of a test of hypothesis in Section 8.1. We then show how to conduct a large-sample test of hypothesis about a population mean in Sections 8.2 and 8.3. In Section 8.4, we utilize small samples to conduct tests about means. Large-sample tests about binomial probabilities are the subject of Section 8.5, and some advanced methods for determining the reliability of a test are covered in optional Section 8.6. Finally, we show how to conduct a test about a population variance in optional Section 8.7.

8.1 The Elements of a Test of Hypothesis

Suppose building specifications in a certain city require that the average breaking strength of residential sewer pipe be more than 2,400 pounds per foot of length (i.e., per linear foot). Each manufacturer that wants to sell pipe in that city must demonstrate that its product meets the specification. Note that we are interested in making an inference about the mean μ of a population. However, in this example we are less interested in estimating the value of μ than we are in testing a *hypothesis* about its value. That is, *we want to decide whether the mean breaking strength of the pipe exceeds 2,400 pounds per linear foot.*

The method used to reach a decision is based on the rare-event concept explained in earlier chapters. We define two hypotheses: (1) The **null hypothesis** represents the status quo to the party performing the sampling experiment; it is the hypothesis that will be supported unless the data provide convincing evidence that it is false. (2) The **alternative,** or **research, hypothesis** will be accepted only if the data provide convincing evidence of its truth. From the point of view of the city conducting the tests, the null hypothesis is that the manufacturer's pipe does *not* meet specifications unless the tests provide convincing evidence otherwise. The null and alternative hypotheses are therefore

Null hypothesis (H_0): $\mu \leq 2,400$
  (i.e., the manufacturer's pipe does not meet specifications)
Alternative (research) hypothesis (H_a): $\mu > 2,400$
  (i.e., the manufacturer's pipe meets specifications)

Now Work Exercise 8.8

How can the city decide when enough evidence exists to conclude that the manufacturer's pipe meets specifications? Since the hypotheses concern the value of the population mean μ, it is reasonable to use the sample mean $\bar{x}$ to make the inference, just as we did when we formed confidence intervals for μ in Sections 7.2 and 7.3. The city will conclude that the pipe meets specifications only when the sample mean $\bar{x}$ convincingly indicates that the population mean exceeds 2,400 pounds per linear foot.

"Convincing" evidence in favor of the alternative hypothesis will exist when the value of $\bar{x}$ exceeds 2,400 by an amount that cannot be readily attributed to sampling variability. To decide, we compute a **test statistic,** which is the z-value that measures the distance between the value of $\bar{x}$ and the value of μ specified in the null hypothesis. When the null hypothesis contains more than one value of μ, as in this case (H_0: $\mu \leq 2,400$), we use the value of μ closest to the values specified in the alternative hypothesis. The idea is that if the hypothesis that μ *equals* 2,400 can be rejected in favor of $\mu > 2,400$, then μ *less than or equal to* 2,400 can certainly be rejected. Thus, the test statistic is

$$z = \frac{\bar{x} - 2,400}{\sigma_{\bar{x}}} = \frac{\bar{x} - 2,400}{\sigma/\sqrt{n}}$$

Note that a value of $z = 1$ means that $\bar{x}$ is 1 standard deviation above $\mu = 2,400$, a value of $z = 1.5$ means that $\bar{x}$ is 1.5 standard deviations above $\mu = 2,400$, etc. How large must z be before the city can be convinced that the null hypothesis can be rejected in favor of the alternative hypothesis and conclude that the pipe meets specifications?

If you examine Figure 8.1, you will note that the chance of observing $\bar{x}$ more than 1.645 standard deviations above 2,400 is only .05—*if in fact the true mean μ is* 2,400. Thus, if the sample mean is more than 1.645 standard deviations above 2,400, either H_0 is true and a relatively rare event has occurred (one with .05 probability) or H_a is true and the population mean exceeds 2,400. Since we would most likely reject the notion that a rare event has occurred, we would reject the null hypothesis ($\mu \leq 2,400$) and conclude that the alternative hypothesis ($\mu > 2,400$) is true.

Now, what is the probability that the procedure just set forth will lead us to an incorrect decision? Such an incorrect decision—deciding that the null hypothesis is false when in fact it is true—is called a **Type I decision error.** As indicated in Figure 8.1, the risk of making a Type I error is denoted by the symbol α. That is,

$\alpha = P\,(\text{Type I error})$

  $= P\,(\text{Rejecting the null hypothesis when in fact the null hypothesis is true})$

In this example,

$$\alpha = P\,(z > 1.645 \text{ when in fact } \mu = 2,400) = .05$$

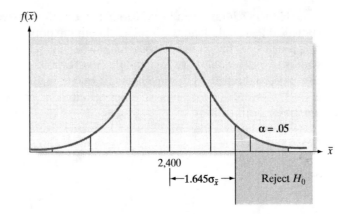

FIGURE 8.1
The sampling distribution of $\bar{x}$, assuming that $\mu = 2,400$

We now summarize the elements of the test:

H_0: $\mu \leq 2,400$ (Mean breaking strength is less than or equal to 2,400 pounds.)

H_a: $\mu > 2,400$ (Mean breaking strength exceeds 2,400 pounds.)

Test statistic: $z = \dfrac{\bar{x} - 2,400}{\sigma_{\bar{x}}}$

Rejection region: $z > 1.645$, which corresponds to $\alpha = .05$

Note that the **rejection region** refers to the values of the test statistic for which we will *reject the null hypothesis.*

To illustrate the use of the test, suppose we test 50 sections of sewer pipe and find the mean and standard deviation for these 50 measurements to be, respectively,

$\bar{x} = 2,460$ pounds per linear foot   and $s = 200$ pounds per linear foot

As in the case of estimation, we can use s to approximate σ when s is calculated from a large set of sample measurements.

The test statistic is

$$z = \frac{\bar{x} - 2,400}{\sigma_{\bar{x}}} = \frac{\bar{x} - 2,400}{\sigma/\sqrt{n}} \approx \frac{\bar{x} - 2,400}{s/\sqrt{n}}$$

Substituting $\bar{x} = 2,460$, $n = 50$, and $s = 200$, we have

$$z \approx \frac{2,460 - 2,400}{200/\sqrt{50}} = \frac{60}{28.28} = 2.12$$

Therefore, the sample mean lies $2.12\sigma_{\bar{x}}$ above the hypothesized value of $\mu = 2,400$, as shown in Figure 8.2. Since this value of z exceeds 1.645, it falls into the rejection region. That is, we reject the null hypothesis that $\mu = 2,400$ and conclude that $\mu > 2,400$. Thus, it appears that the company's pipe has a mean strength that exceeds 2,400 pounds per linear foot.

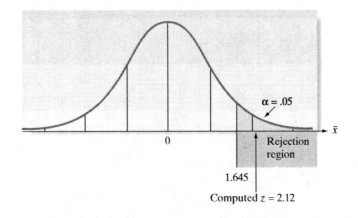

FIGURE 8.2
Location of the test statistic for a test of the hypothesis
H_0: $\mu \leq 2,400$

How much faith can be placed in this conclusion? What is the probability that our statistical test could lead us to reject the null hypothesis (and conclude that the company's pipe meets the city's specifications) when in fact the null hypothesis is true? The answer is $\alpha = .05$. That is, we selected the level of risk, α, of making a Type I error when we constructed the test. Thus, the chance is only 1 in 20 that our test would lead us to conclude the manufacturer's pipe satisfies the city's specifications when in fact the pipe does *not* meet specifications.

Now, suppose the sample mean breaking strength for the 50 sections of sewer pipe turned out to be $\bar{x} = 2,430$ pounds per linear foot. Assuming that the sample standard deviation is still $s = 200$, we now find that the test statistic is

$$z = \frac{2,430 - 2,400}{2/\sqrt{50}} = \frac{30}{28.28} = 1.06$$

Therefore, the sample mean $\bar{x} = 2,430$ is only 1.06 standard deviations above the null hypothesized value of $\mu = 2,400$. As shown in Figure 8.3, this value does not fall into the rejection region ($z > 1.645$). Therefore, we know that we cannot reject H_0 if we use $\alpha = .05$. Even though the sample mean exceeds the city's specification of 2,400 by 30 pounds per linear foot, it does not exceed the specification by enough to provide *convincing* evidence that the *population mean* exceeds 2,400.

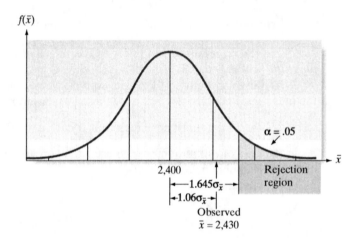

FIGURE 8.3

Location of the test statistic when $\bar{x} = 2,430$

Should we accept the null hypothesis $H_0: \mu \leq 2,400$ and conclude that the manufacturer's pipe does not meet specifications? To do so would be to risk a **Type II error:** concluding that the null hypothesis is true (the pipe does not meet specifications) when in fact it is false (the pipe does meet specifications). We denote the probability of committing a Type II error by β, and we show in optional Section 8.6 that β is often difficult to determine precisely. Rather than make a decision (accept H_0) for which the probability of error (β) is unknown, we avoid the potential Type II error by avoiding the conclu-

Biography

EGON S. PEARSON (1895–1980)—
The Neyman–Pearson Lemma

Egon Pearson was the only son of noteworthy British statistician Karl Pearson. (See Biography, p. 746). As you might expect, Egon developed an interest in the statistical methods developed by his father and, upon completing graduate school, accepted a position to work for Karl in the Department of Applied Statistics at University College, London. Egon is best known for his collaboration with Jerzy Neyman (see Biography, p. 371) on the development of the theory of hypothesis testing. One of the basic concepts in the Neyman–Pearson approach was that of the "null" and "alternative" hypotheses. Their famous "Neyman–Pearson" lemma was published in *Biometrika* in 1928. Egon Pearson made numerous other contributions to statistics and was known as an excellent teacher and lecturer. In his last major work, Egon fulfilled a promise made to his father by publishing an annotated version of Karl Pearson's lectures on the early history of statistics.

TABLE 8.1 Conclusions and Consequences for a Test of Hypothesis

Conclusion	True State of Nature	
	H_0 True	H_a True
Accept H_0 (Assume H_0 True)	Correct decision	Type II error (probability β)
Reject H_0 (Assume H_a True)	Type I error (probability α)	Correct decision

sion that the null hypothesis is true. Instead, we will simply state that *the sample evidence is insufficient to reject H_0 at $\alpha = .05$.* Since the null hypothesis is the "status quo" hypothesis, the effect of not rejecting H_0 is to maintain the status quo. In our pipe-testing example, the effect of having insufficient evidence to reject the null hypothesis that the pipe does not meet specifications is probably to prohibit the utilization of the manufacturer's pipe unless and until there is sufficient evidence that the pipe does meet specifications. That is, until the data indicate convincingly that the null hypothesis is false, we usually maintain the status quo implied by its truth.

Table 8.1 summarizes the four possible outcomes of a test of hypothesis. The "true state of nature" columns in the table refer to the fact that either the null hypothesis H_0 is true or the alternative hypothesis H_a is true. Note that the true state of nature is unknown to the researcher conducting the test. The "conclusion" rows in the table refer to the action of the researcher, assuming that he or she will conclude either that H_0 is true or that H_a is true, on the basis of the results of the sampling experiment. Note that a Type I error can be made *only* when the alternative hypothesis is accepted (equivalently, when the null hypothesis is rejected) and a Type II error can be made *only* when the null hypothesis is accepted. Our policy will be to make a decision only when we know the probability of making the error which corresponds to that decision. Since α is usually specified by the analyst (typically, $\alpha = .05$ in research), we will generally be able to reject H_0 (accept H_a) when the sample evidence supports that decision. However, since β is usually *not* specified, *we will generally avoid the decision to accept H_0, preferring instead to state that the sample evidence is insufficient to reject H_0 when the test statistic is not in the rejection region.*

Caution

Be careful not to "accept H_0" when conducting a test of hypothesis, since the measure of reliability, $\beta = P(\text{Type II error})$, is almost always unknown. If the test statistic does not fall into the rejection region, it is better to state the conclusion as "insufficient evidence to reject H_0."*

The elements of a test of hypothesis are summarized in the next box. Note that the first four elements are all specified *before* the sampling experiment is performed. In no case will the results of the sample be used to determine the hypotheses: The data are collected to *test* the predetermined hypotheses, not to formulate them.

Elements of a Test of Hypothesis

1. *Null hypothesis* (H_0): A theory about the values of one or more population parameters. The theory generally represents the status quo, which we adopt until it is proven false. By convention, the theory is stated as H_0: parameter = value.
2. *Alternative (research) hypothesis* (H_a): A theory that contradicts the null hypothesis. The theory generally represents that which we will accept only when sufficient evidence exists to establish its truth.

(continued)

---

*In many practical applications of hypothesis testing, nonrejection leads the researcher to behave as if the null hypothesis were accepted. Accordingly, the distinction between "accept H_0" and "fail to reject H_0" is frequently blurred in practice. We discuss the issues connected with accepting H_0 and the calculation of β in more detail in (optional) Section 8.6.

3. *Test statistic:* A sample statistic used to decide whether to reject the null hypothesis.

4. *Rejection region:* The numerical values of the test statistic for which the null hypothesis will be rejected. The rejection region is chosen so that the probability is α that it will contain the test statistic when the null hypothesis is true, thereby leading to a Type I error. The value of α is usually chosen to be small (e.g., .01, .05, or .10) and is referred to as the **level of significance** of the test.

5. *Assumptions:* Clear statements of any assumptions made about the population(s) being sampled.

6. *Experiment and calculation of test statistic:* Performance of the sampling experiment and determination of the numerical value of the test statistic.

7. *Conclusion:*
   a. If the numerical value of the test statistic falls into the rejection region, we reject the null hypothesis and conclude that the alternative hypothesis is true. We know that the hypothesis-testing process will lead to this conclusion incorrectly (a Type I error) only $100\alpha\%$ of the time when H_0 is true.
   b. If the test statistic does not fall into the rejection region, we do not reject H_0. Thus, we reserve judgment about which hypothesis is true. We do not conclude that the null hypothesis is true because we do not (in general) know the probability β that our test procedure will lead to an incorrect acceptance of H_0 (a Type II error).

As with confidence intervals, the methodology for testing hypotheses varies with the target population parameter. In this chapter, we develop methods for testing a population mean, a population proportion, and a population variance. Some key words and the type of data associated with these target parameters are listed in the following box:

Determining the Target Parameter

Parameter	Key Words or Phrases	Type of Data
μ	Mean; average	Quantitative
p	Proportion; percentage; fraction; rate	Qualitative
σ^2	Variance; variability; spread	Quantitative

ACTIVITY 8.1: *Challenging a Claim:* Tests of Hypotheses

Use the Internet or a newspaper or magazine to find an example of a claim made by a political or special-interest group about some characteristic (e.g., favor gun control) of the U.S. population. In this activity, you represent a rival group that believes the claim may be false.

1. In your example, what kinds of evidence might exist which would cause one to suspect that the claim might be false and therefore worthy of a statistical study? Be specific. If the claim were false, how would consumers be hurt?

2. Explain the steps necessary to reject the group's claim at level α. State the null and alternative hypotheses. If you reject the claim, does it mean that the claim is false?

3. If you reject the claim when the claim is actually true, what type of error has occurred? What is the probability of this error occurring?

4. If you were to file a lawsuit against the group based on your rejection of its claim, how might the group use your results to defend itself?

STATISTICS IN ACTION REVISITED

Identifying the Key Elements of a Hypothesis Test Relevant to the KLEENEX® Survey

In Kimberly-Clark Corporation's survey of people with colds, each of 250 customers was asked to keep count of his or her use of KLEENEX® tissues in diaries. One goal of the company was to determine how many tissues to package in a cold-care box of KLEENEX®; consequently, the total number of tissues used was recorded for each person surveyed. Since number of tissues is a quantitative variable, the parameter of interest is either μ, the mean number of tissues used by all customers with colds, or σ^2, the variance of the number of tissues used.

Now, according to a *Wall Street Journal* report, there was "little doubt that the company should put 60 tissues" in a cold-care box of KLEENEX® tissues. This statement was based on a claim made by marketing experts that 60 is the average number of times a person will blow his or her nose during a cold. The key word *average* implies that the target parameter is μ, and the marketers are claiming that $\mu = 60$. Suppose we disbelieve the claim that $\mu = 60$, believing instead that the population mean is smaller than 60 tissues. In order to test the claim against our belief, we set up the following null and alternative hypotheses:

$$H_0: \mu = 60 \qquad H_a: \mu < 60$$

We'll conduct this test in the next Statistics in Action Revisited, on p. 371.

Exercises 8.1–8.17

Understanding the Principles

8.1 Which hypothesis, the null or the alternative, is the status quo hypothesis? Which is the research hypothesis?

8.2 Which element of a test of hypothesis is used to decide whether to reject the null hypothesis in favor of the alternative hypothesis?

8.3 What is the level of significance of a test of hypothesis?

8.4 What is the difference between Type I and Type II errors in hypothesis testing? How do α and β relate to Type I and Type II errors?

8.5 List the four possible results of the combinations of decisions and true states of nature for a test of hypothesis.

8.6 We (generally) reject the null hypothesis when the test statistic falls into the rejection region, but we do not accept the null hypothesis when the test statistic does not fall into the rejection region. Why?

8.7 If you test a hypothesis and reject the null hypothesis in favor of the alternative hypothesis, does your test prove that the alternative hypothesis is correct? Explain.

ᴀᴘᴘʟᴇᴛ Applet Exercise 8.1

Use the applet entitled *Hypotheses Test for a Mean* to investigate the frequency of Type I and Type II errors. For this exercise, use $n = 100$ and the normal distribution with mean 50 and standard deviation 10.

    a. Set the null mean equal to 50 and the alternative to *not equal*. Run the applet one time. How many times was the null hypothesis rejected at level .05? In this case, the null hypothesis is true. Which type of error occurred each time the true null hypothesis was rejected? What is the probability of rejecting a true null hypothesis at level .05? How does the proportion of times the null hypothesis was rejected compare with this probability?

    b. Clear the applet, then set the null mean equal to 47, and keep the alternative at *not equal*. Run the applet one

time. How many times was the null hypothesis *not* rejected at level .05? In this case, the null hypothesis is false. Which type of error occurred each time the null hypothesis was *not* rejected? Run the applet several more times without clearing. Based on your results, what can you conclude about the probability of failing to reject the null hypothesis for the given conditions?

Applying the Concepts—Basic

8.8 **Calories in school lunches.** A University of Florida economist conducted a study of Virginia elementary school lunch menus. During the state-mandated testing period, school lunches averaged 863 calories. (*National Bureau of Economic Research*, November 2002.) The economist claimed that after the testing period end, the average caloric content of Virginia school lunches dropped significantly. Set up the null and alternative hypothesis to test the economist's claim.

8.9 **A camera that detects liars.** According to *New Scientist* (January 2, 2002), a new thermal imaging camera that detects small temperature changes is now being used as a polygraph device. The United States Department of Defense Polygraph Institute (DDPI) claims that the camera can detect liars correctly 75% of the time by monitoring the temperatures of their faces. Give the null hypothesis for testing the claim made by the DDPI.

8.10 **Effectiveness of online courses.** The Sloan Survey of Online Learning, "Making the Grade: Online Education in the United States, 2006," reported that 60% of college presidents believe that their online education courses are as good as or superior to courses that utilize traditional face-to-face instruction. (*Inside Higher Ed*, Nov. 2006.) Give the null hypothesis for testing the claim made by the Sloan Survey.

8.11 **Use of herbal therapy.** According to the *Journal of Advanced Nursing* (January 2001), 45% of senior women (i.e., women over the age of 65) use herbal therapies to prevent or treat health problems. Also senior women who use herbal therapies use an average of 2.5 herbal products in a year.

a. Give the null hypothesis for testing the first claim by the journal.

b. Give the null hypothesis for testing the second claim by the journal.

8.12 Infant's listening time. *Science* (January 1, 1999) reported that the mean listening time of 7-month-old infants exposed to a three-syllable sentence (e.g., "ga ti ti") is 9 seconds. Set up the null and alternative hypotheses for testing the claim.

8.13 DNA-reading tool for quick identification of species. A biologist and a zoologist at the University of Florida were the first scientists to test the effectiveness of a high-tech hand-held device designed to instantly identify the DNA of an animal species. (*PLOS Biology*, Dec. 2005.) They used the DNA-reading device on tissue samples collected from mollusks with brightly colored shells. The scientists discovered that the error rate of the device is less than 5 percent. Set up the null and alternative hypotheses if you want to support the findings.

Applying the Concepts—Intermediate

8.14 Susceptibility to hypnosis. The Computer-Assisted Hypnosis Scale (CAHS) is designed to measure a person's susceptibility to hypnosis. CAHS scores range from 0 (no susceptibility to hypnosis) to 12 (extremely high susceptibility to hypnosis). *Psychological Assessment* (March 1995) reported that University of Tennessee undergraduates had a mean CAHS score of $\mu = 4.6$. Suppose you want to test whether undergraduates at your college or university are more susceptible to hypnosis than University of Tennessee undergraduates.

a. Set up H_0 and H_a for the test.

b. Describe a Type I error for this test.

c. Describe a Type II error for this test.

8.15 Mercury levels in wading birds. According to a University of Florida wildlife ecology and conservation researcher, the average level of mercury uptake in wading birds in the Everglades has declined over the past several years. (*UF News*, December 15, 2000.) Five years ago, the average level was 15 parts per million.

a. Give the null and alternative hypotheses for testing whether the average level today is less than 15 ppm.

b. Describe a Type I error for this test.

c. Describe a Type II error for this test.

Applying the Concepts—Advanced

8.16 Jury trial outcomes. Sometimes, the outcome of a jury trial defies the "commonsense" expectations of the general public (e.g., the O. J. Simpson verdict in the "Trial of the Century"). Such a verdict is more acceptable if we understand that the jury trial of an accused murderer is analogous to the statistical hypothesis-testing process. The null hypothesis in a jury trial is that the accused is innocent. (The status quo hypothesis in the U.S. system of justice is innocence, which is assumed to be true until proven *beyond a reasonable doubt*.) The alternative hypothesis is guilt, which is accepted only when sufficient evidence exists to establish its truth. If the vote of the jury is unanimous in favor of guilt, the null hypothesis of innocence is rejected and the court concludes that the accused murderer is guilty. Any vote other than a unanimous one for guilt results in a "not guilty" verdict. The court never accepts the null hypothesis; that is, the court never declares the accused "innocent." A "not guilty" verdict (as in the O. J. Simpson case) implies that the court could not find the defendant guilty *beyond a reasonable doubt*.

a. Define Type I and Type II errors in a murder trial.

b. Which of the two errors is the more serious? Explain.

c. The court does not, in general, know the values of α and β, but ideally, both should be small. One of these probabilities is assumed to be smaller than the other in a jury trial. Which one, and why?

d. The court system relies on the belief that the value of α is made very small by requiring a unanimous vote before guilt is concluded. Explain why this is so.

e. For a jury prejudiced against a guilty verdict as the trial begins, will the value of α increase or decrease? Explain.

f. For a jury prejudiced against a guilty verdict as the trial begins, will the value of β increase or decrease? Explain.

8.17 Intrusion detection systems. Refer to the *Journal of Research of the National Institute of Standards and Technology* (November–December 2003) study of a computer intrusion detection system (IDS), presented in Exercise 3.83 (p. 151). Recall that an IDS is designed to provide an alarm whenever unauthorized access (e.g., an intrusion) to a computer system occurs. The probability of the system giving a false alarm (i.e., providing a warning when, in fact, no intrusion occurs) is defined by the symbol α, while the probability of a missed detection (i.e., no warning given, when, in fact, an intrusion occurs) is defined by the symbol β. These symbols are used to represent Type I and Type II error rates, respectively, in a hypothesis-testing scenario.

a. What is the null hypothesis H_0?

b. What is the alternative hypothesis H_a?

c. According to actual data on the EMERALD system collected by the Massachusetts Institute of Technology Lincoln Laboratory, only 1 in 1,000 computer sessions with no intrusions resulted in a false alarm. For the same system, the laboratory found that only 500 of 1,000 intrusions were actually detected. Use this information to estimate the values of α and β.

8.2 Large-Sample Test of Hypothesis about a Population Mean

In Section 8.1, we learned that the null and alternative hypotheses form the basis for a test-of-hypothesis inference. The null and alternative hypotheses may take one of several forms. In the sewer pipe example, we tested the null hypothesis that the population mean strength of the pipe is less than or equal to 2,400 pounds per linear foot against the alternative hypothesis that the mean strength exceeds 2,400. That is, we tested

$$H_0: \mu \le 2{,}400$$
$$H_a: \mu > 2{,}400$$

This is a **one-tailed** (or **one-sided**) **statistical test,** because the alternative hypothesis specifies that the population parameter (the population mean μ, in this example) is strictly greater than a specified value (2,400, in this example). If the null hypothesis had been $H_0: \mu \geq 2,400$ and the alternative hypothesis had been $H_a: \mu < 2,400$, the test would still be one sided, because the parameter is still specified to be on "one side" of the null-hypothesis value. Some statistical investigations seek to show that the population parameter is *either larger or smaller* than some specified value. Such an alternative hypothesis is called a **two-tailed** (or **two-sided**) **hypothesis.**

While alternative hypotheses are always specified as strict inequalities, such as $\mu < 2,400$, $\mu > 2,400$, or $\mu \neq 2,400$, null hypotheses are usually specified as equalities, such as $\mu = 2,400$. *Even when the null hypothesis is an inequality, such as $\mu \leq 2,400$, we specify $H_0: \mu = 2,400$, reasoning that if sufficient evidence exists to show that $H_a: \mu > 2,400$ is true when tested against $H_0: \mu = 2,400$, then surely sufficient evidence exists to reject $\mu < 2,400$ as well.* Therefore, the null hypothesis is specified as the value of μ closest to a one-sided alternative hypothesis and as the only value *not* specified in a two-tailed alternative hypothesis. The steps for selecting the null and alternative hypotheses are summarized in the following box:

Steps for Selecting the Null and Alternative Hypotheses

1. Select the *alternative hypothesis* as that which the sampling experiment is intended to establish. The alternative hypothesis will assume one of three forms:

    a. One tailed, upper tailed   *Example: H_a: $\mu > 2,400$*
    b. One tailed, lower tailed   *Example: H_a: $\mu < 2,400$*
    c. Two tailed   *Example: H_a: $\mu \neq 2,400$*

2. Select the *null hypothesis* as the status quo—that which will be presumed true unless the sampling experiment conclusively establishes the alternative hypothesis. The null hypothesis will be specified as that parameter value closest to the alternative in one-tailed tests and as the complementary (or only unspecified) value in two-tailed tests.

    Example: $H_0: \mu = 2,400$

The rejection region for a **two-tailed test** differs from that for a one-tailed test. When we are trying to detect departure from the null hypothesis in *either* direction, we must establish a rejection region in both tails of the sampling distribution of the test statistic. Figures 8.4a and 8.4b show the one-tailed rejection regions for lower- and upper-tailed tests, respectively. The two-tailed rejection region is illustrated in Figure 8.4c. Note that a rejection region is established in each tail of the sampling distribution for a two-tailed test.

The rejection regions corresponding to typical values selected for α are shown in Table 8.2 for one- and two-tailed tests. Note that the smaller α you select, the more evidence (the larger z) you will need before you can reject H_0.

FIGURE 8.4
Rejection regions corresponding to one- and two-tailed tests

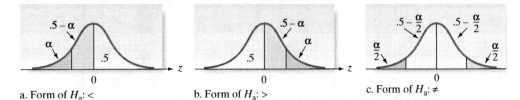

a. Form of H_a: <   b. Form of H_a: >   c. Form of H_a: ≠

TABLE 8.2   Rejection Regions for Common Values of α

	Alternative Hypotheses		
	Lower Tailed	Upper Tailed	Two Tailed
$\alpha = .10$	$z < -1.28$	$z > 1.28$	$z < -1.645$ or $z > 1.645$
$\alpha = .05$	$z < -1.645$	$z > 1.645$	$z < -1.96$ or $z > 1.96$
$\alpha = .01$	$z < -2.33$	$z > 2.33$	$z < -2.575$ or $z > 2.575$

EXAMPLE 8.1

SETTING UP A HYPOTHESIS TEST FOR μ—Mean Drug Response Time

Problem The effect of drugs and alcohol on the nervous system has been the subject of considerable research. Suppose a research neurologist is testing the effect of a drug on response time by injecting 100 rats with a unit dose of the drug, subjecting each rat to a neurological stimulus, and recording its response time. The neurologist knows that the mean response time for rats not injected with the drug (the "control" mean) is 1.2 seconds. She wishes to test whether the mean response time for drug-injected rats differs from 1.2 seconds. Set up the test of hypothesis for this experiment, using $\alpha = .01$.

Solution Since the neurologist wishes to detect whether the mean response time μ for drug-injected rats differs from the control mean of 1.2 seconds in *either* direction—that is, $\mu < 1.2$ or $\mu > 1.2$—we conduct a two-tailed statistical test. Following the procedure for selecting the null and alternative hypotheses, we specify as the alternative hypothesis that the mean differs from 1.2 seconds, since determining whether the drug-injected mean differs from the control mean is the purpose of the experiment. The null hypothesis is the presumption that drug-injected rats have the same mean response time as control rats unless the research indicates otherwise. Thus,

H_0: $\mu = 1.2$ (Mean response time is 1.2 seconds)

H_a: $\mu \neq 1.2$ (Mean response time is less than 1.2 or greater than 1.2 seconds)

The test statistic measures the number of standard deviations between the observed value of $\bar{x}$ and the null-hypothesized value $\mu = 1.2$:

$$\text{Test statistic:} \quad z = \frac{\bar{x} - 1.2}{\sigma_{\bar{x}}}$$

The rejection region must be designated to detect a departure from $\mu = 1.2$ in *either* direction, so we will reject H_0 for values of z that are either too small (negative) or too large (positive). To determine the precise values of z that constitute the rejection region, we first select α, the probability that the test will lead to incorrect rejection of the null hypothesis. Then we divide α equally between the lower and upper tail of the distribution of z, as shown in Figure 8.5. In this example, $\alpha = .01$, so $\alpha/2 = .005$ is placed in each tail. The areas in the tails correspond to $z = -2.575$ and $z = 2.575$, respectively (from Table 8.2), so

$$\text{Rejection region:} \ z < -2.575 \ \text{or} \ z > 2.575 \qquad \text{(see Figure 8.5)}$$

Assumptions: Since the sample size of the experiment is large enough ($n > 30$), the central limit theorem will apply, and no assumptions need be made about the population of response time measurements. The sampling distribution of the sample mean response of 100 rats will be approximately normal, regardless of the distribution of the individual rats' response times.

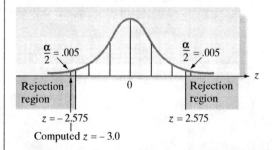

FIGURE 8.5
Two-tailed rejection region:
$\alpha = .01$

Look Back Note that the test is set up *before* the sampling experiment is conducted. The data are not used to develop the test. Evidently, the neurologist wants to conclude that the mean response time for the drug-injected rats differs from the control mean only when the evidence is very convincing, because the value of α has been set quite low at .01. If the experiment results in the rejection of H_0, she can be 99% confident that the mean response time of the drug-injected rats differs from the control mean.

Now Work Exercise 8.21

Once the test is set up, she is ready to perform the sampling experiment and conduct the test. The test is performed in Example 8.2.

EXAMPLE 8.2
CARRYING OUT A HYPOTHESIS TEST FOR μ—
Mean Drug Response Time

Problem Refer to the neurological response-time test set up in Example 8.1. The sample of 100 drug-injected rats yielded the results (in seconds) shown in Table 8.3. Use these data to conduct the test of hypothesis.

DRUGRAT

TABLE 8.3 Drug Response Times for 100 Rats, Example 8.2

1.90	2.17	0.61	1.17	0.66	1.86	1.41	1.30	0.70	0.56
2.00	1.27	0.98	1.55	0.64	0.60	1.55	0.93	0.48	0.39
0.86	1.19	0.79	1.37	1.31	0.85	0.71	1.21	1.23	0.89
1.84	0.80	0.64	1.08	0.74	0.93	1.71	1.05	1.44	0.42
0.70	0.54	1.40	1.06	0.54	0.17	0.98	0.89	1.28	0.68
0.98	1.14	1.16	1.64	1.16	1.01	1.09	0.77	1.58	0.99
0.57	0.27	0.51	1.27	1.81	0.88	0.31	0.92	0.93	1.66
0.21	0.79	0.94	0.45	1.19	1.60	0.14	0.99	1.08	1.57
0.55	1.65	0.81	1.00	2.55	1.96	1.31	1.88	1.51	1.48
0.61	0.05	1.21	0.48	1.63	1.45	0.22	0.49	1.29	1.40

Solution To carry out the test, we need to find the values of $\bar{x}$ and s. These values, $\bar{x} = 1.05$ and $s = .5$, are shown (highlighted) on the MINITAB printout of Figure 8.6. Now we substitute these sample statistics into the test statistic and obtain

$$z = \frac{\bar{x} - 1.2}{\sigma_{\bar{x}}} = \frac{\bar{x} - 1.2}{\sigma/\sqrt{n}} \approx \frac{1.05 - 1.2}{.5/\sqrt{100}} = -3.0$$

The implication is that the sample mean, 1.05, is (approximately) three standard deviations below the null-hypothesized value of 1.2 in the sampling distribution of $\bar{x}$. You can see in Figure 8.5 that this value of z is in the lower-tail rejection region, which consists of all values of $z < -2.575$. This sampling experiment provides sufficient evidence to reject H_0 and conclude, at the $\alpha = .01$ level of significance, that the mean response time for drug-injected rats differs from the control mean of 1.2 seconds. It appears that the rats receiving an injection of the drug have a mean response time that is less than 1.2 seconds.

FIGURE 8.6

MINITAB descriptive statistics for fill amounts, Example 8.2

Descriptive Statistics: TIME

Variable	N	Mean	StDev	Minimum	Q1	Median	Q3	Maximum
TIME	100	1.0517	0.4982	0.0500	0.6650	0.9950	1.4000	2.5500

Look Back Three points about the test of hypothesis in this example apply to all statistical tests:

1. Since z is less than -2.575, it is tempting to state our conclusion at a significance level lower than $\alpha = .01$. We resist this temptation because the level of α is determined *before* the sampling experiment is performed. If we decide that we are willing to tolerate a 1% Type I error rate, the result of the sampling experiment should have no effect on that decision. *In general, the same data should not be used both to set up and to conduct the test.*

2. When we state our conclusion at the .01 level of significance, we are referring to the failure rate of the *procedure*, not the result of this particular test. We know that the test procedure will lead to the rejection of the null hypothesis only 1% of the time when in fact $\mu = 1.2$. *Therefore, when the test statistic falls into the rejection region, we infer that the alternative $\mu \neq 1.2$ is true and express our confidence in the procedure by quoting either the α level of significance or the $100(1 - \alpha)\%$ confidence level.*

3. Although a test may lead to a "statistically significant" result (i.e., rejecting H_0 at significance level α, as in the preceding test), it may not be "practically significant." For example, suppose the neurologist tested $n = 100,000$ drug-injected rats, resulting in $\bar{x} = 1.1995$ and $s = .05$. Now a two-tailed hypothesis test of H_0: $\mu = 1.2$ results in a test statistic of

$$z = \frac{(1.1995 - 1.2)}{.05/\sqrt{100,000}} = -3.16$$

This result at $\alpha = .05$ leads us to "reject H_0" and conclude that the mean μ is "statistically different" from 1.2. However, for all practical purposes, the sample mean $\bar{x} = 1.1995$ and the hypothesized mean $\mu = 1.2$ are the same. Because the result is not "practically significant," the neurologist is not likely to consider a unit dose of the drug as an inhibitor to response time in rats. Consequently, *not all "statistically significant" results are "practically significant."*

Now Work Exercise 8.26

The setup of a large-sample test of hypothesis about a population mean is summarized in the next box. Both the one- and two-tailed tests are shown.

Large-Sample Test of Hypothesis about μ

One-Tailed Test

H_0: $\mu = \mu_0$

H_a: $\mu < \mu_0$ (or H_a: $\mu > \mu_0$)

Test statistic: $z = \dfrac{\bar{x} - \mu_0}{\sigma_{\bar{x}}}$

Rejection region: $z < -z_\alpha$
   (or $z > z_\alpha$ when H_a: $\mu > \mu_0$)

where z_α is chosen so that
   $P(z < -z_\alpha) = \alpha$

Two-Tailed Test

H_0: $\mu = \mu_0$

H_a: $\mu \neq \mu_0$

Test statistic: $z = \dfrac{\bar{x} - \mu_0}{\sigma_{\bar{x}}}$

Rejection region: $z < -z_{\alpha/2}$ or $z > z_{\alpha/2}$

where $z_{\alpha/2}$ is chosen so that
   $P(z > z_{\alpha/2}) = \alpha/2$

Note: μ_0 is the symbol for the numerical value assigned to μ under the null hypothesis.

Conditions Required for a Valid Large-Sample Hypothesis Test for μ

1. A random sample is selected from the target population.

2. The sample size n is large (i.e., $n \geq 30$). (Due to the central limit theorem, this condition guarantees that the test statistic will be approximately normal regardless of the shape of the underlying probability distribution of the population.)

Once the test has been set up, the sampling experiment is performed and the test statistic is calculated. The following box contains possible **conclusions** for a test of hypothesis, depending on the result of the sampling experiment.

Possible Conclusions for a Test of Hypothesis

1. If the calculated test statistic falls into the rejection region, reject H_0 and conclude that the alternative hypothesis H_a is true. State that you are rejecting H_0 at the α level of significance. Remember that the confidence is in the testing *process*, not the particular result of a single test.

(continued)

> **2.** If the test statistic does not fall into the rejection region, conclude that the sampling experiment does not provide sufficient evidence to reject H_0 at the α level of significance. [Generally, we will not "accept" the null hypothesis unless the probability β of a Type II error has been calculated. (See optional Section 8.6.)]

Exercises 8.18–8.35

Understanding the Principles

8.18 Explain the difference between a one-tailed and a two-tailed test.

8.19 What conditions are required for a valid large-sample test for μ?

8.20 For what values of the test statistic do you reject H_0? fail to reject H_0?

Learning the Mechanics

8.21 For each of the following rejection regions, sketch the sampling distribution for z and indicate the location of the rejection region.
  a. $z > 1.96$
  b. $z > 1.645$
  c. $z > 2.575$
  d. $z < -1.28$
  e. $z < -1.645$ or $z > 1.645$
  f. $z < -2.575$ or $z > 2.575$
  g. For each of the rejection regions specified in parts **a–f**, what is the probability that a Type I error will be made?

8.22 Suppose you are interested in conducting the statistical test of H_0: $\mu = 200$ against H_a: $\mu > 200$, and you have decided to use the following decision rule: Reject H_0 if the sample mean of a random sample of 100 items is more than 215. Assume that the standard deviation of the population is 80.
  a. Express the decision rule in terms of z.
  b. Find α, the probability of making a Type I error, by using this decision rule.

8.23 A random sample of 100 observations from a population with standard deviation 60 yielded a sample mean of 110.
  a. Test the null hypothesis that $\mu = 100$ against the alternative hypothesis that $\mu > 100$, using $\alpha = .05$. Interpret the results of the test.
  b. Test the null hypothesis that $\mu = 100$ against the alternative hypothesis that $\mu \neq 100$, using $\alpha = .05$. Interpret the results of the test.
  c. Compare the results of the two tests you conducted. Explain why the results differ.

8.24 A random sample of 64 observations produced the following summary statistics: $\bar{x} = .323$ and $s^2 = .034$.
  a. Test the null hypothesis that $\mu = .36$ against the alternative hypothesis that $\mu < .36$, using $\alpha = .10$.
  b. Test the null hypothesis that $\mu = .36$ against the alternative hypothesis that $\mu \neq .36$, using $\alpha = .10$. Interpret the result.

APPLET Applet Exercise 8.2

Use the applet entitled *Hypotheses Test for a Mean* to investigate the effect of the underlying distribution on the proportion of Type I errors. For this exercise, take $n = 100$, mean $= 50$, standard deviation $= 10$, null mean $= 50$, and alternative $<$.
  a. Select the normal distribution and run the applet several times without clearing. What happens to the proportion of times the null hypothesis is rejected at the .05 level as the applet is run more and more times?
  b. Clear the applet and then repeat part **a**, using the right-skewed distribution. Do you get similar results? Explain.
  c. Describe the effect that the underlying distribution has on the probability of making a Type I error.

APPLET Applet Exercise 8.3

Use the applet entitled *Hypotheses Test for a Mean* to investigate the effect of the underlying distribution on the proportion of Type II errors. For this exercise, take $n = 100$, mean $= 50$, standard deviation $= 10$, null mean $= 52$, and alternative $<$.
  a. Select the normal distribution and run the applet several times without clearing. What happens to the proportion of times the null hypothesis is rejected at the .01 level as the applet is run more and more times? Is this what you would expect? Explain.
  b. Clear the applet and then repeat part **a**, using the right-skewed distribution. Do you get similar results? Explain.
  c. Describe the effect that the underlying distribution has on the probability of making a Type II error.

APPLET Applet Exercise 8.4

Use the applet entitled *Hypotheses Test for a Mean* to investigate the effect of the null mean on the probability of making a Type II error. For this exercise, take $n = 100$, mean $= 50$, standard deviation $= 10$, and alternative $<$ with the normal distribution. Set the null mean to 55 and run the applet several times without clearing. Record the proportion of Type II errors that occurred at the .01 level. Clear the applet and repeat for null means of 54, 53, 52, and 51. What can you conclude about the probability of a Type II error as the null mean gets closer to the actual mean? Can you offer a reasonable explanation for this behavior?

Applying the Concepts—Basic

8.25 **Teacher perceptions of child behavior.** *Developmental Psychology* (Mar. 2003) published a study on teacher perceptions of the behavior of elementary school children. Teachers rated the aggressive behavior of a sample of 11,160 New York City public school children by responding to the statement "This child threatens or bullies others in order to get his/her own way." Responses were measured on a scale ranging from 1 (*never*) to 5 (*always*). Summary statistics for the sample of 11,160 children were reported as $\bar{x} = 2.15$ and $s = 1.05$. Let μ represent the mean response for the population of all New York City public school children. Suppose you want to test H_0: $\mu = 3$ against H_a: $\mu \neq 3$.
  a. In the words of the problem, define a Type I error and a Type II error.

b. Use the sample information to conduct the test at a significance level of $\alpha = .05$.

c. Conduct the test from part **b** at a significance level of $\alpha = .10$.

8.26 **Latex allergy in health-care workers.** Refer to the *Current Allergy & Clinical Immunology* (March 2004) study of $n = 46$ hospital employees who were diagnosed with a latex allergy from exposure to the powder on latex gloves, presented in Exercise 7.13 (p. 314). The number of latex gloves used per week by the sampled workers is summarized as follows: $\bar{x} = 19.3$ and $s = 11.9$. Let μ represent the mean number of latex gloves used per week by all hospital employees. Consider testing $H_0: \mu = 20$ against $H_a: \mu < 20$.

a. Give the rejection region for the test at a significance level of $\alpha = .01$.

b. Calculate the value of the test statistic.

c. Use the results from parts **a** and **b** to draw the appropriate conclusion.

8.27 **Heart rate during laughter.** Laughter is often called "the best medicine," since studies have shown that laughter can reduce muscle tension and increase oxygenation of the blood. In the *International Journal of Obesity* (Jan., 2007), researchers at Vanderbilt University investigated the physiological changes that accompany laughter. Ninety subjects (18–34 years old) watched film clips designed to evoke laughter. During the laughing period, the researchers measured the heart rate (beats per minute) of each subject, with the following summary results: $\bar{x} = 73.5$, $s = 6$. It is well known that the mean resting heart rate of adults is 71 beats per minute. At $\alpha = .05$, is there sufficient evidence to indicate that the true mean heart rate during laughter exceeds 71 beats per minute?

8.28 **Analyzing remote-sensing data to identify type of land cover.** Geographers use remote-sensing data from satellite pictures to identify urban land cover as either grassland, commercial, or residential. In *Geographical Analysis* (Oct. 2006), researchers from Arizona State, Florida State, and Louisiana State Universities collaborated on a new method for analyzing remote-sensing data. A satellite photograph of an urban area was divided into 4×4-meter areas (called pixels). Of interest is a numerical measure of the distribution of the sizes of gaps, or holes, in the pixel, a property called *lacunarity*. The mean and standard deviation of the lacunarity measurements for a sample of 100 pixels randomly selected from a specific urban area are 225 and 20, respectively. It is known that the mean lacunarity measurement for all grassland pixels is 220. Do the data suggest that the area sampled is grassland? Test at $\alpha = .01$.

Applying the Concepts—Intermediate

8.29 **Post-traumatic stress of POWs.** *Psychological Assessment* (March 1995) published the results of a study of World War II aviators captured by German forces after having been shot down. Having located a total of 239 World War II aviator POW survivors, the researchers asked each veteran to participate in the study; 33 responded to the letter of invitation. Each of the 33 POW survivors was administered the Minnesota Multiphasic Personality Inventory, one component of which measures level of post-traumatic stress disorder (PTSD). [*Note:* The higher the score, the higher is the level of PTSD.] The aviators produced a mean PTSD score of $\bar{x} = 9.00$ and a standard deviation of $s = 9.32$.

a. Set up the null and alternative hypotheses for determining whether the true mean PTSD score of all World War II aviator POWs is less than 16. [*Note:* The value 16 represents the mean PTSD score established for Vietnam POWs.]

b. Conduct the test from part **a**, using $\alpha = .10$. What are the practical implications of the test?

c. Discuss the representativeness of the sample used in the study and its ramifications.

8.30 **Point spreads of NFL games.** During the National Football League (NFL) season, Las Vegas oddsmakers establish a point spread on each game for betting purposes. For example, the Indianapolis Colts were established as 7-point favorites over the Chicago Bears in the 2007 Super Bowl. The final scores of NFL games were compared against the final point spreads established by the oddsmakers in *Chance* (Fall 1998). The difference between the outcome of the game and the point spread (called a point-spread error) was calculated for 240 NFL games. The mean and standard deviation of the point-spread errors are $\bar{x} = -1.6$ and $s = 13.3$. Use this information to test the hypothesis that the true mean point-spread error for all NFL games is 0. Conduct the test at $\alpha = .01$ and interpret the result.

8.31 **Bone fossil study.** Humerus bones from the same species of animal tend to have approximately the same length-to-width ratios. When fossils of humerus bones are discovered, archeologists can often determine the species of animal by examining the length-to-width ratios of the bones. It is known that species A exhibits a mean ratio of 8.5. Suppose 41 fossils of humerus bones were unearthed at an archeological site in East Africa, where species A is believed to have lived. (Assume that the unearthed bones were all from the same unknown species.) The length-to-width ratios of the bones were calculated and listed, as shown in the following table:

BONES

10.73	8.89	9.07	9.20	10.33	9.98	9.84	9.59
8.48	8.71	9.57	9.29	9.94	8.07	8.37	6.85
8.52	8.87	6.23	9.41	6.66	9.35	8.86	9.93
8.91	11.77	10.48	10.39	9.39	9.17	9.89	8.17
8.93	8.80	10.02	8.38	11.67	8.30	9.17	12.00
9.38							

a. Test whether the population mean ratio of all bones of this particular species differs from 8.5. Use $\alpha = .01$.

b. What are the practical implications of the test you conducted in part **a**?

8.32 **Cooling method for gas turbines.** During periods of high demand for electricity—especially in the hot summer months—the power output from a gas turbine engine can drop dramatically. One way to counter this drop in power is by cooling the inlet air to the turbine. An increasingly popular cooling method uses high-pressure inlet fogging. The performance of a sample of 67 gas turbines augmented with high-pressure inlet fogging was investigated in the *Journal of Engineering for Gas Turbines and Power* (Jan. 2005). One measure of performance is heat rate (kilojoules per kilowatt per hour). Heat rates for the 67 gas turbines, saved in the **GASTURBINE** file, are listed in the next table. Suppose that a standard gas turbine has, on average, a heat rate of 10,000 kJ/kWh.

a. Conduct a test to determine whether the mean heat rate of gas turbines augmented with high-pressure inlet fogging exceeds 10,000 kJ/kWh. Use $\alpha = .05$.

b. Identify a Type I error for this study. Identify a Type II error.

◉ GASTURBINE

14622	13196	11948	11289	11964	10526	10387	10592	10460	10086
14628	13396	11726	11252	12449	11030	10787	10603	10144	11674
11510	10946	10508	10604	10270	10529	10360	14796	12913	12270
11842	10656	11360	11136	10814	13523	11289	11183	10951	9722
10481	9812	9669	9643	9115	9115	11588	10888	9738	9295
9421	9105	10233	10186	9918	9209	9532	9933	9152	9295
16243	14628	12766	8714	9469	11948	12414			

8.33 Salaries of postgraduates. The *Economics of Education Review* (Vol. 21, 2002) published a paper on the relationship between education level and earnings. The data for the research were obtained from the National Adult Literacy Survey of over 25,000 respondents. The survey revealed that males with a postgraduate degree had a mean salary of \$61,340 (with standard error $s_{\bar{x}} = \$2,185$) while females with a postgraduate degree had a mean of \$32,227 (with standard error $s_{\bar{x}} = \$932$).

a. The article reports that a 95% confidence interval for μ_M, the population mean salary of all males with postgraduate degrees, is (\$57,050, \$65,631). Based on this interval, is there evidence that μ_M differs from \$60,000? Explain.

b. Use the summary information to test the hypothesis that the true mean salary of males with postgraduate degrees differs from \$60,000. Take $\alpha = .05$. (*Note*: $s_{\bar{x}} = s/\sqrt{n}$)

c. Explain why the inferences in parts **a** and **b** agree.

d. The article reports that a 95% confidence interval for μ_F, the population mean salary of all females with postgraduate degrees, is (\$30,396, \$34,058). Based on this interval, is there evidence that μ_F differs from \$33,000? Explain.

e. Use the summary information to test the hypothesis that the true mean salary of females with postgraduate de-

grees differs from \$33,000. Take $\alpha = .05$ (*Note*: $s_{\bar{x}} = s/\sqrt{n}$.)

f. Explain why the inferences in parts **d** and **e** agree.

8.34 Cyanide in soil. *Environmental Science & Technology* (October 1993) reported on a study of contaminated soil in the Netherlands. Seventy-two 400-gram soil specimens were sampled, dried, and analyzed for the con taminant cyanide. The cyanide concentration [in milligrams per kilogram (mg/kg) of soil] of each soil specimen was determined by an infrared microscopic method. The sample resulted in a mean cyanide level of $\bar{x} = 84$ mg/kg and a standard deviation of $s = 80$ mg/kg.

a. Test the hypothesis that the true mean cyanide level in soil in the Netherlands exceeds 100 mg/kg. Use $\alpha = .10$.

b. Would you reach the same conclusion as in part **a** if you took $\alpha = .05$? $\alpha = .01$? Why can the conclusion of a test change when the value of α is changed?

Applying the Concepts—Advanced

8.35 Social interaction of mental patients. The *Community Mental Health Journal* (Aug. 2000) presented the results of a survey of over 6,000 clients of the Department of Mental Health and Addiction Services (DMHAS) in Connecticut. One of the many variables measured for each mental health patient was frequency of social interaction (on a 5-point scale, where 1 = very infrequently, 3 = occasionally, and 5 = very frequently). The 6,681 clients who were evaluated had a mean social interaction score of 2.95 with a standard deviation of 1.10.

a. Conduct a hypothesis test (at $\alpha = .01$) to determine whether the true mean social interaction score of all Connecticut mental health patients differs from 3.

b. Examine the results of the study from a practical view, and then discuss why "statistical significance" does not always imply "practical significance."

c. Because the variable of interest is measured on a 5-point scale, it is unlikely that the population of ratings will be normally distributed. Consequently, some analysts may perceive the test from part **a** to be invalid and search for alternative methods of analysis. Defend or refute this position.

8.3 Observed Significance Levels: *p*-Values

According to the statistical test procedure described in Section 8.2, the rejection region and, correspondingly, the value of α are selected prior to conducting the test and the conclusions are stated in terms of rejecting or not rejecting the null hypothesis. A second method of presenting the results of a statistical test reports the extent to which the test statistic disagrees with the null hypothesis and leaves to the reader the task of deciding whether to reject the null hypothesis. This measure of disagreement is called the *observed significance level* (or *p-value*) for the test.

Definition 8.1

The **observed significance level,** or ***p-value,*** for a specific statistical test is the probability (assuming that H_0 is true) of observing a value of the test statistic that is at least as contradictory to the null hypothesis, and supportive of the alternative hypothesis, as the actual one computed from the sample data.

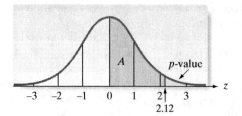

FIGURE 8.7

Finding the p-value for an upper-tailed test when $z = 2.12$

For example, the value of the test statistic computed for the sample of $n = 50$ sections of sewer pipe was $z = 2.12$. Since the test is one tailed [i.e., the alternative (research) hypothesis of interest is $H_a: \mu > 2{,}400$], values of the test statistic even more contradictory to H_0 than the one observed would be values larger than $z = 2.12$. Therefore, the observed significance level (p-value) for this test is

$$p\text{-value} = P(z \geq 2.12)$$

or, equivalently, the area under the standard normal curve to the right of $z = 2.12$. (See Figure 8.7)

The area A in Figure 8.7 is given in Table IV in Appendix A as .4830. Therefore, the upper-tail area corresponding to $z = 2.12$ is

$$p\text{-value} = .5 - .4830 = .0170$$

Consequently, we say that these test results are "statistically significant"; that is, they disagree (rather strongly) with the null hypothesis $H_0: \mu = 2{,}400$ and favor $H_a: \mu > 2{,}400$. Hence, the probability of observing a z value as large as 2.12 is only .0170 if in fact the true value of μ is 2,400.

If you are inclined to select $\alpha = .05$ for this test, then you would reject the null hypothesis because the p-value for the test, .0170, is less than .05. In contrast, if you choose $\alpha = .01$, you would not reject the null hypothesis, because the p-value for the test is larger than .01. Thus, the use of the observed significance level is identical to the test procedure described in the preceding sections, except that the choice of α is left to you.

The steps for calculating the p-value corresponding to a test statistic for a population mean are given in the following box:

Steps for Calculating the p-Value for a Test of Hypothesis

1. Determine the value of the test statistic z corresponding to the result of the sampling experiment.

   a. If the test is one-tailed, the p-value is equal to the tail area beyond z in the same direction as the alternative hypothesis. Thus, if the alternative hypothesis is of the form $>$, the p-value is the area to the right of, or above, the observed z-value. Conversely, if the alternative is of the form $<$, the p-value is the area to the left of, or below, the observed z-value. (See Figure 8.8.)

   b. If the test is two tailed, the p-value is equal to twice the tail area beyond the observed z-value in the direction of the sign of z. That is, if z is positive, the p-value is twice the area to the right of, or above, the observed z value. Conversely, if z is negative, the p-value is twice the area to the left of, or below, the observed z-value. (See Figure 8.9.)

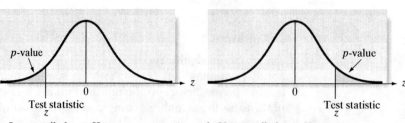

FIGURE 8.8

Finding the p-value for a one-tailed test

a. Lower–tailed test, $H_a: \mu < \mu_0$

b. Upper–tailed test, $H_a: \mu > \mu_0$

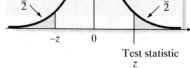

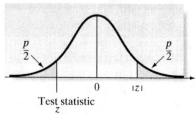

FIGURE 8.9

Finding the *p*-value for a two-tailed test: *p*-value = 2(*p*/2)

a. Test statistic *z* negative

b. Test statistic *z* positive

EXAMPLE 8.3

COMPUTING A
***p*-VALUE—Test**
on Mean Drug
Response Time

Problem Find the observed significance level for the test of the mean response time for drug-injected rats in Examples 8.1 and 8.2.

Solution Example 8.1 presented a two-tailed test of the hypothesis

$$H_0: \mu = 1.2 \text{ seconds}$$

against the alternative hypothesis

$$H_a: \mu \neq 1.2 \text{ seconds}$$

The observed value of the test statistic in Example 8.2 was $z = -3.0$, and any value of z less than -3.0 or greater than $+3.0$ (because this is a two-tailed test) would be even more contradictory to H_0. Therefore, the observed significance level for the test is

$$p\text{-value} = P(z < -3.0 \text{ or } z > +3.0)$$

Thus, we calculate the area below the observed *z*-value, $z = -3.0$, and double it. Consulting Table IV in Appendix A, we find that $P(z < -3.0) = .5 - .4987 = .0013$. Therefore, the *p*-value for this two-tailed test is

$$2P(z < -3.0) = 2(.0013) = .0026$$

This *p*-value can also be obtained with statistical software. The *p*-value is shown (highlighted) on the SAS printout of Figure 8.10.

```
Sample Statistics for TIME

     N          Mean       Std. Dev.       Std. Error
  ------------------------------------------------------
    100          1.05        0.50            0.05

Hypothesis Test

   Null hypothesis:    Mean of TIME =  1.2
   Alternative:        Mean of TIME ^= 1.2

With a specified known standard deviation of 0.5
```

FIGURE 8.10

SAS test of mean response time, Example 8.3

Z Statistic	Prob > Z
-3.000	0.0027

Look Back We can interpret this *p*-value as a strong indication that the mean reaction time of drug-injected rats differs from the control mean ($\mu \neq 1.2$), since we would observe a test statistic this extreme or more extreme only 26 in 10,000 times if the drug-injected mean were equal to the control mean ($\mu = 1.2$). The extent to which the mean differs from 1.2 could be better determined by calculating a confidence interval for μ.

Now Work Exercise 8.42

When publishing the results of a statistical test of hypothesis in journals, case studies, reports, etc., many researchers make use of *p*-values. Instead of selecting α beforehand and then conducting a test, as outlined in this chapter, the researcher computes (usually with the aid of a statistical software package) and reports the value of the appropriate test statistic and its associated p-value. It is left to the reader of the report to judge the significance of the result (i.e., the reader must determine, on the basis of the reported p-value, whether to reject the null hypothesis in favor of the alternative hypothesis. Usually, the null hypothesis is rejected if the observed significance level is *less than* the fixed significance level α chosen by the reader. The inherent advantage of reporting test results in this manner is twofold: (1) Readers are permitted to select the maximum value of α that they would be willing to tolerate if they actually carried out a standard test of hypothesis in the manner outlined in this chapter, and (2) a measure of the degree of significance of the result (i.e., the p-value) is provided.

Reporting Test Results as p-Values: How to Decide Whether to Reject H_0

1. Choose the maximum value of α that you are willing to tolerate.
2. If the observed significance level (p-value) of the test is less than the chosen value of α, reject the null hypothesis. Otherwise, do not reject the null hypothesis.

EXAMPLE 8.4
USING p-VALUES— Test of Mean Hospital Length of Stay

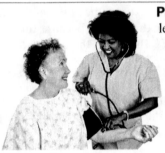

Problem The lengths of stay (in days) for 100 randomly selected hospital patients, first presented in Table 7.1, are reproduced in Table 8.4. Suppose we want to test the hypothesis that the true mean length of stay (LOS) at the hospital is less than 5 days; that is,

H_0: $\mu = 5$ (Mean LOS is 5 days.)
H_a: $\mu < 5$ (Mean LOS is less than 5 days.)

Assuming that $\sigma = 3.68$, use the data in the table to conduct the test at $\alpha = .05$.

 HOSPLOS

TABLE 8.4 Lengths of Stay for 100 Hospital Patients

2	3	8	6	4	4	6	4	2	5
8	10	4	4	4	2	1	3	2	10
1	3	2	3	4	3	5	2	4	1
2	9	1	7	17	9	9	9	4	4
1	1	1	3	1	6	3	3	2	5
1	3	3	14	2	3	9	6	6	3
5	1	4	6	11	22	1	9	6	5
2	2	5	4	3	6	1	5	1	6
17	1	2	4	5	4	4	3	2	3
3	5	2	3	3	2	10	2	4	2

Solution The data were entered into a computer and MINITAB was used to conduct the analysis. The MINITAB printout for the lower-tailed test is displayed in Figure 8.11. Both the test statistic, $z = -1.28$, and the p-value of the test, $p = .101$, are highlighted on the MINITAB printout. Since the p-value exceeds our selected α value, $\alpha = .05$, we

---

One-Sample Z: LOS

```
Test of mu = 5 vs < 5
The assumed standard deviation = 3.68
```

FIGURE 8.11
MINITAB lower-tailed test of mean LOS, Example 8.4

Variable	N	Mean	StDev	SE Mean	95% Upper Bound	Z	P
LOS	100	4.530	3.678	0.368	5.135	-1.28	0.101

cannot reject the null hypothesis. Hence, there is insufficient evidence (at $\alpha = .05$) to conclude that the true mean LOS at the hospital is less than 5 days.

Now Work Exercise 8.49

Note: Some statistical software packages (e.g., SPSS) will conduct only two-tailed tests of hypothesis. For these packages, you obtain the *p*-value for a one-tailed test as shown in the next box.

Converting a Two-Tailed *p*-Value from a Printout to a One-Tailed *p*-Value:

$$p = \frac{\text{Reported } p\text{-value}}{2} \quad \text{if} \begin{cases} H_a \text{ is of form} & > & \text{and } z \text{ is positive} \\ H_a \text{ is of form} & < & \text{and } z \text{ is negative} \end{cases}$$

$$p = 1 - \left(\frac{\text{Reported } p\text{-value}}{2} \right) \quad \text{if} \begin{cases} H_a \text{ is of form} & > & \text{and } z \text{ is negative} \\ H_a \text{ is of form} & < & \text{and } z \text{ is positive} \end{cases}$$

Hypothesis Test for a Population Mean (Large-Sample Case)
Using The TI-84/TI-83 Graphing Calculator

Step 1   *Enter the Data. (Skip to Step 2 if you have summary statistics, not raw data.)*
Press **STAT** and select **1: Edit**.
Note: If the list already contains data, clear the old data. Use the up **ARROW** to highlight "**L1**".
Press **CLEAR ENTER**.
Use the **ARROW** and **ENTER** keys to enter the data set into **L1**.

Step 2   *Access the Statistical Tests Menu.*

Press **STAT**.
Arrow right to **TESTS**.
Press **ENTER** to select **Z-Test**.

Step 3   *Choose "**Data**" or "**Stats**". ("Data" is selected when you have entered the raw data into a List. "Stats" is selected when you are given only the mean, standard deviation, and sample size.)*

Press **ENTER**.
If you selected "Data", enter the values for the hypothesis test, where $\mu_0 =$ the value for μ in the null hypothesis and $\sigma =$ assumed value of the population standard deviation.
Set **List** to **L1**.
Set **Freq** to **1**.
Use the **ARROW** to highlight the appropriate alternative hypothesis.
Press **ENTER**.
Arrow down to "**Calculate**".
Press **ENTER**.

If you selected "Stats", enter the values for the hypothesis test, where $\mu_0 =$ the value for μ in the null hypothesis and $\sigma =$ assumed value of the population standard deviation.
Enter the sample mean and sample size.
Use the **ARROW** to highlight the appropriate alternative hypothesis.
Press **ENTER**.
Arrow down to "**Calculate**".
Press **ENTER**.

The chosen test will be displayed, as will the z-test statistic, the *p*-value, the sample mean, and the sample size.

Example   A manufacturer claims that the average life expectancy of a particular model of light bulb is at least 10,000 hours, with $\sigma = 1,000$ hours. A simple random sample

(continued)

of 40 bulbs shows a sample mean of 9,755 hours. Using $\sigma = .05$, test the manufacturer's claim.

For this problem, the hypotheses will be

$$H_0: \mu \geq 10{,}000$$
$$H_a: \mu < 10{,}000$$

The screens are shown at the right:

As you can see, the p-value is 0.061. Since $p > .05$, ***do not*** reject H_0.

```
Z-Test
  Inpt:Data Stats
  μo:10000
  σ:1000
  x̄:9755
  n:40
  μ:≠μo  <μo  >μo
  Calculate Draw
```

```
Z-Test
  μ<10000
  z=-1.549516053
  p=.0606288707
  x̄=9755
  n=40
```

STATISTICS IN ACTION REVISITED

Testing a Population Mean in the KLEENEX® Survey

Refer to Kimberly-Clark Corporation's survey of 250 people who kept a count of their use of KLEENEX® tissues in diaries (p. 351). We want to test the claim made by marketing experts that $\mu = 60$ is the average number of tissues used by people with colds against our belief that the population mean is smaller than 60 tissues. That is, we want to test

$$H_0: \mu = 60 \qquad H_a: \mu < 60$$

We will select $\alpha = .05$ as the level of significance for the test.

The survey results for the 250 sampled KLEENEX® users are stored in the **TISSUES** data file. A MINITAB analysis of the data yielded the printout displayed in Figure SIA8.1

The observed significance level of the test, highlighted on the printout, is p-value = 018. Since this p-value is less than $\alpha = .05$, we have sufficient evidence to reject H_0; therefore, we conclude that the mean number of tissues used by a person with a cold is less than 60 tissues. [*Note:* If we conduct the same test, but with $\alpha = .01$ as the level of significance, we would have insufficient evidence to reject H_0, since p-value = .018 is greater than $\alpha = .01$. Thus, at $\alpha = .01$, there is no evidence to support our alternative hypothesis that the population mean is less than 60.]

```
Test of mu = 60 vs < 60
```

Variable	N	Mean	StDev	SE Mean	95% Upper Bound	T	P
NUMUSED	250	56.6760	25.0343	1.5833	59.2900	-2.10	0.018

FIGURE SIA8.1
MINITAB test of $\mu = 60$ for KLEENEX® survey

Exercises 8.36–8.53

Understanding the Principles

8.36 How does the observed significance level (p-value) of a test differ from the value of α?

8.37 In general, do large p-values or small p-values support the alternative hypothesis H_a?

8.38 If a hypothesis test using $\alpha = .05$ were conducted, for which of the following p-values would the null hypothesis be rejected?

a. .06   **b.** .10
c. .01   **d.** .001
e. .251   **f.** .042

8.39 For each pair consisting of α and an observed significance level (p-value), indicate whether the null hypothesis would be rejected.
a. $\alpha = .05$, p-value = .10
b. $\alpha = .10$, p-value = .05

c. $\alpha = .01$, p-value $= .001$
d. $\alpha = .025$, p-value $= .05$
e. $\alpha = .10$, p-value $= .45$

Learning the Mechanics

8.40 An analyst tested the null hypothesis $\mu \geq 20$ against the alternative hypothesis $\mu < 20$. The analyst reported a p-value of .06. What is the smallest value of α for which the null hypothesis would be rejected?

8.41 In a test of $H_0: \mu = 100$ against $H_a: \mu > 100$, the sample data yielded the test statistic $z = 2.17$. Find the p-value for the test.

8.42 In a test of $H_0: \mu = 100$ against $H_a: \mu \neq 100$, the sample data yielded the test statistic $z = 2.17$. Find the p-value for the test.

8.43 In a test of the hypothesis $H_0: \mu = 50$ versus $H_a: \mu > 50$, a sample of $n = 100$ observations possessed mean $\bar{x} = 49.4$ and standard deviation $s = 4.1$. Find and interpret the p-value for this test.

8.44 In a test of the hypothesis $H_0: \mu = 10$ versus $H_a: \mu \neq 10$, a sample of $n = 50$ observations possessed mean $\bar{x} = 10.7$ and standard deviation $s = 3.1$. Find and interpret the p-value for this test.

8.45 Consider a test of $H_0: \mu = 75$ performed with the computer. SPSS reports a two-tailed p-value of .1032. Make the appropriate conclusion for each of the following situations:
a. $H_a: \mu < 75$, $z = -1.63$, $\alpha = .05$
b. $H_a: \mu < 75$, $z = 1.63$, $\alpha = .10$
c. $H_a: \mu > 75$, $z = 1.63$, $\alpha = .10$
d. $H_a: \mu \neq 75$, $z = -1.63$, $\alpha = .01$

Applying the Concepts—Basic

8.46 **Teacher perceptions of child behavior.** Refer to the *Developmental Psychology* (Mar. 2003) study on the aggressive behavior of elementary school children, presented in Exercise 8.25 (p. 363). Recall that you tested $H_0: \mu = 3$ against $H_a: \mu \neq 3$, where μ is the mean level of aggressiveness for the population of all New York City public school children, as perceived by their teachers and based on the summary statistics $n = 11,160$, $\bar{x} = 2.15$, and $s = 1.05$.
a. Compute the p-value of the test.

b. Compare the p-value with $\alpha = .10$ and make the appropriate conclusion.

8.47 **Latex allergy in health-care workers.** Refer to the *Current Allergy & Clinical Immunology* (March 2004) study of latex allergy in health-care workers, presented on Exercise 8.26 (p. 364). Recall that you tested $H_0: \mu = 20$ against $H_a: \mu < 20$, where μ is the mean number of latex gloves used per week by all hospital employees, based on the summary statistics $n = 46$, $\bar{x} = 19.3$, and $s = 11.9$.
a. Compute the p-value of the test.
b. Compare the p-value with $\alpha = .01$ and make the appropriate conclusion.

HYBRIDCARS

8.48 **Prices of hybrid cars.** *BusinessWeek.com* provides consumers with retail prices of new cars at dealers from across the country. The July 2006 prices for the hybrid Toyota Prius were obtained from a sample of 160 dealers. These 160 prices are saved in the **HYBRIDCARS** file.
a. Give the null and alternative hypotheses for testing whether the mean July 2006 dealer price of the Toyota Prius, μ, differs from \$25,000.

b. Data from the **HYBRIDCARS** file were analyzed with MINITAB. The resulting printout is shown below. Find and interpret the p-value of the test.
c. State the appropriate conclusion for the test from part **a** if $\alpha = .05$.
d. State the appropriate conclusion for the test from part **a** if $\alpha = .01$.

8.49 **Bone fossil study.** In Exercise 8.31 (p. 364), you tested $H_0: \mu = 8.5$ versus $H_a: \mu \neq 8.5$, where μ is the population mean length-to-width ratio of humerus bones of a particular species of animal. A SAS printout for the hypothesis test is shown at the bottom of the page. Locate the p-value on the printout and interpret it.

Applying the Concepts—Intermediate

8.50 **Colored string preferred by chickens.** Refer to the *Applied Animal Behaviour Science* (October 2000) study of domestic chickens exposed to a pecking stimulus, presented in Exercise 7.19 (p. 315). Recall that the average number of

MINITAB output for Exercise 8.48

```
Test of mu = 25000 vs not = 25000

Variable    N     Mean    StDev   SE Mean      95% CI            T      P
PRICE     160   25476.7   2429.8    192.1   (25097.3, 25856.1)  2.48  0.014
```

SAS printout for Exercise 8.49

```
Sample Statistics for LWRATIO

    N         Mean        Std. Dev.      Std. Error
------------------------------------------------------
   41         9.26          1.20            0.19

Hypothesis Test

    Null hypothesis:    Mean of LWRATIO =  8.5
    Alternative:        Mean of LWRATIO ^= 8.5

With a specified known standard deviation of 1.2

         Z Statistic      Prob > Z
         -----------      --------
            4.042          <.0001
```

pecks a chicken takes at a white string over a specified time interval is known to be $\mu = 7.5$ pecks. In an experiment in which 72 chickens were exposed to blue string, the average number of pecks was $\bar{x} = 1.13$ pecks, with a standard deviation of $s = 2.21$ pecks.

a. On average, are chickens more apt to peck at white string than at blue string? Conduct the appropriate test of hypothesis, using $\alpha = .05$.

b. Compare your answer to part **a** with your answer to Exercise 7.17**b**.

c. Find the p-value for the test and interpret it.

8.51 Feminizing human faces. Research published in *Nature* (August 27, 1998) revealed that people are more attracted to "feminized" faces, regardless of gender. In one experiment, 50 human subjects viewed both a Japanese female and a Caucasian male face on a computer. Using special computer graphics, each subject could morph the faces (by making them more feminine or more masculine) until they attained the "most attractive" face. The level of feminization x (measured as a percentage) was measured.

a. For the Japanese female face, $\bar{x} = 10.2\%$ and $s = 31.3\%$. The researchers used this sample information to test the null hypothesis of a mean level of feminization equal to 0%. Verify that the test statistic is equal to 2.3.

b. Refer to part **a**. The researchers reported the p-value of the test as $p \approx .02$. Verify and interpret this result.

c. For the Caucasian male face, $\bar{x} = 15.0\%$ and $s = 25.1\%$. The researchers reported the test statistic (for the test of the null hypothesis stated in part **a**) as 4.23, with an associated p-value of approximately 0. Verify and interpret these results.

8.52 Post-traumatic stress of POWs. Refer to the *Psychological Assessment* study of World War II aviator POWs, presented in Exercise 8.29 (p. 364). You tested whether the true mean post-traumatic stress disorder score of World War II aviator POWs is less than 16. Recall that $\bar{x} = 9.00$ and $s = 9.32$ for a sample of $n = 33$ POWs.

a. Compute the p-value of the test.

b. Refer to part **a**. Would the p-value have been larger or smaller if $\bar{x}$ had been larger?

Applying the Concepts—Advanced

8.53 Ages of cable TV shoppers. In a paper presented at the 2000 Conference of the International Association for Time Use Research, professor Margaret Sanik of Ohio State University reported the results of her study on American cable TV viewers who purchase items from one of the home-shopping channels. She found that the average age of these cable TV shoppers was 51 years. Suppose you want to test the null hypothesis $H_0: \mu = 51$, using a sample of $n = 50$ cable TV shoppers.

a. Find the p-value of a two-tailed test if $\bar{x} = 52.3$ and $s = 7.1$.

b. Find the p-value of an upper-tailed test if $\bar{x} = 52.3$ and $s = 7.1$.

c. Find the p-value of a two-tailed test if $\bar{x} = 52.3$ and $s = 10.4$.

d. For each of the tests in parts **a–c**, give a value of α that will lead to a rejection of the null hypothesis.

e. If $\bar{x} = 52.3$, give a value of s that will yield a p-value of .01 or less for a one-tailed test.

8.4 Small-Sample Test of Hypothesis about a Population Mean

Most water-treatment facilities monitor the quality of their drinking water on an hourly basis. One variable monitored is pH, which measures the degree of alkalinity or acidity in the water. A pH below 7.0 is acidic, one above 7.0 is alkaline, and a pH of 7.0 is neutral. One water-treatment plant has a target pH of 8.5. (Most try to maintain a slightly alkaline level.) The mean and standard deviation of 1 hour's test results, based on 17 water samples at this plant, are

$$\bar{x} = 8.42 \qquad s = .16$$

Does this sample provide sufficient evidence that the mean pH level in the water differs from 8.5?

This inference can be placed in a test-of-hypothesis framework. We establish the target pH as the null hypothesized value and then utilize a two-tailed alternative that the true mean pH differs from the target:

$$H_0: \mu = 8.5 \text{ (Mean pH level is 8.5.)}$$

$$H_a: \mu \neq 8.5 \text{ (Mean pH level differs from 8.5.)}$$

Recall from Section 7.3 that when we are faced with making inferences about a population mean from the information in a small sample, two problems emerge:

1. The normality of the sampling distribution for $\bar{x}$ does not follow from the central limit theorem when the sample size is small. We must assume that the distribution of measurements from which the sample was selected is approximately normally distributed in order to ensure the approximate normality of the sampling distribution of $\bar{x}$.

2. If the population standard deviation σ is unknown, as is usually the case, then we cannot assume that s will provide a good approximation for σ when the sample size is small. Instead, we must use the *t*-distribution rather than the standard normal *z*-distribution to make inferences about the population mean μ.

Therefore, as the test statistic of a small-sample test of a population mean, we use the *t*-statistic:

$$\textit{Test statistic: } t = \frac{\bar{x} - \mu_0}{s/\sqrt{n}} = \frac{\bar{x} - 8.5}{s/\sqrt{n}}$$

In this equation, μ_0 is the null-hypothesized value of the population mean μ. In the example here, $\mu_0 = 8.5$.

To find the rejection region, we must specify the value of α, the probability that the test will lead to rejection of the null hypothesis when it is true, and then consult the *t* table (Table VI of Appendix A). With $\alpha = .05$, the two-tailed rejection region is

$$\textit{Rejection region: } t_{\alpha/2} = t_{.025} = 2.120 \text{ with } n - 1 = 16 \text{ degrees of freedom}$$
$$\text{Reject } H_0 \text{ if } t < -2.120 \text{ or } t > 2.120$$

The rejection region is shown in Figure 8.12.

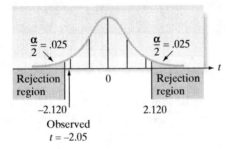

FIGURE 8.12

Two-tailed rejection region for small-sample *t*-test

We are now prepared to calculate the test statistic and reach a conclusion:

$$t = \frac{\bar{x} - \mu_0}{s/\sqrt{n}} = \frac{8.42 - 8.50}{.16/\sqrt{17}} = \frac{-.08}{.039} = -2.05$$

Since the calculated value of *t* does not fall into the rejection region (Figure 8.12), we cannot reject H_0 at the $\alpha = .05$ level of significance. Thus, the water-treatment plant should not conclude that the mean pH differs from the 8.5 target on the basis of the sample evidence.

It is interesting to note that the calculated *t* value, -2.05, is *less than* the .05-level *z*-value, -1.96. The implication is that if we had *incorrectly* used a *z* statistic for this test, we would have rejected the null hypothesis at the .05 level and concluded that the mean pH level differs from 8.5. The important point is that the statistical procedure to be used must always be closely scrutinized and all the assumptions understood. Many statistical lies are the result of misapplications of otherwise valid procedures.

The technique for conducting a small-sample test of hypothesis about a population mean is summarized in the following boxes:

Small-Sample Test of Hypothesis About μ

One-Tailed Test	**Two-Tailed Test**

One-Tailed Test

$H_0: \mu = \mu_0$

$H_a: \mu < \mu_0$ (or $H_a: \mu > \mu_0$)

$$\textit{Test statistic: } t = \frac{\bar{x} - \mu_0}{s/\sqrt{n}}$$

Rejection region: $t < -t_\alpha$

(or $t > t_\alpha$ when $H_a: \mu > \mu_0$)

Two-Tailed Test

$H_0: \mu = \mu_0$

$H_a: \mu \neq \mu_0$

$$\textit{Test statistic: } t = \frac{\bar{x} - \mu_0}{s/\sqrt{n}}$$

Rejection region: $t < -t_{\alpha/2}$ or $t > t_{\alpha/2}$

where t_α and $t_{\alpha/2}$ are based on $(n - 1)$ degrees of freedom

> **Conditions Required for a Valid Small-Sample Hypothesis Test for μ**
>
> 1. A random sample is selected from the target population.
> 2. The population from which the sample is selected has a distribution that is approximately normal.

EXAMPLE 8.5

A SMALL-SAMPLE
TEST FOR μ—
Does a New Engine
Meet Air-Pollution
Standards?

Problem A major car manufacturer wants to test a new engine to determine whether it meets new air-pollution standards. The mean emission μ of all engines of this type must be less than 20 parts per million of carbon. Ten engines are manufactured for testing purposes, and the emission level of each is determined. The data (in parts per million) are listed in Table 8.5.

 EMISSIONS

TABLE 8.5 Emission Levels for Ten Engines									
15.6	16.2	22.5	20.5	16.4	19.4	19.6	17.9	12.7	14.9

Do the data supply sufficient evidence to allow the manufacturer to conclude that this type of engine meets the pollution standard? Assume that the manufacturer is willing to risk a Type I error with probability $\alpha = .01$.

Solution The manufacturer wants to support the research hypothesis that the mean emission level μ for all engines of this type is less than 20 parts per million. The elements of this small-sample one-tailed test are as follows:

$$H_0: \mu = 20 \text{ (Mean emission level is 20 ppm.)}$$
$$H_a: \mu < 20 \text{ (Mean emission level is less than 20 ppm.)}$$

$$\text{Test statistic: } t = \frac{\bar{x} - 20}{s/\sqrt{n}}$$

Rejection region: For $\alpha = .01$ and df $= n - 1 = 9$, the one-tailed rejection region (see Figure 8.13) is $t < -t_{.01} = -2.821$.

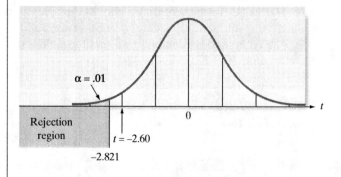

FIGURE 8.13
A *t*-distribution with 9 df and
the rejection region for
Example 8.5

Assumption: The relative frequency distribution of the population of emission levels for all engines of this type is approximately normal. Based on the shape of the MINITAB stem-and-leaf display of the data shown in Figure 8.14, this assumption appears to be reasonably satisfied.

To calculate the test statistic, we analyzed the **EMISSIONS** data with MINITAB. The MINITAB printout is shown at the bottom of Figure 8.14. From the printout, we ob-

Stem-and-Leaf Display: E-LEVEL

```
Stem-and-leaf of E-LEVEL   N  = 10
Leaf Unit = 1.0


   1    1   2
   3    1   45
  (3)   1   667
   4    1   99
   2    2   0
   1    2   2
```

FIGURE 8.14

MINITAB analysis of 10 emission levels, Example 8.5

One-Sample T: E-LEVEL

```
Test of mu = 20 vs < 20


                                         95%
                                       Upper
Variable    N     Mean    StDev  SE Mean   Bound      T      P
E-LEVEL    10  17.5700   2.9522   0.9336  19.2814  -2.60  0.014
```

tain $\bar{x} = 17.57$ and $s = 2.95$. Substituting these values into the test statistic formula and rounding, we get

$$t = \frac{\bar{x} - 20}{s/\sqrt{n}} = \frac{17.57 - 20}{2.95/\sqrt{10}} = -2.60$$

Since the calculated t falls outside the rejection region (see Figure 8.13), the manufacturer cannot reject H_0. There is insufficient evidence to conclude that $\mu < 20$ parts per million and that the new type of engine meets the pollution standard.

Look Back Are you satisfied with the reliability associated with this inference? The probability is only $\alpha = .01$ that the test would support the research hypothesis if in fact it were false.

Now Work Exercise 8.59a–b

EXAMPLE 8.6
THE *p*-VALUE FOR A SMALL-SAMPLE TEST OF μ

Problem Find the observed significance level for the test described in Example 8.5. Interpret the result.

Solution The test of Example 8.5 was a lower-tailed test: H_0: $\mu = 20$ versus H_a: $\mu < 20$. Since the value of t computed from the sample data was $t = -2.60$, the observed significance level (or p-value) for the test is equal to the probability that t would assume a value less than or equal to -2.60 if in fact H_0 were true. This is equal to the area in the lower tail of the t-distribution (highlighted in Figure 8.15).

One way to find this area (i.e., the p-value for the test) is to consult the t-table (Table VI in Appendix A). Unlike the table of areas under the normal curve, Table VI gives only the t values corresponding to the areas .100, .050, .025, .010, .005, .001, and .0005. Therefore, we can only approximate the p-value for the test. Since the

FIGURE 8.15

The observed significance level for the test of Example 8.5

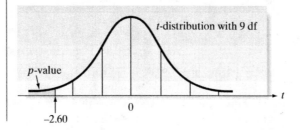

observed t value was based on nine degrees of freedom, we use the df = 9 row in Table VI and move across the row until we reach the t values that are closest to the observed $t = -2.60$. [*Note:* We ignore the minus sign.] The t values corresponding to p-values of .010 and .025 are 2.821 and 2.262, respectively. Since the observed t value falls between $t_{.010}$ and $t_{.025}$, the p-value for the test lies between .010 and .025. In other words, $.010 < p\text{-value} < .025$. Thus, we would reject the null hypothesis $H_0: \mu = 20$ parts per million for any value of α larger than .025 (the upper bound of the p-value).

A second, more accurate, way to obtain the p-value is to use a statistical software package to conduct the test of hypothesis. Both the test statistic (-2.60) and the p-value $(.014)$ are highlighted on the MINITAB printout of Figure 8.14.

You can see that the actual p-value of the test falls within the bounds obtained from Table VI. Thus, the two methods agree and we will reject $H_0: \mu = 20$ in favor of $H_a: \mu < 20$ for any α level larger than .025.

Now Work Exercise 8.59c

Small-sample inferences typically require more assumptions and provide less information about the population parameter than do large-sample inferences. Nevertheless, the t-test is a method of testing a hypothesis about a population mean of a normal distribution when only a small number of observations is available.

What Can Be Done if the Population Relative Frequency Distribution Departs Greatly from Normal?

Answer: Use one of the nonparametric statistical methods of Chapter 14.

ACTIVITY 8.2: *Keep the Change:* Tests of Hypotheses

In this activity, we will test claims that the mean amount transferred for any single purchase is $0.50 and that the mean amount that Bank of America matches for a customer during the first 90 days of enrollment is at least $25. We will be working with data sets from Activity 1.1 (p. 12) and Activity 6.1 (p. 293).

1. On the basis of the assumption that all transfer amounts between $0.00 and $0.99 seem to be equally likely to occur, one may conclude that the mean of the amounts transferred is about $0.50. Explain how someone who doesn't believe this conclusion would use a test of hypothesis to argue that the conclusion is false.

2. Suppose that your original data set *Amounts Transferred* from Activity 1.1 represents a random sample of amounts transferred for all Bank of America customers' purchases. Does your sample meet the requirements for performing either a large-sample or a small-sample test of hypothesis about the population mean? Explain. If your data meet the criteria for one of the tests, perform that test at $\alpha = .05$.

3. Use the pooled data set of *Amounts Transferred* from Activity 6.1 to represent a random sample of amounts transferred for all Bank of America customers' purchases. Explain how the conditions for the large-sample test of hypothesis about a population mean are met. Then perform the test at $\alpha = .05$. Do your results suggest that the mean may be something other than $0.50? Explain.

4. A friend suggests to you that the mean amount the bank matches for a customer during the first 90 days is at least $25. Explain how you could use a test of hypothesis to argue that your friend is wrong.

5. Suppose that your data set *Bank Matching* from Activity 1.1 represents a random sample of all Bank of America customers' bank matching. Perform an appropriate test of hypothesis at $\alpha = .05$. against your friend's claim. If necessary, assume that the underlying distribution is normal. Does the test provide evidence that your friend's claim is false?

Keep the results from this activity for use in other activities.

Exercises 8.54–8.72

Understanding the Principles

8.54 In what ways are the distributions of the z-statistic and t-statistic alike? How do they differ?

8.55 Under what circumstances should you use the t-distribution in testing a hypothesis about a population mean?

Learning the Mechanics

8.56 For each of the following rejection regions, sketch the sampling distribution of t and indicate the location of the rejection region on your sketch:
a. $t > 1.440$, where df = 6

b. $t < -1.782$, where df $= 12$

c. $t < -2.060$ or $t > 2.060$, where df $= 25$

8.57 For each of the rejection regions defined in Exercise 8.56, what is the probability that a Type I error will be made?

8.58 A random sample of n observations is selected from a normal population to test the null hypothesis that $\mu = 10$. Specify the rejection region for each of the following combinations of H_a, α, and n:

a. $H_a: \mu \neq 10$; $\alpha = .05$; $n = 14$

b. $H_a: \mu > 10$; $\alpha = .01$; $n = 24$

c. $H_a: \mu > 10$; $\alpha = .10$; $n = 9$

d. $H_a: \mu < 10$; $\alpha = .01$; $n = 12$

e. $H_a: \mu \neq 10$; $\alpha = .10$; $n = 20$

f. $H_a: \mu < 10$; $\alpha = .05$; $n = 4$

8.59 A sample of five measurements, randomly select ed from a **NW** normally distributed population, resulted in the following summary statistics: $\bar{x} = 4.8$, $s = 1.3$.

a. Test the null hypothesis that the mean of the population is 6 against the alternative hypothesis, $\mu < 6$. Use $\alpha = .05$.

b. Test the null hypothesis that the mean of the population is 6 against the alternative hypothesis, $\mu \neq 6$. Use $\alpha = .05$.

c. Find the observed significance level for each test.

8.60 The following sample of six measurements was randomly selected from a normally distributed population: 1, 3, −1, 5, 1, 2.

a. Test the null hypothesis that the mean of the population is 3 against the alternative hypothesis, $\mu < 3$. Use $\alpha = .05$.

b. Test the null hypothesis that the mean of the population is 3 against the alternative hypothesis, $\mu \neq 3$. Use $\alpha = .05$.

c. Find the observed significance level for each test.

8.61 Suppose you conduct a t-test for the null hypothesis $H_0: \mu = 1,000$ versus the alternative hypothesis $H_a: \mu > 1,000$, based on a sample of 17 observations. The test results are $t = 1.89$, p-value $= .038$.

a. What assumptions are necessary for the validity of this procedure?

b. Interpret the results of the test.

c. Suppose the alternative hypothesis had been the two-tailed $H_a: \mu \neq 1,000$. If the t-statistic were unchanged, what would the p-value be for this test? Interpret the p-value for the two-tailed test.

Applying the Concepts—Basic

JAPANESE

8.62 **Reading Japanese books.** Refer to the *Reading in a Foreign Language* (April 2004) experiment to improve the Japanese reading comprehension levels of University of Hawaii students presented in Exercise 2.31 (p. 46). Recall that 14 students participated in a 10-week extensive reading program in a second-semester Japanese course. The data on number of books read by each student are saved in the **JAPANESE** file. An SPSS printout giving descriptive statistics for the data is shown below.

a. State the null and alternative hypotheses for determining whether the average number of books read by all students who participated in the extensive reading program exceeds 25.

b. Find the rejection region for the test, using $\alpha = .05$.

c. Compute the test statistic.

d. State the appropriate conclusion for the test.

e. What conditions are required for the test results to be valid?

8.63 **A new dental bonding agent.** When bonding teeth, orthodontists must maintain a dry field. A new bonding adhesive (called "Smartbond") has been developed to eliminate the necessity of a dry field. However, there is concern that the new bonding adhesive is not as strong as the current standard, a composite adhesive. (*Trends in Biomaterials & Artificial Organs*, January 2003.) Tests on a sample of 10 extracted teeth bonded with the new adhesive resulted in a mean breaking strength (after 24 hours) of $\bar{x} = 5.07$ Mpa and a standard deviation of $s = .46$ Mpa, where Mpa = megapascal, a measure of force per unit area. Orthodontists want to know if the true mean breaking strength of the new bonding adhesive is less than 5.70 Mpa, the mean breaking strength of the composite adhesive.

a. Set up the null and alternative hypotheses for the test.

b. Find the rejection region for the test, using $\alpha = .01$.

c. Compute the test statistic.

d. State the appropriate conclusion for the test.

e. What conditions are required for the test results to be valid?

8.64 **Al Qaeda attacks on the United States.** Refer to the *Studies in Conflict & Terrorism* (Vol. 29, 2006) analysis of recent incidents involving suicide terrorist attacks, presented in Exercise 7.33 (p. 323). Data on the number of individual suicide bombings that occurred in each of 21 sampled Al Qaeda attacks against the United States are reproduced in the table on p. 378.

a. Do the data indicate that the true mean number of suicide bombings for all Al Qaeda attacks against the United States differs from 2.5?. Use $\alpha = .10$ and the MINITAB printout (p. 378) to answer the question.

b. In Exercise 7.33, you found a 90% confidence interval for the mean μ of the population. This interval is also shown on the MINITAB printout. Answer the question in part **a** on the basis of the 90% confidence interval.

c. Do the inferences derived from the test (part **a**) and confidence interval (part **b**) agree? Explain why or why not.

SPSS output for Exercise 8.62

Descriptive Statistics

	N	Minimum	Maximum	Mean	Std. Deviation
BOOKS	14	16	53	31.64	10.485
Valid N (listwise)	14				

MINITAB output for
Exercise 8.64

One-Sample T: ATTACKS

Test of mu = 2.5 vs not = 2.5

Variable	N	Mean	StDev	SE Mean	90% CI	T	P
ATTACKS	21	1.857	1.195	0.261	(1.407, 2.307)	-2.46	0.023

d. What assumption about the data must be true for the inferences to be valid?

e. Use a graph to check whether the assumption you made in part **d** is reasonably satisfied. Comment on the validity of the inference.

ALQAEDA

1	1	2	1	2	4	1	1	1	1	2	3	4	5	1	1	1	2	2	2	1

Source: Moghadam, A. "Suicide terrorism, occupation, and the globalization of martyrdom: A critique of *Dying to Win*," *Studies in Conflict & Terrorism*, Vol. 29, No. 8, 2006 (Table 3).

8.65 Dental anxiety study. Refer to the *Psychological Reports* (August 1997) study of college students who completed the Dental Anxiety Scale, presented in Exercise 5.36 (p. 247). Recall that scores range from 0 (no anxiety) to 20 (extreme anxiety). Summary statistics for the scores of the 27 students who completed the questionnaire are $\bar{x} = 10.7$ and $s = 3.6$. Conduct a test of hypothesis to determine whether the mean Dental Anxiety Scale score for the population of college students differs from $\mu = 11$. Use $\alpha = .05$.

8.66 Crab spiders hiding on flowers. Refer to the *Behavioral Ecology* (Jan. 2005) experiment on crab spiders' use of camouflage to hide from predators (e.g., birds) on flowers, presented in Exercise 2.36 (p. 48). Researchers at the French Museum of Natural History collected a sample of 10 adult female crab spiders, each sitting on the yellow central part of a daisy, and measured the chromatic contrast between each spider and the flower. The data (for which higher values indicate a greater contrast, and, presumably, an easier detection by predators) are shown in the accompanying table. The researchers discovered that a contrast of 70 or greater allows birds to see the spider. Of interest is whether or not the true mean chromatic contrast of crab spiders on daisies is less than 70.

SPIDER

57	75	116	37	96	61	56	2	43	32

Data adapted from Thery, M., et al. "Specific color sensitivities of prey and predator explain camouflage in different visual systems," *Behavioral Ecology*, Vol. 16, No. 1, Jan. 2005 (Table 1).

a. Define the parameter of interest, μ

b. Set up the null and alternative hypotheses of interest.

c. Find $\bar{x}$ and s for the sample data, and then use these values to compute the test statistic.

d. Give the rejection region for $\alpha = .10$.

e. State the appropriate conclusion in the words of the problem.

Applying the Concepts—Intermediate

LICHEN

8.67 Radioactive lichen. Refer to the 2003 Lichen Radionuclide Baseline Research project to monitor the level of radioactivity in lichen, presented in Exercise 7.35 (p. 324). Recall that University of Alaska researchers collected nine lichen specimens and measured the amount of the radioactive element cesium-137 (in microcuries per milliliter) in each specimen. (The natural logarithms of the data values are saved in the **LICHEN** file.) Assume that in previous years the mean cesium amount in lichen was $\mu = .003$ microcurie per milliliter. Is there sufficient evidence to indicate that the mean amount of cesium in lichen specimens differs from this value? Use the SAS printout below to conduct a complete test of hypothesis at $\alpha = .10$.

8.68 Testing a mosquito repellent. A study was conducted to evaluate the effectiveness of a new mosquito repellent designed by the U.S. Army to be applied as camouflage face paint. (*Journal of the Mosquito Control Association*, June 1995.) The repellent was applied to the forearms of five volunteers who then were exposed to 15 active mosquitos for a 10-hour period. The percentage of the forearm surface area protected from bites (called percent repellency) was calculated for each of the five volunteers. For one color of paint (loam), the following summary statistics were obtained:

$$\bar{x} = 83\% \quad s = 15\%$$

a. The new repellent is considered effective if it provides a repellency of at least 95 percent. Conduct a test to determine whether the mean repellency of the new mosquito repellent is less than 95 percent. Use $\alpha = .10$.

b. What assumptions are required for the hypothesis test in part **a** to be valid?

SAS Output for Exercise 8.67

Sample Statistics for CESIUM

N	Mean	Std. Dev.	Std. Error
9	0.0090	0.0049	0.0016

Hypothesis Test

Null hypothesis: Mean of CESIUM = 0.003
Alternative: Mean of CESIUM ^= 0.003

t Statistic	Df	Prob > t
3.725	8	0.0058

8.69 Minimizing tractor skidding distance. Refer to the *Journal of Forest Engineering* (July 1999) study of minimizing tractor skidding distances along a new road in a European forest, presented in Exercise 7.40 (p. 325). The skidding distances (in meters) were measured at 20 randomly selected road sites. The data are repeated in the accompanying table. Recall that a logger working on the road claims that the mean skidding distance is at least 425 meters. Is there sufficient evidence to refute this claim? Use $\alpha = .10$.

SKIDDING

488	350	457	199	285	409	435	574	439	546
385	295	184	261	273	400	311	312	141	425

Source: Tujek, J. & Pacola, E. "Algorithms for skidding distance modeling on a raster Digital Terrain Model," *Journal of Forest Engineering*, Vol. 10, No. 1, July 1999 (Table 1).

8.70 Mongolian desert ants. Refer to the *Journal of Biogeography* (December 2003) study of ants in Mongolia (central

GOBIANTS

Site	Region	Number of Ant Species
1	Dry Steppe	3
2	Dry Steppe	3
3	Dry Steppe	52
4	Dry Steppe	7
5	Dry Steppe	5
6	Gobi Desert	49
7	Gobi Desert	5
8	Gobi Desert	4
9	Gobi Desert	4
10	Gobi Desert	5
11	Gobi Desert	4

Source: Pfeiffer, M., et al. "Community organization and species richness of ants in Mongolia along an ecological gradient from steppe to Gobi desert," *Journal of Biogeography*, Vol. 30, No. 12, Dec. 2003.

Asia), presented in Exercise 2.66 (p. 60). Recall that botanists placed seed baits at 11 study sites and observed the number of ant species attracted to each site. A portion of the data is provided in the accompanying table. Do these data indicate that the average number of ant species at Mongolian desert sites differs from 5? Conduct the appropriate test at $\alpha = .05$. Are the conditions required for a valid test satisfied?

8.71 Head trauma study. The SCL-90-R is a 90-item symptom inventory checklist designed to reflect the psychological status of an individual. Each symptom (e.g., obsessive–compulsive behavior) is scored on a scale of 0 (none) to 4 (extreme). The total of these scores yields an individual's Positive Symptom Total (PST). "Normal" individuals are known to have a mean PST of about 40. The *Journal of Head Trauma Rehabilitation* (April 1995) reported that a sample of 23 patients diagnosed with mild to moderate traumatic brain injury had a mean PST score of $\bar{x} = 48.43$ and a standard deviation of $s = 20.76$. Is there sufficient evidence to claim that the true mean PST score of all patients with mild-to-moderate traumatic brain injury exceeds the "normal" value of 40? Test, using $\alpha = .05$.

Applying the Concepts—Advanced

8.72 Lengths of great white sharks. One of the most feared predators in the ocean is the great white shark. It is known that the white shark grows to a mean length of 21 feet; however, one marine biologist believes that great white sharks off the Bermuda coast grow much longer owing to unusual feeding habits. To test this claim, some full-grown great white sharks were captured off the Bermuda coast, measured, and then set free. However, because the capture of sharks is difficult, costly, and very dangerous, only three specimens were sampled. Their lengths were 24, 20, and 22 feet. Do these data support the marine biologist's claim?

8.5 Large-Sample Test of Hypothesis about a Population Proportion

Inferences about population proportions (or percentages) are often made in the context of the probability p of "success" for a binomial distribution. We saw how to use large samples from binomial distributions to form confidence intervals for p in Section 7.4. We now consider tests of hypotheses about p.

Consider, for example, a method currently used by doctors to screen women for breast cancer. The method fails to detect cancer in 20% of the women who actually have the disease. Suppose a new method has been developed that researchers hope will detect cancer more accurately. This new method was used to screen a random sample of 140 women known to have breast cancer. Of these, the new method failed to detect cancer in 12 women. Does this sample provide evidence that the failure rate of the new method differs from the one currently in use?

We first view this experiment as a binomial one with 140 screened women as the trials and failure to detect breast cancer as "Success" (in binomial terminology). Let p represent the probability that the new method fails to detect the breast cancer on the one hand, if the new method is no better than the current one, then the failure rate is $p = .2$. On the other hand, if the new method is either better or worse than the current method, then the failure rate is either smaller or larger than 20%; that is, $p \neq .2$.

We can now place the problem in the context of a test of hypothesis:

$$H_0: p = .2$$

$$H_a: p \neq .2$$

Recall that the sample proportion $\hat{p}$ is really just the sample mean of the outcomes of the individual binomial trials and, as such, is approximately normally distributed (for large samples) according to the central limit theorem. Thus, for large samples we can use the standard normal z as the test statistic:

$$\textit{Test statistic:} \quad z = \frac{\text{Sample proportion} - \text{Null hypothesized proportion}}{\text{Standard deviation of sample proportion}}$$

$$= \frac{\hat{p} - p_0}{\sigma_{\hat{p}}}$$

Note that we used the symbol p_0 to represent the null hypothesized value of p.

We use the standard normal distribution to find the appropriate rejection region for the specified value of α. Using $\alpha = .05$, the two-tailed rejection region is

$$z < -z_{\alpha/2} = -z_{.025} = -1.96 \quad \text{or} \quad z > z_{\alpha/2} = z_{.025} = 1.96$$

(See Figure 8.16.)

We are now prepared to calculate the value of the test statistic. Before doing so, however, we want to be sure that the sample size is large enough to ensure that the normal approximation for the sampling distribution of $\hat{p}$ is reasonable. To check this, we calculate a three-standard-deviation interval around the null-hypothesized value p_0, which is assumed to be the true value of p until our test procedure proves otherwise. Recall that $\sigma_{\hat{p}} = \sqrt{pq/n}$ and that we need an estimate of the product pq in order to calculate a numerical value of the test statistic z. Since the

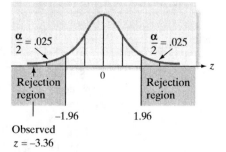

FIGURE 8.16

Rejection region for breast cancer example

null-hypothesized value is generally the value that is accepted until proven otherwise, we use the value of $p_0 q_0$ (where $q_0 = 1 - p_0$) to estimate pq in the calculation of z. Thus,

$$\sigma_{\hat{p}} = \sqrt{\frac{pq}{n}} \approx \sqrt{\frac{p_0 q_0}{n}} = \sqrt{\frac{(.2)(.8)}{140}} = .034$$

and the three-standard-deviation interval around p_0 is

$$p_0 \pm 3\sigma_{\hat{p}} \approx .2 \pm 3(.034) = (.098, .302)$$

As long as this interval does not contain 0 or 1 (i.e., as long as it is completely contained in the interval from 0 to 1), as is the case here, the normal distribution will provide a reasonable approximation for the sampling distribution of $\hat{p}$.

Returning to the hypothesis test at hand, the proportion of the screenings that failed to detect breast cancer is

$$\hat{p} = \frac{12}{140} = .086$$

Finally, we calculate the number of standard deviations (the z value) between the sampled and hypothesized values of the binomial proportion:

$$z = \frac{\hat{p} - p_0}{\sigma_{\hat{p}}} = \frac{\hat{p} - p_0}{\sqrt{p_0 q_0/n}} = \frac{.086 - .2}{.034} = \frac{-.114}{.034} = -3.36$$

The implication is that the observed sample proportion is (approximately) 3.36 standard deviations below the null-hypothesized proportion, .2 (Figure 8.16). Therefore, we reject the null hypothesis, concluding at the .05 level of significance that the true failure rate of the new method for detecting breast cancer differs from .20. Since $\hat{p} = .086$, it appears that the new method is better (i.e., has a smaller failure rate) than the method currently in use. (To estimate the magnitude of the failure rate for the new method, a confidence interval can be constructed.)

The test of hypothesis about a population proportion p is summarized in the next box. Note that the procedure is entirely analogous to that used for conducting large-sample tests about a population mean.

Large-Sample Test of Hypothesis about p

One-Tailed Test

$H_0: p = p_0$
$H_a: p < p_0 \ (\text{or } H_a: p > p_0)$

Test statistic: $z = \dfrac{\hat{p} - p_0}{\sigma_{\hat{p}}}$

where p_0 = hypothesized value of p, $\sigma_{\hat{p}} = \sqrt{p_0 q_0/n}$, and $q_0 = 1 - p_0$

Rejection region: $z < -z_\alpha$
(or $z > z_\alpha$ when $H_a: p > p_0$)

Two-Tailed Test

$H_0: p = p_0$
$H_a: p \neq p_0$

Test statistic: $z = \dfrac{\hat{p} - p_0}{\sigma_{\hat{p}}}$

Rejection region: $z < -z_{\alpha/2}$
or $z > z_{\alpha/2}$

Conditions Required for a Valid Large-Sample Hypothesis Test for p

1. A random sample is selected from a binomial population.
2. The sample size n is large. (This condition will be satisfied if np_0 and nq_0 are both at least 15.)

EXAMPLE 8.7
A HYPOTHESIS TEST FOR p—
Proportion of Defective Batteries

Problem The reputations (and hence sales) of many businesses can be severely damaged by shipments of manufactured items that contain a large percentage of defectives. For example, a manufacturer of alkaline batteries may want to be reasonably certain that less than 5% of its batteries are defective. Suppose 300 batteries are randomly selected from a very large shipment; each is tested and 10 defective batteries are found. Does this outcome provide sufficient evidence for the manufacturer to conclude that the fraction defective in the entire shipment is less than .05? Use $\alpha = .01$.

Solution The objective of the sampling is to determine whether there is sufficient evidence to indicate that the fraction defective, p, is less than .05. Consequently, we will test the null hypothesis that $p = .05$ against the alternative hypothesis that $p < .05$. The elements of the test are

$H_0: p = .05$ (Fraction of defective batteries equals .05.)
$H_a: p < .05$ (Fraction of defective batteries is less than .05.)

Test statistic: $z = \dfrac{\hat{p} - p_0}{\sigma_{\hat{p}}}$

Rejection region: $z < -z_{.01} = -2.33$ (see Figure 8.17)

Before conducting the test, we check to determine whether the sample size is large enough to use the normal approximation to the sampling distribution *of* $\hat{p}$. Since $np_0 = (300)(.05) = 15$ and $nq_0 = (300)(.95) = 285$ are both at least 15, the normal approximation will be adequate.

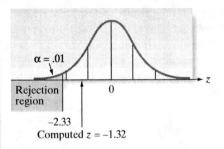

FIGURE 8.17
Rejection region for
Example 8.7

We now calculate the test statistic:

$$z = \frac{\hat{p} - .05}{\sigma_{\hat{p}}} = \frac{(10/300) - .05}{\sqrt{p_0 q_0/n}} = \frac{.03333 - .05}{\sqrt{p_0 q_0/300}}$$

Notice that we use p_0 to calculate $\sigma_{\hat{p}}$ because, in contrast to calculating $\sigma_{\hat{p}}$ for a confidence interval, the test statistic is computed on the assumption that the null hypothesis is true—that is, $p = p_0$. Therefore, substituting the values for $\hat{p}$ and p_0 into the z statistic, we obtain

$$z \approx \frac{-.01667}{\sqrt{(.05)(.95)/300}} = \frac{-.01667}{.0126} = -1.32$$

As shown in Figure 8.17, the calculated z-value does not fall into the rejection region. Therefore, there is insufficient evidence at the .01 level of significance to indicate that the shipment contains less than 5% defective batteries.

Now Work Exercise 8.76a–b

EXAMPLE 8.8

FINDING THE p-VALUE FOR A TEST ABOUT A POPULATION PROPORTION p

Problem In Example 8.7, we found that we did not have sufficient evidence at the $\alpha = .01$ level of significance to indicate that the fraction defective, p, of alkaline batteries was less than $p = .05$. How strong was the weight of evidence favoring the alternative hypothesis ($H_a: p < .05$)? Find the observed significance level (p-value) for the test.

Solution The computed value of the test statistic z was $z = -1.32$. Therefore, for this lower-tailed test, the observed significance level is

$$p\text{-value} = P(z \le -1.32)$$

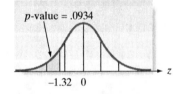

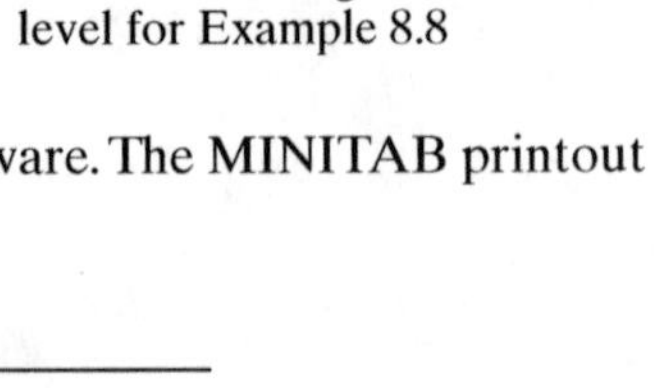

This lower-tail area is shown in Figure 8.18. The area between $z = 0$ and $z = 1.32$ is given in Table IV in Appendix A as .4066. Therefore, the observed significance level is $.5 - .4066 = .0934$.

FIGURE 8.18
The observed significance
level for Example 8.8

Note: The p-value can also be obtained with statistical software. The MINITAB printout shown in Figure 8.19 gives the p-value (highlighted).

Test and CI for One Proportion

Test of p = 0.05 vs p < 0.05

Sample	X	N	Sample p	95% Upper Bound	Z-Value	P-Value
1	10	300	0.033333	0.050380	-1.32	0.093

Using the normal approximation.

FIGURE 8.19
MINITAB lower-tailed test
of p, Example 8.8

Look Back Note that this probability is quite small. Although we did not reject H_0: $p = .05$ at $\alpha = .01$, the probability of observing a z-value as small as or smaller than -1.35 is only .0885 if in fact H_0 is true. Therefore, we would reject H_0 if we choose $\alpha = .10$ (since the observed significance level is less than .10), and we would not reject H_0 (the conclusion of Example 8.7) if we choose $\alpha = .05$ or $\alpha = .01$.

Now Work Exercise 8.76c

Small-sample test procedures are also available for p, although most surveys use samples that are large enough to employ the large-sample tests presented in this section. A test of proportions that can be applied to small samples is discussed in Chapter 13.

STATISTICS IN ACTION REVISITED

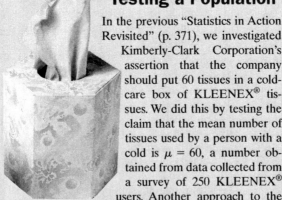

Testing a Population Proportion in the KLEENEX® Survey

In the previous "Statistics in Action Revisited" (p. 371), we investigated Kimberly-Clark Corporation's assertion that the company should put 60 tissues in a cold-care box of KLEENEX® tissues. We did this by testing the claim that the mean number of tissues used by a person with a cold is $\mu = 60$, a number obtained from data collected from a survey of 250 KLEENEX® users. Another approach to the problem is to consider the proportion of KLEENEX® users who use fewer than 60 tissues when they have a cold. Now the population parameter of interest is p, the proportion of all KLEENEX® users who use fewer than 60 tissues when they have a cold.

Kimberly-Clark Corporation's belief that the company should put 60 tissues in a cold-care box will be supported if half of the KLEENEX® users surveyed use less than 60 tissues and half use more than 60 tissues (i.e., if $p = .5$). Is there evidence to indicate that the population proportion differs from .5? To answer this question, we set up the following null and alternative hypotheses:

$$H_0: p = .5 \quad H_a: p \neq .5$$

Recall that the survey results for the 250 sampled KLEENEX® users are stored in the **TISSUES** data file. In addition to the number of tissues used by each person, the file contains a qualitative variable—called USED60—representing whether the person used fewer or more than 60 tissues. (The values of USED60 in the data set are "BELOW" or "ABOVE.") A MINITAB analysis of this variable yielded the printout displayed in Figure SIA8.2.

On the MINITAB printout, x represents the number of the 250 people with colds that used fewer than 60 tissues. Note that $x = 143$. This value is used to compute the test statistic $z = 2.28$, highlighted on the printout. The p-value of the test, also highlighted on the printout, is p-value = .023. Since this value is less than $\alpha = .05$, there is sufficient evidence (at $\alpha = .05$) to reject H_0; we conclude that the proportion of all KLEENEX® users who use fewer than 60 tissues when they have a cold differs from .5. However, if we test at $\alpha = .01$, there is insufficient evidence to reject H_0. Consequently, our choice of α (as in the previous "Statistics in Action Revisited") is critical to our decision.

```
Test of p = 0.5 vs p not = 0.5

Event = BELOW


Variable   X    N   Sample p        95% CI         Z-Value  P-Value
USED60    143  250  0.572000  (0.510666, 0.633334)   2.28    0.023
```

FIGURE SIA8.2
MINITAB test of $p = .5$ for KLEENEX® survey

Exercises 8.73–8.91

Understanding the Principles

8.73 What type of data, quantitative or qualitative, is typically associated with making inferences about a population proportion p?

8.74 What conditions are required for a valid large-sample test for p?

Learning the Mechanics

8.75 For the binomial sample sizes and null-hypothesized values of p in each part, determine whether the sample size is large enough to use the normal approximation methodology presented in this section to conduct a test of the null hypothesis H_0: $p = p_0$.

a. $n = 500, p_0 = .05$
b. $n = 100, p_0 = .99$
c. $n = 50, p_0 = .2$
d. $n = 20, p_0 = .2$
e. $n = 10, p_0 = .4$

8.76 Suppose a random sample of 100 observations from a bino-
NW mial population gives a value of $\hat{p} = .69$ and you wish to test
the null hypothesis that the population parameter p is equal
to .75 against the alternative hypothesis that p is less than .75.

a. Noting that $\hat{p} = .69$, what does your intuition tell you?
Does the value of $\hat{p}$ appear to contradict the null
hypothesis?

b. Use the large-sample z-test to test $H_0: p = .75$ against
the alternative hypothesis $H_a: p < .75$. Use $\alpha = .05$.
How do the test results compare with your intuitive decision from part **a**?

c. Find and interpret the observed significance level of the
test you conducted in part **b**.

8.77 Suppose the sample in Exercise 8.76 has produced $\hat{p} = .84$
and we wish to test $H_0: p = .9$ against the alternative
$H_a: p < .9$.

a. Calculate the value of the z statistic for this test.

b. Note that the numerator of the z statistic
($\hat{p} - p_0 = .84 - .90 = -.06$) is the same as for Exercise 8.76. Considering this, why is the absolute value of
z for this exercise larger than that calculated in Exercise 8.76?

c. Complete the test, using $\alpha = .05$, and interpret the
result.

d. Find the observed significance level for the test and interpret its value.

8.78 A random sample of 100 observations is selected from a binomial population with unknown probability of success, p.
The computed value of $\hat{p}$ is equal to .74.

a. Test $H_0: p = .65$ against $H_a: p > .65$. Use $\alpha = .01$.

b. Test $H_0: p = .65$ against $H_a: p > .65$. Use $\alpha = .10$.

c. Test $H_0: p = .90$ against $H_a: p \neq .90$. Use $\alpha = .05$.

d. Form a 95% confidence interval for p.

e. Form a 99% confidence interval for p.

SNACK

8.79 Refer to Exercise 7.50 (p. 332), in which 50 consumers
taste-tested a new snack food.

a. Test $H_0: p = .5$ against $H_a: p > .5$, where p is the proportion of customers who do not like the snack food.
Use $\alpha = .10$.

b. Report the observed significance level of your test.

APPLET Applet Exercise 8.5

Use the applet entitled *Hypotheses Test for a Proportion* to investigate the relationships between the probabilities of Type I
and Type II errors occurring at levels .05 and .01. For this exercise, use $n = 100$, true $p = 0.5$, and alternative *not equal*.

a. Set null $p = .5$. What happens to the proportion of times
the null hypothesis is rejected at the .05 level and at the .01
level as the applet is run more and more times? What type
of error has occurred when the null hypothesis is rejected
in this situation? Based on your results, is this type of error
more likely to occur at level .05 or at level .01? Explain.

b. Set null $p = .6$. What happens to the proportion of times
the null hypothesis is *not* rejected at the .05 level and at
the .01 level as the applet is run more and more times?

What type of error has occurred when the null hypothesis is *not* rejected in this situation? Based on your results,
is this type of error more likely to occur at level .05 or at
level .01? Explain.

c. Use your results from parts **a** and **b** to make a general
statement about the probabilities of Type I and Type II
errors at levels .05 and .01.

APPLET Applet Exercise 8.6

Use the applet entitled *Hypotheses Test for a Proportion* to investigate the effect of the true population proportion p on the probability of a Type I error occurring. For this exercise, use $n = 100$
and alternative *not equal*.

a. Set true $p = .5$ and null $p = .5$. Run the applet several
times, and record the proportion of times the null hypothesis is rejected at the .01 level.

b. Clear the applet and repeat part **a** for true $p = .1$ and
null $p = .1$. Then repeat one more time for true $p = .01$
and null $p = .01$.

c. Based on your results from parts **a** and **b**, what can you
conclude about the probability of a Type I error occurring as the true population proportion gets closer to 0?

Applying the Concepts—Basic

8.80 "Made in the USA" survey. Refer to the *Journal of Global
Business* (Spring 2002) study of what "Made in the USA"
means to consumers, presented in Exercise 2.13 (p. 36). Recall that 64 of 106 randomly selected shoppers believed that
"Made in the USA" means that 100% of labor and materials
are from the United States. Let p represent the true proportion of consumers who believe "Made in the USA" means
that 100% of labor and materials are from the United States.

a. Calculate a point estimate for p.

b. A claim is made that $p = .70$. Set up the null and alternative hypothesis to test this claim.

c. Calculate the test statistic for the test you carried out in
part **b**.

d. Find the rejection region for the test if $\alpha = .01$.

e. Use the results from parts **c** and **d** to draw the appropriate conclusion.

8.81 Accuracy of price scanners at Wal-Mart. Refer to Exercise
7.73 (p. 338) and the study of the accuracy of checkout scanners at Wal-Mart Stores in California. Recall that the National Institute for Standards and Technology (NIST) mandates
that, for every 100 items scanned through the electronic
checkout scanner at a retail store, no more than 2 should
have an inaccurate price. A study of random items purchased
at California Wal-Mart stores found that 8.3% had the wrong
price (*Tampa Tribune*, Nov. 22, 2005). Assume that the study
included 1,000 randomly selected items.

a. Identify the population parameter of interest in the
study.

b. Set up H_0 and H_a for a test to determine whether the
true proportion of items scanned at California Wal-
Mart stores exceeds the 2% NIST standard.

c. Find the test statistic and rejection region (at $\alpha = .05$)
for the test.

d. Give a practical interpretation of the test.

e. What conditions are required for the inference made in
part **d** to be valid? Are these conditions met?

8.82 Killing insects with low oxygen. A group of Australian entomological toxicologists investigated the impact of exposure to low oxygen on the mortality of insects. (*Journal of Agricultural, Biological, and Environmental Statistics*, Sep. 2000.) Thousands of adult rice weevils were placed in a chamber filled with wheat grain, and the chamber was exposed to nitrogen gas for 4 days. Insects were assessed as dead or alive 24 hours after exposure. At the conclusion of the experiment, 31,386 weevils, were dead and 35 weevils were found alive. Previous studies had shown a 99% mortality rate in adult rice weevils exposed to carbon dioxide for 4 days. For this study, the parameter of interest is the mortality rate for all adult rice weevils exposed to nitrogen.

   a. Give a point estimate of the population parameter.

   b. Set up H_0 and H_a for testing whether the true mortality rate for weevils exposed to nitrogen is higher than 99%.

   c. Conduct the test from part **b** using $\alpha = .10$. Draw the appropriate conclusion in the words of the problem.

   d. What conditions are required for the inference made in part **c** to be valid? Do they appear to be satisfied?

8.83 Single-parent families. Examining data collected on 835 males from the National Youth Survey (a longitudinal survey of a random sample of U.S. households), researchers at Carnegie Mellon University found that 401 of the male youths were raised in a single-parent family. (*Sociological Methods & Research*, February 2001.) Does this information allow you to conclude that more than 45% of male youths are raised in a single-parent family? Test at $\alpha = .05$.

8.84 Graduation rates of student–athletes. Are student–athletes at Division I universities poorer students than nonathletes? The National Collegiate Athletic Association (NCAA) measures the academic outcomes of student–athletes with the Graduation Success Rate (GSR)—the percentage of eligible athletes who graduate within six years of entering college. According to the NCAA, the GSR for all scholarship athletes at Division I institutions is 63% (*Inside Higher Ed*, Nov. 10, 2006.) It is well known that the GSR for all students at Division I colleges is 60%.

   a. Suppose the NCAA report was based on a sample of 500 student–athletes, of which 315 graduated within six years. Is this sufficient information to conclude that the GSR for all scholarship athletes at Division I institutions differs from 60%? Test, using $\alpha = .01$.

   b. The GSR statistics were also broken down by gender and sport. For example, men's Division I college basketball players had a GSR of 42% (compared with a known GSR of 58% for all male college students). Suppose this statistic was based on a sample of 200 male basketball players, of which 84 graduated within six years. Is this sufficient information to conclude that the GSR for all male basketball players at Division I institutions differs from 58%? Test, using $\alpha = .01$.

Applying the Concepts—Intermediate

8.85 Federal civil trial appeals. Refer to the *Journal of the American Law and Economics Association* (Vol. 3, 2001) study of appeals of federal civil trials, presented in Exercise 3.55 (p. 137). A breakdown of 678 civil cases that were originally tried in front of a judge and appealed by either the plaintiff or the defendant is reproduced in the accompanying table. Do the data provide sufficient evidence to indicate that the percentage of civil cases appealed that are actually reversed is less than 25%? Test, using $\alpha = .01$.

Outcome of Appeal	Number of Cases
Plaintiff trial win—reversed	71
Plaintiff trial win—affirmed/dismissed	240
Defendant trial win—reversed	68
Defendant trial win—affirmed/dismissed	299
TOTAL	678

8.86 Verbs and double-object datives. Any sentence that contains an animate noun as a direct object and another noun as a second object (e.g., "Sue offered Ann a cookie") is termed a double-object dative (DOD). The connection between certain verbs and a DOD was investigated in *Applied Psycholinguistics* (June 1998). The subjects were 35 native English speakers who were enrolled in an introductory English composition course at a Hawaiian community college. After viewing pictures of a family, each subject was asked to write a sentence about the family, using a specified verb. Of the 35 sentences using the verb "buy," 10 had a DOD structure. Conduct a test to determine whether the true fraction of sentences with the verb "buy" that are DODs is less than $\frac{1}{3}$. Use $\alpha = .05$.

8.87 Astronomy students and the Big Bang Theory. Indiana University professors investigated first-year college students' knowledge of astronomy. (*Astronomy Education Review*, Vol. 2, 2003.) One concept of interest was the Big Bang theory of the creation of the universe. In a sample of 148 freshmen students, 37 believed that the Big Bang theory accurately described the creation of planetary systems. Based on this information, would you be willing to state that more than 20% of all freshmen college students believe in the Big Bang theory? How confident are you of your decision?

8.88 Study of lunar soil. *Meteoritics* (March 1995) reported the results of a study of lunar soil evolution. Data were obtained from the *Apollo 16* mission to the moon, during which a 62-cm core was extracted from the soil near the landing site. Monomineralic grains of lunar soil were separated out and examined for coating with dust and glass fragments. Each grain was then classified as coated or uncoated. Of interest is the "coat index"—that is, the proportion of grains that are coated. According to soil evolution theory, the coat index will exceed .5 at the top of the core, equal .5 in the middle of the core, and fall below .5 at the bottom of the core. Use the summary data in the accompanying table to test each part of the three-part theory. Use $\alpha = .05$ for each test.

	Location (depth)		
	Top (4.25 cm)	Middle (28.1 cm)	Bottom (54.5 cm)
Number of grains sampled	84	73	81
Number coated	64	35	29

Source: Basu, A., and McKay, D. S. "Lunar soil evolution processes and Apollo 16 core 60013/60014," *Meteoritics*, Vol. 30, No. 2, Mar. 1995, p. 166 (Table 2).

8.89 Effectiveness of skin cream. Pond's Age-Defying Complex, a cream with alpha-hydroxy acid, advertises that it can reduce wrinkles and improve the skin. In a study published in *Archives of Dermatology* (June 1996), 33 middle-aged women used a cream with alpha-hydroxy acid for 22 weeks. At the end of the study period, a dermatologist judged whether each woman exhibited any improvement in the condition of her skin. The results for the 33 women (where I = improved skin and N = no improvement) are listed in the accompanying table.

a. Do the data provide sufficient evidence to conclude that the cream will improve the skin of more than 60% of middle-aged women? Test, using $\alpha = .05$.

b. Find and interpret the *p*-value of the test.

⊘ **SKINCREAM**

I	I	N	I	N	N	I	I	I	I	I
N	I	I	I	N	I	I	I	N	I	N	I
I	I	I	I	I	N	I	I	N		

Applying the Concepts—Advanced

8.90 Parents who condone spanking. In Exercise 4.64 (p. 209) you read about a nationwide survey which claimed that 60% of parents with young children condone spanking their child as a regular form of punishment. (*Tampa Tribune*, October 5, 2000.) In a random sample of 100 parents with young children, how many parents would need to say that they condone spanking as a form of punishment in order to refute the claim?

8.91 Testing the placebo effect. The *placebo effect* describes the phenomenon of improvement in the condition of a patient taking a placebo—a pill that looks and tastes real, but contains no medically active chemicals. Physicians at a clinic in La Jolla, California, gave what they thought were drugs to 7,000 asthma, ulcer, and herpes patients. Although the doctors later learned that the drugs were really placebos, 70% of the patients reported an improved condition. (*Forbes*, May 22, 1995.) Use this information to test (at $\alpha = .05$) the placebo effect at the clinic. Assume that if the placebo is ineffective, the probability of a patient's condition improving is .5.

8.6 Calculating Type II Error Probabilities: More about β (Optional)

In our introduction to hypothesis testing in Section 8.1, we showed that the probability of committing a Type I error, α, can be controlled by the selection of the rejection region for the test. Thus, when the test statistic falls into the rejection region and we make the decision to reject the null hypothesis, we do so knowing the error rate for incorrect rejections of H_0. The situation corresponding to accepting the null hypothesis, and thereby risking a Type II error, is not generally as controllable. For that reason, we adopted a policy of nonrejection of H_0 when the test statistic does not fall in to the rejection region, rather than risking an error of unknown magnitude.

To see how β, the probability of a Type II error, can be calculated for a test of hypothesis, recall the example in Section 8.1 in which a city tests a manufacturer's pipe to see whether it meets the requirement that the mean strength exceed 2,400 pounds per linear foot. The setup for the test is as follows:

H_0: $\mu = 2,400$
H_a: $\mu > 2,400$

Test statistic: $z = \dfrac{\bar{x} - 2,400}{\sigma/\sqrt{n}}$

Rejection region: $z > 1.645$ for $\alpha = .05$

Figure 8.20a shows the rejection region for the **null distribution**—that is, the distribution of the test statistic, assuming that the null hypothesis is true. The area in the rejection region is .05, and this area represents α, the probability that the test statistic leads to rejection of H_0 when in fact H_0 is true.

The Type II error probability β is calculated under the assumption that the null hypothesis is false, because it is defined as the *probability of accepting H_0 when it is false*. Since H_0 is false for any value of μ exceeding 2,400, one value of β exists for each possible value of μ greater than 2,400 (an infinite number of possibilities). Figures 8.20b, 8.20c, and 8.20d show three of the possibilities, corresponding to alternative-hypothesis values of μ equal to 2,425, 2,450, and 2,475, respectively. Note that β is the area in the *nonrejection* (or *acceptance*) *region* in each of these distributions and that β decreases as the true value of μ moves farther from the null-hypothesized

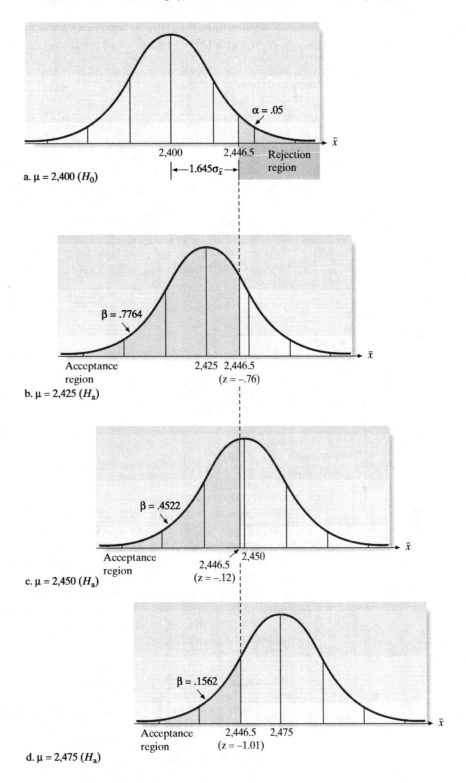

FIGURE 8.20

Values of α and β for various values of μ

value of $\mu = 2,400$. This behavior is sensible because the probability of incorrectly accepting the null hypothesis should decrease as the distance between the null and alternative values of μ increases.

In order to calculate the value of β for a specific value of μ in H_a, we proceed as follows:

1. We calculate the value of $\bar{x}$ that corresponds to the border between the acceptance and rejection regions. For the sewer pipe example, this is the value of $\bar{x}$ that lies 1.645 standard deviations above $\mu = 2,400$ in the sampling distribution of $\bar{x}$.

Denoting this value by $\bar{x}_0$, corresponding to the largest value of $\bar{x}$ that supports the null hypothesis, we find (recalling that $s = 200$ and $n = 50$) that

$$\bar{x}_0 = \mu_0 + 1.645\sigma_{\bar{x}} = 2{,}400 + 1.645\left(\frac{\sigma}{\sqrt{n}}\right)$$

$$\approx 2{,}400 + 1.645\left(\frac{s}{\sqrt{n}}\right) = 2{,}400 + 1.645\left(\frac{200}{\sqrt{50}}\right)$$

$$= 2{,}400 + 1.645(28.28) = 2{,}446.5$$

2. For a particular alternative distribution corresponding to a value of μ denoted by μ_a, we calculate the z-value corresponding to $\bar{x}_0$, the border between the rejection and acceptance regions. We then use this z-value and Table IV of Appendix A to determine the area in the *acceptance region* under the alternative distribution. This area is the value of β corresponding to the particular alternative μ_a. For example, for the alternative $\mu_a = 2{,}425$, we calculate

$$z = \frac{\bar{x}_0 - 2{,}425}{\sigma_{\bar{x}}} = \frac{\bar{x} - 2{,}425}{\sigma/\sqrt{n}}$$

$$\approx \frac{\bar{x}_0 - 2{,}425}{s/\sqrt{n}} = \frac{2{,}446.5 - 2{,}425}{28.28} = .76$$

Note in Figure 8.20b that the area in the acceptance region is the area to the left of $z = .76$. This area is

$$\beta = .5 + .2764 = .7764$$

Thus, the probability that the test procedure will lead to an incorrect acceptance of the null hypothesis $\mu = 2{,}400$ when in fact $\mu = 2{,}425$ is about .78. As the average strength of the pipe increases to 2,450, the value of β decreases to .4522 (Figure 8.20c). If the mean strength is further increased to 2,475, the value of β is further decreased to .1562 (Figure 8.20d). Thus, even if the true mean strength of the pipe exceeds the minimum specification by 75 pounds per linear foot, the test procedure will lead to an incorrect acceptance of the null hypothesis (rejection of the pipe) approximately 16% of the time. The upshot is that the pipe must be manufactured so that the mean strength well exceeds the minimum requirement if the manufacturer wants the probability of its acceptance by the city to be large (i.e., β to be small).

The steps for calculating β for a large-sample test about a population mean are summarized in the following box:

Steps for Calculating β for a Large-Sample Test about μ

1. Calculate the value(s) of $\bar{x}$ corresponding to the border(s) of the rejection region. There will be one border value for a one-tailed test and two for a two-tailed test. The formula is one of the following, corresponding to a test with level of significance α:

$$Upper\text{-}tailed\ test: \bar{x}_0 = \mu_0 + z_\alpha\sigma_{\bar{x}} \approx u_0 + z_\alpha\left(\frac{s}{\sqrt{n}}\right)$$

$$Lower\text{-}tailed\ test: \bar{x}_0 = \mu_0 + z_\alpha\sigma_{\bar{x}} \approx u_0 - z_\alpha\left(\frac{s}{\sqrt{n}}\right)$$

$$Two\text{-}tailed\ test: \bar{x}_{0,\ L} = \mu_0 - z_{\alpha/2}\sigma_{\bar{x}} \approx u_0 - z_{\alpha/2}\left(\frac{s}{\sqrt{n}}\right)$$

$$\bar{x}_{0,\ U} = \mu_0 + z_{\alpha/2}\sigma_{\bar{x}} \approx \mu_0 + z_{\alpha/2}\left(\frac{s}{\sqrt{n}}\right)$$

(continued)

2. Specify the value of μ_a in the alternative hypothesis for which the value of β is to be calculated. Then convert the border value(s) of $\bar{x}_0$ to z-value(s), using the alternative distribution with mean μ_a. The general formula for the z value is

$$z = \frac{\bar{x}_0 - \mu_a}{\sigma_{\bar{x}}}$$

Sketch the alternative distribution (centered at μ_a), and shade the area in the acceptance (nonrejection) region. Use the z-statistic(s) and Table IV of Appendix A to find the shaded area, which is β.

Following the calculation of β for a particular value of μ_a, you should interpret the value in the context of the hypothesis-testing application. It is often useful to interpret the value of $1 - \beta$, which is known as the power of the test corresponding to a particular alternative, μ_a. Since β is the probability of accepting the null hypothesis when the alternative hypothesis is true with $\mu = \mu_a$, $1 - \beta$ is the probability of the complementary event, or the probability of rejecting the null hypothesis when the alternative $H_a: \mu = \mu_a$ is true. That is, the power $(1 - \beta)$ measures the likelihood that the test procedure will lead to the correct decision (reject H_0) for a particular value of the mean in the alternative hypothesis.

Definition 8.2

The **power of a test** is the probability that the test will correctly lead to the rejection of the null hypothesis for a particular value of μ in the alternative hypothesis. The power is equal to $(1 - \beta)$ for the particular alternative considered.

For example, in the sewer pipe example, we found that $\beta = .7764$ when $\mu = 2,425$. This is the probability that the test leads to the (incorrect) acceptance of the null hypothesis when $\mu = 2,425$. Or, equivalently, the power of the test is $1 - .7764 = .2236$, which means that the test will lead to the (correct) rejection of the null hypothesis only 22% of the time when the pipe exceeds specifications by 25 pounds per linear foot. When the manufacturer's pipe has a mean strength of 2,475 (that is, 75 pounds per linear foot in excess of specifications), the power of the test increases to $1 - .1562 = .8438$. That is, the test will lead to the acceptance of the manufacturer's pipe 84% of the time if $\mu = 2,475$.

EXAMPLE 8.9
FINDING THE POWER OF A TEST

Problem Recall the drug experiment in Examples 8.1 and 8.2, in which we tested to determine whether the mean response time for rats injected with a drug differs from the control mean response time of $\mu = 1.2$ seconds. The test setup is repeated here:

$H_0: \mu = 1.2$

$H_a: \mu \neq 1.2$ (i.e., $\mu < 1.2$ or $\mu > 1.2$)

Test statistic: $z = \dfrac{\bar{x} - 1.2}{\sigma_{\bar{x}}}$

Rejection region: $z < -1.96$ or $z > 1.96$ for $\alpha = .05$

$\quad\quad\quad\quad\quad\quad\quad z < -2.575$ or $z > 2.575$ for $\alpha = .01$

Note that two rejection regions have been specified, corresponding to values of $\alpha = .05$ and $\alpha = .01$, respectively. Assume that $n = 100$ and $s = .5$.

a. Suppose drug-injected rats have a mean response time of 1.1 seconds; that is, $\mu = 1.1$. Calculate the values of β corresponding to the two rejection regions. Discuss the relationship between the values of α and β.

b. Calculate the power of the test for each of the rejection regions when $\mu = 1.1$.

Solution

a. We first consider the rejection region corresponding to $\alpha = .05$. The first step is to calculate the border values of $\bar{x}$ corresponding to the two-tailed rejection region, $z < -1.96$ or $z > 1.96$:

$$\bar{x}_{0,L} = \mu_0 - 1.96\sigma_{\bar{x}} \approx \mu_0 - 1.96\left(\frac{s}{\sqrt{n}}\right) = 1.2 - 1.96\left(\frac{.5}{10}\right) = 1.102$$

$$\bar{x}_{0,U} = \mu_0 + 1.96\sigma_{\bar{x}} \approx \mu_0 + 1.96\left(\frac{s}{\sqrt{n}}\right) = 1.2 + 1.96\left(\frac{.5}{10}\right) = 1.298$$

These border values are shown in Figure 8.21.

Next, we convert these values to z-values in the alternative distribution with $\mu_a = 1.1$:

$$z_L = \frac{\bar{x}_{0,L} - \mu_a}{\sigma_{\bar{x}}} \approx \frac{1.102 - 1.1}{.05} = .04$$

$$z_U = \frac{\bar{x}_{0,U} - \mu_a}{\sigma_{\bar{x}}} \approx \frac{1.298 - 1.1}{.05} = 3.96$$

These z-values are shown in Figure 8.21b. You can see that the acceptance (or non-rejection) region is the area between them. Using Table IV of Appendix A, we find

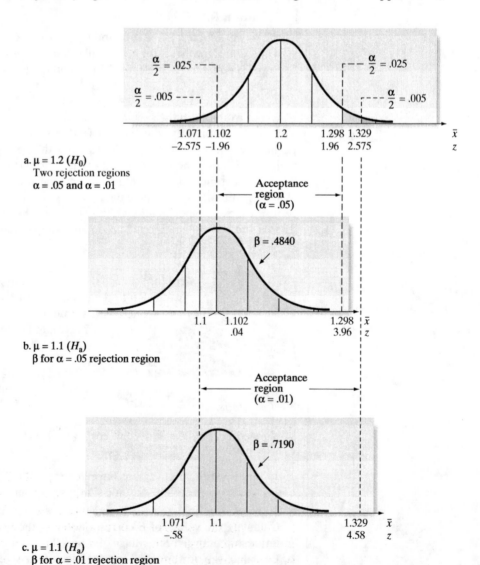

a. $\mu = 1.2$ (H_0)
Two rejection regions
$\alpha = .05$ and $\alpha = .01$

b. $\mu = 1.1$ (H_a)
β for $\alpha = .05$ rejection region

c. $\mu = 1.1$ (H_a)
β for $\alpha = .01$ rejection region

FIGURE 8.21

Calculation of β for drug-injected rate (Example 8.9)

that the area between $z = 0$ and $z = .04$ is .0160 and the area between $z = 0$ and $z = 3.96$ is (approximately) .5 (since $z = 3.96$ is off the scale of Table IV). Then the area between $z = .04$ and $z = 3.96$ is approximately

$$\beta = .5 - .0160 = .4840$$

Thus, the test with $\alpha = .05$ will lead to a Type II error about 48% of the time when the mean reaction time for drug-injected rats is .1 second less than the control mean response time.

For the rejection region corresponding to $\alpha = .01, z < -2.575$ or $z > 2.575$, we find that

$$\bar{x}_{0,L} = 1.2 - 2.575\left(\frac{.5}{10}\right) = 1.0712$$

$$\bar{x}_{0,U} = 1.2 + 2.575\left(\frac{.5}{10}\right) = 1.3288$$

These border values of the rejection region are shown in Figure 8.21c.

Converting these two border values to z-values in the alternative distribution with $\mu_a = 1.1$, we find that $z_L = -.58$ and $z_U = 4.58$. The area between these values is approximately

$$\beta = .2190 + .5 = .7190$$

Thus, the chance that the test procedure with $\alpha = .01$ will lead to an incorrect acceptance of H_0 is about 72%.

Note that the value of β increases from .4840 to .7190 when we decrease the value of α from .05 to .01. This is a general property of the relationship between α and β: *As α is decreased (increased), β is increased (decreased).*

b. The power is defined to be the probability of (correctly) rejecting the null hypothesis when the alternative is true. When $\mu = 1.1$ and $\alpha = .05$, we find that

$$\text{Power} = 1 - \beta = 1 - .4840 = .5160$$

When $\mu = 1.1$ and $\alpha = .01$, we get

$$\text{Power} = 1 - \beta = 1 - .7190 = .2810$$

You can see that the power of the test is decreased as the level of α is decreased. This means that as the probability of incorrectly rejecting the null hypothesis is decreased, the probability of correctly accepting the null hypothesis for a given alternative is also decreased.

Look Back A key point in this example is that the value of α must be selected carefully, with the realization that a test is made less capable of detecting departures from the null hypothesis when the value of α is decreased.

Most statistical software packages now have options for computing the power of standard tests of hypothesis. Usually, you will need to specify the type of test (z-test or t-test), the form of H_a ($<, >$, or $\neq$), the standard deviation, the sample size, and the value of the parameter in H_a (or the difference between the value in H_0 and the value in H_a). The MINITAB power analysis for Example 8.9 when $\alpha = .05$ is displayed in Figure 8.22. The power of the test (.516) is highlighted on the printout.

We have shown that the probability of committing a Type II error, β, is inversely related to α (Example 8.9), and that the value of β decreases as the value of μ_a moves farther from the null-hypothesis value. Consider again the sewer pipe example. The sample size n also affects β. Remember that the standard deviation of the sampling distribution of

---

Power and Sample Size

```
1-Sample Z Test

Testing mean = null (versus not = null)
Calculating power for mean = null + difference
Alpha = 0.05  Assumed standard deviation = 0.5
```

FIGURE 8.22

MINITAB power analysis for
Example 8.9

```
                      Sample
       Difference      Size      Power
              0.1       100    0.516005
```

$\bar{x}$ is inversely proportional to the square root of the sample size ($\sigma_{\bar{x}} = \sigma/\sqrt{n}$). Thus, as illustrated in Figure 8.23, the variability of both the null and alternative sampling distributions is decreased as n is increased. If the value of α is specified and remains fixed, then the value of β decreases as n increases, as illustrated in Figure 8.23. Conversely, the power of the test for a given alternative hypothesis is increased as the sample size is increased.

The properties of β and power are summarized in the following box:

> ### Properties of β and Power
>
> 1. For fixed n and α, the value of β decreases and the power increases as the distance between the specified null value μ_0 and the specified alternative value μ_a increases. (See Figure 8.20).
> 2. For fixed n, μ_0, and μ_a, the value of β increases and the power decreases as the value of α is decreased. (See Figure 8.21).
> 3. For fixed α, μ_0, and μ_a, the value of β decreases and the power increases as the sample size n is increased. (See Figure 8.23).

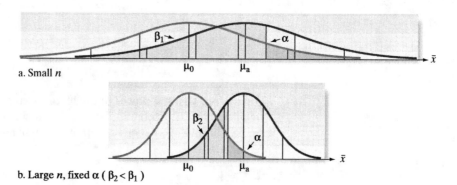

FIGURE 8.23

Relationship between α, β, and n

a. Small n

b. Large n, fixed α ($\beta_2 < \beta_1$)

Exercises 8.92–8.103

Understanding the Principles

8.92 Define the power of a test.

8.93 What is the relationship between β (the probability of committing a Type II error) and the power of the test?

8.94 List three factors that will increase the power of the test.

Learning the Mechanics

8.95 Suppose you want to test $H_0: \mu = 1{,}000$ against $H_a: \mu > 1{,}000$, using $\alpha = .05$. The population in question is normally distributed with standard deviation 120. A random sample of size $n = 36$ will be used.

a. Sketch the sampling distribution of $\bar{x}$, assuming that H_0 is true.

b. Find the value of $\bar{x}_0$, that value of $\bar{x}$ above which the null hypothesis will be rejected. Indicate the rejection region on your graph of part **a**. Shade the area above the rejection region and label it α.

c. On your graph of part **a**, sketch the sampling distribution of $\bar{x}$ if $\mu = 1{,}020$. Shade the area under this distribution which corresponds to the probability that $\bar{x}$ falls in the nonrejection region when $\mu = 1{,}020$. Label this area β.

d. Find β.

e. Compute the power of this test for detecting the alternative $H_a: \mu = 1{,}020$.

8.96 Refer to Exercise 8.95.
  a. If $\mu = 1,040$ instead of 1,020, what is the probability that the hypothesis test will incorrectly fail to reject H_0? That is, what is β?
  b. If $\mu = 1,040$, what is the probability that the test will correctly reject the null hypothesis? That is, what is the power of the test?
  c. Compare β and the power of the test when $\mu = 1,040$ to with values you obtained in Exercise 8.95 for $\mu = 1,020$. Explain the differences.

8.97 It is desired to test $H_0: \mu = 50$ against $H_a: \mu < 50$, using $\alpha = .10$. The population in question is uniformly distributed with standard deviation 20. A random sample of size 64 will be drawn from the population.
  a. Describe the (approximate) sampling distribution of $\bar{x}$ under the assumption that H_0 is true.
  b. Describe the (approximate) sampling distribution of $\bar{x}$ under the assumption that the population mean is 45.
  c. If μ were really equal to 45, what is the probability that the hypothesis test would lead the investigator to commit a Type II error?
  d. What is the power of this test for detecting the alternative $H_a: \mu = 45$?

8.98 Refer to Exercise 8.97.
  a. Find β for each of the following values of the population mean: 49, 47, 45, 43, and 41.
  b. Plot each value of β you obtained in part **a** against its associated population mean. Show β on the vertical axis and μ on the horizontal axis. Draw a curve through the five points on your graph.
  c. Use your graph from part **b** to find the approximate probability that the hypothesis test will lead to a Type II error when $\mu = 48$.
  d. Convert each of the β values you calculated in part **a** to the power of the test at the specified value of μ. Plot the power on the vertical axis against μ on the horizontal axis. Compare the graph of part **b** with the *power curve* you plotted here.
  e. Examine the graphs of parts **b** and **d**. Explain what they reveal about the relationships among the distance between the true mean μ and the null-hypothesized mean μ_0, the value of β, and the power.

8.99 Suppose you want to conduct the two-tailed test of $H_0: \mu = 10$ against $H_a: \mu \neq 10$ using $\alpha = .05$. A random sample of size 100 will be drawn from the population in question. Assume the population has a standard deviation equal to 1.0.
  a. Describe the sampling distribution of $\bar{x}$ under the assumption that H_0 is true.
  b. Describe the sampling distribution of $\bar{x}$ under the assumption that $\mu = 9.9$.
  c. If μ were really equal to 9.9, find the value of β associated with the test.
  d. Find the value of β for the alternative $H_a: \mu = 10.1$.

Applying the Concepts—Intermediate

8.100 **Post-traumatic stress of POWs.** Refer to Exercise 8.29 (p. 364), in which the null hypothesis that the mean PTSD score of World War II POWs is 16 is tested against the alternative hypothesis that the mean is less than 16. Recall that 33 POWs were included in the sample. Assume that

the resulting standard deviation of is a good estimate of the true standard deviation.
  a. Plot the power of the test for the mean values of 15.5, 15.0, 14.5, 14.0, and 13.5.
  b. Plot the power of the test on the vertical axis against the mean on the horizontal axis. Draw a curve through the points.
  c. Use the power curve of part **b** to estimate the power for the mean value $\mu = 14.25$. Calculate the power for this value of μ, and compare it with your approximation.
  d. Use the power curve to approximate the power of the test when $\mu = 12.10$. If the true value of the mean PTSD score for WWII POWs is really 10, what (approximately) are the chances that the test will fail to reject the null hypothesis that the mean is 16?

8.101 **Increasing the sample size.** Refer to Exercise 8.100. Show what happens to the power curve when the sample size is increased from $n = 33$ to $n = 100$. Assume that the standard deviation is $\sigma = 9.32$.

8.102 **Gas mileage of the Honda Civic.** According to the Environmental Protection Agency (EPA) *Fuel Economy Guide*, the 2006 Honda Civic automobile obtains a mean of 38 miles per gallon (mpg) on the highway. Suppose Honda claims that the EPA has underestimated the Civic's mileage. To support its assertion, the company selects 36 model 2006 Civic cars and records the mileage obtained for each car over a driving course similar to the one used by the EPA. The following data result: $\bar{x} = 40.3$ mpg, $s = 6.4$ mpg.
  a. If Honda wishes to show that the mean mpg for 2006 Civic autos is greater than 38 mpg, what should the alternative hypothesis be? the null hypothesis?
  b. Do the data provide sufficient evidence to support the auto manufacturer's claim? Test, using $\alpha = .05$. List any assumptions you make in conducting the test.
  c. Calculate the power of the test for the mean values of 38.5, 39.0, 39.5, 40.0, and 40.5, assuming that $s = 6.4$ is a good estimate of σ.
  d. Plot the power of the test on the vertical axis against the mean on the horizontal axis. Draw a curve through the points.
  e. Use the power curve of part **d** to estimate the power for the mean value $\mu = 39.75$. Calculate the power for this value of μ, and compare it with your approximation.
  f. Use the power curve to approximate the power of the test when $\mu = 43$. If the true value of the mean mpg for this model is really 43, what (approximately) are the chances that the test will fail to reject the null hypothesis that the mean is 38?

⚙ **GASTURBINE**

8.103 **Cooling method for gas turbines.** Refer to the *Journal of Engineering for Gas Turbines and Power* (Jan. 2005) study of a new cooling method for gas turbine engines, presented in Exercise 8.32 (p. 364). The heat rates (kilojoules per kilowatt per hour) for 67 gas turbines cooled with the new method are saved in the GASTURBINE file. Assume that the standard deviation of the population of heat rates is $\sigma = 1,600$. In Exercise 8.32, you tested whether the true mean heat rate μ exceeded 10,000 kJ/kWh at $\alpha = .05$. If the true mean is really $\mu = 10,500$, what is the chance that you will make a Type II error?

8.7 Test of Hypothesis about a Population Variance (Optional)

Although many practical problems involve inferences about a population mean (or proportion), it is sometimes of interest to make an inference about a population variance σ^2. To illustrate, a quality control supervisor in a cannery knows that the exact amount each can contains will vary, since there are certain uncontrollable factors that affect the amount of fill. The mean fill per can is important, but equally important is the variance of the fill. If σ^2 is large, some cans will contain too little and others too much. Suppose regulatory agencies specify that the standard deviation of the amount of fill in 16-ounce cans should be less than .1 ounce. To determine whether the process is meeting this specification, the supervisor randomly selects 10 cans and weighs the contents of each. The results are given in Table 8.6.

 FILLAMOUNTS

TABLE 8.6 Fill Weights (ounces) of 10 Cans

16.00	15.95	16.10	16.02	15.99
16.06	16.04	16.05	16.03	16.02

Do these data provide sufficient evidence to indicate that the variability is as small as desired? To answer this question, we need a procedure for testing a hypothesis about σ^2.

Intuitively, it seems that we should compare the sample variance σ^2 with the hypothesized value of σ^2 (or s with σ) in order to make a decision about the population's variability. The quantity

$$\frac{(n - 1)s^2}{\sigma^2}$$

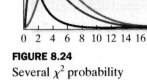

FIGURE 8.24
Several χ^2 probability distributions

has been shown to have a sampling distribution called a **chi-square** (χ^2) **distribution** when the population from which the sample is taken is *normally distributed*. Several chi-square distributions are shown in Figure 8.24.

The upper-tail areas for this distribution have been tabulated and are given in Table VII of Appendix A, a portion of which is reproduced in Table 8.7. The table gives the values of χ^2, denoted as χ^2_α, that locate an area of α in the upper tail of the chi-square distribution; that is, $P(\chi^2 > \chi^2_\alpha) = \alpha$. In this case, as with the t-statistic, the shape of the chi-square distribution depends on the number of degrees of freedom associated with s^2, namely, $(n - 1)$. Thus, for $n = 10$ and an upper-tail value $\alpha = .05$, you will have $n - 1 = 9$ df and $\chi^2_{.05} = 16.9190$ (the highlighted area in Table 8.7). To further illustrate the use of Table VII, we return to the can-filling example.

Now Work Exercise 8.108

TABLE 8.7   Reproduction of Part of Table VII in Appendix A: Critical Values of Chi-Square

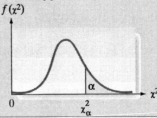

Degrees of Freedom	$\chi^2_{.100}$	$\chi^2_{.050}$	$\chi^2_{.025}$	$\chi^2_{.010}$	$\chi^2_{.005}$
1	2.70554	3.84146	5.02389	6.63490	7.87944
2	4.60517	5.99147	7.37776	9.21034	10.5966
3	6.25139	7.81473	9.34840	11.3449	12.8381
4	7.77944	9.48773	11.1433	13.2767	14.8602
5	9.23635	11.0705	12.8325	15.0863	16.7496
6	10.6446	12.5916	14.4494	16.8119	18.5476
7	12.0170	14.0671	16.0128	18.4753	20.2777
8	13.3616	15.5073	17.5346	20.0902	21.9550
	14.6837		19.0228	21.6660	23.5893
10	15.9871	18.3070	20.4831	23.2093	25.1882
11	17.2750	19.6751	21.9200	24.7250	26.7569
12	18.5494	21.0261	23.3367	26.2170	28.2995
13	19.8119	22.3621	24.7356	27.6883	29.8194
14	21.0642	23.6848	26.1190	29.1413	31.3193
15	22.3072	24.9958	27.4884	30.5779	32.8013
16	23.5418	26.2862	28.8454	31.9999	34.2672
17	24.7690	27.5871	30.1910	33.4087	35.7185
18	25.9894	28.8693	31.5264	34.8053	37.1564
19	27.2036	30.1435	32.8523	36.1908	38.5822

EXAMPLE 8.10
A TEST FOR σ^2— Fill Weight Variance

Problem Refer to the fill weights for the sample of ten 16-ounce cans in Table 8.6. Is there sufficient evidence to conclude that the true standard deviation σ of the fill measurements of 16-ounce cans is less than .1 ounce?

Solution Here, we want to test whether $\sigma < .1$. Since the null and alternative hypotheses must be stated in terms of σ^2 (rather than σ), we want to test the null hypothesis that $\sigma^2 = (.1)^2 = .01$ against the alternative that $\sigma^2 < .01$. Therefore, the elements of the test are

$H_0: \sigma^2 = .01$ (Fill variance equals .01—i.e., process specifications are not met)
$H_a: \sigma^2 < .01$ (Fill variance is less than .01—i.e., process specifications are met)

Test statistic: $\chi^2 = \dfrac{1(n-1)s^2}{\sigma^2}$

Assumption: The distribution of the amounts of fill is approximately normal.
Rejection region: The smaller the value of s^2 we observe, the stronger is the evidence in favor of H_a. Thus, we reject H_0 for "small values" of the test statistic. With $\alpha = .05$ and 9 df, the χ^2 value for rejection is found in Table VII and pictured in Figure 8.25. We will reject H_0 if $\chi^2 < 3.32511$.

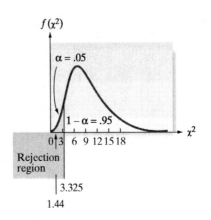

FIGURE 8.25
Rejection region for Example 8.10

(Remember that the area given in Table VII is the area to the *right* of the numerical value in the table. Thus, to determine the lower-tail value, which has $\alpha = .05$ to its *left*, we used the $\chi^2_{.95}$ column in Table VII.)

A SAS printout of the analysis is displayed in Figure 8.26. The value of s (highlighted on the printout) is $s = .0412$. Substituting into the formula for the test statistic, we have

$$\chi^2 = \frac{(n-1)s^2}{\sigma^2} = \frac{9(.0412)^2}{.01} = 1.53$$

Since the value of the test statistic is less than 3.32511, the supervisor can conclude that the variance σ^2 of the population of all amounts of fill is less than .01 (i.e., $\sigma < .1$), with probability of a Type I error equal to $\alpha = .05$. If this procedure is repeatedly used, it will incorrectly reject H_0 only 5% of the time. Thus, the quality control super visor is confident in the decision that the cannery is operating within the desired limits of variability.

FIGURE 8.26
SAS test of fill amount variance, Example 8.10

```
Sample Statistics for FILLAMT

     N        Mean      Std. Dev.      Variance
    ------------------------------------------------
    10       16.026       0.0412        0.0017


Hypothesis Test

    Null hypothesis:       Variance of FILLAMT => 0.01
    Alternative:           Variance of FILLAMT <  0.01

          Chi-square        Df          Prob
         ---------------------------------------
            1.524            9         0.0030
```

Look Back Note that both the test statistic and the one-tailed *p*-value of the test are shown on the SAS printout. Note also that the *p*-value (.003) is less than $\alpha = .05$, thus confirming our conclusion to reject H_0.

Now Work Exercise 8.113

One-tailed and two-tailed tests of hypothesis for σ^2 are given in the following box.*

Test of Hypothesis about σ^2

One-Tailed Test	**Two-Tailed Test**
$H_0: \sigma^2 = \sigma_0^2$	$H_0: \sigma^2 = \sigma_0^2$
$H_a: \sigma^2 < \sigma_0^2$ (or $H_a: \sigma^2 > \sigma_0^2$)	$H_a: \sigma^2 \neq \sigma_0^2$
Test statistic: $\chi^2 = \dfrac{(n-1)s^2}{\sigma_0^2}$	Test statistic: $\chi^2 = \dfrac{(n-1)s^2}{\sigma_0^2}$
Rejection region: $\chi^2 < \chi^2_{(1-\alpha)}$	Rejection region: $\chi^2 < \chi^2_{(1-\alpha/2)}$
(or $\chi^2 > \chi^2_\alpha$ when $H_a: \sigma^2 > \sigma_0^2$)	or $\chi^2 > \chi^2_{(\alpha/2)}$

where σ_0^2 is the hypothesized variance and the distribution of χ^2 is based on $(n-1)$ degrees of freedom.

*A confidence interval for σ^2 can also be formed by using the χ^2 distribution with $(n-1)$ degrees of freedom. A $(1-\alpha)100\%$ confidence interval is

$$\frac{(n-1)s^2}{\chi^2_{\alpha/2}} < \sigma^2 < \frac{(n-1)s^2}{\chi^2_{(1-\alpha/2)}}$$

> **Conditions Required for a Valid Large-Sample Hypothesis Test for σ^2**
> 1. A random sample is selected from the target population.
> 2. The population from which the sample is selected has a distribution that is approximately normal.

Caution

The procedure for conducting a hypothesis test for σ^2 in the preceding examples requires an assumption regardless of whether the sample size n is large or small. We must assume that the population from which the sample is selected has an approximate normal distribution. Unlike small-sample tests for μ based on the t-statistic, *slight to moderate departures from normality will render the χ^2 test invalid*.

Exercises 8.104–8.122

Understanding the Principles

8.104 What sampling distribution is used to make inferences about σ^2?

8.105 What conditions are required for a valid test for σ^2?

8.106 *True or False.* The null hypotheses $H_0: \sigma^2 = .25$ and $H_0: \sigma = .5$ are equivalent.

8.107 *True or False.* When the sample size n is large, no assumptions about the population are necessary to test the population variance σ^2.

Learning the Mechanics

8.108 Let χ_0^2 be a particular value of χ^2. Find the value of χ_0^2 such that
NW
   a. $P(\chi^2 > \chi_0^2) = .10$ for $n = 12$
   b. $P(\chi^2 > \chi_0^2) = .05$ for $n = 9$
   c. $P(\chi^2 > \chi_0^2) = .025$ for $n = 5$

8.109 A random sample of n observations is selected from a normal population to test the null hypothesis that $\sigma^2 = 25$. Specify the rejection region for each of the following combinations of H_a, α, and n:
   a. $H_a: \sigma^2 \neq 25; \alpha = .05; n = 16$

   b. $H_a: \sigma^2 > 25; \alpha = .01; n = 23$
   c. $H_a: \sigma^2 > 25; \alpha = .10; n = 15$
   d. $H_a: \sigma^2 < 25; \alpha = .01; n = 13$
   e. $H_a: \sigma^2 \neq 25; \alpha = .10; n = 7$

   f. $H_a: \sigma^2 < 25; \alpha = .05; n = 25$

8.110 A random sample of seven measurements gave $\bar{x} = 9.4$ and $s^2 = 1.84$.
   a. What assumptions must you make concerning the population in order to test a hypothesis about σ^2?
   b. Suppose the assumptions in part **a** are satisfied. Test the null hypothesis $\sigma^2 = 1$ against the alternative hypothesis $\sigma^2 > 1$. Use $\alpha = .05$.
   c. Test the null hypothesis $\sigma^2 = 1$ against the alternative hypothesis $\sigma^2 \neq 1$. Use $\alpha = .05$.

8.111 Refer to Exercise 8.110. Suppose we had $n = 100$, $\bar{x} = 9.4$, and $s^2 = 1.84$.
   a. Test the null hypothesis $H_0: \sigma^2 = 1$ against the alternative hypothesis $H_a: \sigma^2 > 1$.
   b. Compare your test result with that of Exercise 8.110.

8.112 A random sample of $n = 7$ observations from a normal population produced the following measurements: 4, 0, 6, 3, 3, 5, 9. Do the data provide sufficient evidence to indicate that $\sigma^2 < 2$? Test, using $\alpha = .05$.

Applying the Concepts—Basic

8.113 **Latex allergy in health-care workers.** Refer to the *Current*
NW *Allergy & Clinical Immunology* (March 2004) study of $n = 46$ hospital employees who were diagnosed with a latex allergy from exposure to the powder on latex gloves, presented in Exercise 8.26 (p. 364). Recall that the number of latex gloves used per week by the sampled workers is summarized as follows: $\bar{x} = 19.3$ and $s = 11.9$. Let σ^2 represent the variance in the number of latex gloves used per week by all hospital employees. Consider testing $H_0: \sigma^2 = 100$ against $H_a: \sigma^2 \neq 100$.
   a. Give the rejection region for the test at a significance level of $\alpha = .01$.
   b. Calculate the value of the test statistic.

   c. Use the results from parts **a** and **b** to draw the appropriate conclusion.

8.114 **A new dental bonding agent.** Refer to the *Trends in Biomaterials & Artificial Organs* (January 2003) study of a new bonding adhesive for teeth called "Smartbond," presented in Exercise 8.63 (p. 377). Recall that tests on a sample of 10 extracted teeth bonded with the new adhesive resulted in a mean breaking strength (after 24 hours) of $\bar{x} = 5.07$ Mpa and a standard deviation of $s = .46$ Mpa. In addition to requiring a good mean breaking strength, orthodontists are concerned about the variability in breaking strength of the new bonding adhesive.
   a. Set up the null and alternative hypothesis for a test to determine whether the breaking strength variance differs from .5 Mpa.
   b. Find the rejection region for the test, using $\alpha = .01$.

   c. Compute the test statistic.
   d. Give the appropriate conclusion for the test.

   e. What conditions are required for the test results to be valid?

8.115 **Birthweights of cocaine babies.** A group of researchers at the University of Texas-Houston conducted a comprehensive study of pregnant cocaine-dependent women. (*Journal of Drug Issues*, Summer 1997.) All the women in the study used cocaine on a regular basis (at least three times a week) for more than a year. One of the many variables measured was birth weight (in grams) of the baby delivered. For a sample of 16 cocaine-dependent women, the mean birth weight was 2,971 grams and the standard deviation was 410 grams. Test (at $\alpha = .01$) to determine whether the variance in birth weights of babies delivered by cocaine-dependent women is less than 200,000 grams^2.

8.116 **Analyzing remote-sensing data to identify type of land cover.** Refer to the *Geographical Analysis* (Oct. 2006) study of a new method for analyzing remote-sensing data from satellite pixels, presented in Exercise 8.28 (p. 364). Recall that the method uses a numerical measure of the distribution of gaps, or the sizes of holes, in the pixel, called *lacunarity*. Summary statistics for the lacunarity measurements in a sample of 100 grassland pixels are $\bar{x} = 225$ and $s = 20$. As stated in Exercise 8.28, it is known that the mean lacunarity measurement for all grassland pixels is 220. The method will be effective in identifying land cover if the standard deviation of the measurements is 10% (or less) of the true mean (i.e., if the standard deviation is less than 22).

   a. Give the null and alternative hypothesis for a test to determine whether, in fact, the standard deviation of all grassland pixels is less than 22.

   b. A MINITAB analysis of the data is below. Locate and interpret the *p*-value of the test. Use $\alpha = .10$.

Applying the Concepts—Intermediate

8.117 **Point spreads for NFL games.** Refer to the *Chance* (Fall 1998) study of point-spread errors in NFL games, Presented in Exercise 8.30 (p. 364). Recall that the difference between the actual outcome of the game and the point spread established by oddsmakers—the point-spread error—was calculated for 240 NFL games. The results are summarized as follows: $\bar{x} = -1.6$, $s = 13.3$. Suppose the researcher wants to know whether the true standard deviation of the point-spread errors exceeds 15. Conduct the analysis using $\alpha = .05$.

GOBIANTS

8.118 **Mongolian desert ants.** Refer to the *Journal of Biogeography* (December 2003) study of ants in Mongolia (central Asia), presented in Exercise 8.70 (p. 379). Data

on the number of ant species attracted to 11 randomly selected desert sites are saved in the **GOBIANTS** file. Do these data indicate that the standard deviation of the number of ant species at all Mongolian desert sites exceeds 15 species? Conduct the appropriate test at $\alpha = .05$. Are the conditions required for a valid test satisfied?

8.119 **Extracting toxic substances.** A new technique for extracting toxic organic compounds was evaluated in *Chromatographia* (March 1995). Uncontaminated fish fillets were injected with a toxic substance, and the method was used to extract the toxicant. To test the precision of the new method, seven measurements were obtained on a single fish fillet injected with a toxin. Summary statistics on the percentage of toxin recovered are $\bar{x} = 99$ and $s = 9$. Determine whether the standard deviation of the percentage recovered with the new method differs from 15. (Use $\alpha = .10$.)

GASTURBINE

8.120 **Cooling method for gas turbines.** Refer to the *Journal of Engineering for Gas Turbines and Power* (Jan. 2005) study of the performance of augmented gas turbine engines, presented in Exercise 8.32 (p. 364). Recall that the performance of each in a sample of 67 gas turbines was measured by heat rate (kilojoules per kilowatt per hour). The data are saved in the **GASTURBINE** file. Suppose that standard gas turbines have heat rates with a standard deviation of 1,500 kJ/kWh. Is there sufficient evidence to indicate that the heat rates of the augmented gas turbine engine are more variable than the heat rates of the standard gas turbine engine? Test, using $\alpha = 0.5$.

8.121 **Laser Spectroscopy of rocks.** Geologists use laser Raman microprobe (LRM) spectroscopy to analyze *fluid inclusions* (pockets of gas or liquid) in rock. A chip of natural Brazilian quartz was artificially injected with several fluid inclusions of liquid carbon dioxide (CO_2) and then subjected to LRM spectroscopy. (*Applied Spectroscopy*, February 1986.) The amount of CO_2 present in the inclusion was recorded for the same inclusion on four different days. The data (in mole percent) are as follows:

CO2

86.6	84.6	85.5	85.9

MINITAB output for
Exercise 8.116

Test for One Standard Deviation

```
Method
Null hypothesis         Sigma = 22
Alternative hypothesis  Sigma = < 22

The standard method is only for the normal distribution.

Statistics
N    StDev  Variance
100  20.0        400


Tests
Method      Chi-Square  DF  P-Value
Standard         81.82  99    0.105
```

a. Do the data indicate that the variation in the CO_2 concentration measurements obtained with the LRM method differs from 1?

b. What assumption is required for the test to be valid?

Applying the Concepts—Advanced

8.122 Homogeneity of brain signals. To improve the signal-to-noise ratio (SNR) in the electrical activity of the brain, neurologists repeatedly stimulate subjects and average the responses, a procedure with assumes that signal responses are homogeneous. A study was conducted to test the homogeneous-signal theory. (*IEEE Engineering in Medicine and Biology Magazine*, March 1990.) In this study, the variance of the SNR readings of subjects equaled .54 under the homogeneous-signal theory. If the SNR variance exceeded .54, the researchers concluded that the signals were nonhomogeneous. Signal-to-noise ratios recorded for a sample of 41 normal children ranged from .03 to 3.0. Use this information to test the theory at $\alpha = .10$.

KEY TERMS

Note: Starred (*) terms are from the optional sections in this chapter.

Alternative (research) hypothesis   352
Chi-square distribution*   394
Conclusion   362
Level of significance   356
Lower-tailed test   359

Null distribution*   386
Null hypothesis   352
Observed significance level (*p*-value)   365
One-tailed (one-sided) statistical test   359
Power of a test*   389
Rejection region   353

Test of hypothesis   351
Test statistic   352
Two-tailed (two-sided) hypothesis   359
Two-tailed test   359
Type I decision error   352
Type II error   354
Upper-tailed test   359

CHAPTER NOTES

Key Words for Identifying the Target Parameter:

μ—Mean, Average
p—Proportion, Fraction, Percentage, Rate, Probability
σ^2—Variance, Variability, Spread

Key Symbols

μ	Population mean
p	Population proportion, $P(\text{Success})$, in binomial trial
σ^2	Population variance
$\bar{x}$	Sample mean (estimator of μ)
$\hat{p}$	Sample proportion (estimator of p)
s^2	Sample variance (estimator of σ^2)
H_0	Null hypothesis
H_a	Alternative hypothesis
α	Probability of a Type I error
β	Probability of a Type II error
χ^2	Chi-square (sampling distribution of s^2 for normal data)

Elements of a Hypothesis Test:

1. *Null hypothesis (H_o)*
2. *Alternative hypothesis (H_a)*
3. *Test statistic ($z, t,$ or X^2)*
4. *Significance level (α)*
5. *p-value*
6. *Conclusion*

Type I Error = Reject H_0 when H_0 is true (occurs with probability α)
Type II Error = Accept H_0 when H_0 is false (occurs with probability β)
Power of a Test = P (Reject H_0 when H_0 is false)
= $1 - \beta$

Forms of Alternative Hypothesis:

Lower tailed: $H_a: \mu_0 < 50$
Upper tailed: $H_a: \mu_0 > 50$
Two tailed: $H_a: \mu_0 \neq 50$

Using *p*-values to Decide:

1. Choose significance level (α)
2. Obtain *p*-value of the test
3. If $\alpha > p$-value, Reject H_0

GUIDE TO SELECTING A ONE-SAMPLE HYPOTHESIS TEST

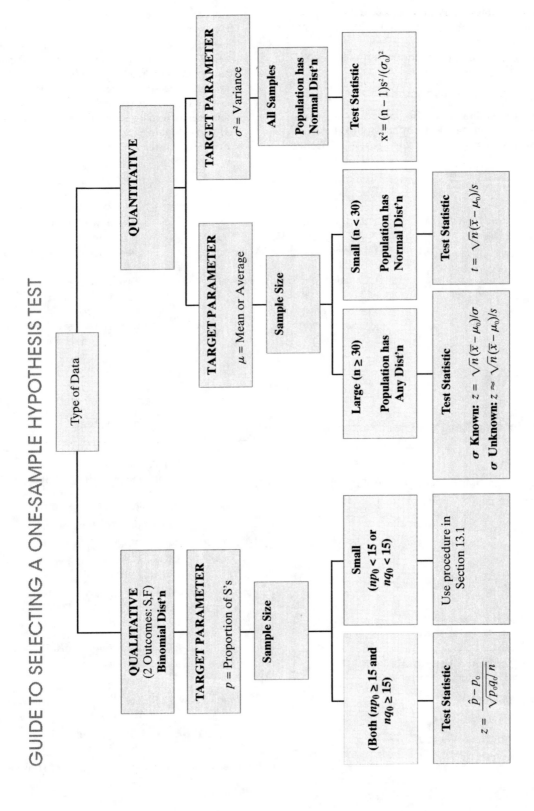

SUPPLEMENTARY EXERCISES 8.123–8.155

Note: List the assumptions necessary for the valid implementation of the statistical procedures you use in solving all these exercises. Starred (*) exercises refer to the optional sections in this chapter.

Understanding the Principles

8.123 *Complete the following statement:* The smaller the p-value associated with a test of hypothesis, the stronger is the support for the _____ hypothesis. Explain your answer.

8.124 Specify the differences between a large-sample and small-sample test of hypothesis about a population mean μ. Focus on the assumptions and test statistics.

8.125 Which of the elements of a test of hypothesis can and should be specified *prior* to analyzing the data that are to be utilized to conduct the test?

8.126 If the rejection of the null hypothesis of a particular test would cause your firm to go out of business, would you want α to be small or large? Explain.

8.127 *Complete the following statement:* The larger the p-value associated with a test of hypothesis, the stronger is the support for the _____ hypothesis. Explain your answer.

Learning the Mechanics

8.128 A random sample of 20 observations selected from a normal population produced $\bar{x} = 72.6$ and $s^2 = 19.4$.
  a. From a 90% confidence interval for the population mean.
  b. Test H_0: $\mu = 80$ against H_a: $\mu < 80$. Use $\alpha = .05$.
  c. Test H_0: $\mu = 80$ against H_a: $\mu \neq 80$. Use $\alpha = .01$.
  d. Form a 99% confidence interval for μ.
  e. How large a sample would be required to estimate μ to within 1 unit with 95% confidence?

8.129 A random sample of $n = 200$ observations from a binomial population yields $\hat{p} = .29$.
  a. Test H_0: $p = .35$ against H_a: $p < .35$. Use $\alpha = .05$.
  b. Test H_0: $p = .35$ against H_a: $p \neq .35$. Use $\alpha = .05$.
  c. Form a 95% confidence interval for p.
  d. Form a 99% confidence interval for p.
  e. How large a sample would be required to estimate p to within .05 with 99% confidence?

8.130 A random sample of 175 measurements possessed a mean of $\bar{x} = 8.2$ and a standard deviation of $s = .79$.
  a. Form a 95% confidence interval for μ.
  b. Test H_0: $\mu = 8.3$ against H_a: $\mu \neq 8.3$. Use $\alpha = .05$.
  c. Test H_0: $\mu = 8.4$ against H_a: $\mu \neq 8.4$. Use $\alpha = .05$.

8.131 A random sample of 41 observations from a normal population possessed a mean of $\bar{x} = 88$ and a standard deviation of $s = 6.9$.
  a. Test H_0: $\sigma^2 = 30$ against H_a: $\sigma^2 > 30$. Use $\alpha = .05$.
  b. Test H_0: $\sigma^2 = 30$ against H_a: $\sigma^2 \neq 30$. Use $\alpha = .05$.

8.132 A t-test is conducted for the null hypothesis H_0: $\mu = 10$ versus the alternative hypothesis H_a: $\mu > 10$ for a random sample of $n = 17$ observations. The test results are $t = 1.174$ and p-value $= .1288$.
  a. Interpret the p-value.
  b. What assumptions are necessary for the validity of this test?
  c. Calculate and interpret the p-value, assuming that the alternative hypothesis was instead H_a: $\mu \neq 10$.

Applying the Concepts—Basic

8.133 **FDA mandatory new-drug testing.** When a new drug is formulated, the pharmaceutical company must subject it to lengthy and involved testing before receiving the necessary permission from the Food and Drug Administration (FDA) to market the drug. The FDA requires the pharmaceutical company to provide substantial evidence that the new drug is safe for potential consumers.
  a. If the new-drug testing were to be placed in a test-of-hypothesis framework, would the null hypothesis be that the drug is safe or unsafe? the alternative hypothesis?
  b. Given the choice of null and alternative hypotheses in part **a**, describe Type I and Type II errors in terms of this application. Define α and β in terms of this application.
  c. If the FDA wants to be very confident that the drug is safe before permitting it to be marketed, is it more important that α or β be small? Explain.

8.134 **Cell phone use by drivers.** Refer to the U.S. Department of Transportation (July 2001) study of the level of cell phone use by drivers while they are in the act of driving a motor passenger vehicle, presented in Exercise 7.91 (p. 343). Recall that in a random sample of 1,165 drivers selected across the country, 35 were found using their cell phone.
  a. Conduct a test (at $\alpha = .05$) to determine whether p, the true driver cell phone use rate, differs from .02.
  b. Does the conclusion, you drew in part **a** agree with the inference you derived from the 95% confidence interval for p in Exercise 7.91? Explain why or why not.

8.135 **Sleep deprivation study.** In a British study, 12 healthy college students deprived of one night's sleep received an array of tests intended to measure their thinking time, fluency, flexibility, and originality of thought. The overall test scores of the sleep-deprived students were compared with the average score expected from students who received their accustomed sleep (*Sleep*, January 1989). Suppose the overall scores of the 12 sleep-deprived students had a mean of $\bar{x} = 63$ and a standard deviation of 17. (Lower scores are associated with a decreased ability to think creatively.)
  a. Test the hypothesis that the true mean score of sleep-deprived subjects is less than 80, the mean score of subjects who received sleep prior to taking the test. Use $\alpha = .05$.
  b. What assumption is required for the hypothesis test of part **a** to be valid?

8.136 **The "Pepsi challenge."** "Take the Pepsi Challenge" was a marketing campaign used by the Pepsi-Cola Company. Coca-Cola drinkers participated in a blind taste test in which they tasted unmarked cups of Pepsi and Coke and were asked to select their favorite. Pepsi claimed that "in recent blind taste tests, more than half the Diet Coke drinkers surveyed said they preferred the taste of Diet Pepsi." (*Consumer's Research*, May 1993.) Suppose 100 Diet Coke drinkers took the Pepsi Challenge and 56 preferred the taste of Diet Pepsi. Test the hypothesis that more than half of all Diet Coke drinkers will select Diet Pepsi in a blind taste test. Use $\alpha = .05$.

8.137 **Masculinizing human faces.** Refer to the *Nature* (August 27, 1998) study of facial characteristics that are deemed attractive, presented in Exercise 8.51 (p. 372). In another experiment, 67 human subjects viewed side by side an image of a Caucasian male face and the same image 50% masculinized. Each subject was asked to select the facial image they deemed more attractive. Fifty-eight of the 67 subjects felt that masculinization of face shape decreased attractiveness of the male face. The researchers used this sample information to test whether the subjects showed a preference for either the unaltered or the morphed male face.

a. Set up the null and alternative hypotheses for this test.

b. Compute the test statistic.

c. The researchers reported a p-value ≈ 0 for the test. Do you agree?

d. Make the appropriate conclusion in the words of the problem. Use $\alpha = .01$.

MATHCPU

*8.138 Time taken to solve a math programming problem. Refer to the *IEEE Transactions* (June 1990) study of a new hybrid algorithm for solving polynomial 0/1 mathematical programs, presented in Exercise 7.103 (p. 344). A SAS printout giving descriptive statistics for the sample of 52 solution times is reproduced here. Use this information to determine whether the variance of the solution times differs from 2. Use $\alpha = .05$.

8.139 Alkalinity of river water. In Exercise 5.117 (p. 270), you learned that the mean alkalinity level of water specimens collected from the Han River in Seoul, Korea, is 50 milligrams per liter. (*Environmental Science & Engineering*, September 1, 2000.) Consider a random sample of 100 water specimens collected from a tributary of the Han River. Suppose the mean and standard deviation of the alkalinity levels for the sample are, respectively, $\bar{x} = 67.8$ mpl and $s = 14.4$ mpl. Is there sufficient evidence (at $\alpha = .01$) to indicate that the population mean alkalinity level of water in the tributary exceeds 50 mpl?

Applying the Concepts—Intermediate

8.140 Errors in medical tests. Medical tests have been developed to detect many serious diseases. A medical test is designed to minimize the probability that it will produce a "false positive" or a "false negative." A false positive is a positive test result for an individual who does not have the disease, whereas a false negative is a negative test result for an individual who does have the disease.

a. If we treat a medical test for a disease as a statistical test of hypothesis, what are the null and alternative hypotheses for the medical test?

b. What are the Type I and Type II errors for the test? Relate each to false positives and false negatives.

c. Which of these errors has graver consequences? Considering this error, is it more important to minimize α or β? Explain.

8.141 Crop weights of pigeons. In Exercise 7.95 (p. 343), you analyzed data from a study of the diets of spinifex pigeons. The data, extracted from the *Australian Journal of Zoology*, are reproduced in the accompanying table. Each measurement in the data set represents the weight (in grams) of the contents of the crop of a spinifex pigeon. Conduct a test at $\alpha = .05$ to determine whether the mean weight of the crops of all spinifex pigeons differs from 1 gram. Test the validity of any assumptions you make.

PIGEONS

.457	3.751	.238	2.967	2.509	1.384	1.454	.818
.335	1.436	1.603	1.309	.201	.530	2.144	.834

8.142 Cracks in highway pavement. Using van-mounted state-of-the-art video technology the Mississippi Department of Transportation collected data on the number of cracks (called *crack intensity*) in an undivided two-lane highway. (*Journal of Infrastructure Systems*, March 1995.) The mean number of cracks found in a sample of eight 50-meter sections of the highway was $\bar{x} = .210$, with a variance of $s^2 = .011$. Suppose the American Association of State Highway and Transportation Officials (AASHTO) recommends a maximum mean crack intensity of .100 for safety purposes.

a. Test the hypothesis that the true mean crack intensity of the Mississippi highway exceeds the AASHTO recommended maximum. Use $\alpha = .01$.

b. Define a Type I error and a Type II error for this study.

8.143 Inbreeding of tropical wasps. Refer to the *Science* (November 1988) study of inbreeding in tropical swarm-founding wasps, presented in Exercise 7.101 (p. 344). A sample of 197 wasps, captured, frozen, and subjected to a series of genetic tests, yielded a sample mean inbreeding coefficient of $\bar{x} = .044$ with a standard deviation of $s = .884$. Recall that if the wasp has no tendency to inbreed, the true mean inbreeding coefficient μ for the species will equal 0.

a. Test the hypothesis that the true mean inbreeding coefficient μ for this species of wasp exceeds 0. Use $\alpha = .05$.

b. Compare the inference you made in part **a** with the inference you obtained in Exercise 7.97, using a confidence interval. Do the inferences agree? Explain.

*8.144 Weights of parrot fish. A marine biologist wishes to use parrot fish for experimental purposes due to the belief that their weight is fairly stable (i.e., the variability in weights among parrot fish is small). The biologist randomly samples 10 parrot fish and finds that their mean weight is 4.3 pounds and the standard deviation is 1.4 pounds. The biologist will use the parrot fish only if there is evidence that the variance of their weights is less than 4.

a. Is there sufficient evidence for the biologist to claim that the variability in weights among parrot fish is small enough to justify their use in the experiment? Test at $\alpha = .05$.

SAS output for Exercise 8.138

The MEANS Procedure

Analysis Variable : CPU

Mean	Std Dev	Variance	N	Minimum	Maximum
0.8121923	1.5047603	2.2643035	52	0.0360000	8.7880000

b. State any assumptions that are needed for the test mentioned in part **a** to be valid.

8.145 PCB in plant discharge. The EPA sets a limit of 5 parts per million (ppm) on PCB (polychlorinated biphenyl, a dangerous substance) in water. A major manufacturing firm producing PCB for electrical insulation discharges small amounts from the plant. The company management, attempting to control the PCB in its discharge, has given instructions to halt production if the mean amount of PCB in the effluent exceeds 3 ppm. A random sample of 50 water specimens produced the following statistics: $\bar{x} = 3.1$ ppm and $s = .5$ ppm.

a. Do these statistics provide sufficient evidence to halt the production process? Use $\alpha = .01$.

b. If you were the plant manager, would you want to use a large or a small value for α for the test in part **a**?

*8.146 PCB in plant discharge (cont'd). Refer to Exercise 8.145.

a. In the context of the problem, define a Type II error.

b. Calculate β for the test described in part **a** of Exercise 8.145, assuming that the true mean is $\mu = 3.1$ ppm.

c. What is the power of the test to detect the effluent's departure from the standard of 3.0 ppm when the mean is 3.1 ppm?

d. Repeat parts **b** and **c**, assuming that the true mean is 3.2 ppm. What happens to the power of the test as the plant's mean PCB departs farther from the standard?

*8.147 PCB in plant discharge (cont'd). Refer to Exercises 8.145 and 8.146.

a. Suppose an α value of .05 is used to conduct the test. Does this change favor the manufacturer? Explain.

b. Determine the value of β and the power for the test when $\alpha = .05$ and $\mu = 3.1$.

c. What happens to the power of the test when α is increased?

8.148 Psychological study of obese adolescents. Research reported in the *Journal of Psychology* (March 1991) studied the personality characteristics of obese individuals. One variable, the locus of control (LOC), measures the individual's degree of belief that he or she has control over situations. High scores on the LOC scale indicate *less* perceived control. For one sample of 19 obese adolescents, the mean LOC score was 10.89, with a standard deviation of 2.48. Suppose we wish to test whether the mean LOC score for all obese adolescents exceeds 10, the average for "normal" individuals.

a. Specify the null and alternative hypotheses for this test.

b. Conduct the test mentioned in part **a**, and make the proper conclusion.

8.149 Choosing portable grill displays. Refer to the *Journal of Consumer Research* (March 2003) experiment on influencing the choices of others by offering undesirable alternatives, presented in Exercise 3.25 (p. 126). Recall that each of 124 college students selected three portable grills out of five to display on the showroom floor. The students were instructed to include Grill #2 (a smaller-sized grill) and select the remaining two grills in the display to maximize purchases of Grill #2. If the six possible grill display combinations (1–2–3, 1–2–4, 1–2–5, 2–3–4, 2–3–5, and 2–4–5) are selected at random, then the proportion of students selecting any display will be $1/6 = .167$. One theory tested by the researcher is that the students will tend to choose the three-grill display so that Grill #2 is a compromise between a more desirable and

a less desirable grill. Of the 124 students, 85 students selected a three-grill display that was consistent with that theory. Use this information to test the theory proposed by the researcher at $\alpha = .05$.

*8.150 Interocular eye pressure. Ophthalmologists require an instrument that can rapidly measure interocular pressure for glaucoma patients. The device now in general use is known to yield readings of this pressure with a variance of 10.3. The variance of five pressure readings on the same eye by a newly developed instrument is equal to 9.8. Does this sample variance provide sufficient evidence to indicate that the new instrument is more reliable than the instrument currently in use? (Use $\alpha = .05$.)

Applying the Concepts—Advanced

8.151 Polygraph test error rates. A group of physicians subjected the *polygraph* (or *lie detector*) to the same careful testing given to medical diagnostic tests. They found that if 1,000 people were subjected to the polygraph and 500 told the truth and 500 lied, the polygraph would indicate that approximately 185 of the truth tellers were liars and that approximately 120 of the liars were truth tellers (*Discover*, 1986).

a. In the application of a polygraph test, an individual is presumed to be a truth teller (H_0) until "proven" a liar (H_a). In this context, what is a Type I error? A Type II error?

b. According to the study, what is the probability (approximately) that a polygraph test will result in a Type I error? A Type II error?

8.152 NCAA March Madness. For three weeks each March, the National Collegiate Athletic Association (NCAA) holds its annual men's basketball championship tournament. The 64 best college basketball teams in the nation play a single-elimination tournament—a total of 63 games—to determine the NCAA champion. Tournament followers, from hard-core gamblers to the casual fan who enters the office betting pool, have a strong interest in handicapping the games. To provide insight into this phenomenon, statisticians Hal Stern and Barbara Mock analyzed data from 13 previous NCAA tournaments and published their results in *Chance* (Winter 1998). The results of first-round games are summarized in the table on p. 404.

a. A common perception among fans, the media, and gamblers is that the higher seeded team has a better than 50–50 chance of winning a first-round game. Is there evidence to support this perception? Conduct the appropriate test for each matchup. What trends do you observe?

b. Is there evidence to support the claim that a 1-, 2-, 3-, or 4-seeded team will win by an average of more than 10 points in first-round games? Conduct the appropriate test for each matchup.

c. Is there evidence to support the claim that a 5-, 6-, 7-, or 8-seeded team will win by an average of less than 5 points in first-round games? Conduct the appropriate test for each matchup.

*d. For each matchup, test the null hypothesis that the standard deviation of the victory margin is 11 points.

e. The researchers also calculated the difference between the outcome of the game (victory margin, in points) and the point spread established by Las Vegas oddsmakers for a sample of 360 recent NCAA tournament games. The mean difference is .7 and the standard deviation of the difference is 11.3. If the true mean difference is 0,

Summary of First-Round NCAA Tournament Games, 1985–1997

Matchup (Seeds)	Number of Games	Number Won by favorite (Higher Seed)	Margin of Victory (Points)	
			Mean	Standard Deviation
1 vs 16	52	52	22.9	12.4
2 vs 15	52	49	17.2	11.4
3 vs 14	52	41	10.6	12.0
4 vs 13	52	42	10.0	12.5
5 vs 12	52	37	5.3	10.4
6 vs 11	52	36	4.3	10.7
7 vs 10	52	35	3.2	10.5
8 vs 9	52	22	−2.1	11.0

Source: Stern, H. S., and Mock, B. "College basketball upsets: Will a 16-seed ever beat a 1-seed?" *Chance*, Vol. 11, No. 1, Winter 1998, p. 29 (Table 3).

then the point spread can be considered a good predictor of the outcome of the game. Use this sample information to test the hypothesis that the point spread, on average, is a good predictor of the victory margin in NCAA tournament games.

8.153 Solar joint inspections. X-rays and lasers are used to inspect solder-joint defects on printed circuit boards (PCBs). (*Quality Congress Transactions*, 1986.) A particular manufacturer of laser-based inspection equipment claims that its product can inspect at least 10 solder joints per second, on average, when the joints are spaced .1 inch apart. The equipment was tested by a potential buyer on 48 different PCBs. In each case, the equipment was operated for exactly 1 second. The number of solder joints inspected on each run is as follows:

PCB

10	9	10	10	11	9	12	8	8	9	6	10
7	10	11	9	9	13	9	10	11	10	12	8
9	9	9	7	12	6	9	10	10	8	7	9
11	12	10	0	10	11	12	9	7	9	9	10

a. The potential buyer doubts the manufacturer's claim. Do you agree?

b. Assume that the standard deviation of the number of solder joints inspected on each run is 1.2, and the true mean number of solder joints that can be inspected is really equal to 9.5. How likely is the buyer to correctly conclude that the claim is false?

Critical Thinking Challenges

8.154 The Hot Tamale caper. "Hot Tamales" are chewy, cinnamon-flavored candies. A bulk vending machine is known to dispense, on average, 15 Hot Tamales per bag. *Chance* (Fall 2000) published an article on a classroom project in which students were required to purchase bags of Hot Tamales from the machine and count the number of candies per bag. One student group claimed it purchased five bags that had the following candy counts: 25, 23, 21, 21, and 20. There was some question as to whether the students had fabricated the data. Use a hypothesis test to gain insight into whether or not the data collected by the students were fabricated. Use a level of significance that gives the benefit of the doubt to the students.

8.155 Verifying voter petitions. To get their names on the ballot of a local election, political candidates often must obtain petitions bearing the signatures of a minimum number of registered voters. In Pinellas County, Florida, a certain political candidate obtained petitions with 18,200 signatures. (*St. Petersburg Times*, April 7, 1992.) To verify that the names on the petitions were signed by actual registered voters, election officials randomly sampled 100 of the signatures and checked each for authenticity. Only 2 were invalid signatures.

a. Is 98 out of 100 verified signatures sufficient to believe that more than 17,000 of the total 18,200 signatures are valid? Use $\alpha = .01$.

b. Repeat part **a** if only 16,000 valid signatures are required.

SUMMARY ACTIVITY: Testing the "Efficient Market" Theory

The "efficient market" theory postulates that the best predictor of a stock's price at some point in the future is the current price of the stock (with some adjustments for inflation and transaction costs, which we shall assume to be negligible for the purpose of this exercise). To test the theory, select a random sample of 25 stocks on the New York Stock Exchange and record the closing prices on the last days of two recent consecutive months. Calculate the increase or decrease in the stock price over the 1-month period.

a. Define μ as the mean change in price of all stocks over a 1-month period. Set up the appropriate null and alternative hypotheses in terms of μ.

b. Use the sample of 25 stock price differences to conduct the test of hypothesis established in part **a**. Take $\alpha = .05$.

c. Tabulate the number of rejections and nonrejections of the null hypothesis in your class. If the null hypothesis were true, how many rejections of the null hypothesis would you expect among those in your class? How does this expectation compare with the actual number of nonrejections? What does the result of this exercise indicate about the efficient market theory?

REFERENCES

Snedecor, G. W., and Cochran, W. G. *Statistical Methods*, 7th ed. Ames, IA: Iowa State University Press, 1980.

Wackerly, D., Mendenhall, W., and Scheaffer, R. *Mathematical Statistics with Applications*, 6th ed. North Scituate, MA: Duxbury, 2002.

Using Technology

Tests of Hypothesis with MINITAB

MINITAB can be used to obtain one-sample tests for a population mean, a population proportion, and a population variance.

Testing μ: To generate a hypothesis test for the mean with the use of a previously created sample data set, first access the MINITAB data worksheet. Next, click on the "Stat" button on the MINITAB menu bar, and then click on "Basic Statistics" and "1-Sample t," as shown in Figure 8.M.1. The dialog box shown in Figure 8.M.2 appears. Click on "Samples in Columns"; then specify the quantitative variable of interest in the open box. Next, check "Perform hypothesis test" and specify the value of μ_0 for the null hypothesis in the open box. Now click on the "Options" button at the bottom of the dialog box and specify the form of the alternative hypothesis, as shown in Figure 8.M.3. Click "OK" to return to the "1-Sample t" dialog box, and then click "OK" again to produce the hypothesis test.

If you want to produce a test for the mean from summary information (e.g., the sample mean, sample standard deviation, and sample size), then click on "Summarized data" in the "1-Sample t" dialog box, enter the values of the summary statistics and μ_0, and then click "OK."

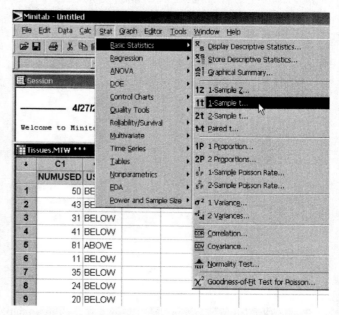

FIGURE 8.M.1
MINITAB menu options for a test about μ

[*Important Note*: The MINITAB one-sample *t*-procedure uses the *t*-statistic to generate the hypothesis test. When the sample size *n* is small, this is the appropriate method. When the sample size *n* is large, the *t*-value will be approximately equal to the large- sample *z*-value and the resulting test will still be valid. If you have a large sample and you know the value of the population standard deviation σ (which is rarely the case), then select "1-sample Z" from the "Basic Statistics" menu options (see Figure 8.M.1) and make the appropriate selections.]

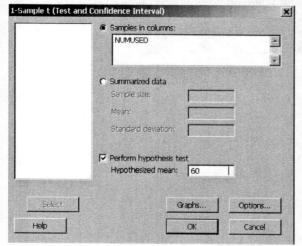

FIGURE 8.M.2
MINITAB one-sample t dialog box

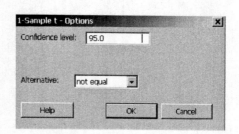

FIGURE 8.M.3
MINITAB one-sample t options

   Testing p: To generate a test for a population proportion with the use of a previously created sample data set, first ac-cess the MINITAB data worksheet. Next, click on the "Stat" button on the MINITAB menu bar, and then click on "Basic Statistics" and "1 Proportion." (See Figure 8.M.1.) The dialog box shown in Figure 8.M.4 appears. Click on "Samples in Columns"; then specify the qualitative variable of interest in the open box. Select "Perform hypothesis test" and enter the null-hypothesis value p_0 in the open box. Click on the "Options" button at the bottom of the dialog box and specify the form of the alternative hypothesis in the resulting dialog box, as shown in Figure 8.M.5. Also, check the "Use test and in-terval based on normal distribution" box at the bottom. Click "OK" to return to the "1-Proportion" dialog box, and then click "OK" again to produce the test results.

   If you want to produce a test for a proportion from summary information (e.g., the number of successes and the sample size), then click on "Summarized data" in the "1-Proportion" dialog box. (See Figure 8.M.4.) Enter the value for the num-ber of trials (i.e., the sample size) and the number of events (i.e., the number of successes), and then click "OK."

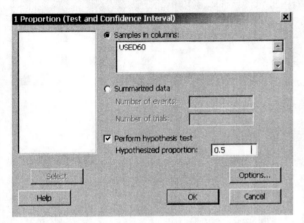

FIGURE 8.M.4
MINITAB one-proportion dialog box

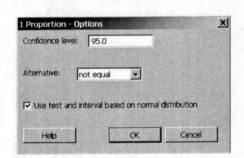

FIGURE 8.M.5
MINITAB one-proportion options

   Testing σ^2: To generate a hypothesis test for the variance with the use of a previously created sample data set, first ac-cess the MINITAB data worksheet. Next, click on the "Stat" button on the MINITAB menu bar, and then click on "Basic Statistics" and "1 Variance." (See Figure 8.M.1.) The dialog box shown in Figure 8.M.6 appears. Click on "Samples in Columns"; then specify the quantitative variable of interest in the open box. Check "Perform hypothesis test" and specify the null-hypothesis value of the standard deviation σ_0 in the open box. Now click on the "Options" button at the bottom of the dialog box and specify the form of the alternative hypothesis, as shown in Figure 8.M.7. Click "OK" twice to pro-duce the hypothesis test.

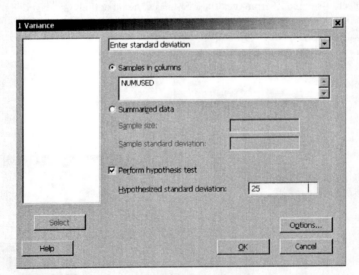

FIGURE 8.M.6
MINITAB one variance dialog box

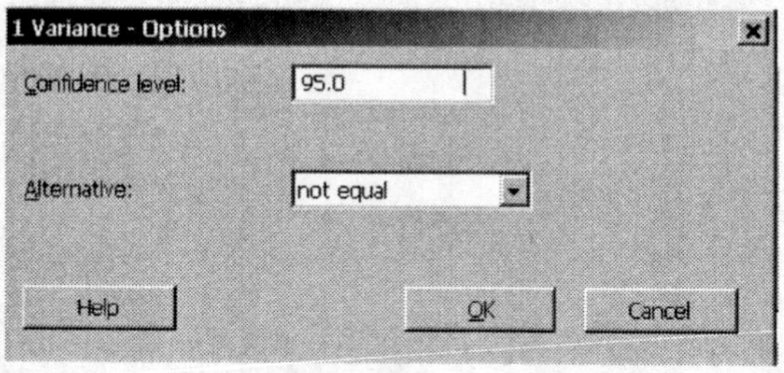

FIGURE 8.M.7
MINITAB one variance options

If you want to produce a test for the variance from summary information (e.g., the sample standard deviation and sample size), then click on "Summarized data" in the "1 Variance" dialog box and enter the values of the summary statistics.

CHAPTER 9

Inferences Based on Two Samples

Confidence Intervals and Tests of Hypotheses

CONTENTS

STATISTICS IN ACTION

Do Homework Assignments Designed to Involve Family Members Really Work?

USING TECHNOLOGY

Two-Sample Inferences with MINITAB

WHERE WE'VE BEEN

- Explored two methods for making statistical inferences: *confidence intervals* and *tests of hypotheses*

- Studied confidence intervals and tests for a single population mean μ, a single population proportion p, and a single population variance σ^2

- Learned how to select the sample size necessary to estimate a population parameter with a specified margin of error

WHERE WE'RE GOING

- Learn how to compare two populations by using confidence intervals and tests of hypotheses.

- Apply these inferential methods to problems in which we want to compare two population means, two population proportions, or two population variances.

- Determine the sizes of the samples necessary to estimate the difference between two population parameters with a specified margin of error.

STATISTICS IN ACTION

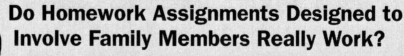

Do Homework Assignments Designed to Involve Family Members Really Work?

"Educators are increasingly aware of the importance of involving parents in the education of their children. Research shows that parent involvement improves student achievement.
When parents are involved, children do better in school. Parental encouragement and assistance contribute to students' higher achievement, report card grades, better attitudes, and higher aspirations."

The preceding quote is taken from the website for TIPS Interactive Homework. TIPS, an acronym for *Teachers Involve Parents in Schoolwork*, is an interactive homework process designed to improve the quality of homework assignments for elementary, middle, and high school students. TIPS homework assignments require students to interact with family partners (parents, guardians, etc.) while completing the homework. Frances Van Voorhis, a de-

velopmental psychology researcher at John Hopkins University, conducted a study to investigate the effects of TIPS on science, mathematics, and language arts homework assignments. (*Journal of Educational Research*, July/Aug. 2003.)

Dr. Van Voorhis's study involved a sample of 128 middle school students, each of whom was assigned to complete TIPS homework assignments, and a second sample of 98 students, each of whom was given traditional, noninteractive homework assignments (called ATIPS). At the end of the study, all students reported on the level of family involvement in their homework on a 5-point scale (0 = never, 1 = rarely, 2 = sometimes, 3 = frequently, 4 = always). Three scores were recorded for each student: one for science homework, one for math homework, and one for language arts homework. The data for the study, saved in the **HWSTUDY** file, are described in detail in Table SIA9.1.

In this chapter, several Statistics in Action Revisited examples demonstrate how we can use the methodology of the chapter to determine whether the TIPS program is effective in involving a student's family in his or her homework.

 HWSTUDY

TABLE SIA9.1 Description of Data Saved in the HWSTUDY file

Number of observations: 226

Variable	Type	Description
HWCOND	QL	Homework condition (TIPS or ATIPS)
SCIENCE	QN	Level of family involvement in science homework (5-point scale)
MATH	QN	Level of family involvement in math homework (5-point scale)
LANGUAGE	QN	Level of family involvement in language arts homework (5-point scale)

Statistics in Action Revisited

- Comparing the Mean Family Involvement in Homework Scores for TIPS and ATIPS Students (p. 423)

- Comparing the Proportions of Frequent Family Involvement in Homework for TIPS and ATIPS students (p. 449)

9.1 Identifying the Target Parameter

Many experiments involve a comparison of two populations. For instance, a sociologist may want to estimate the difference in mean life expectancy between inner-city and suburban residents. Or a consumer group may want to test whether two major brands of food freezers differ in the average amount of electricity they use. Or a political candidate might want to estimate the difference in the proportions of voters in two districts who favor his or her candidacy. Or a professional golfer might be interested in comparing the variability in the distance that two competing brands of golf balls travel when struck with the same club. In this chapter, we consider techniques for using two samples to compare the populations from which they were selected.

The same procedures that are used to estimate and test hypotheses about a single population can be modified to make inferences about two populations. As in Chapters 7 and 8, the methodology used will depend on the sizes of the samples and the parameter of interest (i.e., the *target parameter*). Some key words and the type of data associated with the parameters covered in this chapter are listed in the following box.

Determining the Target Parameter

Parameter	Key Words or Phrases	Type of Data
$\mu_1 - \mu_2$	Mean difference; difference in averages	Quantitative
$p_1 - p_2$	Difference between proportions, percentages, fractions, or rates; compare proportions	Qualitative
$(\sigma_1)^2/(\sigma_2)^2$	Ratio of variances; difference in variability or spread; compare variation	Quantitative

You can see that the key words *difference* and *compare* help identify the fact that two populations are to be compared. In the previous examples, the words *mean* in *mean life expectancy* and *average* in *average amount of electricity* imply that the target parameter is the difference in population means, $\mu_1 - \mu_2$. The word *proportions* in *proportions of voters in two districts* indicates that the target parameter is the difference in proportions, $p_1 - p_2$. Finally, the key word *variability* in *variability in the distance* identifies the ratio of population variances, $(\sigma_1)^2/(\sigma_2)^2$, as the target parameter.

As with inferences about a single population, the type of data (quantitative or qualitative) collected on the two samples is also indicative of the target parameter. With quantitative data, you are likely to be interested in comparing the means or variances of the data. With qualitative data with two outcomes (success or failure), a comparison of the proportions of successes is likely to be of interest.

We consider methods for comparing two population means in Sections 9.2 and 9.3. A comparison of population proportions is presented in Section 9.4 and population variances in optional Section 9.6. We show how to determine the sample sizes necessary for reliable estimates of the target parameters in Section 9.5.

9.2 Comparing Two Population Means: Independent Sampling

In this section, we develop both large-sample and small-sample methodologies for comparing two population means. In the large-sample case, we use the z-statistic; in the small-sample case, we use the t-statistic.

Large Samples:

EXAMPLE 9.1

A LARGE-SAMPLE CONFIDENCE INTERVAL FOR $(\mu_1 - \mu_2)$: Comparing Mean Weight Loss for Two Diets

Problem A dietitian has developed a diet that is low in fats, carbohydrates, and cholesterol. Although the diet was initially intended to be used by people with heart disease, the dietitian wishes to examine the effect this diet has on the weights of obese people. Two random samples of 100 obese people each are selected, and one group of 100 is placed on the low-fat diet. The other 100 are placed on a diet that contains approximately the same quantity of food, but is not as low in fats, carbohydrates, and cholesterol. For each person, the amount of weight lost (or gained) in a three-week period is recorded. The data, saved in the **DIETSTUDY** file, are listed in Table 9.1. Form a 95% confidence interval for the difference between the population mean weight losses for the two diets. Interpret the result.

 DIETSTUDY

TABLE 9.1   Diet Study Data, Example 9.1

Weight Losses for Low-Fat Diet

8	10	10	12	9	3	11	7	9	2
21	8	9	2	2	20	14	11	15	6
13	8	10	12	1	7	10	13	14	4
8	12	8	10	11	19	0	9	10	4
11	7	14	12	11	12	4	12	9	2
4	3	3	5	9	9	4	3	5	12
3	12	7	13	11	11	13	12	18	9
6	14	14	18	10	11	7	9	7	2
16	16	11	11	3	15	9	5	2	6
5	11	14	11	6	9	4	17	20	10

Weight Losses for Regular Diet

6	6	5	5	2	6	10	3	9	11
14	4	10	13	3	8	8	13	9	3
4	12	6	11	12	9	8	5	8	7
6	2	6	8	5	7	16	18	6	8
13	1	9	8	12	10	6	1	0	13
11	2	8	16	14	4	6	5	12	9
11	6	3	9	9	14	2	10	4	13
8	1	1	4	9	4	1	1	5	6
14	0	7	12	9	5	9	12	7	9
8	9	8	10	5	8	0	3	4	8

Solution Recall that the general form of a large-sample confidence interval for a single mean μ is $\bar{x} \pm z_{\alpha/2}\sigma_{\bar{x}}$. That is, we add and subtract $z_{\alpha/2}$ standard deviations of the sample estimate $\bar{x}$ to the value of the estimate. We employ a similar procedure to form the confidence interval for the difference between two population means.

Let μ_1 represent the mean of the conceptual population of weight losses for all obese people who could be placed on the low-fat diet. Let μ_2 be similarly defined for the other diet. We wish to form a confidence interval for $(\mu_1 - \mu_2)$. An intuitively appealing estimator for $(\mu_1 - \mu_2)$ is the difference between the sample means, $(\bar{x}_1 - \bar{x}_2)$. Thus, we will form the confidence interval of interest with

$$(\bar{x}_1 - \bar{x}_2) \pm z_{\alpha/2}\sigma_{(\bar{x}_1 - \bar{x}_2)}$$

Assuming that the two samples are independent, we write the standard deviation of the difference between the sample means as

$$\sigma_{(\bar{x}_1 - \bar{x}_2)} = \sqrt{\frac{\sigma_1^2}{n_1} + \frac{\sigma_2^2}{n_2}} \approx \sqrt{\frac{s_1^2}{n_1} + \frac{s_2^2}{n_2}}$$

Group Statistics

	DIET	N	Mean	Std. Deviation	Std. Error Mean
WTLOSS	LOWFAT	100	9.31	4.668	.467
	REGULAR	100	7.40	4.035	.404

Independent Samples Test

		Levene's Test for Equality of Variances		t-test for Equality of Means					95% Confidence Interval of the Difference	
		F	Sig.	t	df	Sig. (2-tailed)	Mean Difference	Std. Error Difference	Lower	Upper
WTLOSS	Equal variances assumed	1.367	.244	3.095	198	.002	1.910	.617	.693	3.127
	Equal variances not assumed			3.095	193.940	.002	1.910	.617	.693	3.127

FIGURE 9.1

SPSS analysis of diet study data.

Summary statistics for the diet data are displayed at the top of the SPSS printout shown in Figure 9.1. Note that $\bar{x}_1 = 9.31$, $\bar{x}_2 = 7.40$, $s_1 = 4.67$, and $s_2 = 4.04$. Using these values and observing that $\alpha = .05$ and $z_{.025} = 1.96$, we find that the 95% confidence interval is, approximately,

$$(9.31 - 7.40) \pm 1.96 \sqrt{\frac{(4.67)^2}{100} + \frac{(4.04)^2}{100}} = 1.91 \pm (1.96)(.62) = 1.91 \pm 1.22$$

or $(.69, 3.13)$. This interval (rounded) is highlighted in Figure 9.1.

Using this estimation procedure over and over again for different samples, we know that approximately 95% of the confidence intervals formed in this manner will enclose the difference in population means $(\mu_1 - \mu_2)$. Therefore, we are highly confident that the mean weight loss for the low-fat diet is between .69 and 3.13 pounds more than the mean weight loss for the other diet. With this information, the dietitian better understands the potential of the low-fat diet as a weight-reduction diet.

Look Back If the confidence interval for $(\mu_1 - \mu_2)$ contains 0 [e.g., $(-2.5, 1.3)$], then it is possible for the difference between the population means to be 0 (i.e., $\mu_1 - \mu_2 = 0$). In this case, we could not conclude that a significant difference exists between the mean weight losses for the two diets.

Now Work Exercise 9.6a

The justification for the procedure used in Example 9.1 to estimate $(\mu_1 - \mu_2)$ relies on the properties of the sampling distribution of $(\bar{x}_1 - \bar{x}_2)$. The performance of the estimator in repeated sampling is pictured in Figure 9.2, and its properties are summarized in the following box:

Properties of the Sampling Distribution of $(\bar{x}_1 - \bar{x}_2)$

1. The mean of the sampling distribution of $(\bar{x}_1 - \bar{x}_2)$ is $(\mu_1 - \mu_2)$.

2. If the two samples are independent, the standard deviation of the sampling distribution is

$$\sigma_{(\bar{x}_1 - \bar{x}_2)} = \sqrt{\frac{\sigma_1^2}{n_1} + \frac{\sigma_2^2}{n_2}}$$

where σ_1^2 and σ_2^2 are the variances of the two populations being sampled and n_1 and n_2 are the respective sample sizes. We also refer to $\sigma_{(\bar{x}_1 - \bar{x}_2)}$ as the **standard error** of the statistic $(\bar{x}_1 - \bar{x}_2)$.

3. By the central limit theorem, the sampling distribution of $(\bar{x}_1 - \bar{x}_2)$ is approximately normal *for large samples*.

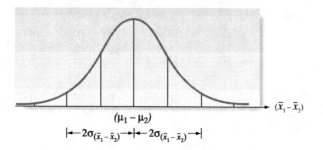

FIGURE 9.2
Sampling distribution of $(\bar{x}_1 - \bar{x}_2)$

In Example 9.1, we noted the similarity in the procedures for forming a large-sample confidence interval for one population mean and a large-sample confidence interval for the difference between two population means. When we are testing hypotheses, the procedures are again similar. The general large-sample procedures for forming confidence intervals and testing hypotheses about $(\mu_1 - \mu_2)$ are summarized in the following boxes:

Large Sample Confidence Interval for $(\mu_1 - \mu_2)$

$$(\bar{x}_1 - \bar{x}_2) \pm z_{\alpha/2}\sigma_{(\bar{x}_1-\bar{x}_2)} = (\bar{x}_1 - \bar{x}_2) \pm z_{\alpha/2}\sqrt{\frac{\sigma_1^2}{n_1} + \frac{\sigma_2^2}{n_2}}$$

$$\approx (\bar{x}_1 - \bar{x}_2) \pm z_{\alpha/2}\sqrt{\frac{s_1^2}{n_1} + \frac{s_2^2}{n_2}}$$

Large-Sample Test of Hypothesis for $(\mu_1 - \mu_2)$

One-Tailed Test

$H_0: (\mu_1 - \mu_2) = D_0$
$H_a: (\mu_1 - \mu_2) < D_0$
  [or $H_a: (\mu_1 - \mu_2) > D_0$]

Two-Tailed Test

$H_0: (\mu_1 - \mu_2) = D_0$
$H_a: (\mu_1 - \mu_2) \neq D_0$

where D_0 = Hypothesized difference between the means (this difference is often hypothesized to be equal to 0)

Test statistic:

$$z = \frac{(\bar{x}_1 - \bar{x}_2) - D_0}{\sigma_{(\bar{x}_1-\bar{x}_2)}} \quad \text{where} \quad \sigma_{(\bar{x}_1-\bar{x}_2)} = \sqrt{\frac{\sigma_1^2}{n_1} + \frac{\sigma_2^2}{n_2}} \approx \sqrt{\frac{s_1^2}{n_1} + \frac{s_2^2}{n_2}}$$

Rejection region: $z < -z_\alpha$
  [or $z > z_\alpha$ when
  $H_a: (\mu_1 - \mu_2) > D_0$]

Rejection region: $|z| > z_{\alpha/2}$

Conditions Required for Valid Large-Sample Inferences about $(\mu_1 - \mu_2)$

1. The two samples are randomly selected in an independent manner from the two target populations.
2. The sample sizes, n_1 and n_2, are both large (i.e., $n_1 \geq 30$ and $n_2 \geq 30$). (By the central limit theorem, this condition guarantees that the sampling distribution of $(\bar{x}_1 - \bar{x}_2)$ will be approximately normal, regardless of the shapes of the underlying probability distributions of the populations. Also, s_1^2 and s_2^2 will provide good approximations to σ_1^2 and σ_2^2 when both samples are large.)

EXAMPLE 9.2

A LARGE-SAMPLE TEST FOR $(\mu_1 - \mu_2)$: Comparing Mean Weight Loss for Two Diets:

Problem Refer to the study of obese people on a low-fat diet and a regular diet presented in Example 9.1. Another way to compare the mean weight losses for the two different diets is to conduct a test of hypothesis. Use the information on the SPSS printout shown in Figure 9.1 to conduct the test. Take $\alpha = .05$.

Solution Again, we let μ_1 and μ_2 represent the population mean weight losses of obese people on the low-fat diet and regular diet, respectively. If one diet is more effective in reducing the weights of obese people, then either $\mu_1 < \mu_2$ or $\mu_2 < \mu_1$; that is, $\mu_1 \neq \mu_2$.

Thus, the elements of the test are as follows:

$H_0: (\mu_1 - \mu_2) = 0$ (i.e., $\mu_1 = \mu_2$; note that $D_0 = 0$ for this hypothesis test)

$H_a: (\mu_1 - \mu_2) \neq 0$ (i.e., $\mu_1 \neq \mu_2$)

Test statistic: $z = \dfrac{(\bar{x}_1 - \bar{x}_2) - D_0}{\sigma_{(\bar{x}_1 - \bar{x}_2)}} = \dfrac{\bar{x}_1 - \bar{x}_2 - 0}{\sigma_{(\bar{x}_1 - \bar{x}_2)}}$

Rejection region: $z < -z_{\alpha/2} = -1.96$ or $z > z_{\alpha/2} = 1.96$ (see Figure 9.3)

Substituting the summary statistics given in Figure 9.1 into the test statistic, we obtain

$$z = \frac{(\bar{x}_1 - \bar{x}_2) - 0}{\sigma_{(\bar{x}_1 - \bar{x}_2)}} = \frac{9.31 - 7.40}{\sqrt{\dfrac{\sigma_1^2}{n_1} + \dfrac{\sigma_2^2}{n_2}}}$$

$$\approx \frac{1.91}{\sqrt{\dfrac{s_1^2}{n_1} + \dfrac{s_2^2}{n_2}}} = \frac{1.91}{\sqrt{\dfrac{(4.67)^2}{100} + \dfrac{(4.04)^2}{100}}} = \frac{1.91}{.617} = 3.09$$

[*Note:* The value of the test statistic is highlighted in the SPSS printout of Figure 9.1.]

As you can see in Figure 9.3, the calculated z-value clearly falls into the rejection region. Therefore, the samples provide sufficient evidence, at $\alpha = .05$, for the dietitian to conclude that the mean weight losses for the two diets differ.

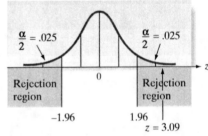

FIGURE 9.3
Rejection region for Example 9.2

Look Back This conclusion agrees with the inference drawn from the 95% confidence interval in Example 9.1. However, the confidence interval provides more information on the mean weight losses. From the hypothesis test, we know only that the two means differ; that is, $\mu_1 \neq \mu_2$. From the confidence interval in Example 9.1, we found that the mean weight loss μ_1 of the low-fat diet was between .69 and 3.13 pounds more than the mean weight loss μ_2 of the regular diet. In other words, the test tells us that the means differ, but the confidence interval tells us how large the difference is. Both inferences are made with the same degree of reliability—namely, 95% confidence (or at $\alpha = .05$).

EXAMPLE 9.3

THE p-VALUE FOR A TEST OF $(\mu_1 - \mu_2)$

Problem Find the observed significance level for the test in Example 9.2. Interpret the result.

Solution The alternative hypothesis in Example 9.2, $H_a: \mu_1 - \mu_2 \neq 0$, required a two-tailed test using

$$z = \frac{\bar{x}_1 - \bar{x}_2}{\sigma_{(\bar{x}_1 - \bar{x}_2)}}$$

as a test statistic. Since the z-value calculated from the sample data was 3.09, the observed significance level (p-value) for the two-tailed test is the probability of observing a value of z at least as contradictory to the null hypothesis as $z = 3.09$; that is,

$$p\text{-value} = 2 \cdot P(z \geq 3.09)$$

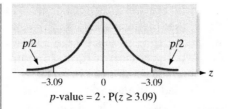

FIGURE 9.4

The observed significance level for Example 9.2

$p\text{-value} = 2 \cdot P(z \geq 3.09)$

This probability is computed under the assumption that H_0 is true and is equal to the highlighted area shown in Figure 9.4.

The tabulated area corresponding to $z = 3.09$ in Table IV of Appendix A is .4990. Therefore,

$$P(z \geq 3.09) = .5 - .4990 = .0010$$

and the observed significance level for the test is

$$p\text{-value} = 2(.001) = .002$$

Since our selected α value, .05, exceeds this p-value, we have sufficient evidence to reject $H_0: \mu_1 - \mu_2 = 0$.

Look Back The p-value of the test is more easily obtained from a statistical software package. The p-value is highlighted at the bottom of the SPSS printout shown in Figure 9.1. This value agrees with our calculated p-value.

Now Work Exercise 9.6b

Small Samples

In comparing two population means with small samples (say, $n_1 < 30$ and $n_2 < 30$), the methodology of the previous three examples is invalid. The reason? When the sample sizes are small, estimates of σ_1^2 and σ_2^2 are unreliable and the central limit theorem (which guarantees that the z statistic is normal) can no longer be applied. But as in the case of a single mean (Section 8.4), we use the familiar Student's t-distribution described in Chapter 7.

To use the t-distribution, both sampled populations must be approximately normally distributed with equal population variances, and the random samples must be selected independently of each other. The assumptions of normality and equal variances imply relative frequency distributions for the populations that would appear as shown in Figure 9.5.

Since we assume that the two populations have equal variances ($\sigma_1^2 = \sigma_2^2 = \sigma^2$), it is reasonable to use the information contained in both samples to construct a **pooled sample estimator σ^2** for use in confidence intervals and test statistics. Thus, if s_1^2 and s_2^2 are the two sample variances (each estimating the variance σ^2 common to both populations), the pooled estimator of σ^2, denoted as s_p^2, is

$$s_p^2 = \frac{(n_1 - 1)s_1^2 + (n_2 - 1)s_2^2}{(n_1 - 1) + (n_2 - 1)} = \frac{(n_1 - 1)s_1^2 + (n_2 - 1)s_2^2}{n_1 + n_2 - 2}$$

or

$$s_p^2 = \frac{\overbrace{\sum(x_1 - \bar{x}_1)^2}^{\text{From sample 1}} + \overbrace{\sum(x_2 - \bar{x}_2)^2}^{\text{From sample 2}}}{n_1 + n_2 - 2}$$

FIGURE 9.5

Assumptions for the two-sample t: (1) normal populations; (2) equal variances

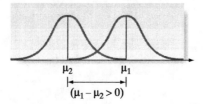

μ_2 μ_1

$(\mu_1 - \mu_2 > 0)$

where x_1 represents a measurement from sample 1 and x_2 represents a measurement from sample 2. Recall that the term *degrees of freedom* was defined in Section 7.2 as 1 less than the sample size. Thus, in this case, we have $(n_1 - 1)$ degrees of freedom for sample 1 and $(n_2 - 1)$ degrees of freedom for sample 2. Since we are pooling the information on σ^2 obtained from both samples, the number of degrees of freedom associated with the pooled variance s_p^2 is equal to the sum of the numbers of degrees of freedom for the two samples, namely, the denominator of s_p^2; that is, $(n_1 - 1) + (n_2 - 1) = n_1 + n_2 - 2$.

Note that the second formula given for s_p^2 shows that the pooled variance is simply a *weighted average* of the two sample variances s_1^2 and s_2^2. The weight given each variance is proportional to its number of degrees of freedom. If the two variances have the same number of degrees of freedom (i.e., *if the sample sizes are equal*), *then the pooled variance is a simple average of the two sample variances*. The result is an average, or "pooled," variance that is a better estimate of σ^2 than either s_1^2 or s_2^2 alone.

Biography

**BRADLEY EFRON
(1938–PRESENT)—
The Bootstrap Method**

Bradley Efron was raised in St. Paul, Minnesota, the son of a truck driver who was the amateur statistician for his bowling and baseball leagues. Efron received a B.S. in mathematics from the California Institute of Technology in 1960, but, by his own admission, had no talent for modern abstract math. His interest in the science of statistics developed after he read a book by Harold Cramer from cover to cover. Efron went to the University of Stanford to study statistics, and he earned his Ph.D there in 1964. He has been a faculty member in Stan-

ford's Department of Statistics since 1966. Over his career, Efron has received numerous awards and prizes for his contributions to modern statistics, including the MacArthur Prize Fellow (1983), the American Statistical Association Wilks Medal (1990), and the Parzen Prize for Statistical Innovation (1998). In 1979, Efron invented a method—called the *bootstrap*—of estimating and testing population parameters in situations in which either the sampling distribution is unknown or the assumptions are violated. The method involves repeatedly taking samples of size n (with replacement) from the original sample and calculating the value of the point estimate. Efron showed that the sampling distribution of the estimator is simply the frequency distribution of the bootstrap estimates.

Both the confidence interval and the test-of-hypothesis procedures for comparing two population means with small samples are summarized in the following boxes:

Small-Sample Confidence Interval for $(\mu_1 - \mu_2)$: Independent Samples

$$(\bar{x}_1 - \bar{x}_2) \pm t_{\alpha/2}\sqrt{s_p^2\left(\frac{1}{n_1} + \frac{1}{n_2}\right)}$$

where $s_p^2 = \dfrac{(n_1 - 1)s_1^2 + (n_2 - 1)s_2^2}{n_1 + n_2 - 2}$

and $t_{\alpha/2}$ is based on $(n_1 + n_2 - 2)$ degrees of freedom.

Small-Sample Test of Hypothesis for $(\mu_1 - \mu_2)$: Independent Samples

One-Tailed Test	**Two-Tailed Test**
$H_0: (\mu_1 - \mu_2) = D_0$	$H_0: (\mu_1 - \mu_2) = D_0$
$H_a: (\mu_1 - \mu_2) < D_0$	$H_a: (\mu_1 - \mu_2) \neq D_0$
[or $H_a: (\mu_1 - \mu_2) > D_0$]	

(continued)

Test statistic:

$$t = \frac{(\bar{x}_1 - \bar{x}_2) - D_0}{\sqrt{s_p^2\left(\dfrac{1}{n_1} + \dfrac{1}{n_2}\right)}}$$

Rejection region: $t < -t_\alpha$
[or $t > t_\alpha$ when
$H_a: (\mu_1 - \mu_2) > D_0$]

Rejection region: $|t| > t_{\alpha/2}$

where t_α and $t_{\alpha/2}$ are based on $(n_1 + n_2 - 2)$ degrees of freedom.

Conditions Required for Valid Small-Sample Inferences about $(\mu_1 - \mu_2)$

1. The two samples are randomly selected in an independent manner from the two target populations.
2. Both sampled populations have distributions that are approximately normal.
3. The population variances are equal (i.e., $\sigma_1^2 = \sigma_2^2$).

EXAMPLE 9.4

A SMALL-SAMPLE CONFIDENCE INTERVAL FOR $(\mu_1 - \mu_2)$: Comparing Two Methods of Teaching

Problem Suppose you wish to compare a new method of teaching reading to "slow learners" with the current standard method. You decide to base your comparison on the results of a reading test given at the end of a learning period of six months. Of a random sample of 22 "slow learners," 10 are taught by the new method and 12 are taught by the standard method. All 22 children are taught by qualified instructors under similar conditions for the designated six-month period. The results of the reading test at the end of this period are given in Table 9.2.

   READING

TABLE 9.2 Reading Test Scores for Slow Learners

New Method				Standard Method			
80	80	79	81	79	62	70	68
76	66	71	76	73	76	86	73
70	85			72	68	75	66

a. Use the data in the table to estimate the true mean difference between the test scores for the new method and the standard method. Use a 95% confidence interval.
b. Interpret the interval you found in part a.
c. What assumptions must be made in order that the estimate be valid? Are they reasonably satisfied?

Solution

a. For this experiment, let μ_1 and μ_2 represent the mean reading test scores of "slow learners" taught with the new and standard methods, respectively. Then the objective is to obtain a 95% confidence interval for $(\mu_1 - \mu_2)$.

The first step in constructing the confidence interval is to obtain summary statistics (e.g., $\bar{x}$ and s) on reading test scores for each method. The data of Table 9.2 were entered into a computer, and SAS was used to obtain these descriptive statistics. The SAS printout appears in Figure 9.6. Note that $\bar{x}_1 = 76.4$, $s_1 = 5.8348$, $\bar{x}_2 = 72.333$, and $s_2 = 6.3437$.

```
                          Two Sample t-test for the Means of SCORE within METHOD

        Sample Statistics

              Group          N      Mean      Std. Dev.    Std. Error
              --------------------------------------------------------
              NEW           10      76.4        5.8348        1.8451
              STD           12   72.33333       6.3437        1.8313

        Hypothesis Test

              Null hypothesis:      Mean 1 - Mean 2 =  0
              Alternative:          Mean 1 - Mean 2 ^= 0

              If Variances Are    t statistic      Df        Pr > t
              --------------------------------------------------------
              Equal                 1.552          20        0.1364
              Not Equal             1.564        19.77       0.1336

        95% Confidence Interval for the Difference between Two Means

                          Lower Limit      Upper Limit
                          -----------      -----------
                            -1.40             9.53
```

FIGURE 9.6

SAS printout for Example 9.4

Next, we calculate the pooled estimate of variance to obtain

$$s_p^2 = \frac{(n_1 - 1)s_1^2 + (n_2 - 1)s_2^2}{n_1 + n_2 - 2}$$

$$= \frac{(10 - 1)(5.8348)^2 + (12 - 1)(6.3437)^2}{10 + 12 - 2} = 37.45$$

where s_p^2 is based on $(n_1 + n_2 - 2) = (10 + 12 - 2) = 20$ degrees of freedom. Also, we find $t_{\alpha/2} = t_{.025} = 2.086$ (based on 20 degrees of freedom) from Table VI of Appendix A.

Finally, the 95% confidence interval for $(\mu_1 - \mu_2)$, the difference between mean test scores for the two methods, is

$$(\bar{x}_1 - \bar{x}_2) \pm t_{\alpha/2}\sqrt{s_p^2\left(\frac{1}{n_1} + \frac{1}{n_2}\right)} = (76.4 - 72.33) \pm t_{.025}\sqrt{37.45\left(\frac{1}{10} + \frac{1}{12}\right)}$$

$$= 4.07 \pm (2.086)(2.62)$$

$$= 4.07 \pm 5.47$$

or $(-1.4, 9.54)$. This interval agrees (except for rounding) with the one shown at the bottom of the SAS printout of Figure 9.6.

b. The interval can be interpreted as follows: With a confidence coefficient equal to .95, we estimate that the difference in mean test scores between using the new method of teaching and using the standard method falls into the interval from -1.4 to 9.54. In other words, we estimate (with 95% confidence) the mean test score for the new method to be anywhere from 1.4 points less than, to 9.54 points more than, the mean test score for the standard method. Although the sample means seem to suggest that the new method is associated with a higher mean test score, there is insufficient evidence to indicate that $(\mu_1 - \mu_2)$ differs from 0 because the interval includes 0 as a possible value for $(\mu_1 - \mu_2)$. To demonstrate a difference in mean test scores (if it exists), you could increase the sample size and thereby narrow the width of the confidence interval for $(\mu_1 - \mu_2)$. Alternatively, you can design the experiment differently. This possibility is discussed in the next section.

c. To use the small-sample confidence interval properly, the following assumptions must be satisfied:

1. The samples are randomly and independently selected from the populations of "slow learners" taught by the new method and the standard method.

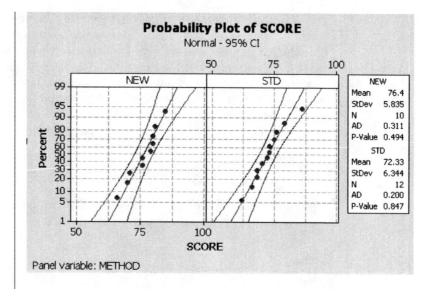

FIGURE 9.7

MINITAB normal probability plots for Example 9.4

2. The test scores are normally distributed for both teaching methods.
3. The variance of the test scores is the same for the two populations; that is, $\sigma_1^2 = \sigma_2^2$.

On the basis of the information provided about the sampling procedure in the description of the problem, the first assumption is satisfied. To check the plausibility of the remaining two assumptions, we resort to graphical methods. Figure 9.7 is a MINITAB printout that gives normal probability plots for the test scores of the two samples of "slow learners." The near straight-line trends on both plots indicate that the distributions of the scores are approximately mound shaped and symmetric. Consequently, each sample data set appears to come from a population that is approximately normal.

One way to check the third assumption is to test the null hypothesis $H_0: \sigma_1^2 = \sigma_2^2$. This test is covered in Section 9.6. Another approach is to examine box plots of the sample data. Figure 9.8 is a MINITAB printout that shows side-by-side vertical box plots of the test scores in the two samples. Recall from Section 2.9 that the box plot represents the "spread" of a data set. The two box plots appear to have about the same spread; thus, the samples appear to come from populations with approximately the same variance.

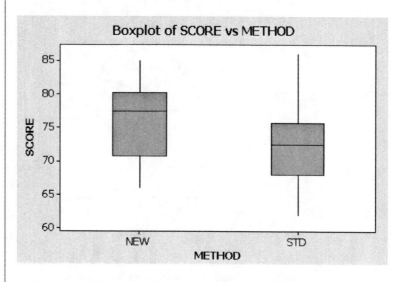

FIGURE 9.8

MINITAB box plots for Example 9.4

Look Back All three assumptions, then, appear to be reasonably satisfied for this application of the small-sample confidence interval.

Now Work Exercise 9.9

The two-sample t-statistic is a powerful tool for comparing population means when the assumptions are satisfied. It has also been shown to retain its usefulness when the sampled populations are only approximately normally distributed. And when the sample sizes are equal, the assumption of equal population variances can be relaxed. That is, if $n_1 = n_2$, then σ_1^2 and σ_2^2 can be quite different, and the test statistic will still possess, approximately, a Student's t-distribution. In the case where $\sigma_1^2 \neq \sigma_2^2$ and $n_1 \neq n_2$, an approximate small-sample confidence interval or test can be obtained by modifying the number of degrees of freedom associated with the t-distribution.

Confidence Interval for $(\mu_1 - \mu_2)$

Using the TI-84/TI-83 Graphing Calculator

Step 1 *Enter the data. (Skip to Step 2 if you have summary statistics, not raw data.)*

Press **STAT** and select **1:Edit.**

Note: If the lists already contain data, clear the old data. Use the up ARROW to highlight '**L1**'.

Press **CLEAR ENTER.**

Use the up ARROW to highlight '**L2**'

Press **CLEAR ENTER.**

Use the **ARROW** and **ENTER** keys to enter the first data set into **L1**.

Use the **ARROW** and **ENTER** keys to enter the second data set into **L2**.

Step 2 *Access the Statistical Tests Menu.*

Press **STAT**.
Arrow right to **TESTS**.
Arrow down to **2-SampTInt**.
Press **ENTER**.

```
EDIT CALC TESTS
4↑2-SampTTest…
5:1-PropZTest…
6:2-PropZTest…
7:ZInterval…
8:TInterval…
9:2-SampZInt…
0:2-SampTInt…
```

Step 3 *Choose "**Data**" or "**Stats**". ("Data" is selected when you have entered the raw data into the Lists. "Stats" is selected when you are given only the means, standard deviations, and sample sizes.)*

Press **ENTER**.
If you selected "Data", set **List1** to **L1** and **List2** to **L2**.
Set **Freq1** to **1** and set **Freq2** to **1**.
Set **C-Level** to the confidence level.
If you are assuming that the two populations have equal variances, select **Yes** for **Pooled**.
If you are not assuming equal variances, select **No**.
Press **ENTER**.
Arrow down to "**Calculate**".
Press **ENTER**.

If you selected "Stats", enter the means, standard deviations, and sample sizes.
Set **C-Level** to the confidence level.
If you are assuming that the two populations have equal variances, select **Yes** for **Pooled**.
If you are not assuming equal variances, select **No**.
Press **ENTER**.
Arrow down to "**Calculate**".
Press **ENTER**.

(The accompanying screen is set up for an example with a mean of 100, a standard deviation of 10, and a sample size of 15 for the first data set and a mean of 105, a standard deviation of 12, and a sample size of 18 for the second data set.)

The confidence interval will be displayed with the number of degrees of freedom, the sample statistics, and the pooled standard deviation (when appropriate).

Example Compute a 95% confidence interval for $(\mu_1 - \mu_2)$, using the following data (in this example, assume that the population variances are equal):

Group 1: 65 58 78 60 68 69 66 70 53 71 63 63

Group 2: 62 53 36 34 56 50 42 57 46 68 48 42 52 53 43

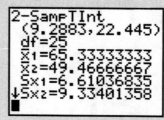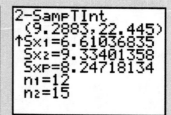

As you can see from the screens, the 95% confidence interval for $(\mu_1 - \mu_2)$ is **(9.2883, 22.445)**.

Also, notice that the output includes the means, standard deviations, sample sizes, and pooled standard deviation.

Hypothesis Test for $(\mu_1 - \mu_2)$

Using the TI-84/TI-83 Graphing Calculator

Step 1 *Enter the data. (Skip to Step 2 if you have summary statistics, not raw data.)*

Press **STAT** and select **1:Edit**.
Note: If the lists already contain data, clear the old data. Use the up **ARROW** to highlight '**L1**'.
Press **CLEAR ENTER**.
Use the up **ARROW** to highlight '**L2**'.
Press **CLEAR ENTER**.
Use the **ARROW** and **ENTER** keys to enter the first data set into **L1**.
Use the **ARROW** and **ENTER** keys to enter the second data set into **L2**.

Step 2 *Access the Statistical Tests Menu.*

Press **STAT**.
Arrow right to **TESTS**.
Arrow down to **2-SampTTest**.
Press **ENTER**.

Step 3 *Choose "**Data**" or "**Stats**". ("Data" is selected when you have entered the raw data into the Lists. "Stats" is selected when you are given only the means, standard deviations, and sample sizes.)*

Press **ENTER**.
If you selected "Data", set **List1** to **L1** and **List2** to **L2**.
Set **Freq1** to **1** and set **Freq2** to **1**.
Use the **ARROW** to highlight the appropriate alternative hypothesis.
Press **ENTER**.
If you are assuming that the two populations have equal variances, select **Yes** for **Pooled**.
If you are not assuming equal variances, select **No.**
Press **ENTER**.
Arrow down to "**Calculate**".
Press **ENTER**.

If you selected "Stats", enter the means, standard deviations, and sample sizes.

(continued)

Use the **ARROW** to highlight the appropriate alternative hypothesis.
Press **ENTER**.
If you are assuming that the two populations have equal variances, select **Yes** for
Pooled.
If you are not assuming equal variances, select **No**.
Press **ENTER**.
Arrow down to "**Calculate**".
Press **ENTER**.
(The screen that follows is set up for an example with a mean of 100, a standard
deviation of 10, and a sample size of 15 for the first data set and a mean of 120, a
standard deviation of 12, and a sample size of 18 for the second data set.)

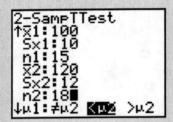

The results of the hypothesis test will be displayed with the *p*-value, the number of
degrees of freedom, the sample statistics, and the pooled standard deviation (when
appropriate).

Example   Test the hypotheses with the following data (in this example, assume that the
population variances are equal):

    Group 1: 65 58 78 60 68 69 66 70 53 71 63 63

    Group 2: 62 53 36 34 56 50 42 57 46 68 48 42 52 53 43

```
2-SampTTest        2-SampTTest
 μ1>μ2              μ1>μ2
 t=4.96746167      ↑Sx1=6.61036835
 P=2.0272631E-5     Sx2=9.33401358
 df=25              SxP=8.24718134
 x̄1=65.33333333     n1=12
↓x̄2=49.46666667     n2=15
```

As you can see from the screens, $t = 4.967$ and the *p*-value is 0.00002.
Also, notice the output includes the means, standard deviations, sample sizes, and
pooled standard deviation.

The next box gives the approximate small-sample procedures to use when the assumption of equal variances is violated. The test for the case of "unequal sample sizes" is
based on Satterthwaite's (1946) approximation.

Approximate Small-Sample Procedures when $\sigma_1^2 \neq \sigma_2^2$

Equal Sample Sizes ($n_1 = n_2 = n$)

Confidence interval: $(\bar{x}_1 - \bar{x}_2) \pm t_{\alpha/2}\sqrt{(s_1^2 + s_2^2)/n}$

Test statistic for $H_0: (\mu_1 - \mu_2) = 0$: $t = (\bar{x}_1 - \bar{x}_2)/\sqrt{(s_1^2 + s_2^2)/n}$

where *t* is based on $\nu = n_1 + n_2 - 2 = 2(n - 1)$ degrees of freedom.

(continued)

Unequal Sample Sizes ($n_1 \neq n_2$)

Confidence interval: $$(\bar{x}_1 - \bar{x}_2) \pm t_{\alpha/2}\sqrt{(s_1^2/n_1) + (s_2^2/n_2)}$$

Test statistic for H_0: $(\mu_1 - \mu_2) = 0$: $$t = (\bar{x}_1 - \bar{x}_2)/\sqrt{(s_1^2/n_1) + (s_2^2/n_2)}$$

where t is based on degrees of freedom equal to

$$\nu = \frac{(s_1^2/n_1 + s_2^2/n_2)^2}{\dfrac{(s_1^2/n_1)^2}{n_1 - 1} + \dfrac{(s_2^2/n_2)^2}{n_2 - 1}}$$

Note: The value of ν will generally not be an integer. Round ν down to the nearest integer to use the t-table.

When the assumptions are not clearly satisfied, you can select larger samples from the populations or you can use other available statistical tests (**nonparametric statistical tests,** described in Chapter 14).

What Should You Do if the Assumptions Are Not Satisfied?

Answer: If you are concerned that the assumptions are not satisfied, use the Wilcoxon rank sum test for independent samples to test for a shift in population distributions. (See Chapter 14).

STATISTICS IN ACTION REVISITED

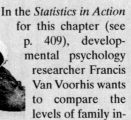

Comparing the Mean Family Involvement in Homework Scores of TIPS and ATIPS Students

In the *Statistics in Action* for this chapter (see p. 409), developmental psychology researcher Francis Van Voorhis wants to compare the levels of family involvement for students assigned to the two homework conditions TIPS and ATIPS. TIPS homework assignments require students to conduct interactions with family partners while completing their homework, while ATIPS homework assignments are the traditional, noninteractive type. One way to analyze the data is to compare the mean family involvement scores for the two groups of students.

Here, we let μ_1 represent the population mean family involvement score for ATIPS students and μ_2 represent the population mean family involvement score for TIPS students. Dr. Van Voorhis speculates that $\mu_1 < \mu_2$ (i.e., the mean family involvement score for students in the ATIPS group is less than the mean score for TIPS students). Of interest, then, is the one-tailed test, H_0: $(\mu_1 - \mu_2) = 0$ versus H_a: $(\mu_1 - \mu_2) < 0$, for each

of the three types of homework: science, math, and language arts. An examination of the data saved in the **HWSTUDY** file reveals that both samples are large ($n_1 = 98$ and $n_2 = 128$); thus, the large-sample z-test is appropriate, and no assumptions about the distributions of the family involvement scores are required. We conducted these tests with MINITAB. The output is shown in Figure SIA9.1.

The one-tailed p-values of the three tests are highlighted in Figure SIA9.1. Only one of the three types of homework (SCIENCE) shows a significant difference at $\alpha = .05$ (p-value ≈ 0). Therefore, for science homework, there is sufficient evidence to conclude that the mean family involvement score for ATIPS students is significantly lower than the mean family involvement score for TIPS students. Consequently, at least in science, there is support for the claim that the TIPS programs leads to a greater level of family involvement in homework assignments. Note, however, that the sample means of TIPS students in both math and language arts exceed the respective means of ATIPS students. Although these means are not significantly different, the results lend support for the TIPS program.

(continued)

```
Two-Sample T-Test and CI: SCIENCE, HWCOND

Two-sample T for SCIENCE

HWCOND    N  Mean  StDev  SE Mean
ATIPS    98  1.43   1.06     0.11
TIPS    128  2.55   1.27     0.11


Difference = mu (ATIPS) - mu (TIPS)
Estimate for difference:  -1.126
95% upper bound for difference:  -0.869
T-Test of difference = 0 (vs <): T-Value = -7.24   P-Value = 0.000   DF = 222
```

```
Two-Sample T-Test and CI: MATH, HWCOND

Two-sample T for MATH

HWCOND    N  Mean  StDev  SE Mean
ATIPS    98  1.48   1.22     0.12
TIPS    128  1.56   1.27     0.11


Difference = mu (ATIPS) - mu (TIPS)
Estimate for difference:  -0.083
95% upper bound for difference:  0.193
T-Test of difference = 0 (vs <): T-Value = -0.50   P-Value = 0.310   DF = 212
```

```
Two-Sample T-Test and CI: LANGUAGE, HWCOND

Two-sample T for LANGUAGE

HWCOND    N  Mean  StDev  SE Mean
ATIPS    98  1.01   1.09     0.11
TIPS    128  1.20   1.12    0.099


Difference = mu (ATIPS) - mu (TIPS)
Estimate for difference:  -0.185
95% upper bound for difference:  0.059
T-Test of difference = 0 (vs <): T-Value = -1.25   P-Value = 0.106   DF = 211
```

FIGURE SIA9.1
MINITAB comparison of means for two homework groups

Exercises 9.1–9.29

Understanding the Principles

9.1 Describe the sampling distribution of $(\bar{x}_1 - \bar{x}_2)$ when the samples are large.

9.2 To use the t-statistic to test for a difference between the means of two populations, what assumptions must be made about the two populations? About the two samples?

9.3 Two populations are described in each of the cases that follow. In which cases would it be appropriate to apply the small-sample t-test to investigate the difference between the population means?

  a. Population 1: Normal distribution with variance σ_1^2
     Population 2: Skewed to the right with variance $\sigma_2^2 = \sigma_1^2$

  b. Population 1: Normal distribution with variance σ_1^2
     Population 2: Normal distribution with variance $\sigma_2^2 \neq \sigma_1^2$

  c. Population 1: Skewed to the left with variance σ_1^2
     Population 2: Skewed to the left with variance $\sigma_2^2 = \sigma_1^2$

  d. Population 1: Normal distribution with variance σ_1^2
     Population 2: Normal distribution with variance $\sigma_2^2 = \sigma_1^2$

  e. Population 1: Uniform distribution with variance σ_1^2
     Population 2: Uniform distribution with variance $\sigma_2^2 = \sigma_1^2$

9.4 A confidence interval for $(\mu_1 - \mu_2)$ is $(-10, 4)$. Which of the following inferences is correct?

  a. $\mu_1 > \mu_2$
  b. $\mu_1 < \mu_2$
  c. $\mu_1 = \mu_2$
  d. no significant difference between means

9.5 A confidence interval for $(\mu_1 - \mu_2)$ is $(-10, -4)$. Which of the following inferences is correct?
 a. $\mu_1 > \mu_2$
 b. $\mu_1 < \mu_2$
 c. $\mu_1 = \mu_2$
 d. no significant difference between means

Learning the Mechanics

9.6 In order to compare the means of two populations, independent random samples of 400 observations are selected from each population, with the following results:

Sample 1	Sample 2
$\bar{x}_1 = 5{,}275$	$\bar{x}_2 = 5{,}240$
$s_1 = 150$	$s_2 = 200$

 a. Use a 95% confidence interval to estimate the difference between the population means $(\mu_1 - \mu_2)$. Interpret the confidence interval.
 b. Test the null hypothesis $H_0: (\mu_1 - \mu_2) = 0$ versus the alternative hypothesis $H_a: (\mu_1 - \mu_2) \neq 0$. Give the significance level of the test, and interpret the result.
 c. Suppose the test in part **b** were conducted with the alternative hypothesis $H_a: (\mu_1 - \mu_2) > 0$. How would your answer to part **b** change?
 d. Test the null hypothesis $H_0: (\mu_1 - \mu_2) = 25$ versus the alternative $H_a: (\mu_1 - \mu_2) \neq 25$. Give the significance level, and interpret the result. Compare your answer with that obtained from the test conducted in part **b**.
 e. What assumptions are necessary to ensure the validity of the inferential procedures applied in parts **a–d**?

9.7 Independent random samples of 100 observations each are chosen from two normal populations with the following means and standard deviations:

Population 1	Population 2
$\mu_1 = 14$	$\mu_2 = 10$
$\sigma_1 = 4$	$\sigma_2 = 3$

 Let $\bar{x}_1$ and $\bar{x}_2$ denote the two sample means.
 a. Give the mean and standard deviation of the sampling distribution of $\bar{x}_1$.
 b. Give the mean and standard deviation of the sampling distribution of $\bar{x}_2$.
 c. Suppose you were to calculate the difference $(\bar{x}_1 - \bar{x}_2)$ between the sample means. Find the mean and standard deviation of the sampling distribution of $(\bar{x}_1 - \bar{x}_2)$.
 d. Will the statistic $(\bar{x}_1 - \bar{x}_2)$ be normally distributed? Explain.

9.8 Assume that $\sigma_1^2 = \sigma_2^2 = \sigma^2$. Calculate the pooled estimator of σ^2 for each of the following cases:
 a. $s_1^2 = 200, s_2^2 = 180, n_1 = n_2 = 25$
 b. $s_1^2 = 25, s_2^2 = 40, n_1 = 20, n_2 = 10$
 c. $s_1^2 = .20, s_2^2 = .30, n_1 = 8, n_2 = 12$
 d. $s_1^2 = 2{,}500, s_2^2 = 1{,}800, n_1 = 16, n_2 = 17$
 e. Note that the pooled estimate is a weighted average of the sample variances. To which of the variances does the pooled estimate fall nearer in each of cases **a–d**?

9.9 Independent random samples from normal populations produced the following results:

🕑 **LM9_9**

Sample 1	Sample 2
1.2	4.2
3.1	2.7
1.7	3.6
2.8	3.9
3.0	

 a. Calculate the pooled estimate of σ^2.
 b. Do the data provide sufficient evidence to indicate that $\mu_2 > \mu_1$? Test, using $\alpha = .10$.
 c. Find a 90% confidence interval for $(\mu_1 - \mu_2)$.
 d. Which of the two inferential procedures, the test of hypothesis in part **b** or the confidence interval in part **c**, provides more information about $(\mu_1 - \mu_2)$?

9.10 Two independent random samples have been selected, 100 observations from population 1 and 100 from population 2. Sample means $\bar{x}_1 = 70$ and $\bar{x}_2 = 50$ were obtained. From previous experience with these populations, it is known that the variances are $\sigma_1^2 = 100$ and $\sigma_2^2 = 64$.
 a. Find $\sigma_{(\bar{x}_1 - \bar{x}_2)}$.
 b. Sketch the approximate sampling distribution $(\bar{x}_1 - \bar{x}_2)$, assuming that $(\mu_1 - \mu_2) = 5$.
 c. Locate the observed value of $(\bar{x}_1 - \bar{x}_2)$ on the graph you drew in part **b**. Does it appear that this value contradicts the null hypothesis $H_0: (\mu_1 - \mu_2) = 5$?
 d. Use the z-table to determine the rejection region for the test of $H_0: (\mu_1 - \mu_2) = 5$ against $H_a: (\mu_1 - \mu_2) \neq 5$. Use $\alpha = .05$. $|z| > 1.96$
 e. Conduct the hypothesis test of part **d** and interpret your result.
 f. Construct a 95% confidence interval for $(\mu_1 - \mu_2)$. Interpret the interval.
 g. Which inference provides more information about the value of $(\mu_1 - \mu_2)$, the test of hypothesis in part **e** or the confidence interval in part **f**?

9.11 Independent random samples are selected from two populations and are used to test the hypothesis $H_0: (\mu_1 - \mu_2) = 0$ against the alternative $H_a: (\mu_1 - \mu_2) \neq 0$. An analysis of 233 observations from population 1 and 312 from population 2 yielded a p-value of .115.
 a. Interpret the results of the computer analysis.
 b. If the alternative the alternative hypothesis had been $H_a: (\mu_1 - \mu_2) < 0$, how would the p-value change? Interpret the p-value for this one-tailed test.

9.12 Independent random samples selected from two normal populations produced the following sample means and standard deviations:

Sample 1	Sample 2
$n_1 = 17$	$n_2 = 12$
$\bar{x}_1 = 5.4$	$\bar{x}_2 = 7.9$
$s_1 = 3.4$	$s_2 = 4.8$

a. Conduct the test $H_0: (\mu_1 - \mu_2) = 0$ against $H_a: (\mu_1 - \mu_2) \neq 0$.

b. Find and interpret the 95% confidence interval for $(\mu_1 - \mu_2)$.

Applying the Concepts—Basic

9.13 Children's recall of TV ads. Marketing professors at Robert Morris and Kent State Universities examined children's recall and recognition of television advertisements. (*Journal of Advertising,* Spring 2006.) Two groups of children were shown a 60-second commercial for Sunkist FunFruit Rock-n-Roll Shapes. One group (the A/V group) was shown the ad with both audio and video; the second group (the video-only group) was shown only the video portion of the commercial. Following the viewing, the children were asked to recall 10 specific items from the ad. The number of items recalled correctly by each child is summarized in the accompanying table. The researchers theorized that "children who receive an audiovisual presentation will have the same level of mean recall of ad information as those who receive only the visual aspects of the ad."

Video-Only Group	A/V Group
$n_1 = 20$	$n_2 = 20$
$\overline{x}_1 = 3.70$	$\overline{x}_2 = 3.30$
$s_1 = 1.98$	$s_2 = 2.13$

Source: Maher, J. K., Hu, M. Y., and Kolbe, R. H. "Children's recall of television ad elements," *Journal of Advertising,* Vol. 35, No. 1, Spring 2006 (Table 1).

a. Set up the appropriate null and alternative hypotheses to test the researchers' theory.

b. Find the value of the test statistic.

c. Give the rejection region for $\alpha = .10$.

d. Make the appropriate inference. What can you say about the researchers' theory?

e. The researchers' reported the *p*-value of the test as *p*-value $= .62$. Interpret this result.

f. What conditions are required for the inference to be valid?

9.14 Index of Biotic Integrity. The Ohio Environmental Protection Agency used the Index of Biotic Integrity (IBI) to measure the biological condition, or "health," of an aquatic region. The IBI is the sum of metrics that measure the presence, abundance, and health of fish in the region. (Higher values of the IBI correspond to healthier fish populations.) Researchers collected IBI measurements for sites located in different Ohio river basins. (*Journal of Agricultural, Biological, and Environmental Sciences,* June 2005.) Summary data for two river basins, Muskingum and Hocking, are given in the accompanying table.

a. Use a 90% confidence interval to compare the mean IBI values of the two river basins. Interpret the interval.

b. Conduct a test of hypothesis (at $\alpha = .10$) to compare the mean IBI values of the two river basins. Explain why

River Basin	Sample Size	Mean	Standard Deviation
Muskingum	53	.035	1.046
Hocking	51	.340	.960

Source: Boone, E. L., Keying, Y., and Smith, E. P. "Evaluating the relationship between ecological and habitat conditions using hierarchical models," *Journal of Agricultural, Biological, and Environmental Sciences,* Vol. 10, No. 2, June 2005 (Table 1).

the result will agree with the inference you derived from the 90% confidence interval in part **a**.

9.15 Reading Japanese books. Refer to the *Reading in a Foreign Language* (Apr. 2004) experiment to improve the Japanese reading comprehension levels of University of Hawaii students, presented in Exercise 2.31 (p. 46). Recall that 14 students participated in a 10-week extensive reading program in a second-semester Japanese course. The numbers of books read by each student and the student's course grade are repeated in the following table:

JAPANESE

Number of Books	Course Grade	Number of Books	Course Grade
53	A	30	A
42	A	28	B
40	A	24	A
40	B	22	C
39	A	21	B
34	A	20	B
34	A	16	B

Source: Hitosugi, C. I., and Day, R. R. "Extensive Reading in Japanese," *Reading in a Foreign Language,* Vol. 16, No. 1, Apr. 2004 (Table 4).

a. Consider two populations of students who participate in the reading program prior to taking a second-semester Japanese course: those who earn an A grade and those who earn a B or C grade. Of interest is the difference in the mean number of books read by the two populations of students. Identify the parameter of interest in words and in symbols.

b. Form a 95% confidence interval for the target parameter identified in part **a**.

c. Give a practical interpretation of the confidence interval you formed in part **b**.

d. Compare the inference in part **c** with the inference you derived from stem-and-leaf plots in Exercise 2.31b.

9.16 Rating service at five-star hotels. A study published in the *Journal of American Academy of Business, Cambridge* (March 2002) examined whether the perception of the quality of service at five-star hotels in Jamaica differed by gender. Hotel guests were randomly selected from the lobby and restaurant areas and asked to rate 10 service-related items (e.g., "the personal attention you received from our employees"). Each item was rated on a five-point scale (1 = "much worse than I expected," 5 = "much better than I expected"), and the sum of the items for each guest was determined. A summary of the guest scores are provided in the following table:

Gender	Sample Size	Mean Score	Standard Deviation
Males	127	39.08	6.73
Females	114	38.79	6.94

a. Construct a 90% confidence interval for the difference between the population mean service-rating scores given by male and female guests at Jamaican five-star hotels. $.29 \pm 1.452$

b. Use the interval you constructed in part **a** to make an inference about whether the perception of the quality of service at five-star hotels in Jamaica differs by gender.

9.17 Heights of grade school repeaters. Are children who repeat a grade in elementary school shorter, on average, than their peers? To answer this question, researchers compared the heights of Australian schoolchildren who repeated a grade with the heights of those who did not. (*Archives of Disease in Childhood*, Apr. 2000.) All height measurements were standardized with the use of z-scores. A summary of the results, by gender, is shown in the following table:

	Never Repeated	Repeated a Grade
Boys	$n = 1,349$	$n = 86$
	$\bar{x} = .30$	$\bar{x} = -.04$
	$s = .97$	$s = 1.17$
Girls	$n = 1,366$	$n = 43$
	$\bar{x} = .22$	$\bar{x} = .26$
	$s = 1.04$	$s = .94$

Source: Wake, M., Coghlan, D., and Hesketh, K. "Does height influence progression through primary school grades?" *The Archives of Disease in Childhood*, Vol. 82, Apr. 2000 (Table 3).

a. Set up the null and alternative hypothesis for determining whether the average height of Australian boys who repeated a grade is less than the average height of boys who never repeated.

b. Conduct the test you set up part **a**, using $\alpha = .05$.

c. Repeat parts **a** and **b** for Australian girls.

9.18 Short-term memory study. A group of University of Florida psychologists investigated the effects of age and gender on the short-term memory of adults. (*Cognitive Aging Conference*, Apr. 1996.) Each in a sample of 152 adults was asked to place 20 common household items (e.g., eyeglasses, keys, hat, hammer) into the rooms of a computer-image house. After performing some unrelated activities, each subject was asked to recall the locations of the objects they had placed. The number of correct responses (out of 20) was recorded.

a. The researchers theorized that women would have a higher mean recall score than men. Set up the null and alternative hypotheses to test this theory.

b. Refer to part **a**. The 43 men in the study had a mean recall score of 13.5, while the 109 women had a mean recall score of 14.4. The observed significance level for comparing these two means was found to be $p = .0001$. Interpret this value.

c. The researchers also hypothesized that younger adults would have a higher mean recall score than older adults. Set up H_0 and H_a to test this theory.

d. The observed significance level for the test of part **c** was reported as $p = .0001$. Interpret this result.

9.19 Bulimia study. The "fear of negative evaluation" (FNE) scores for 11 female students known to suffer from the eating disorder bulimia and 14 female students with normal eating habits, first presented in Exercise 2.38 (p. 48), are re-

produced on the bottom of the page. (Recall that the higher the score, the greater is the fear of a negative evaluation.)

a. Find a 95% confidence interval for the difference between the population means of the FNE scores for bulimic and normal female students. Interpret the result.

b. What assumptions are required for the interval of part **a** to be statistically valid? Are these assumptions reasonably satisfied? Explain.

Applying the Concepts—Intermediate

9.20 Patent infringement case. *Chance* (Fall 2002) described a lawsuit charging Intel Corp. with infringing on a patent for an invention used in the automatic manufacture of computer chips. In response, Intel accused the inventor of adding material to his patent notebook after the patent was witnessed and granted. The case rested on whether a patent witness' signature was written on top of or under key text in the notebook. Intel hired a physicist who used an X-ray beam to measure the relative concentrations of certain elements (e.g., nickel, zinc, potassium) at several spots on the notebook page. The zinc measurements for three notebook locations—on a text line, on a witness line, and on the intersection of the witness and text line—are provided in the following table:

PATENT

Text line:	.335	.374	.440			
Witness line:	.210	.262	.188	.329	.439	.397
Intersection:	.393	.353	.285	.295	.319	

a. Use a test or a confidence interval (at $\alpha = .05$) to compare the mean zinc measurement for the text line with the mean for the intersection.

b. Use a test or a confidence interval (at $\alpha = .05$) to compare the mean zinc measurement for the witness line with the mean for the intersection.

c. From the results you obtained in parts **a** and **b**, what can you infer about the mean zinc measurements at the three notebook locations?

d. What assumptions are required for the inferences to be valid? Are they reasonably satisfied?

9.21 How do you choose to argue? Educators frequently lament weaknesses in students' oral and written arguments. In *Thinking and Reasoning* (Oct. 2006), researchers at Columbia University conducted a series of studies to assess the cognitive skills required for successful arguments. One study focused on whether students would choose to argue by weakening the opposing position or by strengthening the favored position. (For example, suppose you are told you would do better at basketball than soccer, but you like soccer. An argument that weakens the opposing position is "You need to be tall to play basketball," An argument that strengthens the favored position is "With practice, I can become really good at

BULIMIA

Bulimic students	21	13	10	20	25	19	16	21	24	13	14			
Normal students	13	6	16	13	8	19	23	18	11	19	7	10	15	20

Source: Randles, R. H. "On neutral responses (zeros) in the sign test and ties in the Wilcoxon-Mann-Whitney test." *The American Statistician*, Vol. 55, No. 2, May 2001 (Figure 3).

soccer.") A sample of 52 graduate students in psychology was equally divided into two groups. Group 1 was presented with 10 items such that the argument always attempts to strengthens the favored position. Group 2 was presented with the same 10 items, but in this case the argument always attempts to weaken the nonfavored position. Each student then rated the 10 arguments on a five-point scale from very weak (1) to very strong (5). The variable of interest was the sum of the 10 item scores, called the *total rating*. Summary statistics for the data are shown in the accompanying table. Use the methodology of this chapter to compare the mean total ratings for the two groups at $\alpha = .05$. Give a practical interpretation of the results in the words of the problem.

	Group 1 (support favored position)	Group 2 (weaken opposing position)
Sample size	26	26
Mean	28.6	24.9
Standard deviation	12.5	12.2

Source: Kuhn, D., and Udell, W. "Coordinating own and other perspectives in argument," *Thinking and Reasoning,* October 2006.

9.22 Pig castration study. Two methods of castrating male piglets were investigated in *Applied Animal Behaviour Science* (Nov. 1, 2000). Method 1 involved an incision in the spermatic cords, while Method 2 involved pulling and severing the cords. Forty-nine male piglets were randomly allocated to one of the two methods. During castration, the researchers measured the number of high-frequency vocal responses (squeals) per second over a 5-second period. The data are summarized in the accompanying table. Conduct a test of hypothesis to determine whether the population mean number of high-frequency vocal responses differs for piglets castrated by the two methods. Use $\alpha = .05$.

	Method 1	Method 2
Sample size	24	25
Mean number of squeals	.74	.70
Standard deviation	.09	.09

Source: Taylor, A. A., and Weary, D. M. "Vocal responses of piglets to castration: Identifying procedural sources of pain," *Applied Animal Behaviour Science,* Vol. 70, No. 1, November 1, 2000.

9.23 Mongolian desert ants. Refer to the *Journal of Biogeography* (Dec. 2003) study of ants in Mongolia (central Asia), presented in Exercise 2.66 (p. 60). Recall that botanists placed seed baits at 5 sites in the Dry Steppe region and 6 sites in the Gobi Desert and observed the number of ant species attracted to each site. These data are listed in the next table. Is there evidence to conclude that a difference exists between the average number of ant species found at sites in the two regions of Mongolia? Draw the appropriate conclusion, using $\alpha = .05$.

9.24 Accuracy of mental maps. To help students organize global information about people, places, and environments, geographers encourage them to develop "mental maps" of the world. A series of lessons was designed to aid students in the development of mental maps. (*Journal of Geography,* May/June 1997.) In one experiment, a class of 24 seventh-grade geography students was given mental map lessons, while a second class of 20 students received

GOBIANTS

Site	Region	Number of Ant Species
1	Dry Steppe	3
2	Dry Steppe	3
3	Dry Steppe	52
4	Dry Steppe	7
5	Dry Steppe	5
6	Gobi Desert	49
7	Gobi Desert	5
8	Gobi Desert	4
9	Gobi Desert	4
10	Gobi Desert	5
11	Gobi Desert	4

Source: Pfeiffer, M., et al. "Community organization and species richness of ants in Mongolia along an ecological gradient from steppe to Gobi desert," *Journal of Biogeography,* Vol. 30, No. 12, Dec. 2003.

traditional instruction. All of the students were asked to sketch a map of the world, and each portion of the map was evaluated for accuracy on a five-point scale (1 = low accuracy, 5 = high accuracy).

a. The mean accuracy scores of the two groups of seventh-graders were compared with the use of a test of hypothesis. State H_0 and H_a for a test to determine whether the mental map lessons improve a student's ability to sketch a world map.

b. What assumptions (if any) are required for the test to be statistically valid?

c. The observed significance level of the test for comparing the mean accuracy scores for continents drawn is .0507. Interpret this result.

d. The observed significance level of the test for comparing the mean accuracy scores for labeling oceans is .7371. Interpret the result.

e. The observed significance level of the test for comparing the mean accuracy scores for the entire map is .0024. Interpret the result.

9.25 Masculinity and crime. The *Journal of Sociology* (July 2003) published a study on the link between the level of masculinity and criminal behavior in men. Using a sample of newly incarcerated men in Nebraska, the researcher identified 1,171 violent events and 532 events in which violence was avoided that the men were involved in. (A violent event involved the use of a weapon, throwing of objects, punching, choking, or kicking. An event in which violence was avoided included pushing, shoving, grabbing, or threats of violence that did not escalate into a violent event.) Each of the sampled men took the Masculinity–Femininity Scale (MFS) test to determine his level of masculinity, based on common male stereotyped traits. MFS scores ranged from 0 to 56 points, with lower scores indicating a more masculine orientation. One goal of the research was to compare the mean MFS scores for two groups of men: those involved in violent events and those who avoided violent events.

a. Identify the target parameter for this study.

b. The sample mean MFS score for the violent-event group was 44.50, while the sample mean MFS score for the avoided-violent-event group was 45.06. Is this sufficient information to make the comparison desired by the researcher? Explain.

c. In a large-sample test of hypothesis to compare the two means, the test statistic was computed to be $z = 1.21$. Compute the two-tailed p-value of the test.

d. Make the appropriate conclusion, using $\alpha = .10$.

MILK

9.26 Detection of rigged school milk prices. Each year, the state of Kentucky invites bids from dairies to supply half-pint containers of fluid milk products for its school districts. In several school districts in northern Kentucky (called the "tricounty" market), two suppliers—Meyer Dairy and Trauth Dairy—were accused of price-fixing—that is, conspiring to allocate the districts so that the winning bidder was predetermined and the price per pint was set above the competitive price. These two dairies were the only two bidders on the milk contracts in the tricounty market between 1983 and 1991. (In contrast, a large number of different dairies won the milk contracts for school districts in the remainder of the northern Kentucky market, called the "surrounding" market.) Did Meyer and Trauth conspire to rig their bids in the tricounty market? Economic theory states that, if so, the mean winning price in the rigged tricounty market will be higher than the mean winning price in the competitive surrounding market. Data on all bids received from the dairies competing for the milk contracts between 1983 and 1991 are saved in the **MILK** file. A MINITAB printout of the comparison of mean prices bid for whole white milk for the two Kentucky milk markets is shown below. Is there support for the claim that the dairies in the tricounty market participated in collusive practices? Explain in detail.

9.27 Children's use of pronouns. Refer to the *Journal of Communication Disorders* (Mar. 1995) study of specifically language-impaired (SLI) children, presented in Exercise 2.65 (p. 60). The data on deviation intelligence quotient (DIQ) for 10 SLI children and 10 younger, normally developing children are reproduced in the accompanying table. Use the methodology of this section to compare the mean DIQ of the two groups of children. (Take $\alpha = .10$.) What do you conclude?

SLI

SLI Children			YND Children		
86	87	84	110	90	105
94	86	107	92	92	96
89	98	95	86	100	92
110			90		

9.28 Personalities of cocaine abusers. Do cocaine abusers have radically different personalities than nonabusing college students? This was one of the questions researched in *Psychological Assessment* (June 1995). Zuckerman–Kuhlman's Personality Questionnaire (ZKPQ) was administered to a sample of 450 cocaine abusers and a sample of 589 college students. The ZKPQ yields scores (measured on a 20-point scale) on each of five dimensions: impulsive–sensation seeking, sociability, neuroticism–anxiety, aggression–hostility, and activity. The results are summarized in the accompanying table. Compare the mean ZKPQ scores of the two groups on each dimension, using a statistical test of hypothesis. Interpret the results at $\alpha = .01$.

	Cocaine Abusers ($n = 450$)		College Students ($n = 589$)	
ZKPQ Dimension	Mean	Std. Dev.	Mean	Std. Dev.
Impulsive–sensation seeking	9.4	4.4	9.5	4.4
Sociability	10.4	4.3	12.5	4.0
Neuroticism–anxiety	8.6	5.1	9.1	4.6
Aggression–hostility	8.6	3.9	7.3	4.1
Activity	11.1	3.4	8.0	4.1

Source: Ball, S. A. "The validity of an alternative five-factor measure of personality in cocaine abusers." *Psychological Assessment*, Vol. 7, No. 2, June 1995, p. 150 (Table 1).

Applying the Concepts—Advanced

9.29 Ethnicity and pain perception. An investigation of ethnic differences in reports of pain perception was presented at the annual meeting of the American Psychosomatic Society (March 2001). A sample of 55 blacks and 159 whites participated in the study. Subjects rated (on a 13-point scale) the intensity and unpleasantness of pain felt when a bag of ice was placed on their foreheads for two minutes. (Higher ratings correspond to higher pain intensity.) A summary of the results is provided in the following table:

	Blacks	Whites
Sample size	55	159
Mean pain intensity	8.2	6.9

a. Why is it dangerous to draw a statistical inference from the summarized data? Explain.

b. Give values of the missing sample standard deviations that would lead you to conclude (at $\alpha = .05$) that blacks, on average, have a higher pain intensity rating than whites.

c. Give values of the missing sample standard deviations that would lead you to an inconclusive decision (at $\alpha = .05$) regarding whether blacks or whites have a higher mean intensity rating.

MINITAB Output for Exercise 9.26

Two-Sample T-Test and CI: WWBID, Market

```
Two-sample T for WWBID

Market       N    Mean    StDev   SE Mean
SURROUND    254   0.1331  0.0158  0.00099
TRI-COUNTY  100   0.1431  0.0133  0.0013


Difference = mu (SURROUND) - mu (TRI-COUNTY)
Estimate for difference:  -0.009970
95% upper bound for difference:  -0.007232
T-Test of difference = 0 (vs <): T-Value = -6.02   P-Value = 0.000   DF = 213
```

9.3 Comparing Two Population Means: Paired Difference Experiments

In Example 9.4, we compared two methods of teaching reading to "slow learners" by means of a 95% confidence interval. Suppose it is possible to measure the "reading IQs" of the "slow learners" *before* they are subjected to a teaching method. Eight pairs of "slow learners" with similar reading IQs are found, and one member of each pair is randomly assigned to the standard teaching method while the other is assigned to the new method. The data are given in Table 9.3. Do the data support the hypothesis that the population mean reading test score for "slow learners" taught by the new method is greater than the mean reading test score for those taught by the standard method?

 PAIREDSCORES

TABLE 9.3 Reading Test Scores for Eight Pairs of "Slow Learners"

Pair	New Method (1)	Standard Method (2)
1	77	72
2	74	68
3	82	76
4	73	68
5	87	84
6	69	68
7	66	61
8	80	76

We want to test

$$H_0: (\mu_1 - \mu_2) = 0$$

$$H_a: (\mu_1 - \mu_2) > 0$$

Many researchers mistakenly use the t statistic for two independent samples (Section 9.2) to conduct this test. The analysis is shown on the MINITAB printout of Figure 9.9. The test statistic, $t = 1.26$, and the p-value of the test, $p = .115$., are highlighted on the printout. At $\alpha = .10$, the p-value exceeds α. Thus, from *this* analysis, we might conclude that we do not have sufficient evidence to infer a difference in the mean test scores for the two methods.

If you examine the data in Table 9.3 carefully, however, you will find this result difficult to accept. The test score of the new method is larger than the corresponding test score for the standard method *for every one of the eight pairs of "slow learners."* This, in itself, seems to provide strong evidence to indicate that μ_1 exceeds μ_2. Why, then, did the t-test fail to detect the difference? The answer is, *the independent samples t-test is not a valid procedure to use with this set of data.*

The t-test is inappropriate because the assumption of independent samples is invalid. We have randomly chosen *pairs of test scores;* thus, once we have chosen the sample for the new method, we have *not* independently chosen the sample for the standard

---

FIGURE 9.9

MINITAB analysis of reading test scores in Table 9.3

```
Two-sample T for NEW vs STANDARD

          N    Mean   StDev   SE Mean
NEW       8   76.00    6.93     2.4
STANDARD  8   71.63    7.01     2.5


Difference = mu (NEW) - mu (STANDARD)
Estimate for difference:  4.37500
95% lower bound for difference:  -1.76200
T-Test of difference = 0 (vs >): T-Value = 1.26   P-Value = 0.115   DF = 14
Both use Pooled StDev = 6.9687
```

method. The dependence between observations within pairs can be seen by examining the pairs of test scores, which tend to rise and fall together as we go from pair to pair. This pattern provides strong visual evidence of a violation of the assumption of independence required for the two-sample t-test of Section 9.2. Note also that

$$s_p^2 = \frac{(n_1 - 1)s_1^2 + (n_2 - 1)s_2^2}{n_1 + n_2 - 2} = \frac{(8 - 1)(6.93)^2 + (8 - 1)(7.01)^2}{8 + 8 - 2} = 48.58$$

Hence, there is a *large variation within samples* (reflected by the large value of s_p^2) in comparison to the relatively *small difference between the sample means*. Because s_p^2 is so large, the t-test of Section 9.2 is unable to detect a difference between μ_1 and μ_2.

TABLE 9.4 Differences in Reading Test Scores

Pair	New Method	Standard Method	Difference (New Method − Standard Method)
1	77	72	5
2	74	68	6
3	82	76	6
4	73	68	5
5	87	84	3
6	69	68	1
7	66	61	5
8	80	76	4

We now consider a valid method of analyzing the data of Table 9.3. In Table 9.4, we add the column of differences between the test scores of the pairs of "slow learners." We can regard these differences in test scores as a random sample of differences for all pairs (matched on reading IQ) of "slow learners," past and present. Then we can use this sample to make inferences about the mean of the population of differences, μ_d, which is equal to the difference $(\mu_1 - \mu_2)$. That is, the mean of the population (and sample) of differences equals the difference between the population (and sample) means. Thus, our test becomes

$$H_0: \mu_d = 0 \quad (\mu_1 - \mu_2 = 0)$$

$$H_a: \mu_d > 0 \quad (\mu_1 - \mu_2 > 0)$$

The test statistic is a one-sample t (Section 8.4), since we are now analyzing a single sample of differences for small n. Thus,

$$\text{Test statistic:} \quad t = \frac{\bar{x}_d - 0}{s_d/\sqrt{n_d}}$$

where

$$\bar{x}_d = \text{Sample mean difference}$$

$$s_d = \text{Sample standard deviation of differences}$$

$$n_d = \text{Number of differences} = \text{Number of pairs}$$

Assumptions: The population of differences in test scores is approximately normally distributed. The sample differences are randomly selected from the population differences. [*Note:* We do not need to make the assumption that $\sigma_1^2 = \sigma_2^2$.]

Rejection region: At significance level $\alpha = .05$, we will reject H_0 if $t > t_{.05}$, where $t_{.05}$ is based on $(n_d - 1)$ degrees of freedom.

Referring to Table VI in Appendix A, we find the t-value corresponding to $\alpha = .05$ and $n_d - 1 = 8 - 1 = 7$ df to be $t_{.05} = 1.895$. Then we will reject the null hypothesis if $t > 1.895$. (See Figure 9.10.) Note that the number of degrees of freedom decreases from $n_1 + n_2 - 2 = 14$ to 7 when we use the paired difference experiment rather than the two independent random samples design.

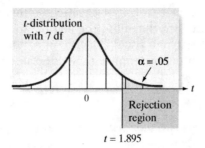

FIGURE 9.10
Rejection region for
Example 9.4

Summary statistics for the $n_d = 8$ differences are shown in the MINITAB printout of Figure 9.11. Note that $\bar{x}_d = 4.375$ and $s_d = 1.685$. Substituting these values into the formula for the test statistic, we have

$$t = \frac{\bar{x}_d - 0}{s_d/\sqrt{n_d}} = \frac{4.375}{1.685/\sqrt{8}} = 7.34$$

Because this value of t falls into the rejection region, we conclude (at $\alpha = .05$) that the population mean test score for "slow learners" taught by the new method exceeds the population mean score for those taught by the standard method. We can reach the same conclusion by noting that the p-value of the test, highlighted in Figure 9.11, is much smaller than $\alpha = .05$.

```
Paired T for NEW - STANDARD


                N      Mean    StDev   SE Mean
NEW             8   76.0000   6.9282    2.4495
STANDARD        8   71.6250   7.0089    2.4780
Difference      8    4.37500  1.68502   0.59574
```

FIGURE 9.11
MINITAB paired difference
analysis of reading test scores

```
95% lower bound for mean difference: 3.24632
T-Test of mean difference = 0 (vs > 0): T-Value = 7.34   P-Value = 0.000
```

Now Work Exercises 9.35ab

This kind of experiment, in which observations are paired and the differences are analyzed, is called a **paired difference experiment.** In many cases, a paired difference experiment can provide more information about the difference between population means than an independent samples experiment can. The idea is to compare population means by comparing the differences between pairs of experimental units (objects, people, etc.) that were similar prior to the experiment. The differencing removes sources of variation that tend to inflate σ^2. For example, when two children are taught to read by two different methods, the observed difference in achievement may be due to a difference in the effectiveness of the two teaching methods, *or* it may be due to differences in the initial reading levels and IQs of the two children (random error). To reduce the effect of differences in the children on the observed differences in reading achievement, the two methods of reading are imposed on two children who are more likely to possess similar intellectual capacity, namely, children with nearly equal IQs. The effect of this pairing is to remove the larger source of variation that would be present if children with different abilities were randomly assigned to the two samples. Making comparisons within groups of similar experimental units is called **blocking,** and the paired difference experiment is a simple example of a **randomized block experiment.** In our example, pairs of children with matching IQ scores represent the blocks.

Some other examples for which the paired difference experiment might be appropriate are the following:

1. Suppose you want to estimate the difference $(\mu_1 - \mu_2)$ in mean price per gallon between two major brands of premium gasoline. If you choose two independent

random samples of stations for each brand, the variability in price due to geographic location may be large. To eliminate this source of variability, you could choose pairs of stations of similar size, one station for each brand, in close geographic proximity and use the sample of differences between the prices of the brands to make an inference about $(\mu_1 - \mu_2)$.

2. Suppose a college placement center wants to estimate the difference $(\mu_1 - \mu_2)$ in mean starting salaries for men and women graduates who seek jobs through the center. If it independently samples men and women, the starting salaries may vary because of their different college majors and differences in grade point averages. To eliminate these sources of variability, the placement center could match male and female job seekers according to their majors and grade point averages. Then the differences between the starting salaries of each pair in the sample could be used to make an inference about $(\mu_1 - \mu_2)$.

3. Suppose you wish to estimate the difference $(\mu_1 - \mu_2)$ in mean absorption rate into the bloodstream for two drugs that relieve pain. If you independently sample people, the absorption rates might vary because of age, weight, sex, blood pressure, etc. In fact, there are many possible sources of nuisance variability, and pairing individuals who are similar in all the possible sources would be quite difficult. However, it may be possible to obtain two measurements *on the same person*. First, we administer one of the two drugs and record the time until absorption. After a sufficient amount of time, the other drug is administered and a second measurement on absorption time is obtained. The differences between the measurements for each person in the sample could then be used to estimate $(\mu_1 - \mu_2)$. This procedure would be advisable only if the amount of time allotted between drugs is sufficient to guarantee little or no carry-over effect. Otherwise, it would be better to use different people matched as closely as possible on the factors thought to be most important.

Now Work Exercise 9.33

The hypothesis-testing procedures and the method of forming confidence intervals for the difference between two means in a paired difference experiment are summarized in the following boxes for both large and small n:

Paired Difference Confidence Interval for $\mu_d = \mu_1 - \mu_2$

Large Sample

$$\overline{x}_d \pm z_{\alpha/2}\frac{\sigma_d}{\sqrt{n_d}} \approx \overline{x}_d \pm z_{\alpha/2}\frac{s_d}{\sqrt{n_d}}$$

Small Sample

$$\overline{x}_d \pm t_{\alpha/2}\frac{s_d}{\sqrt{n_d}}$$

where $t_{\alpha/2}$ is based on $(n_D - 1)$ degrees of freedom

---

Paired Difference Test of Hypothesis for $\mu_d = \mu_1 - \mu_2$

One-Tailed Test

$H_0: \mu_d = D_0$
$H_a: \mu_d < D_0$
$\quad$ [or $H_a: \mu_d > D_0$]

Two-Tailed Test

$H_0: \mu_d = D_0$
$H_a: \mu_d \neq D_0$

(continued)

Large Sample

Test statistic: $z = \dfrac{\bar{x}_d - D_0}{\sigma_d/\sqrt{n_d}} \approx \dfrac{\bar{x}_d - D_0}{s_d/\sqrt{n_d}}$

Rejection region: $z < -z_\alpha$ Rejection region: $|z| > z_{\alpha/2}$

[or $z > z_\alpha$ when $H_a: \mu_d > D_0$]

Small Sample

Test statistic: $t = \dfrac{\bar{x}_d - D_0}{s_d/\sqrt{n_d}}$

Rejection region: $t < -t_\alpha$ Rejection region: $|t| > t_{\alpha/2}$

[or $t > t_\alpha$ when $H_a: \mu_d > D_0$]

where t_α and $t_{\alpha/2}$ are based on $(n_d - 1)$ degrees of freedom

---

Conditions Required for Valid Large-Sample Inferences about μ_d

1. A random sample of differences is selected from the target population of differences.
2. The sample size n_d is large (i.e., $n_d \geq 30$). (By the central limit theorem, this condition guarantees that the test statistic will be approximately normal, regardless of the shape of the underlying probability distribution of the population.)

Conditions Required for Valid Small-Sample Inferences about μ_d

1. A random sample of differences is selected from the target population of differences.
2. The population of differences has a distribution that is approximately normal.

EXAMPLE 9.5

CONFIDENCE INTERVAL FOR μ_d: Comparing Mean Salaries of Males and Females

Problem An experiment is conducted to compare the starting salaries of male and female college graduates who find jobs. Pairs are formed by choosing a male and a female with the same major and similar grade point averages (GPAs). Suppose a random sample of 10 pairs is formed in this manner and the starting annual salary of each person is recorded. The results are shown in Table 9.5. Compare the mean starting salary μ_1 for males with the mean starting salary μ_2 for females, using a 95% confidence interval. Interpret the results.

 GRADPAIRS

TABLE 9.5 Data on Annual Salaries for Matched Pairs of College Graduates

Pair	Male	Female	Difference Male − Female	Pair	Male	Female	Difference Male − Female
1	$29,300	$28,800	$ 500	6	$37,800	$38,000	$−200
2	41,500	41,600	−100	7	69,500	69,200	300
3	40,400	39,800	600	8	41,200	40,100	1,100
4	38,500	38,500	0	9	38,400	38,200	200
5	43,500	42,600	900	10	59,200	58,500	700

The MEANS Procedure

Analysis Variable : DIFF

Mean	Std Dev	N	Minimum	Maximum
400.0000000	434.6134937	10	-200.0000000	1100.00

Two Sample Paired t-test for the Means of MALE and FEMALE

Sample Statistics

Group	N	Mean	Std. Dev.	Std. Error
MALE	10	43930	11665	3688.8
FEMALE	10	43530	11617	3673.6

Hypothesis Test

Null hypothesis: Mean of (MALE - FEMALE) = 0
Alternative: Mean of (MALE - FEMALE) ^= 0

t Statistic	Df	Prob > t
2.910	9	0.0173

95% Confidence Interval for the Difference between Two Paired Means

Lower Limit	Upper Limit
89.10	710.90

FIGURE 9.12

SAS analysis of salary differences

Solution Since the data on annual salary are collected in pairs of males and females matched on GPA and major, a paired difference experiment is performed. To conduct the analysis, we first compute the differences between the salaries, as shown in Table 9.5. Summary statistics for these $n = 10$ differences are displayed at the top of the SAS printout shown in Figure 9.12.

The 95% confidence interval for $\mu_d = (\mu_1 - \mu_2)$ for this small sample is

$$\bar{x}_d \pm t_{\alpha/2} \frac{s_d}{\sqrt{n_d}}$$

where $t_{\alpha/2} = t_{.025} = 2.262$ (obtained from Table VI, Appendix A) is based on $n_d - 1 = 9$ degrees of freedom. Substituting the values of $\bar{x}_d$ and s_d shown on the printout, we obtain

$$\bar{x}_d \pm 2.262 \frac{s_d}{\sqrt{n_d}} = 400 \pm 2.262 \left(\frac{434.613}{\sqrt{10}} \right)$$

$$= 400 \pm 310.88 \approx 400 \pm 311 = (\$89, \$711)$$

[*Note:* This interval is also shown highlighted at the bottom of the SAS printout of Figure 9.12.] Our interpretation is that the true mean difference between the starting salaries of males and females falls between $89 and $711, with 95% confidence. Since the interval falls above 0, we infer that $\mu_1 - \mu_2 > 0$; that is, the mean salary for males exceeds the mean salary for females.

Look Back Remember that $\mu_d = \mu_1 - \mu_2$. So if $\mu_d > 0$, then $\mu_1 > \mu_2$. Alternatively, if $\mu_d < 0$, then $\mu_1 < \mu_2$.

Now Work Exercise 9.42

To measure the amount of information about $(\mu_1 - \mu_2)$ gained by using a paired difference experiment in Example 9.5 rather than an independent samples experiment, we can compare the relative widths of the confidence intervals obtained by the two methods.

Group Statistics

	GENDER	N	Mean	Std. Deviation	Std. Error Mean
SALARY	M	10	43930.00	11665.148	3688.844
	F	10	43530.00	11616.946	3673.601

Independent Samples Test

		Levene's Test for Equality of Variances		t-test for Equality of Means					95% Confidence Interval of the Difference	
		F	Sig.	t	df	Sig. (2-tailed)	Mean Difference	Std. Error Difference	Lower	Upper
SALARY	Equal variances assumed	.000	.991	.077	18	.940	400.00	5206.046	-10537.5	11337.50
	Equal variances not assumed			.077	18.000	.940	400.00	5206.046	-10537.5	11337.51

FIGURE 9.13

SPSS analysis of salaries, assuming independent samples

A 95% confidence interval for $(\mu_1 - \mu_2)$ obtained from a paired difference experiment is, from Example 9.5, ($89, $711). If we analyzed the same data as though this were an independent samples experiment,* we would first obtain the descriptive statistics shown in the SAS printout of Figure 9.13. Then we substitute the sample means and standard deviations shown on the printout into the formula for a 95% confidence interval for $(\mu_1 - \mu_2)$ using independent samples. The result is

$$(\bar{x}_1 - \bar{x}_2) \pm t_{.025}\sqrt{s_p^2\left(\frac{1}{n_1} + \frac{1}{n_2}\right)}$$

where

$$s_p^2 = \frac{(n_1 - 1)s_1^2 + (n_2 - 1)s_2^2}{n_1 + n_2 - 2}$$

SPSS performed these calculations and obtained the interval ($-10,537.50, $11,337.50), highlighted in Figure 9.13.

Notice that the independent samples interval includes 0. Consequently, if we were to use this interval to make an inference about $(\mu_1 - \mu_2)$, we would incorrectly conclude that the mean starting salaries of males and females do not differ! You can see that the confidence interval for the independent sampling experiment is about 35 times wider than for the corresponding paired difference confidence interval. Blocking out the variability due to differences in majors and grade point averages significantly increases the information about the difference in males' and females' mean starting salaries by providing a much more accurate (a smaller confidence interval for the same confidence coefficient) estimate of $(\mu_1 - \mu_2)$.

You may wonder whether a paired difference experiment is always superior to an independent samples experiment. The answer is, Most of the time, but not always. We sacrifice half the degrees of freedom in the t-statistic when a paired difference design is used instead of an independent samples design. This is a loss of information, and unless that loss is more than compensated for by the reduction in variability obtained by blocking (pairing), the paired difference experiment will result in a net loss of information about $(\mu_1 - \mu_2)$. Thus, we should be convinced that the pairing will significantly reduce variability before performing a paired difference experiment. Most of the time, this will happen.

One final note: The pairing of the observations is determined *before* the experiment is performed (i.e., by the *design* of the experiment). A paired difference experiment is *never* obtained by pairing the sample observations *after* the measurements have been acquired.

*This is done only to provide a measure of the increase in the amount of information obtained by a paired design in comparison to an unpaired design. Actually, if an experiment were designed that used pairing, an unpaired analysis would be invalid because the assumption of independent samples would not be satisfied.

What Do You Do When the Assumption of a Normal Distribution for the Population of Differences Is Not Satisfied?

Answer: Use the Wilcoxon signed rank test for the paired difference design (Chapter 14).

ACTIVITY 9.1   *Box Office Receipts:* Comparing Population Means

Use the Internet to find the daily box office receipts for two different hit movies during the first eight weeks after their releases. In this activity, you will compare the mean daily box office receipts of these movies in two different ways.

1. Independently select random samples of size $n = 30$ from the data sets for each of the movies' daily box office receipts. Find the mean and standard deviation of each sample. Then find a confidence interval for the difference of the means.

2. Now pair the data for the two movies by day; that is the box office receipts for the day of release of each movie are paired, the box office receipts for each movie's second day are paired, etc. Calculate the difference in box office re-

ceipts for each day, and select a random sample of size $n = 30$ from the daily differences. Then find a confidence interval for the sample mean.

3. Compare the confidence intervals from Exercises 1 and 2. Explain how the sampling for the paired difference experiment is different from the independent sampling. How might the paired difference sampling technique yield a better comparison of the two means in the box office example?

4. Compute the actual means for the daily box office receipts for each of the movies, and then find the difference of the means. Does the difference of the means lie in both confidence intervals you found? Is the exact difference remarkably closer to one of the estimates? Explain.

Confidence Interval for a Paired Difference Mean

Using the TI-84/TI-83 Graphing Calculator

Note: There is no paired difference option on the calculator. The following instructions demonstrate how to calculate the differences and then use the one-sample *t*-interval:

Step 1   *Enter the data and calculate the differences.*

Press **STAT** and select **1:Edit**.
Note: If the lists already contain data, clear the old data. Use the up **ARROW** to highlight 'L1'.
Press **CLEAR ENTER**.
Use the up **ARROW** to highlight 'L2'.
Press **CLEAR ENTER**.
Use the **ARROW** and **ENTER** keys to enter the first data set into **L1**.
Use the **ARROW** and **ENTER** keys to enter the second data set into **L2**.
The differences will be calculated in **L3**.
Use the up **ARROW** to highlight 'L3'.
Press **CLEAR**. This will clear any old data, but **L3** will remain highlighted.
To enter the equation
$L3 = L1 - L2$, use the following keystrokes:
Press **2ND '1'**. (This will enter L1.)
Press the **MINUS** button.
Press **2ND '2'**. (This will enter L2.)
(Notice the equation at the bottom of the screen.)
Press **ENTER**. (The differences should be calculated in L3.)

L1	L2	⬛3	3
65	62	3	
58	53	5	
78	36	42	
60	34	26	
68	56	12	
69	50	19	
66	42	24	

L3 =L₁-L₂▮

(continued)

Step 2   *Access the Statistical Tests Menu.*

Press **STAT**.
Arrow right to **TESTS**.
Arrow down to **TInterval (even for large sample case).**
Press **ENTER**.

```
EDIT CALC TESTS
2↑T-Test…
3:2-SampZTest…
4:2-SampTTest…
5:1-PropZTest…
6:2-PropZTest…
7:ZInterval…
8↓TInterval…
```

Step 3   *Choose "Data".*

Press **ENTER**.
Set **List** to **L3**.
Set **Freq** to **1**.
Set **C-Level** to the confidence level.
Arrow down to "**Calculate**".
Press **ENTER**.

```
TInterval
 Inpt:DATA Stats
 List:L₃
 Freq:1
 C-Level:.95
 Calculate
```

The confidence interval will be displayed with the mean, standard deviation, and sample size of the differences.

Hypothesis Test for a Paired Difference Mean

Using the TI-84/TI-83 Graphing Calculator

Note: There Is no paired difference option on the calculator. The following instructions demonstrate how to calculate the differences and then use the one-sample *t*-test:

Step 1   *Enter the data and calculate the differences.*

Press **STAT** and select **1:Edit**.
Note: If the lists already contain data, clear the old data. Use the up **ARROW** to highlight 'L1'.
Press **CLEAR ENTER**.
Use the up **ARROW** to highlight 'L2'.
Press **CLEAR ENTER**.
Use the **ARROW** and **ENTER** keys to enter the first data set into **L1**.
Use the **ARROW** and **ENTER** keys to enter the second data set into **L2**.
The differences will be calculated in **L3**.
Use the up **ARROW** to highlight 'L3'.
Press **CLEAR**. This will clear any old data, but **L3** will remain highlighted.
To enter the equation L3 = L1 − L2, use the following keystrokes:
Press 2ND '**1**'. (This will enter L1.)
Press the **MINUS** button.
Press 2ND '**2**'. (This will enter L2.)
(Notice the equation at the bottom of the screen.)
Press **ENTER**. (The differences should be calculated in L3.)

L1	L2	L3	3
65	62	3	
58	53	5	
78	36	42	
60	34	26	
68	56	12	
69	50	19	
66	42	24	

L3 =L₁−L₂

Step 2   *Access the Statistical Tests Menu.*

Press **STAT**.
Arrow right to **TESTS**.
Arrow down to **T-Test (even for a large-sample case).**
Press **ENTER**.

```
EDIT CALC TESTS
1:Z-Test…
2:T-Test…
3:2-SampZTest…
4:2-SampTTest…
5:1-PropZTest…
6:2-PropZTest…
7↓ZInterval…
```

Step 3   *Choose "Data".*

Press **ENTER**.
Enter the values for the hypothesis test, where $\mu_0 =$ the value for μ_d in the null hypothesis.
Set **List** to **L3**.
Set **Freq** to **1**.
Use the **ARROW** to highlight the appropriate alternative hypothesis.
Press **ENTER**.
Arrow down to "**Calculate**".
Press **ENTER**.

The test statistic and the p-value will be displayed, as will the sample mean, standard deviation, and sample size of the differences.

Exercises 9.30–9.49

Understanding the Principles

9.30 What are the advantages of using a paired difference experiment over an independent samples design?

9.31 In a paired difference experiment, when should the observations be paired, before or after the data are collected?

9.32 What conditions are required for valid large-sample inferences about μ_d? small-sample inferences?

Learning the Mechanics

9.33 A paired difference experiment yielded n_d pairs of observations. In each case, what is the rejection region for testing
NW $H_0: \mu_d = 2$ against $H_a: \mu_d > 2$?
a. $n_d = 10, \alpha = .05$
b. $n_d = 20, \alpha = .10$
c. $n_d = 5, \alpha = .025$
d. $n_d = 9, \alpha = .01$

9.34 A paired difference experiment produced the following data:

$$n_d = 16 \quad \bar{x}_1 = 143 \quad \bar{x}_2 = 150 \quad \bar{x}_d = -7 \quad s_d^2 = 64$$

a. Determine the values of t for which the null hypothesis $\mu_1 - \mu_2 = 0$ would be rejected in favor of the alternative hypothesis $\mu_1 - \mu_2 < 0$. Use $\alpha = .10$.
b. Conduct the paired difference test described in part **a**. Draw the appropriate conclusions.
c. What assumptions are necessary so that the paired difference test will be valid?
d. Find a 90% confidence interval for the mean difference μ_d.
e. Which of the two inferential procedures, the confidence interval of part **d** or the test of hypothesis of part **b**, provides more information about the difference between the population means?

9.35 The data for a random sample of six paired observations
NW are shown in the following table:

🖳 **LM9_35**

Pair	Sample from Population 1	Sample from Population 2
1	7	4
2	3	1
3	9	7
4	6	2
5	4	4
6	8	7

a. Calculate the difference between each pair of observations by subtracting observation 2 from observation 1. Use the differences to calculate $\bar{x}_d$ and s_d^2.
b. If μ_1 and μ_2 are the means of populations 1 and 2, respectively, express μ_d in terms of μ_1 and μ_2.
c. Form a 95% confidence interval for μ_d.
d. Test the null hypothesis $H_0: \mu_d = 0$ against the alternative hypothesis $H_a: \mu_d \neq 0$. Use $\alpha = .05$.

9.36 The data for a random sample of 10 paired observations are shown in the following table:

🖳 **LM9_36**

Pair	Population 1	Population 2
1	19	24
2	25	27
3	31	36
4	52	53
5	49	55
6	34	34
7	59	66
8	47	51
9	17	20
10	51	55

a. If you wish to test whether these data are sufficient to indicate that the mean for population 2 is larger than that for population 1, what are the appropriate null and alternative hypotheses? Define any symbols you use.

b. Conduct the test from part **a**, using $\alpha = .10$. What is your decision?

c. Find a 90% confidence interval for μ_d. Interpret this interval.

d. What assumptions are necessary to ensure the validity of the preceding analysis?

9.37 A paired difference experiment yielded the following results:

$$n_d = 40$$
$$\bar{x}_d = 11.7$$
$$s_d = 6.$$

a. Test $H_0: \mu_d = 10$ against $H_a: \mu_d \neq 10$, where $\mu_d = (\mu_1 - \mu_2)$. Use $\alpha = .05$.

b. Report the p-value for the test you conducted in part **a**. Interpret the p-value.

Applying the Concepts—Basic

9.38 Laughter among deaf signers. The *Journal of Deaf Studies and Deaf Education* (Fall 2006) published an article on vocalized laughter among deaf users of American Sign Language (ASL). In videotaped ASL conversations among deaf participants, 28 laughed at least once. The researchers wanted to know if they laughed more as speakers (while signing) or as audience members (while listening). For each of the 28 deaf participants, the number of laugh episodes as a speaker and the number of laugh episodes as an audience member were determined. One goal of the research was to compare the mean numbers of laugh episodes of speakers and audience members.

a. Explain why the data should be analyzed as a paired difference experiment.

b. Identify the study's target parameter.

c. The study yielded a sample mean of 3.4 laughter episodes for speakers and a sample mean of 1.3 laughter episodes for audience members. Is this sufficient evidence to conclude that the population means are different? Explain.

d. A paired difference t-test resulted in $t = 3.14$ and p-value $< .01$. Interpret the results in the words of the problem.

9.39 Animal-assisted therapy for heart patients. Refer to the *American Heart Association Conference* (Nov. 2005) study to gauge whether animal-assisted therapy can improve the physiological responses of heart failure patients, presented in Exercise 2.102 (p. 74). Recall that a sample of $n = 26$ heart patients was visited by a human volunteer accompanied by a trained dog; the anxiety level of each patient was measured (in points) both before and after the visits. The drop (before minus after) in anxiety level for patients is summarized as follows: $\bar{x}_d = 10.5$, $s_d = 7.6$. Does animal-assisted therapy significantly reduce the mean anxiety level of heart failure patients? Support your answer with a 95% confidence interval.

9.40 Life expectancy of Oscar winners. Does winning an Academy of Motion Picture Arts and Sciences award lead to long-term mortality for movie actors? In an article in the *Annals of Internal Medicine* (May 15, 2001), researchers

sampled 762 Academy Award winners and matched each one with another actor of the same sex who was in the same winning film and was born in the same era. The life expectancies (ages) of the pairs of actors were compared.

a. Explain why the data should be analyzed as a paired difference experiment.

b. Set up the null hypothesis for a test to compare the mean life expectancies of Academy Award winners and nonwinners.

c. The sample mean life expectancies of Academy Award winners and nonwinners were reported as 79.7 years and 75.8 years, respectively. The p-value for comparing the two population means was reported as $p = .003$. Interpret this value in the context of the problem.

9.41 The placebo effect and pain. According to research published in *Science* (Feb. 20, 2004), the mere belief that you are receiving an effective treatment for pain can reduce the pain you actually feel. Researchers from the University of Michigan and Princeton University tested this placebo effect on 24 volunteers as follows: Each volunteer was put inside a magnetic resonance imaging (MRI) machine for two consecutive sessions. During the first session, electric shocks were applied to their arms and the blood oxygen level-dependent (BOLD) signal (a measure related to neural activity in the brain) was recorded during pain. The second session was identical to the first, except that, prior to applying the electric shocks, the researchers smeared a cream on the volunteer's arms. The volunteers were informed that the cream would block the pain when, in fact, it was just a regular skin lotion (i.e., a placebo). If the placebo is effective in reducing the pain experience, the BOLD measurements should be higher, on average, in the first MRI session than in the second.

a. Identify the target parameter for this study.

b. What type of design was used to collect the data?

c. Give the null and alternative hypotheses for testing the placebo effect theory.

d. The differences between the BOLD measurements in the first and second sessions were computed and summarized in the study as follows: $n_d = 24$, $\bar{x}_d = .21$, $s_d = .47$. Use this information to calculate the test statistic.

e. The p-value of the test was reported as p-value $= .02$. Make the appropriate conclusion at $\alpha = .05$.

CRASH

9.42 NHTSA new car crash tests. Refer to the National Highway Traffic Safety Administration (NHTSA) crash test data on new cars, saved in the **CRASH** file. Crash test dummies were placed in the driver's seat and front passenger's seat of a new car model, and the car was steered by remote control into a head-on collision with a fixed barrier while traveling at 35 miles per hour. Two of the variables measured for each of the 98 new cars in the data set are (1) the severity of the driver's chest injury and (2) the severity of the passenger's chest injury. (The more points assigned to the chest injury rating, the more severe the injury is.) Suppose the NHTSA wants to determine whether the true mean driver chest injury rating exceeds the true mean passenger chest injury rating and, if so, by how much.

a. State the parameter of interest to the NHTSA.

b. Explain why the data should be analyzed as matched pairs.

c. Find a 99% confidence interval for the true difference between the mean chest injury ratings of drivers and front-seat passengers.

d. Interpret the interval you found in part c. Does the true mean driver chest injury rating exceed the true mean passenger chest injury rating? If so, by how much?

e. What conditions are required for the analysis to be valid? Do these conditions hold for these data?

Applying the Concepts—Intermediate

9.43 Reading tongue twisters. According to *Webster's New World Dictionary*, a tongue twister is "a phrase that is hard to speak rapidly." Do tongue twisters have an effect on the length of time it takes to read silently? To answer this question, 42 undergraduate psychology students participated in a reading experiment. (*Memory & Cognition*, Sept. 1997.) Two lists, each composed of 600 words, were constructed. One list contained a series of tongue twisters, and the other list (called the *control*) did not contain any tongue twisters. Each student read both lists, and the length of time (in minutes) required to complete the lists was recorded. The researchers used a test of hypothesis to compare the mean reading response times for the tongue-twister and control lists.

a. Set up the null hypothesis for the test.

b. Use the information in the accompanying table to find the test statistic and *p*-value of the test.

c. Give the appropriate conclusion. Use $\alpha = .05$.

List Type	Response Time (minutes)	
	Mean	Standard Deviation
Tongue twister	6.59	1.94
Control	6.34	1.92
Difference	.25	.78

Source: Robinson, D. H., and Katayama, A. D. "At-lexical, articulatory interference in silent reading: The 'upstream' tongue-twister effect," *Memory & Cognition*, Vol. 25, No. 5, Sept. 1997, p. 663.

9.44 Visual search and memory study. In searching for an item (e.g., a roadside traffic sign, a lost earring, or a tumor in a mammogram), common sense dictates that you will not re-examine items previously rejected. However, researchers at Harvard Medical School found that a visual search has no memory. (*Nature*, Aug. 6, 1998.) In their experiment, nine subjects searched for the letter "T" mixed among several letters "L." Each subject conducted the search under two conditions: random and static. In the random condition, the locations of the letters were changed every 111 milliseconds; in the static condition, the locations of the letters remained unchanged. In each trial, the reaction time in milliseconds (i.e., the amount of time it took the subject to locate the target letter) was recorded.

a. One goal of the research was to compare the mean reaction times of subjects in the two experimental conditions. Explain why the data should be analyzed as a paired difference experiment.

b. If a visual search has no memory, then the main reaction times in the two conditions will not differ. Specify H_0 and H_a for testing the "no-memory" theory.

c. The test statistic was calculated as $t = 1.52$ with *p*-value = .15. Draw the appropriate conclusion.

9.45 Linking dementia and leisure activities. Does participation in leisure activities in your youth reduce the risk of Alzheimer's disease and other forms of dementia? To answer this question, a group of university researchers studied a sample of 107 same-sex Swedish pairs of twins. (*Journal of Gerontology: Psychological Sciences and Social Sciences*, Sept. 2003.) Each pair of twins was discordant for dementia; that is, one member of each pair was diagnosed with Alzheimer's disease while the other member (the control) was nondemented for at least five years after the sibling's onset of dementia. The level of overall leisure activity (measured on an 80-point scale, where higher values indicate higher levels of leisure activity) of each twin of each pair 20 years prior to the onset of dementia was obtained from the Swedish Twin Registry database. The leisure activity scores (simulated on the basic of summary information presented in the journal article) are saved in the **DEMENTIA** file. The first five and last five observations are shown in the following table:

DEMENTIA (first and last 5 observations)

Pair	Control	Demented
1	27	13
2	57	57
3	23	31
4	39	46
5	37	37
.	.	.
.	.	.
.	.	.
103	22	14
104	32	23
105	33	29
106	36	37
107	24	1

a. Explain why the data should be analyzed as a paired difference experiment.

b. Conduct the appropriate analysis, using $\alpha = .05$. Make an inference about which member of the pair, the demented or control (nondemented) twin, had the largest average level of leisure ac tivity.

9.46 Testing electronic circuits. Japanese researchers have developed a compression–depression method of testing electronic circuits based on Huffman coding. (*IEICE Transactions on Information & Systems*, Jan. 2005.) The new method is designed to reduce the time required for input decompression and output compression—called the compression ratio. Experimental results were obtained by testing a sample of 11 benchmark circuits (all of different sizes) from a SUN Blade 1000 workstation. Each circuit was tested with the standard compression–depression method and the new Huffman-based coding method and the compression ratio recorded. The data are given in the next table. Compare the two methods with a 95% confidence interval. Which method has the smaller mean compression ratio?

CIRCUITS

Circuit	Standard Method	Huffman Coding Method
1	.80	.78
2	.80	.80
3	.83	.86
4	.53	.53
5	.50	.51
6	.96	.68
7	.99	.82
8	.98	.72
9	.81	.45
10	.95	.79
11	.99	.77

Source: Ichihara, H., Shintani, M., and Inoue, T. "Huffman-based test response coding," *IEICE Transactions on Information & Systems,* Vol. E88-D, No. 1, Jan. 2005 (Table 3).

9.47 Light-to-dark transition of genes. *Synechocystis,* a type of cyanobacterium that can grow and survive under a wide range of conditions, is used by scientists to model DNA behavior. In the *Journal of Bacteriology* (July 2002), scientists isolated genes of the bacterium responsible for photosynthesis and respiration and investigated the sensitivity of the genes to light. Each gene sample was grown to midexponential phase in a growth incubator in "full light." The lights were then extinguished, and any growth of the sample was measured after 24 hours in the dark ("full dark"). The lights were then turned back on for 90 minutes ("transient light"), followed immediately by an additional 90 minutes in the dark ("transient dark"). Standardized growth measurements in each light–dark condition were obtained for 103 genes. The complete data set is saved in the **GENEDARK** file. Data on first 10 genes are shown in the following table:

GENEDARK (first 10 observations shown)

Gene ID	FULL-DARK	TR-LIGHT	TR-DARK
SLR2067	−0.00562	1.40989	−1.28569
SLR1986	−0.68372	1.83097	−0.68723
SSR3383	−0.25468	−0.79794	−0.39719
SLL0928	−0.18712	−1.20901	−1.18618
SLR0335	−0.20620	1.71404	−0.73029
SLR1459	−0.53477	2.14156	−0.33174
SLL1326	−0.06291	1.03623	0.30392
SLR1329	−0.85178	−0.21490	0.44545
SLL1327	0.63588	1.42608	−0.13664
SLL1325	−0.69866	1.93104	−0.24820

Source: Gill, R. T., et al. "Genome-wide dynamic transcriptional profiling of the light to dark transition in *Synechocystis Sp.* PCC6803," *Journal of Bacteriology,* Vol. 184, No. 13, July 2002.

a. Treat the data for the first 10 genes as a random sample collected from the population of 103 genes, and test the hypothesis that there is no difference between the mean standardized growth of genes in the full-dark condition and genes in the transient-light condition. Use $\alpha = .01$.

b. Use a statistical software package to compute the mean difference in standardized growth of the 103 genes in the full-dark condition and the transient-light condition. Did the test you carried out in part **a** detect this difference?

c. Repeat parts **a** and **b** for a comparison of the mean standardized growth of genes in the full-dark condition and genes in the transient-dark condition.

d. Repeat parts **a** and **b** for a comparison of the mean standardized growth of genes in the transient-light condition and genes in the transient-dark condition.

Applying the Concepts—Advanced

9.48 Homophone confusion in Alzheimer's patients. A *homophone* is a word whose pronunciation is the same as that of another word having a different meaning and spelling (e.g., *nun* and *none, doe* and *dough,* etc.). *Brain and Language* (Apr. 1995) reported on a study of homophone spelling in patients with Alzheimer's disease. Twenty Alzheimer's patients were asked to spell 24 homophone pairs given in random order. Then the number of homophone confusions (e.g., spelling *doe* given the context, *bake bread dough*) was recorded for each patient. One year later, the same test was given to the same patients. The data for the study are provided in the accompanying table. The researchers posed the following question: "Do Alzheimer's patients show a significant increase in mean homophone confusion errors over time?" Perform an analysis of the data to answer the researchers' question. What assumptions are necessary for the procedure used to be valid? Are they satisfied?

HOMOPHONE

Patient	Time 1	Time 2
1	5	5
2	1	3
3	0	0
4	1	1
5	0	1
6	2	1
7	5	6
8	1	2
9	0	9
10	5	8
11	7	10
12	0	3
13	3	9
14	5	8
15	7	12
16	10	16
17	5	5
18	6	3
19	9	6
20	11	8

Source: Neils, J., Roeltgen, D. P., and Constantinidou, F. "Decline in homophone spelling associated with loss of semantic influence on spelling in Alzheimer's disease," *Brain and Language,* Vol. 49, No. 1, Apr. 1995, p. 36 (Table 3).

9.49 Alcoholic fermentation in wines. Determining alcoholic fermentation in wine is critical to the wine-making process. Must/wine density is a good indicator of the fermentation point, since the density value decreases as sugars are converted into alcohol. For decades, winemakers have measured must/wine density with a hydrometer. Although accurate, the hydrometer employs a manual process that is very time consuming. Consequently, large wineries are searching for more rapid measures of density measurement. An alternative method utilizes the hydrostatic balance instrument (similar to the hydrometer, but digital). A winery in Portugal collected must/wine density measurements on white wine samples randomly selected from the fermentation process for a recent harvest. For each sample, the density of the wine at 20°C was measured with both the hydrometer and the hydrostatic balance. The densities for 40 wine samples are saved in the **WINE40** file. The first five and last five observations are shown in the accompanying table. The winery will use the alternative method of measuring wine density only if it can be demonstrated that the mean difference between the density measurements of the two methods does not exceed .002. Perform the analysis for the winery. Provide the winery with a written report of your conclusions.

WINE40 (first and last five observations)

Sample	Hydrometer	Hydrostatic
1	1.08655	1.09103
2	1.00270	1.00272
3	1.01393	1.01274
4	1.09467	1.09634
5	1.10263	1.10518
.	.	.
.	.	.
36	1.08084	1.08097
37	1.09452	1.09431
38	0.99479	0.99498
39	1.00968	1.01063
40	1.00684	1.00526

Source: Cooperative Cellar of Borba *(Adega Cooperativ a de Borba)*, Portugal.

9.4 Comparing Two Population Proportions: Independent Sampling

Suppose a presidential candidate wants to compare the preferences of registered voters in the northeastern United States with those in the southeastern United States. Such a comparison would help determine where to concentrate campaign efforts. The candidate hires a professional pollster to randomly choose 1,000 registered voters in the northeast and 1,000 in the southeast and interview each to learn her or his voting preference. The objective is to use this sample information to make an inference about the difference $(p_1 - p_2)$ between the proportion p_1 of *all* registered voters in the northeast and the proportion p_2 of *all* registered voters in the southeast who plan to vote for the presidential candidate.

The two samples represent independent binomial experiments. (See Section 4.4 for the characteristics of binomial experiments.) The binomial random variables are the numbers x_1 and x_2 of the 1,000 sampled voters in each area who indicate that they will vote for the candidate. The results are summarized in Table 9.6.

TABLE 9.6 Results of Poll

Northeast	Southeast
$n_1 = 1,000$	$n_2 = 1,000$
$x_1 = 546$	$x_2 = 475$

We can now calculate the sample proportions $\hat{p}_1$ and $\hat{p}_2$ of the voters in favor of the candidate in the northeast and southeast, respectively:

$$\hat{p} = \frac{x_1}{n_1} = \frac{546}{1,000} = .546 \quad \hat{p}_2 = \frac{x_2}{n_2} = \frac{475}{1,000} = .475$$

The difference between the sample proportions $(\hat{p}_1 - \hat{p}_2)$ makes an intuitively appealing point estimator of the difference between the population $(p_1 - p_2)$. For this example, the estimate is

$$(\hat{p}_1 - \hat{p}_2) = .546 - .475 = .071$$

To judge the reliability of the estimator $(\hat{p}_1 - \hat{p}_2)$, we must observe its performance in repeated sampling from the two populations. That is, we need to know the sampling distribution of $(\hat{p}_1 - \hat{p}_2)$. The properties of the sampling distribution are given in the next box. Remember that $\hat{p}_1$ and $\hat{p}_2$ can be viewed as means of the number of successes per trial in the respective samples, so the central limit theorem applies when the sample sizes are large.

Properties of the Sampling Distribution of $(\hat{p}_1 - \hat{p}_2)$

1. The mean of the sampling distribution of $(\hat{p}_1 - \hat{p}_2)$ is $(p_1 - p_2)$; that is,

$$E(\hat{p}_1 - \hat{p}_2) = p_1 - p_2$$

Thus, $(\hat{p}_1 - \hat{p}_2)$ is an unbiased estimator of $(p_1 - p_2)$.

(continued)

2. The standard deviation of the sampling distribution of $(\hat{p}_1 - \hat{p}_2)$ is

$$\sigma_{(\hat{p}_1 - \hat{p}_2)} = \sqrt{\frac{p_1 q_1}{n_1} + \frac{p_2 q_2}{n_2}}$$

3. If the sample sizes n_1 and n_2 are large (see Section 7.3 for a guideline), the sampling distribution of $(\hat{p}_1 - \hat{p}_2)$ is approximately normal.

Since the distribution of $(\hat{p}_1 - \hat{p}_2)$ in repeated sampling is approximately normal, we can use the z-statistic to derive confidence intervals for $(p_1 - p_2)$ or to test a hypothesis about $(p_1 - p_2)$.

For the voter example, a 95% confidence interval for the difference $(p_1 - p_2)$ is

$$(\hat{p}_1 - \hat{p}_2) \pm 1.96\sigma_{(\hat{p}_1 - \hat{p}_2)}, \text{ or } (\hat{p}_1 - \hat{p}_2) \pm 1.96\sqrt{\frac{p_1 q_1}{n_1} + \frac{p_2 q_2}{n_2}}$$

The quantities $p_1 q_1$ and $p_2 q_2$ must be estimated in order to complete the calculation of the standard deviation $\sigma_{(\hat{p}_1 - \hat{p}_2)}$ and, hence, the calculation of the confidence interval. In Section 7.3, we showed that the value of pq is relatively insensitive to the value chosen to approximate p. Therefore, $\hat{p}_1 \hat{q}_1$ and $\hat{p}_2 \hat{q}_2$ will provide satisfactory approximations of $p_1 q_1$ and $p_2 q_2$, respectively. Then

$$\sqrt{\frac{p_1 q_1}{n_1} + \frac{p_2 q_2}{n_2}} \approx \sqrt{\frac{\hat{p}_1 \hat{q}_1}{n_1} + \frac{\hat{p}_2 \hat{q}_2}{n_2}}$$

and we will approximate the 95% confidence interval by

$$(\hat{p}_1 - \hat{p}_2) \pm 1.96\sqrt{\frac{\hat{p}_1 \hat{q}_1}{n_1} + \frac{\hat{p}_2 \hat{q}_2}{n_2}}$$

Substituting the sample quantities yields

$$(.546 - .475) \pm 1.96\sqrt{\frac{(.546)(.454)}{1,000} + \frac{(.475)(.525)}{1,000}}$$

or $.071 \pm .044$. Thus, we are 95% confident that the interval from .027 to .115 contains $(p_1 - p_2)$.

We infer that there are between 2.7% and 11.5% more registered voters in the northeast than in the southeast who plan to vote for the presidential candidate. It seems that the candidate should direct a greater campaign effort in the southeast than in the northeast.

Now Work Exercise 9.59

The general form of a confidence interval for the difference $(p_1 - p_2)$ between population proportions is given in the following box:

Large-Sample 100$(1 - \alpha)$% Confidence Interval for $(p_1 - p_2)$

$$(\hat{p}_1 - \hat{p}_2) \pm z_{\alpha/2}\sigma_{(\hat{p}_1 - \hat{p}_2)} = (\hat{p}_1 - \hat{p}_2) \pm z_{\alpha/2}\sqrt{\frac{p_1 q_1}{n_1} + \frac{p_2 q_2}{n_2}}$$

$$\approx (\hat{p}_1 - \hat{p}_2) \pm z_{\alpha/2}\sqrt{\frac{\hat{p}_1 \hat{q}_1}{n_1} + \frac{\hat{p}_2 \hat{q}_2}{n_2}}$$

The z-statistic,

$$z = \frac{(\hat{p}_1 - \hat{p}_2) - (p_1 - p_2)}{\sigma_{(\hat{p}_1 - \hat{p}_2)}}$$

is used to test the null hypothesis that $(p_1 - p_2)$ equals some specified difference, say, D_0. For the special case where $D_0 = 0$—that is, where we want to test the null hypothesis $H_0: (p_1 - p_2) = 0$ (or, equivalently, $H_0: p_1 = p_2$)—the best estimate of $p_1 = p_2 = p$ is obtained by dividing the total number of successes $(x_1 + x_2)$ for the two samples by the total number of observations $(n_1 + n_2)$ that is,

$$\hat{p} = \frac{x_1 + x_2}{n_1 + n_2}, \quad \text{or} \quad \hat{p} = \frac{n_1\hat{p}_1 + n_2\hat{p}_2}{n_1 + n_2}$$

The second equation shows that $\hat{p}$ is a weighted average of $\hat{p}_1$ and $\hat{p}_2$, with the larger sample receiving more weight. If the sample sizes are equal, then $\hat{p}$ is a simple average of the two sample proportions of successes.

We now substitute the weighted average $\hat{p}$ for both p_1 and p_2 in the formula for the standard deviation of $(\hat{p}_1 - \hat{p}_2)$:

$$\sigma_{(\hat{p} - \hat{p}_2)} = \sqrt{\frac{p_1q_1}{n_1} + \frac{p_2q_2}{n_2}} \approx \sqrt{\frac{\hat{p}\hat{q}}{n_1} + \frac{\hat{p}\hat{q}}{n_2}} = \sqrt{\hat{p}\hat{q}\left(\frac{1}{n_1} + \frac{1}{n_2}\right)}$$

The test is summarized in the following box:

Large-Sample Test of Hypothesis about $(p_1 - p_2)$

One-Tailed Test

$H_0: (p_1 - p_2) = 0$ *

$H_a: (p_1 - p_2) < 0$

[or $H_a: (p_1 - p_2) > 0$]

Two-Tailed Test

$H_0: (p_1 - p_2) = 0$

$H_a: (p_1 - p_2) \neq 0$

Test statistic:

$$z = \frac{(\hat{p}_1 - \hat{p}_2)}{\sigma_{(\hat{p}_1 - \hat{p}_2)}}$$

Rejection region: $z < -z_\alpha$

[or $z > z_\alpha$ when $H_a: (p_1 - p_2) > 0$]

Rejection region: $|z| > z_{\alpha/2}$

Note: $\sigma_{(\hat{p}_1 - \hat{p}_2)} = \sqrt{\frac{p_1q_1}{n_1} + \frac{p_2q_2}{n_2}} \approx \sqrt{\hat{p}\hat{q}\left(\frac{1}{n_1} + \frac{1}{n_2}\right)}$ where $\hat{p} = \frac{x_1 + x_2}{n_1 + n_2}$

Conditions Required for Valid Large-Sample Inferences about $(p_1 - p_2)$

1. The two samples are randomly selected in an independent manner from the two target populations.

2. The sample sizes, n_1 and n_2, are both large, so the sampling distribution of $(\hat{p}_1 - \hat{p}_2)$ will be approximately normal. (This condition will be satisfied if both $n_1\hat{p}_1 \geq 15, n_1\hat{q}_1 \geq 15$, and $n_2\hat{p}_2 \geq 15, n_2\hat{q}_2 \geq 15$.)

---

*The test can be adapted to test for a difference $D_0 \neq 0$. Because most applications call for a comparison of p_1 and p_2, implying that $D_0 = 0$, we will confine our attention to this case.

EXAMPLE 9.6

A LARGE-SAMPLE TEST ABOUT $(p_1 - p_2)$: Comparing Fractions of Smokers for Two Years

Problem In the past decade, intensive antismoking campaigns have been sponsored by both federal and private agencies. Suppose the American Cancer Society randomly sampled 1,500 adults in 1997 and then sampled 1,750 adults in 2007 to determine whether there was evidence that the percentage of smokers had decreased. The results of the two sample surveys are shown in Table 9.7, where x_1 and x_2 represent the numbers of smokers in the 1997 and 2007 samples, respectively. Do these data indicate that the fraction of smokers decreased over this 10-year period? Use $\alpha = .05$.

Solution If we define p_1 and p_2 as the true proportions of adult smokers in 1997 and 2007, respectively, then the elements of our test are

$$H_0: (p_1 - p_2) = 0$$
$$H_a: (p_1 - p_2) > 0$$

(The test is one tailed, since we are interested only in determining whether the proportion of smokers *decreased*.)

TABLE 9.7 Results of Smoking Survey

1997	2007
$n_1 = 1,500$	$n_2 = 1,750$
$x_1 = 555$	$x_2 = 578$

$$\text{Test statistic: } z = \frac{(\hat{p}_1 - \hat{p}_2) - 0}{\sigma_{(\hat{p}_1 - \hat{p}_2)}}$$

$$\text{Rejection region using } \alpha = .05:$$
$$z > z_\alpha = z_{.05} = 1.645 \qquad \text{(see Figure 9.14)}$$

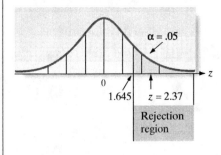

FIGURE 9.14
Rejection region for Example 9.6

We now calculate the sample proportions of smokers:

$$\hat{p}_1 = \frac{555}{1,500} = .37 \qquad \hat{p}_2 = \frac{578}{1,750} = .33$$

Then

$$z = \frac{(\hat{p}_1 - \hat{p}_2) - 0}{\sigma_{(\hat{p}_1 - \hat{p}_2)}} \approx \frac{(\hat{p}_1 - \hat{p}_2)}{\sqrt{\hat{p}\hat{q}\left(\frac{1}{n_1} + \frac{1}{n_2}\right)}}$$

where

$$\hat{p} = \frac{x_1 + x_2}{n_1 + n_2} = \frac{555 + 578}{1,500 + 1,750} = .349$$

Note that $\hat{p}$ is a weighted average of $\hat{p}_1$ and $\hat{p}_2$, with more weight given to the larger (2007) sample.

Thus, the computed value of the test statistic is

$$z = \frac{.37 - .33}{\sqrt{(.349)(.651)\left(\frac{1}{1,500} + \frac{1}{1,750}\right)}} = \frac{.040}{.0168} = 2.38$$

There is sufficient evidence at the $\alpha = .05$ level to conclude that the proportion of adults who smoke has decreased over the 1997–2007 period.

Look Back We could place a confidence interval on $(p_1 - p_2)$ if we were interested in estimating the extent of the decrease.

Now Work Exercise 9.62

EXAMPLE 9.7

FINDING THE OBSERVED SIGNIFICANCE LEVEL OF A TEST FOR $p_1 - p_2$

Problem Use a statistical software package to conduct the test presented in Example 9.6. Find and interpret the p-value of the test.

Solution We entered the sample sizes (n_1 and n_2) and numbers of successes (x_1 and x_2) into MINITAB and obtained the printout shown in Figure 9.15. The test statistic for this one-tailed test, $z = 2.37$, as well as the p-value of the test, are highlighted on the printout. Note that p-value $= .009$ is smaller than $\alpha = .05$. Consequently, we have strong evidence to reject H_0 and conclude that p_1 exceeds p_2.

Test and CI for Two Proportions

```
Sample    X     N   Sample p
1        555  1500  0.370000
2        578  1750  0.330286


Difference = p (1) - p (2)
Estimate for difference:  0.0397143
95% lower bound for difference:  0.0121024
Test for difference = 0 (vs > 0):   Z = 2.37   P-Value = 0.009
```

FIGURE 9.15

MINITAB output for test of two proportions

ACTIVITY 9.2 *Keep the Change:* Inferences Based on Two Samples

In this activity, you will compare the mean amounts transferred for two different Bank of America customers, as well as design some studies that might help the marketing department determine where to allocate more of its advertising budget. You will be working with data sets from Activity 1.1, *Keep the Change: Collecting Data*, (p. 12).

1. You will need to work with another student in the class on this exercise. Each of you should use your data set *Amounts Transferred* from the Activity from Chapter 1 as a random sample from a theoretically larger set of all your amounts ever transferred. Then the means and standard deviations of your data sets will be the sample means and standard deviations. Write a confidence interval for the difference of the two means at the 95% level. Does the interval contain 0? Are your mean amounts transferred significantly different? Explain.

2. Design a study to determine whether there is a significant difference in the mean amount of Bank of America matches for customers in California enrolled in the program and the mean amount of Bank of America matches for customers in Florida enrolled in the program. Be specific about sample sizes, tests used, and how a conclusion will be reached. How might the results of this study help Bank of America estimate costs in the program?

3. Design a study to determine whether there is a significant difference in the percentage of Bank of America customers in California enrolled in the program and the percentage of Bank of America customers in Florida enrolled in the program. Be specific about sample sizes, tests used, and how a conclusion will be reached. How might the results of this study help Bank of America's marketing department?

Keep the results from this activity for use in other activities.

Confidence Interval for $(p_1 - p_2)$

Using the TI-84/TI-83 Graphing Calculator

Step 1   *Access the Statistical Tests Menu.*
           Press **STAT**.
           Arrow right to **TESTS**.
           Arrow down to **2-PropZInt**.
           Press **ENTER**.

(continued)

Step 2 *Enter the values from the sample information and **the confidence level**,*

where x_1 = number of successes in the first sample
n_1 = sample size for the first sample
x_2 = number of successes in the second sample
n_2 = sample size for the second sample

Set **C-Level** to the confidence level.
Arrow down to "**Calculate**".
Press **ENTER**.

Example Find a 95% confidence interval for the difference in the proportions of two leading automobile models that need major repairs.

Model 1: A sample of 400 owners is contacted. Fifty-three owners report that their cars needed major repairs within the first two years after they purchased them.

Model 2: A sample of 500 owners is contacted. Seventy-eight owners report that their cars needed major repairs within the first two years after they purchased them.

The screens for this example are as follows:

```
EDIT CALC TESTS
6↑2-PropZTest…
7:ZInterval…
8:TInterval…
9:2-SampZInt…
0:2-SampTInt…
A:1-PropZInt…
B:2-PropZInt…
```

```
2-PropZInt
(-.0695,.02249)
p̂₁=.1325
p̂₂=.156
n₁=400
n₂=500
```

The 95% confidence interval for the difference in the two proportions is (−.0695, .02249).

Hypothesis Test for ($p_1 - p_2$)

Using the TI-84/TI-83 Graphing Calculator

Step 1 *Access the Statistical Tests Menu.*

Press **STAT**.
Arrow right to **TESTS**.
Arrow down to **2-PropZTest**.
Press **ENTER**.

Step 2 *Enter the values from the sample information and **select the alternative hypothesis**,*

where x_1 = number of successes in the first sample
n_1 = sample size for the first sample
x_2 = number of successes in the second sample
n_2 = sample size for the second sample

Use the **ARROW** to highlight the appropriate alternative hypothesis.
Press **ENTER**.
Arrow down to "**Calculate**".
Press **ENTER**.

Example Test the hypothesis that no difference exists between the proportions of two leading automobile models that need major repairs.

Model 1: A sample of 400 owners is contacted. Fifty-three owners report that their cars needed major repairs within the first two years after they purchased them.

Model 2: A sample of 500 owners is contacted. Seventy-eight owners report that their cars needed major repairs within the first two years after they purchased them.

The screens for this example are as follows:

```
EDIT CALC TESTS
1:Z-Test…
2:T-Test…
3:2-SampZTest…
4:2-SampTTest…
5:1-PropZTest…
6:2-PropZTest…
7↓ZInterval…
```

```
2-PropZTest
 p1≠p2
 z=-.9933568641
 p=.3205360811
 p̂1=.1325
 p̂2=.156
↓p̂=.1455555556
```

Since the *p*-value (.3205) is greater than α (.10). do not reject the null hypothesis. There is insufficient evidence to detect a difference between the population proportions.

STATISTICS IN ACTION REVISITED

Comparing the Proportions of Frequent Family Involvement in Homework for TIPS and ATIPS Students

We now return to the *Statistics in Action* investigation of the effectiveness of the *Teachers Involve Parents in Schoolwork* (TIPS) program (p. 409). Recall that students reported on the level of family involvement in their homework on a five-point scale (0 = never, 1 = rarely, 2 = sometimes, 3 = frequently, 4 = always). In addition to the mean family involvement score, the researcher was interested in the proportion of students with a level of involvement of "sometimes", "frequently" or "always"—that is, the proportion with a score of 2 or more. Call this population parameter the proportion of students with frequent family involvement in their homework.

Another approach to analyzing the data is to compare the proportions for the two groups ATIPS and TIPS. Now the target parameter is $(p_1 - p_2)$, where p_1 is the proportion with frequent family involvement in homework for the ATIPS students and p_2 is the propor-

tion with frequent family involvement in homework for the TIPS students. If, in fact, the TIPS program is effective, then $p_2 > p_1$; this implies that $(p_1 - p_2) < 0$.

The data in the **HWSTUDY** file include the variables INV-SCI, INV-MATH, and INV-LANG. These three variables are qualitative variables with values of "YES" (if the family is involved in homework) or "NO" (if there is no family involvement), for the three classes of science, math, and language arts, respectively. Figure SIA9.2 shows 95% confidence intervals for $(p_1 - p_2)$ for each of these variables.

In science (top of the printout), you can see that 25 of 98 ATIPS students, or 25.5%, experienced family involvement in homework; in contrast, 67 of 128 TIPS students, or 52.3%, experienced family involvement in homework. The corresponding 95% confidence interval (highlighted) for $p_1 - p_2$ is $(-.390, -.146)$. Since all the values in the confidence interval are negative, there is evidence to conclude that $p_2 > p_1$. In fact, we are 95% confident that the percentage of TIPS students with frequent family involvement in their science homework is anywhere from 14.6% to 39.0% higher than the corresponding percentage for ATIPS students.

Test and CI for Two Proportions: INV-SCI, HWCOND

```
Event = YES


HWCOND   X    N   Sample p
ATIPS    25   98  0.255102
TIPS     67  128  0.523438


Difference = p (ATIPS) - p (TIPS)
Estimate for difference:  -0.268335
95% CI for difference:  (-0.390545, -0.146126)
Test for difference = 0 (vs not = 0): Z = -4.07  P-Value = 0.000
```

FIGURE SIA9.2

MINITAB comparison of proportions with frequent family involvement in homework

(continued)

Test and CI for Two Proportions: INV-MATH, HWCOND

```
Event = YES


HWCOND   X     N   Sample p
ATIPS    34    98  0.346939
TIPS     48   128  0.375000


Difference = p (ATIPS) - p (TIPS)
Estimate for difference:  -0.0280612
95% CI for difference:  (-0.154217, 0.0980943)
Test for difference = 0 (vs not = 0):   Z = -0.43   P-Value = 0.664
```

Test and CI for Two Proportions: INV-LANG, HWCOND

```
Event = YES


HWCOND   X     N   Sample p
ATIPS    21    98  0.214286
TIPS     28   128  0.218750


Difference = p (ATIPS) - p (TIPS)
Estimate for difference:  -0.00446429
95% CI for difference:  (-0.112763, 0.103835)
Test for difference = 0 (vs not = 0):   Z = -0.08   P-Value = 0.936
```

FIGURE SIA9.2
Continued

For both the math and language arts classes, note that the 95% confidence intervals (highlighted) include the value 0. Consequently, for both math and language arts, there is insufficient evidence of a difference between the proportions of ATIPS and TIPS students with frequent family involvement in their homework. These results agree with the inferences derived from the tests of means in the previous *Statistics in Action* section.

Exercises 9.50–9.71

Understanding the Principles

9.50 What is the problem with using the z-statistic to make inferences about $p_1 - p_2$ when the sample sizes are both small?

9.51 What conditions are required for valid large-sample inferences about $p_1 - p_2$?

9.52 Consider making an inference about $p_1 - p_2$, where there are x_1 successes in n_1 binomial trials and x_2 successes in n_2 binomial trials.
  a. Describe the distributions of x_1 and x_2.
  b. For large samples, describe the sampling distribution of $(\hat{p}_1 - \hat{p}_2)$.

Learning the Mechanics

9.53 In each case, determine whether the sample sizes are large enough to conclude that the sampling distribution of $(\hat{p}_1 - \hat{p}_2)$ is approximately normal.
  a. $n_1 = 10, n_2 = 12, \hat{p}_1 = .50, \hat{p}_2 = .50$
  b. $n_1 = 10, n_2 = 12, \hat{p}_1 = .10, \hat{p}_2 = .08$
  c. $n_1 = n_2 = 30, \hat{p}_1 = .20, \hat{p}_2 = .30$
  d. $n_1 = 100, n_2 = 200, \hat{p}_1 = .05, \hat{p}_2 = .09$
  e. $n_1 = 100, n_2 = 200, \hat{p}_1 = .95, \hat{p}_2 = .91$

9.54 For each of the following values of α, find the values of z for which $H_0: (p_1 - p_2) = 0$ would be rejected in favor of $H_a: (p_1 - p_2) < 0$.
  a. $\alpha = .01$
  b. $\alpha = .025$
  c. $\alpha = .05$
  d. $\alpha = .10$

9.55 Construct a 95% confidence interval for $(p_1 - p_2)$ in each of the following situations:
  a. $n_1 = 400, \hat{p}_1 = .65; n_2 = 400, \hat{p}_2 = .58$
  b. $n_1 = 180, \hat{p}_1 = .31; n_2 = 250, \hat{p}_2 = .25$
  c. $n_1 = 100, \hat{p}_1 = .46; n_2 = 120, \hat{p}_2 = .61$

9.56 Independent random samples, each containing 800 observations, were selected from two binomial populations. The samples from populations 1 and 2 produced 320 and 400 successes, respectively.
  a. Test $H_0: (p_1 - p_2) = 0$ against $H_a: (p_1 - p_2) \neq 0$. Use $\alpha = .05$.

b. Test H_0: $(p_1 - p_2) = 0$ against H_a: $(p_1 - p_2) \neq 0$. Use $\alpha = .01$.

c. Test H_0: $(p_1 - p_2) = 0$ against H_a: $(p_1 - p_2) < 0$. Use $\alpha = .01$.

d. Form a 90% confidence interval for $(p_1 - p_2)$.

9.57 Random samples of size $n_1 = 50$ and $n_2 = 60$ were drawn from populations 1 and 2, respectively. The samples yielded $\hat{p}_1 = .4$ and $\hat{p}_2 = .2$. Test H_0: $(p_1 - p_2) = .1$ against H_a: $(p_1 - p_2) > .1$, using $\alpha = .05$.

9.58 Sketch the sampling distribution of $(\hat{p}_1 - \hat{p}_2)$ based on independent random samples of $n_1 = 100$ and $n_2 = 200$ observations from two binomial populations with probabilities of success $p_1 = .1$ and $p_2 = .5$, respectively.

Applying the Concepts—Basic

9.59 Bullying behavior study. School bullying is a form of aggressive behavior that occurs when a student is exposed repeatedly to negative actions (e.g., name-calling, hitting, kicking, spreading slander) from another student. In order to study the effectiveness of an antibullying policy at Dutch elementary schools, a survey of over 2,000 elementary school children was conducted (*Health Education Research*, Feb. 2005). Each student was asked if he or she ever bullied another student. In a sample of 1,358 boys, 746 claimed they had never bullied another student. In a sample of 1,379 girls, 967 claimed they had never bullied another student.

a. Estimate the true proportion of Dutch boys who have never bullied another student.

b. Estimate the true proportion of Dutch girls who have never bullied another student.

c. Estimate the difference in the proportions with a 90% confidence interval.

d. Make a statement about how likely the interval you used in part **c** contains the true difference in proportions.

e. Which group is more likely to bully another student, Dutch boys or Dutch girls?

9.60 Executive workout dropouts. Refer to the *Journal of Sport Behavior* (2001) study of variety in exercise workouts, presented in Exercise 7.58 (p. 333). One group of 40 people varied their exercise routine in workouts, while a second group of 40 exercisers had no set schedule or regulations for their workouts. By the end of the study, 15 people had dropped out of the first exercise group and 23 had dropped out of the second group.

a. Find the dropout rates (i.e., the percentage of exercisers who had dropped out of the exercise group) for each of the two groups of exercisers.

b. Find a 90% confidence interval for the difference between the dropout rates of the two groups of exercisers.

c. Give a practical interpretation of the confidence interval you found in part **c**.

9.61 Treating depression with St. John's wort. The *Journal of the American Medical Association* (April 18, 2001) published a study of the effectiveness of using extracts of the herbal medicine St. John's wort in treating major depression. In an eight-week randomized, controlled trial, 200 patients diagnosed with major depression were divided into two groups, one of which ($n_1 = 98$) received St. John's wort extract while the other ($n_2 = 102$) received a placebo (no drug). At the end of the study period, 14 of the St. John's wort patients were in remission, compared with 5 of the placebo patients.

a. Compute the proportion of the St. John's wort patients who were in remission.

b. Compute the proportion of the placebo patients who were in remission.

c. If St. John's wort is effective in treating major depression, then the proportion of St. John's wort patients in remission will exceed the proportion of placebo patients in remission. At $\alpha = .01$, is St. John's wort effective in treating major depression?

d. Repeat part **c**, but use $\alpha = .10$.

e. Explain why the choice of α is critical for this study.

9.62 Planning-habits survey. *American Demographics* (Jan. 2002) reported the results of a survey on the planning habits of men and women. In response to the question "What is your preferred method of planning and keeping track of meetings, appointments, and deadlines?" 56% of the men and 46% of the women answered "I keep them in my head." A nationally representative sample of 1,000 adults participated in the survey; therefore, assume that 500 were men and 500 were women.

a. Set up the null and alternative hypotheses for testing whether the percentage of men who prefer keeping track of appointments in their head is larger than the corresponding percentage of women.

b. Compute the test statistic for the test.

c. Give the rejection region for the test, using $\alpha = .01$.

d. Find the *p*-value for the test.

e. Draw the appropriate conclusion.

9.63 Racial profiling by the LAPD. *Racial profiling* is a term used to describe any police action that relies on ethnicity rather than behavior to target suspects engaged in criminal activities. Does the Los Angeles Police Department (LAPD) invoke racial profiling in stops and searches of Los Angeles drivers? This question was addressed in *Chance* (Spring 2006).

a. Data on stops and searches of both African-Americans and white drivers from January through June 2005 are summarized in the accompanying table. Conduct a test (at $\alpha = .05$) to determine whether there is a disparity in the proportions of African-American and white drivers who are searched by the LAPD after being stopped.

Race	Number Stopped	Number Searched	Number of "Hits"
African-American	61,688	12,016	5,134
White	106,892	5,312	3,006

Source: Khadjavi, L. S. "Driving while black in the City of Angels," *Chance*, Vol. 19, No. 2, Spring 2006 (Tables 1 and 2).

b. The LAPD defines a "hit rate" as the proportion of searches that result in a discovery of criminal activity. Use the data in the table to estimate the disparity in the hit rates for African-American and white drivers under a 95% confidence interval. Interpret the results.

Applying the Concepts—Intermediate

9.64 Angioplasty's benefits challenged. Each year, more than 1 million heart patients undergo an angioplasty. The benefits of an angioplasty were challenged in a recent study of 2,287 patients (2007 Annual Conference of the American College of Cardiology, New Orleans). All the patients had substantial blockage of the arteries, but were medically stable. All were treated with medication such as aspirin and beta-blockers. However, half the patients were randomly assigned to get an angioplasty and half were not. After five years, the researchers found that 211 of the 1,145 patients in the angioplasty group had subsequent heart attacks, compared with 202 of 1,142 patients in the medication-only group. Do you agree with the study's conclusion that "There was no significant difference in the rate of heart attacks for the two groups"? Support your answer with a 95% confidence interval.

9.65 Killing insects with low oxygen. Refer to the *Journal of Agricultural, Biological, and Environmental Statistics* (Sep. 2000) study of the mortality of rice weevils exposed to low oxygen, presented in Exercise 8.82 (p. 385). Recall that 31,386 of 31,421 rice weevils were found dead after exposure to nitrogen gas for 4 days. In a second experiment, 23,516 of 23,676 rice weevils were found dead after exposure to nitrogen gas for 3.5 days. Conduct a test of hypothesis to compare the mortality rates of adult rice weevils exposed to nitrogen at the two exposure times. Is there a significant difference (at $\alpha = .10$) in the mortality rates?

9.66 Effectiveness of drug tests of Olympic athletes. Erythropoietin (EPO) is a banned drug used by athletes to increase the oxygen-carrying capacity of their blood. New tests for EPO were first introduced prior to the 2000 Olympic Games held in Sydney, Australia. *Chance* (Spring 2004) reported that of a sample of 830 world-class athletes, 159 did not compete in the 1999 World Championships (a year prior to the introduction of the new EPO test). Similarly, 133 of 825 potential athletes did not compete in the 2000 Olympic games. Was the new test effective in deterring an athlete from participating in the 2000 Olympics? If so, then the proportion of non participating athletes in 2000 will be more than the proportion of nonparticipating athletes in 1999. Conduct the analysis (at $\alpha = .10$) and draw the proper conclusion.

9.67 "Tip-of-the-tongue" study. Trying to think of a word you know, but can't instantly retrieve, is called the "tip-of-the-tongue" phenomenon. *Psychology and Aging* (Sept. 2001) published a study of this phenomenon in senior citizens. The researchers compared 40 people between 60 and 72 years of age with 40 between 73 and 83 years of age. When primed with the initial syllable of a missing word (e.g., seeing the word *include* to help recall the word *incisor*), the younger seniors had a higher recall rate. Suppose 31 of the 40 seniors in the younger group could recall the word when primed with the initial syllable, while only 22 of the 40 seniors could recall the word. Compare the recall rates of the two groups, using $\alpha = .05$. Does one group of elderly people have a significantly higher recall rate than the other?

MILK

9.68 Detection of rigged school milk prices (cont'd). Refer to the investigation of collusive bidding in the northern Kentucky school milk market, presented in Exercise 9.26 (p. 429). Market allocation is a common form of collusive behavior in bid-rigging conspiracies. Under collusion, the same dairy usually controls the same school districts year after year. The *incumbency rate* for a market is defined as the proportion of school districts that are won by the vendor that won the previous year. Past experience with milk bids in a competitive environment reveals that a typical incumbency rate is .7. That is, 70% of the school districts are expected to purchase their milk from the dairy that won the previous year. Incumbency rates of .9 or higher are strong indicators of collusive bidding. Over the years, when bid collusion was alleged to have occurred in northern Kentucky, there were 51 potential vendor transitions (i.e., changes in milk supplier from one year to the next in a district) in the tricounty market and 134 potential vendor transitions in the surrounding market. These values represent the sample sizes ($n_1 = 134$ and $n_2 = 51$) for calculating incumbency rates. Examining the data saved in the **MILK** file, you'll find that in 50 of the 51 potential vendor transitions for the tricounty market, the winning dairy from the previous year won the bid the next year; similarly, you'll find that in 91 of the 134 potential vendor transitions for the surrounding area, the same dairy won the bid the next year.

a. Estimate the incumbency rates for the tricounty and surrounding milk markets.

b. A MINITAB printout comparing the two incumbency rates is shown below. Give a practical interpretation of the results. Do they show further support for the bid collusion theory?

9.69 Does sleep improve mental performance? Is creativity and problem solving linked to adequate sleep? This question was the subject of research conducted by German scientists at the University of Lübeck (*Nature*, Jan. 22, 2004). One hundred volunteers were divided into two equal-sized groups. Each volunteer took a math test that involved transforming strings of eight digits into a new string that fit a set of given rules, as well as a third, hidden rule. Prior to taking the test, one group received eight hours of sleep, while the other group stayed awake all night. The scientists monitored the volunteers to determine whether and when they figured out the third rule. Of the volunteers who slept, 39 discovered the third rule; of the volunteers who stayed awake all night, 15 discovered the third rule. From the study results, what can you infer about the proportions of volunteers in the two groups who discover the third rule? Support your answer with a 90% confidence interval.

Test and CI for Two Proportions

```
Sample   X    N   Sample p
1       91   134  0.679104
2       50    51  0.980392


Difference = p (1) - p (2)
Estimate for difference:  -0.301288
95% upper bound for difference:  -0.227669
Test for difference = 0 (vs < 0):  Z = -4.30   P-Value = 0.000
```

MINITAB output for Exercise 9.68

Applying the Concepts—Advanced

9.70 Gambling in public high schools. With the rapid growth in legalized gambling in the United States, there is concern that the involvement of youth in gambling activities is also increasing. University of Minnesota professor Randy Stinchfield compared the rates of gambling among Minnesota public school students between 1992 and 1998. (*Journal of Gambling Studies*, Winter 2001.) Based on survey data, the following table shows the percentages of ninth-grade boys who gambled weekly or daily on any game (e.g., cards, sports betting, lotteries) for the two years:

	1992	1998
Number of ninth-grade boys in survey	21,484	23,199
Number who gambled weekly/daily	4,684	5,313

a. Are the percentages of ninth-grade boys who gambled weekly or daily on any game in 1992 and 1998 significantly different? (Use $\alpha = .01$.)

b. Professor Stinchfield states that "because of the large sample sizes, even small differences may achieve statistical significance, so interpretations of the differences should include a judgement regarding the magnitude of the difference and its public health significance." Do you agree with this statement? If not, why not? If so, obtain a measure of the magnitude of the difference between 1992 and 1998 and attach a measure of reliability to the difference.

9.71 Food-craving study. Do you have an insatiable craving for chocolate or some other food? Since many people apparently do, psychologists are designing scientific studies to examine the phenomenon. According to the *New York Times* (Feb. 22, 1995), one of the largest studies of food cravings involved a survey of 1,000 McMaster University (Canada) students. The survey revealed that 97% of the women in the study acknowledged specific food cravings while only 67% of the men did.

a. How large do n_1 and n_2 have to be to conclude that the true proportion of women who acknowledge having food cravings exceeds the corresponding proportion of men? Assume that $\alpha = .01$.

b. Why is it dangerous to conclude from the study that women have a higher incidence of food cravings than men?

9.5 Determining the Sample Size

You can find the appropriate sample size to estimate the difference between a pair of parameters with a specified sampling error (SE) and degree of reliability by using the method described in Section 7.4. That is, to estimate the difference between a pair of parameters correct to within SE units with confidence level $(1 - \alpha)$, let $z_{\alpha/2}$ standard deviations of the sampling distribution of the estimator equal SE. Then solve for the sample size. To do this, you have to solve the problem for a specific ratio between n_1 and n_2. Most often, you will want to have equal sample sizes—that is, $n_1 = n_2 = n$. We will illustrate the procedure with two examples.

EXAMPLE 9.8 FINDING THE SAMPLE SIZES FOR ESTIMATING $(\mu_1 - \mu_2)$: Comparing Mean Crop Yields	**Problem** New fertilizer compounds are often advertised with the promise of increased crop yields. Suppose we want to compare the mean yield μ_1 of wheat when a new fertilizer is used with the mean yield μ_2 from a fertilizer in common use. The estimate of the difference in mean yield per acre is to be correct to within .25 bushel with a confidence coefficient of .95. If the sample sizes are to be equal, find $n_1 = n_2 = n$, the number of 1-acre plots of wheat assigned to each fertilizer. **Solution** To solve the problem, you need to know something about the variation in the bushels of yield per acre. Suppose that, from past records, you know that the yields of wheat possess a range of approximately 10 bushels per acre. You could then approximate $\sigma_1 = \sigma_2 = \sigma$ by letting the range equal 4σ. Thus,

$$4\sigma \approx 10 \text{ bushels}$$
$$\sigma \approx 2.5 \text{ bushels}$$

The next step is to solve the equation

$$z_{\alpha/2}\sigma_{(\bar{x}_1-\bar{x}_2)} = \text{SE, or } z_{\alpha/2}\sqrt{\frac{\sigma_1^2}{n_1} + \frac{\sigma_2^2}{n_2}} = \text{SE}$$

for n, where $n = n_1 = n_2$. Since we want our estimate to lie within SE = .25 of $(\mu_1 - \mu_2)$ with confidence coefficient equal to .95, we have $z_{\alpha/2} = z_{.025} = 1.96$. Then, letting $\sigma_1 = \sigma_2 = 2.5$ and solving for n, we get

$$1.96\sqrt{\frac{(2.5)^2}{n} + \frac{(2.5)^2}{n}} = .25$$

$$1.96\sqrt{\frac{2(2.5)^2}{n}} = .25$$

$$n = 768.32 \approx 769 \text{ (rounding up)}$$

Consequently, you will have to sample 769 acres of wheat for each fertilizer to estimate the difference in mean yield per acre to within .25 bushel.

Look Back Since $n = 769$ would necessitate extensive and costly experimentation, you might decide to allow a larger sampling error (say, SE $= .50$ or SE $= 1$) in order to reduce the sample size, or you might decrease the confidence coefficient. The point is that we can obtain an idea of the experimental effort necessary to achieve a specified precision in our final estimate by determining the approximate sample size *before* the experiment is begun.

Now Work Exercise 9.76

EXAMPLE 9.9

FINDING THE SAMPLE SIZES FOR ESTIMATING $(p_1 - p_2)$: Comparing Defect Rates of Two Machines

Problem A production supervisor suspects that a difference exists between the proportions p_1 and p_2 of defective items produced by two different machines. Experience has shown that the proportion defective for each of the two machines is in the neighborhood of .03. If the supervisor wants to estimate the difference in the proportions to within .005, using a 95% confidence interval, how many items must be randomly sampled from the output produced by each machine? (Assume that the supervisor wants $n_1 = n_2 = n$.)

Solution In this sampling problem, the sampling error SE $= .005$, and for the specified level of reliability, $z_{\alpha/2} = z_{.025} = 1.96$. Then, letting $p_1 = p_2 = .03$ and $n_1 = n_2 = n$, we find the required sample size per machine by solving the following equation for n:

$$z_{\alpha/2}\sigma_{(\hat{p}_1 - \hat{p}_2)} = \text{SE}$$

or

$$z_{\alpha/2}\sqrt{\frac{p_1 q_1}{n_1} + \frac{p_2 q_2}{n_2}} = \text{SE}$$

$$1.96\sqrt{\frac{(.03)(.97)}{n} + \frac{(.03)(.97)}{n}} = .005$$

$$1.96\sqrt{\frac{2(.03)(.97)}{n}} = .005$$

$$n = 8{,}943.2$$

Look Back This large n will likely result in a tedious sampling procedure. If the supervisor insists on estimating $(p_1 - p_2)$ correct to within .005 with 95% confidence, approximately 9,000 items will have to be inspected for each machine.

Now Work Exercise 9.77a

You can see from the calculations in Example 9.9 that $\sigma_{(\hat{p}_1 - \hat{p}_2)}$ (and hence the solution, $n_1 = n_2 = n$) depends on the actual (but unknown) values of p_1 and p_2. In fact, the required sample size $n_1 = n_2 = n$ is largest when $p_1 = p_2 = .5$. Therefore, if you have no prior information on the approximate values of p_1 and p_2, use $p_1 = p_2 = .5$ in the formula for $\sigma_{(\hat{p}_1 - \hat{p}_2)}$. If p_1 and p_2 are in fact close to .5, then the values of n_1 and n_2 that you have calculated will be correct. If p_1 and p_2 differ substantially from .5, then your solutions for n_1 and n_2 will be larger than needed. Consequently, using $p_1 = p_2 = .5$ when solving for n_1 and n_2 is a conservative procedure because the sample sizes n_1 and n_2 will be at least as large as (and probably larger than) needed.

The procedures for determining sample sizes necessary for estimating $(\mu_1 - \mu_2)$ or $(p_1 - p_2)$ for the case $n_1 = n_2$ are given in the following boxes:

Determination of Sample Size for Estimating $(\mu_1 - \mu_2)$

To estimate $(\mu_1 - \mu_2)$ to within a given sampling error SE and with confidence level $(1 - \alpha)$, use the following formula to solve for equal sample sizes that will achieve the desired reliability:

$$n_1 = n_2 = \frac{(z_{\alpha/2})^2(\sigma_1^2 + \sigma_2^2)}{(SE)^2}$$

You will need to substitute estimates for the values of σ_1^2 and σ_2^2 before solving for the sample size. These estimates might be sample variances s_1^2 and s_2^2 from prior sampling (e.g., a pilot study) or from an educated (and conservatively large) guess based on the range—that is, $s \approx R/4$.

Determination of Sample Size for Estimating $p_1 - p_2$

To estimate $(p_1 - p_2)$ to within a given sampling error SE and with confidence level $(1 - \alpha)$, use the following formula to solve for equal sample sizes that will achieve the desired reliability:

$$n_1 = n_2 = \frac{(z_{\alpha/2})^2(p_1q_1 + p_2q_2)}{(SE)^2}$$

You will need to substitute estimates for the values of p_1 and p_2 before solving for the sample size. These estimates might be based on prior samples, obtained from educated guesses or, most conservatively, specified as $p_1 = p_2 = .5$.

Exercises 9.72–9.85

Understanding the Principles

9.72 In determining the sample sizes for estimating $\mu_1 - \mu_2$, how do you obtain estimates of the population variances $(\sigma_1)^2$ and $(\sigma_2)^2$ used in the calculations?

9.73 In determining the sample sizes for estimating $p_1 - p_2$, how do you obtain estimates of the binomial proportions p_1 and p_2 used in the calculations?

9.74 If the sample-size calculation yields a value of n that is too large to be practical, how should you proceed?

Learning the Mechanics

9.75 Suppose you want to estimate the difference between two population means correct to within 2.2 with probability .95. If prior information suggests that the population variances are approximately equal to $\sigma_1^2 = \sigma_2^2 = 15$ and you want to select independent random samples of equal size from the populations, how large should the sample sizes, n_1 and n_2, be?

9.76 Find the appropriate values of n_1 and n_2 (assume that NW $n_1 = n_2$) needed to estimate $(\mu_1 - \mu_2)$ with
  a. A sampling error equal to 3.2 with 95% confidence. From prior experience, it is known that $\sigma_1 \approx 15$ and $\sigma_2 \approx 17$.
  b. A sampling error equal to 8 with 99% confidence. The range of each population is 60.
  c. A 90% confidence interval of width 1.0. Assume that $\sigma_1^2 \approx 5.8$ and $\sigma_2^2 \approx 7.5$.

9.77 Assuming that $n_1 = n_2$, find the sample sizes needed to es-
  NW timate $(p_1 - p_2)$ for each of the following situations:
  a. SE = .01 with 99% confidence. Assume that $p_1 \approx .4$ and $p_2 \approx .7$.
  b. A 90% confidence interval of width .05. Assume there is no prior information available with which to obtain approximate values of p_1 and p_2.
  c. SE = .03 with 90% confidence. Assume that $p_1 \approx .2$ and $p_2 \approx .3$.

9.78 Enough money has been budgeted to collect independent random samples of size $n_1 = n_2 = 100$ from populations 1 and 2 in order to estimate $(p_1 - p_2)$. Prior information indicates that $p_1 = p_2 \approx .6$. Have sufficient funds been allocated to construct a 90% confidence interval for $(p_1 - p_2)$ of width .1 or less? Justify your answer.

Applying the Concepts—Basic

9.79 Bulimia study. Refer to the *American Statistician* (May 2001) study comparing the "fear of negative evaluation" (FNE) scores for bulimic and normal female students, presented in Exercise 9.19 (p. 427). Suppose you want to estimate $(\mu_B - \mu_N)$, the difference between the population means of the FNE scores for bulimic and normal female students, using a 95% confidence interval with a sampling error of two points. Find the sample sizes required to obtain such an estimate. Assume equal sample sizes of $\sigma_B^2 = \sigma_N^2 = 25$.

9.80 Laughter among deaf signers. Refer to the *Journal of Deaf Studies and Deaf Education* (Fall 2006) paired difference study on vocalized laughter among deaf users of sign language, presented in Exercise 9.38 (p. 440). Suppose you want to estimate $\mu_d = (\mu_S - \mu_A)$, the difference between the population mean number of laugh episodes of deaf speakers and deaf audience members, using a 90% confidence interval with a sampling error of .75. Find the number of pairs of deaf people required to obtain such an estimate, assuming that the variance of the paired differences is $\sigma_d^2 = 3$.

9.81 Executive workout dropouts. Refer to the *Journal of Sport Behavior* (2001) study comparing the dropout rates of two groups of exercisers, presented in Exercise 9.60 (p. 451). Suppose you want to reduce the sampling error for estimating $(p_1 - p_2)$ with a 90% confidence interval to .1. Determine the number of exercisers to be sampled from each group in order to obtain such an estimate. Assume equal sample sizes, and assume that $p_1 \approx .4$ and $p_2 \approx .6$.

Applying the Concepts—Intermediate

9.82 Cable-TV home shoppers. All cable television companies carry at least one home-shopping channel. Who uses these home-shopping services? Are the shoppers primarily men or women? Suppose you want to estimate the difference in the percentages of men and women who say they have used or expect to use televised home shopping. You want an 80% confidence interval of width .06 or less.
a. Approximately how many people should be included in your samples?
b. Suppose you want to obtain individual estimates for the two percentages of interest. Will the sample size found in part **a** be large enough to provide estimates of each percentage correct to within .02 with probability equal to .90? Justify your response.

9.83 Health hazards of housework. Is housework hazardous to your health? A study in *Public Health Reports* (July–Aug. 1992) compares the life expectancies of 25-year-old white women in the labor force with those who are housewives. How large a sample would have to be taken from each group in order for you to be 95% confident that the estimate of the difference in mean life expectancies for the two groups is within 1 year of the true difference? Assume that equal sample sizes will be selected from the two groups and that the standard deviation for both groups is approximately 15 years.

9.84 Rat damage in sugarcane. Poisons are used to prevent rat damage in sugarcane fields. The U.S. Department of Agriculture is investigating whether the rat poison should be located in the middle of the field or on the outer perimeter. One way to answer this question is to determine where the greater amount of damage occurs. If damage is measured by the proportion of cane stalks that have been damaged by rats, how many stalks from each section of the field should be sampled in order to estimate the true difference between proportions of stalks damaged in the two sections, to within .02 with 95% confidence?

9.85 Scouting an NFL free agent. In seeking a free-agent NFL running back, a general manager is looking for a player with high mean yards gained per carry and a small standard deviation. Suppose the GM wishes to compare the mean yards gained per carry for two free agents, on the basis of independent random samples of their yards gained per carry. Data from last year's pro football season indicate that $\sigma_1 = \sigma_2 \approx 5$ yards. If the GM wants to estimate the difference in means correct to within 1 yard with a confidence level of .90, how many runs would have to be observed for each player? (Assume equal sample sizes.)

9.6 Comparing Two Population Variances: Independent Sampling (Optional)

Many times, it is of practical interest to use the techniques developed in this chapter to compare the means or proportions of two populations. However, there are also important instances when we wish to compare two population variances. For example, when two devices are available for producing precision measurements (scales, calipers, thermometers, etc.), we might want to compare the variability of the measurements of the devices before deciding which one to purchase. Or when two standardized tests can be used to rate job applicants, the variability of the scores for both tests should be taken into consideration before deciding which test to use.

For problems like these, we need to develop a statistical procedure to compare population variances. The common statistical procedure for comparing population variances σ_1^2 and σ_2^2 makes an inference about the ratio σ_1^2/σ_2^2. In this section, we will show how to test the null hypothesis that the ratio σ_1^2/σ_2^2 equals 1 (the variances are equal) against the alternative hypothesis that the ratio differs from 1 (the variances differ):

$$H_0: \frac{\sigma_1^2}{\sigma_2^2} = 1 \quad (\sigma_1^2 = \sigma_2^2)$$

$$H_a: \frac{\sigma_1^2}{\sigma_2^2} \neq 1 \quad (\sigma_1^2 \neq \sigma_2^2)$$

To make an inference about the ratio σ_1^2/σ_2^2, it seems reasonable to collect sample data and use the ratio of the sample variances, s_1^2/s_2^2. We will use the test statistic

$$F = \frac{s_1^2}{s_2^2}$$

To establish a rejection region for the test statistic, we need to know the sampling distribution of s_1^2/s_2^2. As you will subsequently see, the sampling distribution of s_1^2/s_2^2 is based on two of the assumptions already required for the t-test:

1. The two sampled populations are normally distributed.
2. The samples are randomly and independently selected from their respective populations.

When these assumptions are satisfied and when the null hypothesis is true (i.e., when $\sigma_1^2 = \sigma_2^2$), the sampling distribution of $F = s_1^2/s_2^2$ is the **F-distribution** with $(n_1 - 1)$ numerator degrees of freedom and $(n_2 - 1)$ denominator degrees of freedom, respectively. The shape of the F-distribution depends on the number of degrees of freedom associated with s_1^2 and s_2^2—that is, on $(n_1 - 1)$ and $(n_2 - 1)$. An F-distribution with 7 and 9 df is shown in Figure 9.16. As you can see, the distribution is skewed to the right, since s_1^2/s_2^2 cannot be less than 0, but can increase without bound.

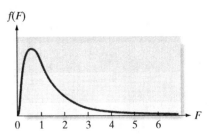

FIGURE 9.16

An F-distribution with 7 numerator and 9 denominator degrees of freedom

Biography

GEORGE W. SNEDECOR (1882–1974)—
Snedecor's F-test

George W. Snedecor's education began at the University of Alabama, where he obtained his bachelor's degree in mathematics and physics. He went on to the University of Michigan for his master's degree in physics and finally earned his Ph.D in mathematics at the University of Kentucky. Snedecor learned of an opening for an assistant professor of mathematics at the University of Iowa, packed his belongings in his car, and began driving to apply for the position. By mistake, he ended up in Ames, Iowa, home of Iowa State University—then an agricultural school that had no need for a mathematics teacher. Nevertheless, Snedecor stayed and founded a statistics laboratory, eventually teaching the first course in statistics at Iowa State in 1915. In 1933, Snedecor turned the statistics laboratory into the first-ever Department of Statistics in the United States. During his tenure as chair of the department, Snedecor published his landmark textbook, *Statistical Methods* (1937). The text contained the first published reference for a test of hypothesis to compare two variances. Although Snedecor named it the F-test in honor of statistician R. A. Fisher (who had developed the F-distribution a few years earlier, many researchers still refer to it as Snedecor's F-test. Now in its ninth edition, *Statistical Methods* (with William Cochran as coauthor) continues to be one of the most frequently cited texts in the statistics field.

We need to be able to find F-values corresponding to the tail areas of this distribution in order to establish the rejection region for our test of hypothesis because we expect the ratio F of the sample variances to be either very large or very small when the population variances are unequal. The upper-tail F values for $\alpha = .10, .05, .025$, and $.01$ can be found in Tables VIII, IX, X, and XI of Appendix A. Table IX is partially reproduced in Table 9.8. It gives F values that correspond to $\alpha = .05$ upper-tail areas for different degrees of freedom; the columns correspond to the number of degrees of freedom, v_1, for the numerator sample variance s_1^2, whereas the rows correspond to the

TABLE 9.8 Reproduction of Part of Table IX in Appendix A: Percentage Points of the *F*-distribution, $\alpha = .05$

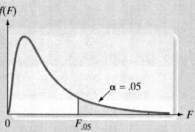

v_1	Numerator Degrees of Freedom								
v_2	1	2	3	4	5	6	7	8	9
1	161.4	199.5	215.7	224.6	230.2	234.0	236.8	238.9	240.5
2	18.51	19.00	19.16	19.25	19.30	19.33	19.35	19.37	19.38
3	10.13	9.55	9.28	9.12	9.01	8.94	8.89	8.85	8.81
4	7.71	6.94	6.59	6.39	6.26	6.16	6.09	6.04	6.00
5	6.61	5.79	5.41	5.19	5.05	4.95	4.88	4.82	4.77
6	5.99	5.14	4.76	4.53	4.39	4.28	4.21	4.15	4.10
7	5.59	4.74	4.35	4.12	3.97	3.87	3.79	3.73	3.68
8	5.32	4.46	4.07	3.84	3.69	3.58	3.50	3.44	3.39
9	5.12	4.26	3.86	3.63	3.48	3.37	3.29	3.23	3.18
10	4.96	4.10	3.71	3.48	3.33	3.22	3.14	3.07	3.02
11	4.84	3.98	3.59	3.36	3.20	3.09	3.01	2.95	2.90
12	4.75	3.89	3.49	3.25	3.11	3.00	2.91	2.85	2.80
13	4.67	3.81	3.41	3.18	3.03	2.92	2.83	2.77	2.71
14	4.60	3.74	3.34	3.11	2.96	2.85	2.76	2.70	2.65

Denominator Degrees of Freedom

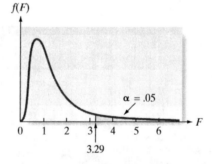

FIGURE 9.17
An *F*-Distribution for $v_1 = 7$ and $v_2 = 9$ df; $\alpha = .05$

number of degrees of freedom v_2, for the denominator sample variance s_2^2. Thus, if the number of degrees of freedom denoted by the numerator is $v_1 = 7$ and the number of degrees of freedom denoted by the denominator is $v_2 = 9$, we look in the seventh column and ninth row to find $F_{.05} = 3.29$. As shown in Figure 9.17, $\alpha = .05$ is the tail area to the right of 3.29 in the *F*-distribution with 7 and 9 df. That is, if $\sigma_1^2 = \sigma_2^2$, then the probability that the *F*-statistic will exceed 3.29 is $\alpha = .05$.

Now Work Exercise 9.90

EXAMPLE 9.10
AN F-TEST APPLICATION:
Comparing Weight Variations in Mice

Problem An experimenter wants to compare the metabolic rates of white mice subjected to different drugs. The weights of the mice may affect their metabolic rates; thus, the experimenter wishes to obtain mice that are relatively homogeneous with respect to weight. Five hundred mice will be needed to complete the study. Currently, 13 mice from supplier 1 and another 18 mice from supplier 2 are available for comparison. The experimenter weighs these mice and obtains the data shown in Table 9.9. Do these data provide sufficient evidence to indicate a difference in the variability of weights of mice obtained from the two suppliers? (Use $\alpha = .10$.) From the results of this analysis, what would you suggest to the experimenter?

MICEWTS

TABLE 9.9 Weights (in ounces) of Experimental Mice

Supplier 1					
4.23	4.35	4.05	3.75	4.41	4.37
4.01	4.06	4.15	4.19	4.52	4.21
4.29					

Supplier 2					
4.14	4.26	4.05	4.11	4.31	4.12
4.17	4.35	4.25	4.21	4.05	4.28
4.15	4.20	4.32	4.25	4.02	4.14

Solution Let

$$\sigma_1^2 = \text{Population variance of weights of white mice from supplier 1}$$
$$\sigma_2^2 = \text{Population variance of weights of white mice from supplier 2}$$

The hypotheses of interest are then

$$H_0: \frac{\sigma_1^2}{\sigma_2^2} = 1 \quad (\sigma_1^2 = \sigma_2^2)$$

$$H_a: \frac{\sigma_1^2}{\sigma_2^2} \neq 1 \quad (\sigma_1^2 \neq \sigma_2^2)$$

The nature of the F-tables given in Appendix A affects the form of the test statistic. To form the rejection region for a two-tailed F-test, we want to make certain that the upper tail is used, because only the upper-tail values of F are shown in Tables VIII, IX, X, and XI. To accomplish that, *we will always place the larger sample variance in the numerator of the F-test statistic.* This has the effect of doubling the tabulated value for α, since we double the probability that the F-ratio will fall in the upper tail by always placing the larger sample variance in the numerator. That is, we establish a one-tailed rejection region by putting the larger variance in the numerator, rather than establishing rejection regions in both tails.

To calculate the value of the test statistic, we require the sample variances. These are shown on the MINITAB printout of Figure 9.18. The sample variances are $s_1^2 = .0409$ and $s_2^2 = .00964$. Therefore,

$$F = \frac{\text{Larger sample variance}}{\text{Smaller sample variance}} = \frac{s_1^2}{s_2^2} = \frac{(.0409)}{(.00964)} = 4.24$$

For our example, we have a numerator s_1^2 with df $= v_1 = n_1 - 1 = 12$ and a denominator s_2^2 with df $= v_2 = n_2 - 1 = 17$. Therefore, we will reject $H_0: \sigma_1^2 = \sigma_2^2$ for $\alpha = .10$ when the calculated value of F exceeds the tabulated value:

$$F_{\alpha/2} = F_{.05} = 2.38 \quad \text{(see Figure 9.19)}$$

Note that $F = 4.24$ falls into the rejection region. Therefore, the data provide sufficient evidence to indicate that the population variances differ. It appears that the weights of mice obtained from supplier 2 tend to be more homogeneous (less variable) than the weights of mice obtained from supplier 1. On the basis of this evidence, we would advise the experimenter to purchase the mice from supplier 2.

Look Back What would you have concluded if the value of F calculated from the samples had not fallen into the rejection region? Would you conclude that the null hypothesis of

Descriptive Statistics: WEIGHT

Variable	SUPPLIER	N	Mean	StDev	Variance	Minimum	Maximum
WEIGHT	1	13	4.1992	0.2021	0.0409	3.7500	4.5200
	2	18	4.1878	0.0982	0.00964	4.0200	4.3500

Test for Equal Variances: WEIGHT versus SUPPLIER

95% Bonferroni confidence intervals for standard deviations

SUPPLIER	N	Lower	StDev	Upper
1	13	0.138579	0.202133	0.361467
2	18	0.070860	0.098193	0.156836

```
F-Test (normal distribution)
Test statistic = 4.24, p-value = 0.007


Levene's Test (any continuous distribution)
Test statistic = 4.31, p-value = 0.047
```

FIGURE 9.18

MINITAB summary statistics and *F*-test for mice weights

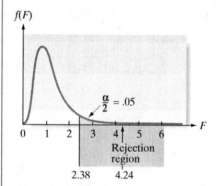

FIGURE 9.19

Rejection region for Example 9.10

equal variances is true? No, because then you risk the possibility of a Type II error (accepting H_0 if H_a is true) without knowing the value of β, the probability of accepting H_0: $\sigma_1^2 = \sigma_2^2$ if in fact it is false. Since we will not consider the calculation of β for specific alternatives in this text, when the *F*-statistic does not fall into the rejection region we simply conclude that the sample possesses insufficient evidence to refute the null hypothesis that $\sigma_1^2 = \sigma_2^2$.

Now Work Exercise 9.95a

EXAMPLE 9.11

THE OBSERVED SIGNIFICANCE LEVEL OF AN *F*-TEST

Problem Find the *p*-value for the test in Example 9.10, using the *F*-tables in Appendix A. Compare this with the exact *p*-value obtained from a computer printout.

Solution Since the observed value of the *F*-statistic in Example 9.10 was found to be 4.24, the observed significance level of the test would equal the probability of observing a value of *F* at least as contradictory to H_0: $\sigma_1^2 = \sigma_2^2$ as $F = 4.24$, is, if in fact H_0 is true. Since we give the *F*-tables in Appendix A just for values of α equal to .10, .05, .025, and .01, we can only approximate the observed significance level. Checking Table XI, we find that $F_{.01} = 3.46$. Since the observed value of *F* is greater than $F_{.01}$, the observed significance level for the test is less than $2(.01) = .02$. (Note that we double the α value shown in Table XI because this is a two-tailed test.) The exact *p*-value, $p = .007$, is highlighted at the bottom of the MINITAB printout shown in Figure 9.18.

Look Back We double the α value in Table XI because this is a two-tailed test.

Now Work Exercise 9.95b

In addition to applying a hypothesis test for σ_1^2/σ_2^2, we can use the F-statistic to estimate the ratio with a confidence interval. The following boxes summarize the confidence interval and testing procedures:

A $(1 - \alpha) \times 100\%$ Confidence Interval for $(\sigma_1)^2/(\sigma_2)^2$

$$\left(\frac{s_1^2}{s_2^2}\right)\left(\frac{1}{F_{L,\alpha/2}}\right) < \left(\frac{\sigma_1^2}{\sigma_2^2}\right) < \left(\frac{s_1^2}{s_2^2}\right)F_{U,\alpha/2}$$

where $F_{L,\alpha/2}$ is the value of F that places an area $\alpha/2$ in the upper tail of an F-distribution with $v_1 = (n_1 - 1)$ numerator and $v_2 = (n_2 - 1)$ denominator degrees of freedom, and $F_{U,\alpha/2}$ is the value of F that places an area $\alpha/2$ in the upper tail of an F-distribution with $v_1 = (n_2 - 1)$ numerator and $v_2 = (n_1 - 1)$ denominator degrees of freedom.

F-Test for Equal Population Variances*

One-Tailed Test

$H_0: \sigma_1^2 = \sigma_2^2$

$H_a: \sigma_1^2 < \sigma_2^2$ (or $H_a: \sigma_1^2 > \sigma_2^2$)

Test statistic:

$$F = \frac{s_2^2}{s_1^2}$$

$$\left(\text{or } F = \frac{s_1^2}{s_2^2} \text{ when } H_a: \sigma_1^2 > \sigma_2^2\right)$$

Rejection region:

$F > F_\alpha$

Two-Tailed Test

$H_0: \sigma_1^2 = \sigma_2^2$

$H_a: \sigma_1^2 \neq \sigma_2^2$

Test statistic:

$$F = \frac{\text{Larger sample variance}}{\text{Smaller sample variance}}$$

$$= \frac{s_1^2}{s_2^2} \text{ when } s_1^2 > s_2^2$$

$$\left(\text{or } \frac{s_2^2}{s_1^2} \text{ when } s_2^2 > s_1^2\right)$$

Rejection region:

$F > F_{\alpha/2}$

where F_α and $F_{\alpha/2}$ are based on v_1 numerator degrees of freedom and v_2 denominator degrees of freedom; and v_1 and v_2 are the degrees of freedom for the numerator and denominator sample variances, respectively.

Conditions Required for Valid Inferences about $(\sigma_1)^2/(\sigma_2)^2$

1. The samples are random and independent.
2. Both populations are normally distributed.

To conclude this section, we consider the comparison of population variances as a check of the assumption $\sigma_1^2 = \sigma_2^2$ needed for the two-sample t-test. Rejection of the null hypothesis $\sigma_1^2 = \sigma_2^2$ would indicate that the assumption is invalid. [*Note:* Nonrejection of the null hypothesis does *not* imply that the assumption is valid.]

*Although a test of a hypothesis of equality of variances is its most common application, the F-test can also be used to test a hypothesis that the ratio between the population variances is equal to some specified value $H_0: \sigma_1^2/\sigma_2^2 = k$. In that case, the test is conducted in exactly the same way as specified in the box, except that we use the test statistic

$$F = \left(\frac{s_1^2}{s_2^2}\right)\left(\frac{1}{k}\right)$$

EXAMPLE 9.12

CHECKING THE ASSUMPTION OF EQUAL VARIANCES

Problem In Example 9.4 (Section 9.2), we used the two-sample t-statistic to compare the mean reading scores of two groups of "slow learners" who had been taught to read by two different methods. The data are repeated in Table 9.10 for convenience. The use of the t-statistic was based on the assumption that the population variances of the test scores were equal for the two methods. Conduct a test of hypothesis to check this assumption at $\alpha = .10$.

⊘ **READING**

TABLE 9.10 Reading Test Scores for "Slow Learners"

New Method				Standard Method			
80	80	79	81	79	62	70	68
76	66	71	76	73	76	86	73
70	85			72	68	75	66

Solution We want to test

$$H_0: \sigma_1^2/\sigma_2^2 = 1 \quad (\text{i.e., } \sigma_1^2 = \sigma_2^2)$$
$$H_a: \sigma_1^2/\sigma_2^2 \neq 1 \quad (\text{i.e., } \sigma_1^2 \neq \sigma_2^2)$$

The data were entered into SAS, and the SAS printout shown in Figure 9.20 was obtained. Both the test statistic, $F = .85$, and the two-tailed p-value, .8148, are highlighted on the printout. Since $\alpha = .10$ is less than the p-value, we do not reject the null hypothesis that the population variances of the reading test scores are equal. It is here that the temptation to misuse the F-test is strongest. *We cannot conclude that the data justify the use of the t-statistic.* Doing so would be equivalent to accepting H_0, and we have repeatedly warned against this conclusion because the probability of a Type II error, β, is unknown. The α level of .10 protects us only against rejecting H_0 if it is true. This use of the F-test may prevent us from abusing the t procedure when we obtain a value of F that leads to a rejection of the assumption that $\sigma_1^2 = \sigma_2^2$. But when the F-statistic does not fall into the rejection region, we know little more about the validity of the assumption than before we conducted the test.

Look Back A 95% confidence interval for the ratio $(\sigma_1)^2/(\sigma_2)^2$ is shown at the bottom of the SAS printout of Figure 9.20. Note that the interval, (.2358, 3.3096), includes 1; hence, we

```
                    Two Sample Test for Variances of SCORE within METHOD


    Sample Statistics

        METHOD
        Group          N        Mean      Std. Dev.     Variance
        ----------------------------------------------------------------
        NEW           10        76.4        5.8348       34.04444
        STD           12     72.33333       6.3437       40.24242


    Hypothesis Test

            Null hypothesis:        Variance 1 / Variance 2 =  1
            Alternative:            Variance 1 / Variance 2 ^= 1

                        - Degrees of Freedom -
             F           Numer.     Denom.            Pr > F
        ----------------------------------------------------------------
           0.85            9          11              0.8148


    95% Confidence Interval of the Ratio of Two Variances

             Lower Limit        Upper Limit
             -----------        -----------
                0.2358             3.3096
```

FIGURE 9.20
SAS F-test for testing assumption of equal variances

cannot conclude that the ratio differs significantly from 1. Thus, the confidence interval leads to the same conclusion that the two-tailed test does: There is insufficient evidence of a difference between the population variances.

Now Work Exercise 9.99

What Do You Do if the Assumption of Normal Population Distributions Is Not Satisfied?

Answer: The F-test is much less robust (i.e., much more sensitive) to departures from normality than the t-test for comparing the population means (Section 9.2). If you have doubts about the normality of the population frequency distributions, use a *nonparametric method* (e.g., Levene's Test) for comparing the two population variances. A method can be found in the nonparametric-statistics texts listed in the references.

Hypothesis Test for (σ_1^2/σ_2^2)

Using the TI-84/TI-83 Graphing Calculator

Step 1   *Enter the data. (Skip to step 2 if you have summary statistics, not raw data.)*

Press **STAT** and select **1:Edit**.
Note: If the lists already contain data, clear the old data. Use the up **ARROW** to highlight '**LI**'.
Press **CLEAR ENTER**.
Use the up **ARROW** highlight '**L2**'.
Press **CLEAR ENTER**.
Use the **ARROW** and **ENTER** keys to enter the first data set into **L1**.
Use the **ARROW** and **ENTER** keys to enter the second data set into **L2**.

```
EDIT CALC TESTS
8↑TInterval…
9:2-SampZInt…
0:2-SampTInt…
A:1-PropZInt…
B:2-PropZInt…
C:χ²-Test…
D:2-SampFTest…
```

Step 2   *Access the Statistical Tests Menu.*

Press **STAT**.
Arrow right to **TESTS**.
Arrow down to **2-SampFTest**.
Press **ENTER**.

Step 3   *Choose "**Data**" or "**Stats**". ("Data" is selected when you have entered the raw data into the Lists. "Stats" is selected when you are given only the means, standard deviations, and sample sizes.)*

Press **ENTER**.
If you selected "Data",
Set **List1** to **L1** and **List2** to **L2**.
Set **Freq1** to **1** and set **Freq2** to **1**.
Use the **ARROW** to highlight the appropriate alternative hypothesis.
Press **ENTER**.
Arrow down to "**Calculate**".
Press **ENTER**.

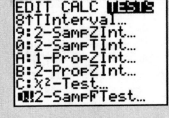

If you selected "Stats", enter the standard deviations and sample sizes.
Use the **ARROW** to highlight the appropriate alternative hypothesis.
Press **ENTER**.
Arrow down to "**Calculate**".
Press **ENTER**.
The results of the hypothesis test will be displayed with the p-value and the input data used.

(continued)

Example Test the hypothesis $H_0: \sigma_1^2 = \sigma_2^2$ vs. $H_a: \sigma_1^2 \neq \sigma_2^2$, using the following data:

Group 1: standard deviation $= 10$; $n = 23$
Group 2: standard deviation $= 12$; $n = 33$

As you can see from the screens, $F = .6944$ and the p-value is .3759. Since this p-value is large, you **do not reject** the null hypothesis. Notice that the output includes the standard deviations and sample sizes.

```
2-SampFTest
σ1≠σ2
F=.6944444444
p=.3759305952
Sx1=10
Sx2=12
↓n1=23
∎
```

Exercises 9.86–9.105

Understanding the Principles

9.86 Describe the sampling distribution of $(s_1)^2/(s_2)^2$ for normal data.

9.87 What conditions are required for valid inferences about $(\sigma_1)^2/(\sigma_2)^2$?

9.88 *True or false.* The F-statistic used for testing $H_0: \sigma_1^2 = \sigma_2^2$ against $H_a: \sigma_1^2 < \sigma_2^2$ is $F = (s_1)^2/(s_2)^2$.

9.89 *True or false.* $H_0: \sigma_1^2 = \sigma_2^2$ is equivalent to $H_0: \sigma_1^2/\sigma_2^2 = 0$.

Learning the Mechanics

9.90 Use Tables VIII, IX, X, and XI of Appendix A to find each
NW of the following F-values:
  a. $F_{.05}$, where $\nu_1 = 8$ and $\nu_2 = 5$
  b. $F_{.01}$, where $\nu_1 = 20$ and $\nu_2 = 14$
  c. $F_{.025}$, where $\nu_1 = 10$ and $\nu_2 = 5$
  d. $F_{.10}$, where $\nu_1 = 20$ and $\nu_2 = 5$

9.91 Given ν_1 and ν_2, find the following probabilities:
  a. $\nu_1 = 2, \nu_2 = 30, P(F \geq 4.18)$
  b. $\nu_1 = 24, \nu_2 = 14, P(F < 1.94)$
  c. $\nu_1 = 9, \nu_2 = 1, P(F \leq 6,022.0)$
  d. $\nu_1 = 30, \nu_2 = 30, P(F > 1.84)$

9.92 For each of the cases that follow, identify the rejection region that should be used to test $H_0: \sigma_1^2 = \sigma_2^2$ against $H_a: \sigma_1^2 > \sigma_2^2$. Assume that $\nu_1 = 20$ and $\nu_2 = 30$.
  a. $\alpha = .10$ **b.** $\alpha = .05$
  c. $\alpha = .025$ **d.** $\alpha = .01$

9.93 For each of the cases that follow, identify the rejection region that should be used to test $H_0: \sigma_1^2 = \sigma_2^2$ against $H_a: \sigma_1^2 \neq \sigma_2^2$. Assume that $\nu_1 = 8$ and $\nu_2 = 40$.
  a. $\alpha = .20$
  b. $\alpha = .10$
  c. $\alpha = .05$
  d. $\alpha = .02$

9.94 Specify the appropriate rejection region for testing against $H_0: \sigma_1^2 = \sigma_2^2$ in each of the following situations:
  a. $H_a: \sigma_1^2 > \sigma_2^2; \alpha = .05, n_1 = 25, n_2 = 20$
  b. $H_a: \sigma_1^2 < \sigma_2^2; \alpha = .05, n_1 = 10, n_2 = 15$
  c. $H_a: \sigma_1^2 \neq \sigma_2^2; \alpha = .10, n_1 = 21, n_2 = 31$
  d. $H_a: \sigma_1^2 < \sigma_2^2; \alpha = .01, n_1 = 31, n_2 = 41$
  e. $H_a: \sigma_1^2 \neq \sigma_2^2; \alpha = .05, n_1 = 7, n_2 = 16$

9.95 Independent random samples were selected from each of two
NW normally distributed populations, $n_1 = 16$ from population 1 and $n_2 = 25$ from population 2. The means and variances for the two samples are shown in the following table:

Sample 1	Sample 2
$n_1 = 16$	$n_2 = 25$
$\bar{x}_1 = 22.5$	$\bar{x}_2 = 28.2$
$s_1^2 = 2.87$	$s_2^2 = 9.85$

  a. Test the null hypothesis $H_0: \sigma_1^2 = \sigma_2^2$ against the alternative hypothesis $H_a: \sigma_1^2 \neq \sigma_2^2$. Use $\alpha = .05$.
  b. Find and interpret the p-value of the test.

9.96 Independent random samples were selected from each of two normally distributed populations, $n_1 = 6$ from population 1 and $n_2 = 4$ from population 2. The data are shown in the following table:

⊙ **LM9_96**

Sample 1	Sample 2
3.1	2.3
4.3	1.4
1.2	3.7
1.7	8.9
.6	
3.4	

  a. Test $H_0: \sigma_1^2 = \sigma_2^2$ against $H_a: \sigma_1^2 < \sigma_2^2$. Use $\alpha = .01$.
  b. Test $H_0: \sigma_1^2 = \sigma_2^2$ against $H_a: \sigma_1^2 \neq \sigma_2^2$. Use $\alpha = .10$.

Applying the Concepts—Basic

9.97 **Rating service at five-star hotels.** Refer to the *Journal of American Academy of Business, Cambridge* (March 2002) study of how guests perceive the quality of service at five-star hotels in Jamaica, presented in Exercise 9.16 (p. 426). A summary of the guest perception scores, by gender, is reproduced in the accompanying table. Let σ_M^2 and σ_F^2 represent the true variances in scores for male and female guests, respectively.

Gender	Sample Size	Mean Score	Standard Deviation
Males	127	39.08	6.73
Females	114	38.79	6.94

  a. Set up H_0 and H_a for determining whether σ_M^2 is less than σ_F^2.
  b. Find the test statistic for the test.

BULIMIA

Bulimic students	21	13	10	20	25	19	16	21	24	13	14			
Normal students	13	6	16	13	8	19	23	18	11	19	7	10	15	20

Source: Randles, R. H. "On neutral responses (zeros) in the sign test and ties in the Wilcoxon-Mann-Whitney test." *American Statistician,* Vol. 55, No. 2, May 2001 (Figure 3).

c. Give the rejection region for the test if $\alpha = .10$.

d. Find the approximate *p*-value of the test.

e. Draw the appropriate conclusion in the words of the problem.

f. What conditions are required for the test results to be valid?

9.98 Bulimia study. Refer to Exercise 9.19 (p. 427). The "fear of negative evaluation" (FNE) scores for the 11 bulimic females and 14 females with normal eating habits are reproduced in the table above. The confidence interval you constructed in Exercise 9.19 requires that the variance of the FNE scores of bulimic females be equal to the variance of the FNE scores of normal females. Conduct a test (at $\alpha = .05$) to determine the validity of this assumption.

GOBIANTS

9.99 How do you choose to argue? Refer to the *Thinking and Reasoning* (Oct. 2006) study of the cognitive skills required for successful arguments, presented in Exercise 9.21 (p. 427). Recall that 52 psychology graduate students were equally divided into two groups. Group 1 was presented with arguments that always attempted to strengthen the favored position. Group 2 was presented with arguments that always attempted to weaken the nonfavored position. Summary statistics for the student ratings of the arguments are reproduced in the accompanying table. In Exercise 9.21, you compared the mean ratings for the two groups with a small-sample *t*-test, assuming equal variances. Determine the validity of this assumption at $\alpha = .05$.

	Group 1 (support favored position)	Group 2 (weaken opposing position)
Sample size	26	26
Mean	28.6	24.9
Standard deviation	12.5	12.2

Source: Kuhn, D., and Udell, W. "Coordinating own and other perspectives in argument," *Thinking and Reasoning,* October 2006.

9.100 Mongolian desert ants. Refer to the *Journal of Biogeography* (Dec. 2003) study of ants in Mongolia (central Asia), presented Exercise 9.23 (p. 428), in which you compared the mean number of ants at two desert sites. Since the sample sizes were small, the variances of the populations at the two sites must be equal in order for the inference to be valid.

a. Set up H_0 and H_a for determining whether the variances are the same.

b. Use the data in the **GOBIANTS** file to find the test statistic for the test.

c. Give the rejection region for the test if $\alpha = .05$.

d. Find the approximate *p*-value of the test.

e. Draw the appropriate conclusion in the words of the problem.

f. What conditions are required for the test results to be valid?

9.101 Gender differences in math test scores. The *American Educational Research Journal* (Fall 1998) published a study comparing the mathematics achievement test scores of male and female students. The researchers hypothesized that the distribution of test scores for males is more variable than the corresponding distribution for females. Use the summary information reproduced in the following table to test this claim at $\alpha = .01$.

	Males	Females
Sample size	1,764	1,739
Mean	48.9	48.4
Standard deviation	12.96	11.85

Source: Bielinski, J., and Davison, M. L. "Gender differences by item difficulty interactions in multiple-choice mathematics items." *American Educational Research Journal,* Vol. 35, No. 3, Fall 1998, p. 464 (Table I).

Applying the Concepts—Intermediate

9.102 Patent infringement case. Refer to the *Chance* (Fall 2002) description of a patent infringement case against Intel Corp., presented in Exercise 9.20 (p. 427). The zinc measurements for three locations listed in the original inventor's notebook—on a text line, on a witness line, and on the intersection of the witness and text line—are reproduced in the following table:

PATENT

Text line:	.335	.374	.440			
Witness line:	.210	.262	.188	.329	.439	.397
Intersection:	.393	.353	.285	.295	.319	

a. Use a test (at $\alpha = .05$) to compare the variation in zinc measurements for the text line with the corresponding variation for the intersection.

b. Use a test (at $\alpha = .05$) to compare the variation in zinc measurements for the witness line with the corresponding variation for the intersection.

c. From your results in parts **a** and **b**, what can you infer about the variation in zinc measurements at the three notebook locations?

d. What assumptions are required for the inferences to be valid? Are they reasonably satisfied? (You checked these assumptions when you answered Exercise 9.20d.)

9.103 Human inspection errors. Tests of product quality by human inspectors can lead to serious errors. (*Journal of Quality Technology,* Apr. 1986.) To evaluate the performance of inspectors in a new company, a quality manager had a sample of 12 novice inspectors evaluate 200 finished products. The same 200 items were also evaluated by 12 experienced inspectors. The quality of each item—defective or nondefective—was known to the manager.

The following table lists the number of errors (classifying a defective item as nondefective or vice versa) made by each inspector:

INSPECT

Novice Inspectors				Experienced Inspectors			
30	35	26	40	31	15	25	19
36	20	45	31	28	17	19	18
33	29	21	48	24	10	20	21

a. Prior to conducting this experiment, the manager believed that the variance in inspection errors was lower for experienced inspectors than for novice inspectors. Do the sample data support her belief? Test, using $\alpha = .05$.

b. What is the appropriate p-value of the test you conducted in part **a?**

MILK

9.104 Detection of rigged school milk prices (cont'd). Refer to the investigation into collusive bidding in the northern Kentucky school milk market, presented in Exercises 9.26 (p. 429) and 9.68 (p. 452). In competitive sealed-bid markets, vendors do not share information about their bids. Consequently, more dispersion or variability among the bids is typically observed than in collusive markets, where vendors communicate about their bids and have a tendency to submit bids in close proximity to one another in an attempt to make the bidding appear competitive. If collusion exists in the tricounty milk market, the variation in winning bid prices in the surrounding ("competitive") market will be significantly larger than the corresponding variation in the tricounty ("rigged") market. A MINITAB analysis of the data on whole white milk in the **MILK** file

yielded the printout below. Is there evidence that the bid-price variance for the surrounding market exceeds the bid-price variance for the tricounty market?

9.105 Following the initial Persian Gulf War, the Pentagon changed its logistics processes to be more corporate-like. The extravagant "just-in-case" mentality was replaced with "just-in-time" systems. Emulating Federal Express and United Parcel Service, the Pentagon now expedites deliveries from factories to foxholes with the use of bar codes, laser cards, radio tags, and databases to track supplies. The following table contains order-to-delivery times (in days) for a sample of shipments from the United States to the Persian Gulf in 1991 and a sample of shipments from the United States to Bosnia in 1995.

ORDTIMES

Persian Gulf	Bosnia
28.0	15.1
20.0	6.4
26.5	5.0
10.6	11.4
9.1	6.5
35.2	6.5
29.1	3.0
41.2	7.0
27.5	5.5

Source: Adapted from Crock, S. "The Pentagon goes to B-school," *Business Week*, Dec. 11, 1995, p. 98.

a. Determine whether the variances in order-to-delivery times for Persian Gulf and Bosnia shipments are equal. Use $\alpha = .05$.

b. Given your answer to part **a,** is it appropriate to construct a confidence interval for the difference between the mean order-to-delivery times? Explain.

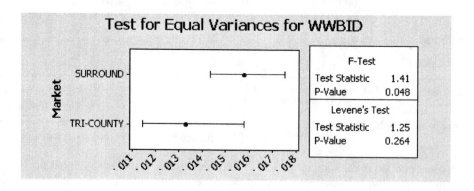

MINITAB output for
Exercise 9.104

KEY TERMS

Note: Starred (*) terms are from the optional section in this chapter.

GUIDE TO SELECTING A TWO-SAMPLE HYPOTHESIS & CONFIDENCE INTERVAL

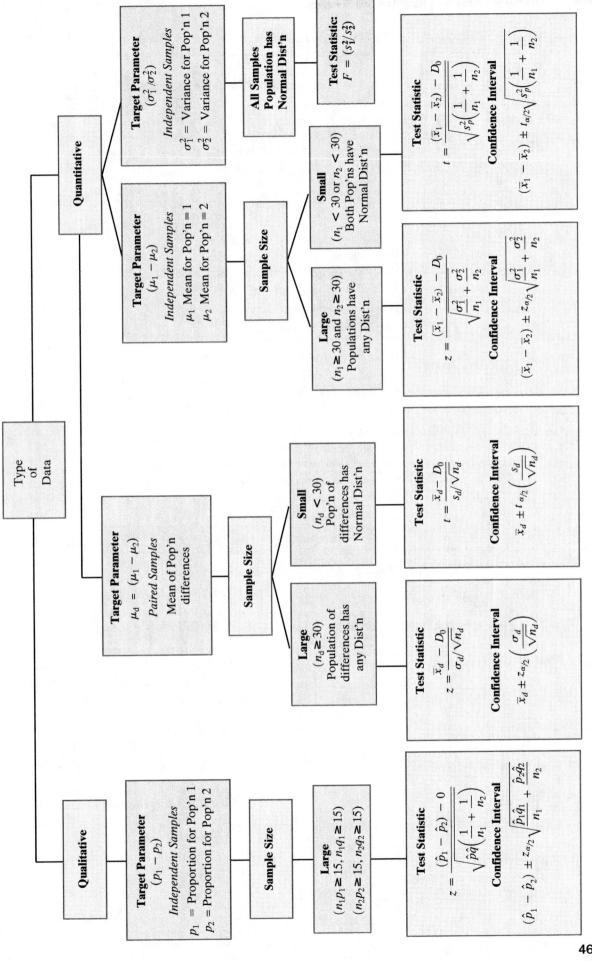

CHAPTER NOTES

Key Words for Identifying the Target Parameter

$\mu_1 - \mu_2$	Difference in Means or Averages
μ_d	Paired Difference in Means or Averages
$p_1 - p_2$	Difference in Proportions, Fractions, Percentages, Rates
σ_1^2/σ_2^2	Ratio (or Difference) in Variances, Spreads

Key Symbols

$\mu_1 - \mu_2$	Difference between population means
μ_d	Paired difference in population means
$p_1 - p_2$	Difference between population proportions
σ_1^2/σ_2^2	Ratio of population variances
D_0	Hypothesized value of difference
$\bar{x}_1 - \bar{x}_2$	Difference between sample means
$\bar{x}_d$	Mean of sample differences
$\hat{p}_1 - \hat{p}_2$	Difference between sample proportions
s_1^2/s_2^2	Ratio of sample variances
$\sigma_{(\bar{x}_1 - \bar{x}_2)}$	Standard error for $\bar{x}_1 - \bar{x}_2$
$\sigma_{\bar{d}}$	Standard error for $\bar{d}$
$\sigma_{(\hat{p}_1 - \hat{p}_2)}$	Standard error for $\hat{p}_1 - \hat{p}_2$
F_a	Critical value for F-distribution
v_1	Numerator degrees of freedom for F-distribution
v_2	Denominator degrees of freedom for F-distribution
SE	Sampling error in estimation

Determining the Sample Size

Estimating $\mu_1 - \mu_2$: $n_1 = n_2 = (z_{a/2})^2(\sigma_1^2 + \sigma_2^2)/(\text{SE})^2$

Estimating $p_1 - p_2$: $n_1 = n_2 = (z_{a/2})^2(p_1q_1 + p_2q_2)/(\text{SE})^2$

Conditions Required for Inferences about $\mu_1 - \mu_2$

Large samples:
1. Independent random samples
2. $n_1 \geq 30, n_2 \geq 30$

Small samples:
1. Independent random samples
2. Both populations normal
3. $\sigma_1^2 = \sigma_2^2$

Conditions Required for Inferences about σ_1^2/σ_2^2

Large or small samples:
1. Independent random samples
2. Both populations normal

Conditions Required for Inferences about μ_d

Large Samples:
1. Random sample of paired differences
2. $n_d \geq 30$

Small samples:
1. Random sample of paired differences
2. Population of differences is normal

Conditions Required for Inferences about $p_1 - p_2$

Large samples:
1. Independent random samples
2. $n_1p_1 \geq 15, n_1q_1 \geq 15$
3. $n_2p_2 \geq 15, n_2q_2 \geq 15$

Using a Confidence Interval for $(\mu_1 - \mu_2)$ or $(p_1 - p_2)$ to Determine whether a Difference Exists:

1. If the confidence interval includes all *positive* numbers $(+, +)$: $\rightarrow$ Infer $\mu_1 > \mu_2$ or $p_1 > p_2$
2. If the confidence interval includes all *negative* numbers $(-, -)$ $\rightarrow$ Infer $\mu_1 < \mu_2$ or $p_1 < p_2$
3. If the confidence interval includes 0 $(-, +)$: $\rightarrow$ Infer "no evidence of a difference."

Supplementary Exercises 9.106–9.140

Note: Starred (*) exercises refer to the optional section in this chapter.

Understanding the Principles

9.106 List the assumptions necessary for each of the following inferential techniques:
  a. Large-sample inferences about the difference $(\mu_1 - \mu_2)$ between population means, using a two-sample z-statistic
  b. Small-sample inferences about $(\mu_1 - \mu_2)$, using an independent samples design and a two-sample t-statistic
  c. Small-sample inferences about $(\mu_1 - \mu_2)$, using a paired difference design and a single-sample t-statistic to analyze the differences
  d. Large-sample inferences about the differences $(p_1 - p_2)$ between binomial proportions, using a two-sample z-statistic
  *e. Inferences about the ratio σ_1^2/σ_2^2 of two population variances, using an F-test

9.107 For each of the following, identify the target parameter as $\mu_1 - \mu_2$, $p_1 - p_2$, or σ_1^2/σ_2^2.
  a. Comparison of average SAT scores of males and females.
  b. Difference between mean waiting times at two supermarket checkout lanes
  c. Comparison of proportions of Democrats and Republicans who favor the legalization of marijuana.
  *d. Comparison of variation in salaries of NBA players picked in the first round and the second round.
  e. Difference in dropout rates of college student athletes and regular students

Learning the Mechanics

9.108 Two independent random samples were selected from normally distributed populations with means and variances (μ_1, σ_1^2) and (μ_2, σ_2^2), respectively. The sample sizes, means, and variances are shown in the following table:

Sample 1	Sample 2
$n_1 = 20$	$n_2 = 15$
$\bar{x}_1 = 123$	$\bar{x}_2 = 116$
$s_1^2 = 31.3$	$s_2^2 = 120.1$

  *a. Test H_0: $\sigma_1^2 = \sigma_2^2$ against H_a: $\sigma_1^2 \neq \sigma_2^2$. Use $\alpha = .05$.
  $F = 3.84$
  b. Would you be willing to use a t-test to test the null hypothesis H_0: $(\mu_1 - \mu_2) = 0$ against the alternative hypothesis H_a: $(\mu_1 - \mu_2) \neq 0$? Why?

9.109 Independent random samples were selected from two normally distributed populations with means μ_1 and μ_2, re-

spectively. The sample sizes, means, and variances are shown in the following table:

Sample 1	Sample 2
$n_1 = 12$	$n_2 = 14$
$\bar{x}_1 = 17.8$	$\bar{x}_2 = 15.3$
$s_1^2 = 74.2$	$s_2^2 = 60.5$

  a. Test H_0: $(\mu_1 - \mu_2) = 0$ against H_a: $(\mu_1 - \mu_2) > 0$. Use $\alpha = .05$.
  b. Form a 99% confidence interval for $(\mu_1 - \mu_2)$.
  c. How large must n_1 and n_2 be if you wish to estimate $(\mu_1 - \mu_2)$ to within two units with 99% confidence? Assume that $n_1 = n_2$.

9.110 Independent random samples were selected from two binomial populations. The size and number of observed successes for each sample are shown in the following table:

Sample 1	Sample 2
$n_1 = 200$	$n_2 = 200$
$x_1 = 110$	$x_2 = 130$

  a. Test H_0: $(p_1 - p_2) = 0$ against H_a: $(p_1 - p_2) < 0$. Use $\alpha = .10$.
  b. Form a 95% confidence interval for $(p_1 - p_2)$.
  c. What sample sizes would be required if we wish to use a 95% confidence interval of width $.01$ to estimate $(p_1 - p_2)$?

9.111 Two independent random samples are taken from two populations. The results of these samples are summarized in the following table:

Sample 1	Sample 2
$n_1 = 135$	$n_2 = 148$
$\bar{x}_1 = 12.2$	$\bar{x}_2 = 8.3$
$s_1^2 = 2.1$	$s_2^2 = 3.0$

  a. Form a 90% confidence interval for $(\mu_1 - \mu_2)$.
  b. Test H_0: $(\mu_1 - \mu_2) = 0$ against H_a: $(\mu_1 - \mu_2) \neq 0$. Use $\alpha = .01$.
  c. What sample size would be required if you wish to estimate $(\mu_1 - \mu_2)$ to within $.2$ with 90% confidence? Assume that $n_1 = n_2$.

9.112 A random sample of five pairs of observations were selected, one observation from a population with mean μ_1, the other from a population with mean μ_2. The data are shown in the following table:

LM9_112

Pair	Value from Population 1	Value from Population 2
1	28	22
2	31	27
3	24	20
4	30	27
5	22	20

a. Test the null hypothesis $H_0: \mu_d = 0$ against $H_a: \mu_d \neq 0$, where $\mu_d = \mu_1 - \mu_2$. Use $\alpha = .05$.
b. Form a 95% confidence interval for μ_d.
c. When are the procedures you used in parts **a** and **b** valid?

Applying the Concepts—Basic

EVOS

9.113 Oil spill impact on seabirds. Refer to the *Journal of Agricultural, Biological, and Environmental Statistics* (Sept. 2000) study of the impact of a tanker oil spill on the seabird population in Alaska, presented in Exercise 2.181 (p. 105). Recall that for each of 96 shoreline locations (called transects), the number of seabirds found, the length (in kilometers) of the transect, and whether or not the transect was in an oiled area were recorded. (The data are saved in the **EVOS** file.) *Observed seabird density* is defined as the observed count divided by the length of the transect. A comparison of the mean densities of oiled and unoiled transects is displayed in the MINITAB printout below. Use this information to make an inference about the difference in the population mean seabird densities of oiled and unoiled transects.

OILSPILL

9.114 Hull failure of oil tankers. Refer to the *Marine Technology* (Jan. 1995) study of major oil spills from tankers and carriers, presented in Exercise 2.186 (p. 106). The data for the 50 spills are saved in the **OILSPILL** file.
a. Construct a 90% confidence interval for the difference between the mean spillage amount in accidents caused by collision and the mean spillage amount in accidents caused by fires or explosions. Interpret the result.

b. Conduct a test of hypothesis to compare the mean spillage amount in accidents caused by grounding with the corresponding mean in accidents caused by hull failure. Use $\alpha = .05$.
c. Refer to parts **a** and **b**. State any assumptions required for the inferences derived from the analyses to be valid. Are these assumptions reasonably satisfied?
***d.** Conduct a test of hypothesis to compare the variation in spillage amounts in accidents caused by collision and accidents caused by grounding. Use $\alpha = .02$.

9.115 Effect of altitude on climbers. Dr. Philip Lieberman, a neuroscientist at Brown University, recently conducted a field experiment to gauge the effect of high altitude on a person's ability to think critically. (*New York Times*, Aug. 23, 1995.) The subjects of the experiment were five males who took part in an American expedition climbing Mount Everest. At the base camp, Lieberman read sentences to the climbers while they looked at simple pictures in a book. The length of time (in seconds) it took for each climber to match the picture with a sentence was recorded. Using a radio, Lieberman repeated the task when the climbers reached a camp 5 miles above sea level. At this altitude, he noted that the climbers took 50% longer to complete the task.
a. What is the variable measured in this experiment?
b. What are the experimental units?
c. Discuss how the data should be analyzed.

9.116 Tapeworms in brill fish. The *Journal of Fish Biology* (Aug. 1990) reported on a study comparing the incidence of parasites (tapeworms) in species of Mediterranean and Atlantic fish. In the Mediterranean Sea, 588 brill were captured and dissected, and 211 were found to be infected by the parasite. In the Atlantic Ocean, 123 brill were captured and dissected, and 26 were found to be infected. Compare the proportions of infected brill at the two capture sites, using a 90% confidence interval. Interpret the interval.

9.117 Self-concepts of female students. A study reported in the *Journal of Psychology* (Mar. 1991) measures the change in female students' self-concepts as they move from high school to college. A sample of 133 Boston College female students was selected for the study. Each participant was asked to evaluate several aspects of her life at two points in time: at the end of her senior year of high school and during her sophomore year of college. Each student was asked to evaluate where she believed she stood on a scale that ranged from the top 10% of the

---

Two-Sample T-Test and CI: Density, Oil

```
Two-sample T for Density

Oil   N   Mean   StDev   SE Mean
no    36  3.27   6.70    1.1
yes   60  3.50   5.97    0.77


Difference = mu (no ) - mu (yes)
Estimate for difference:  -0.221165
95% CI for difference:   (-2.927767, 2.485436)
T-Test of difference = 0 (vs not =): T-Value = -0.16  P-Value = 0.871  DF = 67
```

MINITAB output for Exercise 9.113

class (1) to the lowest 10% of the class (5). The results for three of the traits evaluated are reported in the following table:

Trait	n	Senior Year of High School $\bar{x}_1$	Sophomore Year of College $\bar{x}_2$
Leadership	133	2.09	2.33
Popularity	133	2.48	2.69
Intellectual self-confidence	133	2.29	2.55

a. What null and alternative hypotheses would you test to determine whether the mean self-concept of females decreases between the senior year of high school and the sophomore year of college, as measured by each of the three traits listed?

b. Are these traits more appropriately analyzed with an independent samples test or a paired difference test? Explain.

c. Noting the size of the sample, state what assumptions are necessary to ensure the validity of the tests.

d. The article reports that the leadership test results in a p-value greater than .05, while the tests for popularity and intellectual self-confidence result in p-values less than .05. Interpret these results.

*9.118 Bear vs. pig bile study. Bear gallbladder is used in Chinese medicine to treat inflammation. A study in the *Journal of Ethnopharmacology* (June 1995) examined the easier-to-obtain pig gallbladder as an effective substitute for bear gallbladder. Twenty male mice were divided randomly into two groups: Ten were given a dosage of bear bile and 10 were given a dosage of pig bile. All the mice then received an injection of croton oil in the left earlobe to induce inflammation. Four hours later, both the left and right earlobes were weighed, with the difference (in milligrams) representing the degree of swelling. Summary statistics on the degree of swelling are provided in the following table:

Bear Bile	Pig Bile
$n_1 = 10$	$n_2 = 10$
$\bar{x}_1 = 9.19$	$\bar{x}_2 = 9.71$
$s_1 = 4.17$	$s_2 = 3.33$

a. Use a hypothesis test (at $\alpha = .05$) to compare the variation in degree of swelling for mice treated with bear bile and mice treated with pig bile.

b. What assumptions are necessary for the inference you made in part **a** to be valid?

9.119 The "winner's curse" in auction bidding. In auction bidding, the "winner's curse" is the phenomenon of the winning (or highest) bid price being above the expected value of the item being auctioned. *The Review of Economics and Statistics* (Aug. 2001) published a study on whether experience in bidding affects the likelihood of the winner's curse occurring. Two groups of bidders in a sealed-bid auction were compared: (1) superexperienced bidders and (2) less experienced bidders. In the superexperienced group, 29 of 189 winning bids were above the item's expected value; in the less experienced group, 32 of 149 winning bids were above the item's expected value.

a. Find an estimate of p_1, the true proportion of superexperienced bidders who fall prey to the winner's curse.

b. Find an estimate of p_2, the true proportion of less experienced bidders who fall prey to the winner's curse.

c. Construct a 90% confidence interval for $p_1 - p_2$.

d. Give a practical interpretation of the confidence interval you constructed in part **c**. Make a statement about whether experience in bidding affects the likelihood of the winner's curse occurring.

9.120 Environmental impact study. Some power plants are located near rivers or oceans so that the available water can be used to cool the condensers. Suppose that, as part of an environmental impact study, a power company wants to estimate the difference in mean water temperature between the discharge of its plant and the offshore waters. How many sample measurements must be taken at each site in order to estimate the true difference between means to within .2°C with 95% confidence? Assume that the range in readings will be about 4°C at each site and that the same number of readings will be taken at each site.

9.121 Impact of exam question order. Do the early questions in an exam affect your performance on later questions? Research reported in the *Journal of Psychology* (Jan. 1991) investigated this relationship by conducting the following experiment: 140 college students were randomly assigned to two groups. Group A took an exam that contained 15 difficult questions followed by 5 moderate questions. Group B took an exam that contained 15 easy questions followed by the same 5 moderate questions. One of the goals of the study was to compare the average scores of the two groups on the moderate questions.

a. The researchers hypothesized that the students who had the easy questions would score better than the students who had the difficult questions. Set up the appropriate null and alternative hypotheses to test their research hypothesis, defining any symbols you use.

b. Suppose the p-value for this test was reported as .3248. What conclusion would you reach on the basis of this p-value?

c. What assumptions are necessary to ensure the validity of this conclusion?

9.122 Students' attitudes toward parents. Researchers at the University of South Alabama compared the attitudes of male college students toward their fathers with their attitudes toward their mothers. (*Journal of Genetic Psychology*, March 1998.) Each of a sample of 13 males was asked to complete the following statement about each of his parents: My relationship with my father (mother) can best be described as (1) Awful, (2) Poor, (3) Average, (4) Good, or (5) Great. The following data were obtained:

FMATTITUDES

Student	Attitude toward Father	Attitude toward Mother
1	2	3
2	5	5
3	4	3
4	4	5
5	3	4
6	5	4
7	4	5
8	2	4
9	4	5
10	5	4
11	4	5
12	5	4
13	3	3

Source: Adapted from Vitulli, W. F., and Richardson, D. K. "College students' attitudes toward relationships with parents: A five-year comparative analysis." *Journal of Genetic Psychology*, Vol. 159, No. 1, (March 1998), pp. 45–52.

a. Specify the appropriate hypotheses for testing whether male students' attitudes toward their fathers differ from their attitudes toward their mothers, on average.

b. Conduct the test of part **a** at $\alpha = .05$. Interpret the results in the context of the problem.

Applying the Concepts—Intermediate

9.123 Depo-Provera drug study. Hypersexual behavior caused by traumatic brain injury (TBI) is often treated with the drug Depo-Provera. In one clinical study, eight young male TBI patients who exhibited hypersexual behavior were treated weekly with 400 milligrams of Depo-Provera for six months. (*Journal of Head Trauma Rehabilitation,* June 1995.) The testosterone levels (in nanograms per deciliter) of the patients both prior to treatment and at the end of the six-month treatment period are given in the following table:

DEPOPROV

Patient	Pretreatment	After 6 months on Depo-Provera
1	849	96
2	903	41
3	890	31
4	1,092	124
5	362	46
6	900	53
7	1,006	113
8	672	174

Source: Emory, L. E., Cole, C. M., and Meyer, W. J. "Use of Depo-Provera to control sexual aggression in persons with traumatic brain injury," *Journal of Head Trauma Rehabilitation,* Vol. 10, No. 3, June 1995, p. 52 (Table 2).

a. Construct a 99% confidence interval for the true mean difference between the pretreatment and after-treatment testosterone levels of young male TBI patients.

b. Use the interval you found in part **a** to make an inference about the effectiveness of Depo-Provera in reducing testosterone levels of young male TBI patients.

9.124 Mating habits of snails. Hermaphrodites are animals that possess the reproductive organs of both sexes. *Genetical Research* (June 1995) published a study of the mating systems of hermaphroditic snail species. The mating habits of the snails were classified into two groups: (1) self-fertilizing (selfing) snails that mate with snails of the same sex and (2) cross-fertilizing (outcrossing) snails that mate with snails of the opposite sex. One variable of interest in the study was the effective population size of the snail species. The means and standard deviations of the effective population size for independent random samples of 17 outcrossing snail species and 5 selfing snail species are given in the accompanying table.

Snail Mating System	Effective Population Size		
	Sample Size	Mean	Standard Deviation
Outcrossing	17	4,894	1,932
Selfing	5	4,133	1,890

Source: Jarne, P. "Mating system, bottlenecks, and genetic polymorphism in hermaphroditic animals." *Genetical Research,* Vol. 65, No. 3, June 1995, p. 197 (Table 4).

a. Compare the mean effective population sizes of the two types of snail species with a 90% confidence interval. Interpret the result.

b. Geneticists are often more interested in comparing the variation in population size of the two types of mating systems. Conduct this analysi for the researcher. Interpret the result.

9.125 Teaching nursing skills. A traditional approach to teaching basic nursing skills was compared with an innovative approach in the *Journal of Nursing Education* (Jan. 1992). The innovative approach utilizes Vee heuristics and concept maps to link theoretical concepts with practical skills. Forty-two students enrolled in an upper-division nursing course participated in the study. Half (21) were randomly assigned to laboratories that utilized the innovative approach. After completing the course, all students were given short-answer questions about scientific principles underlying each of 10 nursing skills. The objective of the research was to compare the mean scores of the two groups of students.

a. What is the appropriate test to use to compare the two groups?

b. Are any assumptions required for the test?

c. One question dealt with the use of clean or sterile gloves. The mean scores for this question were 3.28 (traditional) and 3.40 (innovative). Is there sufficient information to perform the test?

d. Refer to part **c.** The p-value for the test was reported to be $p = .79$. Interpret this result.

e. Another question concerned the choice of a stethoscope. The mean scores of the two groups were 2.55 (traditional) and 3.60 (innovative), with an associated p-value of .02. Interpret these results.

9.126 Identical twins reared apart. Because they share an identical genotype, twins make ideal subjects for investigating the degree to which various environmental conditions affect personality. The classical method of studying this phenomenon, and the subject of an interesting book by Susan Farber (*Identical Twins Reared Apart,* New York: Basic Books, 1981), is the study of identical twins separated early in life and reared apart. Much of Farber's discussion focuses on a comparison of IQ scores. The data for this analysis appear in the accompanying table. One member (A) of each of the $n = 32$ pairs of twins was reared by a natural parent; the other member (B) was reared by a relative or some other person. Is there a significant difference between the average IQ scores of identical twins when one member of the pair is reared by the natural parents and the other member of the pair is not? Use $\alpha = .05$ to draw your conclusion.

TWINSIQ

Pair ID	Twin A	Twin B	Pair ID	Twin A	Twin B
112	113	109	228	100	88
114	94	100	232	100	104
126	99	86	236	93	84
132	77	80	306	99	95
136	81	95	308	109	98
148	91	106	312	95	100
170	111	117	314	75	86
172	104	107	324	104	103
174	85	85	328	73	78
180	66	84	330	88	99
184	111	125	338	92	111
186	51	66	342	108	110
202	109	108	344	88	83
216	122	121	350	90	82
218	97	98	352	79	76
220	82	94	416	97	98

Source: Adapted from *Identical Twins Reared Apart,* by Susan L. Farber © 1981 by Basic Books, Inc.

9.127 Treatments for panic disorder. Inositol is a complex cyclic alcohol found to be effective against clinical depression. Medical researchers believe that inositol may also be used to treat panic disorder. To test this theory, a double-blind, placebo-controlled study of 21 patients diagnosed with panic disorder was conducted. (*American Journal of Psychiatry,* July 1995.) Patients completed diaries recording

INOSITOL

Patient	Placebo	Inositol	Patient	Placebo	Inositol
1	0	0	12	0	2
2	2	1	13	3	1
3	0	3	14	3	1
4	1	2	15	3	4
5	0	0	16	4	2
6	10	5	17	6	4
7	2	0	18	15	21
8	6	4	19	28	8
9	1	1	20	30	0
10	1	0	21	13	0
11	1	3			

Source: Benjamin, J., et al. "Double-blind, placebo-controlled, crossover trial of inositol treatment for panic disorder," *American Journal of Psychiatry,* Vol. 152, No. 7, July 1995, p. 1085 (Table 1).

the occurrence of their panic attacks. The data for a week in which patients received a glucose placebo and for a week when they were treated with inositol are provided in the accompanying table. [*Note:* Neither the patients nor the treating physicians knew which week the placebo was given.] Analyze the data and interpret the results. Comment on the validity of the assumptions.

9.128 Aerobic exercise study. Excess postexercise oxygen consumption (EPOC) describes energy expended during the body's recovery period immediately following aerobic exercise. *The Journal of Sports Medicine and Physical Fitness* (Dec. 1994) published a study designed to investigate the effect of fitness level on the magnitude and duration of EPOC. Ten healthy young adult males volunteered for the study. Five were endurance trained and made up the fit group; the other five were not engaged in any systematic training and constituted the sedentary group. Each volunteer engaged in a weight-supported exercise on a cycle ergometer until 300 kilocalories were expended. The magnitude (in kilocalories) and duration (in minutes) of the EPOC of each exerciser were measured. The study results are summarized in the following table:

Variable		Fit ($n = 5$)	Sedentary ($n = 5$)	p-value
Magnitude (kcal)	Mean	12.2	12.2	.998
	Std. dev.	3.1	4.3	
Duration (min)	Mean	16.6	20.4	.344
	Std. dev.	3.1	7.8	

Source: Sedlock, D. A. "Fitness levels and postexercise energy expenditure," *The Journal of Sports Medicine and Physical Fitness,* Vol. 34, No. 4, Dec. 1994, p. 339 (Table III).

a. Conduct a test of hypothesis to determine whether the true mean magnitude of EPOC differs for fit and sedentary young adult males. Use $\alpha = .10$.

b. The *p*-value for the test you conducted in part **a** is given in the table. Interpret this value.

c. Conduct a test of hypothesis to determine whether the true mean duration of EPOC differs for fit and sedentary young adult males. Use $\alpha = .10$.

d. The *p*-value for the test you conducted in part **c** is given in the table. Interpret this value.

9.129 Switching majors in college. When female undergraduates switch from science, mathematics, and engineering (SME) majors into disciplines that are not based on science, are their reasons different from those of their male counterparts? This question was investigated in *Science Education* (July 1995). A sample of 335 junior/senior undergraduates—172 females and 163 males—at two large research universities were identified as "switchers"; that is, they left a declared SME major for a non-SME major. Each student listed one or more factors that contributed to the switching decision.

a. Of the 172 females in the sample, 74 listed lack or loss of interest in SME (i.e., they were "turned off" by science) as a major factor, compared with 72 of the 163 males. Conduct a test (at $\alpha = .10$) to determine whether the proportion of female switchers who give "lack of interest in SME" as a major reason for switching differs from the corresponding proportion of males.

b. Thirty-three of the 172 females in the sample indicated that they because discouraged or lost confidence because of low grades in SME during their early years, compared with 44 of 163 males. Construct a 90% confidence interval for the difference between the proportions of female and male switchers who lost confidence due to low grades in SME. Interpret the result.

9.130 Swim maze study. Merck Research Labs used the single-T swim maze to conduct an experiment to evaluate the effect of a new drug. Nineteen impregnated dam rats were allocated a dosage of 12.5 milligrams of the drug. One male and one female rat pup were randomly selected from each resulting litter to perform in the swim maze. Each pup was placed in the water at one end of the maze and allowed to swim until it escaped at the opposite end. If the pup failed to escape after a certain period of time, it was placed at the beginning of the maze and given another chance. The experiment was repeated until each pup accomplished three successful escapes. The accompanying table reports the number of swims required by each pup to perform three successful escapes. Is there sufficient evidence of a difference between the mean number of swims required by male and female pups? Conduct the test (at $\alpha = .10$). Comment on the assumptions required for the test to be valid.

RATPUPS

Litter	Male	Female	Litter	Male	Female
1	8	5	11	6	5
2	8	4	12	6	3
3	6	7	13	12	5
4	6	3	14	3	8
5	6	5	15	3	4
6	6	3	16	8	12
7	3	8	17	3	6
8	5	10	18	6	4
9	4	4	19	9	5
10	4	4			

Source: Thomas E. Bradstreet, Merck Research Labs, BL 3–2, West Point, PA 19486.

9.131 Rating music teachers. Students enrolled in music classes at the University of Texas (Austin) participated in a study to compare the observations and teacher evaluations of music education majors and nonmusic majors. (*Journal of Research in Music Education*, Winter 1991.) Independent random samples of 100 music majors and 100 nonmajors rated the overall performance of their teacher, using a six-point scale, where 1 was the lowest rating and 6 the highest. Use the information in the accompanying table to compare the mean teacher ratings of the two groups of music students with a 95% confidence interval. Interpret the result.

	Music Majors	Nonmusic Majors
Sample size	100	100
Mean "overall" rating	4.26	4.59
Standard deviation	.81	.78

Source: Duke, R. A., and Blackman, M. D. "The relationship between observers' recorded teacher behavior and evaluation of music instruction," *Journal of Research in Music Education*, Vol. 39, No. 4, Winter 1991 (Table 2).

9.132 Identifying the target parameter. For each of the following studies, give the parameter of interest and state any assumptions that are necessary for the inferences to be invalid.

a. To investigate a possible link between jet lag and memory impairment, a University of Bristol (England) neurologist recruited 20 female flight attendants who worked flights across several time zones. Half of the attendants had only a short recovery time between flights, and half had a long recovery time between flights. The average size of the right temporal lobe of the brain for the short-recovery group was significantly smaller than the average size of the right temporal lobe of the brain for the long-recovery group. (*Tampa Tribune*, May 23, 2001.)

b. In a study presented at the March 2001 meeting of the Association for the Advancement of Applied Sport Psychology, researchers revealed that the proportion of athletes who have a good self-image of their body is 20% higher than the corresponding proportion of nonathletes.

c. A University of Florida animal sciences professor has discovered that feeding chickens corn oil causes them to produce larger eggs. (*UF News*, April 11, 2001.) The weight of eggs produced by each of a sample of chickens on a regular feed diet was recorded. Then the same chickens were fed a diet supplemented by corn oil, and the weight of eggs produced by each was recorded. The mean weight of the eggs produced with corn oil was 3 grams heavier than the mean weight produced with the regular diet.

*9.133 Instrument precision. The quality control department of a paper company measures the brightness (a measure of reflectance) of finished paper on a periodic basis throughout the day. Two instruments that are available to measure the paper specimens are subject to error, but they can be adjusted so that the mean readings for a control paper specimen are the same for both instruments. Suppose you are concerned about the precision of the two instruments and want to compare the variability in the readings of instrument 1 with those of instrument 2. Five brightness measurements were made on a single paper specimen, using each of the two instruments. The data are shown in the following table:

BRIGHT

Instrument 1	Instrument 2
29	26
28	34
30	30
28	32
30	28

a. Is the variance of the measurements obtained by instrument 1 significantly different from the variance of the measurements obtained by instrument 2?

b. What assumptions must be satisfied for the test in part **a** to be valid?

9.134 Students attitudes towards parents. Refer to the *Journal of Genetic Psychology* (Mar. 1998) study comparing male students' attitudes toward their fathers and mothers, presented in Exercise 9.122 (p. 471). Suppose you want to estimate $\mu_D = (\mu_F - \mu_M)$, the difference between the population mean attitudes toward fathers and mothers, using a 90% confidence interval with a sampling error of .3. Find the number of male students required to obtain such an estimate. Assume that the variance of the paired differences is $\sigma_D^2 = 1$.

9.135 Kicking the cigarette habit. Can taking an antidepressant drug help cigarette smokers kick their habit? The *New England Journal of Medicine* (Oct. 23, 1997) published a study in which 615 smokers (all of whom wanted to give up smoking) were randomly assigned to receive either Zyban (an antidepressant) or a placebo (a dummy pill) for six weeks. Of the 309 patients who received Zyban, 71 were not smoking one year later. Of the 306 patients who received a placebo, 37 were not smoking one year later. Conduct a test of hypothesis (at $\alpha = .05$) to answer the research question posed in the first sentence of this exercise.

9.136 Muscle properties of crayfish. Marine biochemists at the University of Tokyo studied the properties of crustacean striated muscles. (*The Journal of Experimental Zoology*, Sept. 1993.) The main purpose of the experiment was to compare the biochemical properties of fast and slow muscles of crayfish. Using crayfish obtained from a local supplier, the researchers excised 12 fast-muscle fiber bundles and tested each one for uptake of calcium. Twelve slow-muscle fiber bundles were excised from a second sample of crayfish, and their calcium uptake was measured. The results of the experiment are summarized here. (All calcium measurements are in moles per milligram.) Analyze the data, using a 95% confidence interval. Make an inference about the difference between the calcium uptake means of fast and slow muscles.

Fast Muscle	Slow Muscle
$n_1 = 12$	$n_2 = 12$
$\bar{x}_1 = .57$	$\bar{x}_2 = .37$
$s_1 = .104$	$s_2 = .035$

Source: Ushio, H., and Watabe, S. "Ultrastructural and biochemical analysis of the sarcoplasmic reticulum from crayfish fast and slow striated muscles," *Journal of Experimental Zoology*, Vol. 267, Sept. 1993, p. 16 (Table 1). Copyright © 1993 John Wiley & Sons, Inc. Reprinted with permission.

Applying the Concepts—Advanced

9.137 Isolation timeouts for students. Researchers at Rochester Institute of Technology investigated the use of isolation time-out as a behavioral management technique (*Exceptional Children*, Feb. 1995.) Subjects for the study were 155 emotionally disturbed students enrolled in a special-education facility. The students were randomly assigned to one of two types of classrooms: Option II classrooms (one teacher, one paraprofessional, and a maximum of 12 students) and Option III classrooms (one teacher, one paraprofessional, and a maximum of 6 students). Over the academic year, the number of behavioral incidents resulting in an isolation time-out was recorded for each student. Summary statistics for the two groups of students are shown in the following table:

	Option II	Option III
Number of students	100	55
Mean number of time-out incidents	78.67	102.87
Standard deviation	59.08	69.33

Source: Costenbader, V., and Reading-Brown, M. "Isolation timeout used with students with emotional disturbance," *Exceptional Children*, Vol. 61, No. 4, Feb. 1995, p. 359 (Table 3).

Do you agree with the following statement: "On average, students in Option III classrooms had significantly more time-out incidents than students in Option II classrooms?"

9.138 Feeding habits of sea urchins. The *Florida Scientist* (Summer/Autumn 1991) reported on a study of the feeding habits of sea urchins. A sample of 20 urchins was captured from Biscayne Bay (Miami), placed in marine aquaria, and then starved for 48 hours. Each sea urchin was then fed a 5-cm blade of turtle grass. Ten of the urchins received only green blades, while the other half received only decayed blades. (Assume that the two samples of 10 sea urchins each were randomly and independently selected.) The ingestion time, measured from the time the blade first made contact with the urchin's mouth to the time the urchin had finished ingesting the blade, was recorded. A summary of the results is provided in the following table:

	Green Blades	Decayed Blades
Number of sea urchins	10	10
Mean ingestion time (hours)	3.35	2.36
Standard deviation (hours)	.79	.47

Source: Montague, J. R., et al. "Laboratory measurement of ingestion rate for the sea urchin *Lytechinus variegatus*," *Florida Scientist*, Vol. 54, Nos. 3/4, Summer/Autumn, 1991 (Table 1).

According to the researchers, "The difference in rates at which the urchins ingested the blades suggest that green, unblemished turtle grass may not be a particularly palatable food compared with decayed turtle grass. If so, urchins in the field may find it more profitable to selectively graze on decayed portions of the leaves." Do the results support this conclusion?

Critical Thinking Challenges

9.139 Self-managed work teams and family life. To improve quality, productivity, and timeliness, more and more American industries are utilizing self-managed work teams (SMWTs). A team typically consists of 5 to 15 workers who are collectively responsible for making decisions and performing all tasks related to a particular project. Researchers L. Stanley-Stevens (Tarleton State University), D. E. Yeatts, and R. R. Seward (both from the University of North Texas) investigated the connection between SMWTs, work characteristics, and workers' perceptions of positive spillover into family life (*Quality Management Journal*, Summer 1995.) Survey data were collected from 114 AT&T [employees who worked on 1 of 15 SMWTs at an AT&T technical division. The workers were divided into two groups: (1) those who reported a positive spillover of work skills to family life and (2) those who did not report any such positive work spillover. The two groups were compared on a variety of job and demographic characteristics, several of which are shown in the accompanying table. All but the demographic characteristics were measured on a seven-point scale, ranging from 1 = "strongly disagree" to 7 = "strongly agree"; thus, the larger the number, the more the characteristic was indicated.

SPILLOVER
Variables Measured in the SMWT Survey

Characteristic	Variable
Information Flow	Use of creative ideas (seven-point scale)
Information Flow	Utilization of information (seven-point scale)
Decision Making	Participation in decisions regarding personnel matters (seven-point scale)
Job	Good use of skills (seven-point scale)
Job	Task identity (seven-point scale)
Demographic	Age (years)
Demographic	Education (years)
Demographic	Gender (male or female)
Comparison	Group (positive spillover or no spillover)

The file named **SPILLOVER** includes the values of the variables listed in the table for each of the 114 survey participants. The researchers' objectives were to compare the two groups of workers on each characteristic. In particular, they wanted to know which job-related characteristics are most highly associated with positive work spillover. Conduct a complete analysis of the data for the researchers.

9.140 **MS and exercise study**. A study published in *Clinical Kinesiology* (Spring 1995) was designed to examine the metabolic and cardiopulmonary responses during exercise of persons diagnosed with multiple sclerosis (MS). Leg-cycling and arm-cranking exercises were performed by 10 MS patients and 10 healthy (non-MS) control subjects. Each member of the control group was selected on the basis of gender, age, height, and weight to match (as closely as possible) with one member of the MS group. Consequently, the researchers compared the MS and non-MS groups by matched-pairs t-tests on such outcome variables as oxygen uptake, carbon dioxide output, and peak aerobic power. The data on the matching variables used in the experiment are shown in the table below. Have the researchers successfully matched the MS and non-MS subjects?

MSSTUDY

	MS Subjects				Non-MS Subjects			
Matched Pair	Gender	Age (years)	Height (cm)	Weight (kg)	Gender	Age (years)	Height (cm)	Weight (kg)
1	M	48	171.0	80.8	M	45	173.0	76.3
2	F	34	158.5	75.0	F	34	158.0	75.6
3	F	34	167.6	55.5	F	34	164.5	57.7
4	M	38	167.0	71.3	M	34	161.3	70.0
5	M	45	182.5	90.9	M	39	179.0	96.0
6	F	42	166.0	72.4	F	42	167.0	77.8
7	M	32	172.0	70.5	M	34	165.8	74.7
8	F	35	166.5	55.3	F	43	165.1	71.4
9	F	33	166.5	57.9	F	31	170.1	60.4
10	F	46	175.0	79.9	F	43	175.0	77.9

Source: Ponichtera-Mulcare, J. A., et al. "Maximal aerobic exercise of individuals with multiple sclerosis using three modes of ergometry," *Clinical Kinesiology,* Vol. 49, No. 1, Spring 1995, p. 7 (Table 1).

SUMMARY ACTIVITY: Paired Vs. Unpaired Experiments

We have now discussed two methods of collecting data to compare two population means. In many experimental situations, a decision must be made either to collect two independent samples or to conduct a paired difference experiment. The importance of this decision cannot be overemphasized, since the amount of information obtained and the cost of the experiment are both directly related to the method of experimentation that is chosen.

Choose two populations (pertinent to your school major) that have unknown means and for which you could both collect two independent samples and collect paired observations. Before conducting the experiment, state which method of sampling you think will provide more information (and why). Compare the two methods, first performing the independent sampling procedure by collecting 10 observations from each population (a total of 20 measurements) and then performing the paired difference experiment by collecting 10 pairs of observations.

Construct two 95% confidence intervals, one for each experiment you conduct. Which method provides the narrower confidence interval and hence more information on this performance of the experiment? Does your result agree with your preliminary expectations?

REFERENCES

Freedman, D., Pisani, R., and Purves, R. *Statistics*. New York: W. W. Norton and Co., 1978.

Gibbons, J. D. *Nonparametric Statistical Inference*, 2d ed. New York: McGraw-Hill, 1985.

Hollander, M., and Wolfe, D. A. *Nonparametric Statistical Methods*. New York: Wiley, 1973.

Mendenhall, W., Beaver, R. J., and Beaver, B. *Introduction to Probability and Statistics*, 11th ed. North Scituate, MA: Duxbury, 2002.

Satterthwaite, F. W. "An approximate distribution of estimates of variance components." *Biometrics Bulletin*, Vol. 2, 1946, pp. 110–114.

Snedecor, G. W., and Cochran, W. *Statistical Methods*, 7th ed. Ames, IA: Iowa State University Press, 1980.

Steel, R. G. D., and Torrie, J. H. *Principles and Procedures of Statistics*, 2d ed. New York: McGraw-Hill, 1980.

Using Technology

Two-Sample Inferences with MINITAB

MINITAB can be used to make two-sample inferences about $(\mu_1 - \mu_2)$ for independent samples, μ_d for paired samples, $(p_1 - p_2)$, and σ_1^2/σ_2^2.

To carry out an analysis for $(\mu_1 - \mu_2,)$ first access the MINITAB worksheet that contains the sample data. Next, click on the "Basic Statistics" button on the MINITAB menu bar, and then click on "2-Sample t", as shown in Figure 9.M.1. The dialog box shown in Figure 9.M.2 then appears.

If the worksheet contains data for one quantitative variable (on which the means will be computed) and one qualitative variable (which represents the two groups or populations), select "Samples in one column", and then specify the quantitative variable in the "Samples" area and the qualitative variable in the "Subscripts" area. (See Figure 9.M.2.)

If the worksheet contains the data for the first sample in one column and the data for the second sample in another column, select "Samples in different columns" and then specify the "First" and "Second" variables. Alternatively, if you have only summarized data (i.e., sample sizes, sample means, and sample standard deviations), select "Summarized data" and enter these summarized values in the appropriate boxes.

Once you have made the appropriate menu selection, click the "Options" button on the MINITAB "2-Sample T" dialog box. Specify the confidence level for a confidence interval, the null-hypothesized value of the difference $(\mu_1 - \mu_2)$, and the form of the alternative hypothesis (lower tailed, two tailed, or upper tailed) in the resulting dialog box, as shown in Figure 9.M.3. Click "OK" to return to the "2-Sample T" dialog box, and then click "OK" again to generate the MINITAB printout.

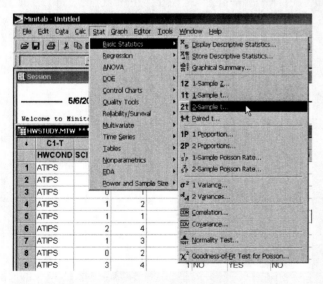

FIGURE 9.M.1
MINITAB menu options for inferences about two means

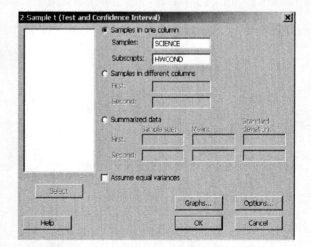

FIGURE 9.M.2
MINITAB two-sample t dialog box

(continued)

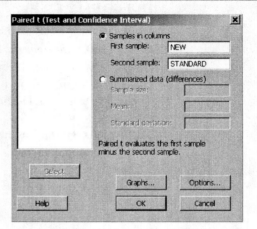

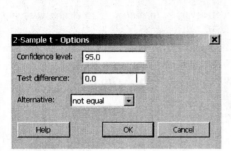

FIGURE 9.M.3
MINITAB two-sample t options

FIGURE 9.M.4
MINITAB paired samples dialog box

[*Important Note:* The MINITAB two-sample *t*-procedure uses the *t*-statistic to conduct the test of hypothesis. When the sample sizes are small, this is the appropriate method. When the sample sizes are large, the *t*-value will be approximately equal to the large-sample *z*-value and the resulting test will still be valid.]

To carry out an analysis of μ_d for matched pairs, first access the MINITAB worksheet that contains the sample data. The data file should contain two quantitative variables: one with the data values for the first group (or population) and one with the data values for the second group. (*Note:* The sample size should be the same for each group.) Next, click on the "Basic Statistics" button on the MINITAB menu bar, and then click on "Paired t" (see Figure 9.M.1). The dialog box shown in Figure 9.M.4 then appears.

Select the "Samples in columns" option, and specify the two quantitative variables of interest in the "First sample" and "Second sample" boxes, as shown in Figure 9.M.4. [Alternatively, if you have only summarized data of the paired differences, select the "Summarized data (differences)" option and enter the sample size, sample mean, and sample standard deviation in the appropriate boxes.]

Next, click the "Options" button and specify the confidence level for a confidence interval, the null-hypothesized value μ_d, of the difference, and the form of the alternative hypothesis (lower tailed, two tailed, or upper tailed) in the resulting dialog box. (See Figure 9.M.3.) Click "OK" to return to the "Paired t" dialog box, and then click "OK" again to generate the MINITAB printout.

To analyze the difference between two proportions ($p_1 - p_2$), first access the MINITAB worksheet that contains the sample data. Next, click on the "Basic Statistics" button on the MINITAB menu bar, and then and click on "2 Proportions", as shown in Figure 9.M.1. The dialog box shown in Figure 9.M.5 then appears. Select the data option ("Samples in one column", "Samples in different columns", or "Summarized data"), and make the appropriate menu choices. (Figure 9.M.5 shows the menu options when you select "Summarized data".)

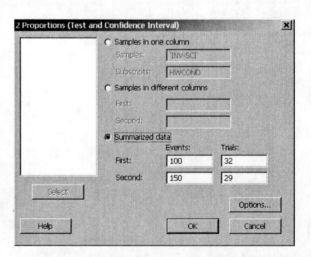

FIGURE 9.M.5
MINITAB two-proportions
dialog box

Next, click the "Options" button and specify the confidence level for a confidence interval, the null-hypothesized value of the difference, and the form of the alternative hypothesis (lower tailed, two tailed, or upper tailed) in the resulting dialog box, as shown in Figure 9.M.6. (If you desire a pooled estimate of p for the test, be sure to check the appropriate box.) Click "OK" to return to the "2 Proportions" dialog box, and then click "OK" again to generate the MINITAB printout.

To carry out an analysis for the ratio of two variances, σ_1^2/σ_2^2, first access the MINITAB worksheet that contains the sample data. Next, click on the "Basic Statistics" button on the MINITAB menu bar, and then click on "2 Variances", as shown in Figure 9.M.1. The dialog box shown in Figure 9.M.7 then appears. The menu selections and options are similar to those for the two-sample t-test. Once the selections are made, click "OK" to produce the MINITAB F-test printout.

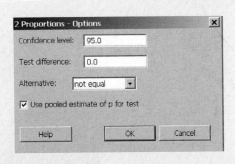

FIGURE 9.M.6

MINITAB two-proportions options

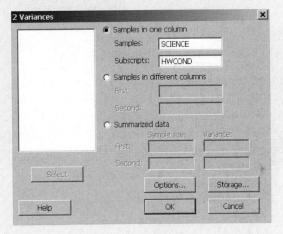

FIGURE 9.M.7

MINITAB two-variances dialog box

10
Analysis of Variance

Comparing More than Two Means

CONTENTS

STATISTICS IN ACTION
On the Trail of the Cockroach:
　　Do Roaches Travel at Random?

USING TECHNOLOGY
Analysis of Variance with MINITAB

WHERE WE'VE BEEN
- Presented methods for estimating and testing hypotheses about a single population mean
- Presented methods for comparing two population means

WHERE WE'RE GOING
- Discuss the critical elements in the *design* of a sampling experiment
- Learn how to set up three of the more popular experimental designs for comparing more than two population means: *completely randomized, randomized block*, and *factorial designs*
- Show how to analyze data collected from a designed experiment using a technique called an *analysis of variance*

STATISTICS IN ACTION

On the Trail of the Cockroach: Do Roaches Travel at Random?

Entomologists have long established that insects such as ants, bees, caterpillars, and termites use chemical or "odor" trails for navigation. These trails are used as highways between sources of food and the insects' nest. Until recently, however, "bug" researchers believed that the navigational behavior of cockroaches scavenging for food was random and not linked to a chemical trail.

One of the first researchers to challenge the "random-walk" theory about cockroaches was professor and entomologist Dini Miller of Virginia Tech University. According to Miller, "The idea that roaches forage randomly means that they would have to come out of their hiding places every night and bump into food and water by accident. But roaches never seem to go hungry." Since cockroaches had never before been evaluated for trail-following behavior, Miller designed an experiment to test a cockroach's ability to follow a trail of their fecal material (*Explore*, Research at the University of Florida, Fall 1998).

First, Miller developed a methanol extract from roach feces—called a pheromone. She theorized that "pheromones are communication devices between cockroaches. If you have an infestation and have a lot of fecal material around, it advertises, 'Hey, this is a good cockroach place.'" Then she created a chemical trail with the pheromone on a strip of white chromatography paper and placed the paper at the bottom of a plastic, V-shaped container, 122 square centimeters in area. German cockroaches were released into the container at the beginning of the trail, one at a time, and a video surveillance camera was used to monitor the roaches' movements.

In addition to the trail containing the fecal extract (the treatment), a trail using methanol only was created. This second trail served as a control against which the treated trail could be compared. Because Miller also wanted to determine whether trail-following ability differed among cockroaches of different age, sex, and reproductive status, four roach groups were utilized in the experiment: adult males, adult females, gravid (pregnant) females, and nymphs (immatures). Twenty roaches of each type were randomly assigned to the treatment trail, and 10 of each type were randomly assigned to the control trail. Thus, a total of 120 roaches were used in the experiment.

The movement pattern of each cockroach tested was translated into *xy*-coordinates every one-tenth of a second by the Dynamic Animal Movement Analyzer (DAMA) program. Miller measured the perpendicular distance of each *xy*-coordinate from the trail and then averaged all the distances, or deviations, for each cockroach. The average trail deviations (measured in pixels, where 1 pixel equals approximately 2 centimeters) for each of the 120 cockroaches in the study are stored in the data file named **ROACH**.

We apply the statistical methodology presented in this chapter to the cockroach data in several Statistics in Action Revisited sections.

Statistics in Action Revisited

- A One-Way Analysis of the Cockroach Data (p. 498)
- Ranking the Means of the Cockroach Groups (p. 508)
- A Two-Way Analysis of the Cockroach Data (p. 537)

Most of the data analyzed in previous chapters were collected in *observational* sampling experiments rather than *designed* sampling experiments. In *observational experiments*, the analyst has little or no control over the variables under study and merely observes their values. In contrast, in *designed experiments* the analyst attempts to control the levels of one or more variables to determine their effect on a variable of interest. Although many practical situations do not present the opportunity for such control, it is instructive, even with observational experiments, to have a working knowledge of the analysis and interpretation of data that result from designed experiments and to know the basics of how to design experiments when the opportunity arises.

We first present the basic elements of an experimental design in Section 10.1. We then discuss two of the simpler, and more popular, experimental designs in Sections 10.2 and 10.4. Slightly more complex experiments are discussed in Section 10.5. Methods for ranking means from a designed experiment are presented in Section 10.3.

10.1 Elements of a Designed Experiment

Certain elements are common to almost all designed experiments, regardless of the specific area of application. For example, the *response* is the variable of interest in the experiment. The response might be the SAT scores of a high school senior, the total sales of a firm last year, or the total income of a particular household this year. We will also refer to the response as the *dependent variable*.

> **Definition 10.1**
>
> The **response variable** is the variable of interest to be measured in the experiment. We also refer to the response as the **dependent variable**.

The intent of most statistical experiments is to determine the effect of one or more variables on the response. These variables are usually referred to as the *factors* in a designed experiment. Factors are either *quantitative* or *qualitative*, depending on whether the variable is measured on a numerical or a nonnumerical scale. For example, we might want to explore the effect of the qualitative factor Gender on the response SAT score. In other words, we might want to compare the SAT scores of male and female high school seniors. Or we might wish to determine the effect of the quantitative factor Number of salespeople on the response Total sales for retail firms. Often, two or more factors are of interest. For example, we might want to determine the effect of the quantitative factor Number of wage earners and the qualitative factor Location on the response Household income.

> **Definition 10.2**
>
> **Factors** are those variables whose effect on the response is of interest to the experimenter. **Quantitative factors** are measured on a numerical scale, whereas **qualitative factors** are not (naturally) measured on a numerical scale.

Levels are the values of the factors that are utilized in the experiment. The levels of qualitative factors are usually nonnumerical. For example, the levels of Gender are Male and Female, and the levels of Location might be North, East, South, and West.* The levels of quantitative factors are the numerical values of the variable utilized in the experiment. The Number of salespeople in each of a set of companies, the Number of wage earners in each of a set of households, and the GPAs for a set of high school seniors all represent levels of the respective quantitative factors.

> **Definition 10.3**
>
> **Factor levels** are the values of the factor utilized in the experiment.

When a *single factor* is employed in an experiment, the *treatments* of the experiment are the levels of the factor. For example, if the effect of the factor Gender on the response SAT score is being investigated, the treatments of the experiment are the two levels of

---

*The levels of a qualitative variable may bear numerical labels. For example, Locations could be numbered 1, 2, 3, and 4. However, in such cases the numerical labels for a qualitative variable will usually be codes representing nonnumerical levels.

Gender: Female and Male. Or if the effect of the Number of wage earners on Household income is the subject of the experiment, the numerical values assumed by the quantitative factor Number of wage earners are the treatments. If *two or more factors* are utilized in an experiment, the treatments are the factor–level combinations used. For example, if the effects of the factors Gender and Socioeconomic status (SES) on the response SAT score are being investigated, the treatments are the combinations of the levels of Gender and SES used; thus, (Female, high SES) and (Male, low SES) would be treatments.

> ### Definition 10.4
>
> The **treatments** of an experiment are the factor–level combinations utilized.

The objects on which the response variable and factors are observed are the *experimental units*. For example, SAT score, High school GPA and Gender are all variables that can be observed on the same experimental unit: a high school senior. Similarly, Total sales, Earnings per share, and Number of salespeople can be measured on a particular firm in a particular year, and the firm–year combination is the experimental unit. Likewise, Total income, Number of female wage earners, and Location can be observed for a household at a particular point in time, and the household–time combination is the experimental unit. Every experiment, whether observational or designed, has experimental units on which the variables are observed. However, the identification of the experimental units is more important in designed experiments, when the experimenter must actually sample the experimental units and measure the variables.

> ### Definition 10.5
>
> An **experimental unit** is the object on which the response and factors are observed or measured.*

When the specification of the treatments and the method of assigning the experimental units to each of the treatments are controlled by the analyst, the experiment is said to be *designed*. In contrast, if the analyst is just an observer of the treatments on a sample of experimental units, the experiment is *observational*. For example, if, on the one hand, you specify the number of female and male high school students within each GPA range to be randomly selected in order to evaluate the effect of gender and GPA on SAT scores, you are designing the experiment. If, on the other hand, you simply observe the SAT scores, gender, and GPA for all students who took the SAT test last month at a particular high school, the experiment is observational.

> ### Definition 10.6
>
> A **designed experiment** is an experiment in which the analyst controls the specification of the treatments and the method of assigning the experimental units to each treatment. An **observational experiment** is an experiment in which the analyst simply observes the treatments and the response on a sample of experimental units.

Figure 10.1 provides an overview of the experimental process and a summary of the terminology introduced in this section. Note that the experimental unit is at the core of the process. The method by which the sample of experimental units is selected from the population determines the type of experiment. The level of every factor (the treatment) and the response are all variables that are observed or measured on each experimental unit.

*Recall (Chapter 1) that the set of all experimental units is the population.

Biography

SIR RONALD A. FISHER
(1890–1962)—
The Founder of Modern Statistics

At a young age, Ronald Fisher demonstrated special abilities in mathematics, astronomy, and biology. (Fisher's biology teacher once divided all his students into two groups on the basis of their "sheer brilliance": Fisher and the rest.) Fisher graduated from prestigious Cambridge University in London in 1912 with a B.A. degree in astronomy. After several years teaching mathematics, he found work at the Rothamsted Agricultural Experiment station, where he began his extraordinary career as a statistician. Many consider Fisher to be the leading founder of modern statistics. His contributions to the field include the notion of unbiased statistics, the

development of *p*-values for hypothesis tests, the invention of analysis of variance for designed experiments, the maximum-likelihood estimation theory, and the formulation of the mathematical distributions of several well-known statistics. Fisher's book, *Statistical Methods for Research Workers* (written in 1925), revolutionized applied statistics, demonstrating with very readable and practical examples how to analyze data and interpret the results. In 1935, Fisher wrote *The Design of Experiments*, in which he first described his famous experiment on the "lady tasting tea." (Fisher showed, through a designed experiment, that the lady really could determine whether tea poured into milk tastes better than milk poured into tea.) Before his death, Fisher was elected a Fellow of the Royal Statistical Society, was awarded numerous medals, and was knighted by the Queen of England.

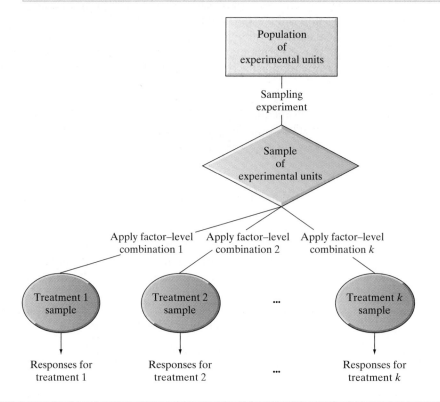

FIGURE 10.1

Sampling experiment: process and terminology

EXAMPLE 10.1

THE KEY ELEMENTS OF A DESIGNED EXPERIMENT— Testing Golf Ball Brands

Problem The United States Golf Association (USGA) regularly tests golf equipment to ensure that it conforms to the association's standards. Suppose the USGA wishes to compare the mean distances traveled by four different brands of golf balls struck by a driver (the club used to maximize distance). The following experiment is conducted: 10 balls of each brand are randomly selected. Each ball is struck with a driver by "Iron Byron" (the USGA's golf robot named for the famous golfer Byron Nelson), and the distance traveled is recorded. Identify each of the following elements in this experiment: response, factors, types of factor, levels, treatments, and experimental units.

Solution The response is the variable of interest, Distance traveled. The only factor being investigated is Brand of golf ball, and it is nonnumerical and therefore qualitative. The four brands (say, A, B, C, and D) represent the levels of this factor. Since only one factor is utilized, the treatments are the four levels of that factor—that is, the four brands. The experimental unit is a golf ball; more specifically, it is a golf ball at a particular position in the striking sequence, since the distance traveled can be recorded only when the ball is struck, and we would expect the distance to be different (due to random factors such as wind resistance, landing place, and so forth) if the same ball is struck a second time. Note that 10 experimental units are sampled for each treatment, generating a total of 40 observations.

Look Back This experiment, like many real applications, is a blend of designed and observational: The analyst cannot control the assignment of the brand to each golf ball (observational), but he or she can control the assignment of each ball to the position in the striking sequence (designed).

Now Work Exercise 10.5

EXAMPLE 10.2

A TWO-FACTOR EXPERIMENT— Testing Golf Ball Brands

Problem Suppose the USGA is also interested in comparing the mean distances the four brands of golf balls travel when struck by a five-iron and by a driver. Ten balls of each brand are randomly selected, five to be struck by the driver and five by the five-iron. Identify the elements of this experiment, and construct a schematic diagram similar to Figure 10.1 to provide an overview of the experiment.

Solution The response is the same as in Example 10.1, Distance traveled. The experiment now has two factors: Brand of golf ball and Club utilized. There are four levels of Brand (A, B, C, and D) and two of Club (driver and five-iron, or 1 and 5). Treatments are factor–level combinations, so there are $4 \times 2 = 8$ treatments in this experiment: (A, 1), (A, 5), (B, 1), (B, 5), (C, 1), (C, 5), (D, 1), and (D, 5). The experimental units are still the combinations of golf ball and hitting position. Note that five experimental units are sampled per treatment, generating 40 observations. The experiment is summarized in Figure 10.2.

Look Back Whenever there are two or more factors in an experiment, remember to combine the levels of the factors—one from each factor—to obtain the treatments.

Now Work Exercise 10.10

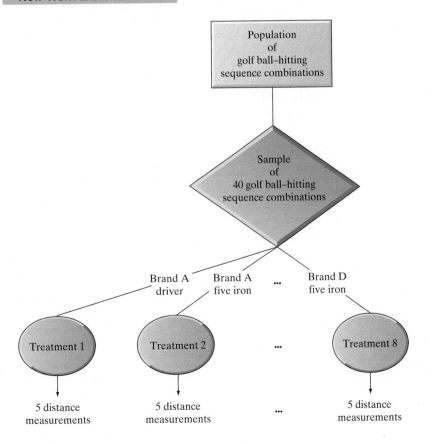

FIGURE 10.2

Two-factor golf experiment summary: Example 10.2

ACTIVITY 10.1: Designed versus Observational Experiments

In this Activity, you will revisit Activity 9.1 (p. 437) and Activity 9.2 (p. 447) and consider two new, but similar, experiments.

1. Explain why each of the situations in *Box Office Receipts: Comparing Population Means*, (p. 437), and *Keep the Change: Inferences Based on Two Samples*, (p. 447), are observational experiments. What key elements of a designed experiment are missing in each situation?

2. A movie company wishes to measure the effect of advertising on box office receipts. Thirty U.S. cities with similar demographics are chosen for an experiment. The 30 cities are randomly divided into three groups of 10 cities each. In each city, a trailer for a new film will be run on local cable during prime time in the week leading up to the release of the film. In the first group of 10 cities the trailer will be run 500 times, in the second group the trailer will be run 1,000 times, and in the third group it will be run 1,500 times. The company will collect the box office receipts for the opening weekend of the film in each city and compare the mean box office receipts.

    Explain why this is a designed experiment. Identify the factor and the response variable. Is the factor quantitative or qualitative? Identity the factor levels and the experimen-

tal units. What part of choosing the cities is not necessarily random? Explain why it might be difficult to randomize this part of the experiment.

3. Suppose Bank of America wants to determine whether e-mail and postcard reminders of the benefits of the *Keep the Change* program result in customers using their debit cards more often. A random sample of customers is chosen and split into four groups. The customers in one group are sent an e-mail reminder, those in the second group are sent a postcard, the customers in the third group are sent both, and those in the last group are sent neither. The bank keeps track of how many more times each customer uses his or her debit card in the two weeks after the reminders are sent, as opposed to the two weeks before the reminders are sent. The means for the four groups are then compared.

    Explain why this is a designed experiment. Identify the factors and the response variable. Is the factor quantitative or qualitative? Identify the factor levels, the treatments, and the experimental units. Comparing this experiment with that in Exercise 2, state why it is more realistic to choose a random sample for the experiment.

Our objective in designing an experiment is usually to maximize the amount of information obtained about the relationship between the treatments and the response. Of course, we are almost always subject to constraints on budget, time, and even the availability of experimental units. Nevertheless, designed experiments are generally preferred to observational experiments: Not only do we have better control over the amount and quality of the information collected, but we also avoid the biases that are inherent in observational experiments in the selection of the experimental units representing each treatment. Inferences based on observational experiments always carry the implicit assumption that the sample has no hidden bias which was not considered in the statistical analysis. A better understanding of the potential problems with observational experiments is a by-product of our study of experimental design in the remainder of this chapter.

Exercises 10.1–10.12

Understanding the Principles

10.1 What are the treatments for a designed experiment that utilizes one qualitative factor with four levels: A, B, C, and D?

10.2 What are the treatments for a designed experiment with two factors, one qualitative with two levels (A and B) and one quantitative with five levels (50, 60, 70, 80, and 90)?

10.3 What is the difference between an observational and a designed experiment?

Applying the Concepts—Basic

10.4 What are the experimental units on which each of the following responses are observed?
   a. GPA of a college student
   b. Household income
   c. Your time in running the 100-yard dash
   d. A patient's reaction to a new drug

10.5 **Identifying the type of experiment.** Determine whether
NW each of the following experiments is observational or designed, and explain your reasoning:
   a. An economist obtains the unemployment rate and gross state product for a sample of states over the past 10 years, with the objective of examining the relationship between the unemployment rate and the gross state product by census region.
   b. A psychologist tests the effects of three different feedback programs by randomly assigning five rats to each program and recording their response times at specified intervals during the program.
   c. A marketer of notebook computers runs ads in each of four national publications for one quarter and keeps track of the number of sales that are attributable to each publication's ad.
   d. An electric utility engages a consultant to monitor the discharge from its smokestack on a monthly basis over a one-

year period in order to relate the level of sulfur dioxide in the discharge to the load on the facility's generators.

e. Intrastate trucking rates are compared before and after governmental deregulation of prices charged, with the comparison also taking into account distance of haul, goods hauled, and the price of diesel fuel.

f. An agriculture student compares the amount of rainfall in four different states over the past five years.

10.6 Extinct New Zealand birds. Refer to the *Evolutionary Ecology Research* (July 2003) study of extinction in the New Zealand bird population, presented in Exercise 1.18 (p. 20). Recall that biologists measured the body mass (in grams) and type of habitat (aquatic, ground terrestrial, or aerial terrestrial) for each bird species. One objective is to compare the body mass means of birds with the three different types of habitat.

a. Identify the response variable of the study.
b. Identify the experimental units of the study.
c. Identify the factor(s) in the study.
d. Identify the treatments in the study

10.7 CT scanning for lung cancer. Refer to Exercise 1.23 (p. 20) and the University of South Florida clinical trial of 50,000 smokers to compare the effectiveness of CT scans with X-rays in detecting lung cancer. (*Today's Tomorrows*, Fall 2002.) Recall that each participating smoker will be randomly assigned to one of two screening methods—CT or chest X-ray—and the age (in years) at which the scanning method first detects a tumor will be determined. One goal of the study is to compare the mean ages when cancer is first detected by the two screening methods.

a. Identify the response variable of the study.
b. Identify the experimental units of the study.
c. Identify the factor(s) in the study.
d. Identify the treatments in the study.

Applying the Concepts—Intermediate

10.8 Treatment for tendon pain. Chronic Achilles tendon pain (i.e., tendinosis) is common among middle-aged recreational athletes. A group of Swedish physicians investigated the use of heavy-load eccentric calf muscle training to treat Achilles tendinosis. (*British Journal of Sports Medicine*, Feb. 1, 2004.) A sample of 25 patients with chronic Achilles tendinosis undertook the treatment. Data on tendon thickness (measured in millimeters) were collected by ultrasonography both before and following treatment of each patient. The researchers want to compare the mean tendon thickness before treatment with the mean tendon thickness after treatment.

a. Is this a designed experiment or an observational study? Explain.
b. What is the experimental unit of the study?
c. What is the response variable of the study?

d. What are the treatments in this experiment?

e. After reading Section 10.3, you will learn that patients represent a blocking factor in this study. How many levels are in the blocking factor?

10.9 Taste preferences of cockatiels. *Applied Animal Behaviour Science* (Oct. 2000) published a study of the taste preferences of caged cockatiels. A sample of birds bred at the University of California at Davis was randomly divided into

three experimental groups. Group 1 was fed purified water in bottles on both sides of the cage. Group 2 was fed water on one side and a liquid sucrose (sweet) mixture on the opposite side of the cage. Group 3 was fed water on one side and a liquid sodium chloride (salty) mixture on the opposite side of the cage. One variable of interest to the researchers was total consumption of liquid by each cockatiel.

a. What is the experimental unit of this study?
b. Is the study a designed experiment? Why?
c. What are the factors in the study?
d. Give the levels of each factor.
e. How many treatments are in the study? Identify them.
f. What is the response variable?

10.10 Exam performance study. In *Teaching of Psychology* (Aug. 1998), a study investigated whether final exam performance is affected by whether or not students take a practice test. Students in an introductory psychology class at Pennsylvania State University were initially divided into three groups based on their class standing: Low, Medium, and High. Within each group, the students were randomly assigned to either attend a review session or take a practice test prior to the final exam. Thus, six groups were formed: (Low, Review), (Low, Practice exam), (Medium, Review), (Medium, Practice exam), (High, Review), and (High, Practice exam). One goal of the study was to compare the mean final exam scores of the six groups of students.

a. What is the experimental unit of this study?
b. Is the study a designed experiment? Why?
c. What are the factors in the study?
d. Give the levels of each factor.
e. How many treatments are in the study? Identify them.
f. What is the response variable?

10.11 Baker's versus brewer's yeast. The *Electronic Journal of Biotechnology* (Dec. 15, 2003) published an article comparing two yeast extracts: baker's yeast and brewer's yeast. Brewer's yeast is a surplus by-product obtained from a brewery; hence, it is less expensive than primary-grown baker's yeast. Samples of both yeast extracts were prepared at four different temperatures (45, 48, 51, and 54°C), and the autolysis yield (recorded as a percentage) was measured for each of the yeast–temperature combinations. The goal of the analysis is to investigate the impact of yeast extract and temperature on mean autolysis yield.

a. Identify the factors (and factor levels) in the experiment.
b. Identify the response variable.
c. How many treatments are included in the experiment?
d. What type of experimental design is employed?

Applying the Concepts—Advanced

10.12 Testing a new pain-relief tablet. Paracetamol is the active ingredient in drugs designed to relieve mild to moderate pain and fever. The properties of paracetamol tablets derived from khaya gum were studied in the *Tropical Journal of Pharmaceutical Research* (June 2003). Three factors believed to affect the properties of parcetamol tablets are (1) the nature of the binding agent, (2) the concentration of the binding agent, and (3) the relative density of the tablet. In the experiment, binding agent was set at two levels (khaya gum and PVP), binding concentration at two levels (.5% and 4.0%), and relative density at two levels (low and high). One of the dependent variables investigated in the study was tablet dissolution time (i.e., the amount of time, in minutes, for 50% of the tablet to dissolve). The goal of the study was to determine the effect of binding agent, binding concentration, and relative density on mean dissolution time.

a. Identify the dependent (response) variable in the study.
b. What are the factors investigated in the study? Give the levels of each.
c. How many treatments are possible in the study? List them.

10.2 The Completely Randomized Design

The simplest experimental design, the *completely randomized design*, consists of the *independent random selection* of experimental units representing each treatment. For example, we could independently select random samples of 20 female and 15 male high school seniors in order to compare their mean SAT scores. Or we could randomly assign cancer patients to receive one of three experimental treatments and then compare the mean pain levels of patients in the treatment groups. In both examples, our objective is to compare treatment means by selecting random, independent samples for each treatment.

> **Definition 10.7**
>
> The **completely randomized design** is a design in which treatments are randomly assigned to the experimental units or in which independent random samples of experimental units are selected for each treatment.*

EXAMPLE 10.3

ASSIGNING TREATMENTS IN A COMPLETELY RANDOMIZED DESIGN— Comparing Bottled Water Brands

Problem Suppose we want to compare the taste preferences of consumers for three different brands of bottled water (say, Brands A, B, and C), using a random sample of 15 consumers of bottled water. Set up a completely randomized design for this purpose. That is, assign the treatments to the experimental units for this design.

Solution In this study, the experimental units are the 15 consumers and the treatments are the three brands of bottled water. One way to set up the completely randomized design is to randomly assign one of the three brands to each consumer to taste. Then we could measure (say, on a 1- to 10-point scale) the taste preference of each consumer. A good practice is to assign the same number of consumers to each brand—in this case, five consumers to each of the three brands. (When an equal number of experimental units is assigned to each treatment, we call the design a **balanced design**.)

A random-number table (Table 1, Appendix A) or computer software can be used to make the random assignments. Figure 10.3 is

CRD3brands.MTW ***

↓	C1	C2	C3	C4	C5
	Consumer	BrandA	BrandB	BrandC	
1	1	2	15	6	
2	2	11	14	5	
3	3	1	7	12	
4	4	13	10	9	
5	5	3	8	4	
6	6				
7	7				
8	8				
9	9				
10	10				
11	11				
12	12				
13	13				
14	14				
15	15				
16					

FIGURE 10.3

MINITAB random assignments of consumers to brands

---

*We use *completely randomized design* to refer to both designed and observational experiments. Thus, the only requirement is that the experimental units to which treatments are applied (designed) or on which treatments are observed (observational) be independently selected for each treatment.

a MINITAB worksheet showing the random assignments made with the MINITAB "Random Data" function. You can see that MINITAB randomly assigned consumers numbered 2, 11, 1, 13, and 3 to taste Brand A; consumers numbered 15, 14, 7, 10, and 8 to taste Brand B; and consumers numbered 6, 5, 12, 9, and 4 to taste Brand C.

Look Back In some experiments, it will not be possible to randomly assign treatments to the experimental units: The units will already be associated with one of the treatments. (For example, if the treatments are "Male" and "Female," you cannot change a person's gender.) In this case, a completely randomized design is a design in which you select independent random samples of experimental units from each treatment.

The objective of a completely randomized design is usually to compare the treatment means. If we denote the true, or population, means of the k treatments as $\mu_1, \mu_2, \ldots, \mu_k$, then we will test the null hypothesis that the treatment means are all equal against the alternative that at least two of the treatment means differ:

$$H_0: \mu_1 = \mu_2 = \cdots = \mu_k$$
$$H_a: \text{At least two of the } k \text{ treatment means differ}$$

The μ's might represent the means of *all* female and male high school seniors' SAT scores or the means of *all* households' income in each of four census regions.

To conduct a statistical test of these hypotheses, we will use the means of the independent random samples selected from the treatment populations in a completely randomized design. That is, we compare the k sample means $\bar{x}_1, \bar{x}_2, \ldots, \bar{x}_k$.

For example, suppose you select independent random samples of five female and five male high school seniors and obtain sample mean SAT scores of 550 and 590, respectively. Can we conclude that males score 40 points higher, on average, than females? To answer this question, we must consider the amount of sampling variability among the experimental units (students). If the scores are as depicted in the dot plot shown in Figure 10.4, then the difference between the means is small relative to the sampling variability of the scores within the treatments, namely, Female and Male. We would be inclined not to reject the null hypothesis of equal population means in this case.

In contrast, if the data are as depicted in the dot plot of Figure 10.5, then the sampling variability is small relative to the difference between the two means. In this case, we would be inclined to favor the alternative hypothesis that the population means differ.

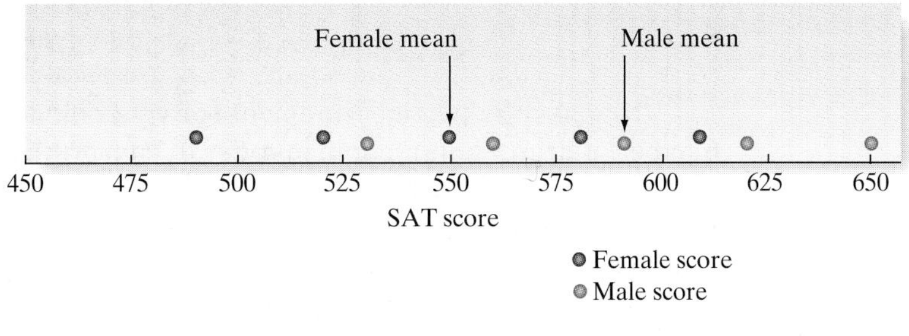

FIGURE 10.4
Dot plot of SAT scores: difference between means dominated by sampling variability.

FIGURE 10.5
Dot plot of SAT scores: difference between means large relative to sampling variability

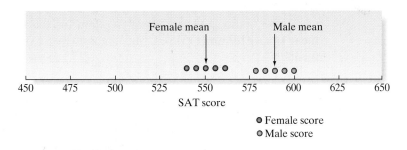

Now Work Exercise 10.19a

You can see that the key is to compare the difference between the treatment means with the amount of sampling variability. To conduct a formal statistical test of the hypothesis requires numerical measures of the difference between the treatment means and the sampling variability within each treatment. The variation between the treatment means is measured by the **sum of squares for treatments** (SST), which is calculated by squaring the distance between each treatment mean and the overall mean of *all* sample measurements, then multiplying each squared distance by the number of sample measurements for the treatment, and, finally, adding the results over all treatments:

$$\text{SST} = \sum_{i=1}^{k} n_i(\bar{x}_i - \bar{x})^2 = 5(550 - 570)^2 + 5(590 - 570)^2 = 4{,}000$$

In this equation, we use $\bar{x}$ to represent the overall mean response of all sample measurements—that is, the mean of the combined samples. The symbol n_i is used to denote the sample size for the ith treatment. You can see that the value of SST is 4,000 for the two samples of five female and five male SAT scores depicted in Figures 10.4 and 10.5.

Next, we must measure the sampling variability within the treatments. We call this the **sum of squares for error** (SSE), because it measures the variability around the treatment means that is attributed to sampling error. Suppose the 10 measurements in the first dot plot (Figure 10.4) are 490, 520, 550, 580, and 610 for females and 530, 560, 590, 620, and 650 for males. Then the value of SSE is computed by summing the squared distance between each response measurement and the corresponding treatment mean and then adding the squared differences over all measurements in the entire sample:

$$\text{SSE} = \sum_{j=1}^{n_1}(x_{1j} - \bar{x}_1)^2 + \sum_{j=1}^{n_2}(x_{2j} - \bar{x}_2)^2 + \cdots \sum_{j=1}^{n_k}(x_{kj} - \bar{x}_k)^2$$

Here, the symbol x_{1j} is the jth measurement in sample 1, x_{2j} is the jth measurement in sample 2, and so on. This rather complex-looking formula can be simplified by recalling the formula for the sample variance s^2 given in Chapter 2:

$$s^2 = \sum_{i=1}^{n} \frac{(x_i - \bar{x})^2}{n - 1}$$

Note that each sum in SSE is simply the numerator of s^2 for that particular treatment. Consequently, we can rewrite SSE as

$$\text{SSE} = (n_1 - 1)s_1^2 + (n_2 - 1)s_2^2 + \cdots + (n_k - 1)s_k^2$$

where $s_1^2, s_2^2, \ldots, s_k^2$ are the sample variances for the k treatments. For our samples of SAT scores, we find that $s_1^2 = 2{,}250$ (for females) and $s_2^2 = 2{,}250$ (for males); then we have

$$\text{SSE} = (5 - 1)(2{,}250) + (5 - 1)(2{,}250) = 18{,}000$$

To make the two measurements of variability comparable, we divide each by the number of degrees of freedom in order to convert the sums of squares to mean squares. First, the **mean square for treatments** (MST), which measures the variability *among* the treatment means, is equal to

$$\text{MST} = \frac{\text{SST}}{k - 1} = \frac{4{,}000}{2 - 1} = 4{,}000$$

where the number of degrees of freedom for the k treatments is $(k - 1)$. Next, the **mean square for error** (MSE), which measures the sampling variability *within* the treatments, is

$$\text{MSE} = \frac{\text{SSE}}{n - k} = \frac{18{,}000}{10 - 2} = 2{,}250$$

Finally, we calculate the ratio of MST to MSE—an **F-statistic**:

$$F = \frac{\text{MST}}{\text{MSE}} = \frac{4{,}000}{2{,}250} = 1.78$$

Values of the F-statistic near 1 indicate that the two sources of variation, between treatment means and within treatments, are approximately equal. In this case, the difference between the treatment means may well be attributable to sampling error, which provides little support for the alternative hypothesis that the population treatment means differ. Values of F well in excess of 1 indicate that the variation among treatment means well exceeds that within means and therefore support the alternative hypothesis that the population treatment means differ.

When does F exceed 1 by enough to reject the null hypothesis that the means are equal? This depends on the degrees of freedom for treatments and for error and on the value of α selected for the test. We compare the calculated F-value with an F-value taken from a table (see Tables VIII–XI of Appendix A) with $v_1 = (k - 1)$ degrees of freedom in the numerator and $v_2 = (n - k)$ degrees of freedom in the denominator and corresponding to a Type I error probability of α. For the example of the SAT scores, the F-statistic has $v_1 = (2 - 1)$ numerator degrees of freedom and $v_2 = (10 - 2) = 8$ denominator degrees of freedom. Thus, for $\alpha = .05$, we find (from Table IX of Appendix A) that

$$F_{.05} = 5.32$$

The implication is that MST would have to be 5.32 times greater than MSE before we could conclude, at the .05 level of significance, that the two population treatment means differ. Since the data yielded $F = 1.78$, our initial impressions of the dot plot in Figure 10.4 are confirmed: There is insufficient information to conclude that the mean SAT scores differ for the populations of female and male high school seniors. The rejection region and the calculated F value are shown in Figure 10.6.

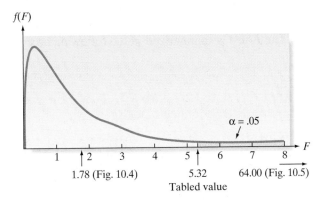

FIGURE 10.6
Rejection region and calculated F-values for SAT score samples

In contrast, consider the dot plot in Figure 10.5. Since the means are the same as in the first example, 550 and 590, respectively, the variation between the means is the same, MST = 4,000. But the variation within the two treatments appears to be considerably smaller. The observed SAT scores are 540, 545, 550, 555, and 560 for females and 580, 585, 590, 595, and 600 for males. These values yield $s_1^2 = 62.5$ and $s_2^2 = 62.5$. Thus, the variation within the treatments is measured by

$$\text{SSE} = (5 - 1)(62.5) + (5 - 1)(62.5) = 500$$
$$\text{MSE} = \frac{\text{SSE}}{n - k} = \frac{500}{8} = 62.5$$

Then the F-ratio is

$$F = \frac{\text{MST}}{\text{MSE}} = \frac{4,000}{62.5} = 64.0$$

Again, our visual analysis of the dot plot is confirmed statistically: $F = 64.0$ well exceeds the table's F value, 5.32, corresponding to the .05 level of significance. We would therefore reject the null hypothesis at that level and conclude that the SAT mean score of males differs from that of females.

Now Work Exercise 10.19b–h

Recall that we performed a hypothesis test for the difference between two means in Section 9.2, using a two-sample t-statistic for two independent samples. When two independent samples are being compared, the t- and F-tests are equivalent. To see this, recall the formula

$$t = \frac{\bar{x}_1 - \bar{x}_2}{\sqrt{s_p^2\left(\frac{1}{n_1} + \frac{1}{n_2}\right)}} = \frac{590 - 550}{\sqrt{(62.5)\left(\frac{1}{5} + \frac{1}{5}\right)}} = \frac{40}{5} = 8$$

where we used the fact that $s_p^2 = \text{MSE}$, which you can verify by comparing the formulas. Note that the calculated F for these samples ($F = 64$) equals the square of the calculated t for the same samples ($t = 8$). Likewise, the table's F-value (5.32) equals the square of the table's t-value at the two-sided .05 level of significance ($t_{.025} = 2.306$ with 8 df). Since both the rejection region and the calculated values are related in the same way, the tests are equivalent. Moreover, the assumptions that must be met to ensure the validity of the t- and F-tests are the same:

1. The probability distributions of the populations of responses associated with each treatment must all be normal.

2. The probability distributions of the populations of responses associated with each treatment must have equal variances.

3. The samples of experimental units selected for the treatments must be random and independent.

In fact, the only real difference between the tests is that the F-test can be used to compare *more than two* treatment means, whereas the t-test is applicable to two samples only. The **F-test** is summarized in the following box:

ANOVA F-Test to Compare k Treatment Means: Completely Randomized Design

H_0: $\mu_1 = \mu_2 = \cdots = \mu_k$

H_a: At least two treatment means differ.

Test statistic: $F = \dfrac{\text{MST}}{\text{MSE}}$

Rejection region: $F > F_\alpha$, where F_α is based on $v_1 = (k - 1)$ numerator degrees of freedom (associated with MST) and $v_2 = (n - k)$ denominator degrees of freedom (associated with MSE).

Conditions Required for a Valid ANOVA F-Test: Completely Randomized Design

1. The samples are randomly selected in an independent manner from the k treatment populations. (This can be accomplished by randomly assigning the experimental units to the treatments.)

2. All k sampled populations have distributions that are approximately normal.

3. The k population variances are equal (i.e., $\sigma_1^2 = \sigma_2^2 = \sigma_3^2 = \cdots = \sigma_k^2$).

Computational formulas for MST and MSE are given in Appendix B. We will rely on statistical software to compute the F statistic, concentrating on the interpretation of the results rather than their calculation.

EXAMPLE 10.4

CONDUCTING AN ANOVA F-TEST— Comparing Golf Ball Brands

Problem Suppose the USGA wants to compare the mean distances reached of four different brands of golf balls struck with a driver. A completely randomized design is employed, with Iron Byron, the USGA's robotic golfer, using a driver to hit a random sample of 10 balls of each brand in a random sequence. The distance is recorded for each hit, and the results are shown in Table 10.1, organized by brand.

a. Set up the test to compare the mean distances for the four brands. Use $\alpha = .10$.

b. Use statistical software to obtain the test statistic and p-value. Interpret the results.

GOLFCRD

TABLE 10.1 Results of Completely Randomized Design: Iron Byron Driver

	Brand A	Brand B	Brand C	Brand D
	251.2	263.2	269.7	251.6
	245.1	262.9	263.2	248.6
	248.0	265.0	277.5	249.4
	251.1	254.5	267.4	242.0
	260.5	264.3	270.5	246.5
	250.0	257.0	265.5	251.3
	253.9	262.8	270.7	261.8
	244.6	264.4	272.9	249.0
	254.6	260.6	275.6	247.1
	248.8	255.9	266.5	245.9
Sample means	250.8	261.1	270.0	249.3

Solution

a. To compare the mean distances of the $k = 4$ brands, we first specify the hypotheses to be tested. Denoting the population mean of the ith brand by μ_i, we test

$$H_0: \mu_1 = \mu_2 = \mu_3 = \mu_4$$
$$H_a: \text{The mean distances differ for at least two of the brands.}$$

The test statistic compares the variation among the four treatment (Brand) means with the sampling variability within each of the treatments:

$$\text{Test statistic:} \quad F = \frac{\text{MST}}{\text{MSE}}$$

$$\text{Rejection region:} \quad F > F_\alpha = F_{.10} \text{ with } v_1 = (k - 1) = 3 \text{ df}$$
$$\text{and } v_2 = (n - k) = 36 \text{ df}$$

From Table VIII of Appendix A, we find that $F_{.10} \approx 2.25$ for 3 and 36 df. Thus, we will reject H_0 if $F > 2.25$. (See Figure 10.7.)

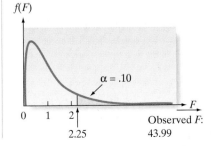

FIGURE 10.7

F-test for completely randomized design: golf ball experiment

The assumptions necessary to ensure the validity of the test are as follows:

1. The samples of 10 golf balls for each brand are selected randomly and independently.
2. The probability distributions of the distances for each brand are normal.
3. The variances of the distance probability distributions for each brand are equal.

b. The MINITAB printout for the data in Table 10.1 resulting from this completely randomized design is given in Figure 10.8. The total sum of squares is designated "Total" and is partitioned into the "Brand" (i.e., treatments) and "Error" sum of squares (SS).

The values of the mean squares, MST and MSE (highlighted on the printout), are 931.5 and 21.2, respectively. The F-ratio, 43.99, also highlighted on the printout, exceeds the table value of 2.25. We therefore reject the null hypothesis at the .10 level of significance, concluding that at least two of the brands differ with respect to mean distance traveled when struck by the driver.

Look Back We can also arrive at the appropriate conclusion by noting that the observed significance level of the F-test (highlighted on the printout) is p-value $= .000$. This implies that we would reject the null hypothesis that the means are equal at any α level.

One-way ANOVA: DISTANCE versus BRAND

```
Source   DF      SS     MS      F      P
BRAND     3  2794.4  931.5  43.99  0.000
Error    36   762.3   21.2
Total    39  3556.7

S = 4.602    R-Sq = 78.57%   R-Sq(adj) = 76.78%


                                    Individual 95% CIs For Mean Based on
                                    Pooled StDev
Level    N    Mean   StDev   --------+---------+---------+---------+-
BrandA   10  250.78   4.74   (---*---)
BrandB   10  261.06   3.87                  (---*---)
BrandC   10  269.95   4.50                              (----*---)
BrandD   10  249.32   5.20   (---*---)
                             --------+---------+---------+---------+-
                               252.0     259.0     266.0     273.0

Pooled StDev = 4.60
```

FIGURE 10.8
MINITAB ANOVA for completely randomized design

Now Work Exercise 10.22

The results of an **analysis of variance (ANOVA)** can be summarized in a simple tabular format similar to that obtained from the MINITAB program in Example 10.4. The general form of the table is shown in Table 10.2, where the symbols df, SS, and MS stand for degrees of freedom, sum of squares, and mean square, respectively. Note that the two sources of variation, Treatments and Error, add to the total sum of squares, SS(Total). The ANOVA summary table for Example 10.4 is given in Table 10.3, and the partitioning of the total sum of squares into its two components is illustrated in Figure 10.9.

TABLE 10.2 General ANOVA Summary Table for a Completely Randomized Design

Source	df	SS	MS	F
Treatments	$k-1$	SST	$MST = \dfrac{SST}{k-1}$	$\dfrac{MST}{MSE}$
Error	$n-k$	SSE	$MSE = \dfrac{SSE}{n-k}$	
Total	$n-1$	SS(Total)		

TABLE 10.3 ANOVA Summary Table for Example 10.4

Source	df	SS	MS	F	p-Value
Brands	3	2,794.39	931.46	43.99	.000
Error	36	762.30	21.18		
Total	39	3,556.69			

FIGURE 10.9

Partitioning of the total sum of squares for the completely randomized design

Total sum of squares
SS(Total)

Sum of squares for treatments
SST

Sum of squares for error
SSE

Suppose the *F*-test results in a rejection of the null hypothesis that the treatment means are equal. Is the analysis then complete? Usually, the conclusion that at least two of the treatment means differ leads to other conclusions and—for instance, other questions. Which of the means differ and by how much? For example, the *F*-test in Example 10.4 leads to the conclusion that at least two of the brands of golf balls have different mean distances traveled when struck with a driver. Now the questions are, Which of the brands differ? and How are the brands ranked with respect to mean distance?

One way to obtain this information is to construct a confidence interval for the difference between the means of any pair of treatments, using the method of Section 9.2. For example, if a 95% confidence interval for $\mu_A - \mu_C$ in Example 10.4 is found to be $(-24, -13)$, we are confident that the mean distance for Brand C exceeds the mean for Brand A (since all differences in the interval are negative). Constructing these confidence intervals for all possible pairs of brands allows you to rank the brand means. A method for conducting these *multiple comparisons*—one that controls for Type I errors—is presented in Section 10.3.

Analysis of Variance

Using the TI-84/TI-83 Graphing Calculator

Computing a One-Way ANOVA

Step 1 *Enter each data set into its own list (i.e., sample 1 into L1, sample 2 into L2, sample 3 into L3, etc.).*

Step 2 *Access the Statistical Test Menu.*

Press **STAT**.
Arrow right to **TESTS**.
Arrow down to **ANOVA**.
Press **ENTER**.
Type in each List name, separated by commas (e.g., *L1, L2, L3, L4*).
Press **ENTER**.

Step 3 *View Display.*

The calculator will display the *F*-test statistic, as well as the *p*-value, the Factor degrees of freedom, the sum of squares, the mean square, and, by arrowing down, the Error degrees of freedom, the sum of squares, the mean square, and the pooled standard deviation.

(continued)

Example   Shown are four different samples. At the $\alpha = .05$ level of significance, test whether the four population means are equal. The null hypothesis will be $H_0: \mu_1 = \mu_2 = \mu_3 = \mu_4$. The alternative hypothesis H_a. At least one mean is different.

SAMPLE1	SAMPLE2	SAMPLE3	SAMPLE4
60	59	55	58
61	52	55	58
56	51	52	55

The screens for this example are as follows:

As you can see from the screen, the p-value is 0.1598, which is **not less than** 0.05; therefore, we should **not reject** H_0. The differences are not significantly different.

EXAMPLE 10.5
CHECKING THE ANOVA ASSUMPTIONS

Problem Refer to the completely randomized ANOVA design conducted in Example 10.4. Are the assumptions required for the test approximately satisfied?

Solution The assumptions for the test are repeated as follows:

1. The samples of golf balls for each brand are selected randomly and independently.
2. The probability distributions of the distances for each brand are normal.
3. The variances of the distance probability distributions for each brand are equal.

Since the sample consisted of 10 randomly selected balls of each brand, and since the robotic golfer Iron Byron was used to drive all the balls, the first assumption of independent random samples is satisfied. To check the next two assumptions, we will employ two graphical methods presented in Chapter 2: histograms and box plots. A MINITAB histogram of driving distances for each brand of golf ball is shown in Figure 10.10, and SAS box plots are shown in Figure 10.11.

The normality assumption can be checked by examining the histograms in Figure 10.10. With only 10 sample measurements for each brand, however, the displays are not very informative. More data would need to be collected for each brand before we could assess whether the distances come from normal distributions. Fortunately, analysis of variance has been shown to be a very **robust method** when the assumption of normality is not satis-

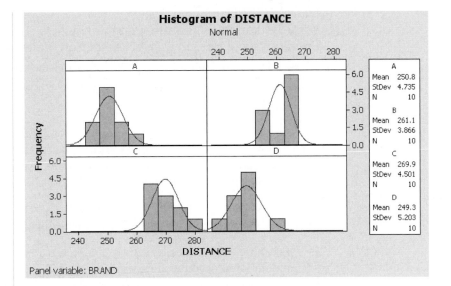

FIGURE 10.10

MINITAB histograms for golf ball driving distances

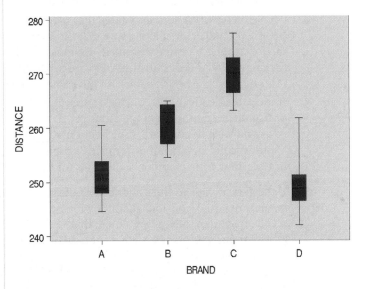

FIGURE 10.11

SAS box plots for golf ball distances

fied exactly. That is, *moderate departures from normality do not have much effect on the significance level of the ANOVA F-test or on confidence coefficients.* Rather than spend the time, energy, or money to collect additional data for this experiment in order to verify the normality assumption, we will rely on the robustness of the ANOVA methodology.

Box plots are a convenient way to obtain a rough check on the assumption of equal variances. With the exception of a possible outlier for Brand D, the box plots in Figure 10.11 show that the spread of the distance measurements is about the same for each brand. Since the sample variances appear to be the same, the assumption of equal population variances for the brands is probably satisfied. Although robust with respect to the normality assumption, ANOVA is *not robust* with respect to the equal-variances assumption. Departures from the assumption of equal population variances can affect the associated measures of reliability (e.g., *p*-values and confidence levels). Fortunately, the effect is slight when the sample sizes are equal, as in this experiment.

Now Work Exercise 10.30

Although graphs can be used to check the ANOVA assumptions as in Example 10.5, no measures of reliability can be attached to these graphs. When you have a plot that is unclear as to whether or not an assumption is satisfied, you can use formal statistical tests that are beyond the scope of this text. Consult the references at the end of the chapter for information on these tests. When the validity of the ANOVA assumptions is in doubt, nonparametric statistical methods are useful.

What Do You Do When the Assumptions Are Not Satisfied for the Analysis of Variance for a Completely Randomized Design?

Answer: Use a nonparametric statistical method such as the Kruskal–Wallis *H*-Test of Section 14.5.

The procedure for conducting an analysis of variance for a completely randomized design is summarized in the next box. Remember that the hallmark of this design is independent random samples of experimental units associated with each treatment. We discuss a design with dependent samples in Section 10.4.

Steps for Conducting an ANOVA for a Completely Randomized Design

1. Make sure that the design is truly completely randomized, with independent random samples for each treatment.
2. Check the assumptions of normality and equal variances.
3. Create an ANOVA summary table that specifies the variabilities attributable to treatments and error, making sure that those variabilities lead to the calculation of the *F*-statistic for testing the null hypothesis that the treatment means are equal in the population. Use a statistical software program to obtain the numerical results. If no such package is available, use the calculation formulas in Appendix B.
4. If the *F*-test leads to the conclusion that the means differ,
   a. Conduct a multiple-comparisons procedure for as many of the pairs of means as you wish to compare. (See Section 10.3.) Use the results to summarize the statistically significant differences among the treatment means.
   b. If desired, form confidence intervals for one or more individual treatment means.
5. If the *F*-test leads to the nonrejection of the null hypothesis that the treatment means are equal, consider the following possibilities:
   a. The treatment means are equal; that is, the null hypothesis is true.
   b. The treatment means really differ, but other important factors affecting the response are not accounted for by the completely randomized design. These factors inflate the sampling variability, as measured by MSE, resulting in smaller values of the *F*-statistic. Either increase the sample size for each treatment, or use a different experimental design (as in Section 10.4) that accounts for the other factors affecting the response.

   [*Note:* Be careful not to automatically conclude that the treatment means are equal since the possibility of a Type II error must be considered if you accept H_0.]

STATISTICS IN ACTION REVISITED

A One-Way Analysis of the Cockroach Data

Consider the experiment designed to investigate the trail-following ability of German cockroaches (p. 481). Recall that an entomologist created a chemical trail with either a methanol extract from roach feces or just methanol (the control). Cockroaches were then released into a container at the beginning of the trail, one at a time, and a video surveillance camera was used to monitor the roaches' movements. The movement pattern of each cockroach was measured by its average deviation (in pixels) from the extract trail and the data stored in the **ROACH** file.

For this application, consider only the cockroaches assigned to the fecal extract trail. Four roach groups were utilized in the experiment—adult males, adult females, gravid females, and nymphs—with 20 roaches of each type independently and randomly selected. Is there sufficient evidence to say that the ability to follow the extract trail differs among cockroaches of different age, sex, and reproductive status? In other words, is there evidence to suggest that the mean trail deviation μ differs for the four roach groups?

To answer this question, we conduct a one-way analysis of variance on the **ROACH** data. The dependent (response) variable of interest is deviation from the extract trail, while the treatments are the four different roach groups. Thus, we want to test the null hypothesis:

$$H_0\text{: } \mu_{\text{Male}} = \mu_{\text{Female}} = \mu_{\text{Gravid}} = \mu_{\text{Nymph}}$$

A MINITAB printout of the ANOVA is displayed in Figure SIA10.1. The p-value of the test (highlighted on the printout) is 0. Since this value is less than, say,

$\alpha = .05$, we reject the null hypothesis and conclude (at the .05 level of significance) that the mean deviation from the extract trail differs among the populations of adult male, adult female, gravid, and nymph cockroaches.

The sample means for the four cockroach groups are also highlighted in Figure SIA10.1. Note that adult males have the smallest sample mean deviation (7.38) while gravids have the largest sample mean deviation (44.03). In the next Statistics in Action application (p. 508), we demonstrate how to rank, statistically, the four population means on the basis of their respective sample means.

Results for Trail = Extract

One-way ANOVA: Deviate versus Group

```
Source   DF      SS     MS      F       P
Group     3   14164   4721  11.61   0.000
Error    76   30918    407
Total    79   45083

S = 20.17    R-Sq = 31.42%    R-Sq(adj) = 28.71%


                            Individual 95% CIs For Mean Based on
                            Pooled StDev
Level    N    Mean   StDev  -+---------+---------+---------+--------
Female   20   21.07  26.13                (-----*-----)
Gravid   20   44.03  24.84                            (-----*-----)
Male     20    7.38   8.61   (-----*-----)
Nymph    20   18.73  15.92             (-----*-----)
                            -+---------+---------+---------+--------
                             0        15        30        45

Pooled StDev = 20.17
```

FIGURE SIA10.1
MINITAB one-way ANOVA for deviation from extract trail

Exercises 10.13–10.36

Understanding the Principles

10.13 Explain how to collect the data for a completely randomized design.

10.14 Explain the concept of a balanced design.

10.15 What conditions are required for a valid ANOVA F-test in a completely randomized design?

10.16 *True or False.* The ANOVA method is robust when the assumption of normality is not exactly satisfied in a completely randomized design.

Learning the Mechanics

10.17 Use Tables VIII, IX, X, and XI of Appendix A to find each of the following F values:
  a. $F_{.05}, v_1 = 3, v_2 = 4$
  b. $F_{.01}, v_1 = 3, v_2 = 4$

  c. $F_{.10}, v_1 = 20, v_2 = 40$
  d. $F_{.025}, v_1 = 12, v_2 = 9$

10.18 Find the following probabilities:
  a. $P(F \leq 3.48)$ for $v_1 = 5, v_2 = 9$
  b. $P(F > 3.09)$ for $v_1 = 15, v_2 = 20$
  c. $P(F > 2.40)$ for $v_1 = 15, v_2 = 15$
  d. $P(F \leq 1.83)$ for $v_1 = 8, v_2 = 40$

10.19 Consider dot plots A and B (shown at the top of p. 500).
  NW Assume that the two samples represent independent random samples corresponding to two treatments in a completely randomized design.
  a. In which dot plot is the difference between the sample means small relative to the variability within the sample observations? Justify your answer.
  b. Calculate the treatment means (i.e., the means of samples 1 and 2) for both dot plots.

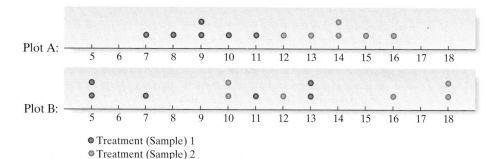

Plot A:

Plot B:

● Treatment (Sample) 1
● Treatment (Sample) 2

Dot Plots for Exercise 10.19

c. Use the means to calculate the sum of squares for treatments (SST) for each dot plot.

d. Calculate the sample variance for each sample and use these values to obtain the sum of squares for error (SSE) for each dot plot.

e. Calculate the total sum of squares [SS(Total)] for the two dot plots by adding the sums of squares for treatment and error. What percentage of SS(Total) is accounted for by the treatments—that is, what percentage of the total sum of squares is the sum of squares for treatment—in each case?

f. Convert the sums of squares for treatment and error to mean squares by dividing each by the appropriate number of degrees of freedom. Calculate the F-ratio of the mean square for treatment (MST) to the mean square for error (MSE) for each dot plot.

g. Use the F-ratios to test the null hypothesis that the two samples are drawn from populations with equal means. Take $\alpha = .05$.

h. What assumptions must be made about the probability distributions corresponding to the responses for each treatment in order to ensure the validity of the F-tests conducted in part **g**?

10.20 Refer to Exercise 10.19. Conduct a two-sample t-test (Section 9.2) of the null hypothesis that the two treatment means are equal for each dot plot. Use $\alpha = .05$ and two-tailed tests. In the course of the test, compare each of the following with the F-tests in Exercise 10.19:

a. The pooled variances and the MSEs

b. The t- and the F-test statistics

c. The tabled values of t and F that determine the rejection regions

d. The conclusions of the t- and F-tests

e. The assumptions that must be made in order to ensure the validity of the t- and F-tests

10.21 Refer to Exercises 10.19 and 10.20. Complete the following ANOVA table for each of the two dot plots:

Source	df	SS	MS	F
Treatments				
Error				
Total				

10.22 A partially completed ANOVA table for a completely
NW   randomized design is shown here:

Source	df	SS	MS	F
Treatments	6	18.4		
Error				
Total	41	45.2		

a. Complete the ANOVA table.

b. How many treatments are involved in the experiment?

c. Do the data provide sufficient evidence to indicate a difference among the population means? Test, using $\alpha = .10$.

d. Find the approximate observed significance level for the test in part **c**, and interpret it.

10.23 Suppose the total sum of squares for a completely randomized design with $p = 5$ treatments and $n = 30$ total measurements (6 per treatment) is equal to 500. In each of the following cases, conduct an F-test of the null hypothesis that the mean responses for the 5 treatments are the same. Use $\alpha = .10$.

a. Sum of squares for treatment (SST) is 20% of SS(Total)

b. SST is 50% of SS(Total)

c. SST is 80% of SS(Total)

d. What happens to the F-ratio as the percentage of the total sum of squares attributable to treatments is increased?

10.24 The data in the following table resulted from an experi-
NW   ment that utilized a completely randomized design:

⌬ **LM10_24**

Treatment 1	Treatment 2	Treatment 3
3.9	5.4	1.3
1.4	2.0	.7
4.1	4.8	2.2
5.5	3.8	
2.3	3.5	

a. Use statistical software (or the formulas in Appendix B) to complete the following ANOVA table:

Source	df	SS	MS	F
Treatments				
Error				
Total				

b. Test the null hypothesis that $\mu_1 = \mu_2 = \mu_3$, where μ_i represents the true mean for treatment i, against the alternative that at least two of the means differ. Use $\alpha = .01$.

Applying the Concepts—Basic

10.25 **College tennis recruiting with a team website.** Most university athletic programs now have a website with information on individual sports and a Prospective Student Athlete Form that allows high school athletes to submit information about their academic and sports achievements directly to the college coach. *The Sport Journal* (Winter 2004) published a study of how important team websites are to the recruitment of college tennis players. A survey was conducted of National Collegiate Athletic Association (NCAA) tennis coaches, of which 53 were from Division I schools, 20 were from Division II schools, and 53 were from Division III schools. Coaches were asked to respond to a series of statements, including "The Prospective Student Athlete Form on the website contributes very little to the recruiting process." Responses were measured on a seven-points scale (where $1 =$ strongly disagree and $7 =$ strongly agree). In order to compare the mean responses of tennis coaches from the three NCAA divisions, the data were analyzed with a completely randomized ANOVA design.

a. Identify the experimental unit, the dependent (response) variable, the factor, and the treatments in this study.

b. Give the null and alternative hypothesis for the ANOVA F-test.

c. The observed significance level of the test was found to be p-value $< .003$. What conclusion can you draw if you want to test at $\alpha = .05$?

10.26 A new dental bonding agent. Refer to the *Trends in Biomaterials & Artificial Organs* (Jan. 2003) study of a new bonding adhesive for teeth, presented in Exercise 8.63 (p. 377). Recall that the new adhesive (called "Smartbond") has been developed to eliminate the necessity of a dry field. In one portion of the study, 30 extracted teeth were bonded with Smartbond and each was randomly assigned one of three different bonding times: 1 hour, 24 hours, or 48 hours. At the end of the bonding period, the breaking strength (in Mpa) of each tooth was determined. The data were analyzed with the use of analysis of variance in order to determine whether the true mean breaking strength of the new adhesive varies with the bonding time.

a. Identify the experimental units, treatments, and response variable for this completely randomized design.

b. Set up the null and alternative hypotheses for the ANOVA.

c. Find the rejection region for the test, using $\alpha = .01$.

d. The test results were $F = 61.62$ and p-value ≈ 0. Give the appropriate conclusion for the test.

e. What conditions are required for the test results to be valid?

10.27 Robots trained to behave like ants. Robotics researchers investigated whether robots could be trained to behave like ants in an ant colony. (*Nature*, Aug. 2000.) Robots were trained and randomly assigned to "colonies" (i.e., groups) consisting of 3, 6, 9, or 12 robots. The robots were assigned the tasks of foraging for "food" and recruiting another robot when they identified a resource-rich area. One goal of the experiment was to compare the mean energy expended (per robot) of the four different sizes of colonies.

a. What type of experimental design was employed?

b. Identify the treatments and the dependent variable.

c. Set up the null and alternative hypotheses of the test.

d. The following ANOVA results were reported: $F = 7.70$, numerator df $= 3$, denominator df $= 56$, p-value $< .001$. Conduct the test at a significance level of $\alpha = .05$ and interpret the result.

⊙ **TVADRECALL**

10.28 Study of recall of TV commercials. Television advertisers seek to promote their products on TV programs that attract the most viewers. Do TV shows with violence and sex impair memory for commercials? To answer this question, Iowa St. professors B. Bushman and A. Bonacci conducted a designed experiment in which 324 adults were randomly assigned to one of three viewer groups of 108 participants each. (*Journal of Applied Psychology*, June 2002.) One group watched a TV program (e.g., *Tour of Duty*) with a violent content code (V) rating, the second group viewed a show (e.g., *Strip Mall*) with a sex content code (S) rating, and the last group watched a neutral TV program (e.g., *Candid Camera*) with neither a V nor an S rating. Nine commercials were embedded into each TV show. After viewing the program, each participant was scored on his or her recall of the brand names in the commercial messages, with scores ranging from 0 (no brands recalled) to 9 (all brands recalled). The data (simulated from information provided in the article) are saved in the **TVADRECALL** file. The researchers compared the mean recall scores of the three viewing groups with an analysis of variance for a completely randomized design.

a. Identify the experimental units in the study.

b. Identify the dependent (response) variable in the study.

c. Identify the factor and treatments in the study.

d. The sample mean recall scores for the three groups were $\bar{x}_V = 2.08$, $\bar{x}_S = 1.71$, and $\bar{x}_{\text{Neutral}} = 3.17$. Explain why one should not draw an inference about differences in the population mean recall scores on the basis of only these summary statistics.

e. An ANOVA on the data in the **TVADRECALL** file yielded the results shown in the accompanying MINITAB printout. Locate the test statistic and p-value on the printout.

f. Interpret the results from part **e**, using $\alpha = 0.01$. What can the researchers conclude about the three groups of TV ad viewers?

One-way ANOVA: VIOLENT, SEX, NEUTRAL

Source	DF	SS	MS	F	P
Factor	2	123.27	61.63	20.45	0.000
Error	321	967.35	3.01		
Total	323	1090.62			

S = 1.736 R-Sq = 11.30% R-Sq(adj) = 10.75%

10.29 Heights of grade school repeaters. Refer to the *Archives of Disease in Childhood* (Apr. 2000) study of whether height influences a child's progression through elementary school, presented in Exercise 9.17 (p. 427). Within each grade, Australian schoolchildren were divided into equal thirds (tertiles) based on age (youngest third, middle third, and oldest third). The researchers compared the average heights of the three groups, using an analysis of variance. (All height measurements were standardized with z-scores.) A summary of the results for all grades combined, by gender, is shown in the next table:

	Sample Size	Youngest Tertile Mean Height	Middle Tertile Mean Height	Oldest Tertile Mean Height	F-Value	p-Value
Boys	1439	0.33	0.33	0.16	4.57	0.01
Girls	1409	0.27	0.18	0.21	0.85	0.43

Source: Wake, M., Coghlan, D., and Hesketh, K. "Does height influence progression through primary school grades?" *The Archives of Disease in Childhood,* Vol. 82, Apr. 2000 (Table 2).

a. What is the null hypothesis for the ANOVA of the boys' data?

b. Interpret the results of the test, part **a**. Use $\alpha = .05$.

c. Repeat parts **a** and **b** for the girls' data.

d. Summarize the results of the hypothesis tests in the words of the problem.

10.30 Most powerful American women. Refer to *Fortune* (Nov. 14, 2002) magazine's study of the most powerful women in America, presented in Exercise 2.58 (p. 59). Recall that the data on age (in years) and title of each of the 50 women in the survey are stored in the **WPOWER50** file. (Some of the data are listed in the accompanying table.) Suppose you want to compare the average ages of the most powerful American women in four groups based on their position (title) within the firm: Group 1 (CEO); Group 2 (Chairman, President CFO, COO, or CRO); Group 3 (EVP, SVP, and Vice Chair); and Group 4 (Founder, Treasurer, or Executive).

WPOWER50

Rank	Name	Age	Company	Title
1	Meg Whitman	49	eBay	CEO/Chairman
2	Anne Mulcahy	52	Xerox	CEO/Chairman
3	Brenda Barnes	51	Sara Lee	CEO/President
4	Oprah Winfrey	51	Harpo	Chairman
5	Andrea Jung	47	Avon	CEO/Chairman
⋮	⋮	⋮	⋮	⋮
49	Safra Catz	43	Oracle	President
50	Kathy Cassidy	51	General Electric	Treasurer

Source: Fortune, Nov. 14, 2005.

a. Give the null and alternative hypotheses to be tested.

b. An SPSS analysis-of-variance printout for the test you stated in part **a** is shown below. The sample means for the four groups appear at the bottom of the printout. Why is it insufficient to make a decision about the null hypothesis based solely on these sample means?

c. Locate the test statistic and p-value on the printout. Use this information to make the appropriate conclusion at $\alpha = .10$.

d. Use the data in the **WPOWER50** file to determine whether the ANOVA assumptions are reasonably satisfied.

Applying the Concepts—Intermediate

10.31 Income and road rage. The phenomenon of road rage has received much media attention in recent years. Is a driver's propensity to engage in road rage related to his or her income? Researchers at Mississippi State University attempted to answer this question by conducting a survey of a representative sample of over 1,000 U.S. adult drivers. (*Accident Analysis and Prevention,* Vol. 34, 2002.) Based on how often each driver engaged in certain road rage behaviors (e.g., making obscene gestures at, tailgating, and thinking about physically hurting another driver), a road rage score was assigned. (Higher scores indicate a greater pattern of road rage behavior.) The drivers were also grouped by annual income: under $30,000, between $30,000 and $60,000, and over $60,000. The data were subjected to an analysis of variance, with the results summarized in the next table. Interpret the results fully. Is a driver's propensity to engage in road rage related to his or her income?

ANOVA

AGE

	Sum of Squares	df	Mean Square	F	Sig.
Between Groups	191.140	3	63.713	2.500	.071
Within Groups	1172.140	46	25.481		
Total	1363.280	49			

AGE

GROUP	Mean	N	Std. Deviation
1	51.07	15	5.216
2	48.11	18	5.603
3	49.57	14	3.502
4	56.00	3	7.000
Total	49.88	50	5.275

SPSS output for Exercise 10.30

Income Group	Sample Size	Mean Road Rage Score
Under $30,000	379	4.60
$30,000 to $60,000	392	5.08
Over $60,000	267	5.15
ANOVA results:	F-value $= 3.90$	p-value $< .01$

10.32 Restoring self-control when intoxicated. Does coffee or some other form of stimulation (e.g., an incentive to stop when seeing a flashing red light on a car) really allow a person suffering from alcohol intoxication to "sober up"? Psychologists from the University of Waterloo investigated the matter in *Experimental and Clinical Psychopharmacology* (February 2005). A sample of 44 healthy male college students participated in the experiment. Each student was asked to memorize a list of 40 words (20 words on a green list and 20 words on a red list). The students were then randomly assigned to one of four different treatment groups (11 students in each group). Students in three of the groups were each given two alcoholic beverages to drink prior to performing a word completion task. Students in Group A received only the alcoholic drinks. Participants in Group AC had caffeine powder dissolved in their drinks. Group AR participants received a monetary award for correct responses on the word completion task. Students in Group P (the placebo group) were told that they would receive alcohol, but instead received two drinks containing a carbonated beverage (with a few drops of alcohol on the surface to provide an alcoholic scent). After consuming their drinks and resting for 25 minutes, the students performed the word completion task. Their scores (simulated on the basis of summary information from the article) are reported in the accompanying table. (*Note:* A task score represents the difference between the proportion of corrects responses on the green list of words and the proportion of incorrect responses on the red list of words.)

a. What type of experimental design is employed in this study?

b. Analyze the data for the researchers, using $\alpha = .05$. Are there differences among the mean task scores for the four groups?

c. What assumptions must be met in order to ensure the validity of the inference you made in part **b**?

DRINKERS

AR	AC	A	P
.51	.50	.16	.58
.58	.30	.10	.12
.52	.47	.20	.62
.47	.36	.29	.43
.61	.39	$-.14$	.26
.00	.22	.18	.50
.32	.20	$-.35$	.44
.53	.21	.31	.20
.50	.15	.16	.42
.46	.10	.04	.43
.34	.02	$-.25$	.40

Adapted from Grattan-Miscio, K.E., and Vogel-Sprott, M. "Alcohol, intentional control, and inappropriate behavior: Regulation by caffeine or an incentive," *Experimental and Clinical Psychopharmacology*, Vol. 13, No. 1, February 2005 (Table 1).

10.33 Effect of scopolamine on memory. The drug scopolamine is often used as a sedative to induce sleep in patients. In *Behavioral Neuroscience* (Feb. 2004), medical researchers examined scopolamine's effects on memory with associated word pairs. A total of 28 human subjects, recruited from a university community, were given a list of related word pairs to memorize. For every word pair in the list (e.g., robber–jail), there was an associated word pair with the same first word, but a different second word (e.g., robber–police). The subjects were then randomly divided into three treatment groups. Group 1 subjects were administered an injection of scopolamine, group 2 subjects were given an injection of glycopyrrolate (an active placebo), and group 3 subjects were not given any drug. Four hours later, subjects were shown 12 word pairs from the list and tested on how many they could recall. The data on number of pairs recalled (simulated on the basis of summary information provided in the research article) are listed in the accompanying table. Prior to the analysis, the researchers theorized that the mean number of word pairs recalled for the scopolamine subjects (group 1) would be less than the corresponding means for the other two groups.

a. Explain why this is a completely randomized design.

b. Identify the treatments and response variable.

c. Find the sample means for the three groups. Is this sufficient information to support the researchers' theory? Explain.

d. Conduct an ANOVA F-test on the data. Is there sufficient evidence (at $\alpha = .05$) to conclude that the mean number of word pairs recalled differs among the three treatment groups?

SCOPOLAMINE

Group 1 (Scopolamine):	5	8	8	6	6	6	6	8	6	4	5	6
Group 2 (Placebo):	8	10	12	10	9	7	9	10				
Group 3 (No drug):	8	9	11	12	11	10	12	12				

10.34 The "name game." Psychologists at Lancaster University (United Kingdom) evaluated three methods of name retrieval in a controlled setting. (*Journal of Experimental Psychology—Applied*, June 2000.) A sample of 139 students was randomly divided into three groups, and each group of students used a different method to learn the names of the other students in the group. Group 1 used the "simple name game," in which the first student states his or her full name, the second student announces his or her name and the name of the first student, the third student says his or her name and the names of the first two students, etc. Group 2 used the "elaborate name game," a modification of the simple name game such that the students state not only their names, but also their favorite activity (e.g., sports). Group 3 used "pairwise introductions," according to which students are divided into pairs and each student must introduce the other member of the pair. One year later, all subjects were sent pictures of the students in their group and asked to state the full name of each. The researchers measured the percentage of names recalled by each student respondent. The data (simulated on the basis of summary statistics provided in the research article) are shown in the next table. Conduct an analysis of variance to determine whether the mean percentages of names recalled differ for the three name-retrieval methods. Use $\alpha = .05$.

NAMEGAME

Simple Name Game

24	43	38	65	35	15	44	44	18	27	0	38	50	31
7	46	33	31	0	29	0	0	52	0	29	42	39	26
51	0	42	20	37	51	0	30	43	30	99	39	35	19
24	34	3	60	0	29	40	40						

Elaborate Name Game

39	71	9	86	26	45	0	38	5	53	29	0	62	0
1	35	10	6	33	48	9	26	83	33	12	5	0	0
25	36	39	1	37	2	13	26	7	35	3	8	55	50

Pairwise Introductions

5	21	22	3	32	29	32	0	4	41	0	27	5	9
66	54	1	15	0	26	1	30	2	13	0	2	17	14
5	29	0	45	35	7	11	4	9	23	4	0	8	2
18	0	5	21	14									

Source: Morris, P. E., and Fritz, C. O. "The name game: Using retrieval practice to improve the learning of names," *Journal of Experimental Psychology—Applied*, Vol. 6, No. 2, June 2000 (data simulated from Figure 1).

10.35 **Estimating the age of glacial drifts.** Refer to the *American Journal of Science* (Jan. 2005) study of the chemical make-up of buried tills (glacial drifts) in Wisconsin, presented in Exercise 2.130 (p. 88). The ratio of the elements aluminum (Al) and beryllium (Be) in sediment is related to the duration of burial. Recall the Al/Be ratios for a sample of 26 buried till specimens were determined and are saved in the TILLRATIO file. The till specimens were obtained from five different boreholes (labeled UMRB-1, UMRB-2, UMRB-3, SWRA, and SD). The data are shown in the accompanying table. Conduct an analysis of variance of the data. Is there sufficient evidence to indicate differences among the mean Al/Be ratios for the five boreholes? Test, using $\alpha = .10$.

TILLRATIO

UMRB-1:	3.75	4.05	3.81	3.23	3.13	3.30	3.21
UMRB-2:	3.32	4.09	3.90	5.06	3.85	3.88	
UMRB-3:	4.06	4.56	3.60	3.27	4.09	3.38	3.37
SWRA:	2.73	2.95	2.25				
SD:	2.73	2.55	3.06				

Source: Adapted from *American Journal of Science*, Vol. 305, No. 1, Jan. 2005, p. 16 (Table 2).

Applying the Concepts—Advanced

10.36 **Animal-assisted therapy for heart patients.** Refer to the *American Heart Association Conference* (Nov. 2005) study to gauge whether animal-assisted therapy can improve the physiological responses of heart failure patients, presented in Exercise 2.102 (p. 74). Recall that 76 heart patients were randomly assigned to one of three groups. Each patient in group T was visited by a human volunteer accompanied by a trained dog, each patient in group V was visited by a volunteer only, and the patients in group C were not visited at all. The anxiety level of each patient was measured (in points) both before and after the visits. The accompanying table gives summary statistics for the drop in anxiety level for patients in the three groups. The mean drops in anxiety levels of the three groups of patients were compared with the use of an analysis of variance. Although the ANOVA table was not provided in the article, sufficient information is given to reconstruct it.

	Sample Size	Mean Drop	Std. Dev.
Group T: Volunteer + Trained Dog	26	10.5	7.6
Group V: Volunteer only	25	3.9	7.5
Group C: Control group (no visit)	25	1.4	7.5

Source: Cole, K., et al. "Animal-assisted therapy decreases hemodynamics, plasma epinephrine and state anxiety in hospitalized heart failure patients," *American Heart Association Conference*, Dallas, Texas, Nov. 2005.

a. Compute SST for the ANOVA, using the formula (on p. 490)

$$\text{SST} = \sum_{i=1}^{3} n_i(\bar{x}_i - \bar{x})^2$$

where $\bar{x}$ is the overall mean drop in anxiety level of all 76 subjects. [Hint: $\bar{x} = (\sum_{i=1}^{3} n_i (\bar{x}_i)/76.]$

b. Recall that SSE for the ANOVA can be written as

$$\text{SSE} = (n_1 - 1)s_1^2 + (n_2 - 1)s_2^2 + (n_3 - 1)s_3^2$$

where s_1^2, s_2^2, and s_3^2 are the sample variances associated with the three treatments. Compute SSE for the ANOVA.

c. Use the results from parts **a** and **b** to construct the ANOVA table.

d. Is there sufficient evidence (at $\alpha = .01$) of differences among the mean drops in anxiety levels by the patients in the three groups?

e. Comment on the validity of the ANOVA assumptions. How might this affect the results of the study?

10.3 Multiple Comparisons of Means

Consider a completely randomized design with three treatments: *A*, *B*, and *C*. Suppose we determine, via the ANOVA *F*-test of Section 10.2, that the treatment means are statistically different. To complete the analysis, we want to rank the three treatment means. As mentioned in Section 10.2, we start by placing confidence intervals on the differences between various pairs of treatment means in the experiment. In the three-treatment experiment, for example, we would construct confidence intervals for the following differences: $\mu_A - \mu_B$, $\mu_A - \mu_C$, and $\mu_B - \mu_C$.

Determining the Number of Pairwise Comparisons of Treatment Means

In general, if there are k treatment means, there are

$$c = k(k - 1)/2$$

pairs of means that can be compared.

If we want to have $100(1 - \alpha)\%$ confidence that each of the c confidence intervals contains the true difference it is intended to estimate, we must use a smaller value of α for each individual confidence interval than we would use for a single interval. For example, suppose we want to rank the means of the three treatments with 95% confidence that all three confidence intervals comparing the means contain the true differences between the treatment means. Then each individual confidence interval will need to be constructed on the basis of a level of significance smaller than $\alpha = .05$.*

Now Work Exercise 10.41

To make **multiple comparisons of a set of treatment means**, we can use a number of procedures which, under various assumptions, ensure that the overall confidence level associated with all the comparisons remains at or above the specified $100(1 - \alpha)\%$ level. Three widely used techniques are the Bonferroni, Scheffé, and Tukey methods. For each of these procedures, the risk of making a Type I error applies to the comparisons of the treatment means in the experiment; thus, the value of α selected is called an **experimentwise error rate** (in contrast to a **comparisonwise error rate**).

The choice of a multiple-comparison method in ANOVA will depend on the type of experimental design used and the comparisons that are of interest to the analyst. For example, **Tukey** (1949) developed his procedure specifically for pairwise comparisons when the sample sizes of the treatments are equal. The **Bonferroni** method (see Miller, 1981), like the Tukey procedure, can be applied when pairwise comparisons are of interest; however, Bonferroni's method does not require equal sample sizes. **Scheffé** (1953) developed a more general procedure for comparing all possible linear combinations of treatment means (called *contrasts*). Consequently, in making pairwise comparisons, the confidence intervals produced by Scheffé's method will generally be wider than the Tukey or Bonferroni confidence intervals.

Biography

**CARLO E. BONFERRONI
(1892–1960)—
Bonferroni Inequalities**

During his childhood years in Turin, Italy, Carlo Bonferroni developed an aptitude for mathematics while studying music. He went on to obtain a degree in mathematics at the University of Turin. Bonferroni's first appointment as a professor of mathematics was at the University of Bari in 1923. Ten years later, he became chair of financial mathematics at the University of Florence, where he re-

mained until his death. Bonferroni was a prolific writer, authoring over 65 research papers and books. His interest in statistics included various methods of calculating a mean and a correlation coefficient. Among statisticians, however, Bonferroni is most well known for developing his Bonferroni inequalities in probability theory in 1935. Later, other statisticians proposed using these inequalities to find simultaneous confidence intervals, which led to the development of the Bonferroni multiple-comparison method in ANOVA. Bonferroni balanced these scientific accomplishments with his music, becoming an excellent pianist and composer.

---

*The reason each interval must be formed at a higher confidence level than that specified for the collection of intervals can be demonstrated as follows:

$$P\ \{\text{At least one of } c \text{ intervals fails to contain the true difference}\}$$
$$= 1 - P\ \{\text{All } c \text{ intervals contain the true differences}\}$$
$$= 1 - (1 - \alpha)^c \geq \alpha$$

Thus, to make this probability of at least one failure equal to α, we must specify the individual levels of significance to be less than α.

The formulas for constructing confidence intervals for differences between treatment means by the Tukey, Bonferroni, or Scheffé methods are provided in Appendix B. However, since these procedures (and many others) are available in the ANOVA programs of most statistical software packages, we will use the computer to conduct the analyses. The programs generate a confidence interval for the difference between two treatment means for all possible pairs of treatments, based on the experimentwise error rate (α) selected by the analyst.

EXAMPLE 10.6

RANKING TREATMENT MEANS— Golf Ball Experiment

Problem Refer to the completely randomized design of Example 10.4, in which we concluded that at least two of the four brands of golf balls are associated with different mean distances traveled when struck with a driver.

a. Use Tukey's multiple comparison procedure to rank the treatment means with an overall confidence level of 95%.

b. Estimate the mean distance traveled for balls manufactured by the brand with the highest rank.

Solution

a. To rank the treatment means with an overall confidence level of .95, we require the experimentwise error rate of $\alpha = .05$. The confidence intervals generated by Tukey's method appear at the bottom of the SAS ANOVA printout, shown in Figure 10.12. Note that for any pair of means μ_i and μ_j, SAS computes two confidence intervals— one for $(\mu_i - \mu_j)$ and one for $(\mu_j - \mu_i)$. Only one of these intervals is necessary to decide whether the means differ significantly.

In this example, we have $k = 4$ brand means to compare. Consequently, the number of relevant pairwise comparisons—that is, the number of nonredundant confidence intervals—is $c = 4(3)/2 = 6$. These six intervals, highlighted in Figure 10.12, are given in Table 10.4.

We are 95% confident that the intervals *collectively* contain all the differences between the true brand mean distances. Note that intervals containing 0, such as the (Brand A–Brand D) interval from −4.08 to 7.00, do not support a conclusion that the true brand mean distances differ. If both endpoints of the interval are positive, as with the (Brand B–Brand D) interval from 6.20 to 17.28, the implication is

The ANOVA Procedure

Tukey's Studentized Range (HSD) Test for DISTANCE

NOTE: This test controls the Type I experimentwise error rate.

Alpha	0.05
Error Degrees of Freedom	36
Error Mean Square	21.17503
Critical Value of Studentized Range	3.80880
Minimum Significant Difference	5.5424

Comparisons significant at the 0.05 level are indicated by ***.

BRAND Comparison		Difference Between Means	Simultaneous 95% Confidence Limits		
C	- B	8.890	3.348	14.432	***
C	- A	19.170	13.628	24.712	***
C	- D	20.630	15.088	26.172	***
B	- C	-8.890	-14.432	-3.348	***
B	- A	10.280	4.738	15.822	***
B	- D	11.740	6.198	17.282	***
A	- C	-19.170	-24.712	-13.628	***
A	- B	-10.280	-15.822	-4.738	***
A	- D	1.460	-4.082	7.002	
D	- C	-20.630	-26.172	-15.088	***
D	- B	-11.740	-17.282	-6.198	***
D	- A	-1.460	-7.002	4.082	

FIGURE 10.12

SAS multiple–comparison printout for Example 10.6

TABLE 10.4 Pairwise Comparisons for Example 10.6

Brand Comparison	Confidence Interval
$(\mu_A - \mu_B)$	$(-15.82, -4.74)$
$(\mu_A - \mu_C)$	$(-24.71, -13.63)$
$(\mu_A - \mu_D)$	$(-4.08, 7.00)$
$(\mu_B - \mu_C)$	$(-14.43, -3.35)$
$(\mu_B - \mu_D)$	$(6.20, 17.28)$
$(\mu_C - \mu_D)$	$(15.09, 26.17)$

Mean: 249.3   250.8   261.1   270.0
Brand: D   A   B   C

FIGURE 10.13

Summary of Tukey multiple comparisons

that the first brand (B) mean distance exceeds the second (D). Conversely, if both endpoints of the interval are negative, as with the (Brand A–Brand C) interval from −24.71 to −13.63, the implication is that the second brand (C) mean distance exceeds the first brand (A) mean distance.

A convenient summary of the results of the Tukey multiple comparisons is a listing of the brand means from highest to lowest, with a solid line connecting those which are *not* significantly different. This summary is shown in Figure 10.13. The interpretation is that brand C's mean distance exceeds all others, brand B's mean exceeds that of brands A and D, and the means of brands A and D do not differ significantly. All these inferences are made with 95% confidence, the overall confidence level of the Tukey multiple comparisons.

b. Brand C is ranked highest; thus, we want a confidence interval for μ_C. Since the samples were selected independently in a completely randomized design, a confidence interval for an individual treatment mean is obtained with the one-sample t confidence interval of Section 7.3, using the standard deviation, $s = \sqrt{MSE}$, as the measure of sampling variability for the experiment. A 95% confidence interval on the mean distance traveled by brand C (apparently the "longest ball" of those tested) is

$$\bar{x}_C \pm t_{.025} s \sqrt{1/n}$$

where $n = 10$, $t_{.025} \approx 2$ (based on 36 degrees of freedom), and $s = 4.602$ (obtained from the MINITAB printout shown in Figure 10.8). Substituting, we obtain

$$270.0 \pm (2)(4.60)(\sqrt{.1})$$
$$270.0 \pm 2.9 \quad \text{or} \quad (267.1, 272.9)$$

Thus, we are 95% confident that the true mean distance traveled for brand C is between 267.1 and 272.9 yards when the ball is hit with a driver by Iron Byron.

Look Back The easiest way to create a summary table like Figure 10.13 is to first list the treatment means in rank order. Begin with the largest mean and compare it to (in order), the second largest mean, the third largest mean, etc., by examining the appropriate confidence intervals shown on the computer printout. If a confidence interval contains 0, then connect the two means with a line. (These two means are not significantly different.) Continue in this manner by comparing the second largest mean with the third largest, fourth largest, etc., until all possible $c = (k)(k - 1)/2$ comparisons are made.

Now Work Exercise 10.43

Many of the available statistical software packages that have multiple-comparison routines will also produce the rankings shown in Figure 10.13. For example, the SAS printout in Figure 10.14 displays the ranking of the mean distances for the four golf ball brands, achieved with Tukey's method.

The experimentwise error rate (.05), MSE value (21.17503), and minimum significant difference (5.5424) used in the analysis are highlighted on the printout. The Tukey

```
                            The ANOVA Procedure

                Tukey's Studentized Range (HSD) Test for DISTANCE

      NOTE: This test controls the Type I experimentwise error rate, but it generally has a higher
                         Type II error rate than REGWQ.


                      Alpha                               0.05
                      Error Degrees of Freedom              36
                      Error Mean Square                21.17503
                      Critical Value of Studentized Range  3.80880
                      Minimum Significant Difference      5.5424


              Means with the same letter are not significantly different.


                   Tukey Grouping          Mean    N    BRAND

                           A             269.950   10   C

                           B             261.060   10   B

                           C             250.780   10   A
                           C
                           C             249.320   10   D
```

FIGURE 10.14

Alternative SAS multiple-comparison output for Example 10.6

rankings of the means are displayed at the bottom of the figure. Instead of a solid line, note that SAS uses a "Tukey Grouping" letter to connect means that are not significantly different. You can see that the mean for brand C is ranked highest, followed by the mean for brand B. These two brand means are significantly different, since they are associated with a different "Tukey Grouping" letter. Brands A and D are ranked lowest, and their means are not significantly different (since they have the same "Tukey Grouping" letter).

Remember that the Tukey method—designed for comparing treatments with equal sample sizes—is just one of numerous multiple-comparison procedures available. Another technique may be more appropriate for the experimental design you employ. Consult the references for details on these other methods and when they should be applied. Guidelines for using the Tukey, Bonferroni, and Scheffé methods are given in the following box:

Guidelines for Selecting a Multiple-Comparison Method in ANOVA

Method	Treatment Sample Sizes	Types of Comparisons
Tukey	Equal	Pairwise
Bonferroni	Equal or unequal	Pairwise
Scheffé	Equal or unequal	General contrasts

Note: For equal sample sizes and pairwise comparisons, Tukey's method will yield simultaneous confidence intervals with the smallest width, and the Bonferroni intervals will have smaller widths than the Scheffé intervals.

STATISTICS IN ACTION REVISITED

Ranking the Means of the Cockroach Groups

Refer to the experiment designed to investigate the trail-following ability of German cockroaches. In the previous Statistics in Action Revisited (p. 498), we applied a one-way ANOVA to the **ROACH** data and discovered statistically significant differences among the mean extract trail deviations for the four groups of cockroaches: adult males, adult females, gravid females, and nymphs. In order to determine which group has the highest degree of trail-following ability, we want

to rank the population means from largest to smallest. That is, we want to follow up the ANOVA by conducting multiple comparisons of the four treatment means.

Figure SIA10.2 is a MINITAB printout of the ANOVA and the multiple-comparison results. MINITAB uses Tukey's method to compare the means. The experimentwise confidence level (95%) is highlighted on the printout; also highlighted are the Tukey confidence intervals for all possible pairs of means. The information contained in these confidence intervals will enable us to rank the treatment (population) means.

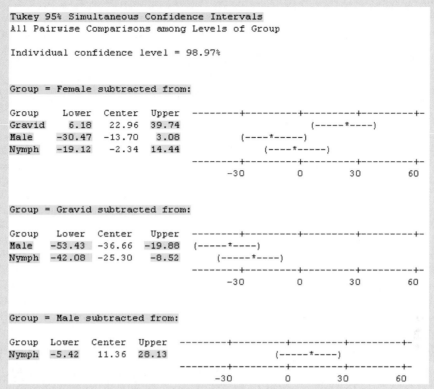

FIGURE SIA10.2
MINITAB multiple comparisons of extract trail deviation means

For example, the confidence interval for $(\mu_{Gravid} - \mu_{Female})$ is (6.18, 39.74). Since the endpoints of the interval are both positive, the difference between the means is positive. This implies that the population mean deviation from the extract trail for gravid cockroaches is greater than the population mean for adult females (i.e., $\mu_{Gravid} > \mu_{Female}$).

Now consider the confidence interval for $(\mu_{Male} - \mu_{Female})$. The interval shown on the printout is $(-30.47, 3.08)$. Since the value 0 is included in the interval, there is no evidence of a significant difference between the two treatment means. Similar interpretations are made for the confidence intervals for $(\mu_{Nymph} - \mu_{Female})$ and $(\mu_{Nymph} - \mu_{Male})$, since both these intervals contain 0.

Finally, note that the confidence intervals for $(\mu_{Male} - \mu_{Gravid})$ and $(\mu_{Nymph} - \mu_{Gravid})$ both have negative endpoints, implying that the differences between the means is negative. Thus, the population mean deviation from the extract trail for gravids is greater than either the population mean for adult males ($\mu_{Gravid} > \mu_{Male}$) or the population mean for nymphs ($\mu_{Gravid} > \mu_{Nymph}$).

The results of these multiple comparisons are summarized in Table SIA10.1. With an overall confidence level of .95, we conclude that gravid cockroaches have a mean extract trail deviation larger than any of the other three groups; there are no significant differences among adult males, adult females, or nymphs.

TABLE SIA10.1 Ranking of the Cockroach Group Means

Treatment Mean:	7.38	18.73	21.07	44.03
Cockroach Group:	Male	Nymph	Female	Gravid

Exercises 10.37–10.55

Understanding the Principles

10.37 Define an experimentwise error rate.

10.38 Define a comparisonwise error rate.

10.39 For each of the following confidence intervals for the difference between two means, $(\mu_1 - \mu_2)$, which mean is significantly larger?
   a. $(-10, 5)$ **b.** $(-10, -5)$ **c.** $(5, 10)$

10.40 Give a situation when it is most appropriate to apply Tukey's multiple-comparison-of-means method.

Learning the Mechanics

10.41 Consider a completely randomized design with p treat-
NW ments. Assume that all pairwise comparisons of treatment means are to be made with the use of a

multiple-comparison procedure. Determine the total number of pairwise comparisons for the following values of k:

a. $k = 3$ **b.** $k = 5$
c. $k = 4$ **d.** $k = 10$

10.42 Consider a completely randomized design with five treatments: A, B, C, D, and E. The ANOVA F-test revealed significant differences among the means. A multiple-comparison procedure was used to compare all possible pairs of treatment means at $\alpha = .05$. The ranking of the five treatment means is summarized here. Identify which pairs of means are significantly different.

a. $\overline{A\ \ C}\ \ E\ \ \overline{B\ \ D}$ **b.** $\overline{A\ \ C\ \ E}\ \ \overline{B\ \ D}$
c. A $\overline{C\ \ E\ \ B}$ D   **d.** $\overline{A\ \ C\ \ E\ \ B\ \ D}$

10.43 A multiple-comparison procedure for comparing four
NW treatment means produced the confidence intervals shown here. Rank the means from smallest to largest. Which means are significantly different?

$(\mu_1 - \mu_2)$: $(2, 15)$
$(\mu_1 - \mu_3)$: $(4, 7)$
$(\mu_1 - \mu_4)$: $(-10, 3)$
$(\mu_2 - \mu_3)$: $(-5, 11)$
$(\mu_2 - \mu_4)$: $(-12, -6)$
$(\mu_3 - \mu_4)$: $(-8, -5)$

Applying the Concepts—Basic

10.44 **College tennis recruiting with a team website.** Refer to *The Sport Journal* (Winter 2004) study comparing the attitudes of Division I, Division II, and Division III college tennis coaches towards team websites as recruiting tools, presented in Exercise 10.25 (p. 500). The mean responses (measured on a seven-point scale) to the statement "The Prospective Student-Athlete Form on the website contributes very little to the recruiting process" are listed and ranked in the accompanying table. The results were obtained with the use of a multiple-comparison procedure with an experimentwise error rate of .05. Interpret the results practically.

Mean:	4.51	3.60	3.21
Division:	I	II	III

10.45 **Chemical properties of whole wheat breads.** Whole wheat breads contain a high amount of phytic acid, which tends to lower the absorption of nutrient minerals. The *Journal of Agricultural and Food Chemistry* (Jan. 2005) published the results of a study to determine whether sourdough can increase the solubility of whole wheat bread. Four types of bread were prepared from whole meal flour: (1) yeast added, (2) sourdough added, (3) no yeast or sourdough added (control), and (4) lactic acid added. Data were collected on the soluble magnesium level (percent of total magnesium) during fermentation for samples of each type of bread and were analyzed with the use of a one-way ANOVA. The four mean soluble magnesium means were compared in pairwise fashion with Bonferroni's method. The results are summarized as follows:

Mean	7%	12.5%	22%	27.5%
Type of Bread	Control	Yeast	Lactate	Sourdough

a. How many pairwise comparisons are made in the Bonferroni analysis?
b. Which treatment(s) yielded the significantly highest mean soluble magnesium level? The lowest?

c. The experimentwise error rate for the analysis was .05. Interpret this value.

10.46 **A new dental bonding agent.** Refer to the *Trends in Biomaterials & Artificial Organs* (Jan. 2003) study of a new bonding adhesive for teeth, presented in Exercise 10.26 (p. 501). A completely randomized design was used to compare the mean breaking strengths of teeth bonded for three different bonding times: 1 hour, 24 hours, and 48 hours. The sample mean breaking strengths were $\overline{x}_{1\text{ hour}} = 3.32$ Mpa, $\overline{x}_{24\text{ hours}} = 5.07$ Mpa, and $\overline{x}_{48\text{ hours}} = 5.03$ Mpa. Using an experimentwise error rate of .05, Tukey's method detected no significant difference between the means at 24 and 48 hours; however, the mean at 1 hour was found to be significantly smaller than the other two means.
a. Illustrate the results of the multiple comparisons of means by ordering the sample means and connecting means that are not significantly different.
b. What practical conclusions can you draw from the analysis?
c. Give a measure of reliability (i.e., overall confidence level) for the inferences drawn in part **b.**

10.47 **Robots trained to behave like ants.** Refer to the *Nature* (Aug. 2000) study of robots trained to behave like ants, presented in Exercise 10.27 (p. 501). Multiple comparisons of mean energy expended for the four colony sizes were conducted with an experimentwise error rate of .05. The results are summarized as follows:

Sample mean:	.97	.95	.93	.80
Group size:	3	6	9	12

a. How many pairwise comparisons are conducted in this analysis?
b. Interpret the results shown.

10.48 **Heights of grade school repeaters.** Refer to *The Archives of Disease in Childhood* (Apr. 2000) comparison of the average heights of three groups of Australian schoolchildren based on age, presented in Exercise 10.29 (p. 501). The three height means for boys were ranked with the Bonferroni method at $\alpha = .05$. The results are summarized as follows. (recall that all height measurements were standardized with the use of z-scores):

Sample mean:	0.16	0.33	0.33
Age group:	Oldest	Youngest	Middle

a. Is there a significant difference between the standardized height means for the oldest and youngest boys?
b. Is there a significant difference between the standardized height means for the oldest and middle boys?
c. Is there a significant difference between the standardized height means for the youngest and middle boys?

d. What is the experimentwise error rate for the inferences made in parts **a–c**? Interpret this value.

e. The researchers did not perform a Bonferroni analysis of the height means for the three groups of girls. Explain why not.

Applying the Concepts—Intermediate

10.49 **Dental fear study.** Does recalling a traumatic dental experience increase your level of anxiety at the dentist's office? In a study published in *Psychological Reports* (Aug. 1997), researchers at Wittenberg University randomly assigned 74 undergraduate psychology students to one of three experimental conditions. Subjects in the "Slide" condition viewed 10 slides of scenes from a dental office. Subjects in the "Questionnaire" condition completed a full dental history questionnaire; one of the questions asked them to describe their worst dental experience. Subjects in the "Control" condition received no actual treatment. All students then completed the Dental Fear Scale, with scores ranging from 27 (no fear) to 135 (extreme fear). The sample dental fear means for the Slide, Questionnaire, and Control groups were reported as 43.1, 53.8, and 41.8, respectively.

a. A completely randomized ANOVA design was carried out on the data, with the following results: $F = 4.43$, p-value $< .05$. Interpret these results.

b. According to the article, a Bonferroni ranking of the three dental fear means (at $\alpha = .05$) "indicated a significant difference between the mean scores on the Dental Fear Scale for the Control and Questionnaire groups, but not for the means between the Control and Slide groups." Summarize these results in a chart similar to Figure 10.13 (p. 507).

10.50 **Study of recall of TV commercials.** Refer to the *Journal of Applied Psychology* (June 2002) completely randomized design study to compare the mean commercial recall scores of viewers of three TV programs, presented in Exercise 10.28 (p. 501). Recall that one program had a violent content code (V) rating, one had a sex content code

(S) rating, and one was a neutral TV program. Using Tukey's method, the researchers conducted multiple comparisons of the three mean recall scores.

a. How many pairwise comparisons were made in this study?

b. The multiple-comparison results are shown in the MINITAB printout below. An experimentwise error rate of .05 was used. Locate the confidence interval for the comparison of the V and S groups. Interpret this result practically.

c. Repeat part **b** for the remaining comparisons. Which of the groups has the largest mean recall score?

d. In the journal article, the researchers concluded that "memory for [television] commercials is impaired after watching violent or sexual programming." Do you agree?

10.51 **Income and road rage.** Refer to the *Accident Analysis and Prevention* (Vol. 34, 2002) study of road rage, Exercise 10.31 (p. 502). Recall that the mean road rage scores of drivers in the three income groups—Under $30 thousand, Between $30 and $60 thousand, and Over $60 thousand— were 4.60, 5.08, and 5.15, respectively.

a. An experimentwise error rate of .01 was used to rank the three means. Give a practical interpretation of this error rate.

b. How many pairwise comparisons are necessary to compare the three means? List them.

c. A multiple-comparisons procedure revealed that the means for the two income groups Between $30 and $60 thousand and Over $60 thousand were not significantly different. All other pairs of means were found to be significantly different. Summarize these results in tabular form.

d. Which of the comparisons of part **b** will yield a confidence interval that does not contain 0?

SCOPOLAMINE

10.52 **Effect of scopolamine on memory.** Refer to the *Behavioral Neuroscience* (Feb. 2004) study of the drug

```
Tukey 95% Simultaneous Confidence Intervals
All Pairwise Comparisons

Individual confidence level = 98.01%


VIOLENT subtracted from:

           Lower   Center   Upper   -------+---------+---------+---------+--
SEX       -0.923  -0.370   0.183           (----*----)
NEUTRAL    0.530   1.083   1.636                      (----*----)
                                   -------+---------+---------+---------+--
                                      -1.2       0.0       1.2       2.4


SEX subtracted from:

           Lower   Center   Upper   -------+---------+---------+---------+--
NEUTRAL    0.901   1.454   2.007                         (---*----)
                                   -------+---------+---------+---------+--
                                      -1.2       0.0       1.2       2.4
```

MINITAB output for Exercise 10.50

scopolamine's effects on memory for word-pair associates, presented in Exercise 10.33 (p. 503). Recall that the researchers theorized that the mean number of word pairs recalled for the scopolamine subjects (group 1) would be less than the corresponding means for the placebo subjects (group 2) and the no-drug subjects (group 3). Conduct multiple comparisons of the three means (using an experimentwise error rate of .05). Do the results support the researchers' theory? Explain.

TILLRATIO

10.53 Estimating the age of glacial drifts. Refer to the *American Journal of Science* (Jan. 2005) study of the chemical makeup of buried tills (glacial drifts) in Wisconsin, presented in Exercise 10.35 (p. 504). Use a multiple-comparisons procedure to compare the mean AI/Be ratios for the five boreholes (labeled UMRB-1, UMRB-2, UMRB-3, SWRA, and SD), with an experimentwise error rate of .10. Identify the means that appear to differ.

Applying the Concepts—Advanced

DRINKERS

10.54 Restoring self-control intoxicated. Refer to the *Experimental and Clinical Psychopharmacology* (February 2005) study of restoring self-control while intoxicated, presented in Exercise 10.32 (p. 503). The researchers theorized that if caffeine can really restore self-control, then students in Group AC

(the group that drank alcohol plus caffeine) will perform the same as students in Group P (the placebo group) on the word completion task. Similarly, if an incentive can restore self-control, then students in Group AR (the group that drank alcohol and got a reward for correct responses on the word completion task) will perform the same as students in Group P. Finally, the researchers theorized that students in Group A (the alcohol-only group) will perform worse on the word completion task than students in any of the other three groups. Access the data in the **DRINKERS** file and conduct Tukey's multiple comparisons of the means, using an experimentwise error rate of .05. Are the researchers' theories supported?

10.55 Animal-assisted therapy for heart patients. Refer to the *American Heart Association Conference* (Nov. 2005) study to gauge whether animal-assisted therapy can improve the physiological responses of heart failure patients, presented in Exercise 10.36 (p. 504). You found evidence of a difference among the treatment means for the three treatments: Group T (volunteer plus trained dog), Group V (volunteer only), and Group C (control). Conduct a Bonferroni analysis to rank the three treatment means. Use an experimentwise error rate of $\alpha = .03$. Interpret the results for the researchers. [*Hint:* As shown in Appendix B, the Bonferroni formula for a confidence interval for the difference $(\mu_i - \mu_j)$ is

$$(\bar{x}_i - \bar{x}_j) \pm t_{\alpha^*/2}(s)\sqrt{(1/n_i) + (1/n_j)}$$

where $\alpha^* = 2\alpha/[(k)(k-1)]$, is the experimentwise error rate, and k is the total number of treatment means compared.]

10.4 The Randomized Block Design

If the completely randomized design results in nonrejection of the null hypothesis that the treatment means are equal because the sampling variability (as measured by MSE) is large, we may want to consider an experimental design that better controls the variability. In contrast to the selection of independent samples of experimental units specified by the completely randomized design, the *randomized block design* utilizes experimental units that are *matched sets*, assigning one from each set to each treatment. The matched sets of experimental units are called *blocks*. The theory behind the randomized block design is that the sampling variability of the experimental units in each block will be reduced, in turn reducing the measure of error, MSE.

Definition 10.8

The **randomized block design** consists of a two-step procedure:

1. Matched sets of experimental units, called **blocks**, are formed, with each block consisting of k experimental units (where k is the number of treatments). The b blocks should consist of experimental units that are as similar as possible.

2. One experimental unit from each block is randomly assigned to each treatment, resulting in a total of $n = bk$ responses.

For example, if we wish to compare SAT scores of female and male high school seniors, we could select independent random samples of five females and five males, and analyze the results of the completely randomized design as outlined in Section 10.2. Or we could select matched pairs of females and males according to their scholastic records and analyze the SAT scores of the pairs. For instance, we could select pairs of students

TABLE 10.5 Randomized Block Design: SAT Score Comparison

Block	Female SAT Score	Male SAT Score	Block Mean
1 (School A, 2.75 GPA)	540	530	535
2 (School B, 3.00 GPA)	570	550	560
3 (School C, 3.25 GPA)	590	580	585
4 (School D, 3.50 GPA)	640	620	630
5 (School E, 3.75 GPA)	690	690	690
Treatment mean	606	594	

with approximately the same GPAs from the same high school. Five such pairs (blocks) are depicted in Table 10.5. Note that this is just a *paired difference experiment*, first discussed in Section 9.3.

As before, the variation between the treatment means is measured by squaring the distance between each treatment mean and the overall mean, multiplying each squared distance by the number of measurements for the treatment, and then summing over treatments:

$$\text{SST} = \sum_{i=1}^{k} b(\bar{x}_{T_i} - \bar{x})^2$$
$$= 5(606 - 600)^2 + 5(594 - 600)^2 = 360$$

Here, $\bar{x}_{T_i}$ represents the sample mean for the ith treatment, b (the number of blocks) is the number of measurements for each treatment, and k is the number of treatments.

The blocks also account for some of the variation among the different responses. That is, just as SST measures the variation between the female and male means, we can calculate a measure of variation among the five block means representing different schools and scholastic abilities. Analogous to the computation of SST, we sum the squares of the differences between each block mean and the overall mean, multiply each squared difference by the number of measurements for each block, and then sum over blocks to calculate the **sum of squares for blocks** (SSB):

$$\text{SSB} = \sum_{i=1}^{b} k(\bar{x}_{B_i} - \bar{x})^2$$
$$= 2(535 - 600)^2 + 2(560 - 600)^2 + 2(585 - 600)^2 +$$
$$2(630 - 600)^2 + 2(690 - 600)^2$$
$$= 30{,}100$$

Here, $\bar{x}_{B_i}$ represents the sample mean for the ith block and k (the number of treatments) is the number of measurements in each block. As we expect, the variation in SAT scores attributable to Schools and Levels of scholastic achievement is apparently large.

As before, we want to compare the variability attributed to treatments with that which is attributed to sampling. In a randomized block design, the sampling variability is measured by subtracting that portion attributed to treatments and blocks from the total sum of squares, SS(Total). The total variation is the sum of the squared differences of each measurement from the overall mean:

$$\text{SS(Total)} = \sum_{i=1}^{n} (x_i - \bar{x})^2$$
$$= (540 - 600)^2 + (530 - 600)^2 + (570 - 600)^2 + (550 - 600)^2 +$$
$$\cdots + (690 - 600)^2$$
$$= 30{,}600$$

The variation attributable to sampling error is then found by subtraction:

$$\text{SSE} = \text{SS(Total)} - \text{SST} - \text{SSB} = 30{,}600 - 360 - 30{,}100 = 140$$

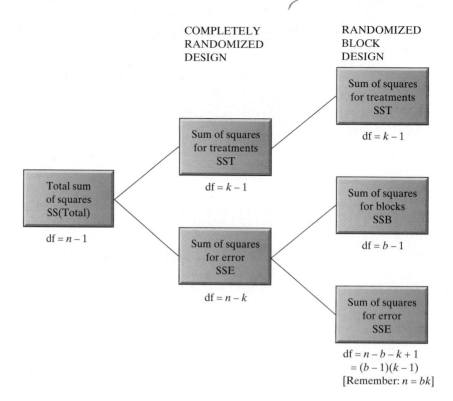

FIGURE 10.15

Partitioning of the total sum of squares for the randomized block design

In sum, the total sum of squares, 30,600, is divided into three components: 360 attributed to treatments (Gender), 30,100 attributed to blocks (Scholastic ability), and 140 attributed to sampling error.

The mean squares associated with each source of variability are obtained by dividing the sum of squares by the appropriate number of degrees of freedom. The partitioning of the total sum of squares and the total number of degrees of freedom for a randomized block experiment are summarized in Figure 10.15.

To determine whether we can reject the null hypothesis that the treatment means are equal in favor of the alternative that at least two of them differ, we calculate

$$\text{MST} = \frac{\text{SST}}{k-1} = \frac{360}{2-1} = 360$$

$$\text{MSE} = \frac{\text{SSE}}{n-b-k+1} = \frac{140}{10-5-2+1} = 35$$

The F-ratio that is used to test the hypothesis is

$$F = \frac{360}{35} = 10.29$$

Comparing this ratio with the tabular F-value corresponding to $\alpha = .05$, $v_1 = (k-1) = 1$ degree of freedom in the numerator, and $v_2 = (n-b-k+1) = 4$ degrees of freedom in the denominator, we find that

$$F = 10.29 > F_{.05} = 7.71$$

which indicates that we should reject the null hypothesis and conclude that the mean SAT scores differ for females and males.

If you review Section 9.3, you will find that the analysis of a paired difference experiment results in a one-sample t-test on the differences between the treatment responses within each block. Applying the procedure to the differences between female and male scores in Table 10.5, we obtain

$$t = \frac{\bar{x}_d}{s_d/\sqrt{n_d}} = \frac{12}{\sqrt{70}/\sqrt{5}} = 3.207$$

At the .05 level of significance with $(n_d - 1) = 4$ degrees of freedom,

$$t = 3.207 > t_{.025} = 2.776$$

Since $t^2 = (3.207)^2 = 10.29$ and $t_{.025}^2 = (2.776)^2 = 7.71$, we find that the paired difference t-test and the ANOVA F-test are equivalent, with both the calculated test statistics and the rejection region related by the formula $F = t^2$. The difference between the tests is that the paired difference t-test can be used to compare only two treatments in a randomized block design, whereas the F-test can be applied to *two or more* treatments in a randomized block design. The F-test is summarized in the following box:

ANOVA F-Test to Compare k Treatment Means: Randomized Block Design

$H_0: \mu_1 = \mu_2 = \cdots = \mu_p$

H_a: At least two treatment means differ

Test statistic: $F = \dfrac{MST}{MSE}$

Rejection region: $F > F_\alpha$, where F_α is based on $(k - 1)$ numerator degrees of freedom and $(n - b - k + 1)$ denominator degrees of freedom.

Conditions Required for a Valid ANOVA F-Test: Randomized Block Design

1. The b blocks are randomly selected, and all k treatments are applied (in random order) to each block.
2. The distributions of observations corresponding to all bk block–treatment combinations are approximately normal.
3. The bk block–treatment distributions have equal variances.

Note that the assumptions concern the probability distributions associated with each block–treatment combination. The experimental unit selected for each combination is assumed to have been randomly selected from all possible experimental units for that combination, and the response is assumed to be normally distributed with the same variance for each of the block–treatment combinations. For example, the F-test comparing female and male SAT score means requires the scores for each combination of gender and scholastic ability (e.g., females with 3.25 GPA) to be normally distributed with the same variance as the other combinations employed in the experiment.

The calculation formulas for randomized block designs are given in Appendix B. We will rely on statistical software packages to analyze randomized block designs and to obtain the necessary ingredients for testing the null hypothesis that the treatment means are equal.

EXAMPLE 10.7
EXPERIMENTAL DESIGN PRINCIPLES

Problem Refer to Examples 10.4–10.6. Suppose the USGA wants to compare the mean distances associated with the four brands of golf balls struck by a driver, but wishes to employ human golfers rather than the robot Iron Byron. Assume that 10 balls of each brand are to be utilized in the experiment.

a. Explain how a completely randomized design could be employed.
b. Explain how a randomized block design could be employed.
c. Which design is likely to provide more information about the differences among the brand mean distances?

Solution

a. Since the completely randomized design calls for independent samples, we can employ such a design by randomly selecting 40 golfers and then randomly assigning 10 golfers to each of the four brands. Finally, each golfer will strike the ball of the assigned brand, and the distance will be recorded. This design is illustrated in Figure 10.16a.

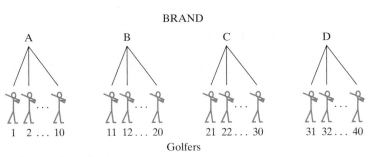

a. Completely randomized design

BRAND

	A	B	C	D
1	Hit 3	Hit 1	Hit 4	Hit 2
2	Hit 2	Hit 4	Hit 3	Hit 1
⋮	⋮	⋮	⋮	⋮
10	Hit 4	Hit 3	Hit 1	Hit 2

GOLFERS

b. Randomized block design

FIGURE 10.16

Illustration of completely randomized design and randomized block design: comparison of four golf ball brands

b. The randomized block design employs blocks of relatively homogeneous experimental units. For example, we could randomly select 10 golfers and permit each golfer to hit four balls, one of each brand, in a random sequence. Then each golfer is a block, with each treatment (brand) assigned to each block (golfer). This design is summarized in Figure 10.16b.

c. Because we expect much more variability among distances generated by "real" golfers than by Iron Byron, we would expect the randomized block design to control the variability better than the completely randomized design does. That is, with 40 different golfers, we would expect the sampling variability among the measured distances within each brand to be greater than that among the four distances generated by each of 10 golfers hitting one ball of each brand.

Now Work Exercise 10.65a,b

EXAMPLE 10.8

A RANDOMIZED BLOCK DESIGN ANOVA—
Comparing Golf Ball Brands

Problem Refer to Example 10.7. Suppose the randomized block design of part **b** is employed, utilizing a random sample of 10 golfers, with each golfer using a driver to hit four balls, one of each brand, in a random sequence.

a. Set up a test of the research hypothesis that the brand mean distances differ. Use $\alpha = .05$.

b. The data for the experiment are given in Table 10.6. Use statistical software to analyze the data, and conduct the test set up in part **a**.

Solution

a. We want to test whether the data in Table 10.6 provide sufficient evidence to conclude that the brand mean distances differ. Denoting the population mean of the ith brand by μ_i, we test

$$H_0: \mu_1 = \mu_2 = \mu_3 = \mu_4$$
$$H_a: \text{The mean distances differ for at least two of the brands.}$$

GOLFRBD

TABLE 10.6 Distance Data for Randomized Block Design

Golfer (Block)	Brand A	Brand B	Brand C	Brand D
1	202.4	203.2	223.7	203.6
2	242.0	248.7	259.8	240.7
3	220.4	227.3	240.0	207.4
4	230.0	243.1	247.7	226.9
5	191.6	211.4	218.7	200.1
6	247.7	253.0	268.1	244.0
7	214.8	214.8	233.9	195.8
8	245.4	243.6	257.8	227.9
9	224.0	231.5	238.2	215.7
10	252.2	255.2	265.4	245.2
Sample means	227.0	233.2	245.3	220.7

The test statistic compares the variation among the four treatment (brand) means with the sampling variability within each of the treatments:

$$\text{Test statistic:}\quad F = \frac{\text{MST}}{\text{MSE}}$$

Rejection region: $F > F_\alpha = F_{.05}$, with $v_1 = (k - 1) = 3$ numerator degrees of freedom and $v_2 = (n - k - b + 1) = 27$ denominator degrees of freedom. From Table IX of Appendix A, we find that $F_{.05} = 2.96$. Thus, we will reject H_0 if $F > 2.96$.

The assumptions necessary to ensure the validity of the test are as follows: (1) The probability distributions of the distances for each brand–golfer combination are normal. (2) The variances of the distance probability distributions for each brand–golfer combination are equal.

b. SPSS was used to analyze the data in Table 10.6, and the result is shown in Figure 10.17. The values of MST and MSE (highlighted on the printout) are 1,099.552 and 20.245, respectively. The F-ratio for Brand (also highlighted on the printout) is $F = 54.312$, which exceeds the tabled value of 2.96. We therefore reject the null hypothesis at the $\alpha = .05$ level of significance, concluding that at least two of the brands differ with respect to mean distance traveled when struck by the driver.

Tests of Between-Subjects Effects

Dependent Variable: DISTANCE

Source	Type III Sum of Squares	df	Mean Square	F	Sig.
Corrected Model	15372.539[a]	12	1281.045	63.276	.000
Intercept	2145032.91	1	2145032.910	105952.6	.000
BRAND	3298.657	3	1099.552	54.312	.000
GOLFER	12073.882	9	1341.542	66.265	.000
Error	546.621	27	20.245		
Total	2160952.07	40			
Corrected Total	15919.160	39			

a. R Squared = .966 (Adjusted R Squared = .950)

FIGURE 10.17

SPSS printout for randomized block design ANOVA of data in Table 10.6

Look Back The result of part **b** is confirmed by noting that the observed significance level of the test, highlighted on the printout, is $p \approx 0$.

Now Work Exercise 10.65c

TABLE 10.7 General ANOVA Summary Table for a Randomized Block Design

Source	df	SS	MS	F
Treatments	$k-1$	SST	MST	MST/MSE
Blocks	$b-1$	SSB	MSB	
Error	$n-k-b+1$	SSE	MSE	
Total	$n-1$	SS(Total)		

TABLE 10.8 ANOVA Table for Example 10.8

Source	df	SS	MS	F	p
Treatment (Brand)	3	3,298.7	1,099.6	54.31	.000
Block (Golfer)	9	12,073.9	1,341.5		
Error	27	546.6	20.2		
Total	39	15,919.2			

The results of an ANOVA for a randomized block design can be summarized in a simple tabular format similar to that utilized for the completely randomized design in Section 10.2. The general form of the table is shown in Table 10.7, and that for Example 10.8 is given in Table 10.8. Note that the randomized block design is characterized by three sources of variation—treatments, blocks, and error—which sum to the total sum of squares. We hope that employing blocks of experimental units will reduce the error variability, thereby making the test for comparing treatment means more powerful.

When the F-test results in the rejection of the null hypothesis that the treatment means are equal, we will usually want to compare the various pairs of treatment means to determine which specific pairs differ. We can employ a multiple-comparison procedure as in Section 10.3. The number of pairs of means to be compared will again be $c = k(k-1)/2$, where p is the number of treatment means. In Example 10.8, $c = 4(3)/2 = 6$; that is, there are six pairs of golf ball brand means to be compared.

EXAMPLE 10.9

RANKING TREATMENT MEANS IN A RANDOMIZED BLOCK DESIGN— Comparing Golf Ball Brands

Problem Bonferroni's procedure is used to compare the mean distances of the four golf ball brands in Example 10.8. The resulting confidence intervals, with an experimentwise error rate of $\alpha = .05$, are shown in the SPSS printout of Figure 10.18. Interpret the results.

Multiple Comparisons

Dependent Variable: DISTANCE
Bonferroni

(I) BRAND	(J) BRAND	Mean Difference (I-J)	Std. Error	Sig.	95% Confidence Interval Lower Bound	95% Confidence Interval Upper Bound
A	B	-6.1300*	2.01222	.031	-11.8586	-.4014
	C	-18.2800*	2.01222	.000	-24.0086	-12.5514
	D	6.3200*	2.01222	.024	.5914	12.0486
B	A	6.1300*	2.01222	.031	.4014	11.8586
	C	-12.1500*	2.01222	.000	-17.8786	-6.4214
	D	12.4500*	2.01222	.000	6.7214	18.1786
C	A	18.2800*	2.01222	.000	12.5514	24.0086
	B	12.1500*	2.01222	.000	6.4214	17.8786
	D	24.6000*	2.01222	.000	18.8714	30.3286
D	A	-6.3200*	2.01222	.024	-12.0486	-.5914
	B	-12.4500*	2.01222	.000	-18.1786	-6.7214
	C	-24.6000*	2.01222	.000	-30.3286	-18.8714

Based on observed means.
*. The mean difference is significant at the .05 level.

FIGURE 10.18

SPSS printout of Bonferroni confidence intervals for the randomized block design

FIGURE 10.19

Listing of brand means for randomized block design [*Note:* All differences are statistically significant.]

Mean: 220.7 227.0 233.2 245.3
Brand: D   A   B   C

Solution Note that 12 confidence intervals are shown in Figure 10.18, rather than 6. SPSS (like SAS) computes intervals for both $\mu_i - \mu_j$ and $\mu_j - \mu_i, i \neq j$. Only half of these are necessary to conduct the analysis, and these are highlighted on the printout. The intervals (rounded) are summarized as follows:

$$(\mu_A - \mu_B): \quad (-11.9, -.4)$$
$$(\mu_A - \mu_C): \quad (-24.0, -12.6)$$
$$(\mu_A - \mu_D): \quad (.6, 12.0)$$
$$(\mu_B - \mu_C): \quad (-17.9, -6.4)$$
$$(\mu_B - \mu_D): \quad (6.7, 18.2)$$
$$(\mu_C - \mu_D): \quad (18.9, 30.3)$$

Note that we are 95% confident that all the brand means differ, because none of the intervals contains 0. The listing of the brand means in Figure 10.19 has no lines connecting them, because there are no nonsignificant differences at the .05 level.

Now Work Exercise 10.65d

Unlike the completely randomized design, the randomized block design cannot, in general, be used to estimate individual treatment means. Whereas the completely randomized design employs a random sample for each treatment, the randomized block design does not necessarily do so: The experimental units within the blocks are assumed to be randomly selected, but the blocks themselves may not be randomly selected.

We can, however, test the hypothesis that the block means are significantly different. We simply compare the variability attributable to differences among the block means with that associated with sampling variability. The ratio of MSB to MSE is an *F*-ratio similar to that formed in testing treatment means. The *F*-statistic is compared with a tabular value for a specific value of α, with $(b - 1)$ numerator degrees of freedom and $(n - k - b + 1)$ denominator degrees of freedom. The test is usually given on the same printout as the test for treatment means. Note in the SPSS printout in Figure 10.17 that the test statistic for comparing the block means is

$$F = \frac{\text{MSB}}{\text{MSE}} = \frac{\text{MS(Golfers)}}{\text{MS(Error)}} = \frac{1,341.5}{20.2} = 66.26$$

with a *p*-value of .000. Since $\alpha = .05$ exceeds this *p*-value, we conclude that the block means are different. The results of the test are summarized in Table 10.9.

In the golf example, the test for block means confirms our suspicion that the golfers vary significantly; therefore, the use of the block design was a good decision. However, be careful not to conclude that the block design was a mistake if the *F*-test for blocks does not result in rejection of the null hypothesis that the block means are the

TABLE 10.9 ANOVA Table for Randomized Block Design: Test for Blocks Included

Source	df	SS	MS	F	p
Treatments (Brands)	3	3,298.7	1,099.6	54.31	.000
Blocks (Golfers)	9	12,073.9	1,341.5	66.26	.000
Error	27	546.6	20.2		
Total	39	15,919.2			

same. Remember that the possibility of a Type II error exists, and we are not controlling its probability as we are the probability α of a Type I error. If the experimenter believes that the experimental units are more homogeneous within blocks than between blocks, then he or she should use the randomized block design regardless of the results of a single test comparing the block means.

The procedure for conducting an analysis of variance for a randomized block design is summarized in the next box. Remember that the hallmark of this design is the utilization of blocks of homogeneous experimental units in which each treatment is represented.

Steps for Conducting an ANOVA for a Randomized Block Design

1. Be sure that the design consists of blocks (preferably, blocks of homogeneous experimental units) and that each treatment is randomly assigned to one experimental unit in each block.

2. If possible, check the assumptions of normality and equal variances for all block–treatment combinations. [*Note:* This may be difficult to do, since the design will likely have only one observation for each block–treatment combination.]

3. Create an ANOVA summary table that specifies the variability attributable to treatments, blocks, and error, and that leads to the calculation of the F-statistic to test the null hypothesis that the treatment means are equal in the population. Use a statistical software package or the calculation formulas in Appendix B to obtain the necessary numerical ingredients.

4. If the F-test leads to the conclusion that the means differ, employ the Bonferroni or Tukey procedure, or a similar procedure, to conduct multiple comparisons of as many of the pairs of means as you wish. Use the results to summarize the statistically significant differences among the treatment means. Remember that, in general, the randomized block design cannot be employed to form confidence intervals for individual treatment means.

5. If the F-test leads to the nonrejection of the null hypothesis that the treatment means are equal, several possibilities exist:
   a. The treatment means *are* equal: that is, the null hypothesis is true.
   b. The treatment means really differ, but other important factors affecting the response are not accounted for by the randomized block design. These factors inflate the sampling variability, as measured by MSE, resulting in smaller values of the F-statistic. Either increase the sample size for each treatment, or conduct an experiment that accounts for the other factors affecting the response (as is to be done in Section 10.5). Do not automatically reach the former conclusion, since the possibility of a Type II error must be considered if you accept H_0.

6. If desired, conduct the F-test of the null hypothesis that the block means are equal. Rejection of this hypothesis lends statistical support to the utilization of the randomized block design.

Note: It is often difficult to check whether the assumptions for a randomized block design are satisfied. When you feel that these assumptions are likely to be violated, a nonparametric procedure is advisable.

What Do You Do When the Assumptions Are Not Satisfied for the Analysis of Variance for a Completely Randomized Design?

Answer: Use a nonparametric statistical method such as the Friedman F_r test of Section 14.b.

ACTIVITY 10.2: **Randomized Block Design**

In this Activity, you will revisit Activity 10.1 (p. 486).

For each of the designed experiments in Exercises 2 and 3 of *Designed versus Observational Experiments* on page 406, you will rework the experiment to produce a randomized block design. Explain how you will choose your experimental units from each population. Then describe the criteria you would use to split the experimental units into matched sets. How do you determine which experimental unit in each matched set receives each level of treatment? What data are collected and how are they compared? Do you believe that there is any benefit to the block design? Explain.

Exercises 10.56–10.72

Understanding the Principles

10.56 When is it advantageous to use a randomized block design over a completely randomized design?

10.57 Explain the difference between a randomized block design and a paired difference experiment.

10.58 What conditions are required for valid inferences from a randomized block ANOVA design?

Learning the Mechanics

10.59 A randomized block design yielded the ANOVA table shown here:

Source	df	SS	MS	F
Treatments	4	501	125.25	9.109
Blocks	2	225	112.50	8.182
Error	8	110	13.75	
Total	14	836		

a. How many blocks and treatments were used in this experiment?

b. How many observations were collected in the experiment?

c. Specify the null and alternative hypotheses you would use to compare the treatment means.

d. What test statistic should be used to conduct the hypothesis test of part **c**?

e. Specify the rejection region for the test of parts **c** and **d**. Use $\alpha = .01$.

f. Conduct the test of parts **c–e**, and state the proper conclusion.

g. What assumptions are necessary to ensure the validity of the test you conducted in part **f**?

10.60 An experiment was conducted that used a randomized block design. The data from the experiment are displayed in the following table:

⊘ **LM10_60**

Treatment	Block 1	2	3
1	2	3	5
2	8	6	7
3	7	6	5

a. Fill in the missing entries in the following ANOVA table:

Source	df	SS	MS	F
Treatments		21.5555		
Blocks				
Error				
Total		30.2222		

b. Specify the null and alternative hypotheses you would use to investigate whether a difference exists among the treatment means.

c. What test statistic should be used in conducting the test of part **b**?

d. Describe the Type I and Type II errors associated with the hypothesis test of part **b**.

e. Conduct the hypothesis test of part **b**, using $\alpha = .05$.

10.61 A randomized block design was used to compare the mean responses for three treatments. Four blocks of three homogeneous experimental units were selected, and each treatment was randomly assigned to one experimental unit within each block. The data are shown in the following table, and a MINITAB ANOVA printout for this experiment is displayed on p. 522:

⊘ **LM10_61**

Treatment	Block 1	2	3	4
A	3.4	5.5	7.9	1.3
B	4.4	5.8	9.6	2.8
C	2.2	3.4	6.9	.3

a. Use the printout to fill in the entries in the following ANOVA table:

Source	df	SS	MS	F
Treatments				
Blocks				
Error				
Total				

b. Do the data provide sufficient evidence to indicate that the treatment means differ? Use $\alpha = .05$.

c. Do the data provide sufficient evidence to indicate that blocking was effective in reducing the experimental error? Use $\alpha = .05$.

Two-way ANOVA: X versus Treatment, Block

```
Source       DF       SS       MS        F       P
Treatment     2   12.0317   6.0158    50.96   0.000
Block         3   71.7492  23.9164   202.59   0.000
Error         6    0.7083   0.1181
Total        11   84.4892

S = 0.3436    R-Sq = 99.16%    R-Sq(adj) = 98.46%

Tukey 95.0% Simultaneous Confidence Intervals
Response Variable X
All Pairwise Comparisons among Levels of Treatment
Treatment = A  subtracted from:

Treatment   Lower   Center    Upper    -+---------+---------+---------+-----
B           0.379    1.125   1.8706                                 (----*---)
C          -2.071   -1.325  -0.5794              (----*----)
                                       -+---------+---------+---------+-----
                                     -3.0      -1.5       0.0       1.5


Treatment = B  subtracted from:

Treatment   Lower   Center    Upper    -+---------+---------+---------+-----
C          -3.196   -2.450   -1.704    (----*----)
                                       -+---------+---------+---------+-----
                                     -3.0      -1.5       0.0       1.5
```

MINITAB output
for Exercise 10.61

d. Use the printout to rank the treatment means at $\alpha = .05$.

e. What assumptions are necessary to ensure the validity of the inferences made in parts **b, c,** and **d**?

10.62 Suppose an experiment utilizing a randomized block design has four treatments and nine blocks, for a total of $4 \times 9 = 36$ observations. Assume that the total sum of squares for the response is SS(Total) = 500. For each of the following partitions of SS(Total), test the null hypothesis that the treatment means are equal and the null hypothesis that the block means are equal (use $\alpha = .05$ for each test):

a. The sum of squares for treatments (SST) is 20% of SS(Total), and the sum of squares for blocks (SSB) is 30% of SS(Total).

b. SST is 50% of SS(Total), and SSB is 20% of SS(Total).

c. SST is 20% of SS(Total), and SSB is 50% of SS(Total).

d. SST is 40% of SS(Total), and SSB is 40% of SS(Total).

e. SST is 20% of SS(Total), and SSB is 20% of SS(Total).

Applying the Concepts—Basic

10.63 **Rotary oil rigs.** An economist wants to compare the average monthly number of rotary oil rigs running in three states: California, Utah, and Alaska. In order to account for month-to-month variation, three months were randomly selected over a two-year period and the number of oil rigs running in each state in each month was obtained from data provided from *World Oil* (Jan. 2002) magazine. The data, reproduced in the accompanying table, were analyzed by means of a randomized block design. The MINITAB printout is shown at the top of p. 523.

OILRIGS

Month	California	Utah	Alaska
1	27	17	11
2	34	20	14
3	36	15	14

a. Why is a randomized block design preferred over a completely randomized design for comparing the mean number of oil rigs running monthly in California, Utah, and Alaska?

b. Identify the treatments for the experiment.

c. Identify the blocks for the experiment.

d. State the null hypothesis for the ANOVA F-test.

e. Locate the test statistic and p-value on the MINITAB printout. Interpret the results.

NUMRIGS

Tukey HSD[a,b]

STATE	N	Subset 1	Subset 2
AL	3	13.00	
UT	3	17.33	
CAL	3		32.33
Sig.		.262	1.000

Means for groups in homogeneous subsets are displayed.
Based on Type III Sum of Squares
The error term is Mean Square(Error) = 8.111.

a. Uses Harmonic Mean Sample Size = 3.000.

b. Alpha = .05.

SPSS output for Exercise 10.63

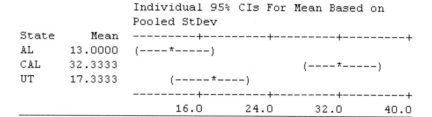

Two-way ANOVA: NumRigs versus State, Month

```
Source   DF       SS        MS       F      P
State     2  617.556   308.778   38.07  0.002
Month     2   30.889    15.444    1.90  0.262
Error     4   32.444     8.111
Total     8  680.889

S = 2.848   R-Sq = 95.23%   R-Sq(adj) = 90.47%


                       Individual 95% CIs For Mean Based on
                       Pooled StDev
State     Mean    ---------+---------+---------+---------+
AL     13.0000    (----*-----)
CAL    32.3333                                 (----*-----)
UT     17.3333          (-----*----)
                   ---------+---------+---------+---------+
                        16.0      24.0      32.0      40.0
```

MINITAB output for Exercise 10.63

f. A Tukey multiple comparison of means (at $\alpha = .05$) is summarized in the SPSS printout at the bottom of p. 522. Which state(s) have the significantly largest mean number of oil rigs running monthly?

10.64 Treatment for tendon pain. Refer to the *British Journal of Sports Medicine* (Feb. 1, 2004) study of chronic Achilles tendon pain, presented in Exercise 10.8 (p. 487). Recall that each in a sample of 25 patients with chronic Achilles tendinosis was treated with heavy-load eccentric calf mus-

TENDON

Patient	Before Thickness (millimeters)	After Thickness Patient (millimeters)
1	11.0	11.5
2	4.0	6.4
3	6.3	6.1
4	12.0	10.0
5	18.2	14.7
6	9.2	7.3
7	7.5	6.1
8	7.1	6.4
9	7.2	5.7
10	6.7	6.5
11	14.2	13.2
12	7.3	7.5
13	9.7	7.4
14	9.5	7.2
15	5.6	6.3
16	8.7	6.0
17	6.7	7.3
18	10.2	7.0
19	6.6	5.3
20	11.2	9.0
21	8.6	6.6
22	6.1	6.3
23	10.3	7.2
24	7.0	7.2
25	12.0	8.0

Source: Ohberg, L., et al. "Eccentric training in patients with chronic Achilles tendinosis: normalized tendon structure and decreased thickness at follow up." *British Journal of Sports Medicine*, Vol. 38, No. 1, Feb. 1, 2004 (Table 2).

cle training. Tendon thickness (in millimeters) was measured both before and following the treatment of each patient. These experimental data are shown in the accompanying table.

a. What experimental design was employed in this study?
b. How many treatments are used in this study? How many blocks?
c. Give the null and alternative hypothesis for determining whether the mean tendon thickness before treatment differs from the mean after treatment.
d. Compute the test statistic for the test in part **c**, using the paired difference t formula of Section 9.3.
e. Use statistical software (or the formulas in Appendix B) to compute the ANOVA F-statistic for the test in part **c**.
f. Compare the test statistics you computed in parts **d** and **e**. You should find that $F = t^2$.
g. Show that the two tests from parts **d** and **e** yield identical p-values.
h. Give the appropriate conclusion, using $\alpha = .05$.

10.65 Endangered dwarf shrubs. Rugel's pawpaw (yellow squirrel banana) is an endangered species of a dwarf shrub. Biologists from Stetson University conducted an experiment to determine the effects of fire on the shrub's growth. (*Florida Scientist*, Spring 1997.) Twelve experimental plots of land were selected in a pasture where the shrub is abundant. Within each plot, three pawpaws were randomly selected and treated as follows: One shrub was subjected to fire, another to clipping, and the third left unmanipulated (a control). After five months, the number of flowers produced by each of the 36 shrubs was determined. The objective of the study was to compare the mean number of flowers produced by pawpaws for the three treatments (fire, clipping, and control).

a. Identify the type of experimental design employed, including the treatments, response variable, and experimental units.
b. Illustrate the layout of the design, using a graphic similar to Figure 10.16.
c. The ANOVA of the data resulted in a test statistic of $F = 5.42$ for treatments with p-value $= .009$. Interpret this result.

d. The three treatment means were compared by Tukey's method at $\alpha = .05$. Interpret the results, shown as follows:

Mean number of flowers:	1.17	10.58	17.08
Treatment:	Control	Clipping	Burning

10.66 Studies on treating Alzheimer's disease. Refer to the *eCAM* (November 2006) study of the quality of the research methodology used in journal articles that investigate the effectiveness of treatments for Alzheimer's disease, presented in Exercise 7.38 (p. 324). For each in a sample of 13 research papers, the quality of the methodology on each of nine dimensions was measured with the Wong scale, with scores ranging from 1 (low quality) to 3 (high quality). In Exercise 7.38, the total (sum) of the Wong scores across the dimensions was reported for each paper. The data in the following table give the individual dimension scores for the sample of 13 papers . (Note: The researchers labeled the nine dimensions as What-A, What-B, What-C, Who-A, Who-B, Who-C, How-A, How-B, and How-C.)

a. One goal of the study was to compare the mean Wong scores of the nine research methodology dimensions. Set up the null and alternative hypotheses for this test.

b. The researchers used a completely randomized ANOVA design to analyze the data. Explain why a randomized block ANOVA is a more appropriate method.

c. The SAS output for a randomized block ANOVA of the data (with Dimensions as treatments and Papers as blocks) appears below. Interpret the *p*-values of the tests shown.

d. The SAS printout also reports the results of a Tukey multiple-comparison analysis of the nine Dimension means. Which pairs of means are significantly different?

e. The experimentwise error rate used in the analysis in part **d** is .05. Interpret this value.

Applying the Concepts—Intermediate

10.67 Prompting walkers to walk. A study was conducted to investigate the effect of prompting in a walking program. (*Health Psychology*, Mar. 1995.) Five groups of walkers—27 in each group—agreed to participate by walking for 20 minutes at

TREATAD2

Paper	What-A	What-B	What-C	Who-A	Who-B	Who-C	How-A	How-B	How-C
1	3	3	2	2	2	3	2	2	3
2	3	3	2	1	3	2	3	2	2
3	2	2	3	1	2	2	1	2	3
4	2	3	3	2	1	3	2	1	2
5	2	3	2	2	2	3	1	3	2
6	2	3	2	1	1	1	2	2	1
7	2	3	2	2	1	3	2	2	2
8	2	2	2	1	2	3	3	2	3
9	1	2	2	2	2	3	1	1	1
10	2	3	2	1	2	2	2	3	3
11	2	2	1	1	1	2	3	2	3
12	2	3	3	2	1	3	1	2	3
13	3	3	2	2	1	3	2	2	3

Source: Chiappelli, F., et al. "Evidence-based research in complementary and alternative medicine III: Treatment of patients with Alzheimer's disease," *eCAM*, Vol. 3, No. 4, Nov. 2006 (Table 1).

Source	DF	Type III SS	Mean Square	F Value	Pr > F
DIMENSION	8	15.86324786	1.98290598	5.40	<.0001
PAPER	12	6.44444444	0.53703704	1.46	0.1520

Means with the same letter are not significantly different.

Tukey Grouping			Mean	N	DIMENSION
	A		2.6923	13	WHAT-B
	A				
B	A		2.5385	13	WHO-C
B	A				
B	A		2.3846	13	HOW-C
B	A				
B	A	C	2.1538	13	WHAT-C
B	A	C			
B	A	C	2.1538	13	WHAT-A
B	A	C			
B	A	C	2.0000	13	HOW-B
B		C			
B		C	1.9231	13	HOW-A
		C			
		C	1.6154	13	WHO-B
		C			
		C	1.5385	13	WHO-A

SAS output for Exercise 10.66

WALKERS

Week	Control	Frequent/Low	Frequent/High	Infrequent/Low	Infrequent/High
1	7	23	25	21	19
4	2	19	25	10	12
8	2	18	19	9	9
12	2	7	20	8	2
16	2	18	18	8	7
24	1	17	17	7	6

Source: Lombard, D. N., et al. "Walking to meet health guidelines: The effect of prompting frequency and prompt structure," *Health Psychology,* Vol. 14, No. 2, Mar. 1995, p. 167 (Table 2).

least one day per week over a 24-week period. The participants were prompted to walk each week via telephone calls, but different prompting schemes were used for each group. Walkers in the control group received no prompting phone calls, walkers in the "frequent/low" group received a call once a week with low structure (e.g., "just touching base"), walkers in the "frequent/high" group received a call once a week with high structure (i.e., goals are set), walkers in the "infrequent/low" group received a call once every 3 weeks with low structure, and walkers in the "infrequent/high" group received a call once every 3 weeks with high structure. The table above lists the number of participants in each group who actually walked the minimum requirement each week for weeks 1, 4, 8, 12, 16, and 24. The data were subjected to an analysis of variance for a randomized block design, with the five walker groups representing the treatments and the six periods (weeks) representing the blocks.

a. What is the purpose of blocking on weeks in this study?

b. Use statistical software (or the formulas in Appendix B) to construct an ANOVA summary table.

c. Is there sufficient evidence of a difference in the mean number of walkers per week among the five walker groups? Use $\alpha = .05$.

d. Use Tukey's technique to compare all pairs of treatment means with an experimentwise error rate of $\alpha = .05$. Interpret the results.

e. What assumptions must hold to ensure the validity of the inferences you made in parts **c** and **d**?

10.68 Effect of massage on boxers. Eight amateur boxers participated in an experiment to investigate the effect of massage on boxing performance. (*British Journal of Sports Medicine,* Apr. 2000.) The punching power of each boxer (measured

in newtons) was recorded in the round following each of four different interventions: (M1) in round 1, following a pre-bout sports massage; (R1) in round 1, following a pre-bout period of rest; (M5) in round 5, following a sports massage between rounds; and (R5) in round 5, following a period of rest between rounds. Based on information provided in the article, the data in the accompanying table were obtained. The main goal of the experiment was to compare the punching power means of the four interventions.

a. Set up H_0 and H_a for this analysis.

b. Identify the treatments and blocks in the experiment.

c. Conduct the test set up in part **a**. What conclusions can you draw regarding the effect of massage on punching power?

10.69 Plants and stress reduction. Plant therapists believe that plants can reduce the stress levels of humans. A Kansas State University study was conducted to investigate this phenomenon. Two weeks prior to final exams, 10 undergraduate students took part in an experiment to determine what effect the presence of a live plant, a photo of a plant, or the absence of a plant has on the student's ability to relax while isolated in a dimly lit room. Each student participated in three sessions: one with a live plant, one with a photo of a plant, and one with no plant (the control).* During each session, finger temperature was measured at one-minute intervals for 20 minutes. Since increasing finger temperature indicates an increased level of relaxation, the maximum temperature (in degrees) was used as the response variable. The data for the experiment are provided in the accompanying table. Conduct an ANOVA and make the proper inferences at $\alpha = .10$.

BOXING

Boxer	Intervention			
	M1	R1	M5	R5
1	1,243	1,244	1,291	1,262
2	1,147	1,053	1,169	1,177
3	1,247	1,375	1,309	1,321
4	1,274	1,235	1,290	1,285
5	1,177	1,139	1,233	1,238
6	1,336	1,313	1,366	1,362
7	1,238	1,279	1,275	1,261
8	1,261	1,152	1,289	1,266

Source: Hemmings, B., Smith, M., Graydon, J., and Dyson, R. "Effects of massage on physiological restoration, perceived recovery, and repeated sports performance." *British Journal of Sports Medicine,* Vol. 34, No. 2, Apr. 2000 (adapted from Table 3).

PLANTS

Student	Live Plant	Plant Photo	No Plant (control)
1	91.4	93.5	96.6
2	94.9	96.6	90.5
3	97.0	95.8	95.4
4	93.7	96.2	96.7
5	96.0	96.6	93.5
6	96.7	95.5	94.8
7	95.2	94.6	95.7
8	96.0	97.2	96.2
9	95.6	94.8	96.0
10	95.6	92.6	96.6

Source: Elizabeth Schreiber, Department of Statistics, Kansas State University, Manhattan, Kansas.

*The experiment is simplified for this exercise. The actual experiment involved 30 students who participated in 12 sessions.

10.70 Absentee rates at a jeans plant. A plant that manufactures denim jeans in the United Kingdom recently introduced a computerized automated handling system. The new system delivers garments to the assembly-line operators by means of an overhead conveyor. Although the automated system minimizes operator handling time, it inhibits operators from working ahead and taking breaks to be away from their machine. A study in *New Technology, Work, and Employment* (July 2001) investigated the impact of the new handling system on worker absentee rates at the jeans plant. One theory is that the mean absentee rate will vary by day of the week, as operators decide to indulge in one-day absences to relieve work pressure. Nine weeks were randomly selected, and the absentee rate (percentage of workers absent) was determined for each day (Monday through Friday) of the work week. The data are listed in the accompanying table. Conduct a complete analysis of the data to determine whether the mean absentee rate differs across the five days of the workweek.

JEANS

Week	Monday	Tuesday	Wednesday	Thursday	Friday
1	5.3	0.6	1.9	1.3	1.6
2	12.9	9.4	2.6	0.4	0.5
3	0.8	0.8	5.7	0.4	1.4
4	2.6	0.0	4.5	10.2	4.5
5	23.5	9.6	11.3	13.6	14.1
6	9.1	4.5	7.5	2.1	9.3
7	11.1	4.2	4.1	4.2	4.1
8	9.5	7.1	4.5	9.1	12.9
9	4.8	5.2	10.0	6.9	9.0

Source: Boggis, J. J. "The eradication of leisure," *New Technology, Work, and Employment,* Volume 16, Number 2, July 2001 (Table 3).

10.71 Light-to-dark transition of genes. Refer to the *Journal of Bacteriology* (July 2002) study of the sensitivity of bacteria genes to light, presented in Exercise 9.47 (p. 442). Recall that scientists isolated 103 genes of the bacterium responsible for photosynthesis and respiration. Each gene was grown to midexponential phase in a growth incubator in "full light" and then was exposed to three alternative light/dark conditions: "full dark" (lights extinguished for 24 hours), "transient light" (lights kept on for another minutes), and "transient dark" (lights turned off for 90 minutes). At the end of each light/dark condition, the standardized growth measurement was determined for each of the 103 genes. The complete data set is saved in the **GENEDARK** file. (Data for the first 10 genes are shown in the accompanying table.) Assume that the goal of the experiment is to compare the mean standardized growth measurements for the three light/dark conditions.

a. Explain why the data should be analyzed as a randomized block design.

b. Specify the null and alternative hypotheses for comparing the light/dark condition means.

c. Using a statistical software package, conduct the test you set up in part **b.** Interpret the results at $\alpha = .05$.

d. If necessary, employ a multiple-comparison procedure to rank the light/dark condition means. Use an experimentwise error rate of .05.

GENEDARK (first 10 observations shown)

Gene ID	FULL-DARK	TR-LIGHT	TR-DARK
SLR2067	−0.00562	1.40989	−1.28569
SLR1986	−0.68372	1.83097	−0.68723
SSR3383	−0.25468	−0.79794	−0.39719
SLL0928	−0.18712	−1.20901	−0.18618
SLR0335	−0.20620	1.71404	−0.73029
SLR1459	−0.53477	2.14156	−0.33174
SLL1326	−0.06291	1.03623	−0.30392
SLR1329	−0.85178	−0.21490	0.44545
SLL1327	0.63588	1.42608	−0.13664
SLL1325	−0.69866	1.93104	−0.24820

Source: Gill, R. T., et al. "Genome-wide dynamic transcriptional profiling of the light to dark transition in *Synechocystis Sp.* PCC6803," *Journal of Bacteriology,* Vol. 184, No. 13, July 2002.

Applying the Concepts—Advanced

10.72 Listening ability of infants. *Science* (Jan. 1, 1999) reported on the ability of seven-month-old infants to learn an unfamiliar language. In one experiment, 16 infants were trained in an artificial language. Then each infant was presented with two 3-word sentences that consisted entirely of new words (e.g., "wo fe wo"). One sentence was consistent (i.e., constructed from the same grammar the infants got in the training session), and one sentence was inconsistent (i.e., constructed from grammar in which the infant was not trained). The variable measured in each trial was the time (in seconds) the infant spent listening to the speaker, with the goal being to compare the mean listening times of consistent and inconsistent sentences.

a. The data were analyzed as a randomized block design with the 16 infants representing the blocks and the two types of sentences (consistent and inconsistent) representing the treatments. Do you agree with this data analysis method? Explain.

b. Refer to part **a.** The test statistic for testing treatments was $F = 25.7$ with an associated observed significance level of $p < .001$. Interpret this result.

c. Explain why the data could also be analyzed as a paired difference experiment with a test statistic of $t = 5.07$.

d. The mean listening times and standard deviations for the two treatments are given here. Use this information to calculate the F-statistic for comparing the treatment means in a completely randomized ANOVA design. Explain why this test statistic provides weaker evidence of a difference between treatment means than the test in part **b** provides.

	Consistent Sentences	Inconsistent Sentences
Mean	6.3	9.0
Standard deviation	2.6	2.16

e. Explain why there is no need to control the experimentwise error rate in ranking the treatment means for this experiment.

10.5 Factorial Experiments

All the experiments discussed in Sections 10.2 and 10.4 were **single-factor experiments.** The treatments were levels of a single factor, with the sampling of experimental units performed with either a completely randomized or a randomized block design. However, most responses are affected by more than one factor, and we will therefore often wish to design experiments involving more than one factor.

Consider an experiment in which the effects of two factors on the response are being investigated. Assume that factor A is to be investigated at a levels and factor B at b levels. Recalling that treatments are factor–level combinations, you can see that the experiment has, potentially, ab treatments that could be included in it. A *complete factorial experiment* is a factorial experiment in which all possible ab treatments are utilized.

> ### Definition 10.9
>
> A **complete factorial experiment** is a factorial experiment in which every factor–level combination is utilized. That is, the number of treatments in the experiment equals the total number of factor–level combinations.

For example, suppose the USGA wants to determine the relationship not only between distance and brand of golf ball, but also between distance and the club used to hit the ball. If the USGA decides to use four brands and two clubs (say, driver and five-iron) in the experiment, then a complete factorial experiment would call for utilizing all $4 \times 2 = 8$ Brand–Club combinations. This experiment is referred to more specifically as a *complete 4×2 factorial.* A layout for a two-factor factorial experiment (henceforth, we use the term *factorial* to refer to a *complete factorial*) is given in Table 10.10. The factorial experiment is also referred to as a **two-way classification,** because it can be arranged in the row–column format exhibited in Table 10.10.

In order to complete the specification of the experimental design, the treatments must be assigned to the experimental units. If the assignment of the ab treatments in the factorial experiment is random and independent, the design is completely randomized. For example, if the machine Iron Byron is used to hit 80 golf balls, 10 for each of the eight Brand–Club combinations, in a random sequence, then the design is completely randomized. By contrast, if the assignment is made within homogeneous blocks of experimental units, then the design is a randomized block design. For example, if 10 golfers are employed to hit each of the eight golf balls, and each golfer hits all eight Brand–Club combinations in a random sequence, then the design is a randomized block design, with the golfers serving as blocks. In the remainder of this section, we confine our attention to factorial experiments utilizing completely randomized designs.

If we utilize a completely randomized design to conduct a factorial experiment with ab treatments, we can proceed with the analysis in exactly the same way as we did in Section 10.2. That is, we calculate (or let the computer calculate) the measure of treatment mean variability (MST) and the measure of sampling variability (MSE) and use

TABLE 10.10 Schematic Layout of Two-Factor Factorial Experiment

	Level	Factor B at b Levels				
		1	2	3	$\cdots$	b
Factor A	1	Trt. 1	Trt. 2	Trt. 3	$\cdots$	Trt. b
at a levels	2	Trt. $b+1$	Trt. $b+2$	Trt. $b+3$	$\cdots$	Trt. $2b$
	3	Trt. $2b+1$	Trt. $2b+2$	Trt. $2b+3$	$\cdots$	Trt. $3b$
	$\vdots$	$\vdots$	$\vdots$	$\vdots$	$\cdots$	$\vdots$
	a	Trt. $(a-1)b+1$	Trt. $(a-1)b+2$	Trt. $(a-1)b+3$	$\cdots$	Trt. ab

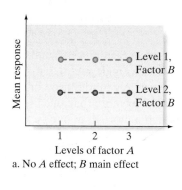

a. No A effect; B main effect

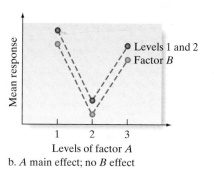

b. A main effect; no B effect

FIGURE 10.20

Illustration of possible treatment effects: factorial experiment

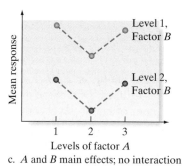

c. A and B main effects; no interaction

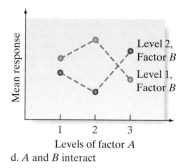

d. A and B interact

the F-ratio of these two quantities to test the null hypothesis that the treatment means are equal. However, if this hypothesis is rejected, because we conclude that some differences exist among the treatment means, important questions remain: Are both factors affecting the response, or only one? If both, do they affect the response independently, or do they interact to affect the response?

For example, suppose the distance data indicate that at least two of the eight treatment (Brand–Club combinations) means differ in the golf experiment. Does the brand of ball (factor A) or the club utilized (factor B) affect mean distance, or do both affect it? Several possibilities are shown in Figure 10.20. In Figure 10.20a, the brand means are equal (only three are shown for the purpose of illustration), but the distances differ for the two levels of factor B (Club). Thus, there is no effect of Brand on distance, but a Club main effect is present. In Figure 10.20b, the Brand means differ, but the Club means are equal for each Brand. Here, a Brand main effect is present, but no effect of Club is present.

Figure 10.20c and Figure 10.20d illustrate cases in which both factors affect the response. In Figure 10.20c, the mean distance between clubs does not change for the three Brands, so the effect of Brand on distance is independent of Club. That is, the two factors Brand and Club *do not interact*. In contrast, Figure 10.20d shows that the difference between mean distances between clubs varies with Brand. Thus, the effect of Brand on distance depends on Club, and the two factors *do interact*.

In order to determine the nature of the treatment effect, if any, on the response in a factorial experiment, we need to break the treatment variability into three components: Interaction between factors A and B, Main effect of factor A, and Main effect of factor B. The **Factor interaction** component is used to test whether the factors combine to affect the response, while the **Factor main effect** components are used to determine whether the factors affect the response separately.

Now Work Exercise 10.87

The partitioning of the total sum of squares into its various components is illustrated in Figure 10.21. Notice that at stage 1 the components are identical to those in the one-factor, completely randomized designs of Section 10.2: The sums of squares for treatment and error sum to the total sum of squares. The degrees of freedom for treatments is equal to $(ab - 1)$, one less than the number of treatments. The degrees of freedom for error is equal to $(n - ab)$, the total sample size minus the number of

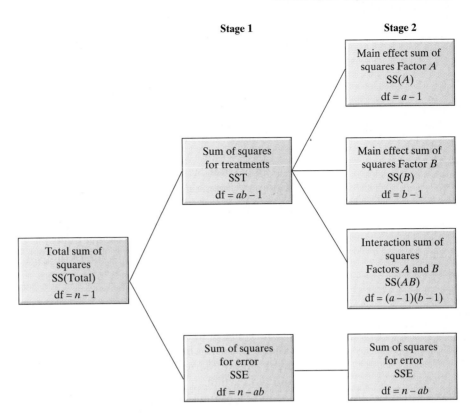

Stage 1   Stage 2

FIGURE 10.21
Partitioning the total sum of
squares for a two-factor
factorial

treatments. Only at stage 2 of the partitioning does the factorial experiment differ from those previously discussed. Here, we divide the treatment sum of squares into its three components: interaction and the two main effects. These components can then be used to test the nature of the differences, if any, among the treatment means.

There are a number of ways to proceed in the testing and estimation of factors in a factorial experiment. We present one approach in the following box:

Procedure for Analysis of Two-Factor Factorial Experiment

1. Partition the total sum of squares into the treatment and error components (stage 1 of Figure 10.21). Use either a statistical software package or the calculation formulas in Appendix C to accomplish the partitioning.

2. Use the F-ratio of the mean square for treatments to the mean square for error to test the null hypothesis that the treatment means are equal.*

    a. If the test results in nonrejection of the null hypothesis, consider refining the experiment by increasing the number of replications or introducing other factors. Also, consider the possibility that the response is unrelated to the two factors.

    b. If the test results in rejection of the null hypothesis, then proceed to step 3.

3. Partition the treatment sum of squares into the main effect and the interaction sum of squares (stage 2 of Figure 10.21). Use either a statistical software package or the calculation formulas in Appendix B to accomplish the partitioning.

4. Test the null hypothesis that factors A and B do not interact to affect the response by computing the F-ratio of the mean square for interaction to the mean square for error.

    a. If the test results in nonrejection of the null hypothesis, proceed to step 5.

    b. If the test results in rejection of the null hypothesis, conclude that the two factors interact to affect the mean response. Then proceed to step 6a.

(continued)

---

*Some analysts prefer to proceed directly to test the interaction and main-effect components, skipping the test of treatment means. We begin with this test to be consistent with our approach in the one-factor completely randomized design.

5. Conduct tests of two null hypotheses that the mean response is the same at each level of factor A and factor B. Compute two F-ratios by comparing the mean square for each factor main effect with the mean square for error.

   a. If one or both tests result in rejection of the null hypothesis, conclude that the factor affects the mean response. Proceed to step 6b.

   b. If both tests result in nonrejection, an apparent contradiction has occurred. Although the treatment means seemingly differ (step 2 test), the interaction (step 4) and main-effect (step 5) tests have not supported that result. Further experimentation is advised.

6. Compare the means:

   a. If the test for interaction (step 4) is significant, use a multiple-comparison procedure to compare any or all pairs of the treatment means.

   b. If the test for one or both main effects (step 5) is significant, use a multiple-comparison procedure to compare the pairs of means corresponding to the levels of the significant factor(s).

We assume that the completely randomized design is a **balanced design**, meaning that the same number of observations are made for each treatment. That is, we assume that r experimental units are randomly and independently selected for each treatment. The numerical value of r must exceed 1 in order to have any degrees of freedom with which to measure the sampling variability. [Note that if $r = 1$, then $n = ab$, and the number of degrees of freedom associated with error (Figure 10.21) is df $= n - ab = 0$.] The value of r is often referred to as the number of **replicates of the factorial experiment**, since we assume that all ab treatments are repeated, or replicated, r times. Whatever approach is adopted in the analysis of a factorial experiment, several tests of hypotheses are usually conducted. The tests are summarized in the following box.

Tests Conducted in Analyses of Factorial Experiments: Completely Randomized Design, r Replicates per Treatment

Test for Treatment Means

H_0: No difference among the ab treatment means
H_a: At least two treatment means differ

Test statistic: $F = \dfrac{\text{MST}}{\text{MSE}}$

Rejection region: $F \geq F_\alpha$, based on $(ab - 1)$ numerator and $(n - ab)$ denominator degrees of freedom [*Note: n = abr.*]

Test for Factor Interaction

H_0: Factors A and B do not interact to affect the response mean
H_a: Factors A and B do interact to affect the response mean

Test statistic: $F = \dfrac{\text{MS}(AB)}{\text{MSE}}$

Rejection region: $F \geq F_\alpha$, based on $(a - 1)(b - 1)$ numerator and $(n - ab)$ denominator degrees of freedom

Test for Main Effect of Factor A

H_0: No difference among the a mean levels of factor A
H_a: At least two factor A mean levels differ

(continued)

Test statistic: $F = \dfrac{MS(A)}{MSE}$

Rejection region: $F \geq F_\alpha$, based on $(a - 1)$ numerator and $(n - ab)$ denominator degrees of freedom

Test for Main Effect of Factor B

H_0: No difference among the b mean levels of factor B

H_a: At least two factor B mean levels differ

Test statistic: $F = \dfrac{MS(B)}{MSE}$

Rejection region: $F \geq F_\alpha$, based on $(b - 1)$ numerator and $(n - ab)$ denominator degrees of freedom

Conditions Required for Valid F-Tests in Factorial Experiments

1. The response distribution for each factor–level combination (treatment) is normal.
2. The response variance is constant for all treatments.
3. Random and independent samples of experimental units are associated with each treatment.

EXAMPLE 10.10

CONDUCTING A FACTORIAL ANOVA—Golf Ball Driving Distances

Problem Suppose the USGA tests four different brands (A, B, C, D) of golf balls and two different clubs (driver, five-iron) in a 4 × 2 factorial design. Each of the eight Brand–Club combinations (treatments) is randomly and independently assigned to four experimental units, each consisting of a specific position in the sequence of hits by Iron Byron. The distance response is recorded for each of the 32 hits, and the results are shown in Table 10.11.

GOLFFAC1

TABLE 10.11 Distance Data for 4 × 2 Factorial Golf Experiment

Club	Brand			
	A	B	C	D
Driver	226.4	238.3	240.5	219.8
	232.6	231.7	246.9	228.7
	234.0	227.7	240.3	232.9
	220.7	237.2	244.7	237.6
Five-iron	163.8	184.4	179.0	157.8
	179.4	180.6	168.0	161.8
	168.6	179.5	165.2	162.1
	173.4	186.2	156.5	160.3

a. Use statistical software to partition the total sum of squares into the components necessary to analyze this 4 × 2 factorial experiment.
b. Conduct the appropriate ANOVA tests and interpret the results of your analysis. Use $\alpha = .10$ for the tests you conduct.
c. If appropriate, conduct multiple comparisons of the treatment means. Use an experimentwise error rate of .10. Illustrate the comparisons with a graph.

```
Dependent Variable: DISTANCE
```

Source	DF	Sum of Squares	Mean Square	F Value	Pr > F
Model	7	33659.80875	4808.54411	140.35	<.0001
Error	24	822.24000	34.26000		
Corrected Total	31	34482.04875			

R-Square	Coeff Var	Root MSE	DISTANCE Mean
0.976155	2.896461	5.853204	202.0813

Source	DF	Type III SS	Mean Square	F Value	Pr > F
CLUB	1	32093.11125	32093.11125	936.75	<.0001
BRAND	3	800.73625	266.91208	7.79	0.0008
CLUB*BRAND	3	765.96125	255.32042	7.45	0.0011

FIGURE 10.22

SAS printout for factorial ANOVA of golf data

Solution

a. The SAS printout that partitions the total sum of squares for this factorial experiment is given in Figure 10.22. The partitioning takes place in two stages. First, the total sum of squares is partitioned into the model (treatment) and error sums of squares at the top of the printout. Note that SST is 33,659.8 with 7 degrees of freedom and SSE is 822.2 with 24 degrees of freedom, adding to 34,482.0 and 31 degrees of freedom. In the second stage of partitioning, the treatment sum of squares is further divided into the main-effect and interaction sums of squares. From the highlighted values at the bottom of the printout, we see that SS(Club) is 32,093.1 with 1 degree of freedom, SS(Brand) is 800.7 with 3 degrees of freedom, and SS(Club $\times$ Brand) is 766.0 with 3 degrees of freedom, adding to 33,659.8 and 7 degrees of freedom.

b. Once partitioning is accomplished, our first test is

H_0: The eight treatment means are equal.

H_a: At least two of the eight means differ.

Test statistic: $F = \dfrac{\text{MST}}{\text{MSE}} = 140.35$ (highlighted, top of printout)

Observed significance level: $p < .0001$ (highlighted, top of printout)

Since $\alpha = .10$ exceeds p, we reject this null hypothesis and conclude that at least two of the Brand–Club combinations differ in mean distance.

After accepting the hypothesis that the treatment means differ, and therefore that the factors Brand and/or Club somehow affect the mean distance, we want to determine how the factors affect the mean response. We begin with a test of interaction between Brand and Club:

H_0: The factors Brand and Club do not interact to affect the mean response.

H_a: Brand and Club interact to affect mean response.

Test statistic: $F = \dfrac{\text{MS}(AB)}{\text{MSE}} = \dfrac{\text{MS(Brand} \times \text{Club)}}{\text{MSE}}$

$= \dfrac{255.32}{34.26} = 7.45$ (highlighted, bottom of printout)

Observed significance level: $p = .0011$ (highlighted, bottom of printout)

Since $\alpha = .10$ exceeds the p-value, we conclude that the factors Brand and Club interact to affect mean distance.

Because the factors interact, we do not test the main effects for Brand and Club. Instead, we compare the treatment means in an attempt to learn the nature of the interaction.

c. Rather than compare all $8(7)/2 = 28$ pairs of treatment means, we test for differences only between pairs of brands within each club. That differences exist *between* clubs can be assumed. Therefore, only $4(3)/2 = 6$ pairs of means need to be com-

```
------------------------------------- CLUB=5IRON -------------------------------------

                              The ANOVA Procedure

                  Tukey's Studentized Range (HSD) Test for DISTANCE

     NOTE: This test controls the Type I experimentwise error rate, but it generally has a higher
                          Type II error rate than REGWQ.


                    Alpha                                        0.1
                    Error Degrees of Freedom                      12
                    Error Mean Square                        36.10792
                    Critical Value of Studentized Range       3.62071
                    Minimum Significant Difference             10.878


            Means with the same letter are not significantly different.


                 Tukey Grouping          Mean      N    BRAND

                        A             182.675      4    B

                        B             171.300      4    A
                        B
                        B             167.175      4    C
                        B
                        B             160.500      4    D


------------------------------------- CLUB=DRIVER ------------------------------------

                              The ANOVA Procedure

                  Tukey's Studentized Range (HSD) Test for DISTANCE

     NOTE: This test controls the Type I experimentwise error rate, but it generally has a higher
                          Type II error rate than REGWQ.


                    Alpha                                        0.1
                    Error Degrees of Freedom                      12
                    Error Mean Square                        32.41208
                    Critical Value of Studentized Range       3.62071
                    Minimum Significant Difference             10.307


            Means with the same letter are not significantly different.


                 Tukey Grouping          Mean      N    BRAND

                        A             243.100      4    C
                        A
                    B   A             233.725      4    B
                    B
                    B             229.750      4    D
                    B
                    B             228.425      4    A
```

FIGURE 10.23

SAS printout of Tukey rankings of golf ball brand means for each club

pared for each club, or a total of 12 comparisons for the two clubs. The results of these comparisons, obtained from Tukey's method with an experimentwise error rate of $\alpha = .10$ for each club, are displayed in the SAS printout shown in Figure 10.23. For each club, the brand means are listed in descending order in the Figure, and those not significantly different are connected by the same letter in the "Tukey Grouping" column.

As shown in Figure 10.23, the picture is unclear with respect to Brand means. For the five-iron (top of figure), the brand B mean significantly exceeds all other brands. However, when the brand B golf balls hit with a driver (bottom of figure), brand B's mean is not significantly different from any of the other brands. The Club × Brand interaction can be seen in the SPSS plot of means shown in Figure 10.24. Note that the difference between the mean distances of the two clubs (driver and five-iron) varies with the brand. The biggest difference appears for Brand C, while the smallest difference is for Brand B.

Look Back Note the nontransitive nature of the multiple comparisons. For example, for the driver, the brand C mean can be "the same" as the brand B mean, and the brand B mean can be "the same" as the brand D mean, yet the brand C mean can significantly exceed the brand D mean. The reason lies in the definition of "the same": We must be careful not to conclude that two means are equal simply because they are connected by a line or a letter. The line indicates only that *the connected means are not significantly different*. You should conclude (at the overall α level of significance) only that means which are *not* connected are different, while withholding judgment on those which are

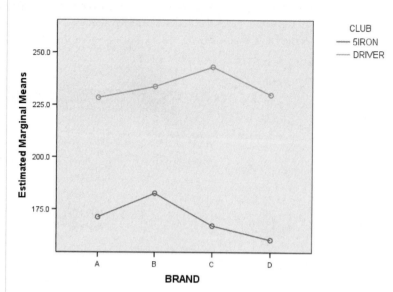

FIGURE 10.24

SPSS means plot for factorial golf ball experiment

connected. The picture of which means differ and by how much will become clearer as we increase the number of replicates of the factorial experiment.

Now Work Exercise 10.90

As with completely randomized and randomized block designs, the results of a factorial ANOVA are typically presented in an ANOVA summary table. Table 10.12 gives the general form of the ANOVA table, while Table 10.13 gives the ANOVA table for the golf ball data analyzed in Example 10.10. A two-factor factorial is characterized by four sources of variation—factor A, factor B, $A \times B$ interaction, and error—that sum to the total sum of squares.

TABLE 10.12 General ANOVA Summary Table for a Two-Factor Factorial Experiment with r Replicates, Where Factor A Has a Levels and Factor B Has b Levels

Source	df	SS	MS	F
A	$a - 1$	SSA	MSA	MSA/MSE
B	$b - 1$	SSB	MSB	MSB/MSE
AB	$(a - 1)(b - 1)$	SSAB	MSAB	MSAB/MSE
Error	$ab(r - 1)$	SSE	MSE	
Total	$n - 1$	SS(Total)		

TABLE 10.13 ANOVA Summary Table for Example 10.10

Source	df	SS	MS	F
Brand	1	32,093.11	32,093.11	936.75
Club	3	800.74	266.91	7.79
Interaction	3	765.96	255.32	7.45
Error	24	822.24	34.26	
Total	31	34,482.05		

EXAMPLE 10.11

MORE PRACTICE ON CONDUCTING A FACTORIAL ANOVA—Golf Ball Driving Distances

Problem Refer to Example 10.10. Suppose the same factorial experiment is performed on four other brands (E, F, G, and H), and the results are as shown in Table 10.14. Repeat the factorial analysis and interpret the results.

 **GOLFFAC2**

TABLE 10.14   Distance Data for Second Factorial Golf Experiment

Club	Brand			
	E	F	G	H
Driver	238.6	261.4	264.7	235.4
	241.9	261.3	262.9	239.8
	236.6	254.0	253.5	236.2
	244.9	259.9	255.6	237.5
Five-iron	165.2	179.2	189.0	171.4
	156.9	171.0	191.2	159.3
	172.2	178.0	191.3	156.6
	163.2	182.7	180.5	157.4

Solution An SPSS printout for the second factorial experiment is shown in Figure 10.25. We conduct several tests, as outlined in the box on page 529.

Test for Equality of Treatment Means

The F-ratio for Treatments is $F = 290.1$ (highlighted at the top of the printout), which exceeds the tabular value of $F_{.10} = 1.98$ for seven numerator and 24 denominator degrees of freedom. (Note that the same rejection regions will apply in this example as in Example 10.10, since the factors, treatments, and replicates are the same.) We conclude that at least two of the Brand–Club combinations have different mean distances.

Test for Interaction

We next test for interaction between Brand and Club. The F-value (highlighted on the SPSS printout) is

$$F = \frac{\text{MS(Brand} \times \text{Club)}}{\text{MSE}} = 1.425$$

Since this F-ratio does *not* exceed the tabled value of $F_{.10} = 2.33$ with 3 and 24 df, we cannot conclude at the .10 level of significance that the factors interact. In fact, note that the observed significance level (highlighted on the SPSS printout) for the test of interaction is .260. Thus, at any level of significance lower than $\alpha = .26$, we could not conclude that the factors interact. We therefore test the main effects for Brand and Club.

Tests of Between-Subjects Effects

Dependent Variable: DISTANCE

Source	Type III Sum of Squares	df	Mean Square	F	Sig.
Corrected Model	49959.375[a]	7	7137.054	290.120	.000
Intercept	1423532.83	1	1423532.828	57866.45	.000
BRAND	3410.316	3	1136.772	46.210	.000
CLUB	46443.900	1	46443.900	1887.939	.000
BRAND * CLUB	105.158	3	35.053	1.425	.260
Error	590.407	24	24.600		
Total	1474082.61	32			
Corrected Total	50549.782	31			

a. R Squared = .988 (Adjusted R Squared = .985)

FIGURE 10.25

SPSS printout of second factorial ANOVA

Test for Brand Main Effect

We first test for the Brand main effect:

H_0: No difference exists among the true Brand mean distances.
H_a: At least two Brand mean distances differ.
Test statistic:

$$F = \frac{MS(Brand)}{MSE} = \frac{1{,}136.772}{24.600} = 46.210 \quad \text{(highlighted on printout)}$$

Observed significance level: $p = .000$ (highlighted on printout)

Since $\alpha = .10$ exceeds the p-value, we conclude that at least two of the brand means differ. We will subsequently determine which brand means differ by using Tukey's multiple-comparison procedure. But first, we want to test for the Club main effect:

Test for Club Main Effect

H_0: No differences exist between the Club mean distances.
H_a: The Club mean distances differ.
Test statistic:

$$F = \frac{MS(Club)}{MSE} = \frac{46{,}443.900}{24.600} = 1{,}887.939 \quad \text{(highlighted on printout)}$$

Observed significance level: $p = .000$ (highlighted on printout)

Since $\alpha = .10$ exceeds the p-value, we conclude that the two clubs are associated with different mean distances. Since only two levels of Club were utilized in the experiment, this F-test leads to the inference that the mean distance differs for the two clubs. It is no surprise (to golfers) that the mean distance for balls hit with the driver is significantly greater than the mean distance for those hit with the five-iron.

Ranking of Means

To determine which of the Brands' mean distances differ, we wish to compare the four Brand means by using Tukey's method at $\alpha = .10$. The results of these multiple comparisons are displayed in the SPSS printout shown in Figure 10.26. The Brand means are shown, grouped by subset, in the figure, with means that are not significantly different in the same subset. Brands G and F (subset 2) are associated with significantly greater mean distances than brands E and H (subset 1). However, since G and F are in the same Tukey subset, and since E and H are in the same subset, we cannot distinguish between brands G and F or between brands E and H by means of these data.

DISTANCE

Tukey HSD[a,b]

		Subset	
BRAND	N	1	2
H	8	199.2000	
E	8	202.4375	
F	8		218.4375
G	8		223.5875
Sig.		.568	.189

Means for groups in homogeneous subsets are displayed.
Based on Type III Sum of Squares
The error term is Mean Square(Error) = 24.600.
   a. Uses Harmonic Mean Sample Size = 8.000.
   b. Alpha = .05.

FIGURE 10.26
SPSS printout of Tukey rankings of brand means

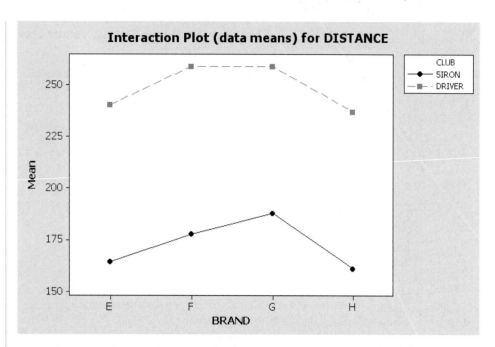

FIGURE 10.27
MINITAB means plot for second factorial golf ball experiment

Look Back Since the interaction between Brand and Club was not significant, we conclude that this difference among brands applies to both clubs. The sample means for all Club–Brand combinations are shown in the MINITAB graph of Figure 10.27 and appear to support the conclusions of the tests and comparisons. Note that the Brand means maintain their relative positions for each Club: Brands F and G dominate brands E and H for both the driver and the five-iron.

Now Work Exercise 10.85

Analysis-of-factorial experiments can become complex if the number of factors is increased. Even the two-factor experiment becomes more difficult to analyze if some factor combinations have different numbers of observations than others. We have provided an introduction to these important experiments by using two-factor factorials with equal numbers of observations for each treatment. Although similar principles apply to most factorial experiments, you should consult the references at the end of this chapter if you need to design and analyze more complex factorials.

STATISTICS IN ACTION REVISITED

A Two-Way Analysis of the Cockroach Data

We now return to the study of the trail-following ability of German cockroaches (p. 481). Recall that an entomologist created a chemical trail with either a methanol extract from roach feces or just methanol (control). Cockroaches from one of four age–sex groups were released into a container at the beginning of the trail, one at a time, and the movement pattern of each cockroach—the deviation from the trail (in pixels)—was measured. The layout for the experimental design is shown in Figure SIA10.3. You

		Roach Type			
		Adult Male	Adult Female	Gravid Female	Nymph
Trail	Extract	$n = 20$	$n = 20$	$n = 20$	$n = 20$
	Control	$n = 10$	$n = 10$	$n = 10$	$n = 10$

FIGURE SIA10.3
Layout of experimental design for cockroach study

(continued)

```
General Linear Model: Deviate versus Trail, Group

Factor   Type    Levels   Values
Trail    fixed        2   Control, Extract
Group    fixed        4   Female, Gravid, Male, Nymph


Analysis of Variance for Deviate, using Adjusted SS for Tests

Source         DF     Seq SS     Adj SS     Adj MS       F       P
Trail           1    46445.5    46445.5    46445.5   63.34   0.000
Group           3    16271.2    13000.6     4333.5    5.91   0.001
Trail*Group     3     2245.2     2245.2      748.4    1.02   0.386
Error         112    82131.7    82131.7      733.3
Total         119   147093.6


S = 27.0799    R-Sq = 44.16%    R-Sq(adj) = 40.67%
```

FIGURE SIA10.4

MINITAB two-way ANOVA for extract trail deviation

can see that 20 roaches of each type were randomly assigned to the treatment trail and 10 of each type were randomly assigned to the control trail. Thus, a total of 120 roaches were used in the experiment. The design is a factorial with two factors: Trail (extract or control) and Group (adult males, adult females, gravid females, or nymphs).

The entomologist wants to determine whether cockroaches in different age–sex groups differ in their ability to follow either the extract trail or the control trail. In other words, how do the two factors age–sex group and type of trail affect the cockroaches' mean deviation from the trail? To answer this question, we conduct a two-way factorial analysis of variance on the data saved in the **ROACH** file. A MINITAB printout of the ANOVA is displayed in Figure SIA10.4.

First, note that the p-value for the test for factor interaction (highlighted on the printout) is .386. Thus, there is insufficient evidence (at $\alpha = .05$) of interaction between the two factors. This implies that the impact of one factor (say, age–sex group) on mean trail deviation does not depend on the level of the other

```
            Bonferroni (Dunn) t Tests for DEVIATE

NOTE: This test controls the Type I experimentwise error rate, but it generally has a higher
                 Type II error rate than REGWQ.


            Alpha                                0.05
            Error Degrees of Freedom              112
            Error Mean Square                733.3187
            Critical Value of t               2.68593
            Minimum Significant Difference      18.78


            Means with the same letter are not significantly different.

            Bon Grouping          Mean       N     GROUP

                         A       53.747      30     Gravid
                         A
                       B A       37.077      30     Nymph
                       B A
                       B A       35.110      30     Female
                       B
                       B        20.917      30     Male


            Bonferroni (Dunn) t Tests for DEVIATE

NOTE: This test controls the Type I experimentwise error rate, but it generally has a higher
                 Type II error rate than REGWQ.


            Alpha                                0.05
            Error Degrees of Freedom              112
            Error Mean Square                733.3187
            Critical Value of t               1.98137
            Minimum Significant Difference      10.39
            Harmonic Mean of Cell Sizes      53.33333

                 NOTE: Cell sizes are not equal.


            Means with the same letter are not significantly different.

            Bon Grouping          Mean       N     TRAIL

                         A       64.535      40     Control

                         B       22.801      80     Extract
```

FIGURE SIA10.5

SAS Bonferroni rankings of group means and trail means

factor (type of trail). With no evidence of interaction, it is appropriate to conduct main-effect tests on the two factors.

The p-values for the main effects of type of trail and age–sex group (both highlighted on the printout) are .000 and .001, respectively. Since both p-values are less than $\alpha = .05$, there is sufficient evidence of (1) a difference between the mean deviations of cockroaches following the fecal extract trail and the control, and (2) differences in mean deviations among the four age–sex groups. To determine which main effect means are largest, we perform multiple comparisons of the means for both main effects.

Figure SIA10.5 is a SAS printout showing (at the top) the Bonferroni rankings of the age–sex group means and (at the bottom) the Bonferroni rankings of the trail-type means. Both comparisons are made with an experimentwise error rate of .05. On the basis of the "Bon Grouping" letters shown at the top of the printout, the only significant difference between age–sex group means is for the adult male and gravid cockroaches: Adult males have a significantly smaller mean deviation from the trail than gravids have. No other pair of age–sex group means is significantly different. The bottom of Figure SIA10.5 shows that the mean deviation for cockroaches following the fecal extract trail is significantly smaller than the mean for cockroaches following the control.

The final conclusions of the entomologist were as follows: There is evidence that cockroaches exhibit more of an ability to follow a fecal extract trail than a control (methanol) trail. Also, adult males appear to have more of an ability to follow a trail than gravid (pregnant female) cockroaches have.

Exercises 10.73–10.95

Understanding the Principles

10.73 Describe how the treatments are formed in a complete factorial experiment.

10.74 What is a balanced factorial design?

10.75 What conditions are required for valid inferences from a factorial ANOVA?

10.76 Describe what is meant by factor interaction.

10.77 Suppose you conduct a 3×5 factorial experiment.
  a. How many factors are used in this experiment?
  b. Can you determine the type(s) of factors—qualitative or quantitative—from the information given? Explain.
  c. Can you determine the number of levels used for each factor? Explain.
  d. Describe a treatment for the experiment, and determine the number of treatments used.
  e. What problem is caused by using a single replicate of this experiment? How is the problem solved?

Learning the Mechanics

10.78 The partially complete ANOVA table given here is for a two-factor factorial experiment:

Source	df	SS	MS	F
A	3		.75	
B	1	.95		
AB			.30	
Error				
Total	23	6.5		

  a. Give the number of levels for each factor.
  b. How many observations were collected for each factor–level combination?
  c. Complete the ANOVA table.
  d. Test to determine whether the treatment means differ. Use $\alpha = .10$.

e. Conduct the tests of factor interaction and mean effects, each at the $\alpha = .10$ level of significance. Which of the tests are warranted as part of the factorial analysis? Explain.

10.79 Following is a partially completed ANOVA table for a 3×4 factorial experiment with two replications:

Source	df	SS	MS	F
A		.8		
B		5.3		
AB		9.6		
Error				
Total		18.1		

  a. Complete the ANOVA table.
  b. Which sums of squares are combined to find the sum of squares for treatment? Do the data provide sufficient evidence to indicate that the treatment means differ? Use $\alpha = .05$.
  c. Does the result of the test in part **b** warrant further testing? Explain.
  d. What is meant by factor interaction, and what is the practical implication if it exists?
  e. Test to determine whether these factors interact to affect the response mean. Use $\alpha = .05$, and interpret the result.
  f. Does the result of the interaction test warrant further testing? Explain.

10.80 The following two-way table gives data for a 2×3 factorial experiment with two observations for each factor–level combination:

LM10_80

	Level	Factor B 1	2	3
Factor A	1	3.1, 4.0	4.6, 4.2	6.4, 7.1
	2	5.9, 5.3	2.9, 2.2	3.3, 2.5

Two-way ANOVA: RESPONSE versus A, B

```
Source        DF      SS        MS      F       P
A              1    4.4408   4.44083  18.06  0.005
B              2    4.1267   2.06333   8.39  0.018
Interaction    2   18.0067   9.00333  36.62  0.000
Error          6    1.4750   0.24583
Total         11   28.0492

S = 0.4958    R-Sq = 94.74%    R-Sq(adj) = 90.36%
```

MINITAB output for Exercise 10.80

a. Identify the treatments for this experiment. Calculate and plot the treatment means, using the response variable as the y-axis and the levels of factor B as the x-axis. Use the levels of factor A as plotting symbols. Do the treatment means appear to differ? Do the factors appear to interact?

b. The MINITAB ANOVA printout for this experiment is shown above. Test to determine whether the treatment means differ at the $\alpha = .05$ level of significance. Does the test support your visual interpretation from part **a**?

c. Does the result of the test in part **b** warrant a test for interaction between the two factors? If so, perform it, using $\alpha = .05$.

d. Do the results of the previous tests warrant tests of the two factor main effects? If so, perform them, using $\alpha = .05$.

e. Interpret the results of the tests. Do they support your visual interpretation from part **a**?

10.81 Suppose a 3×3 factorial experiment is conducted with three replications. Assume that SS(Total) = 1,000. For each of the following scenarios, form an ANOVA table, conduct the appropriate tests, and interpret the results:

a. The sum of squares of factor A main effect [SS(A)] is 20% of SS(Total), the sum of squares of factor B main effect [SS(B)] is 10% of SS(Total), and the sum of squares of interaction [SS(AB)] is 10% of SS(Total).

b. SS(A) is 10%, SS(B) is 10%, and SS(AB) is 50% of SS(Total).

c. SS(A) is 40%, SS(B) is 10%, and SS(AB) is 20% of SS(Total).

d. SS(A) is 40%, SS(B) is 40%, and SS(AB) is 10% of SS(Total).

10.82 The following two-way table gives data for a 2×2 factorial experiment with two observations per factor–level combination:

LM10_82

		Factor B	
Level		1	2
Factor A	1	29.6, 35.2	47.3, 42.1
	2	12.9, 17.6	28.4, 22.7

a. Identify the treatments for this experiment. Calculate and plot the treatment means, using the response variable as the y-axis and the levels of factor B as the x-axis. Use the levels of factor A as plotting symbols. Do the

treatment means appear to differ? Do the factors appear to interact?

b. Construct an ANOVA table for this experiment.

c. Test to determine whether the treatment means differ at the $\alpha = .05$ level of significance. Does the test support your visual interpretation from part **a**?

d. Does the result of the test in part **c** warrant a test for interaction between the two factors? If so, perform it, using $\alpha = .05$.

e. Do the results of the previous tests warrant tests of the two factor main effects? If so, perform them, using $\alpha = .05$.

f. Interpret the results of the tests. Do they support your visual interpretation from part **a**?

g. Given the results of your tests, which pairs of means, if any, should be compared?

Applying the Concepts—Basic

10.83 Removing bacteria from water. A coagulation–microfiltration process for removing bacteria from water was investigated in *Environmental Science & Engineering* (Sept. 1, 2000). Chemical engineers at Seoul National University performed a designed experiment to estimate the effect of both the level of the coagulant and the acidity (pH) level on the coagulation efficiency of the process. Six levels of coagulant (5, 10, 20, 50, 100, and 200 milligrams per liter) and six pH levels (4.0, 5.0, 6.0, 7.0, 8.0, and 9.0) were employed. Water specimens collected from the Han River in Seoul, Korea, were placed in jars, and each jar was randomly assigned to receive one of the $6 \times 6 = 36$ combinations of coagulant level and pH level.

a. What type of experimental design was applied in this study?

b. Give the factors, factor levels, and treatments for the study.

10.84 Insomnia and education. Refer to the *Journal of Abnormal Psychology* (Feb. 2005) study of whether insomnia is related to education status, presented in Exercise 1.26 (p. 21). A random-digit telephone dialing procedure was employed to collect data on 575 study participants. In addition to insomnia status (normal sleeper or chronic insomnia), the researchers classified each participant into one of four education categories (college graduate, some college, high school graduate, and high school dropout). One dependent variable of interest to the researchers was a quantitative measure of daytime functioning called the Fatigue Severity Scale (FSS). The data were analyzed as a 2×4 factorial experiment, with Insomnia status and Education level as the two factors.

a. Determine the number of treatments for this study. List them.

b. The researchers reported that "the Insomnia × Education interaction was not statistically significant." Interpret this result practically. (Illustrate with a graph.)

c. The researchers discovered that the sample mean FSS for people with insomnia was greater than the sample mean FSS for normal sleepers and that this difference was statistically significant. Interpret this result practically.

d. The researchers reported that the main effect of Education was statistically significant. Interpret this result practically.

e. Refer to part **d**. In a follow-up analysis, the sample mean FSS values for the four Education levels were compared with the use of Tukey's method ($\alpha = .05$), with the results shown in the accompanying table. What do you conclude?

Mean:	3.3	3.6	3.7	4.2
Education:	College graduate	Some college	High school graduate	High school dropout

10.85 Mussel settlement patterns on algae. Mussel larvae are in great abundance in the drift material that washes up on Ninety Mile Beach in New Zealand. These larvae tend to settle on algae. Environmentalists at the University of Auckland investigated the impact of the type of algae on the abundance of mussel larvae in drift material. (*Malacologia*, Feb. 8, 2002.) Drift material from three different wash-up events on Ninety Mile Beach was collected; for each washup, the algae was separated into four strata: coarse-branching, medium-branching, fine-branching, and hydroid algae. Two samples were randomly selected for each of the $3 \times 4 = 12$ event–strata combinations, and the mussel density (percent per square centimeter) was measured for each. The data were analyzed as a complete 3×4 factorial design. The ANOVA summary table is as follows:

Source	df	F	p-Value
Event	2	.35	>.05
Strata	3	217.33	<.05
Interaction	6	1.91	>.05
Error	12		
Total	23		

a. Identify the factors (and levels) in this experiment.
b. How many treatments are included in the experiment?
c. How many replications are included in the experiment?
d. What is the total sample size for the experiment?
e. What is the response variable measured?
f. Which ANOVA F-test should be conducted first? Conduct this test (at $\alpha = .05$) and interpret the results.
g. If appropriate, conduct the F-tests (at $\alpha = .05$) for the main effects. Interpret the results.
h. Tukey multiple comparisons of the four algae strata means (at $\alpha = .05$) are summarized in the accompanying table. Which means are significantly different?

Mean abundance ($\%/cm^2$):	9	10	27	55
Algae stratum	Coarse	Medium	Fine	Hydroid

10.86 Are you lucky? Parapsychologists define "lucky" people as individuals who report that seemingly chance events consistently tend to work out in their favor. A team of British psychologists designed a study to examine the effects of luckiness and competition on performance in a guessing task. (*The Journal of Parapsychology*, Mar. 1997.) Each in a sample of 56 college students was classified as lucky, unlucky, or uncertain on the basis of their responses to a Luck-

iness Questionnaire. In addition, the participants were randomly assigned to either a competitive or a noncompetitive condition. All students were then asked to guess the outcomes of 50 flips of a coin. The response variable measured was percentage of coin flips correctly guessed.

a. A 2×3 factorial ANOVA design was conducted on the data. Identify the factors and their levels for this design.
b. The results of the ANOVA are summarized in the accompanying table. Interpret the results fully.

Source	df	F	p-Value
Luckiness (L)	2	1.39	.26
Competition (C)	1	2.84	.10
L $\times$ C	2	0.72	.72
Error	50		
Total	55		

10.87 Impact of paper color on exam scores. A study published in *Teaching Psychology* (May 1998) examined how external clues influence student performance. Introductory psychology students were randomly assigned to one of four different midterm examinations. Form 1 was printed on blue paper and contained difficult questions, while form 2 was also printed on blue paper, but contained simple questions. Form 3 was printed on red paper with difficult questions; form 4 was printed on red paper with simple questions. The researchers were interested in the impact that Color (red or blue) and Question (simple or difficult) had on mean exam score.

a. What experimental design was employed in this study? Identify the factors and treatments.
b. The researchers conducted an ANOVA and found a significant interaction between Color and Question (p-value $< .03$). Interpret this result.
c. The sample mean scores (percentage correct) for the four exam forms are listed in the accompanying table. Plot the four means on a graph to illustrate the Color $\times$ Question interaction.

Form	Color	Question	Mean Score
1	Blue	Difficult	53.3
2	Blue	Simple	80.0
3	Red	Difficult	39.3
4	Red	Simple	73.6

10.88 Virtual-reality–based rehabilitation systems. In *Robotica* (Vol. 22, 2004), researchers described a study of the effectiveness of display devices for three virtual-reality (VR)-based hand rehabilitation systems. Display device A is a projector, device B is a desktop computer monitor, and device C is a head-mounted display. Twelve nondisabled right-handed male subjects were randomly assigned to the three VR display devices, four subjects in each group. In addition, within each group two subjects were randomly assigned to use an auxiliary lateral image and two subjects were not. Consequently, a 3×2 factorial design was employed, with the VR display device at three levels (A, B, or C) and an auxiliary lateral image at two levels (yes or no). Using the assigned VR system, each subject carried out a "pick-and-place" procedure and the collision frequency (number of collisions between moved objects) was measured.

a. Give the sources of variation and associated degrees of freedom in an ANOVA summary table for this design.

b. How many treatments are investigated in this experiment?

c. The factorial ANOVA resulted in the following p-values: Display main effect (.045), Auxiliary lateral image main effect (.003), and Interaction (.411). Interpret, these results practically. Use $\alpha = .05$ for each test you conduct.

Applying the Concepts—Intermediate

10.89 The thrill of a close game. Do women enjoy the thrill of a close basketball game as much as men do? To answer this question, male and female undergraduate students were recruited to participate in an experiment. (*Journal of Sport & Social Issues*, Feb. 1997.) The students watched one of eight live televised games of a recent NCAA basketball tournament. (None of the games involved a home team to which the students could be considered emotionally committed.) The "suspense" of each game was classified into one of four categories according to the closeness of scores at the game's conclusions: minimal (15–point or greater differential), moderate (10–14-point differential), substantial (5–9-point differential), and extreme (1–4-point differential). After the game, each student rated his or her enjoyment on an 11-point scale ranging from 0 (not at all) to 10 (extremely). The enjoyment rating data were analyzed as a 4×2 factorial design, with suspense (four levels) and gender (two levels) as the two factors. The $4 \times 2 = 8$ treatment means are shown in the following table:

	Gender	
Suspense	Male	Female
Minimal	1.77	2.73
Moderate	5.38	4.34
Substantial	7.16	7.52
Extreme	7.59	4.92

Source: Gan, Su-lin, et al. "The thrill of a close game: Who enjoys it and who doesn't?" *Journal of Sport & Social Issues*, Vol. 21, No. 1, Feb. 1997, pp. 59–60.

a. Plot the treatment means in a graph similar to Figure 10.24. Does the pattern of means suggest interaction between suspense and gender? Explain.

b. The ANOVA F-test for interaction yielded the following results: numerator df = 3, denominator df = 68, $F = 4.42$, p-value = .007. What can you infer from these results?

c. On the basis of the test carried out in part **b,** is the difference between the mean enjoyment levels of males and females the same, regardless of the suspense level of the game?

10.90 Baker's versus brewer's yeast. The *Electronic Journal of Biotechnology* (Dec. 15, 2003) published an article on a comparison of two yeast extracts: baker's yeast and brewer's yeast. Brewer's yeast is a surplus by-product obtained from a brewery; hence, it is less expensive than primary-grown baker's yeast. Samples of both yeast extracts were prepared at four different temperatures (45, 48, 51, and 54°C); thus, a 2×4 factorial design with yeast extract at two levels and temperature at four levels was employed. The response variable was the autolysis yield (recorded as a percentage).

a. How many treatments are included in the experiment?

b. An ANOVA found sufficient evidence of factor interaction at $\alpha = .05$. Interpret this result practically.

c. Give the null and alternative hypotheses for testing the main effects of yeast extract and temperature.

d. Explain why the tests allowed to in part **c** should not be conducted.

e. Multiple comparisons of the four temperature means were conducted for each of the two yeast extracts. Interpret the results, shown as follows:

Baker's yeast:	Mean yield (%):	41.1	47.5	48.6	50.3
	Temperature (°C):	54	45	48	51
Brewer's yeast:	Mean yield (%):	39.4	47.3	49.2	49.6
	Temperature (°C):	54	51	48	45

10.91 Learning from picture book reading. *Developmental Psychology* (Nov. 2006) published an article that examined toddlers's ability to learn from reading picture books. The experiment involved 36 children at each of three different ages: 18, 24, and 30 months. The children were randomly assigned into one of three different reading book conditions: book with color photographs (Photos), book with colored pencil drawings (Drawings), and book with no photographs or drawing (Control). Thus, a 3×3 factorial experiment was employed (with age at three levels and reading book condition at three levels). After a book-reading session, the children were scored on their ability to reenact the target actions in the book. Scores ranged from 0 (low) to 3 (high). An ANOVA of the reenactment scores is summarized in the following table:

Source	df	F	p-value
Age	–	11.93	< .001
Book	–	23.64	< .001
Age × Book	–	2.99	< .05
Error	–		
Total	107		

a. Fill in the missing degrees-of-freedom (df) values in the table.

b. How many treatments are investigated in this experiment? List them.

c. Conduct a test for Age × Book interaction at $\alpha = .05$. Interpret the result practically.

d. On the basis of the test you conducted in part **c,** do you need to conduct tests for Age and Book main effects? Explain.

e. At each age level, the researchers performed multiple comparisons of the reading book condition means at $\alpha = .05$. The results are summarized in the accompanying table. What can you conclude from this analysis? Support you answer with a plot of the means.

Age = 18 months:	.40 Control	.75 Drawings	1.20 Photos
Age = 24 months:	.60 Control	1.61 Drawings	1.63 Photos
Age = 30 months:	.50 Control	2.20 Drawings	2.21 Photos

10.92 Violent lyrics and aggressiveness. In the *Journal of Personality and Social Psychology* (May 2003), psychologists investigated the potentially harmful effects of violent music lyrics. The researchers theorized that listening to a song with violent lyrics will lead to more violent thoughts and actions. A total of 60 undergraduate college students participated in an experiment designed by the researchers. Half of the students were volunteers, and half were required to participate as part of their introductory psychology class. Each student listened to a song by the group "Tool," with half the students randomly assigned a song with violent lyrics and half assigned a song with nonviolent lyrics. Consequently, the experiment used a 2×2 factorial design with the factors Song (violent, nonviolent) and Pool (volunteer, psychology class). After listening to the song, each student was given a list of word pairs and asked to rate the similarity of each word in the pair on a seven-point scale. One word in each pair was aggressive in meaning (e.g., *choke*) and the other was ambiguous (e.g., *night*). An aggressive cognition score was assigned on the basis of the average word-pair scores. (The higher the score, the more the subject associated an ambiguous word with a violent word.) The data (simulated) are shown in the accompanying table. Conduct a complete analysis of variance on the data.

⊘ **LYRICS**

	Volunteer	Psychology Class
Violent Song	4.1 3.5 3.4 4.1 3.7 2.8 3.4 4.0 2.5 3.0 3.4 3.5 3.2 3.1 3.6	3.4 3.9 4.2 3.2 4.3 3.3 3.1 3.2 3.8 3.1 3.8 4.1 3.3 3.8 4.5
Nonviolent Song	2.4 2.4 2.5 2.6 3.6 4.0 3.3 3.7 2.8 2.9 3.2 2.5 2.9 3.0 2.4	2.5 2.9 2.9 3.0 2.6 2.4 3.5 3.3 3.7 3.3 2.8 2.5 2.8 2.0 3.1

10.93 Impact of vitamin-B supplement. In the *Journal of Nutrition* (July 1995), University of Georgia researchers examined the impact of a vitamin-B supplement (nicotinamide) on the kidney. The experimental "subjects" were 28 Zucker rats—a species that tends to develop kidney problems. Half of the rats were classified as obese and half as lean. Within each group, half were randomly assigned to receive a vitamin-B-supplemented diet and half were not. Thus, a 2×2 factorial experiment was conducted, with seven rats assigned to each of the four combinations of size (lean or obese) and diet

⊘ **VITAMINB**

Rat Size	Diet			
	Regular		Vitamin-B Supplement	
Lean	1.62	1.47	1.51	1.63
	1.80	1.37	1.65	1.35
	1.71	1.71	1.45	1.66
	1.81		1.44	
Obese	2.35	2.84	2.93	2.63
	2.97	2.05	2.72	2.61
	2.54	2.82	2.99	2.64
	2.93		2.19	

(supplemental or not). One of the response variables measured was weight (in grams) of the kidney at the end of a 20-week feeding period. The data (simulated from summary information provided in the journal article) are shown in the accompanying table:
a. Conduct an analysis of variance on the data. Summarize the results in an ANOVA table.
b. Conduct the appropriate ANOVA *F*-tests at $\alpha = .01$. Interpret the results.

Applying the Concepts—Advanced

10.94 Testing a new pain-relief tablet. Refer to the *Tropical Journal of Pharmaceutical Research* (June 2003) study of the impact of binding agent, binding concentration, and relative density on the mean dissolution time of pain-relief tablets, presented in Exercise 10.12 (p. 487). Recall that binding agent was set at two levels (khaya gum and PVP), binding concentration at two levels (.5% and 4.0%), and relative density at two levels (low and high); thus, a $2 \times 2 \times 2$ factorial design was employed. The sample mean dissolution times for the treatments associated with the factors binding agent and relative density when the other factor (binding concentration) is held fixed at .5% are $\bar{x}_{\text{Gum/Low}} = 4.70$, $\bar{x}_{\text{Gum/High}} = 7.95$, $\bar{x}_{\text{PVP/Low}} = 3.00$, and $\bar{x}_{\text{PVP/High}} = 4.10$. Do the results suggest that there is an interaction between binding agent and relative density? Explain.

10.95 Impact of flavor name on consumer choice. Do consumers react favorably to products with ambiguous colors or names? Marketing professors E. G. Miller and B. E. Kahn investigated this phenomenon in the *Journal of Consumer Research* (June 2005). As a "reward" for participating in an unrelated experiment, 100 consumers were told that they could have some jelly beans available in several cups on a table. Half the consumers were assigned to take jelly beans with common descriptive flavor names (e.g., watermelon green), while the other half were assigned to take jelly beans with ambiguous flavor names (e.g., monster green). Within each group, half of the consumers took the jelly beans and left (low cognitive load condition), while the other half were asked questions designed to distract them while they were taking their jelly beans (high cognitive load condition). Consequently, a 2×2 factorial experiment was employed—with Flavor name (common or ambiguous) and Cognitive load (low or high) as the two factors—with 25 consumers assigned to each of four treatments. The dependent variable of interest was the number of jelly beans taken by each consumer. The means and standard deviations of the four treatments are shown in the following table:

	Ambiguous		Common	
	Mean	Std. Dev.	Mean	Std. Dev.
Low Load	18.0	15.0	7.8	9.5
High Load	6.1	9.5	6.3	10.0

Source: Miller, E. G. & Kahn, B. E. "Shades of meaning: The effect of color and flavor names on consumer choice," *Journal of Consumer Research*, Vol. 32, June 2005 (Table 1).

a. Calculate the total of the $n = 25$ measurements for each of the four categories in the 2×2 factorial experiment.

b. Calculate the correction for mean, CM. (See Appendix C for computational formulas.)

c. Use the results of parts **a** and **b** to calculate the sums of squares for Load, Name, and Load × Name interaction.

d. Calculate the sample variance for each treatment. Then calculate the sum of squares of deviations within each sample for the four treatments.

e. Calculate SSE. (*Hint*: SSE is the pooled sum of squares for the deviations calculated in part **d**.)

f. Now that you know SS(Load), SS(Name), SS(Load × Name), and SSE, find SS(Total).

g. Summarize the calculations in an ANOVA table.

h. The researchers reported the *F*-value for Load × Name interaction as $F = 5.34$. Do you agree?

i. Conduct a complete analysis of these data. Use $\alpha = .05$ for any inferential techniques you employ. Illustrate your conclusions graphically.

j. What assumptions are necessary to ensure the validity of the inferential techniques you utilized? State them in terms of this experiment.

KEY TERMS

Analysis of variance (ANOVA)   494
Balanced design   530
Blocks   512
Bonferroni multiple-comparison
   procedure   505
Comparisonwise error rate   505
Complete factorial experiment   527
Completely randomized design   488
Dependent variable   482
Designed experiment   483
Experimental unit   483
Experimentwise error rate   505
Factor interaction   528
Factor levels   482

Factor main effect   528
Factors   482
F-statistic   490
F-test   492
Mean square for error   490
Mean square for treatments   490
Multiple comparisons of a set
   of treatment means   505
Observational experiment   483
Qualitative factors   482
Quantitative factors   482
Randomized block design   512
Replicates of the factorial
   experiment   530

Response variable   482
Robust method   496
Scheffé multiple-comparison
   procedure   505
Single-factor experiments   527
Sum of squares for blocks   513
Sum of squares for error   490
Sum of squares for treatments   490
Treatments   483
Tukey multiple-comparison
   procedure   505
Two-way classification   527

GUIDE TO CONDUCTING ANOVA *F*-TESTS

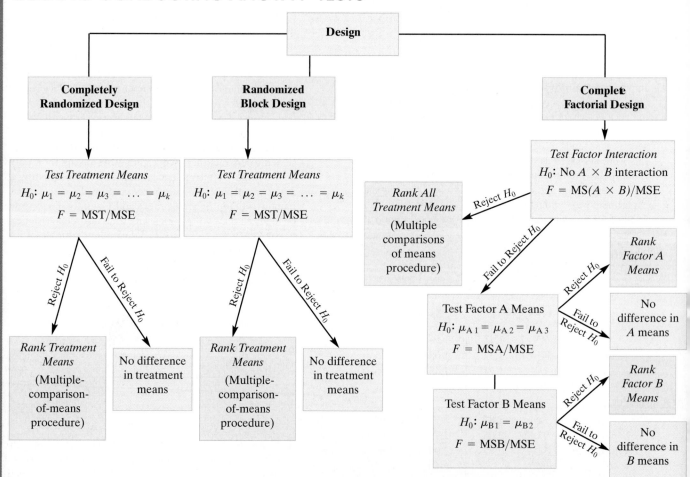

GUIDE TO SELECTING AN EXPERIMENTAL DESIGN

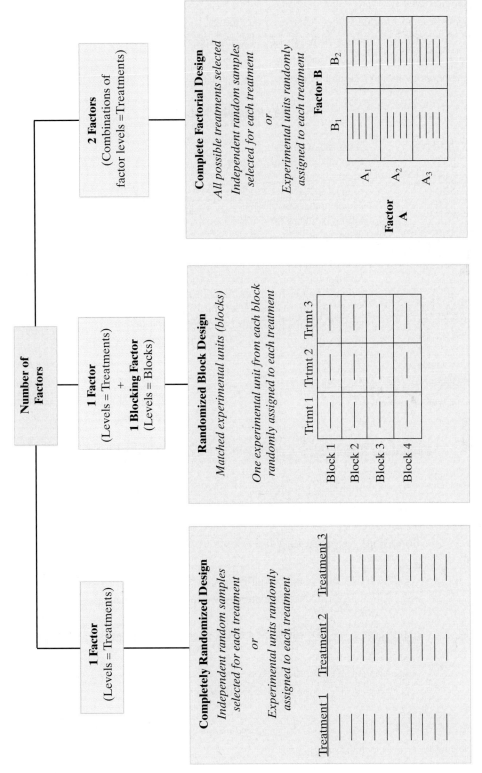

Number of Factors

1 Factor
(Levels = Treatments)

1 Factor
(Levels = Treatments)
+
1 Blocking Factor
(Levels = Blocks)

2 Factors
(Combinations of factor levels = Treatments)

Completely Randomized Design
Independent random samples selected for each treatment
or
Experimental units randomly assigned to each treatment

Treatment 1   Treatment 2   Treatment 3

Randomized Block Design
Matched experimental units (blocks)

One experimental unit from each block randomly assigned to each treatment

Trtmt 1   Trtmt 2   Trtmt 3

Block 1
Block 2
Block 3
Block 4

Complete Factorial Design
All possible treatments selected
Independent random samples selected for each treatment
or
Experimental units randomly assigned to each treatment

Factor B
B_1 B_2

Factor A
A_1
A_2
A_3

CHAPTER NOTES

Key Elements of a Designed Experiment:

1. *Response (dependent) variable*—quantitative
2. *Factors (independent variables)*—quantitative or qualitative
3. *Factor levels (values of factors)*—selected by the experimenter
4. *Treatments*—combinations of factor levels
5. *Experimental units*—assign treatments to experimental units and measure response for each

Key Symbols/Notation

ANOVA	Analysis of variance
SST	Sum of squares for treatments
MST	Mean square for treatments
SSB	Sum of squares for blocks
MSB	Mean square for blocks
SSE	Sum of squares for error
MSE	Mean square for error
$a \times b$ factorial	Factorial design with one factor at a levels and the other factor at b levels
SS(A)	Sum of squares for main-effect factor A
MS(A)	Mean square for main-effect factor A
SS(B)	Sum of squares for main-effect factor B
MS(B)	Mean square for main-effect factor B
SS(AB)	Sum of squares for factor $A \times B$ interaction
MS(AB)	Mean square for factor $A \times B$ interaction

Balanced design

Sample sizes for each treatment are equal.

Tests for main effects in a factorial design

appropriate only if the test for factor interaction is nonsignificant

Conditions Required for Valid *F*-Test in a Completely Randomized Design

1. All k treatment populations are approximately normal.
2. $\sigma_1^2 = \sigma_2^2 = \ldots = \sigma_k^2$

Conditions Required for Valid *F*-Tests in a Randomized Block Design

1. All treatment-block populations are approximately normal.
2. All treatment-block populations have the same variance.

Conditions Required for Valid *F*-Tests in a Complete Factorial Design

1. All treatment populations are approximately normal.
2. All treatment populations have the same variance.

Robust method

Slight to moderate departures from normality have no impact on the validity on the ANOVA results.

Experimentwise error rate

Risk of making at least one Type I error when making multiple comparisons of means in ANOVA

Number of pairwise comparisons with k treatment means:

$$c = k(k-1)/2$$

Multiple-Comparison-of-Means Methods

Tukey
1. Balanced design
2. Pairwise comparisons of means

Bonferroni
1. Either balanced or unbalanced design
2. Pairwise comparisons of means

Scheffé
1. Either balanced or unbalanced design
2. General contrasts of means

SUPPLEMENTARY EXERCISES 10.96–10.124

Understanding the Principles

10.96 What is the difference between a one-way ANOVA and a two-way ANOVA?

10.97 Explain the difference between an experiment that utilizes a completely randomized design and one that utilizes a randomized block design.

10.98 What are the treatments in a two-factor experiment with factor A at three levels and factor B at two levels?

10.99 Why does the experimentwise error rate of a multiple-comparison procedure differ from the significance level for each comparison (assuming that the experiment has more than two treatments)?

Learning the Mechanics

10.100 A completely randomized design is utilized to compare four treatment means. The data are shown in the accompanying table.
  a. Given that SST = 36.95 and SS(Total) = 62.55, complete an ANOVA table for this experiment.
  b. Is there evidence that the treatment means differ? Use $\alpha = .10$.

LM10_100

Treatment 1	Treatment 2	Treatment 3	Treatment 4
8	6	9	12
10	9	10	13
9	8	8	10
10	8	11	11
11	7	12	11

10.101 An experiment utilizing a randomized block design was conducted to compare the mean responses for four treatments, A, B, C, and D. The treatments were randomly assigned to the four experimental units in each of five blocks. The data are shown in the next table:
  a. Given that SS(Total) = 22.31, SS(Block) = 10.688, and SSE = .288, complete an ANOVA table for the experiment.
  b. Do the data provide sufficient evidence to indicate a difference among treatment means? Test, using $\alpha = .05$

c. Does the result of the test in part **b** warrant further comparison of the treatment means? If so, how many pairwise comparisons need to be made?
d. Is there evidence that the block means differ? Use $\alpha = .05$.

LM10_101

Treatment	Block 1	2	3	4	5
A	8.6	7.5	8.7	9.8	7.4
B	7.3	6.3	7.3	8.4	6.3
C	9.1	8.3	9.0	9.9	8.2
D	9.3	8.2	9.2	10.0	8.4

10.102 The following table shows a partially completed ANOVA table for a two-factor factorial experiment:

Source	df	SS	MS	F
A	3	2.6		
B	5	9.2		
$A \times B$			3.1	
Error		18.7		
Total	47			

  a. Complete the ANOVA table.
  b. How many levels were used for each factor? How many treatments were used? How many replications were performed?
  c. Find the value of the sum of squares for treatments. Test to determine whether the data provide evidence that the treatment means differ. Use $\alpha = .05$.
  d. Is further testing of the nature of factor effects warranted? If so, test to determine whether the factors interact. Use $\alpha = .05$. Interpret the result.

Applying the Concepts—Basic

10.103 **Strength of fiberboard boxes.** The *Journal of Testing and Evaluation* (July 1992) published an investigation of the mean compression strength of corrugated fiberboard shipping containers. Comparisons were made for boxes of five different sizes: A, B, C, D, and E. Twenty identical boxes of each size were tested, and the peak compression strength (in pounds) was recorded for each box. The accompanying figure shows the sample means for the five types of box, as well as the variation around each sample mean.

a. Explain why the data are collected as a completely randomized design.

b. Refer to box types B and D. On the basis of the graph, does it appear that the mean compressive strengths of these two types of box are significantly different? Explain.

c. On the basis of the graph, does it appear that the mean compressive strengths of all five types of box are significantly different? Explain.

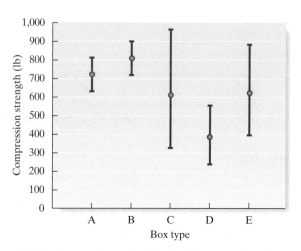

Source: Singh, S. P., et al. "Compression of single-wall corrugated shipping containers using fixed and floating test platens," *Journal of Testing and Evaluation*, Vol. 20, No. 4, July 1992, p. 319 (Figure 3). Copyright American Society for Testing and Materials.

10.104 **Shoulder rotation experiment.** *Physical Therapy* (Aug. 1986) reported on a study of the medial rotation of the shoulder. Ten college students who exhibited no evidence of disease or limitation of movement in their shoulders served as the subjects for the study. For each subject, the medial rotation was measured (in degrees) at each of three positions: (1) beginning position, (2) point at which rotation changed directions, and (3) ending position. The goal of the analysis was to compare the mean medial rotation measurements of the three positions.

a. Explain why a randomized block design is appropriate in this experiment.

b. Identify the treatments in the experiment.

c. Identify the blocks in the experiment.

d. Identify the response variable.

10.105 **Ethics of salespeople.** Within marketing, the area of personal sales has long suffered from a poor ethical image, particularly in the eyes of college students. An article in *Journal of Business Ethics* (Vol. 15, 1996) investigated whether such opinions by college students are a function of the type of sales jobs (high tech versus low tech) and/or the sales task (new = account development versus account maintenance). Four different samples of college students were confronted with the four different situations (new = account development in a high-tech sales task; new = account development in a low-tech sales task;

account maintenance in a high-tech sales task; and account maintenance in a low-tech sales task) and were asked to evaluate the ethical behavior of the salesperson on a Seven-point scale ranging from 1 (not a serious ethical violation) to 7 (a very serious ethical violation). Identify each of the following elements of the experiment:

a. Response

b. Factor(s) and factor level(s)

c. Treatments

d. Experimental units

10.106 **Alcohol-and-marriage study.** An experiment was conducted to examine the effects of alcohol on the marital interactions of husbands and wives (*Journal of Abnormal Psychology*, Nov. 1998). A total of 135 couples participated in the experiment. The husband in each couple was classified as aggressive (60 husbands) or nonaggressive (75 husbands), on the basis of an interview and his response to a questionnaire. Before the marital interactions of the couples were observed, each husband was randomly assigned to one of three groups: receive no alcohol, receive several alcoholic mixed drinks, or receive placebos (nonalcoholic drinks disguised as mixed drinks). Consequently, a 2 × 3 factorial design was employed, with husband's aggressiveness at two levels (aggressive or nonaggressive) and husband's alcohol condition at three levels (no alcohol, alcohol, and placebo). The response variable observed during the marital interaction was severity of conflict (measured on a 100-point scale).

a. A partial ANOVA table is shown. Fill in the missing degrees of freedom.

Source	df	F
Aggressiveness (A)	–	$16.43 \ (p < .001)$
Alcohol Condition (C)	–	$6.00 \ (p < .01)$
A × C	–	–
Error	129	
Total	–	

b. Interpret the *p*-value of the *F*-test for Aggressiveness.

c. Interpret the *p*-value of the *F*-test for Alcohol Condition.

d. The *F*-test for interaction was omitted from the article. Discuss the dangers of making inferences based on the tests in parts **b** and **c** without knowing the result of the interaction test.

10.107 **Children's use of pronouns.** Refer to the *Journal of Communication Disorders* (Mar. 1995) study of pronoun misusage by specifically language-impaired (SLI) children, presented in Exercise 2.65 (p. 60). Recall that percentage of pronoun errors was recorded for three

Source	df	SS	MS	F	*p*-Value
Groups	2	11,292.45	5,646.22	8.295	.0016
Error	27	18,377.65	680.65		
Total	29	29,670.10			
Mean percentage of errors:			0.00	30.17	46.88
Group:			OND	SLI	YND

Source: Moore, M. E. "Error analysis of pronouns by normal and language-impaired children," *Journal of Communication Disorders*, Vol. 28, No. 1, Mar. 1995, p. 67 (Table 6).

groups of children: 10 five-year-old SLI children, 10 younger (three-year-old) normally developing (YND) children, and 10 older (five-year-old) normally developing (OND) children. A completely randomized ANOVA design with multiple comparisons of means was conducted on the data, producing the results shown in the accompanying table. Interpret these results.

DDT

10.108 Contaminated fish in the Tennessee River. Refer to the U.S. Army Corps of Engineers data on contaminated fish, saved in the **DDT** file. The results of an ANOVA and Tukey multiple-comparison analysis to compare the three fish species (channel catfish, largemouth bass, and smallmouth buffalo) on the dependent variable length (in centimeters) are shown in the accompanying MINITAB printout.

    a. Is there sufficient evidence (at $\alpha = .01$) to conclude that the mean lengths differ among the three fish species?

    b. What is the experimentwise error rate for the Tukey multiple comparisons?

    c. Locate the confidence interval for the difference $(\mu_{bass} - \mu_{catfish})$. Are the two means significantly different? If so, which mean is significantly larger?

    d. Locate the confidence interval for the difference $(\mu_{buffalo} - \mu_{catfish})$. Are the two means significantly different? If so, which mean is significantly larger?

One-way ANOVA: LENGTH versus SPECIES

```
Source    DF      SS      MS      F       P
SPECIES    2   3533.1  1766.5  76.88  0.000
Error    141   3239.9    23.0
Total    143   6772.9

S = 4.794    R-Sq = 52.16%    R-Sq(adj) = 51.49%


Level             N   Mean    StDev
CHANNELCATFISH   96  44.729   4.581
LARGEMOUTHBASS   12  26.542   4.480
SMALLMOUTHBUFF   36  43.125   5.413


Pooled StDev = 4.794


Tukey 95% Simultaneous Confidence Intervals
All Pairwise Comparisons among Levels of SPECIES

Individual confidence level = 98.08%


SPECIES = CHANNELCATFISH subtracted from:

SPECIES          Lower    Center   Upper
LARGEMOUTHBASS  -21.664  -18.188  -14.711
SMALLMOUTHBUFF   -3.823   -1.604    0.615


SPECIES = LARGEMOUTHBASS subtracted from:

SPECIES          Lower    Center   Upper
SMALLMOUTHBUFF   12.798   16.583   20.368
```

MINITAB output for Exercise 10.108

    e. Locate the confidence interval for the difference $(\mu_{buffalo} - \mu_{bass})$. Are the two means significantly different? If so, which mean is significantly larger?

10.109 Detecting distorted responses. The Minnesota Multiphasic Personality Inventory (MMPI) is a questionnaire used to gauge a person's personality. *Psychological Assessment* (Mar. 1995) published a study that investigated the effectiveness of the MMPI scales in detecting deliberately distorted responses. A completely randomized design with four treatments was employed. The treatments consisted of independent random samples of females in the following four groups: nonforensic psychiatric patients ($n_1 = 65$), forensic psychiatric patients ($n_2 = 28$), college students who were requested to respond honestly ($n_3 = 140$), and college students who were instructed to provide "fake bad" responses ($n_4 = 45$). All 278 participants were given the MMPI, and the score on a scale designed to assess the distortion in their responses was recorded for each. An analysis of variance was conducted on the data.

    a. The ANOVA yielded $F = 39.1$. Do the mean scores of the four groups completing the MMPI differ significantly? Use $\alpha = .05$.

    b. If the MMPI is effective in detecting distorted responses, then the mean score for the "fake bad" treatment group will be the largest score. Based on the information provided, can the researchers make an inference about the effectiveness of the MMPI? Explain.

    c. The Bonferroni method was used to rank the means of the four groups, using an experimentwise error rate of $\alpha = .05$. The results are shown in the accompanying table. Interpret the results.

Mean Score	12.0	12.1	20.8	21.0
Group	FP	NFP	CSH	CSFB

Source: Bagby, R. M., Burs, T., and Nicholson, R. A. "Relative effectiveness of the standard validity scales in detecting fake-bad and fake-good responding: Replication and extension." *Psychological Assessment,* Vol. 7, No. 1, Mar. 1995, p. 86 (Table 1).

Applying the Concepts—Intermediate

10.110 Safety of nuclear power plants. An article in the *American Journal of Political Science* (Jan. 1998) examined the attitudes of three groups of professionals who influence U.S. policy. Random samples of 100 scientists, 100 journalists, and 100 government officials were asked about the safety of nuclear power plants. Responses were made on a seven-point scale, where 1 = very unsafe and 7 = very safe. The mean safety scores for the groups are scientists, 4.1; journalists, 3.7; government officials, 4.2.

    a. Identify the response variable for this study.

    b. How many treatments are included in the study? Describe them.

    c. Specify the null and alternative hypotheses that should be used to investigate whether there are differences in the attitudes of scientists, journalists, and government officials regarding the safety of nuclear power plants.

    d. The MSE for the sample data is 2.355. At least how large must the MST be in order to reject the null hypothesis of the test of part **c**, using $\alpha = .05$?

    e. If the MST = 11.280, what is the approximate p-value of the test of part **c**?

f. Determine the number of pairwise comparisons of treatment means that can be made in this study.

g. With an experimentwise error rate of $\alpha = .05$, Tukey's minimum significant difference for comparing means is .23. Use this information to conduct multiple-comparison analysis of the safety score means. Interpret the results fully.

OILSPILL

10.111 Hull failures of oil tankers Refer to the *Marine Technology* (Jan. 1995) study of major ocean oil spills by tanker vessels, presented in Exercise 2.186 (p. 106). The spillage amounts (thousands of metric tons) and cause of accident for 48 tankers are saved in the **OILSPILL** file. (*Note:* Delete the two tankers with oil spills of unknown cause.)

a. Conduct an analysis of variance (at $\alpha = .01$) to compare the mean spillage amounts for the four types of accident: (1) collision, (2) grounding, (3) fire/explosion, and (4) hull failure. Interpret your results.

b. If appropriate, use Bonferroni's method to rank the spillage means of the four types of accident. Use $\alpha = .01$.

10.112 Exposure to low-frequency sound. *Infrasound* refers to sound frequencies below the audibility range of the human ear. A study of the physiological effects of infrasound was published in the *Journal of Low Frequency Noice, Vibration and Active Control* (Mar. 2004). In the experiment, one group of five university students (Group A) was exposed to infrasound at 4 hertz and 120 decibels for 1 hour, and a second group of five students (Group B) was exposed to infrasound at 2 hertz and 110 decibels, also for 1 hour. The heart rate (beats/minute) of each student was measured both before and after their exposure. The experimental data are provided in the accompanying table. To determine the impact of infrasound, the researchers compared the mean heart rate before exposure to the mean heart rate after exposure.

INFRASOUND

Group A Students	Before Exposure	After Exposure	Group B Students	Before Exposure	After Exposure
A1	70	70	B1	73	79
A2	69	80	B2	68	60
A3	76	84	B3	61	69
A4	77	86	B4	72	77
A5	64	76	B5	61	66

Source: Qibai, C. Y. H., and Shi, H. "An investigation on the physiological and psychological effects of infrasound on persons," *Journal of Low Frequency Noise, Vibration and Active Control*, Vol. 23, No. 1, March 2004 (Tables I–IV).

a. Analyze the data on Group A students with an ANOVA for a randomized block design. Conduct the ANOVA test of interest with $\alpha = .05$.

b. Repeat part **a** for Group B students.

c. Now analyze the data via a paired difference t-test. Show that, for both groups of students, the results are equivalent to the randomized block ANOVA.

10.113 Availability of food for marsh ducks. Ducks inhabiting the Great Salt Lake marshes feed on a variety of animals, including water boatmen, brine shrimp, beetles, and snails. The changes in the availability of these animal species for ducks during the summer was investigated (*Wetlands*, March 1995). The goal was to compare the mean amount (measured as biomass) of a particular duck food species across four different summertime periods: (1) July 9–23, (2) July 24–Aug. 8, (3) Aug. 9–23, and (4) Aug. 24–31. Ten stations in the marshes were randomly selected, and the biomass density in a water specimen collected from each station was measured. Biomass measurements (milligrams per square meter) were collected during each of the four summertime periods at each station, with stations treated as a blocking factor. Thus, the data were analyzed as a randomized block design.

a. Fill in the missing degrees of freedom in the randomized block ANOVA table shown here:

Source	df	F	p-Value
Time Period	—	11.25	.0001
Station	—	—	—
Error	—		
Total	39		

b. The F-value and the corresponding p-value shown in the ANOVA table of part **a** were computed from an analysis of biomass of water boatmen nymphs (a common duck food). Interpret these results.

c. A multiple-comparison analysis of period means was conducted that used an experimentwise error rate of .05. The results are summarized in the table at the bottom of the page. Identify the period(s) with the largest and smallest mean biomass.

10.114 Testing the ability to perform left-handed tasks. Most people are right handed due to the propensity of the left hemisphere of the brain to control sequential movement. Similarly, the fact that some tasks are performed better with the left hand is likely due to the superiority of the right hemisphere of the brain in processing the necessary information. Does such cerebral specialization in spatial processing occur in adults with Down syndrome? A 2×2 factorial experiment was conducted to answer this question. (*American Journal on Mental Retardation*, May 1995.) A sample of adults with Down syndrome was compared with a control group of individuals of a similar age, but not affected by the condition. Thus, one factor was Group at two levels (Down syndrome and control), and the second factor was Handedness (left or right) of the subject. All the subjects performed a task that typically yields a left-hand advantage. The response variable was "laterality index," measured on a -100- to 100-point scale. (A large positive index indicates a right-hand advantage, a large negative index a left-hand advantage.)

Multiple Comparisons for Exercise 10.113

Mean biomass (mg/m²):	19	54.5	90	148
Period:	8/24–8/31	8/9–8/23	7/24–8/8	7/9–7/23

Mean laterality index:	−30	−4	−.5	+.5
Group/Handed:	Down/Left	Control/Right	Control/Left	Down/Right

a. Identify the treatments in this experiment.

b. Construct a graph that would support a finding of no interaction between the two factors.

c. Construct a graph that would support a finding of interaction between the two factors.

d. The F-test for factor interaction yielded an observed significance level of $p < .05$. Interpret this result.

e. Multiple comparisons of all pairs of treatment means yielded the rankings shown in the table above. Interpret the results.

f. The experimentwise error rate for part **e** was .05. Interpret this value.

10.115 Facial expression study. What do people infer from facial expressions of emotion? This was the research question of interest in an article published in the *Journal of Nonverbal Behavior* (Fall 1996). A sample of 36 introductory psychology students was randomly divided into six groups. Each group was assigned to view one of six slides showing a person making a facial expression.* The six expressions were (1) angry, (2) disgusted, (3) fearful, (4) happy, (5) sad, and (6) neutral. After viewing the slides, the students rated the degree of dominance they inferred from the facial expression (on a scale ranging from −15 to +15). The data (simulated from summary information provided in the article) are listed in the accompanying table.

a. Conduct an analysis of variance to determine whether the mean dominance ratings differ among the six facial expressions. Use $\alpha = .10$.

b. Use Tukey's method to rank the six dominance rating means. (Use $\alpha = .05$)

FACES

Angry	Disgusted	Fearful	Happy	Sad	Neutral
2.10	.40	.82	1.71	.74	1.69
.64	.73	−2.93	−.04	−1.26	−.60
.47	−.07	−.74	1.04	−2.27	−.55
.37	−.25	.79	1.44	−.39	.27
1.62	.89	−.77	1.37	−2.65	−.57
−.08	1.93	−1.60	.59	−.44	−2.16

10.116 Effectiveness of geese decoys. Using decoys is a common method of hunting waterfowl. A study in the *Journal of Wildlife Management* (July 1995) compared the effectiveness of three different types of decoy—taxidermy-mounted decoys, plastic shell decoys, and full-bodied plastic decoys—in attracting Canada geese to sunken pit blinds. In order to account for an extraneous source of variation, three pit blinds were used as blocks in the experiment. Thus, a randomized block design with three treatments (types of decoy) and three blocks (pit blinds) was employed. The response variable was the percentage of a goose flock to approach within 46 meters of the pit blind on a given day. The data are given in the following table:*

DECOY

Blind	Shell	Full Bodied	Taxidermy Mounted
1	7.3	13.6	17.8
2	12.6	10.4	17.0
3	16.4	23.4	13.6

Source: Harrey, W. F., Hindman, L. J., and Rhodes, W. E. "Vulnerability of Canada geese to taxidermy-mounted decoys," *Journal of Wildlife Management*, Vol. 59, No. 3, July 1995, p. 475 (Table 1).

a. Use statistical software (for the formulas in Appendix C) to construct an ANOVA table.

b. Interpret the F-statistic for comparing the response means of the three types of decoy.

c. What assumptions are necessary for the validity of the inference made in part **a**?

d. Why is it not necessary to conduct multiple comparisons of the response means for the three types of decoy?

10.117 Price and display marketing study. Complete factorial designs are commonly employed in marketing research to evaluate the effectiveness of sales strategies. At one supermarket, two of the factors were Price level (regular, reduced price, cost to supermarket) and Display level (normal display space, normal display space plus end-of-aisle display, twice the normal display space). Each of the $3 \times 3 = 9$ treatments was applied three times to a particular product for a full week. The dependent variable of interest was unit sales for the week. To minimize treatment carry-over effects, each treatment was preceded and followed by a week in which the product was priced at its regular price and was displayed in its normal manner. The table below reports the data collected.

a. Form an ANOVA table for the study.

b. Do the data indicate that the mean sales differ among the nine treatments? Test, using $\alpha = .10$.

SUPMARK

Display	Regular	Reduced	Cost to Supermarket
Normal	989 1,025 1,030	1,211 1,215 1,182	1,577 1,559 1,598
Normal Plus	1,191 1,233 1,221	1,860 1,910 1,926	2,492 2,527 2,511
Twice Normal	1,226 1,202 1,180	1,516 1,501 1,498	1,801 1,833 1,852

*In the actual experiment, each group viewed all six facial expression slides and the design employed was a Latin Square (beyond the scope of this text).

*The actual design employed in the study was more complex than the randomized block design shown here. In the actual study, each number in the table represented the mean daily percentage of goose flocks attracted to the blind, averaged over 13–17 days.

c. Is the test of interaction between the factors Price and Display warranted as a result of the test conducted in part **b**? If so, conduct the test, using $\alpha = .10$.

d. Are the tests of the main effects for Price and Display warranted as a result of the previous tests? If so, conduct them, using $\alpha = .10$.

e. Which pairs of treatment means should be compared as a result of the tests conducted in parts **b–d**? Perform the comparisons.

10.118 Mosquito insecticide study. A species of Caribbean mosquito is known to be resistant against certain insecticides. The effectiveness of five different types of insecticides—temephos, malathion, fenitrothion, fenthion, and chlorpyrifos—in controlling this mosquito species was investigated in the *Journal of the American Mosquito Control Association* (March 1995). Mosquito larvae were collected from each of seven Caribbean locations. In a laboratory, the larvae from each location were divided into five batches and each batch was exposed to one of the five insecticides. The dosage of insecticide required to kill 50% of the larvae was recorded and divided by the known dosage for a susceptible mosquito strain. The resulting value is called the *resistance ratio*. (The higher the ratio, the more resistant the mosquito species is to the insecticide relative to the susceptible mosquito strain.) The resistance ratios for the study are listed in the table below. The researchers want to compare the mean resistance ratios of the five insecticides.

a. Explain why the experimental design is a randomized block design. Identify the treatments and the blocks.

b. Conduct a complete analysis of the data. Are any of the insecticides more effective than any of the others?

10.119 Short-day traits of lemmings. Many temperate-zone animal species exhibit physiological and morphological changes when the hours of daylight begin to decrease during the autumn months. A study was conducted to investigate the "short-day" traits of collared lemmings. (*Journal of Experimental Zoology*, Sept. 1993.) A total of 124 lemmings were bred in a colony maintained with a photoperiod of 22 hours of light per day. At weaning (19 days of age), the lemmings were weighed and randomly assigned to live under one of two photoperiods: 16 hours or less of light per day and more than 16 hours of light per day. (Each group was assigned the same number of males and females.) After 10 weeks, the lemmings were weighed again. The response variable of interest was the gain in body weight (measured in grams) over the 10-week experimental period. The researchers analyzed the data by means of a 2×2 factorial ANOVA design with the two factors being Photoperiod (at two levels) and Gender (at two levels).

a. Construct an ANOVA table for the experiment, listing the sources of variation and associated degrees of freedom.

b. The F-test for interaction was not significant. Interpret this result practically.

c. The p-values for testing for Photoperiod and Gender main effects were both smaller than .001. Interpret these results practically.

10.120 Ranging behavior of Spanish cattle. The cattle inhabiting the Biological Reserve of Doñana (Spain), live under free-range conditions, with virtually no human interference. The cattle population is organized into four herds (LGN, MTZ, PLC, and QMD). The *Journal of Zoology* (July 1995) investigated the ranging behavior of the four herds across the four seasons. Thus, a 4×4 factorial experiment was employed, with Herd and Season representing the two factors. Three animals from each herd during each season were sampled and the home range of each individual was measured (in square kilometers). The data were subjected to an ANOVA, with the results shown in the following table.

Source	df	F	p-Value
Herd (H)	3	17.2	$p < .001$
Season (S)	3	3.0	$p < .05$
H $\times$ S	9	1.2	$p > .05$
Error	32		
Total	47		

a. Conduct the appropriate ANOVA F-tests and interpret the results.

b. The researcher conducting the experiment ranked the four herd means independently of season. Do you agree with this strategy? Explain.

c. Refer to part **b**. The Bonferroni rankings of the four herd means (at $\alpha = .05$) are shown in the following table. Interpret the results.

Mean (km)^2:	.75	1.0	2.7	3.8
Herd:	PLC	LGN	QMD	MTZ

MOSQUITO

	Insecticide				
Location	Temephos	Malathion	Fenitrothion	Fenthion	Chlorpyrifos
Anguilla	4.6	1.2	1.5	1.8	1.5
Antigua	9.2	2.9	2.0	7.0	2.0
Dominica	7.8	1.4	2.4	4.2	4.1
Guyana	1.7	1.9	2.2	1.5	1.8
Jamaica	3.4	3.7	2.0	1.5	7.1
St. Lucia	6.7	2.7	2.7	4.8	8.7
Suriname	1.4	1.9	2.0	2.1	1.7

Source: Rawlins, S. C., and Oh Hing Wan, J. "Resistance in some Caribbean population of *Aedes aegypti* to several insecticides," *Journal of the American Mosquito Control Association*, Vol. 11, No. 1, Mar. 1995 (Table 1).

Applying the Concepts—Advanced

10.121 **Testing a new insecticide.** Traditionally, people protect themselves from mosquito bites by applying insect repellent to their skin and clothing. Recent research suggests that peremethrin, an insecticide with low toxicity to humans, can provide protection from mosquitoes. A study in the *Journal of the American Mosquito Control Association* (Mar. 1995) investigated whether a tent sprayed with a commercially available 1% peremethrin formulation would protect people, both inside and outside the tent, against biting mosquitoes. Two canvas tents—one treated with peremethrin, the other untreated—were positioned 25 meters apart on flat dry ground in an area infested with mosquitoes. Eight people participated in the experiment, with four randomly assigned to each tent. Of the four stationed at each tent, two were randomly assigned to stay inside the tent (at opposite corners) and two to stay outside the tent (at opposite corners). During a specified 20-minute period during the night, each person kept count of the number of mosquito bites received. The goal of the study was to determine the effect of both Tent type (treated or untreated) and Location (inside or outside the tent) on the mean mosquito bite count.

a. What type of design was employed in the study?

b. Identify the factors and treatments.

c. Identify the response variable.

d. The study found statistical evidence of interaction between Tent type and Location. Give a practical interpretation of this result.

10.122 **Therapy for binge eaters.** Do you experience episodes of excessive eating accompanied by being overweight? If so, you may suffer from binge eating disorder. Cognitive-behavioral therapy (CBT), in which patients are taught how to make changes in specific behavior patterns (e.g., exercise, eat only low-fat foods), can be effective in treating the disorder. A group of Stanford University researchers investigated the effectiveness of interpersonal therapy (IPT) as a second level of treatment for binge eaters. (*Journal of Consulting and Clinical Psychology*, June 1995.) The researchers employed a design that randomly assigned a sample of 41 overweight individuals diagnosed with binge eating disorder to either a treatment group (30 subjects) or a control group (11 subjects). Subjects in the treatment group received 12 weeks of CBT and then were subdivided into two groups. Those who responded successfully to CBT (17 subjects) were assigned to a weight loss therapy (WLT) program for the next 12 weeks. Those CBT subjects who did not respond to treatment (13 subjects) received 12 weeks of IPT. The subjects in the control group received no therapy of any type. Thus, the study ultimately consisted of three groups of overweight binge eaters: the CBT-WLT group, the CBT-IPT group, and the control group. One outcome (response) variable measured for each subject was the number x of binge eating episodes per week. Summary statistics for each of the three groups at the end of the 24-week period are shown in the accompanying table. The data were analyzed as a completely randomized design with three treatments (CBT-WLT, CBT-IPT, and Control). Although the ANOVA tables were not provided in the article, sufficient information is given in the table to reconstruct them. [See Exercise 10.36 (p. 504). Is CBT effective in reducing the mean number of binges experienced per work?

	CBT-WLT	CBT-IPT	Control
Sample size	17	13	11
Mean number of binges per week	0.2	1.9	2.9
Standard deviation	0.4	1.7	2.0

Source: Agras, W. S., et al. "Does interpersonal therapy help patients with binge eating disorder who fail to respond to cognitive–behavioral therapy?" *Journal of Consulting and Clinical Psychology*, Vol. 63, No. 3, June 1995, p. 358 (Table 1).

Critical Thinking Challenges

10.123 **Anticorrosive behavior of steel coated with epoxy.** Organic coatings that use epoxy resins are widely used to protect steel and metal against weathering and corrosion. Researchers at National Technical University in Athens, Greece, examined the steel anticorrosive behavior of different epoxy coatings formulated with zinc pigments in an attempt to find the epoxy coating with the best resistance to corrosion. (*Pigment & Resin Technology*, Vol. 32, 2003.) The experimental units were flat, rectangular panels cut from steel sheets. Each panel was coated with one of four different coating systems: S1, S2, S3, and S4. Three panels, labeled, S1-A, S1-B, S1-C, S2-A, S2-B, . . . , S4-C, were prepared for each coating system. The characteristics of the four coating systems are listed in the following table:

Characteristics of Four Epoxy Coating Systems

Coating System	First Layer	Second Layer
S1	Zinc dust	Epoxy paint, 100 micrometers thick
S2	Zinc phosphate	Epoxy paint, 100 micrometers thick
S2	Zinc phosphate with mica	Finish layer, 100 micrometers thick
S4	Zinc phosphate with mica	Finish layer, 200 micrometers thick

Each coated panel was immersed in deionized and deaerated water and then tested for corrosion. Since exposure time is likely to have a strong influence on anticorrosive behavior, the researchers attempted to remove this extraneous source of variation through the experimental design. Exposure times were fixed at 24 hours, 60 days, and 120 days. For each of the coating systems, one panel was exposed to water for 24 hours, one for 60 days, and one for 120 days, in random order. The design is illustrated in the following diagram:

Diagram of the Experimental Design

Exposure Time	Coating System/Panel Exposed
24 Hours	S1-A, S2-C, S3-C, S4-B
60 Days	S1-C, S2-A, S3-B, S4-A
120 Days	S1-B, S2-B, S3-A, S4-C

Following exposure, the corrosion rate (in nanoamperes per square centimeter) was determined for each panel. The lower the corrosion rate, the greater is the anticorrosion performance of the coating system. The data are shown in the next table. Are there differences among the epoxy treatment means? If so, which of the epoxy coating systems yields the lowest corrosion rate?

EPOXY

Exposure Time	System S1	System S2	System S3	System S4
24 Hours	6.7	7.5	8.2	6.1
60 Days	8.7	9.1	10.5	8.3
120 Days	11.8	12.6	14.5	11.8

Source: Kouloumbi, N., et al. "Anticorrosion performance of epoxy coatings on steel surface exposed to de-ionized water," *Pigment & resin Technology,* Vol. 32, No. 2, 2003 (Table II).

10.124 **Exam performance study.** Refer to the *Teaching of Psychology* (Aug. 1998) study of whether a practice test helps students prepare for a final exam, presented in Exercise 10.10 (p. 487). Recall that students in an introductory psychology class were grouped according to their class standing and whether they attended a review session or took a practice test prior to the final exam. The experimental design was a 3×2 factorial design, with Class Standing at 3 levels (low, medium, high) and Exam Preparation at 2 levels (practice exam, review session). There were 22 students in each of the $3 \times 2 = 6$ treatment groups. After completing the final exam, each student rated her or his exam preparation on an 11-point scale ranging from 0 (not helpful at all) to 10 (extremely helpful). The data for this experiment (simulated from summary statistics provided in the article) are saved in the **PRACEXAM** file. The first five and last five observations in the data set are listed in the accompanying table. Conduct a complete analysis of variance of the helpfulness ratings data, including (if warranted) multiple comparisons of means. Do your findings support the article's conclusion that "Students at all levels of academic ability benefit from a ... practice exam"?

PRACEXAM

Exam Preparation	Class Standing	Helpfulness Rating
PRACTICE	LOW	6
PRACTICE	LOW	7
PRACTICE	LOW	7
PRACTICE	LOW	5
PRACTICE	LOW	3
⋮	⋮	⋮
REVIEW	HI	5
REVIEW	HI	2
REVIEW	HI	5
REVIEW	HI	4
REVIEW	HI	3

Source: Balch, W. R. "Practice versus review exams and final exam performance," *Teaching of Psychology,* Vol. 25, No. 3, Aug. 1998 (adapted from Table 1).

SUMMARY ACTIVITY: Comparing Supermarket Food Prices

Due to ever-increasing food costs, consumers are becoming more discerning in their choice of supermarkets. It is usually more convenient to shop at just one market, as opposed to buying different items at different markets. Thus, it would be useful to compare the mean food expenditure for a market basket of food items from store to store. Since there is a great deal of variability in the prices of products sold at any supermarket, we will consider an experiment that blocks on products.

Choose three (or more) supermarkets in your area that you want to compare. Then choose approximately 10 (or more) food products you typically purchase. For each food item, record the price each store charges in the following manner:

Food Item 1	Food Item 2	· · ·	Food Item 10
Price store 1	Price store 1	· · ·	Price store 1
Price store 2	Price store 2	· · ·	Price store 2
Price store 3	Price store 3	· · ·	Price store 3

Use the data you obtain to test

H_0: Mean expenditures at the stores are the same.

H_a: Mean expenditures for at least two of the stores are different.

Also, test to determine whether blocking on food items is advisable in this kind of experiment. Interpret the results of your analysis fully.

REFERENCES

Cochran, W. G., and Cox, G. M. *Experimental Designs*, 2d ed. New York: Wiley, 1957.

Hsu, J. C. *Multiple Comparisons: Theory and Methods*. London: Chapman & Hall, 1996.

Kramer, C. Y. "Extension of multiple range tests to group means with unequal number of replications." *Biometrics*, Vol. 12, 1956, pp. 307–310.

Mason, R. L., Gunst, R. F., and Hess, J. L. *Statistical Design and Analysis of Experiments*. New York: Wiley, 1989.

Mendenhall, W. *Introduction to Linear Models and the Design and Analysis of Experiments*. Belmont, CA: Wadsworth, 1968.

Miller, R. G., Jr. *Simultaneous Statistical Inference*. New York: Springer-Verlag, 1981.

Neter, J., Kutner, M., Nachtsheim, C., and Wasserman, W. *Applied Linear Statistical Models*, 4th ed. Homewood, IL.: Richard D. Irwin, 1996.

Scheffé, H. "A method for judging all contrasts in the Analysis of Variance," *Biometrica*, Vol. 40, 1953, pp. 87–104.

Scheffé, H. *The Analysis of Variance*. New York: Wiley, 1959.

Snedecor, G. W., and Cochran, W. G. *Statistical Methods*, 7th ed. Ames, IA: Iowa State University Press, 1980.

Steele, R. G. D., and Torrie, J. H. *Principles and Procedures of Statistics: A Biometrical Approach*, 2d ed. New York: McGraw-Hill, 1980.

Tukey, J. "Comparing individual means in the Analysis of Variance," *Biometrics*, Vol. 5, 1949, pp. 99–114.

Winer, B. J. *Statistical Principles in Experimental Design*, 2d ed. New York: McGraw-Hill, 1971.

Using Technology

Analysis of Variance with MINITAB

MINITAB can conduct ANOVAs for all three types of experimental designs discussed in this chapter: completely randomized, randomized block, and factorial designs.

Completely Randomized Design

To conduct a completely randomized ANOVA design, first access the MINITAB worksheet file that contains the sample data. The data file should contain one quantitative variable (the response, or dependent, variable) and one qualitative factor variable with at least two levels. Next, click on the "Stat" button on the MINITAB menu bar, and then click on "ANOVA" and "One-Way," as shown in Figure 10.M.1.

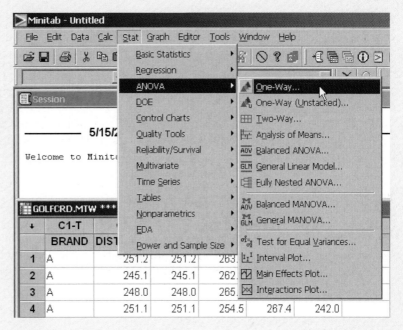

FIGURE 10.M.1

MINITAB menu options for one-way ANOVA

The resulting dialog box appears as shown in Figure 10.M.2. Specify the response variable in the "Response" box and the factor variable in the "Factor" box. Click the "Comparisons" button, and select a multiple-comparison method and experimentwise error rate in the resulting dialog box. (See Figure 10.M.3.) Then click "OK" to return to the "One-Way ANOVA" dialog screen. Click "OK" to generate the MINITAB printout.

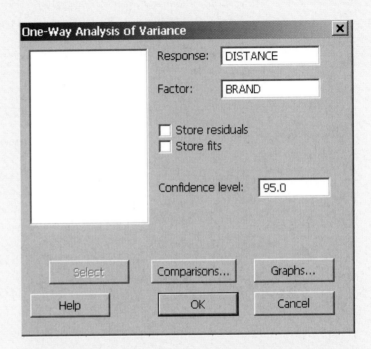

FIGURE 10.M.2
MINITAB one-way ANOVA
dialog box

FIGURE 10.M.3
MINITAB multiple
comparisons dialog box

Randomized Block and Factorial Designs

To conduct either a randomized block or factorial ANOVA design, first access the SPSS spreadsheet file that contains the sample data. The data file should contain one quantitative variable (the response, or dependent, variable) and two other variables that represent the factors and/or blocks. Next, click on the "Stat" button on the MINITAB menu bar, and then click on "ANOVA" and "Two-Way". (See Figure 10.M.1). The resulting dialog box appears as shown in Figure 10.M.4.

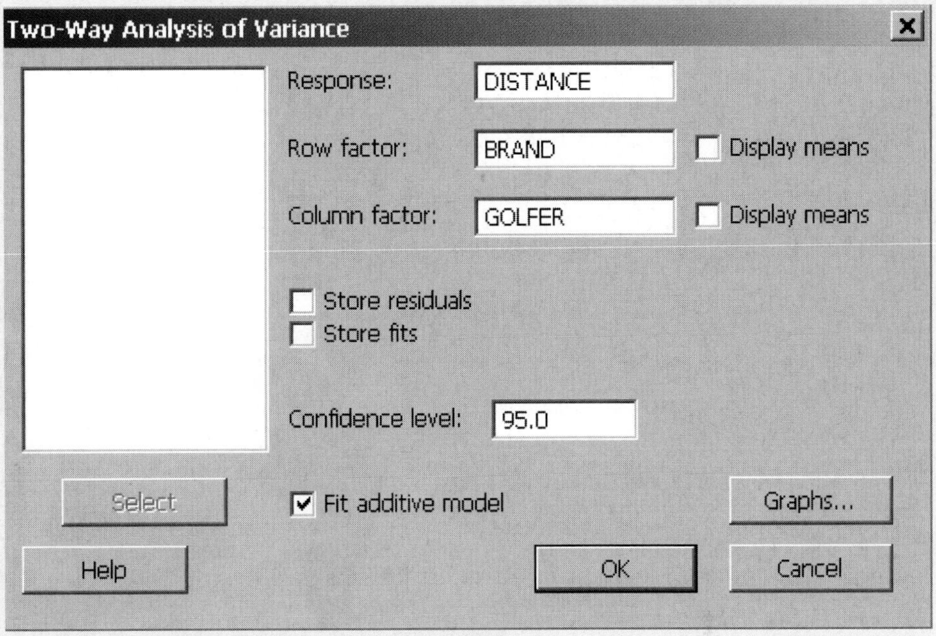

FIGURE 10.M.4
MINITAB two-way ANOVA
dialog box

Specify the response variable in the "Response" box, the first factor variable in the "Row factor" box, and the second factor, or block, variable in the "Column factor" box. If the design is a randomized block, select the "Fit additive model" option as shown in Figure 10.M.4. If the design is factorial, leave the "Fit additive model" option unselected. Click "OK" to generate the MINITAB printout.

[*Note:* Multiple comparisons of treatment means for randomized block and factorial designs are obtained by selecting "Stat", then "ANOVA", then "General Linear Models.".]

11

Simple Linear Regression

STATISTICS IN ACTION

Can Dowsers Really Detect Water?

USING TECHNOLOGY

Simple Linear Regression with MINITAB

WHERE WE'VE BEEN

- Presented methods for estimating and testing population parameters (e.g., the mean, proportion, and variance) for a single sample

- Extended these methods to allow for a comparison of population parameters for multiple samples

WHERE WE'RE GOING

- Introduce the straight-line (*simple linear regression*) model as a means of relating one quantitative variable to another quantitative variable

- Introduce the *correlation coefficient* as a means of relating one quantitative variable to another quantitative variable

- Assess how well the simple linear regression model fits the sample data

- Utilize the simple linear regression model to predict the value of one variable from a specified value of another variable

STATISTICS IN ACTION

Can Dowsers Really Detect Water?

The act of searching for and finding underground supplies of water with the use of nothing more than a divining rod is commonly known as "dowsing." Although widely regarded among scientists as no more than a superstitious relic from medieval times, dowsing remains popular in folklore, and to this day, there are individuals who claim to have this mysterious skill.

Many dowsers in Germany claim that they respond to "earthrays" which emanate from the water source. Earthrays, say the dowsers, are a subtle form of radiation that is potentially hazardous to human health. As a result of these claims, in the mid-1980s the German government conducted a two-year experiment to investigate the possibility that dowsing is a genuine skill. If such a skill could be demonstrated, reasoned government officials, then dangerous levels of radiation in Germany could be detected, avoided, and disposed of.

A group of university physicists in Munich, Germany, was provided a grant of 400,000 marks (about 250,000) to conduct the study. Approximately 500 candidate dowsers were recruited to participate in preliminary tests of their skill. To avoid fraudulent claims, the 43 individuals who seemed to be the most successful in the preliminary tests were selected for the final, carefully controlled, experiment.

The researchers set up a 10-meter-long line on the ground floor of a vacant barn, along which a small wagon could be moved. Attached to the wagon was a short length of pipe, perpendicular to the test line, that was connected by hoses to a pump with running water. The location of the pipe along the line for each trial of the experiment was assigned by a computer-generated random number. On the upper floor of the barn, directly above the experimental line, a 10-meter test line was painted. In each trial, a dowser was admitted to this upper level and required, with his or her rod, stick, or other tool of choice, to ascertain where the pipe with running water on the ground floor was located.

Each dowser participated in at least one test series constituting a sequence of from 5 to 15 trials (typically, 10), with the pipe randomly repositioned after each trial. (Some dowsers undertook only 1 test series, whereas selected others underwent more than 10 test series.) Over the two-year experimental period, the 43 dowsers participated in a total of 843 tests. The experiment was "double blind" in that neither the observer (researcher) on the top floor nor the dowser knew the pipe's location, even after a guess was made. [*Note:* Before the experiment began, a professional magician inspected the entire arrangement for potential deception or cheating by the dowsers.]

For each trial, two variables were recorded: the actual location of the pipe (in decimeters from the beginning of the line) and the dowser's guess (also measured in decimeters). On the basis of an examination of these data, the German physicists concluded in their final report that although most dowsers did not do particularly well in the experiments, "some few dowsers, in particular tests, showed an extraordinarily high rate of success, which can scarcely if at all be explained as due to chance ... a real core of dowser-phenomena can be regarded as empirically proven ... " (Wagner, Betz, and König, 1990. Final Report 01 KB8602, Federal Ministry for Research and Technology.).

This conclusion was critically assessed by Professor J. T. Enright of the University of California at San Diego. (*Skeptical Inquirer*, Jan./Feb. 1999.) In the Statistics in Action Revisited sections of this chapter, we demonstrate how Enright concluded the exact opposite of the German physicists.

Statistics in Action Revisited

- Estimating a Straight-Line Regression Model for the Dowsing Data (p. 571)

- Assessing How Well the Straight-Line Model Fits the Dowsing Data (p. 587)

- Using the Coefficients of Correlation and Determination to Assess the Dowsing Data (p. 598)

- Using the Straight-Line Model to Predict Pipe Location for the Dowsing Data (p. 606)

In Chapters 7–10, we described methods for making inferences about population means. The mean of a population has been treated as a *constant*, and we have shown how to use sample data to estimate or to test hypotheses about this constant mean. In many applications, the mean of a population is not viewed as a constant, but rather as a variable. For example, the mean sale price of residences in a large city might be treated as a variable that depends on the number of square feet of living space in the residence. The relationship might be

$$\text{Mean sale price} = \$30{,}000 + \$60 \, (\text{Square feet})$$

This formula implies that the mean sale price of 1,000-square-foot homes is $90,000, the mean sale price of 2,000-square-foot homes is $150,000, and the mean sale price of 3,000-square-foot homes is $210,000.

In this chapter, we discuss situations in which the mean of the population is treated as a variable, dependent on the value of another variable. The dependence of the residential sale price on the number of square feet of living space is one illustration. Other examples include the dependence of the mean reaction time on the amount of a drug in the bloodstream, the dependence of the mean starting salary of a college graduate on the student's GPA, and the dependence of the mean number of years to which a criminal is sentenced on the number of previous convictions.

Here, we present the simplest of all models relating a populating mean to another variable: the *straight-line model*. We show how to use the sample data to estimate the straight-line relationship between the mean value of one variable, *y*, as it relates to a second variable, *x*. The methodology of estimating and using a straight-line relationship is referred to as *simple linear regression analysis*.

11.1 Probabilistic Models

An important consideration in taking a drug is how it may affect one's perception or general awareness. Suppose you want to model the length of time it takes to respond to a stimulus (a measure of awareness) as a function of the percentage of a certain drug in the bloodstream. The first question to be answered is this: "Do you think that an exact relationship exists between these two variables?" That is, do you think that it is possible to state the exact length of time it takes an individual (subject) to respond if the amount of the drug in the bloodstream is known? We think that you will agree with us that this is *not* possible, for several reasons: The reaction time depends on many variables other than the percentage of the drug in the bloodstream—for example, the time of day, the amount of sleep the subject had the night before, the subject's visual acuity, the subject's general reaction time without the drug, and the subject's age. Even if many variables are included in a model (the topic of Chapter 12), it is still unlikely that we would be able to predict the subject's reaction time *exactly*. There will almost certainly be some variation in response times due strictly to *random phenomena* that cannot be modeled or explained.

If we were to construct a model that hypothesized an exact relationship between variables, it would be called a **deterministic model**. For example, if we believe that *y*, the reaction time (in seconds), will be exactly one-and-one-half times *x*, the amount of drug in the blood, we write

$$y = 1.5x$$

This represents a **deterministic relationship** between the variables *y* and *x*. It implies that *y* can always be determined exactly when the value of *x* is known. *There is no allowance for error in this prediction.*

If, however, we believe that there will be unexplained variation in reaction times—perhaps caused by important, but unincluded, variables or by random phenomena—we discard the deterministic model and use a model that accounts for this **random error**. Our **probabilistic model** will include both a deterministic component and a random-error component. For example, if we hypothesize that the response time *y* is related to the percentage *x* of drug by

$$y = 1.5x + \text{Random error}$$

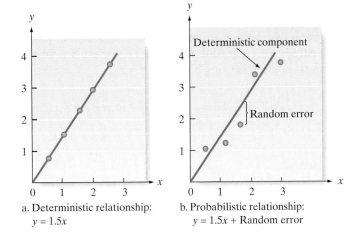

FIGURE 11.1

Possible reaction times y for five different drug percentages x

a. Deterministic relationship:
$y = 1.5x$

b. Probabilistic relationship:
$y = 1.5x +$ Random error

we are hypothesizing a **probabilistic relationship** between y and x. Note that the deterministic component of this probabilistic model is $1.5x$.

Figure 11.1a shows the possible responses for five different values of x, the percentage of drug in the blood, when the model is deterministic. All the responses must fall exactly on the line, because a deterministic model leaves no room for error.

Figure 11.1b shows a possible set of responses for the same values of x when we are using a probabilistic model. Note that the deterministic part of the model (the straight line itself) is the same. Now, however, the inclusion of a random-error component allows the response times to vary from this line. Since we know that the response time does vary randomly for a given value of x, the probabilistic model for y is more realistic than the deterministic model.

General Form of Probabilistic Models

$$y = \text{Deterministic component} + \text{Random error}$$

where y is the variable of interest. We always assume that the mean value of the random error equals 0. This is equivalent to assuming that the mean value of y, $E(y)$, equals the deterministic component of the model; that is,

$$E(y) = \text{Deterministic component}$$

Biography

FRANCIS GALTON
(1822–1911)—
The Law of Universal Regression

Francis Galton was the youngest of seven children born to a middle-class English family of Quaker faith. A cousin of Charles Darwin, Galton attended Trinity College (Cambridge, England) to study medicine. Due to the death of his father, Galton was unable to obtain his degree. His competence in both medicine and mathematics, however, led Galton to pursue a career as a scientist. He made major contributions to the fields of genetics, psychology, meteorology, and anthro-

pology. Some consider Galton to be the first social scientist for his applications of the novel statistical concepts of the time—in particular, regression and correlation. While studying natural inheritance in 1886, Galton collected data on heights of parents and adult children. He noticed the tendency for tall (or short) parents to have tall (or short) children, but that the children were not as tall (or short), on average as their parents. Galton called this phenomenon the "law of universal regression," for the average heights of adult children tended to "regress" to the mean of the population. With the help of his friend and disciple, Karl Pearson, Galton applied the straight-line model to the height data, and the term *regression model* was coined.

In this chapter, we present the simplest of probabilistic models—the **straight-line model**—which gets its name from the fact that the deterministic portion of the model graphs as a straight line. Fitting this model to a set of data is an example of **regression analysis**, or **regression modeling**. The elements of the straight-line model are summarized in the following box:

A First-Order (Straight-Line) Probabilistic Model

$$y = \beta_0 + \beta_1 x + \varepsilon$$

where

y = **Dependent** *or* **response variable** (variable to be modeled)

x = **Independent** *or* **predictor variable** (variable used as a predictor of y)*

$\beta_0 + \beta_1 x = E(y)$ = Deterministic component

ε (epsilon) = Random error component

β_0 (beta zero) = **y-intercept of the line** — that is, the point at which the line intersects, or cuts through, the y-axis (see Figure 11.2)

β_1 (beta one) = **Slope of the line** — that is, the amount of increase (or decrease) in the deterministic component of y for every one-unit increase in x.

[*Note:* A *positive* slope implies that $E(y)$ *increases* by the amount β_1. (See Figure 11.2.) A *negative* slope implies that $E(y)$ *decreases* by the amount β_1.]

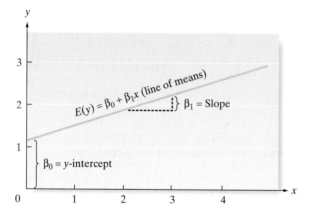

FIGURE 11.2

The straight-line model

In the probabilistic model, the deterministic component is referred to as the **line of means**, because the mean of y, $E(y)$, is equal to the straight-line component of the model. That is,

$$E(y) = \beta_0 + \beta_1 x$$

Note that the Greek symbols β_0 and β_1 respectively represent the y-intercept and slope of the model. They are population parameters that will be known only if we have access to the entire population of (x, y) measurements. Together with a specific value of the independent variable x, they determine the mean value of y, which is just a specific point on the line of means (Figure 11.2).

The values of β_0 and β_1 will be unknown in almost all practical applications of regression analysis. The process of developing a model, estimating the unknown parameters, and using the model can be viewed as the five-step procedure shown in the following box:

*The word *independent* should not be interpreted in a probabilistic sense as defined in Chapter 3. The phrase *independent variable* is used in regression analysis to refer to a predictor variable for the response y.

Step 1   Hypothesize the deterministic component of the model that relates the mean $E(y)$ to the independent variable x (Section 11.2).

Step 2   Use the sample data to estimate unknown parameters in the model (Section 11.2).

Step 3   Specify the probability distribution of the random-error term and estimate the standard deviation of this distribution (Section 11.3).

Step 4   Statistically evaluate the usefulness of the model (Sections 11.4 and 11.5).

Step 5   When satisfied that the model is useful, use it for prediction, estimation, and other purposes (Section 11.6).

Exercises 11.1–11.10

Understanding the Principles

11.1 Why do we generally prefer a probabilistic model to a deterministic model? Give examples for which the two types of models might be appropriate.

11.2 What is the difference between a dependent variable and an independent variable in a probabilistic model?

11.3 What is the line of means?

11.4 If a straight-line probabilistic relationship relates the mean $E(y)$ to an independent variable x, does it imply that every value of the variable y will always fall exactly on the line of means? Why or why not?

Learning the Mechanics

11.5 In each case, graph the line that passes through the given points.
  a. $(1, 1)$ and $(5, 5)$
  b. $(0, 3)$ and $(3, 0)$
  c. $(-1, 1)$ and $(4, 2)$
  d. $(-6, -3)$ and $(2, 6)$

11.6 Give the slope and y-intercept for each of the lines graphed in Exercise 11.5.

11.7 The equation (deterministic) for a straight line is

$$y = \beta_0 + \beta_1 x$$

If the line passes through the point $(-2, 4)$, then $x = -2$, $y = 4$ must satisfy the equation; that is,

$$4 = \beta_0 + \beta_1(-2)$$

Similarly, if the line passes through the point $(4, 6)$, then $x = 4$, $y = 6$ must satisfy the equation; that is,

$$6 = \beta_0 + \beta_1(4)$$

Use these two equations to solve for β_0 and β_1; then find the equation of the line that passes through the points $(-2, 4)$ and $(4, 6)$. $\beta_1 = \frac{1}{3}; \beta_0 = \frac{14}{3}$

11.8 Refer to Exercise 11.7. Find the equations of the lines that pass through the points listed in Exercise 11.5.

11.9 Plot the following lines:
  a. $y = 4 + x$ **b.** $y = 5 - 2x$
  c. $y = -4 + 3x$ **d.** $y = -2x$
  e. $y = x$ **f.** $y = .50 + 1.5x$

11.10 Give the slope and y-intercept for each of the lines defined in Exercise 11.9.

11.2 Fitting the Model: The Least Squares Approach

After the straight-line model has been hypothesized to relate the mean $E(y)$ to the independent variable x, the next step is to collect data and to estimate the (unknown) population parameters, the y-intercept β_0 and the slope β_1.

To begin with a simple example, suppose an experiment involving five subjects is conducted to determine the relationship between the percentage of a certain drug in the bloodstream and the length of time it takes to react to a stimulus. The results are shown in Table 11.1. (The number of measurements and the measurements themselves are unrealistically simple in order to avoid arithmetic confusion in this introductory example.) This set of data will be used to demonstrate the five-step procedure of regression modeling given in the previous section. In the current section, we hypothesize the deterministic component of the model and estimate its unknown parameters (steps 1 and 2). The model's assumptions and the random-error component (step 3) are the subjects of Section 11.3, whereas Sections 11.4 and 11.5 assess the utility of the model (step 4). Finally, we use the model for prediction and estimation (step 5) in Section 11.6.

STIMULUS

TABLE 11.1 Reaction Time versus Drug Percentage

Subject	Percent x of Drug	Reaction Time y (seconds)
1	1	1
2	2	1
3	3	2
4	4	2
5	5	4

Step 1 *Hypothesize the deterministic component of the probabilistic model.* As stated before, we will consider only straight-line models in this chapter. Thus, the complete model relating mean response time $E(y)$ to drug percentage x is given by

$$E(y) = \beta_0 + \beta_1 x$$

Step 2 *Use sample data to estimate unknown parameters in the model.* This step is the subject of this section—namely, how can we best use the information in the sample of five observations in Table 11.1 to estimate the unknown y-intercept β_0 and slope β_1?

To determine whether a linear relationship between y and x is plausible, it is helpful to plot the sample data in a **scattergram**. Recall (Section 2.9) that a scattergram locates each data point on a graph, as shown in Figure 11.3 for the five data points of Table 11.1. Note that the scattergram suggests a general tendency for y to increase as x increases. If you place a ruler on the scattergram, you will see that a line may be drawn through three of the five points, as shown in Figure 11.4. To obtain the equation of this visually fitted line, note that the line intersects the y-axis at $y = -1$, so the y-intercept is -1. Also, y increases exactly one unit for every one-unit increase in x, indicating that the slope is $+1$. Therefore, the equation is

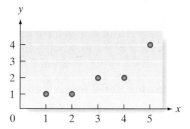

FIGURE 11.3

Scattergram for data in Table 11.1

$$\tilde{y} = -1 + 1(x) = -1 + x$$

where $\tilde{y}$ is used to denote the y that is predicted from the visual model.

One way to decide quantitatively how well a straight line fits a set of data is to note the extent to which the data points deviate from the line. For example, to evaluate the model in Figure 11.4, we calculate the magnitude of the *deviations* (i.e., the differences between the observed and the predicted values of y). These deviations, or **errors of prediction**, are the vertical distances between observed and predicted values (see Figure 11.4). The observed and predicted values of y, their differences, and their squared differences are shown in Table 11.2. Note that the *sum of errors* equals 0 and the *sum of squares of the errors* (SSE), which places a greater emphasis on large deviations of the points from the line, is equal to 2.

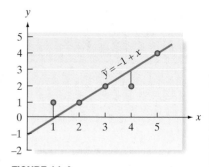

FIGURE 11.4

Visual straight line fitted to the data in Figure 11.3

TABLE 11.2 Comparing Observed and Predicted Values for the Visual Model

x	y	$\tilde{y} = -1 + x$	$(y - \tilde{y})$	$(y - \tilde{y})^2$
1	1	0	$(1 - 0) = 1$	1
2	1	1	$(1 - 1) = 0$	0
3	2	2	$(2 - 2) = 0$	0
4	2	3	$(2 - 3) = -1$	1
5	4	4	$(4 - 4) = 0$	0
			Sum of errors = 0	Sum of squared errors (SSE) = 2

You can see by shifting the ruler around the graph that it is possible to find many lines for which the sum of errors is equal to 0, but it can be shown that there is one (and only one) line for which the SSE is a *minimum*. This line is called the **least squares line**, the **regression line**, or the **least squares prediction equation**. The methodology used to obtain that line is called the **method of least squares**.

Now Work Exercise 11.16a–d

To find the least squares prediction equation for a set of data, assume that we have a sample of n data points consisting of pairs of values of x and y, say, $(x_1, y_1), (x_2, y_2), \ldots, (x_n, y_n)$. For example, the $n = 5$ data points shown in Table 11.2 are $(1, 1), (2, 1), (3, 2), (4, 2),$ and $(5, 4)$. The fitted line, which we will calculate on the basis of the five data points, is written as

$$\hat{y} = \hat{\beta}_0 + \hat{\beta}_1 x$$

The "hats" indicate that the symbols below them are estimates: $\hat{y}$ (y-hat) is an estimator of the mean value of y, $E(y)$, and is a predictor of some future value of y; and $\hat{\beta}_0$ and $\hat{\beta}_1$ are estimators of β_0 and β_1, respectively.

For a given data point—say, the point (x_i, y_i),—the observed value of y is y_i and the predicted value of y would be obtained by substituting x_i into the prediction equation:

$$\hat{y}_i = \hat{\beta}_0 + \hat{\beta}_1 x_i$$

The deviation of the ith value of y from its predicted value is

$$(y_i - \hat{y}_i) = [y_i - (\hat{\beta}_0 + \hat{\beta}_1 x_i)]$$

Then the sum of the squares of the deviations of the y-values about their predicted values for all the n data points is

$$\text{SSE} = \sum [y_i - (\hat{\beta}_0 + \hat{\beta}_1 x_i)]^2$$

The quantities $\hat{\beta}_0$ and $\hat{\beta}_1$ that make the SSE a minimum are called the **least squares estimates** of the population parameters β_0 and β_1, and the prediction equation $\hat{y} = \hat{\beta}_0 + \hat{\beta}_1 x$ is called the *least squares line*.

Definition 11.1

The **least squares line** $\hat{y} = \hat{\beta}_0 + \hat{\beta}_1 x$ is the line that has the following two properties:

1. The sum of the errors (SE) equals 0.
2. The sum of squared errors (SSE) is smaller than that for any other straight-line model

The values of $\hat{\beta}_0$ and $\hat{\beta}_1$ that minimize the SSE are given by the formulas in the following box (proof omitted):*

Formulas for the Least Squares Estimates

Slope: $\hat{\beta}_1 = \dfrac{SS_{xy}}{SS_{xx}}$

y-intercept: $\hat{\beta}_0 = \bar{y} - \hat{\beta}_1 \bar{x}$

where

$$SS_{xy} = \sum(x_i - \bar{x})(y_i - \bar{y}) = \sum x_i y_i - \frac{\left(\sum x_i\right)\left(\sum y_i\right)}{n}$$

$$SS_{xx} = \sum(x_i - \bar{x})^2 = \sum x_i^2 - \frac{\left(\sum x_i\right)^2}{n}$$

n = Sample size

EXAMPLE 11.1

APPLYING THE METHOD OF LEAST SQUARES— Drug Reaction Data

Problem Refer to the reaction data presented in Table 11.1. Consider the straight-line model $E(y) = \beta_0 + \beta_1 x$, where y = reaction time (in seconds) and x = percent of drug received.

a. Use the method of least squares to estimate the values of β_0 and β_1.

b. Predict the reaction time when $x = 2\%$.

c. Find SSE for the analysis.

d. Give practical interpretations of $\hat{\beta}_0$ and $\hat{\beta}_1$.

Solution

a. Preliminary computations for finding the least squares line for the drug reaction example are presented in Table 11.3. We can now calculate

$$SS_{xy} = \sum x_i y_i - \frac{\left(\sum x_i\right)\left(\sum y_i\right)}{5} = 37 - \frac{(15)(10)}{5} = 37 - 30 = 7$$

$$SS_{xx} = \sum x_i^2 - \frac{\left(\sum x_i\right)^2}{5} = 55 - \frac{(15)^2}{5} = 55 - 45 = 10$$

TABLE 11.3 Preliminary Computations for the Drug Reaction Example

	x_i	y_i	x_i^2	$x_i y_i$
	1	1	1	1
	2	1	4	2
	3	2	9	6
	4	2	16	8
	5	4	25	20
Totals	$\sum x_i = 15$	$\sum y_i = 10$	$\sum x_i^2 = 55$	$\sum x_i y_i = 37$

*Students who are familiar with calculus should note that the values of β_0 and β_1 that minimize SSE = $\sum(y_i - \hat{y}_i)^2$ are obtained by setting the two partial derivatives $\partial SSE/\partial \beta_0$ and $\partial SSE/\partial \beta_1$ equal to 0. The solutions of these two equations yield the formulas shown in the box. Furthermore, we denote the sample solutions of the equations by $\hat{\beta}_0$ and $\hat{\beta}_1$, where the "hat" denotes that these are sample estimates of the true population intercept β_0 and slope β_1.

Then the slope of the least squares line is

$$\hat{\beta}_1 = \frac{SS_{xy}}{SS_{xx}} = \frac{7}{10} = .7$$

and the y-intercept is

$$\hat{\beta}_0 = \bar{y} - \hat{\beta}_1\bar{x} = \frac{\sum y_i}{5} - \hat{\beta}_1\frac{\sum x_i}{5}$$

$$= \frac{10}{5} - (.7)\left(\frac{15}{5}\right) = 2 - (.7)(3) = 2 - 2.1 = -.1$$

The least squares line is thus

$$\hat{y} = \hat{\beta}_0 + \hat{\beta}_1 x = -.1 + .7x$$

The graph of this line is shown in Figure 11.5.

b. The predicted value of y for a given value of x can be obtained by substituting into the formula for the least squares line. Thus, when $x = 2$, we predict y to be

$$\hat{y} = -.1 + .7x = -.1 + .7(2) = 1.3$$

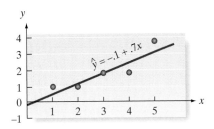

We show how to find a prediction interval for y in Section 11.6.

FIGURE 11.5

The line $\hat{y} = -.1 + .7x$ fitted to the data

c. The observed and predicted values of y, the deviations of the y values about their predicted values, and the squares of these deviations are shown in Table 11.4. Note that the sum of the squares of the deviations, SSE, is 1.10 and (as we would expect) this is less than the SSE = 2.0 obtained in Table 11.2 for the visually fitted line.

d. The estimated y-intercept, $\hat{\beta}_0 = -.1$, appears to imply that the estimated mean reaction time is equal to $-.1$ second when the percent x of drug is equal to 0%. Since negative reaction times are not possible, this seems to make the model nonsensical. However, *the model parameters should be interpreted only within the sampled range of the independent variable*—in this case, for amounts of drug in the bloodstream between 1% and 5%. Thus, the y-intercept—which is, by definition, at $x = 0$ (0% drug)—is not within the range of the sampled values of x and is not subject to meaningful interpretation.

The slope of the least squares line, $\hat{\beta} = .7$, implies that for every unit increase in x, the mean value of y is estimated to increase by .7 unit. In terms of this example, for every 1% increase in the amount of drug in the bloodstream, the mean reaction time is estimated to increase by .7 second *over the sampled range of drug amounts from 1% to 5%*. Thus, the model does not imply that increasing the drug amount from 5% to 10% will result in an increase in mean reaction time of 3.5 seconds, because the range of x in the sample does not extend to 10% ($x = 10$). In fact, 10% might be such a high concentration that the drug would kill the subject! Be careful to interpret the estimated parameters only within the sampled range of x.

TABLE 11.4 Comparing Observed and Predicted Values for the Least Squares Prediction Equation

x	y	$\hat{y} = -.1 + .7x$	$(y - \hat{y})$	$(y - \hat{y})^2$
1	1	.6	$(1 - .6) = .4$	.16
2	1	1.3	$(1 - 1.3) = -.3$	.09
3	2	2.0	$(2 - 2.0) = 0$	.00
4	2	2.7	$(2 - 2.7) = -.7$	.49
5	4	3.4	$(4 - 3.4) = .6$	.36
			Sum of errors $= 0$	SSE $= 1.10$

Look Back The calculations required to obtain $\hat{\beta}_0$, $\hat{\beta}_1$, and SSE in simple linear regression, although straightforward, can become rather tedious. Even with the use of a pocket calculator, the process is laborious and susceptible to error, especially when the sample size is large. Fortunately, the use of statistical computer software can significantly reduce the labor involved in regression calculations. The SAS, SPSS, and MINITAB outputs for the simple linear regression of the data in Table 11.1 are displayed in Figure 11.6a–c. The

Dependent Variable: TIME_Y

Number of Observations Read	5
Number of Observations Used	5

Analysis of Variance

Source	DF	Sum of Squares	Mean Square	F Value	Pr > F
Model	1	4.90000	4.90000	13.36	0.0354
Error	3	1.10000	0.36667		
Corrected Total	4	6.00000			

Root MSE	0.60553	R-Square	0.8167
Dependent Mean	2.00000	Adj R-Sq	0.7556
Coeff Var	30.27650		

Parameter Estimates

Variable	DF	Parameter Estimate	Standard Error	t Value	Pr > |t|
Intercept	1	-0.10000	0.63509	-0.16	0.8849
DRUG_X	1	0.70000	0.19149	3.66	0.0354

FIGURE 11.6a

SAS printout for the time–drug regression

Model Summary

Model	R	R Square	Adjusted R Square	Std. Error of the Estimate
1	.904[a]	.817	.756	.606

a. Predictors: (Constant), DRUG_X

ANOVA[b]

Model		Sum of Squares	df	Mean Square	F	Sig.
1	Regression	4.900	1	4.900	13.364	.035[a]
	Residual	1.100	3	.367		
	Total	6.000	4			

a. Predictors: (Constant), DRUG_X

b. Dependent Variable: TIME_Y

Coefficients[a]

Model		Unstandardized Coefficients		Standardized Coefficients	t	Sig.
		B	Std. Error	Beta		
1	(Constant)	-.100	.635		-.157	.885
	DRUG_X	.700	.191	.904	3.656	.035

a. Dependent Variable: TIME_Y

FIGURE 11.6b

SPSS printout for the time–drug regression

Regression Analysis: TIME_Y versus DRUG_X

```
The regression equation is
TIME_Y = - 0.100 + 0.700 DRUG_X


Predictor      Coef   SE Coef       T      P
Constant    -0.1000    0.6351   -0.16  0.885
DRUG_X       0.7000    0.1915    3.66  0.035


S = 0.605530    R-Sq = 81.7%    R-Sq(adj) = 75.6%


Analysis of Variance

Source          DF       SS       MS       F      P
Regression       1   4.9000   4.9000   13.36  0.035
Residual Error   3   1.1000   0.3667
Total            4   6.0000
```

FIGURE 11.6c

MINITAB printout for the time–drug regression

values of $\hat{\beta}_0$ and $\hat{\beta}_1$ are highlighted on the printouts. These values, $\hat{\beta}_0 = -.1$ and $\hat{\beta}_1 = .7$, agree exactly with our hand-calculated values. The value of SSE $= 1.10$ is also highlighted on the printouts.

Now Work Exercise 11.23

Simple Linear Regression

Using the TI-84/TI-83 Graphing Calculator

I. Finding the least squares regression equation

Step 1 *Enter the data.*
Press **STAT** and select **1:Edit**.
(*Note*: If a list already contains data, clear the old data.)
Use the up arrow to highlight the list name, "**L1**" or "**L2**".
Press **CLEAR ENTER**.
Enter your *x*-data into **L1** and your *y*-data into **L2**.

Step 2 *Find the equation.*

Press **STAT** and highlight **CALC**.
Press **4** for **LinReg(ax + b)**.
Press **ENTER**.
The screen will show the values for *a* and *b* in the equation $y = ax + b$.

Example The following figures show a table of data entered on the TI-84/TI-83 and the regression equation obtained by following the preceding steps.

```
L1      L2    L3    2      LinReg
2       67    ------        y=ax+b
1.9     68                  a=2.495967742
2.3     70                  b=63.3391129
3.9     74
6.4     78
7.4     81
6.8     82

L2(7) =82
```

II. Graphing the least squares line with the scatterplot

Step 1 *Enter the data as shown in part I.*

Step 2 *Set up the data plot.*

Press **Y =** and **CLEAR** all functions from the Y register.
Press **2nd Y =** for **STAT PLOT**.

(continued)

Press **1** for **Plot 1**.
Set the cursor so that **ON** is flashing, and press **ENTER**.
For **Type**, use the **ARROW** and **ENTER** keys to highlight and select the scatterplot (first icon in the first row).
For **Xlist**, choose the column containing the *x*-data.
For **Ylist**, choose the column containing the *y*-data.

Step 3   *Find the regression equation and store the equation in Y1.*

Press **STAT** and highlight **CALC**.
Press **4** for **LinReg(ax + b)** (*Note*: Don't press ENTER here, because you want to store the regression equation in Y1.)
Press **VARS**.
Use the right arrow to highlight **Y-VARS**.
Press **ENTER** to select **1:Function**.
Press **ENTER** to select **1:Y1**.
Press **ENTER**.

Step 4   *View the scatterplot and regression line.*

Press **ZOOM**, and then press **9** to select **9:ZoomStat**.
You should see the data graphed along with the regression line.

Example   The figure shows a graph of the scatterplot and least squares line obtained by following the preceding steps.

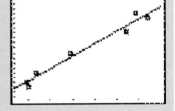

ACTIVITY 11.1: *Keep the Change:* Least Squares Models

In this activity, you will once again use data collected in Activity 1.1, *Keep the Change: Collecting Data* (p. 12). For each student in your class, collect the sum of the data set Purchase Total, the sum of the data set. *Amounts Transferred*, and the number of purchases (the number of data items in the set *Purchase Totals*).

1. For each student in your class, form the ordered pair

(*Sum of Purchase Totals, Sum of Amounts Transferred*)

Use these ordered pairs to create a scattergram. Then use the ordered pairs to find the values of $\hat{\beta}_0$ and $\hat{\beta}_1$ in the least squares line for the data.

2. Suppose that three customers have made only one debit-card purchase each, as shown in the following table:

Customer	Purchases	Actual Amount Transferred	Estimated Amount Transferred	Difference
A	$ 3.49			
B	$ 30.49			
C	$300.49			

Complete the table by first finding the actual amount that will be transferred for each customer. Then use the least squares line $y = \hat{\beta}_0 + \hat{\beta}_1 x$ from Exercise 1 to estimate the amount transferred. Finally, calculate the difference between the actual and estimated amounts for each customer.

3. On the basis of your results in Exercise 2, comment on the utility of using your model from Exercise 1 to estimate the transferred amounts. Do you believe that the least squares model is an appropriate model in this situation? Explain.

4. For each student in your class, form the ordered pair

(*Number of Purchases, Sum of Amounts Transferred*)

Use these ordered pairs to create a scattergram. Then use the ordered pairs to find the values of $\hat{\beta}_0$ and $\hat{\beta}_1$ in the least squares line for the data. Create your own hypothetical data as in Exercise 2 to test your model. Do you believe that this model is more or less useful than the model of Exercise 1? Explain.

Even when the interpretations of the estimated parameters in a simple linear regression are meaningful, we need to remember that they are only estimates based on the sample. As such, their values will typically change in repeated sampling. How much confidence do we have that the estimated slope $\hat{\beta}_1$ accurately approximates the true slope

β_1? Determining this requires statistical inference, in the form of confidence intervals and tests of hypotheses, which we address in Section 11.5.

To summarize, we defined the best-fitting straight line to be the line that minimizes the sum of squared errors around it, and we called it the least squares line. We should interpret the least squares line only within the sampled range of the independent variable. In subsequent sections, we show how to make statistical inferences about the model.

STATISTICS IN ACTION REVISITED

Estimating a Straight-Line Regression Model for the Dowsing Data

After conducting a series of experiments in a Munich barn, a group of German physicists concluded that dowsing (i.e., the ability to find underground water with a divining rod) "can be regarded as empirically proven." This observation was based on the data collected on 3 (of the participating 500) dowsers who had particularly impressive results. All of these "best" dowsers (numbered 99, 18, and 108) performed the experiment multiple times, and the best test series (sequence of trials) for each of them was identified. These data, saved in the **DOWSING** file, are listed in Table SIA11.1.

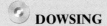 **DOWSING**

TABLE SIA11.1 Dowsing Trial Results: Best Series for the Three Best Dowsers

Trial	Dowser Number	Pipe Location	Dowser's Guess
1	99	4	4
2	99	5	87
3	99	30	95
4	99	35	74
5	99	36	78
6	99	58	65
7	99	40	39
8	99	70	75
9	99	74	32
10	99	98	100
11	18	7	10
12	18	38	40
13	18	40	30
14	18	49	47
15	18	75	9
16	18	82	95
17	108	5	52
18	108	18	16
19	108	33	37
20	108	45	40
21	108	38	66
22	108	50	58
23	108	52	74
24	108	63	65
25	108	72	60
26	108	95	49

Source: Enright, J. T. "Testing dowsing: The failure of the Munich experiments," *Skeptical Inquirer*, Jan./Feb. 1999, p. 45 (Figure 6a).

Recall (p. 559) that for various hidden pipe locations, each dowser guessed where the pipe with running water was located. Let x = dowser's guess (in meters) and y = pipe location (in meters) for each trial. One way to determine whether the "best" dowsers are effective is to fit the straight-line model $E(y) = \beta_0 + \beta_1 x$ to the data in Table SIA11.1.

A MINITAB scatterplot of the data is shown in Figure SIA11.1. The least squares line, obtained from the MINITAB regression printout shown in Figure SIA11.2, is also displayed on the scatterplot. Although the least squares line has a slight upward trend, the variation of the data points around the line is large. It does not appear that a dowser's guess (x) will be a very

(continued)

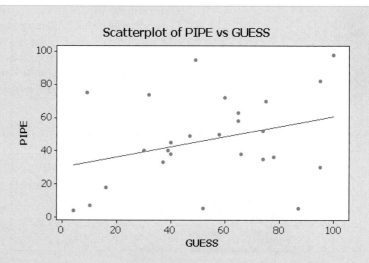

FIGURE SIA11.1
MINITAB scatterplot of dowsing data

good predictor of the actual pipe location (y). In fact, the estimated slope (obtained from Figure SIA11.2) is $\hat{\beta}_1 = .31$. Thus, for every 1-meter increase in a dowser's guess, we estimate that the actual pipe location will increase only .31 meter. In the Statistics in Action Revisited sections that follow, we will provide a measure of reliability for this inference and investigate the phenomenon of dowsing further.

FIGURE SIA11.2
MINITAB simple linear regression for dowsing data

```
Regression Analysis: PIPE versus GUESS

The regression equation is
PIPE = 30.1 + 0.308 GUESS


Predictor     Coef   SE Coef     T       P
Constant     30.07     11.41   2.63   0.015
GUESS       0.3079    0.1900   1.62   0.118


S = 26.0298    R-Sq = 9.9%    R-Sq(adj) = 6.1%


Analysis of Variance

Source           DF        SS       MS      F       P
Regression        1    1778.9   1778.9   2.63   0.118
Residual Error   24   16261.2    677.6
Total            25   18040.2
```

Exercises 11.11–11.31

Understanding the Principles

11.11 In regression, what is an error of prediction?

11.12 Give two properties of the line estimated with the method of least squares.

11.13 *True or False.* The estimates of β_0 and β_1 should be interpreted only within the sampled range of the independent variable, x.

Learning the Mechanics

11.14 The accompanying table is similar to Table 11.3. It is used to make the preliminary computations for finding the least squares line for the given pairs of x and y values.
  a. Complete the table.   **b.** Find SS_{xy}.
  c. Find SS_{xx}.   **d.** Find $\hat{\beta}_1$.
  e. Find $\bar{x}$ and $\bar{y}$.   **f.** Find $\hat{\beta}_0$.
  g. Find the least squares line.

x_i	y_i	x_i^2	$x_i y_i$
7	2	—	—
4	4	—	—
6	2	—	—
2	5	—	—
1	7	—	—
1	6	—	—
3	5	—	—
Totals $\sum x_i =$	$\sum y_i =$	$\sum x_i^2 =$	$\sum x_i y_i =$

11.15 Refer to Exercise 11.14. After the least squares line has been obtained, the following table (which is similar to Table 11.4) can be used (1) to compare the observed and the predicted values of y and (2) to compute SSE.

x	y	$\hat{y}$	$(y - \hat{y})$	$(y - \hat{y})^2$
7	2	—	—	—
4	4	—	—	—
6	2	—	—	—
2	5	—	—	—
1	7	—	—	—
1	6	—	—	—
3	5	—	—	—
		$\sum(y - \hat{y}) =$	SSE $= \sum(y - \hat{y})^2 =$	

a. Complete the table.

b. Plot the least squares line on a scattergram of the data. Plot the following line on the same graph:

$$\hat{y} = 14 - 2.5x$$

c. Show that SSE is larger for the line in part **b** than it is for the least squares line.

11.16 Construct a scattergram of the data in the following
NW table.

x	.5	1	1.5
y	2	1	3

a. Plot the following two lines on your scattergram:

$$\hat{y} = 3 - x \quad \text{and} \quad \hat{y} = 1 + x$$

b. Which of these lines would you choose to characterize the relationship between x and y? Explain.

c. Show that the sum of errors for both of these lines equals 0.

d. Which of these lines has the smaller SSE?

e. Find the least squares line for the data, and compare it with the two lines described in part **a**.

11.17 Consider the following pairs of measurements:

x	5	3	−1	2	7	6	4
y	4	3	0	1	8	5	3

a. Construct a scattergram of these data.

b. What does the scattergram suggest about the relationship between x and y?

c. Given that $SS_{xx} = 43.4286$, $SS_{xy} = 39.8571$, $\bar{y} = 3.4286$, and $\bar{x} = 3.7143$, calculate the least squares estimates of β_0 and β_1.

d. Plot the least squares line on your scattergram. Does the line appear to fit the data well? Explain.

e. Interpret the y-intercept and slope of the least squares line. Over what range of x are these interpretations meaningful?

APPLET Applet Exercise 11.1

Use the applet entitled *Regression by Eye* to explore the relationship between the pattern of data in a scattergram and the corresponding least squares model.

a. Run the applet several times. For each time, attempt to move the green line into a position that appears to minimize the vertical distances of the points from the line. Then click *Show regression line* to see the actual regression line. How close is your line to the actual line? Click *New data* to reset the applet.

b. Click the trash can to clear the graph. Use the mouse to place five points on the scattergram that are approximately in a straight line. Then move the green line to approximate the regression line. Click *Show regression line* to see the actual regression line. How close were you this time?

c. Continue to clear the graph, and plot sets of five points with different patterns among the points. Use the green line to approximate the regression line. How close do you come to the actual regression line each time?

d. On the basis of your experiences with the applet, explain why we need to use more reliable methods of finding the regression line than just "eyeing" it.

Applying the Concepts—Basic

11.18 **Quantitative models of music.** Writing in *Chance* (Fall 2004), University of Konstanz (Germany) statistics professor Jan Beran demonstrated that certain aspects of music can be described by quantitative models. For example, the information content of a musical composition (called *entropy*) can be quantified by determining how many times a certain pitch occurs. In a sample of 147 famous compositions ranging from the 13th to the 20th century, Beran computed the Z12-note entropy (y) and plotted it against the year of birth (x) of the composer. The graph is reproduced here.

a. Do you observe a trend, especially since the year 1400?

b. The least squares line for the data since 1400 is shown on the graph. Is the slope of the line positive or negative? What does this imply?

c. Explain why the line shown is not the true line of means.

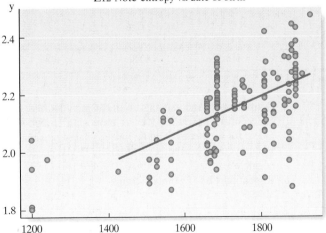

Z12-Note-entropy vs. date of birth

11.19 **Wind turbine blade stress.** Mechanical engineers at the University of Newcastle (Australia) investigated the use of timber in high-efficiency small wind turbine blades (*Wind Engineering*, Jan. 2004). The strengths of two types of timber—radiata pine and hoop pine—were compared.

Twenty specimens (called "coupons") of each timber blade were fatigue tested by measuring the stress (in MPa) on the blade after various numbers of blade cycles. A simple linear regression analysis of the data, one conducted for each type of timber, yielded the following results (where y = stress and x = natural logarithm of number of cycles):

$$\text{Radiata Pine: } \hat{y} = 97.37 - 2.50x$$
$$\text{Hoop Pine: } \hat{y} = 122.03 - 2.36x$$

a. Interpret the estimated slope of each line.
b. Interpret the estimated y-intercept of each line.
c. On the basis of these results, which type of timber blade appears to be stronger and more fatigue resistant? Explain.

11.20 **Winning marathon times.** In *Chance* (Winter 2000), statistician Howard Wainer and two students compared men's and women's winning times in the Boston Marathon. One of the graphs used to illustrate gender differences is reproduced here. The scattergram plots the winning times (in minutes) against the year in which the race was run. Men's times are represented by purple dots and women's times by red dots.

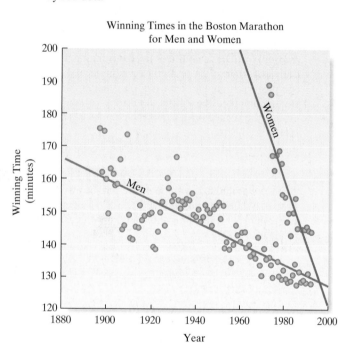

Winning Times in the Boston Marathon for Men and Women

a. Consider only the winning times for men. Is there evidence of a linear trend? If so, propose a straight-line model for predicting winning time (y) based on year (x). Would you expect the slope of this line to be positive or negative?
b. Repeat part **b** for women's times.

c. Which slope, the men's or the women's, will be greater in absolute value?
d. Would you recommend using the straight-line models to predict the winning time in the 2020 Boston Marathon? Why or why not?

11.21 **College protests of labor exploitation.** Refer to the *Journal of World-Systems Research* (Winter 2004) study of student "sit-ins" for a "sweat-free campus" at universities, presented in Exercise 2.145 (p. 93). Recall that the **SITIN** file contains data on the duration (in days) of each sit-in, as well as the number of student arrests. The data for 5 sit-ins in which there was at least one arrest are shown in the accompanying table. Let y = number of arrests and x = duration.
a. Give the equation of a straight-line model relating y to x.
b. SPSS was used to fit the model to the data for the 5 sit-ins. The SPSS printout is shown at the bottom of the page. Give the least squares prediction equation.
c. Interpret the estimates of β_0 and β_1 in the context of the problem.

SITIN2 (Selected observations)

Sit-In	University	Duration (days)	Number of Arrests
12	Wisconsin	4	54
14	SUNY Albany	1	11
15	Oregon	3	14
17	Iowa	4	16
18	Kentucky	1	12

Source: Ross, R. J. S. "From antisweatshop to global justice to antiwar: How the new new left is the same and different from the old new left," *Journal of Word-Systems Research*, Vol. X, No. 1, Winter 2004 (Tables 1 and 3).

GOBIANTS

11.22 **Mongolian desert ants.** Refer to the *Journal of Biogeography* (Dec. 2003) study of ants in Mongolia, presented in Exercise 2.147 (p. 93). Data on annual rainfall, maximum daily temperature, and number of ant species recorded at each of 11 study sites are listed in the next table.
a. Consider a straight-line model relating annual rainfall (y) and maximum daily temperature (x). A MINITAB printout of the simple linear regression is shown (p. 575). Give the least squares prediction equation.
b. Construct a scatterplot for the analysis you performed in part **a**. Include the least square line on the plot. Does the line appear to be a good predictor of annual rainfall?
c. Now consider a straight-line model relating number of ant species (y) to annual rainfall (x). On the basis of the MINITAB printout (p. 575), repeat parts **a** and **b**.

Coefficients[a]

Model		Unstandardized Coefficients		Standardized Coefficients	t	Sig.
		B	Std. Error	Beta		
1	(Constant)	2.522	16.352		.154	.887
	DURATION	7.261	5.576	.601	1.302	.284

SPSS output for Exercise 11.21   a. Dependent Variable: ARRESTS

Regression Analysis: Rain versus Temp

```
The regression equation is
Rain = 295 - 16.4 Temp

Predictor        Coef    SE Coef      T       P
Constant       295.25      22.41  13.18   0.000
Temp          -16.364       2.346  -6.97   0.000

S = 17.5111    R-Sq = 84.4%    R-Sq(adj) = 82.7%

Analysis of Variance
Source            DF      SS       MS       F       P
Regression         1   14915    14915   48.64   0.000
Residual Error     9    2760      307
Total             10   17675
```

Regression Analysis: AntSpecies versus Rain

```
The regression equation is
AntSpecies = 10.5 + 0.016 Rain

Predictor        Coef    SE Coef      T       P
Constant       10.52       22.03   0.48   0.644
Rain          0.0160      0.1480   0.11   0.916

S = 19.6726    R-Sq = 0.1%    R-Sq(adj) = 0.0%

Analysis of Variance
Source            DF      SS       MS       F       P
Regression         1     4.5      4.5    0.01   0.916
Residual Error     9  3483.1    387.0
Total             10  3487.6
```

MINITAB output for
Exercise 11.22

GOBIANTS

Site	Region	Annual Rainfall (mm)	Max. Daily Temp. (°C)	Number of Ant Species
1	Dry Steppe	196	5.7	3
2	Dry Steppe	196	5.7	3
3	Dry Steppe	179	7.0	52
4	Dry Steppe	197	8.0	7
5	Dry Steppe	149	8.5	5
6	Gobi Desert	112	10.7	49
7	Gobi Desert	125	11.4	5
8	Gobi Desert	99	10.9	4
9	Gobi Desert	125	11.4	4
10	Gobi Desert	84	11.4	5
11	Gobi Desert	115	11.4	4

Source: Pfeiffer, M., et al. "Community organization and species richness of ants in Mongolia along an ecological gradient from steppe to Gobi desert." *Journal of Biogeography*, Vol. 30, No. 12, Dec. 2003 (Tables 1 and 2).

11.23 **Redshifts of Quasi Stellar Objects.** Astronomers call a shift in the spectrum of galaxies a "redshift." A correlation between redshift level and apparent magnitude (i.e., brightness on a logarithmic scale) of a quasi-stellar object was discovered and reported in the *Journal of Astrophysics & Astronomy* (Mar./Jun. 2003). Physicist D. Basu (Carleton University, Ottawa) applied simple linear regression to data collected for a sample of over 6,000 quasi-stellar objects with confirmed redshifts. The analysis yielded the following results for a specific range of magnitudes: $\hat{y} = 18.13 + 6.21x$, where y = magnitude and x = redshift level.

a. Graph the least squares line. Is the slope of the line positive or negative?

b. Interpret the estimate of the y-intercept in the words of the problem.

c. Interpret the estimate of the slope in the words of the problem.

Applying the Concepts—Intermediate

11.24 **Extending the life of an aluminum smelter pot.** An investigation of the properties of bricks used to line aluminum smelter pots was published in *The American Ceramic Society Bulletin* (Feb. 2005). Six different commercial bricks were evaluated. The life span of a smelter pot depends on the porosity of the brick lining (the less porosity, the longer is the life); consequently, the researchers measured the apparent porosity of each brick specimen, as well as the mean pore diameter of each brick. The data are given in the next table:

a. Find the least squares line relating porosity (y) to mean pore diameter (x).

b. Interpret the y-intercept of the line.

c. Interpret the slope of the line.

d. Predict the apparent percentage of porosity for a brick with a mean pore diameter of 10 micrometers.

SMELTPOT

Brick	Apparent Porosity (%)	Mean Pore Diameter (micrometers)
A	18.8	12.0
B	18.3	9.7
C	16.3	7.3
D	6.9	5.3
E	17.1	10.9
F	20.4	16.8

Source: Bonadia, P., et al. "Aluminosilicate refractories for aluminum cell linings," *The American Ceramic Society Bulletin*, Vol. 84, No. 2, Feb. 2005 (Table II).

11.25 Ranking driving performance of professional golfers. Refer to *The Sport Journal* (Winter 2007) study of a new method for ranking the total driving performance of golfers on the Professional Golf Association (PGA) tour, presented in Exercise 2.60 (p. 59). Recall that the method computes a driving performance index based on a golfer's average driving distance (yards) and driving accuracy (percent of drives that land in the fairway). Data for the top 40 PGA golfers (as ranked by the new method) are saved in the **PGADRIVER** file. (The first five and last five observations are listed in the accompanying table.)
  a. Write the equation of a straight-line model relating driving accuracy (y) to diving distance (x).
  b. Use simple linear regression to fit the model you found in part **a** to the data. Give the least squares prediction equation.
  c. Interpret the estimated y-intercept of the line.
  d. Interpret the estimated slope of the line.
  e. In Exercise 2.149 (p. 93), you were informed that a professional golfer practicing a new swing to increase his average driving distance is concerned that his driving accuracy will be lower. Which of the two estimates, y-intercept or slope, will help you determine whether the golfer's concern is a valid one? Explain.

PGADRIVER (Selected observations shown)

Rank	Player	Driving Distance (yards)	Driving Accuracy (%)	Driving Performance Index
1	Woods	316.1	54.6	3.58
2	Perry	304.7	63.4	3.48
3	Gutschewski	310.5	57.9	3.27
4	Wetterich	311.7	56.6	3.18
5	Hearn	295.2	68.5	2.82
⋮	⋮	⋮	⋮	⋮
36	Senden	291	66	1.31
37	Mickelson	300	58.7	1.30
38	Watney	298.9	59.4	1.26
39	Trahan	295.8	61.8	1.23
40	Pappas	309.4	50.6	1.17

Source: Wiseman, F. et al. "A New Method for Ranking Total Driving Performance on the PGA Tour," *The Sport Journal*, Vol. 10, No. 1, Winter 2007 (Table 2).

11.26 FCAT scores and poverty. In the state of Florida, elementary school performance is based on the average score obtained by students on a standardized exam, called the Florida Comprehensive Assessment Test (FCAT). An analysis of the link between FCAT scores and sociodemographic factors was published in the *Journal of Educational and Behavioral Statistics* (Spring 2004). Data on average math and reading FCAT scores of third graders, as well as the percentage of students below the poverty level, for a sample of 22 Florida elementary schools are listed in the accompanying table.
  a. Propose a straight-line model relating math score (y) to percentage (x) of students below the poverty level.
  b. Use the method of least squares to fit the model to the data in the FCAT file.
  c. Graph the least squares line on a scattergram of the data. Is there visual evidence of a relationship between the two variables? Is the relationship positive or negative?
  d. Interpret the estimates of the y-intercept and slope in the words of the problem.
  e. Now consider a model relating reading score (y) to percentage (x) of students below the poverty level. Repeat parts **a–d** for this model.

FCAT

Elementary School	FCAT—Math	FCAT—Reading	% Below Poverty
1	166.4	165.0	91.7
2	159.6	157.2	90.2
3	159.1	164.4	86.0
4	155.5	162.4	83.9
5	164.3	162.5	80.4
6	169.8	164.9	76.5
7	155.7	162.0	76.0
8	165.2	165.0	75.8
9	175.4	173.7	75.6
10	178.1	171.0	75.0
11	167.1	169.4	74.7
12	177.0	172.9	63.2
13	174.2	172.7	52.9
14	175.6	174.9	48.5
15	170.8	174.8	39.1
16	175.1	170.1	38.4
17	182.8	181.4	34.3
18	180.3	180.6	30.3
19	178.8	178.0	30.3
20	181.4	175.9	29.6
21	182.8	181.6	26.5
22	186.1	183.8	13.8

Source: Tekwe, C. D., et al. "An empirical comparison of statistical models for value-added assessment of school performance," *Journal of Educational and Behavioral Statistics*, Vol. 29, No. 1, Spring 2004 (Table 2).

11.27 New method of estimating rainfall. Accurate measurements of rainfall are critical for many hydrological and meteorological projects. Two standard methods of monitoring rainfall use rain gauges and weather radar. Both, however, can be contaminated by human and environmental interference. In the *Journal of Data Science* (Apr. 2004), researchers employed artificial neural networks (i.e., computer-based mathematical models) to estimate rainfall at a meteorological station in Montreal. Rainfall estimates were made every 5 minutes over a 70-minute period by each of the three methods. The data (in millimeters) are listed in the next table.

RAINFALL

Time	Radar	Rain Gauge	Neural Network
8:00 A.M.	3.6	0	1.8
8:05	2.0	1.2	1.8
8:10	1.1	1.2	1.4
8:15	1.3	1.3	1.9
8:20	1.8	1.4	1.7
8:25	2.1	1.4	1.5
8:30	3.2	2.0	2.1
8:35	2.7	2.1	1.0
8:40	2.5	2.5	2.6
8:45	3.5	2.9	2.6
8:50	3.9	4.0	4.0
8:55	3.5	4.9	3.4
9:00 A.M.	6.5	6.2	6.2
9:05	7.3	6.6	7.5
9:10	6.4	7.8	7.2

Source: Hessami, M. et al. "Selection of an artificial neural network model for the post-calibration of weather radar rainfall estimation," *Journal of Data Science*, Vol. 2, No. 2, Apr. 2004. (Adapted from Figures 2 and 4.)

a. Propose a straight-line model relating rain gauge amount (y) to weather radar rain estimate (x).

b. Use the method of least squares to fit the model to the data in the **RAINFALL** file.

c. Graph the least squares line on a scattergram of the data. Is there visual evidence of a relationship between the two variables? Is the relationship positive or negative?

d. Interpret the estimates of the y-intercept and slope in the words of the problem.

e. Now consider a model relating rain gauge amount (y) to the artificial neural network rain estimate (x). Repeat parts **a–d** for this model.

11.28 Sweetness of orange juice The quality of the orange juice produced by a manufacturer is constantly monitored. There are numerous sensory and chemical components that combine to make the best-tasting orange juice. For example, one manufacturer has developed a quantitative index of the "sweetness" of orange juice. (The higher the index, the sweeter is the juice.) Is there a relationship between the sweetness index and a chemical measure such as the amount of water-soluble pectin (parts per million) in the orange juice? Data collected on these two variables during 24 production runs at a juice-manufacturing plant are shown in the table (top, right). Suppose a manufacturer wants to use simple linear regression to predict the sweetness (y) from the amount of pectin (x).

a. Find the least squares line for the data.

b. Interpret $\hat{\beta}_0$ and $\hat{\beta}_1$ in the words of the problem.

c. Predict the sweetness index if the amount of pectin in the orange juice is 300 ppm. [*Note:* A measure of reliability of such a prediction is discussed in Section 11.6.]

11.29 Are geography journals worth their cost? Refer to the *Geoforum* (Vol. 37, 2006) study of whether the price of a geography journal is correlated with quality, presented in Exercise 2.144 (p. 92). Several quantitative variables were recorded for each in a sample of 28 geography journals: cost of a one-year subscription (dollars); journal impact factor (JIF), the average number of times articles from the journal

OJUICE

Run	Sweetness Index	Pectin (ppm)
1	5.2	220
2	5.5	227
3	6.0	259
4	5.9	210
5	5.8	224
6	6.0	215
7	5.8	231
8	5.6	268
9	5.6	239
10	5.9	212
11	5.4	410
12	5.6	256
13	5.8	306
14	5.5	259
15	5.3	284
16	5.3	383
17	5.7	271
18	5.5	264
19	5.7	227
20	5.3	263
21	5.9	232
22	5.8	220
23	5.8	246
24	5.9	241

Note: The data in the table are authentic. For reasons of confidentiality, the name of the manufacturer cannot be disclosed.

have been cited; number of citations for the journals over the past five years; and relative price index (RPI). The data for the 28 journals are saved in the **GEOJRNL** file. Selected observations are listed in the accompanying table.

a. Fit a straight-line model relating cost (y) to JIF (x). Give a practical interpretation of the estimated slope of the line.

b. Fit a straight-line model relating cost (y) to number of citations (x). Give a practical interpretation of the estimated slope of the line.

c. Fit a straight-line model relating cost (y) to RPI (x). Give a practical interpretation of the estimated slope of the line.

GEOJRNL (selected observations)

Journal	Cost ($)	JIF	Citations	RPI
J. Econ. Geogr	468	3.139	207	1.16
Prog. Hum. Geog	624	2.943	544	0.77
T. I. Brit. Geogr	499	2.388	249	1.11
Econ. Geogr.	90	2.325	173	0.30
A. A. A. Geogr.	698	2.115	377	0.93
⋮	⋮	⋮	⋮	⋮
Geogr.Anal.	213	0.902	106	0.88
Geogr.J.	223	0.857	81	0.94
Appl.Geogr	646	0.853	74	3.38

Source: Blomley, N. "Is this journal worth US$1118?" *Geoforum*, Vol. 27, 2006.

11.30 The "name game." Refer to the *Journal of Experimental Psychology—Applied* (June 2000) study in which the "name game" was used to help groups of students learn the names of other students in the group, presented in

Exercise 10.34 (p. 503). Recall that the "name game" requires the first student in the group to state his or her full name, the second student to say his or her name and the name of the first student, the third student to say his or her name and the names of the first two students, etc. After making their introductions, the students listened to a seminar speaker for 30 minutes. At the end of the seminar, all students were asked to remember the full name of each of the other students in their group, and the researchers measured the proportion of names recalled for each. One goal of the study was to investigate the linear trend between y = proportion of names recalled and x = position (order) of the student during the game. The data (simulated on the basis of summary statistics provided in the research article) for 144 students in the first eight positions are saved in the **NAMEGAME2** file. The first five and last five observations in the data set are listed in the accompanying table. [*Note:* Since the student in position 1 actually must recall the names of all the other students, he or she is assigned position number 9 in the data set.] Use the method of least squares to estimate the line $E(y) = \beta_0 + \beta_1 x$. Interpret the β estimates in the words of the problem.

NAMEGAME2

Position	Recall
2	0.04
2	0.37
2	1.00
2	0.99
2	0.79
⋮	⋮
9	0.72
9	0.88
9	0.46
9	0.54
9	0.99

Source: Morris, P.E., and Fritz, C.O. "The name game: Using retrieval practice to improve the learning of names," *Journal of Experimental Psychology— Applied,* Vol. 6, No. 2, June 2000 (data simulated from Figure 2).

Applying the Concepts—Advanced

11.31 Spreading rate of spilled liquid. Refer to the *Chemical Engineering Progress* (Jan. 2005) study of the rate which a spilled volatile liquid will spread across a surface, presented in Exercise 2.150 (p. 94). Recall that a DuPont Corp. engineer calculated the mass (in pounds) of a 50-gallon methanol spill after a period ranging from 0 to 60 minutes. Do the data shown in the accompanying table indicate that the mass of the spill tends to diminish as time increases? If so, how much will the mass diminish each minute?

LIQUIDSPILL

Time (minutes)	Mass (pounds)
0	6.64
1	6.34
2	6.04
4	5.47
6	4.94
8	4.44
10	3.98
12	3.55
14	3.15
16	2.79
18	2.45
20	2.14
22	1.86
24	1.60
26	1.37
28	1.17
30	0.98
35	0.60
40	0.34
45	0.17
50	0.06
55	0.02
60	0.00

Source: Barry, J. "Estimating rates of spreading and evaporation of volatile liquids," *Chemical Engineering Progress,* Vol. 101, No. 1, Jan. 2005.

11.3 Model Assumptions

In Section 11.2, we assumed that the probabilistic model relating the drug reaction time y to the percentage x of drug in the bloodstream is

$$y = \beta_0 + \beta_1 x + \varepsilon$$

We also recall that the least squares estimate of the deterministic component of the model, $\beta_0 + \beta_1 x$, is

$$\hat{y} = \hat{\beta}_0 + \hat{\beta}_1 x = -.1 + .7x$$

Now we turn our attention to the random component ε of the probabilistic model and its relation to the errors in estimating β_0 and β_1. We will use a probability distribution to characterize the behavior of ε. We will see how the probability distribution of ε determines how well the model describes the relationship between the dependent variable y and the independent variable x.

Step 3 in a regression analysis requires us to specify the probability distribution of the random error ε. We will make four basic assumptions about the general form of this probability distribution:

Assumption 1 The mean of the probability distribution of ε is 0. That is, the average of the values of ε over an infinitely long series of experiments is 0 for each setting of the independent variable x. This assumption implies that the mean value of y, for a given value of x is $E(y) = \beta_0 + \beta_1 x$.

Assumption 2 The variance of the probability distribution of ε is constant for all settings of the independent variable x. For our straight-line model, this assumption means that the variance of ε is equal to a constant—say, σ^2—for all values of x.

Assumption 3 The probability distribution of ε is normal.

Assumption 4 The values of ε associated with any two observed values of y are independent. That is, the value of ε associated with one value of y has no effect on any of the values of ε associated with any other y values.

The implications of the first three assumptions can be seen in Figure 11.7, which shows distributions of errors for three values of x, namely, 5, 10, and 15. Note that the relative frequency distributions of the errors are normal with a mean of 0 and a constant variance σ^2. (All of the distributions shown have the same amount of spread or variability.) The straight line shown in Figure 11.7 is the line of means; it indicates the mean value of y for a given value of x. We denote this mean value as $E(y)$. Then the line of means is given by the equation

$$E(y) = \beta_0 + \beta_1 x$$

These assumptions make it possible for us to develop measures of reliability for the least squares estimators and to devise hypothesis tests for examining the usefulness of the least squares line. We have various techniques for checking the validity of these assumptions, and we have remedies to apply when they appear to be invalid. Several remedies are discussed in Chapter 12. Fortunately, the assumptions need not hold exactly in order for least squares estimators to be useful. The assumptions will be satisfied adequately for many applications encountered in practice.

It seems reasonable to assume that the greater the variability of the random error ε (which is measured by its variance σ^2), the greater will be the errors in the estimation of the model parameters β_0 and β_1 and in the error of prediction when $\hat{y}$ is used to predict y for some value of x. Consequently, you should not be surprised, as we proceed through this chapter, to find that σ^2 appears in the formulas for all confidence intervals and test statistics that we will be using.

In most practical situations, σ^2 is unknown and we must use our data to estimate its value. The best estimate of σ^2, denoted by s^2, is obtained by dividing the sum of the squares of the deviations of the y values from the prediction line, or

$$\text{SSE} = \sum (y_i - \hat{y}_i)^2$$

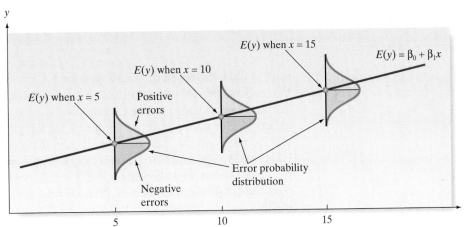

FIGURE 11.7

The probability distribution of ε

by the number of degrees of freedom associated with this quantity. We use 2 df to estimate the two parameters β_0 and β_1 in the straight-line model, leaving $(n - 2)$ df for the estimation of the error variance.

Estimation of σ^2 for a (First-Order) Straight-Line Model

$$s^2 = \frac{\text{SSE}}{\text{Degrees of freedom for error}} = \frac{\text{SSE}}{n - 2}$$

where $\text{SSE} = \sum (y_i - \hat{y}_i)^2 = \text{SS}_{yy} - \hat{\beta}_1 \text{SS}_{xy}$

in which

$$\text{SS}_{yy} = \sum (y_i - \bar{y})^2 = \sum y_i^2 - \frac{\left(\sum y_i \right)^2}{n}$$

To estimate the standard deviation σ of ε, we calculate

$$s = \sqrt{s^2} = \sqrt{\frac{\text{SSE}}{n - 2}}$$

We will refer to s as the **estimated standard error of the regression model**.

Warning

When performing these calculations, you may be tempted to round the calculated values of SS_{yy}, $\hat{\beta}_1$, and SS_{xy}. Be certain to carry at least six significant figures for each of these quantities, to avoid substantial errors in calculating the SSE.

EXAMPLE 11.2

ESTIMATING σ IN REGRESSION—Drug Reaction Data

Problem Refer to Example 11.1 and the simple linear regression of the drug reaction data in Table 11.3.

a. Compute an estimate of σ.
b. Give a practical interpretation of the estimate.

Solution

a. We previously calculated SSE = 1.10 for the least squares line $\hat{y} = -.1 + .7x$. Recalling that there were $n = 5$ data points, we have $n - 2 = 5 - 2 = 3$ df for estimating σ^2. Thus,

$$s^2 = \frac{\text{SSE}}{n - 2} = \frac{1.10}{3} = .367$$

is the estimated variance, and

$$s = \sqrt{.367} = .61$$

is the standard error of the regression model.

b. You may be able to grasp s intuitively by recalling the interpretation of a standard deviation given in Chapter 2 and remembering that the least squares line estimates the mean value of y for a given value of x. Since s measures the spread of the distribution of y values about the least squares line and these errors of prediction are assumed to be normally distributed, we should not be surprised to find that most (about 95%) of the observations lie within $2s$, or $2(.61) = 1.22$, of the least squares line. For this simple example (only five data points), all five data points fall within $2s$ of the least squares line. In Section 11.6, we use s to evaluate the error of prediction when the least squares line is used to predict a value of y to be observed for a given value of x.

Dependent Variable: TIME_Y

Number of Observations Read   5
Number of Observations Used   5

Analysis of Variance

Source	DF	Sum of Squares	Mean Square	F Value	Pr > F
Model	1	4.90000	4.90000	13.36	0.0354
Error	3	1.10000	0.36667		
Corrected Total	4	6.00000			

Root MSE	0.60553	R-Square	0.8167	
Dependent Mean	2.00000	Adj R-Sq	0.7556	
Coeff Var	30.27650			

Parameter Estimates

Variable	DF	Parameter Estimate	Standard Error	t Value	Pr > |t|
Intercept	1	-0.10000	0.63509	-0.16	0.8849
DRUG_X	1	0.70000	0.19149	3.66	0.0354

FIGURE 11.8
SAS printout for the time–drug regression

Look Back The values of s^2 and s can also be obtained from a simple linear regression printout. The SAS printout for the drug reaction example is reproduced in Figure 11.8. The value of s^2 is highlighted on the printout (in the **Mean Square** column in the row labeled **Error**). The value $s^2 = .36667$, rounded to three decimal places, agrees with the one calculated by hand. The value of s is also highlighted in Figure 11.8 (next to the heading **Root MSE**). This value, $s = .60553$, agrees (except for rounding) with our hand-calculated value.

Now Work Exercise 11.36a–b

Interpretation of s, the Estimated Standard Deviation of ε

We expect most ($\approx 95\%$) of the observed y values to lie within $2s$ of their respective least squares predicted values, $\hat{y}$.

Exercises 11.32–11.46

Understanding the Principles

11.32 What are the four assumptions made about the probability distribution of ε in regression?

11.33 Illustrate the assumptions of Exercise 11.32 with a graph.

11.34 Visually compare the scattergrams shown at right. If a least squares line were determined for each data set, which do you think would have the smallest variance s^2? Explain.

Learning the Mechanics

11.35 Calculate SSE and s^2 for each of the following cases:
a. $n = 20$, $SS_{yy} = 95$, $SS_{xy} = 50$, $\hat{\beta}_1 = .75$

b. $n = 40$, $\sum y^2 = 860$, $\sum y = 50$,

   $SS_{xy} = 2{,}700$, $\hat{\beta}_1 = .2$

c. $n = 10$, $\sum (y_i - \bar{y})^2 = 58$,

   $SS_{xy} = 91$, $SS_{xx} = 170$

11.36 Suppose you fit a least squares line to 12 data points and
NW the calculated value of SSE is .429.

a.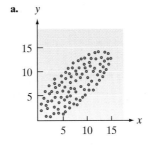

b.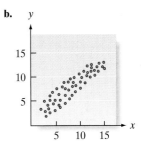

c.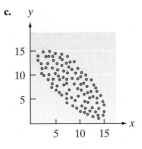

a. Find s^2, the estimator of σ^2 (the variance of the random error term ε).

b. Find s, the estimate of σ.

c. What is the largest deviation that you might expect between any one of the 12 points and the least squares line?

11.37 Refer to Exercises 11.14 and 11.17 (pp. 572, 573). Calculate SSE, s^2, and s for the least squares lines obtained in those exercises. Interpret the standard errors of the regression model for each.

Applying the Concepts—Basic

11.38 **Quantitative models of music.** Refer to the *Chance* (Fall 2004) study on modeling a certain pitch of a musical composition, presented in Exercise 11.18 (p. 573). Recall that the number of times (y) a certain pitch occurs—called entropy—was modeled as a straight-line function of year of birth (x) of the composer. On the basis of the scatterplot of the data (p. 573), the standard deviation σ of the model is estimated to be $s = .1$. For a given year (x), about 95% of the actual entropy values (y) will fall within d units of their predicted values. Find the value of d.

11.39 **Winning marathon times.** Refer to Exercise 11.20 (p. 574) and the *Chance* (Winter 2000) study on predicting the winning time (y) in the Boston Marathon. On the basis of the variation of the data around the scatterplots (p. 574), which simple linear regression model, the men's or the women's, will have the smallest estimate of σ? Explain.

SITIN

11.40 **College protests of labor exploitation.** Refer to the *Journal of World-Systems Research* (Winter 2004) study of college student "sit-ins," presented in Exercise 11.21 (p. 574). The data in the **SITIN** file was used to estimate the straight-line model relating number of arrests (y) to duration of sit-in (x).

a. Give the values of SSE, s^2, and s, shown on the SPSS printout below.

b. Give a practical interpretation of the value of s.

GOBIANTS

11.41 **Mongolian desert ants.** Refer to the *Journal of Biogeography* (Dec. 2003) study of ant sites in Mongolia, presented

in Exercise 11.22 (p. 574). The data in the **GOBIANTS** file was used to estimate the straight-line model relating annual rainfall (y) to maximum daily temperature (x).

a. Give the values of SSE, s^2, and s, shown on the MINITAB printout (p. 575).

b. Give a practical interpretation of the value of s.

Applying the Concepts—Intermediate

SMELTPOT

11.42 **Extending the life of an aluminum smelter pot.** Refer to *The American Ceramic Society Bulletin* (Feb. 2005) study of bricks that line aluminum smelter pots, presented in Exercise 11.24 (p. 575). You fit the simple linear regression model relating brick porosity (y) to mean pore diameter (x) to the data in the **SMELTPOT** file.

a. Find an estimate of the standard deviation σ of the model.

b. In Exercise 11.24d, you predicted brick porosity percentage when $x = 10$ micrometers. Use the result of part **a** to estimate the error of prediction.

FCAT

11.43 **FCAT scores and poverty.** Refer to the *Journal of Educational and Behavioral Statistics* (Spring 2004) study of scores on the Florida Comprehensive Assessment Test (FCAT), presented in Exercise 11.26 (p. 576).

a. Consider the simple linear regression relating math score (y) to percentage (x) of students below the poverty level. Find and interpret the value of s for this regression.

b. Consider the simple linear regression relating reading score (y) to percentage (x) of students below the poverty level. Find and interpret the value of s for this regression.

c. Which dependent variable, math score or reading score, can be more accurately predicted by percentage (x) of students below the poverty level? Explain.

RAINFALL

11.44 **New method of estimating rainfall.** Refer to the *Journal of Data Science* (Apr. 2004) comparison of methods for estimating rainfall, presented in Exercise 11.27 (p. 576).

Model Summary

Model	R	R Square	Adjusted R Square	Std. Error of the Estimate
1	.601[a]	.361	.148	16.913

a. Predictors: (Constant), DURATION

ANOVA[b]

Model		Sum of Squares	df	Mean Square	F	Sig.
1	Regression	485.026	1	485.026	1.696	.284[a]
	Residual	858.174	3	286.058		
	Total	1343.200	4			

a. Predictors: (Constant), DURATION

SPSS output for Exercise 11.40   b. Dependent Variable: ARRESTS

a. Consider the simple linear regression relating rain gauge amount (y) to weather radar rain estimate (x). Find and interpret the value of s for this regression.

b. Consider the simple linear regression relating rain gauge amount (y) to the artificial neural network rain estimate (x). Find and interpret the value of s for this regression.

c. Which independent variable, radar estimate or neural network estimate, is a more accurate predictor of rain gauge amount (y)? Explain.

⊙ **GEOJRNL**

11.45 Are geography journals worth their cost? Refer to the *Geoforum* (Vol. 37, 2006) study of whether the price of a geography journal is correlated with quality, presented in Exercise 11.29 (p. 577). The data are saved in the **GEOJRNL** file.

a. In Exercise 11.29a, you fit a straight-line model relating cost (y) to JIF(x). Within how many dollars can you expect to predict cost with this model?

b. In Exercise 11.29b, you fit a straight-line model relating cost (y) to number of citation(x). Within how many dollars can you expect to predict cost with this model?

c. In Exercise 11.29c, you fit a straight-line model relating cost (y) to RPI(x). Within how many dollars can you expect to predict cost with this model?

Applying the Concepts—Advanced

11.46 Life tests of cutting tools. To improve the quality of the output of any production process, it is necessary first to understand the capabilities of the process (Gitlow, et al.,

Quality Management: Tools and Methods for Improvement, 1995). In a particular manufacturing process, the useful life of a cutting tool is linearly related to the speed at which the tool is operated. The data in the accompanying table were derived from life tests for the two different brands of cutting tools currently used in the production process. For which brand would you feel more confident using the least squares line to predict useful life for a given cutting speed? Explain.

⊙ **CUTTOOL**

Cutting Speed (meters per minute)	Useful Life (hours)	
	Brand A	Brand B
30	4.5	6.0
30	3.5	6.5
30	5.2	5.0
40	5.2	6.0
40	4.0	4.5
40	2.5	5.0
50	4.4	4.5
50	2.8	4.0
50	1.0	3.7
60	4.0	3.8
60	2.0	3.0
60	1.1	2.4
70	1.1	1.5
70	.5	2.0
70	3.0	1.0

11.4 Assessing the Utility of the Model: Making Inferences about the Slope β_1

Now that we have specified the probability distribution of ε and found an estimate of the variance σ^2, we are ready to make statistical inferences about the linear model's usefulness in predicting the response y. This is step 4 in our regression modeling procedure.

Refer again to the data of Table 11.1, and suppose the reaction times are *completely unrelated* to the percentage of drug in the bloodstream. What could then be said about the values of β_0 and β_1 in the hypothesized probabilistic model

$$y = \beta_0 + \beta_1 x + \varepsilon$$

if x contributes no information for the prediction of y? The implication is that the mean of y—that is, the deterministic part of the model $E(y) = \beta_0 + \beta_1 x$—does not change as x changes. In the straight-line model, this means that the true slope, β_1, is equal to 0. (See Figure 11.9.) Therefore, to test the null hypothesis that the linear model contributes no

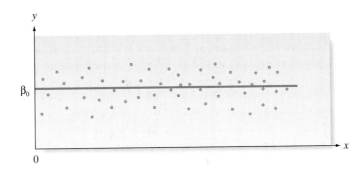

FIGURE 11.9

Graph of the straight-line model when the slope is zero, i.e., $y = \beta_0 + \varepsilon$

information for the prediction of y against the alternative hypothesis that the linear model is useful in predicting y, we test

$$H_0: \beta_1 = 0$$
$$H_a: \beta_1 \neq 0$$

If the data support the alternative hypothesis, we will conclude that x does contribute information for the prediction of y with the straight-line model [although the true relationship between $E(y)$ and x could be more complicated than a straight line]. In effect, then, this is a test of the usefulness of the hypothesized model.

The appropriate test statistic is found by considering the sampling distribution of $\hat{\beta}_1$, the least squares estimator of the slope β_1, as shown in the following box:

Sampling Distribution of $\hat{\beta}_1$

If we make the four assumptions about ε (see Section 11.3), the sampling distribution of the least squares estimator $\hat{\beta}_1$ of the slope will be normal with mean β_1 (the true slope) and standard deviation

$$\sigma_{\hat{\beta}_1} = \frac{\sigma}{\sqrt{SS_{xx}}} \quad \text{(see Figure 11.10)}$$

We estimate $\sigma_{\hat{\beta}_1}$ by $s_{\hat{\beta}_1} = \dfrac{s}{\sqrt{SS_{xx}}}$ and refer to $S_{\hat{\beta}_1}$ as the **estimated standard error of the least squares slope $\hat{\beta}_1$.**

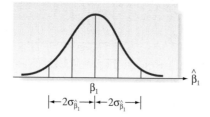

FIGURE 11.10
Sampling distribution of $\hat{\beta}_1$

Since σ is usually unknown, the appropriate test statistic is a t-statistic, formed as:

$$t = \frac{\hat{\beta}_1 - \text{Hypothesized value of } \beta_1}{s_{\hat{\beta}_1}} \quad \text{where} \quad s_{\hat{\beta}_1} = \frac{s}{\sqrt{SS_{xx}}}$$

Thus,

$$t = \frac{\hat{\beta}_1 - 0}{s/\sqrt{SS_{xx}}}$$

Note that we have substituted the estimator s for σ and then formed the estimated standard error $s_{\hat{\beta}_1}$ by dividing s by $\sqrt{SS_{xx}}$. The number of degrees of freedom associated with this t statistic is the same as the number of degrees of freedom associated with s. Recall that this number is $(n - 2)$ df when the hypothesized model is a straight line. (See Section 11.3.) The setup of our test of the usefulness of the straight-line model is summarized in the two boxes on p. 585.

EXAMPLE 11.3
TESTING THE REGRESSION SLOPE, β_1—Drug Reaction Model

Problem Refer to the simple linear regression analysis of the drug reaction data performed in Examples 11.1 and 11.2. Conduct a test (at $\alpha = .05$) to determine whether the reaction time (y) is linearly related to the amount of drug (x).

Solution For the drug reaction example, $n = 5$. Thus, t will be based on $n - 2 = 3$ df, and the rejection region t (at $\alpha = .05$) will be

$$|t| > t_{.025} = 3.182$$

> ### A Test of Model Utility: Simple Linear Regression
>
> **One-Tailed Test**
>
> $H_0: \beta_1 = 0$
> $H_a: \beta_1 < 0$ (or $H_a: \beta_1 > 0$)
>
> **Two-Tailed Test**
>
> $H_0: \beta_1 = 0$
> $H_a: \beta_1 \neq 0$
>
> *Test statistic:* $t = \dfrac{\hat{\beta}_1}{s_{\hat{\beta}_1}} = \dfrac{\hat{\beta}_1}{s/\sqrt{SS_{xx}}}$
>
> *Rejection region:* $t < -t_\alpha$
>
> (or $t > t_\alpha$ when $H_a: \beta_1 > 0$)
>
> *Rejection region:* $|t| > t_{\alpha/2}$
>
> where t_α and $t_{\alpha/2}$ are based on $(n - 2)$ degrees of freedom

> ### Conditions Required for a Valid Test: Simple Linear Regression
> The four assumptions about ε listed in Section 11.3.

We previously calculated $\hat{\beta}_1 = .7$, $s = .61$, and $SS_{xx} = 10$. Thus,

$$t = \frac{\hat{\beta}_1}{s/\sqrt{SS_{xx}}} = \frac{.7}{.61/\sqrt{10}} = \frac{.7}{.19} = 3.7$$

Since this calculated t-value falls into the upper-tail rejection region (see Figure 11.11), we reject the null hypothesis and conclude that the slope β_1 is not 0. The sample evidence indicates that the percentage x of drug in the bloodstream contributes information for the prediction of the reaction time y when a linear model is used.

  [*Note:* We can reach the same conclusion by using the observed significance level (p-value) of the test from a computer printout. The MINITAB printout for the drug reaction example is reproduced in Figure 11.12. The test statistic and the two-tailed

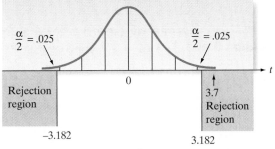

FIGURE 11.11

Rejection region and calculated t value for testing $H_0: \beta_1 = 0$ versus $H_a: \beta_1 \neq 0$

Regression Analysis: TIME_Y versus DRUG_X

```
The regression equation is
TIME_Y = - 0.100 + 0.700 DRUG_X


Predictor      Coef    SE Coef       T       P
Constant    -0.1000     0.6351   -0.16   0.885
DRUG_X       0.7000     0.1915    3.66   0.035


S = 0.605530    R-Sq = 81.7%    R-Sq(adj) = 75.6%


Analysis of Variance

Source           DF       SS       MS       F       P
Regression        1   4.9000   4.9000   13.36   0.035
Residual Error    3   1.1000   0.3667
Total             4   6.0000
```

FIGURE 11.12

MINITAB printout for the time–drug regression

p-value are highlighted on the printout. Since the *p*-value = .035 is smaller than $\alpha = .05$, we will reject H_0.]

Look Back What conclusion can be drawn if the calculated *t*-value does not fall into the rejection region or if the observed significance level of the test exceeds α? We know from previous discussions of the philosophy of hypothesis testing that such a *t*-value does *not* lead us to accept the null hypothesis. That is, we do not conclude that $\beta_1 = 0$. Additional data might indicate that β_1 differs from 0, or a more complicated relationship may exist between *x* and *y*, requiring the fitting of a model other than the straight-line model. We discuss several such models in Chapter 12.

Now Work Exercise 11.54

Interpreting *p*-Values for β Coefficients in Regression

Almost all statistical computer software packages report a *two-tailed p*-value for each of the β parameters in the regression model. For example, in simple linear regression, the *p*-value for the two-tailed test $H_0: \beta_1 = 0$ versus $H_a: \beta_1 \neq 0$ is given on the printout. If you want to conduct a *one-tailed* test of hypothesis, you will need to adjust the *p*-value reported on the printout as follows:

$$\text{Upper-tailed test } (H_a: \beta_1 > 0): \quad p\text{-value} = \begin{cases} p/2 & \text{if } t > 0 \\ 1 - p/2 & \text{if } t < 0 \end{cases}$$

$$\text{Lower-tailed test } (H_a: \beta_1 < 0): \quad p\text{-value} = \begin{cases} p/2 & \text{if } t < 0 \\ 1 - p/2 & \text{if } t > 0 \end{cases}$$

Here, *p* is the *p*-value reported on the printout and *t* is the value of the test statistic.

Another way to make inferences about the slope β_1 is to estimate it with a confidence interval, formed as shown in the following box:

A $100(1 - \alpha)\%$ Confidence Interval for the Simple Linear Regression Slope β_1

$$\hat{\beta}_1 \pm t_{\alpha/2}s_{\hat{\beta}_1}$$

where the estimated standard error of $\hat{\beta}_1$ is calculated by

$$s_{\hat{\beta}_1} = \frac{s}{\sqrt{SS_{xx}}}$$

and $t_{\alpha/2}$ is based on $(n - 2)$ degrees of freedom.

Conditions Required for a Valid Confidence Interval: Simple Linear Regression

The four assumptions about ε listed in Section 11.3.

For the simple linear regression for the drug reaction (Examples 11.1–11.3), $t_{\alpha/2}$ is based on $(n - 2) = 3$ degrees of freedom. Therefore, a 95% confidence interval for the slope β_1, the expected change in reaction time for a 1% increase in the amount of drug in the bloodstream, is

$$\hat{\beta}_1 \pm t_{.025}s_{\hat{\beta}_1} = .7 \pm 3.182\left(\frac{s}{\sqrt{SS_{xx}}}\right) = .7 \pm 3.182\left(\frac{.61}{\sqrt{10}}\right) = .7 \pm .61$$

Coefficients[a]

Model		Unstandardized Coefficients		Standardized Coefficients	t	Sig.	95% Confidence Interval for B	
		B	Std. Error	Beta			Lower Bound	Upper Bound
1	(Constant)	-.100	.635		-.157	.885	-2.121	1.921
	TIME_X	.700	.191	.904	3.656	.035	.091	1.309

a. Dependent Variable: DRUG_Y

FIGURE 11.13

SPSS printout with 95% confidence intervals for the time–drug regression betas

Thus, the estimate of the interval for the slope parameter β_1 is from .09 to 1.31. [*Note:* This interval can also be obtained with statistical software and is highlighted on the SPSS printout shown in Figure 11.13.] In terms of this example, the implication is that we can be 95% confident that the *true* mean increase in reaction time per additional 1% of the drug is between .09 and 1.31 seconds. This inference is meaningful only over the sampled range of x—that is, from 1% to 5% of the drug in the bloodstream.

Now Work Exercise 11.59

Since all the values in this interval are positive, it appears that β_1 is positive and that the mean of y, $E(y)$, increases as x increases. However, the rather large width of the confidence interval reflects the small number of data points (and, consequently, a lack of information) used in the experiment. We would expect a narrower interval if the sample size were increased.

STATISTICS IN ACTION REVISITED

Assessing How Well the Straight-Line Model Fits the Dowsing Data

In the previous Statistics in Action Revisited, we fit the straight-line model $E(y) = \beta_0 + \beta_1 x$, where x = dowser's guess (in meters) and y = pipe location (in meters) for each trial. The MINITAB regression printout is reproduced in Figure SIA11.3. The two-tailed p-value for testing the null hypothesis $H_0: \beta_1 = 0$ (highlighted on the printout) is p-value = .118. Even for an α-level as high as α = .10, there is insufficient evidence to reject H_0. Consequently, the dowsing data in Table SIA11.1 provide no statistical support for the German researchers' claim that the three

best dowsers have an ability to find underground water with a divining rod.

This lack of support for the dowsing theory is made clearer with a confidence interval for the slope of the line. When n = 26, df = $(n - 2)$ = 24 and $t_{.025}$ = 2.064. Substituting the latter value and the relevant values shown on the MINITAB printout, we find that a 95% confidence interval for β_1 is

$$\hat{\beta}_1 \pm t_{.025}(s_{\hat{\beta}_1}) = .31 \pm (2.064)(.19)$$
$$= .31 \pm .39, \text{ or } (-.08, .70)$$

Regression Analysis: PIPE versus GUESS

```
The regression equation is
PIPE = 30.1 + 0.308 GUESS


Predictor     Coef   SE Coef     T       P
Constant     30.07     11.41   2.63   0.015
GUESS       0.3079    0.1900   1.62   0.118



S = 26.0298    R-Sq = 9.9%    R-Sq(adj) = 6.1%



Analysis of Variance

Source            DF        SS       MS      F      P
Regression         1    1778.9   1778.9   2.63  0.118
Residual Error    24   16261.2    677.6
Total             25   18040.2
```

FIGURE SIA11.3

MINITAB simple linear regression for dowsing data

(continued)

Thus, for every 1-meter increase in a dowser's guess, we estimate (with 95% confidence) that the change in the actual pipe location will range anywhere from a decrease of .08 meter to an increase of .70 meter. In other words, we're not sure whether the pipe location will increase or decrease along the 10-meter pipeline!

Keep in mind also that the data in Table SIA11.1 represent the "best" performances of the three dowsers (i.e., the outcome of the dowsing experiment in its most favorable light). When the data for all trials are considered and plotted, there is not even a hint of a trend.

Exercises 11.47–11.65

Understanding the Principles

11.47 In the equation $E(y) = \beta_0 + \beta_1 x$, what is the value of β_1 if x has no linear relationship to y?

11.48 What conditions are required for valid inferences about the β's in simple linear regression?

11.49 How do you adjust the p-value obtained from a computer printout when you perform a one-tailed test of β_1 in simple linear regression?

11.50 For each of the following 95% confidence intervals for β_1 in simple linear regression, decide whether there is evidence of a positive or negative linear relationship between y and x:
a. $(22, 58)$ **b.** $(-30, 111)$ **c.** $(-45, -7)$

Learning the Mechanics

11.51 Construct both a 95% and a 90% confidence interval for β_1 for each of the following cases:
a. $\hat{\beta}_1 = 31$, $s = 3$, $SS_{xx} = 35$, $n = 12$
b. $\hat{\beta}_1 = 64$, $SSE = 1,960$, $SS_{xx} = 30$, $n = 18$
c. $\hat{\beta}_1 = -8.4$, $SSE = 146$, $SS_{xx} = 64$, $n = 24$

11.52 Consider the following pairs of observations:

x	1	5	3	2	6	6	0
y	1	3	3	1	4	5	1

a. Construct a scattergram of the data.
b. Use the method of least squares to fit a straight line to the seven data points in the table.
c. Plot the least squares line on your scattergram of part **a**.
d. Specify the null and alternative hypotheses you would use to test whether the data provide sufficient evidence to indicate that x contributes information for the (linear) prediction of y.
e. What is the test statistic that should be used in conducting the hypothesis test of part **d**? Specify the number of degrees of freedom associated with the test statistic.
f. Conduct the hypothesis test of part **d**, using $\alpha = .05$.
g. Construct a 95% confidence interval for β_1.

11.53 Consider the following pairs of observations:

y	4	2	5	3	2	4
x	1	4	5	3	2	4

a. Construct a scattergram of the data.
b. Use the method of least squares to fit a straight line to the six data points.

c. Plot the least squares line on the scattergram of part **a**.
d. Compute the test statistic for determining whether x and y are linearly related.
e. Carry out the test you set up in part **d**, using $\alpha = .01$.

f. Find a 99% confidence interval for β_1.

Applying the Concepts—Basic

11.54 **English as a second language reading ability.** What are the factors that allow a native Spanish-speaking person to understand and read English? A study published in the *Bilingual Research Journal* (Summer 2006) investigated the relationship of Spanish (first-language) grammatical knowledge to English (second-language) reading. The study involved a sample of $n = 55$ native Spanish-speaking adults who were students in an English as a second language (ESL) college class. Each student took four standardized exams: Spanish grammar (SG), Spanish reading (SR), English grammar (EG), and English reading (ESLR). Simple linear regression was used to model the ESLR score (y) as a function of each of the other exam scores (x). The results are summarized in the following table:

Independent variable (x)	p-value for testing H_0: $\beta_1 = 0$
SG score	.739
SR score	.012
ER score	.022

a. At $\alpha = .05$, is there sufficient evidence to indicate that ESLR score is linearly related to SG score?

b. At $\alpha = .05$, is there sufficient evidence to indicate that ESLR score is linearly related to SR score?
c. At $\alpha = .05$, is there sufficient evidence to indicate that ESLR score is linearly related to ER score?

11.55 **Ranking driving performance of professional golfers.** Refer to *The Sport Journal* (Winter 2007) study of a new method for ranking the total driving performance of golfers on the Professional Golf Association (PGA) tour, presented in Exercise 11.25 (p. 576). You fit a straight-line model relating driving accuracy (y) to driving distance (x) to the data saved in the **PGADRIVER** file.
a. Give the null and alternative hypotheses for testing whether driving accuracy (y) decreases linearly as driving distance (x) increases.
b. Find the test statistic and p-value of the test you set up in part **a**.
c. Make the appropriate conclusion at $\alpha = .01$.

FCAT

11.56 FCAT scores and poverty. Refer to the *Journal of Educational and Behavioral Statistics* (Spring 2004) study of scores on the Florida Comprehensive Assessment Test (FCAT), first presented in Exercise 11.26 (p. 576). Consider the simple linear regression relating math score (y) to percentage (x) of students below the poverty level.
  a. Test whether y is negatively related to x. Use $\alpha = .01$.

  b. Construct a 99% confidence interval for β_1. Interpret the result practically.

RAINFALL

11.57 New method of estimating rainfall. Refer to the *Journal of Data Science* (Apr. 2004) comparison of methods for estimating rainfall, first presented in Exercise 11.27 (p. 577). Consider the simple linear regression relating the rain gauge amount (y) to the artificial neural network rain estimate (x).
  a. Test whether y is positively related to x. Use $\alpha = .10$.

  b. Construct a 90% confidence interval for β_1. Interpret the result practically.

GEOJRNL

11.58 Are geography journals worth their cost? Refer to the *Geoforum* (Vol. 37, 2006) study of whether the price of a geography journal is correlated with the quality of the journal, first presented in Exercise 11.29 (p. 577). The data are saved in the **GEOJRNL** file.
  a. In exercise 11.29a, you fit a straight-line model relating cost (y) to JIF(x). Find and interpret a 95% confidence interval for the slope of the line.
  b. In exercise 11.29b, you fit a straight-line model relating cost (y) to number of citations (x). Find and interpret a 95% confidence interval for the slope of the line.
  c. In exercise 11.29c, you fit a straight-line model relating cost (y) to RPI(x). Find and interpret a 95% confidence interval for the slope of the line.

OJUICE

11.59 Sweetness of orange juice. Refer to Exercise 11.28 **NW** (p. 577) and the simple linear regression relating the sweetness index (y) of an orange juice sample to the amount of water-soluble pectin (x) in the juice. Find a 90% confidence interval for the true slope of the line. Interpret the result.

Applying the Concepts—Intermediate

11.60 Effect of massage on boxers. Refer to the *British Journal of Sports Medicine* (Apr. 2000) study of the effect of massage on boxing performance, presented in Exercise 10.68 (p. 525). Two other variables measured on the boxers were blood lactate concentration (in mM) and the boxer's perceived recovery (on a 28-point scale). On the basis of information provided in the article, the data shown in the accompanying table were obtained for 16 five-round boxing performances in which a massage was given to the boxer between rounds. Conduct a test to determine whether blood lactate level (y) is linearly related to perceived recovery (x). Use $\alpha = .10$.

BOXING2

Blood Lactate Level	Perceived Recovery
3.8	7
4.2	7
4.8	11
4.1	12
5.0	12
5.3	12
4.2	13
2.4	17
3.7	17
5.3	17
5.8	18
6.0	18
5.9	21
6.3	21
5.5	20
6.5	24

Source: Hemmings, B., Smith, M., Graydon, J., and Dyson, R. "Effects of massage on physiological restoration, perceived recovery, and repeated sports performance," *British Journal of Sports Medicine*, Vol. 34, No. 2, Apr. 2000 (data adapted from Figure 3).

11.61 Forest fragmentation study. Refer to the *Conservation Ecology* (Dec. 2003) study on the causes of fragmentation of 54 South American forests, presented in Exercise 2.148 (p. 93). Recall that researchers developed two fragmentation indexes for each forest—one index for anthropogenic (human development activities) fragmentation and one for fragmentation from natural causes. Data on 5 of the 54 forests saved in the **FORFRAG** file are listed in the following table:

FORFRAG (First 5 observations listed)

Ecoregion (forest)	Anthropogenic Index, y	Natural Origin Index, x
Araucaria moist forests	34.09	30.08
Atlantic Coast *restingas*	40.87	27.60
Bahia coastal forests	44.75	28.16
Bahia interior forests	37.58	27.44
Bolivian *Yungas*	12.40	16.75

Source: Wade, T. G., et al. "Distribution and causes of global forest fragmentation," *Conservation Ecology*, Vol. 72, No. 2, Dec. 2003 (Table 6).

  a. Ecologists theorize that a linear relationship exists between the two fragmentation indexes. Write the model relating y to x.
  b. Fit the model to the data in the **FORFRAG** file, using the method of least squares. Give the equation of the least squares prediction equation.
  c. Interpret the estimates of β_0 and β_1 in the context of the problem.
  d. Is there sufficient evidence to indicate that the natural origin index (x) and the anthropogenic index (y) are positively linearly related? Test, using $\alpha = .05$.
  e. Find and interpret a 95% confidence interval for the change in the anthropogenic index (y) for every 1-point increase in the natural origin index (x).

11.62 Pain empathy and brain activity. Empathy refers to being able to understand and vicariously feel what others actually feel. Neuroscientists at University College of London investigated the relationship between brain activity and pain-related empathy in persons who watch others in pain. (*Science,* Feb. 20, 2004.) Sixteen couples participated in the experiment. The female partner watched while painful stimulation was applied to the finger of her male partner. Two variables were measured for each female: y = pain-related brain activity (measured on a scale ranging from -2 to 2) and x = score on the Empathic Concern Scale (0 to 25 points). The data are listed in the accompanying table. The research question of interest was "Do people scoring higher in empathy show higher pain-related brain activity?" Use simple linear regression analysis to answer this question.

BRAINPAIN

Couple	Brain Activity (y)	Empathic Concern (x)
1	.05	12
2	−.03	13
3	.12	14
4	.20	16
5	.35	16
6	0	17
7	.26	17
8	.50	18
9	.20	18
10	.21	18
11	.45	19
12	.30	20
13	.20	21
14	.22	22
15	.76	23
16	.35	24

Source: Singer, T. et al. "Empathy for pain involves the affective but not sensory components of pain," *Science,* Vol. 303, Feb. 20, 2004. (Adapted from Figure 4.)

11.63 Relation of eye and head movements. How do eye and head movements relate to body movements when a person reacts to a visual stimulus? Scientists at the California Institute of Technology designed an experiment to answer this question and reported their results in *Nature* (Aug. 1998). Adult male rhesus monkeys were exposed to a visual stimulus (i.e., a panel of light-emitting diodes), and their eye, head, and body movements were electronically recorded. In one variation of the experiment, two variables were measured: active head movement (x, percent per degree) and body-plus-head rotation (y, percent per degree). The data for $n = 39$ trials were subjected to a simple linear regression analysis, with the following results: $\hat{\beta}_1 = .88$, $s_{\hat{\beta}_1} = .14$

a. Conduct a test to determine whether the two variables, active head movement x and body-plus-head rotation y are positively linearly related. Use $\alpha = .05$.

b. Construct and interpret a 90% confidence interval for β_1.

c. The scientists want to know whether the true slope of the line differs significantly from 1. On the basis of your answer to part **b**, make the appropriate inference.

NAMEGAME2

11.64 The "name game." Refer to the *Journal of Experimental Psychology—Applied* (June 2000) name-retrieval study,

presented in Exercise 11.30 (p. 577). Recall that the goal of the study was to investigate the linear trend between proportion of names recalled (y) and position (order) of the student (x) during the "name game." Is there sufficient evidence (at $\alpha = .01$) of a linear trend? Answer the question by analyzing the data for 144 students saved in the **NAMEGAME2** file. $t = 2.858$

Applying the Concepts—Advanced

11.65 Does elevation affect hitting performance in baseball? The Colorado Rockies play their major league home baseball games in Coors Field, Denver. Each year, the Rockies are among the leaders in team batting statistics (e.g., home runs, batting average, and slugging percentage). Many baseball experts attribute this phenomenon to the "thin air" of Denver—called the "Mile-High City" due to its elevation. *Chance* (Winter 2006) investigated the effects of elevation on slugging percentage in Major League Baseball. Data were compiled on players' composite slugging percentages at each of 29 cities for the 2003 season, as well as on each city's elevation (feet above sea level.) The data are saved in the **MLBPARKS** file. (Selected observations are shown in the accompanying table.) Consider a straight-line model relating slugging percentage (y) to elevation (x).

a. The model was fit to the data with the use of MINITAB, with the results shown in the printout (p. 591). Locate the estimates of the model parameters on the printout.

b. Is there sufficient evidence (at $\alpha = .01$) of a positive linear relationship between elevation (x) and slugging percentage (y)? Use the p-value shown on the printout to make the inference.

c. Construct a scatterplot of the data and draw the least squared line on the graph. Locate the data point for Denver on the graph. What do you observe?

d. Remove the data point for Denver from the data set and refit the straight-line model to the remaining data. Repeat parts **a** and **b**. What conclusions can you draw about the "thin air" theory from this analysis?

MLBPARKS (Selected observations)

City	Slug Pct.	Elevation
Anaheim	.480	160
Arlington	.605	616
Atlanta	.530	1,050
Baltimore	.505	130
Boston	.505	20
⋮	⋮	⋮
Denver	.625	5,277
⋮	⋮	⋮
Seattle	.550	350
San Francisco	.510	63
St. Louis	.570	465
Tampa	.500	10
Toronto	.535	566

Source: Schaffer, J., & Heiny, E.L. "The effects of elevation on slugging percentage in Major League Baseball," *Chance,* Vol. 19, No. 1, Winter 2006 (adapted from Figure 2).

Regression Analysis: SLUGPCT versus ELEVATION

```
The regression equation is
SLUGPCT = 0.515 + 0.000021 ELEVATION

Predictor          Coef      SE Coef        T       P
Constant       0.515140     0.007954    64.76   0.000
ELEVATION    0.00002074   0.00000719     2.89   0.008

S = 0.0369803   R-Sq = 23.6%   R-Sq(adj) = 20.7%

Analysis of Variance

Source            DF        SS         MS      F       P
Regression         1   0.011390   0.011390   8.33   0.008
Residual Error    27   0.036924   0.001368
Total             28   0.048314
```

MINITAB output for
Exercise 11.65

11.5 The Coefficients of Correlation and Determination

In this section, we present two statistics that describe the adequacy of a model: the *coefficient of correlation* and the *coefficient of determination*.

Coefficient of Correlation

Recall (from optional Section 2.9) that a **bivariate relationship** describes a relationship—or correlation—between two variables x and y. Scattergrams are used to describe a bivariate relationship graphically. In this section, we will discuss the concept of **correlation** and how it can be used to measure the linear relationship between two variables x and y. A numerical descriptive measure of correlation is provided by the *Pearson product moment coefficient of correlation*, r.

Definition 11.2

The **coefficient of correlation**,* r, is a measure of the strength of the *linear* relationship between two variables x and y. It is computed (for a sample of n measurements on x and y) as follows:

$$r = \frac{SS_{xy}}{\sqrt{SS_{xx}\,SS_{yy}}}$$

Note that the computational formula for the correlation coefficient r given in Definition 11.2 involves the same quantities that were used in computing the least squares prediction equation. In fact, since the numerators of the expressions for $\hat{\beta}_1$ and r are identical, it is clear that $r = 0$ when $\hat{\beta}_1 = 0$ (the case where x contributes no information for the prediction of y) and that r is positive when the slope is positive and negative when the slope is negative. Unlike $\hat{\beta}_1$, the correlation coefficient r is *scaleless* and assumes a value between -1 and $+1$, regardless of the units of x and y.

A value of r near or equal to 0 implies little or no linear relationship between y and x. In contrast, the closer r comes to 1 or -1, the stronger is the linear relationship between y and x. And if $r = 1$ or $r = -1$, all the sample points fall exactly on the least squares line. Positive values of r imply a positive linear relationship between y and x;

---

*The value of r is often called the *Pearson correlation coefficient* to honor its developer, Karl Pearson. (See Biography, p. 746.)

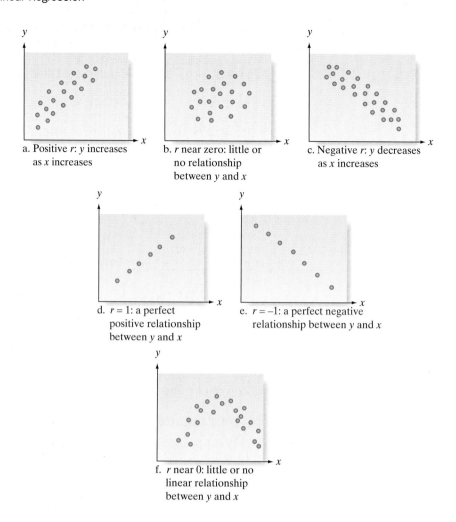

FIGURE 11.14

Values of r and their implications

that is, y increases as x increases. Negative values of r imply a negative linear relationship between y and x; that is, y decreases as x increases. Each of these situations is portrayed in Figure 11.14.

Now Work Exercise 11.69

We use the data in Table 11.1 for the drug reaction example to demonstrate how to calculate the coefficient of correlation, r. The quantities needed to calculate r are SS_{xy}, SS_{xx}, and SS_{yy}. The first two quantities have been calculated previously and are repeated here for convenience:

$$SS_{xy} = 7, \quad SS_{xx} = 10, \quad SS_{yy} = \sum y^2 - \frac{\left(\sum y\right)^2}{n}$$

$$= 26 - \frac{(10)^2}{5} = 26 - 20 = 6$$

We now find the coefficient of correlation:

$$r = \frac{SS_{xy}}{\sqrt{SS_{xx} \, SS_{yy}}} = \frac{7}{\sqrt{(10)(6)}} = \frac{7}{\sqrt{60}} = .904$$

The fact that r is positive and near 1 indicates that the reaction time tends to increase as the amount of drug in the bloodstream increases—*for the given sample of five subjects*. This is the same conclusion we reached when we found the calculated value of the least squares slope to be positive.

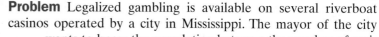

EXAMPLE 11.4

USING THE
CORRELATION
COEFFICIENT—
Relating Crime
Rate and Casino
Employment

Problem Legalized gambling is available on several riverboat casinos operated by a city in Mississippi. The mayor of the city wants to know the correlation between the number of casino employees and the yearly crime rate. The records for the past 10 years are examined, and the results listed in Table 11.5 are obtained. Calculate the coefficient of correlation, r, for the data. Interpret the result.

CASINO

TABLE 11.5 Data on Casino Employees and Crime Rate, Example 11.4

Year	Number x of Casino Employees (thousands)	Crime Rate y (number of crimes per 1,000 population)
1998	15	1.35
1999	18	1.63
2000	24	2.33
2001	22	2.41
2002	25	2.63
2003	29	2.93
2004	30	3.41
2005	32	3.26
2006	35	3.63
2007	38	4.15

Solution Rather than use the computing formula given in Definition 11.2, we resort to a statistical software package. The data of Table 11.5 were entered into a computer and MINITAB was used to compute r. The MINITAB printout is shown in Figure 11.15.

The coefficient of correlation, highlighted at the top of the printout, is $r = .987$. Thus, the size of the casino workforce and crime rate in this city are very highly correlated—at least over the past 10 years. The implication is that a strong positive linear relationship exists between these variables. (See Figure 11.15.) We must be careful, however, not to jump

---

Correlations: EMPLOYEES, CRIMERAT

```
Pearson correlation of EMPLOYEES and CRIMERAT = 0.987
P-Value = 0.000
```

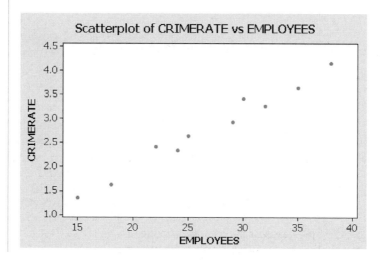

FIGURE 11.15

MINITAB correlation printout and scattergram for Example 11.4

to any unwarranted conclusions. For instance, the mayor may be tempted to conclude that hiring more casino workers next year will increase the crime rate—that is, that there is a *causal relationship* between the two variables. However, high correlation does not imply causality. The fact is, many things have probably contributed both to the increase in the casino workforce and to the increase in crime rate. The city's tourist trade has undoubtedly grown since riverboat casinos were legalized, and it is likely that the casinos have expanded both in services offered and in number. *We cannot infer a causal relationship on the basis of high sample correlation. When a high correlation is observed in the sample data, the only safe conclusion is that a linear trend may exist between x and y.*

Look Back Another variable, such as the increase in tourism, may be the underlying cause of the high correlation between x and y.

> Now Work Exercise 11.75a

Warning

Two caveats apply in using the sample correlation coefficient r to infer the nature of the relationship between x and y: (1) A *high correlation* does not necessarily imply that a causal relationship exists between x and y—only that a linear trend may exist; (2) a *low correlation* does not necessarily imply that x and y are unrelated—only that x and y are not strongly linearly related.

Keep in mind that the correlation coefficient r measures the linear correlation between x values and y values in the sample, and a similar linear coefficient of correlation exists for the population from which the data points were selected. The **population correlation coefficient** is denoted by the symbol ρ (rho). As you might expect, ρ is estimated by the corresponding sample statistic r. Or, instead of estimating ρ, we might want to test the null hypothesis $H_0: \rho = 0$ against $H_a: \rho \neq 0$; that is, we can test the hypothesis that x contributes no information for the prediction of y by using the straight-line model against the alternative that the two variables are at least linearly related.

However, we already performed this *identical* test in Section 11.5 when we tested $H_0: \beta_1 = 0$ against $H_a: \beta_1 \neq 0$. That is, the null hypothesis $H_0: \rho = 0$ is equivalent to the hypothesis $H_0: \beta_1 = 0$.* When we tested the null hypothesis $H_0: \beta_1 = 0$ in connection with the drug reaction example, the data led to a rejection of the null hypothesis at the $\alpha = .05$ level. This rejection implies that the null hypothesis of a 0 linear correlation between the two variables (drug and reaction time) can also be rejected at the $\alpha = .05$ level. The only real difference between the least squares slope $\hat{\beta}_1$ and the coefficient of correlation, r, is the measurement scale. Therefore, the information they provide about the usefulness of the least squares model is to some extent redundant. For this reason, we will use the slope to make inferences about the existence of a positive or negative linear relationship between two variables.

ACTIVITY 11.2: *Keep the Change:* Correlation Coefficients

In this activity, you will use data collected in Activity 1.1 *Keep the Change: Collecting Data* (p. 12), and the results from Activity 11.1, *Keep the Change: Least Squares Models* (p. 570), to study the strength of a linear relationship.

1. For each of the least squares models in Exercises 1 and 4 in Activity 11.1, calculate the corresponding correlation coefficient. Do these values support your conclusion about which model is more useful? Explain?

2. For each purchase in your original data set *Purchase Totals*, form the ordered pair.

   (Purchase Total, Amount Transferred)

   Calculate the correlation coefficient and discuss the strength of the linear relationship between the two variables. Explain why you might expect the slope of the corresponding least squares line to be close to zero. Find the least squares model and comment on its usefulness.

---

*The correlation test statistic that is equivalent to $t = \hat{\beta}_1/s_{\hat{\beta}_1}$ is $t = \dfrac{r}{\sqrt{(1 - r^2)/(n - 2)}}$.

Does the model produce estimated values that are meaningless for large purchase totals? Explain.

3. For each student in your class, form the ordered pair

(*Sum of Amounts Transferred, Bank Matching*)

Calculate the correlation coefficient. How strong is the linear relationship between the two variables? Find the least

squares model. Is the slope $\hat{\beta}_1$ approximately 13 and the y-intercept $\hat{\beta}_0$ approximately 0? Explain why the line should have that slope and y-intercept. How good are the estimates given by the model in this situation?

Coefficient of Determination

Another way to measure the usefulness of a linear model is to measure the contribution of x in predicting y. To accomplish this, we calculate how much the errors of prediction of y were reduced by using the information provided by x. To illustrate, consider the sample shown in the scattergram of Figure 11.16a. If we assume that x contributes no information for the prediction of y, the best prediction for a value of y is the sample mean $\bar{y}$, which is shown as the horizontal line in Figure 11.16b. The vertical line segments in Figure 11.16b are the deviations of the points about the mean $\bar{y}$. Note that the sum of the squares of the deviations for the prediction equation $\hat{y} = \bar{y}$ is

$$SS_{yy} = \sum (y_i - \bar{y})^2$$

Now suppose you fit a least squares line to the same set of data and locate the deviations of the points about the line, as shown in Figure 11.16c. Compare the deviations about the prediction lines in Figures 11.16b and 11.16c. You can see that

1. If x contributes little or no information for the prediction of y, the sums of the squares of the deviations for the two lines

$$SS_{yy} = \sum (y_i - \bar{y})^2 \quad \text{and} \quad SSE = \sum (y_i - \hat{y}_i)^2$$

will be nearly equal.

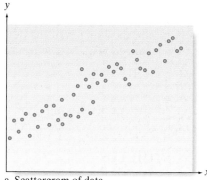

a. Scattergram of data

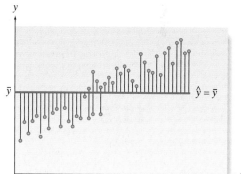

b. Assumption: x contributes no information
for predicting y, $\hat{y} = \bar{y}$

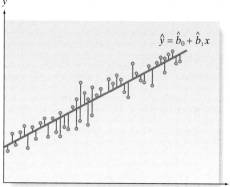

c. Assumption: x contributes information
for predicting y, $\hat{y} = \hat{\beta}_0 + \hat{\beta}_1 x$

FIGURE 11.16
A comparison of the sum of squares of deviations for two models

2. If x does contribute information for the prediction of y, the SSE will be smaller than SS_{yy}. In fact, if all the points fall on the least squares line, then SSE $= 0$.

Consequently, the reduction in the sum of the squares of the deviations that can be attributed to x, expressed as a proportion of SS_{yy}, is

$$\frac{SS_{yy} - SSE}{SS_{yy}}$$

Note that SS_{yy} is the "total sample variability" of the observations around the mean $\bar{y}$ and that SSE is the remaining "unexplained sample variability" after fitting the line $\hat{y}$. Thus, the difference $(SS_{yy} - SSE)$ is the "explained sample variability" attributable to the linear relationship with x. Thus, a verbal description of the proportion is

$$\frac{SS_{yy} - SSE}{SS_{yy}} = \frac{\text{Explained sample variability}}{\text{Total sample variability}}$$

$$= \text{Proportion of total sample variability explained by the linear relationship}$$

In simple linear regression, it can be shown that this proportion—called the *coefficient of determination*—is equal to the square of the simple linear coefficient of correlation, r.

Definition 11.3

The **coefficient of determination** is

$$r^2 = \frac{SS_{yy} - SSE}{SS_{yy}} = 1 - \frac{SSE}{SS_{yy}}$$

and represents the proportion of the total sample variability around $\bar{y}$ that is explained by the linear relationship between y and x. (In simple linear regression, it may also be computed as the square of the coefficient of correlation, r.)

Note that r^2 is always between 0 and 1, because r is between -1 and $+1$. Thus, an r^2 of .60 means that the sum of the squares of the deviations of the y values about their predicted values has been reduced 60% by the use of the least squares equation $\hat{y}$, instead of $\bar{y}$, to predict y.

EXAMPLE 11.5
OBTAINING THE VALUE OF r^2—
Drug Reaction Regression

Problem Calculate the coefficient of determination for the drug reaction example. The data are repeated in Table 11.6 for convenience. Interpret the result.

 **STIMULUS**

TABLE 11.6

Percent x of Drug	Reaction Time y (seconds)
1	1
2	1
3	2
4	2
5	4

Solution From previous calculations,

$$SS_{yy} = 6 \quad \text{and} \quad SSE = \sum(y - \hat{y})^2 = 1.10$$

Then, from Definition 11.3, the coefficient of determination is

$$r^2 = \frac{SS_{yy} - SSE}{SS_{yy}} = \frac{6.0 - 1.1}{6.0} = \frac{4.9}{6.0} = .817$$

Model Summary

Model	R	R Square	Adjusted R Square	Std. Error of the Estimate
1	.904ª	.817	.756	.606

a. Predictors: (Constant), DRUG_X

FIGURE 11.17
Portion of SPSS printout for time-drug regression

Another way to compute r^2 is to recall from Section 11.5 that $r = .904$. Then we have $r^2 = (.904)^2 = .817$. A third way to obtain r^2 is from a computer printout. Its value is highlighted on the SPSS printout in Figure 11.17. Our interpretation is as follows: We know that using the percent x of drug in the blood to predict y with the least squares line

$$\hat{y} = -.1 + .7x$$

accounts for nearly 82% of the total sum of the squares of the deviations of the five sample y values about their mean. Or, stated another way, 82% of the sample variation in reaction time (y) can be "explained" by using the percent x of drug in a straight-line model.

Now Work Exercise 11.75b

Practical Interpretation of the Coefficient of Determination, r^2

$100(r^2)\%$ of the sample variation in y (measured by the total sum of the squares of the deviations of the sample y values about their mean $\bar{y}$) can be explained by (or attributed to) using x to predict y in the straight-line model.

Simple Linear Regression

Using the TI-84/TI-83 Graphing Calculator
Finding r and r^2

Step 1   *Enter the data.*

Press **STAT** and select **1:Edit**.
Note: If a list already contains data, clear the old data. Use the up arrow to highlight the list name, **L1** or **L.2'**.
Press **CLEAR ENTER**.
Enter your x-data into **L1** and your y-data into **L2**.

Step 2   *Turn the diagnostics feature on.*

Press **2nd 0** for **CATALOG**.
Press the key for **D**.
Press the down arrow key until **Diagnostics On** is highlighted.
Press **ENTER** twice.

Step 3   *Find the equation.*

Press **START** and highlight **CALC**.
Press 4 for LinReg (**ax + b**).
Press **ENTER**.
The screen will show the values for a and b in the equation $y = ax + b$.
The values for r and r^2 will appear on the screen as well.

```
LinReg
 y=ax+b
 a=2.495967742
 b=63.3391129
 r²=.9620199454
 r=.9808261545
```

Example   The figure shows the form of the output with the **DiagnosticsOn.**

STATISTICS IN ACTION REVISED

Using the Coefficients of Correlation and Determination to Assess the Dowsing Data

In the previous Statistics in Action Revisited, we discovered that using a dowser's guess (x) in a straight-line model was not statistically useful in predicting actual pipe location (y). Both the coefficient of correlation and the coefficient of determination (highlighted on the MINITAB) printouts in Figure SIA11.4) also support this conclusion. The value of the correlation coef-ficient, $r = .314$, indicates a fairly weak positive linear relationship between the variables. This value, how-ever, is not statistically significant (p-value $= .118$). in other words, there is no evidence to indicate that the population correlation coefficient is different from 0. The coefficient of determination, $r^2 = .099$, implies that only about 10% of the sample variation in pipe location values can be explained by the simple linear model.

Regression Analysis: PIPE versus GUESS

```
The regression equation is
PIPE = 30.1 + 0.308 GUESS


Predictor       Coef   SE Coef       T      P
Constant       30.07     11.41    2.63  0.015
GUESS         0.3079    0.1900    1.62  0.118


S = 26.0298    R-Sq = 9.9%    R-Sq(adj) = 6.1%


Analysis of Variance


Source           DF        SS        MS      F     P
Regression        1    1778.9    1778.9   2.63  0.118
Residual Error   24   16261.2     677.6
Total            25   18040.2
```

FIGURE SIA11.4

MINITAB printouts with coefficients of correlation and determination for the dowsing data

Correlations: PIPE, GUESS

```
Pearson correlation of PIPE and GUESS = 0.314
P-Value = 0.118
```

Exercises 11.66–11.86

Understanding the Principles

11.66 Describe the slope of the least squares line if
    a. $r = .7$ **b.** $r = -.7$ **c.** $r = 0$ **d.** $r^2 = .64$

11.67 *True or False.* The correlation coefficient is a measure of the strength of the linear relationship between x and y.

11.68 *True or False.* A value of the correlation coefficient near 1 or near -1 implies a causal relationship between x and y.

11.69 Explain what each of the following sample correlation co-
NW efficients tells you about the relationship between the x and y values in the sample:
    a. $r = 1$ **b.** $r = -1$
    c. $r = 0$ **d.** $r = .90$
    e. $r = .10$ **f.** $r = -.88$

Learning the Mechanics

11.70 Calculate r^2 for the least squares line in Exercise 11.14 (p. 572).

11.71 Calculate r^2 for the least squares line in Exercise 11.17 (p. 573).

11.72 Construct a scattergram for each data set. Then calculate r and r^2 for each data set. Interpret their values.

a.

x	-2	-1	0	1	2
y	-2	1	2	5	6

b.

x	-2	-1	0	1	2
y	6	5	3	2	0

c.

x	1	2	2	3	3	3	4
y	2	1	3	1	2	3	2

d.

x	0	1	3	5	6
y	0	1	2	1	0

Applet Exercise 11.2

Use the applet entitled *Correlation by the Eye* to explore the relationship between the pattern of data in a scattergram and the corresponding correlation coefficient.

    a. Run the applet several times. Each times, guess the value of the correlation coefficient. Then click *Show r* to see the actual correlation coefficient. How close is your value to the actual value of *r*? Click *New data* to reset the applet.

    b. Click the trash can to clear the graph. Use the mouse to place five points on the scattergram that are approximately in a straight line. Then guess the value of the correlation coefficient. Click *Show r* to see the actual correlation coefficient. How close were you this time?

    c. Continue to clear the graph and plot sets of five points with different patterns among the points. Guess the value of *r*. How close do you come to the actual value of *r* each time?

    d. On the basis of your experiences with the applet, explain why we need to use more reliable methods of finding the correlation coefficient than just "eyeing" it.

Applying the Concepts—Basic

11.73 Physical activity of obese young adults. Refer to the *International Journal of Obesity* (January 2007) study of the physical activity of obese young adults, presented in Exercise 6.35 (p. 296). For two groups of young adults—13 obese and 15 of normal weight—researchers recorded the total number of registered movements (counts) of each your adult over a period of time. *Baseline* physical activity was then computed as the number of counts per minute (cpm). Four years later, physical activity measurements were taken again—called physical activity *at follow-up*.

    a. For the 13 obese young adults, the researchers reported a correlation of $r = .50$ between baseline and follow-up physical activity, with an associated *p*-value of .07. Give a practical interpretation of this correlation coefficient and *p*-value.

    b. Refer to part **a**. Construct a scatterplot of the 13 data points that would yield a value or $r = .50$.

    c. For the 15 young adults of normal weight, the researchers reported a correlation of $r = -.12$ between baseline and follow-up physical activity, with an associated *p*-value of .66. Give a practical interpretation of this correlation coefficient and *p*-value.

    d. Refer to part **c**. Construct a scatterplot of the 15 data points that would yield a value of $r = -12$.

11.74 Wind turbine blade stress. Refer to the *Wind Engineering* (Jan. 2004) study of two types of timber—radiata pine and hoop pine—used in high-efficiency small wind turbine blades, presented in Exercise 11.19 (p. 573). Data on stress (*y*) and the natural logarithm of the number of blade cycles (*x*) for each type of timber were analyzed by means of simple linear regression. The results are as follows, with additional information on the coefficient of determination:

Radiata Pine: $\hat{y} = 97.37 - 2.50x$, $r^2 = .84$
Hoop Pine: $\hat{y} = 122.03 - 2.36x$, $r^2 = .90$

Interpret the value of r^2 for each type of timber.

11.75 Sports news on local TV broadcasts. *The Sports Journal*
NW   (Winter 2004) published the results of a study conducted to assess the factors that affect the time allotted to sports news on local television news broadcasts. Information on total time (in minutes) allotted to sports and on audience ratings of the TV news broadcast (measured on a 100-point scale) was obtained from a national sample of 163 news directors. A correlation analysis of the data yielded $r = .43$.

    a. Interpret the value of the correlation coefficient *r*.

    b. Find and interpret the value of the coefficient of determination r^2.

11.76 English as a second language reading ability. Refer to the *Bilingual Research Journal* (Summer 2006) study of the relationship of Spanish (first-language) grammatical knowledge to English (second-language) reading, presented in Exercise 11.54 (p. 588). Recall that each in a sample of $n = 55$ native Spanish-speaking adults took four standardized exams: Spanish grammar (SG), Spanish reading, (SR), English grammar (EG), and English reading (ESLR). Simple linear regressions were used to model the ESLR score (*y*) as a function of each of the other exam scores (*x*). The coefficient of determination, r^2, for each model is listed in the accompanying table. Give a practical interpretation of each of these values.

Independent Variable (x)	r^2
SG score	.002
SR score	.099
ER score	.078

11.77 Redshifts of quasi-stellar objects. Refer to the *Journal of Astrophysics & Astronomy* (Mar./Jun. 2003) study of redshifts in quasi-stellar objects presented in Exercise 11.23 (p. 575). Recall that simple linear regression was used to model the magnitude (*y*) of a quasu-stellar object as a function of the redshift level (*x*). In addition to the least squares line, $\hat{y} = 18.13 + 6.21x$, the coefficient of correlation was determined to be $r = .84$.

    a. Interpret the value of *r* in the words of the problem.

    b. What is the relationship between *r* and the estimated slope of the line?

    c. Find and interpret the value of r^2.

11.78 Removing metal from water. In the *Electronic Journal of Biotechnology* (Apr. 15, 2004), Egyptian scientists studied a new method for removing heavy metals from water. Metal solutions were prepared in glass vessels, and then biosorption was used to remove the metal ions. Two variables were measured for each test vessel: $y = $ metal uptake (milligrams of metal per gram of biosorbent) and $x = $ final concentration of metal in the solution (milligrams per liter).

    a. Write a simple linear regression model relating *y* to *x*.

    b. For one metal, a simple linear regression analysis yielded $r^2 = .92$. Interpret this result.

Applying the Concepts—Intermediate

11.79 Performance in online courses. Florida State University information scientists assessed the impact of online courses on student performance (*Educational Technology & Society*, Jan. 2005). Each in a sample of 24 graduate students enrolled in an online advanced Web application course was asked, "How many courses per semester (on average) do you take online?" Each student's performance on weekly quizzes was also recorded. The information scientists found that the number of online courses and the weekly quiz grade were negatively correlated at $r = -.726$.

a. Give a practical interpretation of r.

b. The researchers concluded that there was a "significant negative correlation" between the number of online courses and the weekly quiz grade. Do you agree?

11.80 Salary linked to height. Are short people shortchanged when it comes to salary? According to business professors T. A. Judge (University of Florida) and D. M. Cable (University of North Carolina), tall people tend to earn more money over their career than short people earn. (*Journal of Applied Psychology*, June 2004.) Using data collected from participants in the National Longitudinal Surveys begun in 1979, the researchers computed the correlation between average earnings (in dollars) from 1985 to 2000 and height (in inches) for several occupations. The results are given in the following table:

Occupation	Correlation, r	Sample Size, n
Sales	.41	117
Managers	.35	455
Blue Collar	.32	349
Service Workers	.31	265
Professional/Technical	.30	453
Clerical	.25	358
Crafts/Forepersons	.24	250

Source: Judge, T. A., & Cable, D. M. "The effect of physical height on workplace success and income: Preliminary test of a theoretical model," *Journal of Applied Psychology*, Vol. 89, No. 3, June 2004 (Table 5).

a. Interpret the value of r for people in sales occupations.

b. Compute r^2 for people in sales occupations. Interpret the result.

c. Give H_0 and H_a for testing whether average earnings and height are positively correlated.

d. The test statistic for testing H_0 and H_a in part **c** is $t = \dfrac{r\sqrt{n-2}}{\sqrt{1-r^2}}$. Compute the value of t for people in sales occupations.

e. Use the result you obtained in part **d** to conduct the test at $\alpha = .01$. State the appropriate conclusion.

f. Select another occupation and repeat parts **a–e**.

11.81 View of rotated objects. *Perception & Psychophysics* (July 1998) reported on a study of how people view three-dimensional objects projected onto a rotating two-dimensional image. Each in a sample of 25 university students viewed various depth-rotated objects (e.g., a hairbrush, a duck, and a shoe) until they recognized the object. The recognition exposure time—that is, the minimum time (in milliseconds) required for the subject to recognize the object—was recorded for each object. In addition, each subject rated the "goodness of view" of the object on a numerical scale, with lower scale values corresponding to better views. The following table gives the correlation coefficient r between recognition exposure time and goodness of view for several different rotated objects:

Object	r	t
Piano	.447	2.40
Bench	−.057	.27
Motorbike	.619	3.78
Armchair	.294	1.47
Teapot	.949	14.50

a. Interpret the value of r for each object.

b. Calculate and interpret the value of r^2 for each object.

c. The table also includes the t-value for testing the null hypothesis of no correlation (i.e., for testing $H_0: \beta_1 = 0$). Interpret these results.

11.82 Snow geese feeding trial. Botanists at the University of Toronto conducted a series of experiments to investigate the feeding habits of baby snow geese. (*Journal of Applied Ecology*, Vol. 32, 1995.) Goslings were deprived of food until their guts were empty and then were allowed to feed for 6 hours on a diet of plants or Purina® Duck Chow®. For each feeding trial, the change in the weight of the gosling after 2.5 hours was recorded as a percentage of the bird's initial weight. Two other variables recorded were digestion efficiency (measured as a percentage) and amount of acid-detergent fiber in the digestive tract (also measured

SNOWGEESE (First and last 5 observations listed)

Feeding Trial	Diet	Weight Change (%)	Digestion Efficiency (%)	Acid-Detergent Fiber (%)
1	Plants	−6	0	28.5
2	Plants	−5	2.5	27.5
3	Plants	−4.5	5	27.5
4	Plants	0	0	32.5
5	Plants	2	0	32
⋮	⋮	⋮	⋮	⋮
38	Duck Chow	9	59	8.5
39	Duck Chow	12	52.5	8
40	Duck Chow	8.5	75	6
41	Duck Chow	10.5	72.5	6.5
42	Duck Chow	14	69	7

Source: Gadallah, F. L., and Jefferies, R. L. "Forage quality in brood rearing areas of the lesser snow goose and the growth of captive goslings," *Journal of Applied Biology*, Vol. 32, No. 2, 1995, pp. 281–282 (adapted from Figures 2 and 3).

as a percentage). Data on 42 feeding trials are saved in the **SNOWGEESE** file. The first and last 5 observations are listed in the table (bottom, p. 600).

a. The botanists were interested in the correlation between weight change (y) and digestion efficiency (x). Plot the data for these two variables in a scattergram. Do you observe a trend?

b. Find the coefficient of correlation relating weight change y to digestion efficiency x. Interpret this value.

c. Conduct a test to determine whether weight change y is correlated with digestion efficiency x. Use $\alpha = .01$.

d. Repeat parts **b** and **c**, but exclude the data for trials that used duck chow. What do you conclude?

e. The botanists were also interested in the correlation between digestion efficiency y and acid-detergent fibre x. Repeat parts **a–d** for these two variables.

11.83 Dance/movement therapy. In cotherapy, two or more therapists lead a group. An article in the *American Journal of Dance Therapy* (Spring/Summer 1995) examined the use of cotherapy in dance/movement therapy. Two of several variables measured on each of a sample of 136 professional dance/movement therapists were years x of formal training and reported success rate y (measured as a percentage) of coleading dance/movement therapy groups.

a. Propose a linear model relating y to x.

b. The researcher hypothesized that dance/movement therapists with more years in formal dance training will report higher perceived success rates in cotherapy relationships. State the hypothesis in terms of the parameter of the model you proposed in part **a**.

c. The correlation coefficient for the sample data was reported as $r = -.26$. Interpret this result.

d. Does the value of r in part **c** support the hypothesis in part **b**? Test, using $\alpha = .05$. [*Hint:* See the last footnote at the bottom of page 594.]

● **NAMEGAME2**

11.84 The "name game." Refer to the *Journal of Experimental Psychology—Applied* (June 2000) name-retrieval study, first presented in Exercise 11.30 (p. 578). Find and interpret the values of r and r^2 for the simple linear regression relating the proportion of names recalled (y) and the position (order) of the student (x) during the "name game."

● **BOXING2**

11.85 Effect of massage on boxing. Refer to the *British Journal of Sports Medicine* (April 2000) study of the effect of massage on boxing performance, presented in Exercise 11.60 (p. 589). Find and interpret the values of r and r^2 for the simple linear regression relating the blood lactate concentration and the boxer's perceived recovery.

Applying the Concepts—Advanced

11.86 Pain tolerance study. A study published in *Psychosomatic Medicine* (Mar./Apr. 2001) explored the relationship between reported severity of pain and actual pain tolerance in 337 patients who suffer from chronic pain. Each patient reported his or her severity of chronic pain on a seven-point scale ($1 = $ no pain, $7 = $ extreme pain). To obtain a pain tolerance level, a tourniquet was applied to the arm of each patient and twisted. The maximum pain level tolerated was measured on a quantitative scale.

a. According to the researchers, "Correlational analysis revealed a small but significant inverse relationship between [actual] pain tolerance and the reported severity of chronic pain." On the basis of this statement, is the value of r for the 337 patients positive or negative?

b. Suppose that the result reported in part **a** is significant at $\alpha = .05$. Find the approximate value of r for the sample of 337 patients. [*Hint:* Use the formula $t = r\sqrt{(n-2)}/\sqrt{(1-r^2)}$.]

11.6 Using the Model for Estimation and Prediction

If we are satisfied that a useful model has been found to describe the relationship between reaction time and percent of drug in the bloodstream, we are ready for step 5 in our regression modeling procedure: using the model for estimation and prediction.

> *The most common uses of a probabilistic model for making inferences can be divided into two categories. The first is the use of the model for estimating the mean value of y, E(y), for a specific value of x.*

For our drug reaction example, we may want to estimate the mean response time for all people whose blood contains 4% of the drug.

> *The second use of the model entails predicting a new individual y value for a given x.*

That is, we may want to predict the reaction time for a specific person who possesses 4% of the drug in the bloodstream.

In the first case, we are attempting to estimate the mean value of y for a very large number of experiments at the given x value. In the second case, we are trying to predict the outcome of a single experiment at the given x value. Which of these uses of the model—estimating the mean value of y or predicting an individual new value of y (for the same value of x)—can be accomplished with the greater accuracy?

Before answering this question, we first consider the problem of choosing an estimator (or predictor) of the mean (or a new individual) y value. We will use the least squares prediction equation

$$\hat{y} = \hat{\beta}_0 + \hat{\beta}_1 x$$

both to estimate the mean value of y and to predict a specific new value of y for a given value of x. For our example, we found that

$$\hat{y} = -.1 + .7x$$

so the estimated mean reaction time for all people when $x = 4$ (the drug is 4% of the blood content) is

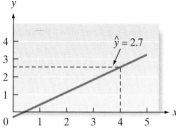

FIGURE 11.18

Estimated mean value and predicted individual value of reaction time y for $x = 4$

$$\hat{y} = -.1 + .7(4) = 2.7 \text{ seconds}$$

The same value is used to predict a new y value when $x = 4$. That is, both the estimated mean and the predicted value of y are $\hat{y} = 2.7$ when $x = 4$, as shown in Figure 11.18.

The difference between these two uses of the model lies in the accuracies of the estimate and the prediction, best measured by the sampling errors of the least squares line when it is used as an estimator and as a predictor, respectively. These errors are reflected in the standard deviations given in the following box:

Sampling Errors for the Estimator of the Mean of y and the Predictor of an Individual New Value of y

1.   The standard deviation of the sampling distribution of the estimator $\hat{y}$ of the mean value of y at a specific value of x, say x_p, is

$$\sigma_{\hat{y}} = \sigma \sqrt{\frac{1}{n} + \frac{(x_p - \overline{x})^2}{SS_{xx}}}$$

where σ is the standard deviation of the random error ε. We refer to $\sigma_{\hat{y}}$ as the standard error of $\hat{y}$.

2.   The standard deviation of the prediction error for the predictor $\hat{y}$ of an individual new y value at a specific value of x is

$$\sigma_{(y-\hat{y})} = \sigma \sqrt{1 + \frac{1}{n} + \frac{(x_p - \overline{x})^2}{SS_{xx}}}$$

where σ is the standard deviation of the random error ε. We refer to $\sigma_{(y-\hat{y})}$ as the standard error of prediction.

The true value of σ is rarely known, so we estimate σ by s and calculate the estimation and prediction intervals as shown in the next two boxes:

A 100$(1 - \alpha)$% Confidence Interval for the Mean Value of y at $x = x_p$

$$\hat{y} + t_{\alpha/2}(\text{Estimated standard error of } \hat{y})$$

or

$$\hat{y} \pm t_{\alpha/2} s \sqrt{\frac{1}{n} + \frac{(x_p - \overline{x})^2}{SS_{xx}}}$$

where $t_{\alpha/2}$ is based on $(n - 2)$ degrees of freedom.

A 100(1 − α)% Prediction Interval* for an Individual New Value of y at x = x_p

$$\hat{y} \pm t_{\alpha/2}(\text{Estimated standard error of prediction})$$

or

$$\hat{y} \pm t_{\alpha/2}s\sqrt{1 + \frac{1}{n} + \frac{(x_p - \bar{x})^2}{SS_{xx}}}$$

where $t_{\alpha/2}$ is based on $(n - 2)$ degrees of freedom.

EXAMPLE 11.6

ESTIMATING THE MEAN OF *y*—Drug Reaction Regression

Problem Refer to the simple linear regression on drug reaction. Find a 95% confidence interval for the mean reaction time when the concentration of the drug in the bloodstream is 4%.

Solution For a 4% concentration, $x = 4$ and the confidence interval for the mean value of *y* is

$$\hat{y} \pm t_{\alpha/2}s\sqrt{\frac{1}{n} + \frac{(x_p - \bar{x})^2}{SS_{xx}}} = \hat{y} \pm t_{.025}s\sqrt{\frac{1}{5} + \frac{(4 - \bar{x})^2}{SS_{xx}}}$$

where $t_{.025}$ is based on $n - 2 = 5 - 2 = 3$ degrees of freedom. Recall that $\hat{y} = 2.7$, $s = .61$, $\bar{x} = 3$, and $SS_{xx} = 10$. From Table VI in Appendix A, $t_{.025} = 3.182$. Thus, we have

$$2.7 \pm (3.182)(.61)\sqrt{\frac{1}{5} + \frac{(4 - 3)^2}{10}} = 2.7 \pm (3.182)(.61)(.55)$$

$$= 2.7 \pm (3.182)(.34)$$

$$= 2.7 \pm 1.1$$

Therefore, when the percentage of drug in the bloodstream is 4%, we can be 95% confident that the mean reaction time for all possible subjects will range from 1.6 to 3.8 seconds.

Look Back Note that we used a small amount of data (a small sample size) for purposes of illustration in fitting the least squares line. The interval would probably be narrower if more information had been obtained from a larger sample.

Now Work Exercise 11.92a–d

EXAMPLE 11.7

PREDICTING AN INDIVIDUAL VALUE OF *y*— Drug Reaction Regression

Problem Refer again to the drug reaction regression. Predict the reaction time for the next performance of the experiment for a subject with a drug concentration of 4%. Use a 95% prediction interval.

Solution To predict the response time for an individual new subject for whom $x = 4$, we calculate the 95% prediction interval as

$$\hat{y} \pm t_{\alpha/2}s\sqrt{1 + \frac{1}{n} + \frac{(x_p - \bar{x})^2}{SS_{xx}}} = 2.7 \pm (3.182)(.61)\sqrt{1 + \frac{1}{5} + \frac{(4 - 3)^2}{10}}$$

$$= 2.7 \pm (3.182)(.61)(1.14)$$

$$= 2.7 \pm (3.182)(.70)$$

$$= 2.7 \pm 2.2$$

---

*The term *prediction interval* is used when the interval formed is intended to enclose the value of a random variable. The term *confidence interval* is reserved for the estimation of population parameters (such as the mean).

Therefore, when the drug concentration for an individual is 4%, we predict with 95% confidence that the reaction time for this new individual will fall into the interval from .5 to 4.9 seconds.

Look Back Like the confidence interval for the mean value of y, the prediction interval for y is quite large. This is because we have chosen a simple example (one with only five data points) to fit the least squares line. The width of the prediction interval could be reduced by using a larger number of data points.

Now Work Exercise 11.92e

Both the confidence interval for $E(y)$ and the prediction interval for y can be obtained from a statistical software package. Figure 11.19 is a MINITAB printout showing the confidence interval and prediction interval, respectively, for the data in the drug example.

The 95% confidence interval for $E(y)$ when $x = 4$, highlighted under "95% CI" in Figure 11.19, is $(1.645, 3.755)$. The 95% prediction interval for y when $x = 4$, highlighted in Figure 11.19 under "95% PI", is $(.503, 4.897)$. These agree with the ones computed in Examples 11.6 and 11.7.

Note that the prediction interval for an individual new value of y is *always* wider than the corresponding confidence interval for the mean value of y. Will this always be true? The answer is "Yes." The error in estimating the mean value of y, $E(y)$, for a given value of x, say, x_p, is the distance between the least squares line and the true line of means, $E(y) = \beta_0 + \beta_1 x$. This error, $[\hat{y} - E(y)]$, is shown in Figure 11.20. In contrast, *the error* $(y_p - \hat{y})$ *in predicting some future value of y is the sum of two errors*: the error in estimating the mean of y, $E(y)$, shown in Figure 11.20, plus the random error that is a component of the value of y that is to be predicted. (See Figure 11.21.) Consequently,

```
Predicted Values for New Observations

New
Obs    Fit   SE Fit      95% CI           95% PI
  1  2.700   0.332  (1.645, 3.755)   (0.503, 4.897)


Values of Predictors for New Observations

New
Obs   DRUG_X
  1    4.00
```

FIGURE 11.19

MINITAB printout giving 95% confidence interval for $E(y)$ and 95% prediction interval for y

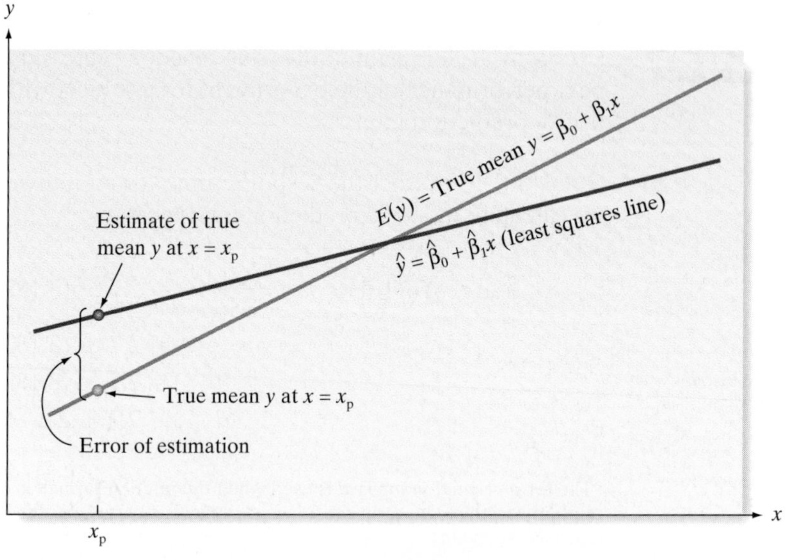

FIGURE 11.20

Error in estimating the mean value of y for a given value of x

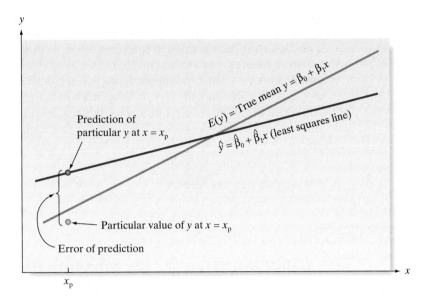

FIGURE 11.21

Error in predicting a future value of y for a given value of x

the error in predicting a particular value of y will be larger than the error in estimating the mean value of y for a particular value of x. Note from their formulas that both the error of estimation and the error of prediction take their smallest values when $x_p = \bar{x}$. The farther x_p lies from $\bar{x}$, the larger will be the errors of estimation and prediction. You can see why this is true by noting the deviations for different values of x_p between the actual line of means $E(y) = \beta_0 + \beta_1 x$ and the predicted line of means $\hat{y} = \hat{\beta}_0 + \hat{\beta}_1 x$ shown in Figure 11.21. The deviation is larger at the extremes of the interval, where the largest and smallest values of x in the data set occur.

Both the confidence intervals for mean values and the prediction intervals for new values are depicted over the entire range of the regression line in Figure 11.22. You can see that the confidence interval is always narrower than the prediction interval and that they are both narrowest at the mean $\bar{x}$, increasing steadily as the distance $|x - \bar{x}|$ increases. In fact, when x is selected far enough away from $\bar{x}$ so that it falls outside the range of the sample data, it is dangerous to make any inferences about $E(y)$ or y.

Caution

Using the least squares prediction equation to estimate the mean value of y or to predict a particular value of y for values of x that fall outside the range of the values of x contained in your sample data may lead to errors of estimation or prediction that are much larger than expected. Although the least squares model may provide a very good fit to the data over the range of x values contained in the sample, it could give a poor representation of the true model for values of x outside that region.

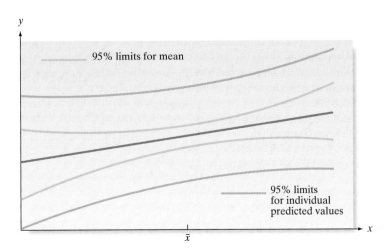

FIGURE 11.22

Confidence intervals for mean values and prediction intervals for new values

The width of the confidence interval grows smaller as n is increased; thus, in theory, you can obtain as precise an estimate of the mean value of y as desired (at any given x) by selecting a large enough sample. The prediction interval for a new value of y also grows smaller as n increases, but there is a lower limit on its width. If you examine the formula for the prediction interval, you will see that the interval can get no smaller than $\hat{y} \pm z_{\alpha/2}\sigma$.* Thus, the only way to obtain more accurate predictions for new values of y is to reduce the standard deviation σ of the regression model. This can be accomplished only by improving the model, either by using a curvilinear (rather than linear) relationship with x or by adding new independent variables to the model (or both). Methods of improving the model are discussed in Chapter 12.

> Now Work Exercise 11.92f

STATISTICS IN ACTION REVISITED

Using the Straight-Line Model to Predict Pipe Location for the Dowsing Data

The group of German physicists who conducted the dowsing experiments stated that the data for the three "best" dowsers empirically support the dowsing theory. If so, then the straight-line model relating a dowser's guess (x) to actual pipe location (y) should yield accurate predictions. The MINITAB printout shown in Figure SIA11.5 gives a 95% prediction interval for y when a dowser guesses $x = 50$ meters (the middle of the 100-meter-long waterpipe). The highlighted interval is $(-9.3, 100.23)$. Thus, we can be 95% confident that the actual pipe location will fall between -9.3 meters and 100.23 meters for this guess. Since the pipe is only 100 meters long, the interval in effect ranges from 0 to 100 meters—the entire length of the pipe! This result, of course, is due to the fact that the straight-line model is not a statistically useful predictor of pipe location, a fact we discovered in the previous Statistics in Action Revisited sections.

```
Predicted Values for New Observations

New
Obs    Fit   SE Fit      95% CI           95% PI
  1  45.47    5.15   (34.83, 56.10)   (-9.30, 100.23)


Values of Predictors for New Observations

New
Obs   GUESS
  1    50.0
```

FIGURE SIA11.5
MINITAB prediction interval for dowsing data

Exercises 11.87–11.103

Understanding the Principles

11.87 Explain the difference between y and $E(y)$ for a given x.

11.88 *True or False*. For a given x, a confidence interval for $E(y)$ will always be wider than a prediction interval for y.

11.89 *True or False*. The greater the deviation between x and $\bar{x}$, the wider the prediction interval for y will be.

11.90 For each of the following, decide whether the proper inference is a prediction interval for y or a confidence interval for $E(y)$:

a. A jeweler wants to predict the selling price of a diamond stone on the basis of its size (number of carats).

b. A psychologist wants to estimate the average IQ of all patients who have a certain income level.

Learning the Mechanics

11.91 In fitting a least squares line to $n = 10$ data points, the following quantities were computed:

$$SS_{xx} = 32, \bar{x} = 3, SS_{yy} = 26, \bar{y} = 4, SS_{xy} = 28$$

---

*The result follows from the facts that, for large n, $t_{\alpha/2} \approx z_{\alpha/2}$, $s \approx \sigma$, and the last two terms under the radical in the standard error of the predictor are approximately 0.

a. Find the least squares line.
b. Graph the least squares line.
c. Calculate SSE.
d. Calculate s^2.
e. Find a 95% confidence interval for the mean value of y when $x_p = 2.5$.
f. Find a 95% prediction interval for y when $x_p = 4$.

11.92 Consider the following pairs of measurements:
NW

🔘 **LM11_92**

x	1	2	3	4	5	6	7
y	3	5	4	6	7	7	10

a. Construct a scattergram of these data.
b. Find the least squares line, and plot it on your scattergram.
c. Find s^2.
d. Find a 90% confidence interval for the mean value of y when $x = 4$. Plot the upper and lower bounds of the confidence interval on your scattergram.
e. Find a 90% prediction interval for a new value of y when $x = 4$. Plot the upper and lower bounds of the prediction interval on your scattergram.
f. Compare the widths of the intervals you constructed in parts **d** and **e**. Which is wider and why?

11.93 Consider the pairs of measurements shown in the following table:
NW

🔘 **LM11_93**

x	4	6	0	5	2	3	2	6	2	1
y	3	5	−1	4	3	2	0	4	1	1

For these data, $SS_{xx} = 38.900$, $SS_{yy} = 33.600$, $SS_{xy} = 32.8$, and $\hat{y} = -.414 + .843x$.

a. Construct a scattergram of the data.
b. Plot the least squares line on your scattergram.
c. Use a 95% confidence interval to estimate the mean value of y when $x_p = 6$. Plot the upper and lower bounds of the interval on your scattergram.
d. Repeat part **c** for $x_p = 3.2$ and $x_p = 0$.
e. Compare the widths of the three confidence intervals you constructed in parts **c** and **d**, and explain why they differ.

11.94 Refer to Exercise 11.93.

a. Using no information about x, estimate and calculate a 95% confidence interval for the mean value of y. [*Hint:* Use the one-sample t methodology of Section 7.3.]

b. Plot the estimated mean value and the confidence interval as horizontal lines on your scattergram.
c. Compare the confidence intervals you calculated in parts **c** and **d** of Exercise 11.93 with the one you calculated in part **a** of this exercise. Does x appear to contribute information about the mean value of y?
d. Check the answer you gave in part **c** with a statistical test of the null hypothesis H_0: $\beta_1 = 0$ against H_a: $\beta_1 \neq 0$. Use $\alpha = .05$.

Applying the Concepts—Basic

11.95 English as a second language reading ability. Refer to the *Bilingual Research Journal* (Summer 2006) study of the relationship of Spanish (first-language) grammatical knowledge to English (second-language) reading, presented in Exercise 11.54 (p. 588). Recall that three simple linear regressions were used to model the English reading (ESLR) score (y) as a function of Spanish grammar (SG), Spanish reading (SR), and English grammar (EG), respectively.

a. If the researchers want to predict the ELSR score (y) of a native Spanish-speaking adult who scored 50% in Spanish grammar (x), how should they proceed?
b. If the researchers want to estimate the mean ELSR score $E(y)$ of all native Spanish-speaking adults who scored 70% in Spanish grammar (x), how should they proceed?

🔘 **PGADRIVER**

11.96 Ranking driving performance of professional golfers. Refer to *The Sport Journal* (Winter 2007) study of a new method for ranking the total driving performance of golfers on the Professional Golf Association (PGA) tour, presented in Exercise 11.25 (p. 576). You fit a straight-line model relating diving accuracy (y) to driving distance (x) to the data saved in the **PGADRIVER** file. A MINITAB printout with prediction and confidence intervals for a driving distance of $x = 300$ yards is shown below.

a. Locate the 95% prediction interval for driving accuracy (y) on the printout, and give a practical interpretation of the result.
b. Locate the 95% prediction interval for mean driving accuracy (y) on the printout, and give a practical interpretation of the result.
c. If you are interested in knowing the average driving accuracy of all PGA golfers who have a driving distance of 300 yards, which of the intervals is relevant? Explain.

🔘 **GOBIANTS**

11.97 Mongolian desert ants. Refer to the *Journal of Biogeography* (Dec. 2003) study of ant sites in Mongolia, presented in Exercise 11.22 (p. 574). You applied the method of least

```
Predicted Values for New Observations

New
Obs     Fit   SE Fit        95% CI             95% PI
  1  61.309   0.357  (60.586, 62.032)   (56.724, 65.894)


Values of Predictors for New Observations

New
Obs   DISTANCE
  1        300
```

MINITAB output for Exercise 11.96

Predictions

Obs	Region	Rain	Temp	Predicted Rain	Lower prediction limit of Rain	Upper prediction limit of Rain
1	DryStepp	196	5.7	201.977	179.525	224.430
2	DryStepp	196	5.7	201.977	179.525	224.430
3	DryStepp	179	7.0	180.704	163.694	197.714
4	DryStepp	197	8.0	164.340	150.594	178.085
5	DryStepp	149	8.5	156.157	143.513	168.802
6	GobiDese	112	10.7	120.156	106.038	134.274
7	GobiDese	125	11.4	108.701	92.298	125.104
8	GobiDese	99	10.9	116.883	102.172	131.595
9	GobiDese	125	11.4	108.701	92.298	125.104
10	GobiDese	84	11.4	108.701	92.298	125.104
11	GobiDese	115	11.4	108.701	92.298	125.104

SAS output for Exercise 11.97

squares to the data in the **GOBIANTS** file to estimate the straight-line model relating annual rainfall (y) and maximum daily temperature (x). An SAS printout giving 95% prediction intervals for the amount of rainfall at each of the 11 sites is shown above. Select the interval associated with site (observation) 7 and interpret it practically.

11.98 Sweetness of orange juice. Refer to the simple linear, regression of sweetness index y and amount of pectin, x, for $n = 24$ orange juice samples, presented in Exercise 11.28 (p. 577). The SPSS printout of the analysis is shown below. A 90% confidence interval for the mean sweetness index $E(y)$ for each value of x is shown on the SPSS spreadsheet. Select an observation and interpret this interval.

Applying the Concepts—Intermediate

11.99 Sports participation survey. The Sasakawa Sports Foundation conducted a national survey to assess the physical activity patterns of Japanese adults. The accompanying table lists the frequency (average number of days in the past year) and the amount of time (average number of minutes per single activity) Japanese adults spent participating in a sample of 11 sports activities.

JAPANSPORTS

Activity	Frequency x (days/years)	Amount of Time y (minutes)
Jogging	135	43
Cycling	68	99
Aerobics	44	61
Swimming	39	60
Volleyball	30	80
Tennis	21	100
Softball	16	91
Baseball	19	127
Skating	7	115
Skiing	10	249
Golf	5	262

Source: J. Bennett, ed. *Statistics in Sport.* London: Arnold, 1998 (adapted from Figure 11.6).

	run	sweet	pectin	lower90m	upper90m
1	1	5.2	220	5.64898	5.83848
2	2	5.5	227	5.63898	5.81613
3	3	6.0	259	5.57819	5.72904
4	4	5.9	210	5.66194	5.87173
5	5	5.8	224	5.64337	5.82560
6	6	6.0	215	5.65564	5.85493
7	7	5.8	231	5.63284	5.80379
8	8	5.6	268	5.55553	5.71011
9	9	5.6	239	5.61947	5.78019
10	10	5.9	212	5.65946	5.86497
11	11	5.4	410	5.05526	5.55416
12	12	5.6	256	5.58517	5.73592
13	13	5.8	306	5.43785	5.65219
14	14	5.5	259	5.57819	5.72904
15	15	5.3	284	5.50957	5.68213
16	16	5.3	383	5.15725	5.57694
17	17	5.7	271	5.54743	5.70434
18	18	5.5	264	5.56591	5.71821
19	19	5.7	227	5.63898	5.81613
20	20	5.3	263	5.56843	5.72031
21	21	5.9	232	5.63125	5.80075
22	22	5.8	220	5.64898	5.83848
23	23	5.8	246	5.60640	5.76091
24	24	5.9	241	5.61587	5.77454

SPSS output for Exercise 11.98

a. Write the equation of a straight-line model relating duration (y) to frequency (x).

b. Find the least squares prediction equation.

c. Is there evidence of a linear relationship between y and x? Test, using $\alpha = .05$.

d. Use the least squares line to predict the amount of time Japanese adults participate in a sport that they play 25 times a year. Form a 95% confidence interval around the prediction and interpret the result.

NAMEGAME2

11.100 The "name game." Refer to the *Journal of Experimental Psychology—Applied* (June 2000) name-retrieval study, presented in Exercise 11.30, (p. 577).

a. Find a 99% confidence interval for the mean recall proportion for students in the fifth position during the "name game." Interpret the result.

b. Find a 99% prediction interval for the recall proportion of a particular student in the fifth position during the "name game." Interpret the result.

c. Compare the intervals you found in parts **a** and **b**. Which interval is wider? Will this always be the case? Explain.

LIQUIDSPILL

11.101 Spreading rate of spilled liquid. Refer to the *Chemical Engineering Progress* (Jan. 2005) study of the rate at which a spilled volatile liquid will spread across a surface, presented in Exercise 11.31 (p. 578). Recall that simple linear regression was used to model y = mass of the spill as a function of y = elapsed time of the spill.

a. Find a 99% confidence interval for the mean mass of all spills with an elapsed time of 15 minutes. Interpret the result.

b. Find a 99% prediction interval for the mass of a single spill with an elapsed time of 15 minutes. Interpret the result.

c. Compare the intervals you found in parts **a** and **b**. Which interval is wider? Will this always be the case? Explain.

SNOWGEESE

11.102 Feeding habits of snow geese. Refer to the *Journal of Applied Ecology* feeding study of the relationship between the weight change y of baby snow geese and their digestion efficiency x, presented in Exercise 11.82 (p. 600).

a. Fit the simple linear regression model to the data.

b. Do you recommend using the model to predict weight change y? Explain.

c. Use the model to form a 95% confidence interval for the mean weight change of all baby snow geese with a digestion efficiency of x = 15%. Interpret the interval.

Applying the Concepts—Advanced

CUTTOOL

11.103 Life tests of cutting tools. Refer to the data saved in the **CUTTOOL** file of Exercise 11.46 (p. 583).

a. Use a 90% confidence interval to estimate the mean useful life of a brand-A cutting tool when the cutting speed is 45 meters per minute. Repeat for brand B. Compare the widths of the two intervals and comment on the reasons for any difference.

b. Use a 90% prediction interval to predict the useful life of a brand-A cutting tool when the cutting speed is 45 meters per minute. Repeat for brand B. Compare the widths of the two intervals with each other and with the two intervals you calculated in part **a**. Comment on the reasons for any differences.

c. Note that the estimation and prediction you performed in parts **a** and **b** were for a value of x that was not included in the original sample. That is, the value x = 45 was not part of the sample. However, the value is within the range of x values in the sample, so that the regression model spans the x value for which the estimation and prediction were made. In such situations, estimation and prediction represent **interpolations**.

Suppose you were asked to predict the useful life of a brand-A cutting tool for a cutting speed of x = 100 meters per minute. Since the given value of x is outside the range of the sample x values, the prediction is an example of **extrapolation**. Predict the useful life of a brand-A cutting tool that is operated at 100 meters per minute, and construct a 95% confidence interval for the actual useful life of the tool. What additional assumption do you have to make in order to ensure the validity of an extrapolation?

11.7 A Complete Example

In the previous sections, we presented the basic elements necessary to fit and use a straight-line regression model. In this section, we will assemble these elements by applying them in an example with the aid of computer software.

Suppose a fire insurance company wants to relate the amount of fire damage in major residential fires to the distance between the burning house and the nearest fire station. The study is to be conducted in a large suburb of a major city; a sample of 15 recent fires in this suburb is selected. The amount of damage, y, and the distance between the fire and the nearest fire station, x, are recorded for each fire. The results are given in Table 11.7.

Step 1   First, we hypothesize a model to relate fire damage, y, to the distance from the nearest fire station, x. We hypothesize a straight-line probabilistic model:

$$y = \beta_0 + \beta_1 x + \varepsilon$$

FIREDAM

TABLE 11.7 Fire Damage Data

Distance from Fire Station, x (miles)	Fire Damage y (thousands of dollars)
3.4	26.2
1.8	17.8
4.6	31.3
2.3	23.1
3.1	27.5
5.5	36.0
.7	14.1
3.0	22.3
2.6	19.6
4.3	31.3
2.1	24.0
1.1	17.3
6.1	43.2
4.8	36.4
3.8	26.1

Step 2 Next, we enter the data of Table 11.7 into a computer and use statistical software to estimate the unknown parameters in the deterministic component of the hypothesized model. The SAS printout for the simple linear regression analysis is shown in Figure 11.23. The least squares estimate of the slope β_1 and intercept β_0, highlighted on the printout, are

$$\hat{\beta}_1 = 4.91933$$
$$\hat{\beta}_0 = 10.27793$$

Dependent Variable: DAMAGE

Analysis of Variance

Source	DF	Sum of Squares	Mean Square	F Value	Pr > F
Model	1	841.76636	841.76636	156.89	<.0001
Error	13	69.75098	5.36546		
Corrected Total	14	911.51733			

Root MSE	2.31635	R-Square	0.9235	
Dependent Mean	26.41333	Adj R-Sq	0.9176	
Coeff Var	8.76961			

Parameter Estimates

Variable	DF	Parameter Estimate	Standard Error	t Value	Pr > |t|	95% Confidence Limits	
Intercept	1	10.27793	1.42028	7.24	<.0001	7.20960	13.34625
DISTANCE	1	4.91933	0.39275	12.53	<.0001	4.07085	5.76781

Output Statistics

Obs	DISTANCE	Dep Var DAMAGE	Predicted Value	Std Error Mean Predict	95% CL Predict		Residual
1	3.4	26.2000	27.0037	0.5999	21.8344	32.1729	-0.8037
2	1.8	17.8000	19.1327	0.8340	13.8141	24.4514	-1.3327
3	4.6	31.3000	32.9068	0.7915	27.6186	38.1951	-1.6068
4	2.3	23.1000	21.5924	0.7112	16.3577	26.8271	1.5076
5	3.1	27.5000	25.5279	0.6022	20.3573	30.6984	1.9721
6	5.5	36.0000	37.3342	1.0573	31.8334	42.8351	-1.3342
7	0.7	14.1000	13.7215	1.1766	8.1087	19.3342	0.3785
8	3	22.3000	25.0359	0.6081	19.8622	30.2097	-2.7359
9	2.6	19.6000	23.0682	0.6550	17.8678	28.2686	-3.4682
10	4.3	31.3000	31.4311	0.7198	26.1908	36.6713	-0.1311
11	2.1	24.0000	20.6085	0.7566	15.3442	25.8729	3.3915
12	1.1	17.3000	15.6892	1.0444	10.1999	21.1785	1.6108
13	6.1	43.2000	40.2858	1.2587	34.5906	45.9811	2.9142
14	4.8	36.4000	33.8907	0.8450	28.5640	39.2175	2.5093
15	3.8	26.1000	28.9714	0.6320	23.7843	34.1585	-2.8714
16	3.5	.	27.4956	0.6043	22.3239	32.6672	.

FIGURE 11.23

SAS printout for fire damage regression

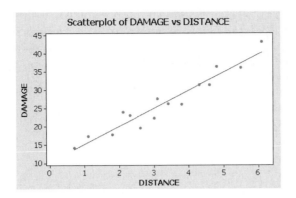

FIGURE 11.24

MINITAB scatterplot with least squares line for fire damage regression analysis

and the least squares equation is (rounded)

$$\hat{y} = 10.28 + 4.92x$$

This prediction equation is graphed by MINITAB in Figure 11.24, along with a plot of the data points.

The least squares estimate of the slope, $\hat{\beta}_1 = 4.92$, implies that the estimated mean damage increases by \$4,920 for each additional mile from the fire station. This interpretation is valid over the range of x, or from .7 to 6.1 miles from the station. The estimated y-intercept, $\hat{\beta}_0 = 10.28$, has the interpretation that a fire 0 miles from the fire station has an estimated mean damage of \$10,280. Although this would seem to apply to the fire station itself, remember that the y-intercept is meaningfully interpretable only if $x = 0$ is within the sampled range of the independent variable. Since $x = 0$ is outside the range, β_0 has no practical interpretation.

Step 3   Now we specify the probability distribution of the random-error component ε. The assumptions about the distribution are identical to those listed in Section 11.3. Although we know that these assumptions are not completely satisfied (they rarely are for practical problems), we are willing to assume that they are approximately satisfied for this example. The estimate of the standard deviation σ of ε, highlighted on the SAS printout, is

$$s = 2.31635$$

This implies that most of the observed fire damage (y) values will fall within approximately $2s = 4.64$ thousand dollars of their respective predicted values when the least squares line is used.

Step 4   We can now check the usefulness of the hypothesized model—in other words, whether x really contributes information for the prediction of y by the straight-line model. First, test the null hypothesis that the slope β_1 is 0—that is, that there is no linear relationship between fire damage and the distance from the nearest fire station—against the alternative hypothesis that fire damage increases as the distance increases. We test

$$H_0: \beta_1 = 0$$
$$H_a: \beta_1 > 0$$

The two-tailed observed significance level for testing $H_a: \beta_1 \neq 0$, highlighted on the SAS printout, is less than .0001. Thus, the p-value for our one-tailed test is less than half of this value (.00005). This small p-value leaves little doubt that mean fire damage and distance between the fire and the fire station are at least linearly related, with mean fire damage increasing as the distance increases.

We gain additional information about the relationship by forming a confidence interval for the slope β_1. A 95% confidence interval, highlighted on the SAS printout, is (4.071, 5.768). Thus, with 95% confidence, we estimate that the interval from $4,071 to $5,768 encloses the mean increase (β_1) in fire damage per additional mile in distance from the fire station.

Another measure of the utility of the model is the coefficient of determination, r^2. The value (also highlighted on the printout) is $r^2 = .9235$, which implies that about 92% of the sample variation in fire damage (y) is explained by the distance (x) between the fire and the fire station.

The coefficient of correlation, r, that measures the strength of the linear relationship between y and x is not shown on the SAS printout and must be calculated. Using the facts that $r = \sqrt{r^2}$ in simple linear regression and that r and $\hat{\beta}_1$ have the same sign, we calculate

$$r = +\sqrt{r^2} = \sqrt{.9235} = .96$$

The high correlation confirms our conclusion that β_1 is greater than 0; it appears that fire damage and distance from the fire station are positively correlated. All signs point to a strong linear relationship between y and x.

Step 5 We are now prepared to use the least squares model. Suppose the insurance company wants to predict the fire damage if a major residential fire were to occur 3.5 miles from the nearest fire station. The predicted value (highlighted at the bottom of the SAS printout) is $\hat{y} = 27.496$, while the 95% prediction interval (also highlighted) is (22.324, 32.667). Therefore, with 95% confidence, we predict fire damage in a major residential fire 3.5 miles from the nearest station to be between $22,324 and $32,667.

Caution

We would not use this model to make predictions for homes less than .7 mile or more than 6.1 miles from the nearest fire station. A look at the data in Table 11.7 reveals that all the x-values fall between .7 and 6.1. It is dangerous to use the model to make predictions outside the region in which the sample data fall. A straight line might not provide a good model for the relationship between the mean value of y and the value of x when stretched over a wider range of x-values.

KEY TERMS

GUIDE TO SIMPLE LINEAR REGRESSION

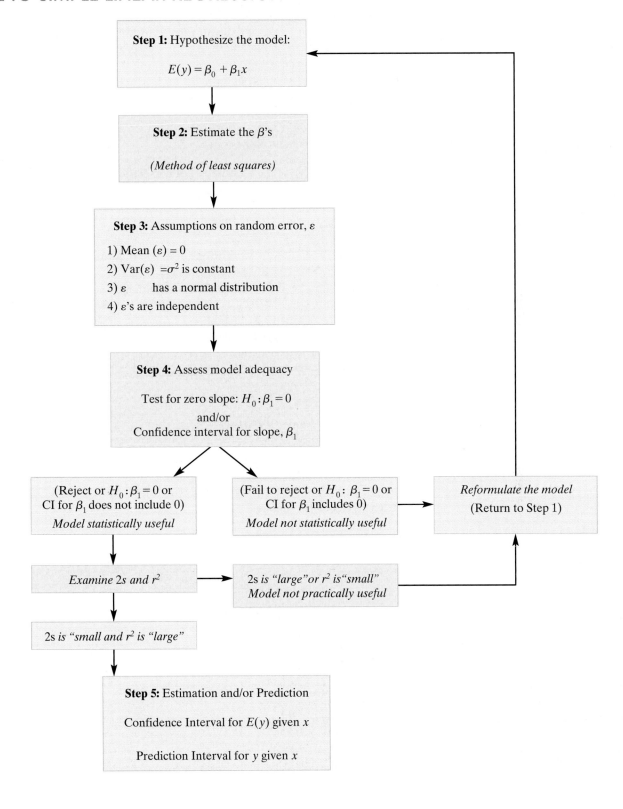

CHAPTER NOTES

Simple linear regression variables:

y = **Dependent** variable (quantitative)

x = **Independent** variable (quantitative)

Method of least squared properties:

1. average error of prediction = 0
2. sum of squared errors is minimum

Practical interpretation of y-interpret:

Predicted y-value when $x = 0$

(no practical interpretation if $x = 0$ is either nonsensical or outside range of sample data)

Practical interpretation of slope:

Increase (or decrease) in y for every one-unit increase in x.

First-order (straight-line) model:

$$E(y) = \beta_0 + \beta_1 x$$

where $E(y)$ = mean of y

β_0 = *y-intercept* of line (point where line intercepts y-axis)

β_1 = **slope** of line (change in y for every one-unit change in x)

Coefficient of correlation, r:

1. ranges between -1 and $+1$
2. measures strength of *linear relationship* between y and x

Coefficient of determination, r^2:

1. ranges between 0 and 1
2. measures proportion of sample variation in y "explained" by the model.

Practical interpretation of model standard deviation s:

Ninety-five percent of y-values fall within $2s$ of their respective predicted values

Width of *confidence interval for $E(y)$* will always be **narrower** than width of *prediction interval for* y

Key Symbols/Notation

y	Dependent variable (variable to be predicted)
x	Independent variable (variable used to predict)
$E(y)$	Expected (mean) of y
β_0	y-intercept of true line
β_1	slope of true line.
$\hat{\beta}_0$	Least squared estimate of y-intercept
$\hat{\beta}_1$	Least squares estimate of slope
ϵ	Random error
$\hat{y}$	Predicted value of y for a given x-value
$(y - \hat{y})$	Estimated error of prediction
SSE	Sum of squared errors of prediction
r	Coefficient of correlation
r^2	Coefficient of determination
x_p	Value of x used to predict y
$r^2 = \dfrac{SS_{yy} - SSE}{SS_{yy}}$	Coefficient of determination
$\hat{y} \pm t_{\alpha/2} s \sqrt{\dfrac{1}{n} + \dfrac{(x_p - \bar{x})^2}{SS_{xx}}}$	$(1 - \alpha)100\%$ confidence interval for $E(y)$ when $x = x_p$
$\hat{y} \pm t_{\alpha/2} s \sqrt{1 + \dfrac{1}{n} + \dfrac{(x_p - \bar{x})^2}{SS_{xx}}}$	$(1 - \alpha)100\%$ prediction interval for y when $x = x_p$

SUPPLEMENTARY EXERCISES 11.104–11.130

Understanding the Principles

11.104 Explain the difference between a probabilistic model and a deterministic model.

11.105 Give the general form of a straight-line model for $E(y)$.

11.106 Outline the five steps in a simple linear regression analysis.

11.107 *True or False.* In simple linear regression, about 95% of the y-values in the sample will fall within $2s$ of their respective predicted values.

Learning the Mechanics

11.108 In fitting a least squares line to $n = 15$ data points, the following quantities were computed: $SS_{xx} = 55$, $SS_{yy} = 198$, $SS_{xy} = -88$, $\bar{x} = 1.3$, and $\bar{y} = 35$.
a. Find the least squares line.
b. Graph the least squares line.
c. Calculate SSE.
d. Calculate s^2.
e. Find a 90% confidence interval for β_1. Interpret this estimate.
f. Find a 90% confidence interval for the mean value of y when $x = 15$.
g. Find a 90% prediction interval for y when $x = 15$.

11.109 Consider the following sample data:

y	5	1	3
x	5	1	3

a. Construct a scattergram for the data.
b. It is possible to find many lines for which $\Sigma(y - \hat{y}) = 0$. For this reason, the criterion $\Sigma(y - \hat{y}) = 0$ is not used to identify the "best-fitting" straight line. Find two lines that have $\Sigma(y - \hat{y}) = 0$.
c. Find the least squares line.
d. Compare the value of SSE for the least squares line with that of the two lines you found in part **b.** What principle of least squares is demonstrated by this comparison?

11.110 Consider the following 10 data points:

◉ LM11_110

x	3	5	6	4	3	7	6	5	4	7
y	4	3	2	1	2	3	3	5	4	2

a. Plot the data on a scattergram.
b. Calculate the values of r and r^2.
c. Is there sufficient evidence to indicate that x and y are linearly correlated? Test at the $\alpha = .10$ level of significance.

Applying the Concepts—Basic

11.111 Arsenic in soil. In Denver, Colorado, environmentalists have discovered a link between high arsenic levels in soil and a crabgrass killer used in the 1950s and 1960s. (*Environmental Science & Technology*, Sept. 1, 2000.) The recent discovery was based, in part, on the accompanying

Scattergrams for
Exercise 11.111

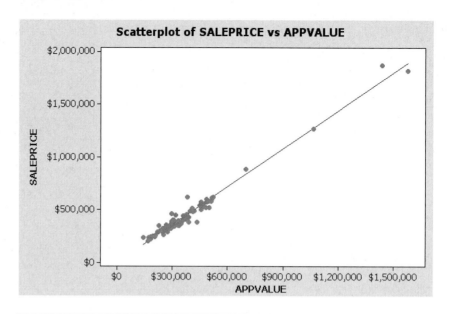

Correlations: SALEPRICE, APPVALUE

```
Pearson correlation of SALEPRICE and APPVALUE = 0.987
P-Value = 0.000
```

Regression Analysis: SALEPRICE versus APPVALUE

```
The regression equation is
SALEPRICE = 184 + 1.20 APPVALUE


Predictor      Coef  SE Coef       T      P
Constant        184     9834    0.02  0.985
APPVALUE    1.19956  0.02234   53.70  0.000


S = 44859.7    R-Sq = 97.4%    R-Sq(adj) = 97.4%


Analysis of Variance

Source           DF           SS           MS        F      P
Regression        1  5.80234E+12  5.80234E+12  2883.31  0.000
Residual Error   76  1.52942E+11   2012390103
Total            77  5.95528E+12


Predicted Values for New Observations

New
Obs    Fit  SE Fit         95% CI              95% PI
  1 480007    5105  (469839, 490175)  (390085, 569930)


Values of Predictors for New Observations

New
Obs  APPVALUE
  1    400000
```

scattergrams (p. 615). The graphs plot the level of the metals cadmium and arsenic, respectively, against the distance from a former smelter plant for samples of soil taken from Denver residential properties.

a. Normally, the metal level in soil decreases as distance from the source (e.g., a smelter plant) increases. Propose a straight-line model relating metal level y to distance x from the plant. On the basis of the theory, would you expect the slope of the line to be positive or negative?

b. Examine the scatterplot for cadmium. Does the plot support the theory you set forth in part **a**?

c. Examine the scatterplot for arsenic. Does the plot support the theory of part **a**? (*Note:* This finding led investigators to discover the link between high arsenic levels and the use of the crabgrass killer.)

11.112 **Predicting sale prices of homes.** Real-estate investors, home buyers, and homeowners often use the appraised value of property as a basis for predicting the sale of that property. Data on sale prices and total appraised value of

78 residential properties sold in 2006 in an upscale Tampa, Florida, neighborhood named Hunter's Green are saved in the **HUNGREEN** file. Selected observations are listed in the following table.

HUNGREEN (selected observations)

Property	Sale Price	Appraised Value
1	$489,900	$418,601
2	1,825,000	1,577,919
3	890,000	687,836
4	250,00	191,620
5	1,275,000	1,063,901
⋮	⋮	⋮
74	325,000	292,702
75	516,000	407,449
76	309,300	272,275
77	370,000	347,320
78	580,000	511,359

Source: Hillsborough Country (Florida) Property Appraiser's Officer.

a. Propose a straight-line model to relate the appraised property value (x) to the sale price (y) for residential properties in this neighborhood.

b. A MINITAB scatterplot of the data with the least squared line is shown (p. 616, top). Does it appear that a straight-line model will be an appropriate fit to the data?

c. A MINITAB simple linear regression printout is also shown (p. 616, bottom). Find the equation of the least squared line. Interpret the estimated slope and y-intercept in the words of the problem.

d. Locate the test statistic and p-value for testing H_0: $\beta_1 = 0$ against H_a: $\beta_1 > 0$. Is there sufficient evidence (at $\alpha = .01$) of a positive linear relationship between appraised property value (x) and sale price (y)?

e. Locate and interpret practically the values of r and r^2 on the printout.

f. Locate and interpret practically the 95% prediction interval for sale price (y) on the printout.

11.113 Baseball batting averages versus wins. Is the number of games won by a major league baseball team in a season related to the team's batting average? In Exercise 2.141 (p. 92), you examined data from the *Baseball Almanac* (2007) on the number of games won and the batting averages for the 14 teams in the American League for the 2006 Major League Baseball season. The data are repeated in the table on p. 618:

a. If you were to model the relationship between the mean (or expected) number of games won by a major league team and the team's batting average x, using a straight line, would you expect the slope of the line to be positive or negative? Explain.

b. Construct a scattergram of the data. Does the pattern revealed by the scattergram agree with your answer to part **a**?

c. A SAS printout of the simple linear regression is shown below. Find the estimates of the β's on the printout and write the equation of the least squares line.

d. Graph the least squares line on your scattergram. Does your least squares line seem to fit the points on your scattergram?

Dependent Variable: WINS

Number of Observations Read	14
Number of Observations Used	14

Analysis of Variance

Source	DF	Sum of Squares	Mean Square	F Value	Pr > F
Model	1	405.26316	405.26316	3.32	0.0936
Error	12	1466.73684	122.22807		
Corrected Total	13	1872.00000			

Root MSE	11.05568	R-Square	0.2165
Dependent Mean	83.00000	Adj R-Sq	0.1512
Coeff Var	13.32010		

Parameter Estimates

Variable	DF	Parameter Estimate	Standard Error	t Value	Pr > |t|
Intercept	1	-85.68421	92.68557	-0.92	0.3735
BATAVG	1	614.03509	337.21750	1.82	0.0936

Obs	BATAVG	Dependent Variable	Predicted Value	Std Error Mean Predict	95% CL Predict		Residual
1	0.285	97.0000	89.3158	4.5564	63.2620	115.3696	7.6842
2	0.284	87.0000	88.7018	4.3053	62.8515	114.5520	-1.7018
3	0.277	70.0000	84.4035	3.0536	59.4133	109.3937	-14.4035
4	0.269	86.0000	79.4912	3.5276	54.2065	104.7760	6.5088
5	0.255	61.0000	70.8947	7.2751	42.0590	99.7304	-9.8947
6	0.28	78.0000	86.2456	3.4507	61.0113	111.4800	-8.2456
7	0.274	95.0000	82.5614	2.9646	57.6222	107.5006	12.4386
8	0.28	90.0000	86.2456	3.4507	61.0113	111.4800	3.7544
9	0.271	62.0000	80.7193	3.2093	55.6367	105.8019	-18.7193
10	0.287	96.0000	90.5439	5.0887	64.0265	117.0613	5.4561
11	0.274	89.0000	82.5614	2.9646	57.6222	107.5006	6.4386
12	0.278	80.0000	85.0175	3.1557	59.9672	110.0679	-5.0175
13	0.272	78.0000	81.3333	3.0933	56.3200	106.3467	-3.3333
14	0.26	93.0000	73.9649	5.7750	46.7883	101.1416	19.0351

SAS output for Exercise 11.113

ALWINS

Team	Games Won	Batting Ave.
New York	97	.285
Toronto	87	.284
Baltimore	70	.277
Boston	86	.269
Tampa Bay	61	.255
Cleveland	78	.280
Detroit	95	.274
Chicago	90	.280
Kansas City	62	.271
Minnesota	96	.287
Los Angeles	89	.274
Texas	80	.278
Seattle	78	.272
Oakland	93	.260

Source: Baseball Almanac, 2007; www.mlb.com

e. Interpret the estimates of β_0 and β_1 in the words of the problem.

f. Conduct a test (at $\alpha = .05$) to determine whether the mean (or expected) number of games won by a major league baseball team is positively linearly related to the team's batting average.

g. Find the coefficient of determination, r^2, and interpret its value.

h. Predict the number of games won by a team with a .285 batting average.

i. Find a 95% prediction interval for the number of games won by a team with a .285 batting average. Interpret the interval.

11.114 Australian seagrass study. The abundance of tropical seagrasses in Australia was the subject of research published in *Aquatic Botany* (Mar. 1995). Simple linear regression was used to relate the standing crop (y, measured in grams per meter squared) of a seagrass species to the percentage (x) of land covered by the plants. Data collected for $n = 12$ sites at Rowes Bay, Australia, yielded the following results:

$$\hat{y} = .031 + .089x \qquad t = 2.34 \qquad p\text{-value} = .042$$

a. Give the practical interpretation, if possible, of the estimated y-intercept of the line.

b. Give the practical interpretation, if possible, of the estimated slope of the line.

c. At what α-level is there sufficient evidence of a linear relationship between standing crop and percentage cover of a seagrass species? Explain.

11.115 Feeding habits of fish. Refer to the *Brain and Behavior Evolution* (Apr. 2000) study of the feeding behavior of black-bream fish, presented in Exercise 2.142 (p. 92). Recall that the zoologists recorded the number of aggressive strikes of two black-bream fish feeding at the bottom of an aquarium in the 10-minute period following the addition of food. The table listing the weekly number of strikes and the age of the fish (in days) is reproduced in the next column:

a. Write the equation of a straight-line model relating number of strikes (y) to age of fish (x).

BLACKBREAM

Week	Number of Strikes	Age of Fish (days)
1	85	120
2	63	136
3	34	150
4	39	155
5	58	162
6	35	169
7	57	178
8	12	184
9	15	190

Source: Shand, J., et al. "Variability in the location of the retinal ganglion cell area centralis is correlated with ontogenetic changes in feeding behavior in the Blackbream, Acanthopagrus 'butcher'." *Brain and Behavior*, Vol. 55, No. 4, Apr. 2000 (Figure H).

b. Fit the model to the data by the method of least squares and give the least squares prediction equation.

c. Give a practical interpretation of the value of $\hat{\beta}_0$ if possible.

d. Give a practical interpretation of the value of $\hat{\beta}_1$ if possible.

e. Test $H_0: \beta_1 = 0$ versus $H_a: \beta_1 < 0$, using $\alpha = .10$. Interpret the result.

11.116 Math anxiety study. Many high school students experience "math anxiety." Does such an attitude carry over to learning computer skills? A researcher at Duquesne University investigated this question and published her results in *Educational Technology* (May–June 1995). A sample of high school students—902 boys and 828 girls—from public schools in Pittsburgh, Pennsylvania, participated in the study. Using five-point Likert scales, where 1 = "strongly disagree" and 5 = "strongly agree," the researcher measured the students' interest and confidence in both mathematics and computers.

a. For boys, math confidence and computer interest were correlated at $r = .14$. Interpret this result fully.

b. For girls, math confidence and computer interest were correlated at $r = .33$. Interpret this result fully.

11.117 "Metaskills" and career management. In today's business environment, effective management of one's own career requires a skill set that includes adaptability, tolerance for ambiguity, self-awareness, and identity change. Management professors at Pace University (New York) used correlation coefficients to investigate the relationship between these "metaskills" and effective career management. (*International Journal of Manpower*, Aug. 2000.) Data were collected on 446 business graduates who had all completed a management "metaskills" course. Two of the many variables measured were self-knowledge skill level (x) and goal-setting ability (y). The correlation coefficient for these two variables was $r = .70$.

a. Give a practical interpretation of the value of r.

b. The p-value for a test of no correlation between the two variables was reported as p-value $= .001$. Interpret this result.

c. Find the coefficient of determination, r^2, and interpret the result.

11.118 Walking study. Refer to the *American Scientist* (July–Aug. 1998) study of the relationship between self-avoiding and unrooted walks, presented in Exercise 2.143 (p. 92). Recall that in a self-avoiding walk you never retrace or cross your own path, while an unrooted walk is a path in which the starting and ending points are impossible to distinguish. The possible number of walks of each type of various lengths are reproduced in the accompanying table. Consider the straight-line model $y = \beta_0 + \beta_1 x + \varepsilon$, where x is walk length (number of steps).

WALK

Walk Length (number of steps)	Unrooted Walks	Self-Avoiding Walks
1	1	4
2	2	12
3	4	36
4	9	100
5	22	284
6	56	780
7	147	2,172
8	388	5,916

Source: Hayes, B. "How to avoid yourself," *American Scientist*, Vol. 86, No. 4, July–Aug. 1988, p. 317 (Figure 5).

a. Use the method of least squares to fit the model to the data if y is the possible number of unrooted walks.
b. Interpret $\hat{\beta}_0$ and $\hat{\beta}_1$ in the estimated model of part **a**.
c. Repeat parts **a** and **b** if y is the possible number of self-avoiding walks.
d. Find a 99% confidence interval for the number of unrooted walks that are possible when the walk length is four steps.
e. Would you recommend using simple linear regression to predict the number of walks that are possible when walk length is 15 steps? Explain.

Applying the Concepts—Intermediate

11.119 Beanie Babies. Refer to Exercise 2.175 (p. 104) and the data on 50 Beanie Babies collector's items, published in *Beanie World Magazine*. Can the age of a Beanie Baby be used to predict its market value? Answer this question by conducting a complete simple linear regression analysis on the data saved in the **BEANIE** file. (The first and last 5 entries are shown in the accompanying table.)

11.120 Organic chemistry experiment. Chemists at Kyushu University (Japan) examined the linear relationship between the maximum absorption rate y (in nanomoles) and the Hammett substituent constant x for metacyclophane compounds (*Journal of Organic Chemistry*, July 1995.) The data for variants of two compounds are given in the accompanying table. The variants of compound 1 are labeled 1a, 1b, 1d, 1e, 1f, 1g, and 1h; the variants of compound 2 are 2a, 2b, 2c, and 2d.

a. Plot the data in a scattergram. Use two different plotting symbols for the two compounds. What do you observe?
b. Using only the data for compound 1, fit the model $E(y) = \beta_0 + \beta_1 x$.
c. Assess the adequacy of the model you fit in part **b**. Use $\alpha = .01$.
d. Repeat parts **b** and **c**, using only the data for compound 2.

ORGCHEM

Compound	Maximum Absorption y	Hammett Constant x
1a	298	0.00
1b	346	.75
1d	303	.06
1e	314	−.26
1f	302	.18
1g	332	.42
1h	302	−.19
2a	343	.52
2b	367	1.01
2c	325	.37
2d	331	.53

Source: Adapted from Tsuge, A., et al. "Preparation and spectral properties of disubstituted [2-2] metacyclophanes," *Journal of Organic Chemistry*, Vol. 60, No. 15, July 1995, pp. 4390–4391 (Table 1 and Figure 1).

11.121 Mortality of predatory birds. Two species of predatory birds—collard flycatchers and tits—compete for nest holes during breeding season on the island of Gotland, Sweden. Frequently, dead flycatchers are found in nest boxes occupied by tits. A field study examined whether the risk of mortality to flycatchers is related to the

BEANIE (First and last 5 observations shown.)

Name	Age (months) as of Sept. 1998	Retired (R)/ Current (C)	Value ($)
1. Ally the Alligator	52	R	55.00
2. Batty the Bat	12	C	12.00
3. Bongo the Brown Monkey	28	R	40.00
4. Blackie the Bear	52	C	10.00
5. Bucky the Beaver	40	R	45.00
⋮	⋮	⋮	⋮
46. Stripes the Tiger (Gold/Black)	40	R	400.00
47. Teddy the 1997 Holiday Bear	12	R	50.00
48. Tuffy the Terrier	17	C	10.00
49. Tracker the Basset Hound	5	C	15.00
50. Zip the Black Cat	28	R	40.00

Source: Beanie World Magazine, Sept. 1998.

degree of competition between the two bird species for nest sites. (*The Condor*, May 1995.) The table gives data on the number y of flycatchers killed at each of 14 discrete locations (plots) on the island, as well as on the nest box tit occupancy x (i.e., the percentage of nest boxes occupied by tits) at each plot. Consider the simple linear regression model $E(y) = \beta_0 + \beta_1 x$.

a. Plot the data in a scattergram. Does the frequency of flycatcher casualties per plot appear to increase linearly with increasing proportion of nest boxes occupied by tits?

b. Use the method of least squares to find the estimates of β_0 and β_1. Interpret their values.

c. Test the utility of the model, using $\alpha = .05$.

d. Find r and r^2 and interpret their values.

e. Find s and interpret the result.

CONDOR2

Plot	Number of Flycatchers Killed y	Nest Box Tit Occupancy x (%)
1	0	24
2	0	33
3	0	34
4	0	43
5	0	50
6	1	35
7	1	35
8	1	38
9	1	40
10	2	31
11	2	43
12	3	55
13	4	57
14	5	64

Source: Merila, J., and Wiggins, D. A. "Interspecific competition for nest holes causes adult mortality in the collard flycatcher." *The Condor*, Vol. 97, No. 2, May 1995, p. 449 (Figure 2), Cooper Ornithological Society.

f. Do you recommend using the model to predict the number of flycatchers killed? Explain.

11.122 Snowmelt runoff erosion. The U.S. Department of Agriculture has developed and adopted the Universal Soil Loss Equation (USLE) for predicting water erosion of soils. In geographic areas where runoff from melting snow is common, calculating the USLE requires an accurate estimate of snowmelt runoff erosion. An article in the *Journal of Soil and Water Conservation* (Mar.–Apr. 1995) used simple linear regression to develop a snowmelt erosion index. Data on 54 climatological stations in Canada were used to model the McCool winter-adjusted rainfall erosivity index y as a straight-line function of the once-in-five-year snowmelt runoff amount x (measured in millimeters).

a. The data points are plotted in the accompanying scattergram. Is there visual evidence of a linear trend?

b. The data for seven stations were removed from the analysis due to lack of snowfall during the study period. Why is this strategy advisable?

c. The simple linear regression on the remaining $n = 47$ data points yielded the following results: $\hat{y} = -6.72 + 1.39x$, $s_{\hat{\beta}_1} = .06$. Use this information to construct a 90% confidence interval for β_1.

d. Interpret the interval you constructed in part **c**.

11.123 Quantum tunneling. At temperatures approaching absolute zero $(-273°C)$, helium exhibits traits that seem to defy many laws of Newtonian physics. An experiment has been conducted with helium in solid form at various temperatures near absolute zero. The solid helium is placed in a dilution refrigerator along with a solid impure substance, and the fraction (in weight) of the impurity passing through the solid helium is recorded. (This phenomenon of solids passing directly through solids is known as *quantum tunneling*.) The data are given in the next table:

a. Find the least squares estimates of the intercept and slope. Interpret them.

b. Use a 95% confidence interval to estimate the slope β_1. Interpret the interval in terms of this application.

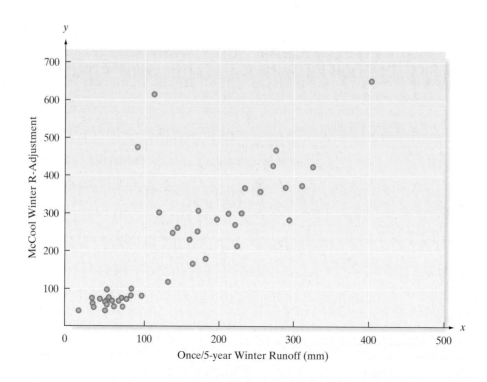

Once/5-year Winter Runoff (mm)

HELIUM

Temperature x(°C)	Proportion of Impurity
−262.0	.315
−265.0	.202
−256.0	.204
−267.0	.620
−270.0	.715
−272.0	.935
−272.4	.957
−272.7	.906
−272.8	.985
−272.9	.987

Does the interval support the hypothesis that temperature contributes information about the proportion of impurity passing through helium?

c. Interpret the coefficient of determination for this model.

d. Find a 95% prediction interval for the percentage of impurity passing through solid helium at −273°C. Interpret the result.

e. Note that the value of x in part **d** is outside the experimental region. Why might this lead to an unreliable prediction?

11.124 Short-term memory study. Neurologists have found that the hippocampus, a structure located in the brain, plays an important role in short-term memory. Refer to the *American Journal of Psychiatry* (July 1995) study of the relationship between hippocampal volume and short-term verbal memory of 21 Vietnam veterans with combat-related post-traumatic stress disorder (PTSD), presented in Exercise 2.146 (p. 93). Recall that magnetic resonance imaging was used to measure the volume x of the right hippocampus (in cubic millimeters) of each subject, while the verbal memory retention y of each subject was measured by the percent retention subscale of the Wechsler Memory Scale. The scattergram for the data is reproduced here:

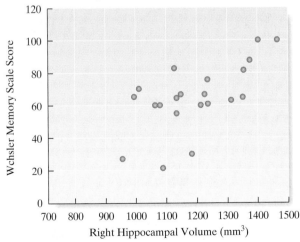

a. Propose a straight-line model relating verbal memory y with right hippocampal volume x to support the theory that a smaller hippocampal volume would be associated with deficits in short-term verbal memory in patients with PTSD.

b. On the basis of the theory, would you expect the slope of the line to be positive or negative? Explain.

c. The coefficient of correlation between right hippocampal volume and verbal retention was $r = .64$. Interpret this value.

d. A statistical test of H_0: $\beta_1 = 0$ versus H_a: $\beta_1 > 0$ resulted in a p-value smaller than .05. Interpret this result.

11.125 Conversing with the hearing impaired. A study was conducted to investigate how people with a hearing impairment communicate with their conversational partners. (*Journal of the Academy of Rehabilitative Audiology*, Vol. 27, 1994.) Each of 13 hearing-impaired subjects, all fitted with a cochlear implant, participated in a structured communication interaction with a familiar conversational partner (a family member) and with an unfamiliar conversational partner (who was instructed not to take the initiative to repair breakdowns in communication). The total number of words used by the subject in each of the two conversations is given in the accompanying table.

HEARAID

Subject	Words with Familiar Partner x	Words with Unfamiliar Partner y
1	65	47
2	160	78
3	55	90
4	83	75
5	0	6
6	140	101
7	49	40
8	164	215
9	62	29
10	56	75
11	207	121
12	207	139
13	93	83

Source: Tye-Murray, N., et al., "Communication breakdowns: Partner contingencies and partner reactions," *Journal of the Academy of Rehabilitative Audiology*, Vol. 27, 1994, pp. 116–117 (Tables 6, 7).

a. Plot the data in a scattergram. Is there visual evidence of a linear relationship between x and y? If so, is it positive or negative?

b. Propose a straight-line model relating y to x.

c. Use the method of least squares to find the estimates of β_0 and β_1.

d. Interpret the values of $\hat{\beta}_0$ and $\hat{\beta}_1$.

11.126 Loneliness in families. Is there a link between the loneliness of parents and that of their offspring? This question was examined in the *Journal of Marriage and Family* (Aug. 1986). The participants in the study were 130 female college undergraduates and their parents. Each triad of daughter, mother, and father completed the UCLA Loneliness Scale, a 20-item questionnaire designed to assess loneliness and several variables theoretically related to loneliness, such as social accessibility to others, difficulty in making friends, and depression.

a. The correlation between daughter's loneliness score y and mother's loneliness score x was determined to be $r = .26$. Interpret this value.

b. The correlation between daughter's loneliness score y and father's loneliness score x was determined to be $r = .19$. Interpret this value.

c. The correlation between daughter's loneliness score y and mother's self-esteem score x was determined to be $r = .14$. Interpret this value.

d. The correlation between daughter's loneliness score y and father's assertiveness score x was determined to be $r = .01$. Interpret this value.

e. Calculate the coefficient of determination r^2 for parts **a–d**. Interpret the results.

Applying the Concepts—Advanced

11.127 Regression through the origin. Sometimes it is known from theoretical considerations that the straight-line relationship between two variables x and y passes through the origin of the xy-plane. Consider the relationship between the total weight y of a shipment of 50-pound bags of flour and the number x of bags in the shipment. Since a shipment containing $x = 0$ bags (i.e., no shipment at all) has a total weight of $y = 0$, a straight-line model of the relationship between x and y should pass through the point $x = 0$, $y = 0$. In such a case, you could assume that $\beta_0 = 0$ and characterize the relationship between x and y with the following model:

$$y = \beta_1 x + \varepsilon$$

The least squares estimate of β_1 for this model is

$$\hat{\beta}_1 = \frac{\Sigma x_i y_i}{\Sigma x_i^2}$$

From the records of past flour shipments, 15 shipments were randomly chosen and the data shown in the following table were recorded:

FLOUR

Weight of Shipment	Number of 50-Pound Bags in Shipment
5,050	100
10,249	205
20,000	450
7,420	150
24,685	500
10,206	200
7,325	150
4,958	100
7,162	150
24,000	500
4,900	100
14,501	300
28,000	600
17,002	400
16,100	400

a. Find the least squares line for the given data under the assumption that $\beta_0 = 0$. Plot the least squares line on a scattergram of the data.

b. Find the least squares line for the given data, using the model

$$y = \beta_0 + \beta_1 x + \varepsilon$$

(i.e., do not restrict β_0 to equal 0). Plot this line on the same scatterplot you constructed in part **a**.

c. Refer to part **b**. Why might $\hat{\beta}_0$ be different from 0 even though the true value of β_0 is known to be 0?

d. The estimated standard error of $\hat{\beta}_0$ is equal to

$$s\sqrt{\frac{1}{n} + \frac{\bar{x}^2}{SS_{xx}}}$$

Use the t-statistic

$$t = \frac{\hat{\beta}_0 - 0}{s\sqrt{(1/n) + (\bar{x}^2/SS_{xx})}}$$

to test the null hypothesis $H_0: \beta_0 = 0$ against the alternative $H_a: \beta_0 \neq 0$. Take $\alpha = .10$. Should you include β_0 in your model?

11.128 Long-jump "takeoff error." The long jump is a track- and-field event in which a competitor attempts to jump a maximum distance into a sandpit after a running start. At the edge of the pit is a takeoff board. Jumpers usually try to plant their toes at the front edge of this board to maximize their jumping distance. The absolute distance between the front edge of the takeoff board and the spot where the toe actually lands on the board prior to jumping is called "takeoff error." Is takeoff error in the long jump linearly related to best jumping distance? To answer this question, kinesiology researchers videotaped the performances of 18 novice long jumpers at a high school track meet. (*Journal of Applied Biomechanics*, May 1995.) The average takeoff error x and the best jumping distance y (out of three jumps) for each jumper are recorded in the table. If a jumper can reduce his or her average takeoff error by .1 meter, how much would you estimate the jumper's best jumping distance to change? On the basis of your answer, comment on the usefulness of the model for predicting best jumping distance.

LONGJUMP

Jumper	Best Jumping Distance y (meters)	Average Takeoff Error x (meters)
1	5.30	.09
2	5.55	.17
3	5.47	.19
4	5.45	.24
5	5.07	.16
6	5.32	.22
7	6.15	.09
8	4.70	.12
9	5.22	.09
10	5.77	.09
11	5.12	.13
12	5.77	.16
13	6.22	.03
14	5.82	.50
15	5.15	.13
16	4.92	.04
17	5.20	.07
18	5.42	.04

Source: Berg, W. P., and Greer, N. L. "A kinematic profile of the approach run of novice long jumpers," *Journal of Applied Biomechanics*, Vol. 11, No. 2, May 1995, p. 147 (Table 1).

Critical Thinking Challenges

11.129 Study of fertility rates. The fertility rate of a country is defined as the number of children a woman citizen bears, on average, in her lifetime. *Scientific American* (Dec. 1993) reported on the declining fertility rate in developing coun-

FERTRATE

Country	Contraceptive Prevalence x	Fertility Rate y
Mauritius	76	2.2
Thailand	69	2.3
Colombia	66	2.9
Costa Rica	71	3.5
Sri Lanka	63	2.7
Turkey	62	3.4
Peru	60	3.5
Mexico	55	4.0
Jamaica	55	2.9
Indonesia	50	3.1
Tunisia	51	4.3
El Salvador	48	4.5
Morocco	42	4.0
Zimbabwe	46	5.4
Egypt	40	4.5
Bangladesh	40	5.5
Botswana	35	4.8
Jordan	35	5.5
Kenya	28	6.5
Guatemala	24	5.5
Cameroon	16	5.8
Ghana	14	6.0
Pakistan	13	5.0
Senegal	13	6.5
Sudan	10	4.8
Yemen	9	7.0
Nigeria	7	5.7

Source: Robey, B., et al. "The fertility decline in developing countries," *Scientific American*, Dec. 1993, p. 62. [*Note:* The data values are estimated from a scatterplot.]

tries. The researchers found that family planning can have a great effect on fertility rate. The accompanying table gives the fertility rate *y* and contraceptive prevalence *x* (measured as the percentage of married women who use contraception) for each of 27 developing countries.

a. According to the researchers, "The data reveal that differences in contraceptive prevalence explain about 90% of the variation in fertility rates." Do you concur?

b. The researchers also concluded that "if contraceptive use increases by 18 percent, women bear, on average, one fewer child." Is this statement supported by the data? Explain.

11.130 **Spall damage in bricks.** A recent civil suit revolved around a five-building brick apartment complex located in the Bronx, New York, which began to suffer *spalling* damage (i.e., a separation of some portion of the face of a brick from its body). The owner of the complex alleged that the bricks were manufactured defectively. The brick manufac-

turer countered that poor design and shoddy management led to the damage. To settle the suit, an estimate of the rate of damage per 1,000 bricks, called the spall rate, was required. (*Chance*, Summer 1994.) The owner estimated the spall rate by using several *scaffold-drop* surveys. (With this method, an engineer lowers a scaffold down at selected places on building walls and counts the number of visible spalls for every 1,000 bricks in the observation area.) The brick manufacturer conducted its own survey by dividing the walls of the complex into 83 wall segments and taking a photograph of each one. (The number of spalled bricks that could be made out from each photo was recorded, and the sum over all 83 wall segments was used as an estimate of total spall damage.) In this court case, the jury was faced with the following dilemma: On the one hand, the scaffold-drop survey provided the most accurate estimate of spall rates in a given wall segment. Unfortunately, however, the drop areas were not selected at random from the entire complex; rather, drops were made at areas with high spall concentrations, leading to an overestimate of the total damage. On the other hand, the photo survey was complete in that all 83 wall segments in the complex were checked for spall damage. But the spall rate estimated by the photos, at least in areas of high spall concentration, was biased low (spalling damage cannot always be seen from a photo), leading to an underestimate of the total damage.

The data in the table are the spall rates obtained from the two methods at 11 drop locations. Use the data, as did expert statisticians who testified in the case, to help the jury estimate the true spall rate at a given wall segment. Then explain how this information, coupled with the data (not given here) on all 83 wall segments, can provide a reasonable estimate of the total spall damage (i.e., total number of damaged bricks).

BRICKS

Drop Location	Drop Spall Rate (per 1,000 bricks)	Photo Spall Rate (per 1,000 bricks)
1	0	0
2	5.1	0
3	6.6	0
4	1.1	.8
5	1.8	1.0
6	3.9	1.0
7	11.5	1.9
8	22.1	7.7
9	39.3	14.9
10	39.9	13.9
11	43.0	11.8

Source: Fairley, W. B., et al. "Bricks, buildings, and the Bronx: Estimating masonry deterioration," *Chance*, Vol. 7. No. 3, Summer 1994, p. 36 (Figure 3). [*Note:* The data points are estimated from the points shown on a scatterplot.]

SUMMARY ACTIVITY: Applying Simple Linear Regression to Your Favorite Data

Many dependent variables in all areas of research serve as the subjects of regression-modeling efforts. We list five such variables here:

1. Crime rate in various communities
2. Daily maximum temperature in your town
3. Grade point average of students who have completed one academic year at your college
4. Gross domestic product of the United States
5. Points scored by your favorite football team in a single game

(continued)

Choose one of these dependent variables, or choose some other dependent variable, for which you want to construct a prediction model. There may be a large number of independent variables that should be included in a prediction equation for the dependent variable you choose. List three potentially important independent variables, x_1, x_2, and x_3, that you think might be (individually) strongly related to your dependent variable. Next, obtain 10 data values, each of which consists of a measure of your dependent variable y and the corresponding values of x_1, x_2, and x_3.

a. Use the least squares formulas given in this chapter to fit three straight-line models—one for each independent variable—for predicting y.

b. Interpret the sign of the estimated slope coefficient $\hat{\beta}_1$ in each case, and test the utility of each model by testing H_0: $\beta_1 = 0$ against H_a: $\beta_1 \neq 0$. What assumptions must be satisfied to ensure the validity of these tests?

c. Calculate the coefficient of determination, r^2, for each model. Which of the independent variables predicts y best for the 10 sampled sets of data? Is this variable necessarily best in general (i.e., for the entire population)? Explain.

Be sure to keep the data and the results of your calculations, since you will need them for the Student Projects section in Chapter 12.

REFERENCES

Chatterjee, S., and Price, B. *Regression Analysis by Example*, 2d ed. New York: Wiley, 1991.

Draper, N., and Smith, H. *Applied Regression Analysis*, 3d ed. New York: Wiley, 1987.

Graybill, F. *Theory and Application of the Linear Model.* North Scituate, MA.: Duxbury, 1976.

Kleinbaum, D., and Kupper, L. *Applied Regression Analysis and Other Multivariable Methods*, 2d ed. North Scituate, MA.: Duxbury, 1997.

Mendenhall, W. *Introduction to Linear Models and the Design and Analysis of Experiments*. Belmont, CA.: Wadsworth, 1968.

Mendenhall, W., and Sincich, T. *A Second Course in Statistics: Regression Analysis*, 6th ed. Upper Saddle River, NJ: Prentice Hall, 2003.

Montgomery, D., Peck, E., and Vining, G. *Introduction to Linear Regression Analysis*, 3d ed. New York: Wiley, 2001.

Mosteller, F., and Tukey, J. W. *Data Analysis and Regression: A Second Course in Statistics.* Reading, MA.: Addison-Wesley, 1977.

Neter, J., Kutner, M., Nachtsheim, C., and Wasserman, W. *Applied Linear Statistical Models*, 4th ed. Homewood, IL.: Richard Irwin, 1996.

Rousseeuw, P. J., and Leroy, A. M. *Robust Regression and Outlier Detection.* New York: Wiley, 1987.

Weisburg, S. *Applied Linear Regression*, 2d ed. New York: Wiley, 1985.

Using Technology

Simple Linear Regression with MINITAB

To conduct a simple linear regression analysis, first access the MINITAB worksheet file that contains the two quantitative variables (the dependent and independent variables). Next, click on the "Stat" button on the MINITAB menu bar, and then click on "Regression" and "Regression" again, as shown in Figure 11.M.1.

The dialog box shown in Figure 11.M.2 then appears. Specify the dependent variable in the "Response" box and the independent variable in the "Predictors" box.

Optionally, you can get MINITAB to produce prediction intervals for y and confidence intervals for $E(y)$ by clicking the "Options" button. The dialog box shown in Figure 11.M.3 then appears. Check "Confidence limits" and/or "Prediction limits", specify the "Confidence level," and enter the value of x in the "Prediction intervals for new observations" box. Click "OK" to return to the main Regression dialog box, and then click "OK" again to produce the MINITAB simple linear regression printout.

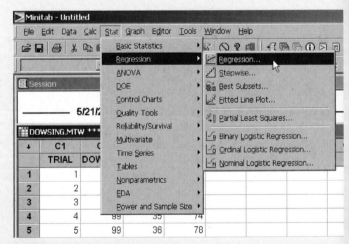

FIGURE 11.M.1

MINITAB menu options for regression

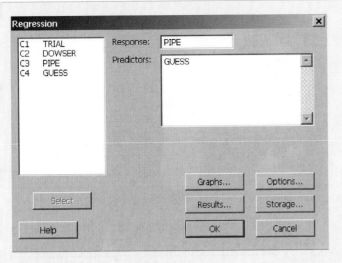

FIGURE 11.M.2
MINITAB regression dialog box

FIGURE 11.M.3
MINITAB regression options

To obtain the correlation coefficient for the two quantitative variables, click on the "Stat" button on the MINITAB main menu bar, then click on "Basic Statistics", and then click on "Correlation", as shown in Figure 11.M.4. The dialog box in Figure 11.M.5 then appears. Enter the two variables of interest in the "Variables" box, and then click "OK" to obtain a printout of the correlation.

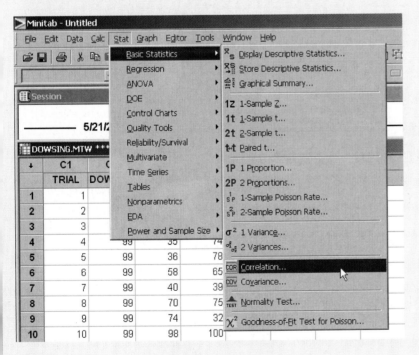

FIGURE 11.M.4
MINITAB menu options for correlation

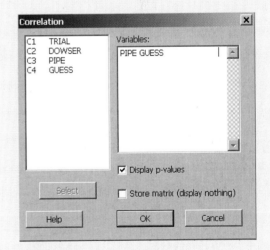

FIGURE 11.M.5
MINITAB correlation dialog box

CHAPTER 12

Multiple Regression and Model Building

CONTENTS

STATISTICS IN ACTION

Modeling Condominium Sales:
What Factors Affect Auction Price?

USING TECHNOLOGY

Multiple Regression with MINITAB

WHERE WE'VE BEEN

- Introduced the straight-line model relating a dependent variable y to a single independent variable x

- Demonstrated how to estimate the parameters of the straight-line model by the method of least squares

- Showed how to statistically assess the adequacy of the model

- Showed how to use the model to estimate $E(y)$ and predict y for a given value of x

■ Introduce a *multiple-regression* model as a means of relating a dependent variable *y* to two or more independent variables.

■ Present several different multiple regression models involving both quantitative and qualitative independent variables.

■ Assess how well the multiple-regression model fits the sample data.

■ Show how an analysis of a model's *residuals* can aid in detecting violations of the model's assumptions and in identifying modifications required by the model.

STATISTICS IN ACTION

Modeling Condominium Sales: What Factors Affect Auction Price?

This application involves an investigation of the factors that affect the sale price of oceanside condominium units. It represents an extension of an analysis of data by Herman Kelting (1979). Although condo sale prices have increased dramatically over the past 20 years, the relationship between these factors and sale prices remain about the same. Consequently, the data provide valuable insight into today's condominium sales market.

Sales data were obtained for a newly built oceanside condominium complex consisting of two adjacent, connected eight-floor buildings. The complex contains 209 units of equal size (approximately 500 square feet each). The locations of the buildings relative to the ocean, the swimming pool, the parking lot, etc., are shown in Figure SIA 12.1.

Among the features of the complex that you should note are the following:

1. The units facing south, called *oceanview*, face the beach and ocean. In addition, units in building 1 have a good view of the pool. Units to the rear of the building, called *bayview*, face the parking lot and an area of land that, ultimately, borders a bay. The view from the upper floors of these units is primarily of

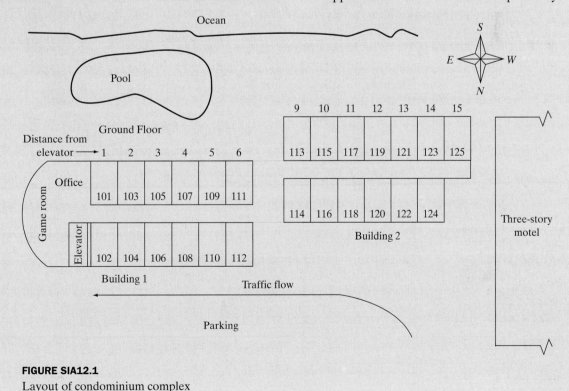

FIGURE SIA12.1
Layout of condominium complex

(continued)

wooded, sandy terrain. The bay is very distant and barely visible.

2. The only elevator in the complex is located at the east end of building 1, next to the office and the game room. People moving to or from the higher floor units in building 2 would probably use the elevator, then move through the passages to their units. Thus, units on the higher floors and at a greater distance from the elevator would be less convenient for their occupants, who would expend greater effort in moving baggage, groceries, etc., and would be farther away from the game room, the office, and the swimming pool. These units also possess an advantage: Because traffic through the hallways in the area would be minimal, these units would be the most private.

3. Because lower floor oceanside units open onto the beach, ocean, and pool, they are most suited to active people. They are within easy reach of the game room, and they are also easily reached from the parking area.

4. Checking Figure SIA 12.1, you will see that the views in some of the units at the center of the complex—units ending in numbers 11 and 14—are partially blocked.

5. The condominium complex was completed at the time of the 1975 recession; sales were slow, and the developer was forced to sell about half of the units at auction approximately 18 months after the complex opened. Many unsold units were furnished by the developer and rented prior to the auction.

This condominium complex is particularly suited to our study. Because the single elevator is located at one end of the complex, it is the source of a remarkably high level of both inconvenience and privacy for the people occupying units on the top floors in building 2. Consequently, the data provide a good opportunity to investigate the relationship that might exist between sale price, height of the unit (floor number), distance of the unit from the elevator, and presence or absence of an ocean view. In addition, the presence or absence of furniture in each of the units permits an investigation of the effect of the availability of furniture on the sale price. Finally, the units sold at auction are completely specified by the buyer and hence are consumer oriented, in contrast to most other real estate units, which are, to a high degree, seller oriented and specified by the broker.

The **CONDO** file contains data on each of the 209 units sold—106 at public auction and 103 at the developer's fixed price. The variables measured for each condominium unit are listed in Table SIA 12.1. We want to build a model for the auction price and, ultimately, to use the model to predict the sale prices of future units.

In several Statistics in Action Revisited sections, we show how to analyze the data by means of a multiple regression analysis.

Statistics in Action Revisited

- A First-Order Model for Condominium Sale Prices (p. 650)

- Building a Model for Condominium Sale Prices (p. 692)

- A Residual Analysis for the Condominium Sale Price Model (p. 716)

 CONDO

TABLE SIA12.1 Variables in the CONDO Data File

Variable Name	Type	Description
PRICE100	Quantitative	Sales price (hundreds of dollars)
FLOOR	Quantitative	Floor height $(1, 2, 3, \ldots, 8)$
DIST	Quantitative	Distance, in units, from the elevator $(1, 2, 3, \ldots, 15)$
VIEW	Qualitative	View $(1 = \text{ocean view}, 0 = \text{non–ocean view})$
END	Qualitative	Location of unit $(1 = \text{end of complex}, 0 = \text{not an end unit})$
FURNISH	Qualitative	Furniture status $(1 = \text{furnished}, 0 = \text{nonfurnished})$
AUCTION	Qualitative	Method of sale $(1 = \text{public auction}, 0 = \text{fixed price})$

12.1 Multiple-Regression Models

Most practical applications of regression analysis utilize models that are more complex than the simple straight-line model. For example, a realistic probabilistic model for reaction time would include more than just the amount of a particular drug in the bloodstream. Factors such as age, a measure of visual perception, and sex of the subject are a few of the many variables that might be related to reaction time. Thus, we would want to incorporate these and other potentially important independent variables into the model in order to make accurate predictions.

Probabilistic models that include more than one independent variable are called **multiple regression models**. The general form of these models is

$$y = \beta_0 + \beta_1 x_1 + \beta_2 x_2 + \cdots + \beta_k x_k + \varepsilon$$

The dependent variable y is now written as a function of k independent variables $x_1, x_2, \ldots, x_k$. The random-error term is added to make the model probabilistic rather than deterministic. The value of the coefficient β_i determines the contribution of the independent variable x_i, and β_0 is the y-intercept. The coefficients $\beta_0, \beta_1, \ldots, \beta_k$ are usually unknown because they represent population parameters.

At first glance, it might appear that the regression model just described would not allow for anything other than straight-line relationships between y and the independent variables, but this is not true. Actually, $x_1, x_2, \ldots, x_k$ can be functions of variables, as long as the functions do not contain unknown parameters. For example, the reaction time y of a subject to a visual stimulus could be a function of the independent variables

$$x_1 = \text{Age of the subject}$$
$$x_2 = (\text{Age})^2 = x_1^2$$
$$x_3 = 1 \text{ if male subject, } 0 \text{ if female subject}$$

The x_2-term is called a **higher order term**, since it is the value of a quantitative variable (x_1) squared (i.e., raised to the second power). The x_3-term is a (qualitative) **coded variable** representing a quality (gender). The multiple-regression model is quite versatile and can be made to model many different types of response variables.

The General Multiple Regression Model

$$y = \beta_0 + \beta_1 x_1 + \beta_2 x_2 + \cdots + \beta_k x_k + \varepsilon$$

where

y is the dependent variable
$x_1, x_2, \ldots, x_k$ are the independent variables
$E(y) = \beta_0 + \beta_1 x_1 + \beta_2 x_2 + \cdots + \beta_k x_k$ is the deterministic portion of the model
β_i determines the contribution of the independent variable x_i

Note: The symbols $x_1, x_2, \ldots, x_k$ may represent higher order terms for quantitative predictors or terms that represent qualitative predictors.

As shown in the following box, the steps used to develop the multiple-regression model are similar to those used for the simple regression model:

Analyzing a Multiple-Regression Model

Step 1   Hypothesize the deterministic component of the model. This component relates the mean $E(y)$ to the independent variables $x_1, x_2, \ldots, x_k$. Involved here is the choice of the independent variables to be included in the model (Sections 12.2, 12.5–12.10).

Step 2   Use the sample data to estimate the unknown parameters $\beta_0, \beta_1, \beta_2, \ldots, \beta_k$ in the model (Section 12.2).

(continued)

Step 3   Specify the probability distribution of the random-error term ε, and estimate the standard deviation σ of this distribution (Section 12.3).

Step 4   Check that the assumptions about ε are satisfied, and make modifications to the model if necessary (Section 12.11).

Step 5   Statistically evaluate the usefulness of the model (Section 12.3).

Step 6   When you are satisfied that the model is useful, use it for prediction, estimation, and other purposes (Section 12.4).

The assumptions we make about the random error ε of the multiple-regression model are similar to those we make about the random error in a simple linear regression and are summarized as follows:

Assumptions about Random Error ε

For any given set of values of $x_1, x_2, \ldots, x_k$, the random error ε has a probability distribution with the following properties:

1. The mean is equal to 0

2. The variance is equal to σ^2

3. The probability distribution is a normal distribution

4. Random errors are independent (in a probabilistic sense)

Throughout this chapter, we introduce several different types of models that form the foundation of **model building** (or useful model construction). In the next several sections, we consider the most basic multiple-regression model, called the *first-order model*.

12.2 The First-Order Model: Estimating and Making Inferences about the β Parameters

A model that includes only terms denoting *quantitative* independent variables, called a **first-order model**, is described in the next box. Note that the first-order model does not include any higher order terms (such as x_1^2).

A First-Order Model in Five Quantitative Independent Variables*

$$E(y) = \beta_0 + \beta_1 x_1 + \beta_2 x_2 + \beta_3 x_3 + \beta_4 x_4 + \beta_5 x_5$$

where $x_1, x_2, \ldots, x_5$ are all quantitative variables that *are not* functions of other independent variables.

Note: β_i represents the slope of the line relating y to x_i when all the other x's are held fixed.

The method of fitting first-order models—and multiple-regression models in general—is identical to that of fitting the simple straight-line model: the method of least squares. That is, we choose the estimated model

$$\hat{y} = \hat{\beta}_0 + \hat{\beta}_1 x_1 + \cdots + \hat{\beta}_k x_k$$

that minimizes

$$\text{SSE} = \sum (y - \hat{y})^2$$

*The terminology "first-order" is derived from the fact that each x in the model is raised to the first power.

As in the case of the simple linear model, the sample estimates $\hat{\beta}_0, \hat{\beta}_1, \ldots, \hat{\beta}_k$ are obtained as a solution of a set of simultaneous linear equations.*

The primary difference between fitting the simple- and multiple-regression models is computational difficulty. The $(k + 1)$ simultaneous linear equations that must be solved to find the $(k + 1)$ estimated coefficients $\hat{\beta}_0, \hat{\beta}_1, \ldots, \hat{\beta}_k$ are difficult (sometimes nearly impossible) to solve with a calculator. Consequently, we resort to the use of computers. Instead of presenting the tedious hand calculations required to fit the models, we present output from SAS, SPSS, and MINITAB.

Biography

GEORGE U. YULE (1871–1951)—
Yule Processes

Born on a small farm in Scotland, George Yule received an extensive childhood education. After graduating from University College (London), where he studied civil engineering, Yule spent a year employed in engineering workshops. However, he made a career change in 1893, accepting a teaching position back at University College under the guidance of statistician Karl Pearson (see p. 746). Inspired by Pearson's work, Yule produced a series of important articles on the statistics of regression and correlation. Yule is considered the first to have applied the method of least squares in regression analysis and he developed the theory of multiple regression. He eventually was appointed a lecturer in statistics at Cambridge University and later became the president of the prestigious Royal Statistical Society. Yule made many other contributions to the field, including the invention of time-series analysis and the development of "Yule" processes and the "Yule" distribution.

EXAMPLE 12.1

FITTING A FIRST-ORDER MODEL:

Price of an Antique Clock

Problem A collector of antique grandfather clocks sold at auction believes that the price received for the clocks depends on both the age of the clocks and the number of bidders at the auction. Thus, he hypothesizes the first-order model

$$y = \beta_0 + \beta_1 x_1 + \beta_2 x_2 + \varepsilon$$

where

$$y = \text{Auction price (dollars)}$$
$$x_1 = \text{Age of clock (years)}$$
$$x_2 = \text{Number of bidders}$$

A sample of 32 auction prices of grandfather clocks, along with their age and the number of bidders, is given in Table 12.1.

a. Use scattergrams to plot the sample data. Interpret the plots.

b. Use the method of least squares to estimate the unknown parameters β_0, β_1, and β_2 of the model.

c. Find the value of SSE that is minimized by the least squares method.

d. Estimate σ, the standard deviation of the model, and interpret the result.

Solution

a. MINITAB side-by-side scatterplots for examining the bivariate relationships between y and x_1 and between y and x_2 are shown in Figure 12.1. Of the two variables, age (x_1) appears to have the strongest linear relationship with auction price (y).

b. The model hypothesized is fit to the data of Table 12.1 with MINITAB. A portion of the printout is reproduced in Figure 12.2. The least squares estimates of the β parameters (highlighted) are $\hat{\beta}_0 = -1{,}339$, $\hat{\beta}_1 = 12.74$, and $\hat{\beta}_2 = 85.95$. Therefore, the equation that minimizes SSE for this data set (i.e., the **least squares prediction equation**) is

$$\hat{y} = -1{,}339 + 12.74 x_1 + 85.95 x_2$$

---

*Students who are familiar with calculus should note that $\hat{\beta}_0, \hat{\beta}_1, \ldots, \hat{\beta}_k$ are the solutions of the set of equations $\partial\text{SSE}/\partial\hat{\beta}_0 = 0, \partial\text{SSE}/\partial\hat{\beta}_1 = 0, \ldots, \partial\text{SSE}/\partial\hat{\beta}_k = 0$. The solution is usually given in matrix form, but we do not present the details here. (See the references for details.)

GFCLOCKS

TABLE 12.1 Auction Price Data

Age x_1	Number of Bidders x_2	Auction Price y	Age x_1	Number of Bidders x_2	Auction Price y
127	13	$1,235	170	14	$2,131
115	12	1,080	182	8	1,550
127	7	845	162	11	1,884
150	9	1,522	184	10	2,041
156	6	1,047	143	6	845
182	11	1,979	159	9	1,483
156	12	1,822	108	14	1,055
132	10	1,253	175	8	1,545
137	9	1,297	108	6	729
113	9	946	179	9	1,792
137	15	1,713	111	15	1,175
117	11	1,024	187	8	1,593
137	8	1,147	111	7	785
153	6	1,092	115	7	744
117	13	1,152	194	5	1,356
126	10	1,336	168	7	1,262

c. The minimum value of the sum of the squared errors, also highlighted in Figure 12.2, is SSE = 516,727.

d. Recall that the estimator of σ^2 for the straight-line model is $s^2 = \text{SSE}/(n-2)$, and note that the denominator is (n − Number of estimated β parameters), which is ($n-2$) in the straight-line model. Since we must estimate the three parameters β_0, β_1, and β_2, for the first-order model, the estimator of σ^2 is

$$s^2 = \frac{\text{SSE}}{n-3} = \frac{\text{SSE}}{32-3} = \frac{516{,}727}{29} = 17{,}818$$

This value, often called the **mean square for error (MSE)** is also highlighted at the bottom of the MINITAB printout in Figure 12.2. The estimate of σ, then, is

$$s = \sqrt{17{,}818} = 133.5$$

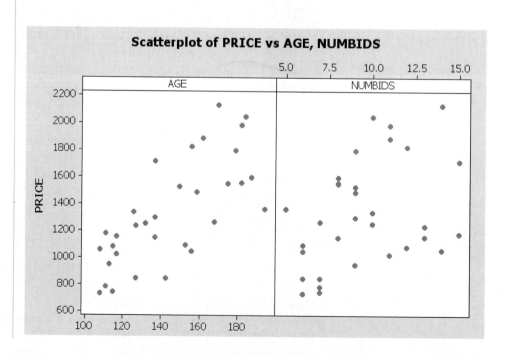

FIGURE 12.1

MINITAB side-by-side scatterplots for the data of table 12.1

Regression Analysis: PRICE versus AGE, NUMBIDS

```
The regression equation is
PRICE = - 1339 + 12.7 AGE + 86.0 NUMBIDS


Predictor      Coef   SE Coef       T      P
Constant    -1339.0     173.8   -7.70  0.000
AGE         12.7406    0.9047   14.08  0.000
NUMBIDS      85.953     8.729    9.85  0.000


S = 133.485    R-Sq = 89.2%    R-Sq(adj) = 88.5%


Analysis of Variance

Source           DF        SS       MS       F      P
Regression        2   4283063  2141531  120.19  0.000
Residual Error   29    516727    17818
Total            31   4799790
```

FIGURE 12.2

MINITAB analysis of the auction price model

which is highlighted in the middle of the printout in Figure 12.2. One useful interpretation of the estimated standard deviation s is that the interval $\pm 2s$ will provide a rough approximation to the accuracy with which the model will predict future values of y for given values of x. Thus, we expect the model to provide predictions of auction price to within about $\pm 2s = \pm 2(133.5) = \pm 267$ dollars.*

Look Back As with simple linear regression, we will use the estimator of σ^2 both to check the utility of the model (Section 12.3) and to provide a measure of the reliability of predictions and estimates when the model is used for those purposes (Section 12.4). Thus, you can see that the estimation of σ^2 plays an important part in the development of a regression model.

Now Work Exercise 12.6a–c

Estimator of σ^2 for a Multiple-Regression Model with k Independent Variables

$$s^2 = \frac{\text{SSE}}{n - \text{Number of estimated } \beta \text{ parameters}} = \frac{\text{SSE}}{n - (k + 1)}$$

After obtaining the least squares prediction equation, the analyst will usually want to make meaningful interpretations of the β estimates. Recall that in the straight-line model (Chapter 11)

$$y = \beta_0 + \beta_1 x + \varepsilon$$

β_0 represents the y-intercept of the line and β_1 represents the slope of the line. From our discussion in Chapter 11, β_1 has a practical interpretation: the mean change in y for every 1-unit increase in x. When the independent variables are quantitative, the β parameters in the first-order model specified in Example 12.1 have similar interpretations. The difference is that when we interpret the β that multiplies one of the variables (e.g., x_1), we must be certain to hold the values of the remaining independent variables (e.g., x_2, x_3) fixed.

*The $\pm 2s$ approximation improves as the sample size is increased. We will provide a more precise methodology for the construction of prediction intervals in Section 12.4.

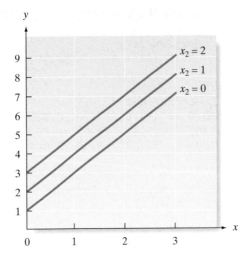

FIGURE 12.3

Graphs of
$E(y) = 1 + 2x_1 + x_2$
for $x_2 = 0, 1, 2$

To see this, suppose that the mean $E(y)$ of a response y is related to two quantitative independent variables x_1 and x_2 by the first-order model

$$E(y) = 1 + 2x_1 + x_2$$

In other words, $\beta_0 = 1$, $\beta_1 = 2$, and $\beta_2 = 1$.

Now, when $x_2 = 0$, the relationship between $E(y)$ and x_1 is given by

$$E(y) = 1 + 2x_1 + (0) = 1 + 2x_1$$

A graph of this relationship (a straight line) is shown in Figure 12.3. Similar graphs of the relationship between $E(y)$ and x_1 for $x_2 = 1$, namely,

$$E(y) = 1 + 2x_1 + (1) = 2 + 2x_1$$

and for $x_2 = 2$, that is,

$$E(y) = 1 + 2x_1 + (2) = 3 + 2x_1$$

also are shown in Figure 12.3. Note that the slopes of the three lines are all equal to $\beta_1 = 2$, the coefficient that multiplies x_1.

Figure 12.3 exhibits a characteristic of all first-order models: If you graph $E(y)$ versus any one variable—say, x_1—for fixed values of the other variables, the result will always be a *straight line* with slope equal to β_1. If you repeat the process for other values of the fixed independent variables, you will obtain a set of *parallel* straight lines. This indicates that the effect of the independent variable x_i on $E(y)$ is independent of all the other independent variables in the model, and this effect is measured by the slope β_i (see note in box on p. 630).

A three-dimensional graph of the model $E(y) = 1 + 2x_1 + x_2$ is shown in Figure 12.4. Note that the graph is a plane. If you slice the plane at a particular value

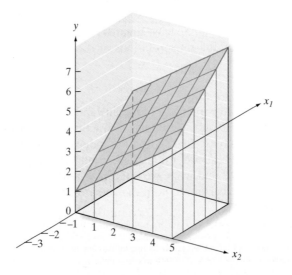

FIGURE 12.4

The plane
$E(y) = 1 + 2x_1 + x_2$

of x_2 (say, $x_2 = 0$), you obtain a straight line relating $E(y)$ to x_1 (e.g., $E(y) = 1 + 2x_1$). Similarly, if you slice the plane at a particular value of x_1, you obtain a straight line relating $E(y)$ to x_2. Since it is more difficult to visualize three-dimensional and, in general, k-dimensional surfaces, we will graph all the models presented in this chapter in two dimensions. The key to obtaining these graphs is to hold fixed all but one of the independent variables in the model.

EXAMPLE 12.2

INTERPRETING THE β ESTIMATES:

Clock Auction Price Model

Problem Refer to the first-order model for auction price y considered in Example 12.1. Interpret the estimates of the β parameters in the model.

Solution The least squares prediction equation, as given in Example 12.1, is $\hat{y} = -1{,}339 + 12.74x_1 + 85.95x_2$. We know that with first-order models β_1 represents the slope of the line relating y to x_1 for fixed x_2. That is, β_1 measures the change in $E(y)$ for every one-unit increase in x_1 when the other independent variable in the model is held fixed. A similar statement can be made about β_2: β_2 measures the change in $E(y)$ for every one-unit increase in x_2 when the other x in the model is held fixed. Consequently, we obtain the following interpretations:

> $\hat{\beta}_1 = 12.74$: We estimate the mean auction price $E(y)$ of an antique clock to increase \$12.74 for every 1-year increase in age (x_1) when the number of bidders (x_2) is held fixed.

> $\hat{\beta}_2 = 85.95$: We estimate the mean auction price $E(y)$ of an antique clock to increase \$85.95 for every 1-bidder increase in the number of bidders (x_2) when age (x_1) is held fixed.

The value $\hat{\beta}_0 = -1{,}339$ does not have a meaningful interpretation in this example. To see this, note that $\hat{y} = \hat{\beta}_0$ when $x_1 = x_2 = 0$. Thus, $\hat{\beta}_0 = -1{,}339$ represents the estimated mean auction price when the values of all the independent variables are set equal to 0. Since an antique clock with these characteristics—an age of 0 years and 0 bidders on the clock—is not practical, the value of $\hat{\beta}_0$ has no meaningful interpretation. In general, $\hat{\beta}_0$ will not have a practical interpretation unless it makes sense to set the values of the x's simultaneously equal to 0.

Look Back In general, $\hat{\beta}_0$ will not have a practical interpretation unless it makes sense to set the values of the x's simultaneously equal to 0.

Now Work Exercise 12.15a–b

Caution

The interpretation of the β parameters in a multiple regression model will depend on the terms specified in the model. The interpretations in Example 12.2 are for a first-order linear model only. In practice, you should be sure that a first-order model is the correct model for $E(y)$ before making β interpretations. [We discuss alternative models for $E(y)$ in Sections 12.5–12.8.]

Inferences about the individual β parameters in a model are obtained with the use of either a confidence interval or a test of hypothesis, as outlined in the following boxes:*

Test of an Individual Parameter Coefficient in the Multiple Regression Model

One-Tailed Test	**Two-Tailed Test**
H_0: $\beta_i = 0$	H_0: $\beta_i = 0$
H_a: $\beta_i < 0$ [or H_a: $\beta_i > 0$]	H_a: $\beta_i \neq 0$

(continued)

---

*The formulas for computing $\hat{\beta}_i$ and its standard error are so complicated that the only reasonable way to present them is by using matrix algebra. We do not assume a prerequisite of matrix algebra for this text, and in any case, we think that the formulas can be omitted in an introductory course without serious loss. They are programmed into almost all statistical software packages with multiple-regression routines and are presented in some of the texts listed in the references.

$$Test\ statistic: t = \frac{\hat{\beta}_i}{s_{\hat{\beta}_i}}$$

Rejection region: $t < -t_\alpha$ *Rejection region:* $|t| > t_{\alpha/2}$

[or $t > t_\alpha$ when H_a: $\beta_i > 0$]

where t_α and $t_{\alpha/2}$ are based on $n - (k + 1)$ degrees of freedom and

$$n = \text{Number of observations}$$
$$k + 1 = \text{Number of } \beta \text{ parameters in the model}$$

A 100(1 − α)% Confidence Interval for a β Parameter

$$\hat{\beta}_i \pm (t_{\alpha/2})s_{\hat{\beta}_1}$$

where $t_{\alpha/2}$ is based on $n - (k + 1)$ degrees of freedom and

$$n = \text{Number of observations}$$
$$k + 1 = \text{Number of } \beta \text{ parameters in the model}$$

Conditions Required for Valid Inferences about Individual β Parameters

The four assumptions about the probability distribution for the random error ε (p. 630).

We illustrate these methods with another example.

EXAMPLE 12.3
INFERENCES ABOUT THE β PARAMETERS:
Auction Price Model

Problem Refer to Examples 12.1 and 12.2. The collector of antique grandfather clocks knows that the price (y) received for the clocks increases linearly with the age (x_1) of the clocks. Moreover, the collector hypothesizes that the auction price (y) of the clocks will increase linearly as the number of bidders (x_2) increases. Use the information on the MINITAB printout shown in Figure 12.2 (p. 633) to

a. Test the hypothesis that the mean auction price of a clock increases as the number of bidders increases when age is held constant (i.e., when $\beta_2 > 0$). (Use $\alpha = .05$.)

b. Find a 90% confidence interval for β_1 and interpret the result.

Solution

a. The hypotheses of interest concern the parameter β_2. Specifically,

$$H_0: \beta_2 = 0$$
$$H_a: \beta_2 > 0$$

The test statistic is a t statistic formed by dividing the sample estimate $\hat{\beta}_2$ of the parameter β_2 by the estimated standard error of $\hat{\beta}_2$ (denoted $s_{\hat{\beta}_2}$). These estimates, $\hat{\beta}_2 = 85.953$ and $s_{\hat{\beta}_2} = 8.729$, as well as the calculated t value,

$$Test\ statistic: t = \frac{\hat{\beta}_2}{s_{\hat{\beta}_2}} = \frac{85.953}{8.729} = 9.85$$

are highlighted on the MINITAB printout in Figure 12.2.

    The rejection region for the test is found in exactly the same way as the rejection regions for the t-tests in previous chapters. That is, we consult Table VI in Appendix A to obtain an upper-tail value of t. This is a value t_α such that $P(t > t_\alpha) = \alpha$. We can then use this value to construct rejection regions for either one-tailed or two-tailed tests.

    For $\alpha = .05$ and $n - (k + 1) = 32 - (2 + 1) = 29$ df, the critical t value obtained from Table VI is $t_{.05} = 1.699$. Therefore,

Rejection region: $t > 1.699$ (see Figure 12.5)

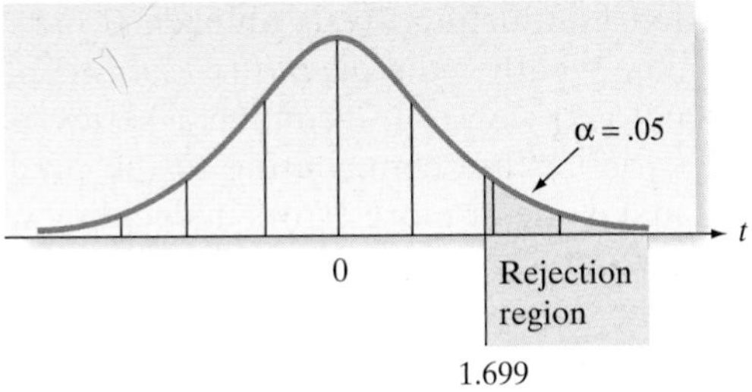

FIGURE 12.5
Rejection region for
$H_0: \beta_2 = 0$ *vs.* $H_a: \beta_2 > 0$

Since the test statistic value, $t = 9.85$, falls into the rejection region, we have sufficient evidence to reject H_0. Thus, the collector can conclude that the mean auction price of a clock increases as the number of bidders increases when age is held constant. Note that the two-tailed observed significance level of the test (highlighted on the printout) is approximately .000. Since the one-tailed p-value (half this value) is also .000, any nonzero α will lead us to reject H_0.

b. From the box on page 636, a 90% confidence interval for β_1 is

$$\hat{\beta}_1 \pm t_{\alpha/2} s_{\hat{\beta}_1} = \hat{\beta}_1 \pm t_{.05} s_{\hat{\beta}_1}$$

Substituting $\hat{\beta}_1 = 12.74$, $s_{\hat{\beta}_i} = .905$ (both obtained from the MINITAB printout in Figure 12.2), and $t_{.05} = 1.699$ (from part **a**) into the equation, we obtain

$$12.74 \pm 1.699(.905) = 12.74 \pm 1.54$$

or (11.20,14.28). Thus, we are 90% confident that β_1 falls between 11.20 and 14.28. Since β_1 is the slope of the line relating the auction price (y) to the age of the clock (x_1), we conclude that the price increases between \$11.20 and \$14.28 for every 1-year increase in age, holding number of bidders (x_2) constant.

Look Back When interpreting the β multiplied by one x, be sure to hold fixed the values of the other x's in the model.

Now Work Exercise 12.15c–d

12.3 Evaluating Overall Model Utility

In section 12.2, we demonstrated the use of t-tests in making inferences about β parameters in a multiple-regression model. There are caveats, however, to conducting these t-tests for the purposes of determining which x's are useful for predicting y. Several such caveats are listed in the following box:

Use Caution When Conducting t-tests on the β Parameters

It is dangerous to conduct t-tests on the individual β parameters in a *first-order linear model* for the purpose of determining which independent variables are useful for predicting y and which are not. If you fail to reject $H_0: \beta_i = 0$, several conclusions are possible:

1. There is no relationship between y and x_i.
2. A straight-line relationship between y and x_i exists (holding the other x's in the model fixed), but a Type II error occurred.
3. A relationship between y and x_i (holding the other x's in the model fixed) exists, but is more complex than a straight-line relationship (e.g., a curvilinear relationship may be appropriate). The most you can say about a β parameter test is that there is either sufficient (if you reject $H_0: \beta_i = 0$) or insufficient (if you do not reject $H_0: \beta_i = 0$) evidence of a *linear* (*straight-line*) relationship between y and x_i.

In addition, conducting t-tests on each β parameter in a model is *not* the best way to determine whether the *overall* model is contributing information relevant to the prediction of y. If we were to conduct a series of t-tests to determine whether the independent variables are contributing to the predictive relationship, we would be very likely to make one or more errors in deciding which terms to retain in the model and which to exclude.

For example, suppose you fit a first-order model in 10 quantitative x variables and decide to conduct t-tests on all 10 of the individual β's in the model, each at $\alpha = .05$. Even if all the β parameters (except β_0) are equal to 0, approximately 40% of the time you will incorrectly reject the null hypothesis at least once and conclude that some β parameter differs from 0.* Thus, in multiple-regression models for which a large number of independent variables are being considered, conducting a series of t-tests may include a large number of insignificant variables and exclude some useful ones. If we want to test the utility of a multiple-regression model, we will need a *global test* (one that encompasses all the β parameters). We would also like to find some statistical quantity that measures how well the model fits the data.

We commence with the easier problem: finding a measure of how well a linear model fits a set of data. For this, we use the multiple-regression equivalent of r^2, the coefficient of determination for the straight-line model (Chapter 11), as given in the next definition.

Definition 12.1

The **multiple coefficient of determination**, R^2, is defined as

$$R^2 = 1 - \frac{\text{SSE}}{\text{SS}_{yy}} = \frac{\text{SS}_{yy} - \text{SSE}}{\text{SS}_{yy}} = \frac{\text{Explained variablilty}}{\text{Total variability}}$$

Just like r^2 in the simple linear model, R^2 represents the fraction of the sample variation of the y-values (measured by SS_{yy}) that is explained by the least squares prediction equation. Thus, $R^2 = 0$ implies a complete lack of fit of the model to the data, and $R^2 = 1$ implies a perfect fit, with the model passing through every data point. In general, the larger the value of R^2, the better the model fits the data.

To illusrate, consider the first-order model for the grandfather clock auction price, presented in Examples 12.1–12.3. A SAS printout of the analysis is shown in Figure 12.6. The value $R^2 = .8923$ is highlighted in Figure 12.6. This high value of R^2 implies that using the independent variables age and number of bidders in a first-order model explains 89.2% of the total *sample variation* (measured by SS_{yy}) in auction price y. Thus, R^2 is a sample statistic that tells how well the model fits the data and thereby represents a measure of the usefulness of the entire model.

A large value of R^2 computed from the *sample* data does not necessarily mean that the model provides a good fit to all of the data points in the *population*. For example, a first-order linear model that contains three parameters will provide a perfect fit to a sample of three data points, and R^2 will equal 1. Likewise, you will always obtain a perfect fit ($R^2 = 1$) to a set of n data points if the model contains exactly n parameters. Consequently, if you want to use the value of R^2 as a measure of how useful the model will be in predicting y, it should be based on a sample that contains substantially more data points than the number of parameters in the model.

---

*The proof of this result (assuming independence of tests) proceeds as follows:

$P(\text{Reject } H_0 \text{ at least once} \mid \beta_1 = \beta_2 = \cdots = \beta_{10} = 0)$

$= 1 - P(\text{Reject } H_0 \text{ no times} \mid \beta_1 = \beta_2 = \cdots = \beta_{10} = 0)$

$\leq 1 - [P(\text{Accept } H_0: \beta_1 = 0 \mid \beta_1 = 0) \cdot P(\text{Accept } H_0: \beta_2 = 0 \mid \beta_2 = 0)] \cdot \cdots \cdot P(\text{Accept } H_0: \beta_{10} = 0 \mid \beta_{10} = 0)]$

$= 1 - [(1 - \alpha)^{10}] = 1 - (.95)^{10} = .401.$

For dependent tests, the Bonferroni inequality states that

$$P(\text{Reject } H_0 \text{ at least once} \mid \beta_1 = \beta_2 = \cdots = \beta_{10} = 0) \leq 10(\alpha) = 10(.05) = .50$$

Dependent Variable: PRICE

Number of Observations Read   32
Number of Observations Used   32

Analysis of Variance

Source	DF	Sum of Squares	Mean Square	F Value	Pr > F
Model	2	4283063	2141531	120.19	<.0001
Error	29	516727	17818		
Corrected Total	31	4799790			

Root MSE	133.48467	R-Square	0.8923	
Dependent Mean	1326.87500	Adj R-Sq	0.8849	
Coeff Var	10.06008			

Parameter Estimates

Variable	DF	Parameter Estimate	Standard Error	t Value	Pr > |t|	90% Confidence Limits	
Intercept	1	-1338.95134	173.80947	-7.70	<.0001	-1634.27571	-1043.62697
AGE	1	12.74057	0.90474	14.08	<.0001	11.20331	14.27784
NUMBIDS	1	85.95298	8.72852	9.85	<.0001	71.12211	100.78385

FIGURE 12.6

SAS analysis of the auction price model

Caution

In a multiple-regression analysis, use the value of R^2 as a measure of how useful a linear model will be in predicting y only if the sample contains substantially more data points than the number of β parameters in the model.

As an alternative to using R^2 as a measure of model adequacy, the *adjusted multiple coefficient of determination*, denoted R_a^2, is often reported. The formula for R_a^2 is given in the next definition.

Definition 12.2

The **adjusted multiple coefficient of determination** is given by

$$R_a^2 = 1 - \left[\frac{(n-1)}{n-(k+1)} \right]\left(\frac{\text{SSE}}{\text{SS}_{yy}} \right)$$

$$= 1 - \left[\frac{(n-1)}{n-(k+1)} \right](1 - R^2)$$

Note: $R_a^2 \leq R^2$.

R^2 and R_a^2 have similar interpretations. However, unlike R^2, R_a^2 takes into account ("adjusts" for) both the sample size n and the number of β parameters in the model. R_a^2 will always be smaller than R^2 and, more importantly, cannot be "forced" to 1 simply by adding more and more independent variables to the model. Consequently, analysts prefer the more conservative R_a^2 in choosing a measure of model adequacy. The value of R_a^2 is also highlighted in Figure 12.6. Note that $R_a^2 = .8849$, a value only slightly smaller than R^2.

Despite their utility, R^2 and R_a^2 are only sample statistics. Therefore, it is dangerous to judge the global usefulness of a model solely on the basis of these values. A better method is to conduct a test of hypothesis involving *all* the β parameters (except β_0) in a model. In particular, for the general multiple-regression model $E(y) = \beta_0 + \beta_1 x_1 + \beta_2 x_2 + \cdots + \beta_k x_k$, we would test

$$H_0: \beta_1 = \beta_2 = \cdots = \beta_k = 0$$
$$H_a: \text{At least one of the coefficients is nonzero}$$

The test statistic used to test this hypothesis is an F-statistic, and several equivalent versions of the formula can be used (although we will usually rely on the computer to calculate the F-statistic):

$$\text{Test statistic: } F = \frac{(\text{SS}_{yy} - \text{SSE})/k}{\text{SSE}/[n - (k + 1)]} = \frac{\text{Mean square (Model)}}{\text{Mean square (Error)}}$$

$$= \frac{R^2/k}{(1 - R^2)/[n - (k + 1)]}$$

Both formulas indicate that the F-statistic is the ratio of the *explained* variability divided by the number of degrees of freedom in the model to the *unexplained* variability divided by the number of degrees of freedom associated with the error. (For this reason, the test is often called the "analysis-of-variance" F-Test.) Thus, the larger the proportion of the total variability accounted for by the model, the larger is the F-statistic.

To determine when the ratio becomes large enough that we can confidently reject the null hypothesis and conclude that the model is more useful than no model at all in predicting y, we compare the calculated F-statistic with a tabulated F-value with k df in the numerator and $[n - (k + 1)]$ df in the denominator. Recall that tabulations of the F-distribution for various values of α are given in Tables VIII, IX, X, and XI of Appendix A. We thus have

Rejection region: $F > F_\alpha$, where F is based on k numerator and
$n - (k + 1)$ denominator degrees of freedom

The analysis-of-variance F-test for testing the overall utility of the multiple-regression model is summarized in the following box:

Testing the Global Usefulness of the Model: The Analysis-of-Variance F-Test

$H_0: \beta_1 = \beta_2 = \cdots = \beta_k = 0$ (All model terms are unimportant in predicting y.)

$H_a:$ At least one $\beta_i \neq 0$ (At least one model term is useful in predicting y.)

$$\text{Test statistic: } F = \frac{(\text{SS}_{yy} - \text{SSE})/k}{\text{SSE}/[n - (k + 1)]} = \frac{R^2/k}{(1 - R^2)/[n - (k + 1)]}$$

$$= \frac{\text{Mean square (Model)}}{\text{Mean square (Error)}}$$

where n is the sample size and k is the number of terms in the model.

Rejection region: $F > F_\alpha$, with k numerator degrees of freedom and $[n - (k + 1)]$ denominator degrees of freedom.

Conditions Required for the Global F-Test to be Valid

The standard regression assumptions about the random error component (Section 12.1).

Caution

A rejection of the null hypothesis $H_0: \beta_1 = \beta_2 = \cdots = \beta_k = 0$ in the **global F-test** leads to the conclusion [with $100(1 - \alpha)\%$ confidence] that the model is statistically useful. However, "useful" does not necessarily mean "best." Another model may prove even more useful in terms of providing more reliable estimates and predictions. This global F-test is usually regarded as a test that the model *must* pass to merit further consideration.

EXAMPLE 12.4

ASSESSING OVERALL MODEL ADEQUACY:

Antique Clock Auction Price Model

Problem Refer to Example 12.3, in which an antique collector modeled the auction price y of grandfather clocks as a function of the age x_1 of the clock and the number x_2 of bidders. Recall that the hypothesized first-order model is

$$y = \beta_0 + \beta_1 x_1 + \beta_2 x_2 + \varepsilon$$

a. Find and interpret the adjusted coefficient of determination, R_a^2, for this example.
b. Conduct the global F-test of model usefulness at the $\alpha = .05$ level of significance.

Solution

a. The R_a^2 value (highlighted in the SAS printout shown in Figure 12.6) is .8849. This implies that the least squares model has explained about 88.5% of the total sample variation in y values (auction prices), after adjusting for sample size and number of independent variables in the model.

b. The elements of the global test of the model are as follows:

$H_0: \beta_1 = \beta_2 = 0$ [*Note: k = 2*]
H_a: At least one of the two model coefficients is nonzero

$$Test \; statistic: F = \frac{MS(Model)}{MSE} = \frac{2,141,531}{17,818} = 120.19 \; (\text{see Figure 12.6})$$

p-value: less than .0001

Conclusion: Since $\alpha = .05$ exceeds the observed significance level, $p < .0001$, the data provide strong evidence that at least one of the model coefficients is nonzero. The overall model appears to be statistically useful in predicting auction prices.

Look Back Can we be sure that the best model for prediction has been found if the global F-test indicates that a model is useful? Unfortunately, we cannot. The addition of other independent variables may improve the usefulness of the model (see caution on page 640). We consider more complex multiple regression models in Sections 12.5–12.8.

Now Work Exercise 12.14

In this section, we discussed several different statistics for assessing the utility of a multiple-regression model: t-tests on the individual β parameters, R^2, R_a^2, and the global F-test. Both R^2 and R_a^2 are indicators of how well the prediction equation fits the data. Intuitive evaluations of the contribution of the model based on R^2 must be examined with care. Unlike R_a^2, the value of R^2 increases as more and more variables are added to the model. Consequently, you could force R^2 to take a value very close to 1 even though the model contributes no information relevant to the prediction of y. In fact, R^2 equals 1 when the number of terms in the model (including β_0) equals the number of data points. Therefore, you should not rely solely on the value of R^2 (or even R_a^2) to tell you whether a model is useful in predicting y.

Conducting t-tests on all the β parameters is also not the best method of testing the global utility of a model, since these multiple tests result in a high probability of making at least one Type I error. Use the F-test for testing the global utility of the model.

After we have used the F-test and determined that the overall model is useful in predicting y, we may elect to conduct one or more t-tests on the individual β parameters. However, the test (or tests) to be conducted should be decided *a priori*—that is, prior to fitting the model. Also, we should limit the number of t-tests conducted, to avoid the potential problem of making too many Type I errors. Generally, the regression analyst will conduct t-tests only on the "most important" β's. We provide insight into identifying the most important β's in a linear model in Sections 12.5–12.8.

Recommendation for Checking the Utility of a Multiple-Regression Model

1. First, use the F-test to conduct a test of the adequacy of the overall model; that is, test H_0: $\beta_1 = \beta_2 = \cdots = \beta_k = 0$. If the model is deemed adequate (i.e., if you reject H_0), then proceed to step 2. Otherwise, you should hypothesize and fit another model. The new model may include more independent variables or higher order terms.

2. Conduct t-tests on those β parameters in which you are particularly interested (i.e., the "most important" β's). These usually involve only the β's associated with higher order terms (x_2, x_1x_2, etc.). However, it is a safe practice to limit the number of β's that are tested. Conducting a series of t-tests leads to a high overall Type I error rate α.

3. Examine the values of R_a^2 and $2s$ to evaluate how well, numerically, the model fits the data.

Exercises 12.1–12.27

Understanding the Principles

12.1 Write a first-order model relating $E(y)$ to
   a. two quantitative independent variables
   b. four quantitative independent variables
   c. five quantitative independent variables

12.2 List the four assumptions about the random error ε required for a multiple-regression analysis.

12.3 Outline the six steps in a multiple-regression analysis.

12.4 What are the caveats to conducting t-tests on all of the individual β parameters in a multiple-regression model?

12.5 How should you test the overall adequacy of a multiple-regression model?

Learning the Mechanics

12.6 MINITAB was used to fit the model $y = \beta_0 + \beta_1x_1 +$
NW $\beta_2x_2 + \varepsilon$ to $n = 20$ data points, and the accompanying printout was obtained.
   a. What are the sample estimates of β_0, β_1, and β_2?
   b. What is the least squares prediction equation?
   c. Find SSE, MSE, and s. Interpret the standard deviation in the context of the problem.
   d. Test H_0: $\beta_1 = 0$ against H_a: $\beta_1 \neq 0$. Use $\alpha = .05$.

e. Use a 95% confidence interval to estimate β_2.
f. Find R^2 and R_a^2 and interpret these values.
g. Use the two formulas given in this section to calculate the test statistic for the null hypothesis H_0: $\beta_1 = \beta_2 = 0$. Compare your results with the test statistic shown on the printout.
h. Find the observed significance level of the test you conducted in part **g**. Interpret the value.

12.7 Suppose you fit the model

$$y = \beta_0 + \beta_1x_1 + \beta_2x_2 + \beta_3x_3 + \varepsilon$$

to $n = 30$ data points and obtain the following result:

$$\hat{y} = 3.4 - 4.6x_1 + 2.7x_2 + .93x_3$$

The estimated standard errors of $\hat{\beta}_2$ and $\hat{\beta}_3$ are 1.86 and .29, respectively.
   a. Test the null hypothesis H_0: $\beta_2 = 0$ against the alternative hypothesis H_a: $\beta_2 \neq 0$. Use $\alpha = .05$.
   b. Test the null hypothesis H_0: $\beta_3 = 0$ against the alternative hypothesis H_a: $\beta_3 \neq 0$. Use $\alpha = .05$.
   c. The null hypothesis H_0: $\beta_2 = 0$ is not rejected. In contrast, the null hypothesis H_0: $\beta_3 = 0$ is rejected. Explain how this can happen even though $\hat{\beta}_2 > \hat{\beta}_3$.

```
The regression equation is
Y = 506.35 - 941.9 X1 - 429.1 X2


Predictor      Coef   SE Coef      T       P
Constant    506.346     45.17   11.21   0.000
X1         -941.900    275.08   -3.42   0.003
X2         -429.060    379.83   -1.13   0.274


S = 94.251    R-Sq = 45.9%    R-Sq(adj) = 39.6%


Analysis of Variance

Source           DF       SS      MS      F      P
Regression        2   128329   64165   7.22  0.005
Residual Error   17   151016    8883
Total            19   279345
```

MINITAB output for
Exercise 12.6

12.8 Suppose you fit the first-order multiple regression model

$$y = \beta_0 + \beta_1 x_1 + \beta_2 x_2 + \varepsilon$$

to $n = 25$ data points and obtain the prediction equation

$$\hat{y} = 6.4 + 3.1 x_1 + .92 x_2$$

The estimated standard deviations of the sampling distributions of $\hat{\beta}_1$ and $\hat{\beta}_2$ are 2.3 and .27, respectively.

a. Test $H_0: \beta_1 = 0$ against $H_a: \beta_1 > 0$. Use $\alpha = .05$.

b. Test $H_0: \beta_2 = 0$ against $H_a: \beta_2 \neq 0$. Use $\alpha = .05$.

c. Find a 90% confidence interval for β_1. Interpret the interval.

d. Find a 99% confidence interval for β_2. Interpret the interval.

12.9 How is the number of degrees of freedom available for estimating σ^2 (the variance of ε) related to the number of independent variables in a regression model?

12.10 Consider the following first-order model equation in three quantitative independent variables:

$$E(y) = 1 + 2x_1 + x_2 - 3x_3$$

a. Graph the relationship between y and x_1 for $x_2 = 1$ and $x_3 = 3$.

b. Repeat part a for $x_2 = -1$ and $x_3 = 1$.

c. How do the graphed lines in parts a and b relate to each other? What is the slope of each line?

d. If a linear model is first order in three independent variables, what type of geometric relationship will you obtain when you graph $E(y)$ as a function of one of the independent variables for various combinations of values of the other independent variables?

12.11 Suppose you fit the first-order model

$$y = \beta_0 + \beta_1 x_1 + \beta_2 x_2 + \beta_3 x_3 + \beta_4 x_4 + \beta_5 x_5 + \varepsilon$$

to $n = 30$ data points and obtain

$$\text{SSE} = .33 \quad R^2 = .92$$

a. Do the values of SSE and R^2 suggest that the model provides a good fit to the data? Explain.

b. Is the model of any use in predicting y? Test the null hypothesis $H_0: \beta_1 = \beta_2 = \cdots = \beta_5 = 0$ against the alternative hypothesis H_a: At least one of the parameters $\beta_1, \beta_2, \cdots, \beta_5$ is nonzero. Use $\alpha = .05$.

12.12 If the analysis-of-variance F-test leads to the conclusion that at least one of the model parameters is nonzero, can you conclude that the model is the best predictor for the dependent variable y? Can you conclude that all of the terms in the model are important in predicting y? What is the appropriate conclusion?

Applying the Concepts—Basic

12.13 **Highway crash data analysis.** Researchers at Montana State University have written a tutorial on an empirical method for analyzing before and after highway crash data (Montana Department of Transportation, Research Report, May 2004). The initial step in the methodology is to develop a safety performance function (SPF)—a mathematical model that estimates the probability of occurrence of a crash for a given segment of roadway. Using data on over 100 segments of roadway, the researchers fit the model $E(y) = \beta_0 + \beta_1 x_1 + \beta_2 x_2$, where $y =$ number of crashes per three years, $x_1 =$ roadway length (miles), and $x_2 =$ average annual daily traffic (number of vehicles) = AADT. The results are shown in the following tables:

Interstate Highways

Variable	Parameter Estimate	Standard Error	t-value
Intercept	1.81231	.50568	3.58
Length (x_1)	.10875	.03166	3.44
AADT (x_2)	.00017	.00003	5.19

Non-Interstate Highways

Variable	Parameter Estimate	Standard Error	t-value
Intercept	1.20785	.28075	4.30
Length (x_1)	.06343	.01809	3.51
AADT (x_2)	.00056	.00012	4.86

a. Give the least squares prediction equation for the interstate highway model.

b. Give practical interpretations of the β estimates you made in part a.

c. Refer to part a. Find a 99% confidence interval for β_1 and interpret the result.

d. Refer to part a. Find a 99% confidence interval for β_2 and interpret the result.

e. Repeat parts a–d for the non-interstate-highway model.

12.14 **Estimation of urban population by means of satellite images.** Can the population of an urban area be estimated without taking a census? In *Geographical Analysis* (Jan. 2007) geography professors at the University of Wisconsin at Milwaukee and Ohio State University demonstrated the use of satellite image maps in estimating urban population. A portion of Columbus, Ohio, was partitioned into $n = 125$ census block groups, and satellite imagery was obtained. For each census block, the following variables were measured: population density (y), proportion of block with low-density residential areas (x_1), and proportion of block with high-density residential areas (x_2). A first-order model for y was fit to the data and produced the following results:

$$\hat{y} = -.0304 + 2.006 x_1 + 5.006 x_2, \quad R^2 = .686$$

a. Give a practical interpretation of each β-estimate in the model.

b. Give a practical interpretation of the coefficient of determination, R^2.

c. State H_0 and H_a for a test of the overall adequacy of the model.

d. Refer to part c. Compute the value of the test statistic.

e. Refer to parts c and d. Make the appropriate conclusion at $\alpha = .01$.

12.15 **Predicting runs scored in baseball.** In *Chance* (Fall 2000), statistician Scott Berry built a multiple-regression model for predicting the total number of runs scored by a Major League Baseball team during a season. Using data on all teams from 1990 to 1998 (a sample with $n = 234$), the results in the next table were obtained.

a. Write the least squares prediction equation for $y =$ total number of runs scored by a team in a season.

b. Give practical interpretations of the β estimates.

c. Conduct a test of $H_0: \beta_7 = 0$ against $H_a: \beta_7 < 0$ at $\alpha = .05$. Interpret the results.

d. Form a 95% confidence interval for β_5. Interpret the results.

Independent Variable	β Estimate	Standard Error
Intercept	3.70	15.00
Walks (x_1)	.34	.02
Singles (x_2)	.49	.03
Doubles (x_3)	.72	.05
Triples (x_4)	1.14	.19
Home Runs (x_5)	1.51	.05
Stolen Bases (x_6)	.26	.05
Caught Stealing (x_7)	−.14	.14
Strikeouts (x_8)	−.10	.01
Outs (x_9)	−.10	.01

Source: Berry, S. M. "A statistician reads the sports pages: Modeling offensive ability in baseball," *Chance,* Vol. 13, No. 4, Fall 2000 (Table 2).

e. Predict the number of runs scored by your favorite Major League Baseball team last year. How close is the predicted value to the actual number of runs scored by your team? (*Note:* You can find data on your favorite team on the Internet at www.majorleaguebaseball.com.)

12.16 Growth of Japanese beetles. In the *Journal of Insect Behavior* (Nov. 2001), biologists at Eastern Illinois University published the results of their study on Japanese beetles. The biologists collected beetles over a period of $n = 13$ summer days in a soybean field. For one portion of the study, the biologists modeled y, the average size (in millimeters) of female beetles as a function of the average daily temperature x_1 (degrees) and Julian date x_2.
a. Write a first-order model for $E(y)$ as a function of x_1 and x_2.
b. The model was fit to the data, with the results shown in the accompanying table. Interpret the estimate of β_1.

Variable	Parameter Estimate	t-value	p-value
Intercept	6.51	26.0	<.0001
Temperature (x_1)	−.002	−0.72	.49
Date (x_2)	−.010	−3.30	.008

c. Conduct a test to determine whether the average size of female Japanese beetles decreases linearly as the temperature increases. Use $\alpha = .05$.

12.17 Study of adolescents with ADHD. Children with attention-deficit/hyperactivity disorder (ADHD) were monitored to evaluate their risk for substance (e.g., alcohol, tobacco, illegal drug) use. (*Journal of Abnormal Psychology,* Aug. 2003.) The following data were collected on 142 adolescents diagnosed with ADHD:

y = frequency of marijuana use the past six months
x_1 = severity of inattention (five-point scale)
x_2 = severity of impulsivity−hyperactivity (five-point scale)
x_3 = level of oppositional-defiant and conduct disorder (five-point scale)

a. Write the equation of a first-order model for $E(y)$.
b. The coefficient of determination for the model is $R^2 = .08$. Interpret this value.

c. The global *F*-test for the model yielded a *p*-value less than .01. Interpret this result.
d. The *t*-test for H_0: $\beta_1 = 0$ resulted in a *p*-value less than .01. Interpret this result.
e. The *t*-test for H_0: $\beta_2 = 0$ resulted in a *p*-value greater than .05. Interpret this result.
f. The *t*-test for resulted in a *p*-value greater than .05. Interpret this result.

12.18 Novelty of a vacation destination. Many tourists choose a vacation destination on the basis of the newness or uniqueness (i.e., the novelty) of the itinerary. Texas A&M University professor J. Petrick investigated the relationship between novelty and vacationing golfers' demographics. (*Annals of Tourism Research,* Vol. 29, 2002.) Data were obtained from a mail survey of 393 golf vacationers to a large coastal resort in the southeastern United States. Several measures of novelty level (on a numerical scale) were obtained for each vacationer, including "change from routine," "thrill," "boredom-alleviation," and "surprise." The researcher employed four independent variables in a regression model to predict each measure of novelty. The independent variables were x_1 = number of rounds of golf per year, x_2 = total number of golf vacations taken, x_3 = number of years the respondent played golf, and x_4 = average golf score.
a. Give the hypothesized equation of a first-order model for y = change from routine.
b. A test of H_0: $\beta_3 = 0$ versus H_a: $\beta_3 < 0$ yielded a *p*-value of .005. Interpret this result if $\alpha = .01$.
c. The estimate of β_3 was found to be negative. On the basis of this result (and the result of part **b**), the researcher concluded that "those who have played golf for more years are less apt to seek change from their normal routine in their golf vacations." Do you agree with this statement? Explain.
d. The regression results for the three other dependent measures of novelty are summarized in the accompanying table. Give the null hypothesis for testing the overall adequacy of each first-order regression model.

Dependent Variable	F-value	p-value	R^2
Thrill	5.56	< .001	.055
Change from routine	3.02	.018	.030
Surprise	3.33	.011	.023

Source: Petrick, J. F. "An examination of golf vacationers' novelty," *Annals of Tourism Research,* Vol. 29, 2002.

e. Give the rejection region for the test mentioned in part **d**. Use $\alpha = .01$.
f. Use the test statistics reported in the table and the rejection region from part **e** to conduct the test for each of the dependent measures of novelty.
g. Verify that the *p*-values in the table support the conclusions you drew in part **f**.
h. Interpret the values of R^2 reported in the table.

Applying the Concepts—Intermediate

12.19 Arsenic in groundwater. *Environmental Science & Technology* (Jan. 2005) reported on a study of the reliability of a commercial kit designed to test for arsenic in groundwater. The field kit was used to test a sample of 328 groundwater wells in Bangladesh. In addition to the arsenic level (in micrograms per liter), the latitude (degrees), longitude (degrees), and depth (feet) of each well was measured. The data are saved in the **ASWELLS** file. The first and last five observations are listed in the following table:

ASWELLS (Data for first and last five wells shown)

Wellid	Latitude	Longitude	Depth	Arsenic
10	23.7887	90.6522	60	331
14	23.7886	90.6523	45	302
30	23.7880	90.6517	45	193
59	23.7893	90.6525	125	232
85	23.7920	90.6140	150	19
.				
.				
7353	23.7949	90.6515	40	48
7357	23.7955	90.6515	30	172
7890	23.7658	90.6312	60	175
7893	23.7656	90.6315	45	624
7970	23.7644	90.6303	30	254

a. Write a first-order model for arsenic level (y) as a function of latitude, longitude, and depth.
b. Use the method of least squares to fit the model to the data.
c. Give practical interpretations of the β estimates.
d. Find the standard deviation s of the model, and interpret its value.
e. Find and interpret the values of R^2 and R_a^2.
f. Conduct a test of overall model utility at $\alpha = .05$.
g. On the basis of the results you obtained in parts **d–f**, would you recommend using the model to predict arsenic level (y)? Explain.

12.20 Study of contaminated fish. Refer to the U.S. Army Corps of Engineers data on fish contaminated from the toxic discharges of a chemical plant located on the banks of the Tennessee River in Alabama, shown below. Recall that the engineers measured the length (in centimeters), weight (in grams), and DDT level (in parts per million) for 144 captured fish. In addition, the number of miles upstream from the river was recorded. The data are saved in the **DDT** file. (The first and last five observations are shown in the table.)
   a. Fit the first-order model $E(y) = \beta_0 + \beta_1 x_1 + \beta_2 x_2 + \beta_3 x_3$ to the data, where y = DDT level, x_1 = mile, x_2 = length, and x_3 = weight. Report the least squares prediction equation.

b. Find the estimate of the standard deviation of ε for the model, and give a practical interpretation of its value.

c. Do the data provide sufficient evidence to conclude that DDT level increases as length increases? Report the observed significance level of the test, and reach a conclusion. Use $\alpha = .05$.
d. Find and interpret a 95% confidence interval for β_3.

e. Test the overall adequacy of the model, using $\alpha = .05$.

12.21 Snow geese feeding trial. Refer to the *Journal of Applied Ecology* (Vol. 32, 1995) study of the feeding habits of baby snow geese, presented Exercise 11.82 (p. 600). Data on gosling weight change, digestion efficiency, acid-detergent fiber (all measured as percentages), and diet (plants or duck chow) for 42 feeding trials are saved in the **SNOWGEESE** file. Selected observations are shown in the table (top, p. 646). The botanists were interested in predicting weight change (y) as a function of the other variables. Consider the first-order model $E(y) = \beta_0 + \beta_1 x_1 + \beta_2 x_2$ where x_1 is digestion efficiency and x_2 is acid-detergent fiber.
   a. Find the least squares prediction equation for weight change y.
   b. Interpret the β-estimates in the equation you found in part **a**.
   c. Conduct a test to determine whether digestion efficiency, x_1, is a useful linear predictor of weight change. Use $\alpha = .01$.
   d. Form a 99% confidence interval for β_2. Interpret the result.
   e. Find and interpret R^2 and R_a^2. Which statistic is the preferred measure of model fit? Explain.
   f. Is the overall model statistically useful in predicting weight change? Test, using $\alpha = .05$.

12.22 Deep-space survey of quasars. A quasar is a distant celestial object (at least 4 billion light-years away) that provides a powerful source of radio energy. The *Astronomical Journal* (July 1995) reported on a study of 90 quasars detected by a deep-space survey. The survey enabled astronomers to measure several different quantitative characteristics of each quasar, including redshift range, line flux ($erg/cm^2 \cdot s$), line luminosity (erg/s), AB_{1450} magnitude, absolute magnitude, and rest-frame equivalent width. The data for a sample of 25 large (redshift) quasars are saved in the **QUASAR** file. (Several quasars are listed in the table, bottom p. 646.)

DDT (First and last five observations listed.)

River	Mile	Species	Length	Weight	DDT
FC	5	CHANNELCATFISH	42.5	732	10.00
FC	5	CHANNELCATFISH	44.0	795	16.00
FC	5	CHANNELCATFISH	41.5	547	23.00
FC	5	CHANNELCATFISH	39.0	465	21.00
FC	5	CHANNELCATFISH	50.5	1252	50.00
⋮	⋮	⋮	⋮	⋮	⋮
TR	345	LARGEMOUTHBASS	23.5	358	2.00
TR	345	LARGEMOUTHBASS	30.0	856	2.20
TR	345	LARGEMOUTHBASS	29.0	793	7.40
TR	345	LARGEMOUTHBASS	17.5	173	0.35
TR	345	LARGEMOUTHBASS	36.0	1433	1.90

SNOWGEESE (First and last five trials shown)

Feeding Trial	Diet	Weight Change (%)	Digestion Efficiency (%)	Acid-Detergent Fibre (%)
1	Plants	−6	0	28.5
2	Plants	−5	2.5	27.5
3	Plants	−4.5	5	27.5
4	Plants	0	0	32.5
5	Plants	2	0	32
⋮	⋮	⋮	⋮	⋮
38	Duck Chow	9	59	8.5
39	Duck Chow	12	52.5	8
40	Duck Chow	8.5	75	6
41	Duck Chow	10.5	72.5	6.5
42	Duck Chow	14	69	7

Source: Gadallah, F. L., and Jefferies, R. L. "Forage quality in brood rearing areas of the lesser snow goose and the growth of captive goslings." *Journal of Applied Biology*, Vol. 32, No. 2, 1995, pp. 281–282 (adapted from Figures 2 and 3).

a. Hypothesize a first-order model for equivalent width y as a function of the first four variables shown in the table.
b. Fit the first-order model to the data. Give the least squares prediction equation.
c. Interpret the β estimates in the model.
d. Test the overall adequacy of the model, using $\alpha = .05$.

e. Test to determine whether redshift (x_1) is a useful linear predictor of equivalent width (y). Use $\alpha = .05$.

12.23 Cooling method for gas turbines. Refer to the *Journal of Engineering for Gas Turbines and Power* (Jan. 2005) study of a high-pressure inlet fogging method for a gas turbine engine, presented in Exercise 8.32 (p. 364). Recall that the heat rate (kilojoules per kilowatt per hour) was measured for each in a sample of 67 gas turbines augmented with high-pressure inlet fogging. In addition, several other variables were measured, including cycle speed (revolutions per minute), inlet temperature (°C), exhaust gas temperature (°C), cycle pressure ratio, and air mass flow rate (kilograms per second). The data are saved in the **GASTURBINE** file. The first and last five observations are listed in the table at right:

a. Write a first-order model for heat rate (y) as a function of speed, inlet temperature, exhaust temperature, cycle pressure ratio, and air mass flow rate.
b. Use the method of least squares to fit the model to the data.

c. Give practical interpretations of the β estimates.
d. Find the standard deviation s of the model, and interpret its value.
e. Find R_a^2 and interpret its value.
f. Is the overall model statistically useful in predicting heat rate (y)? Test, using $\alpha = .01$.

GASTURBINE (Data on first and last five gas turbines)

Rpm	Cpratio	Inlet-Temp	Exh-Temp	Airflow	Heatrate
27245	9.2	1134	602	7	14622
14000	12.2	950	446	15	13196
17384	14.8	1149	537	20	11948
11085	11.8	1024	478	27	11289
14045	13.2	1149	553	29	11964
⋮	⋮	⋮	⋮	⋮	⋮
18910	14.0	1066	532	8	12766
3600	35.0	1288	448	152	8714
3600	20.0	1160	456	84	9469
16000	10.6	1232	560	14	11948
14600	13.4	1077	536	20	12414

Source: Bhargava, R., and Meher-Homji, C. B. "Parametric analysis of existing gas turbines with inlet evaporative and overspray fogging," *Journal of Engineering for Gas Turbines and Power*, Vol. 127, No. 1, Jan. 2005.

12.24 Students ability in science. An article published in the *American Educational Research Journal* (Fall 1998) used

QUASAR (First five quasars listed).

Quasar	Redshift (x_1)	Line Flux (x_2)	Line Luminosity (x_3)	AB_{1450} x_4	Absolute Magnitude (x_5)	Rest-Frame Equivalent Width (y)
1	2.81	−13.48	45.29	19.50	−26.27	117
2	3.07	−13.73	45.13	19.65	−26.26	82
3	3.45	−13.87	45.11	18.93	−27.17	33
4	3.19	−13.27	45.63	18.59	−27.39	92
5	3.07	−13.56	45.30	19.59	−26.32	114

Source: Schmidt, M., Schneider, D. P., and Gunn, J. E. "Spectroscopic CCD surveys for quasars at large redshift," *The Astronomical Journal*, Vol. 110, No. 1, July 1995, p. 70 (Table 1).

Results for Exercise 12.24

Independent Variable	β Estimate	Standard Error	t	p-Value
Prior science attitude (four-point scale)	.60	.07	8.13	$p < .001$
Science ability (standardized test score)	.003	.005	.57	NS
Gender (1 if boy, 0 if girl)	.22	.07	2.98	$p < .01$
Class 1 (1 if classroom 1, 0 if not)	.15	.153	0.98	NS
Class 3 (1 if classroom 3, 0 if not)	−.16	.13	−1.17	NS
Class 4 (1 if classroom 4, 0 if not)	.00	.13	0.00	NS
Class 5 (1 if classroom 5, 0 if not)	.08	.13	0.64	NS
Class 6 (1 if classroom 6, 0 if not)	−.15	.14	−1.12	NS
Active-leading behavior (0 to 1 scale)	.88	.34	2.62	$p < .01$
Passive-assisting behavior (0 to 1 scale)	.43	.51	0.85	NS
Active-manipulating behavior (0 to 1 scale)	.77	.61	1.25	NS

Source: Jovanovic, J., and King, S. S. "Boys and girls in the performance-based science classroom: Who's doing the performing?" *American Educational Research Journal,* Vol. 35, No. 3, Fall 1998, p. 489 (Table 8).
Note: Base level for classroom dummy variables is classroom 2.
NS = not *significant.*

multiple regression to model the students' perceptions of their ability in science classes. The sample consisted of 165 Grade 5–Grade 8 students in six performance-based science classrooms, all of which use hands-on activities as the main teaching tool. The dependent variable of interest, the student's perception of his or her ability (y), was measured on a four-point scale (where 1 = little or no ability and 4 = high ability). The independent variables included in the model, as well as the results of the multiple regression, are listed in the table above.

a. Which independent variables appear to contribute to the prediction of a student's perception of his or her ability in science? Explain.

b. Construct a 95% confidence interval for the β coefficient of the variable active-leading behavior. Interpret the interval.

c. The following statistics for evaluating the overall predictive power of the model were reported: $R^2 = .48$, $F = 12.84$, $p < .001$. Interpret the results.

12.25 Occupational safety study. An important goal in occupational safety is "active caring." Employees demonstrate active caring about the safety of their coworkers when they identify environmental hazards and unsafe work practices and then implement appropriate corrective actions for these unsafe conditions or behaviors. Three factors hypothesized to increase the propensity of an employee to actively care for safety are (1) high self-esteem, (2) optimism, and (3) group cohesiveness. *Applied & Preventive Psychology* (Winter 1995) attempted to establish empirical support for the active-caring hypothesis by fitting the model $E(y) = \beta_0 + \beta_1 x_1 + \beta_2 x_2 + \beta_3 x_3$, where

y = active-caring score (measuring active caring on a 15-point scale)
x_1 = Self-esteem score
x_2 = Optimism score
x_3 = Group cohesion score

The regression analysis, based on data collected for $n = 31$ hourly workers at a large fiber-manufacturing plant, yielded a multiple coefficient of determination of $R^2 = .362$.

a. Interpret the value of R^2.

b. Use the R^2 value to test the global utility of the model. Take $\alpha = .05$.

12.26 R^2 and model fit. Because the coefficient of determination, R^2, always increases when a new independent variable is added to a model, it is tempting to include many variables in the model in order to force R^2 to be near 1. However, doing so reduces the number of degrees of freedom available for estimating σ^2, which adversely affects our ability to make reliable inferences. Suppose you want to use 18 psychological and sociological factors to predict a student's Scholastic Assessment Test (SAT) score. You fit the model

$$y = \beta_0 + \beta_1 x_1 + \beta_2 x_2 + \cdots + \beta_{17} x_{17} + \beta_{18} x_{18} + \varepsilon$$

where y = SAT score and $x_1, x_2, \ldots, x_{18}$ are the psychological and sociological factors. Only 20 years of data ($n = 20$) are used to fit the model, and you obtain $R^2 = .95$. Test to see whether this impressive-looking R^2 is large enough for you to infer that the model is useful—that is, that at least one term in the model is important in predicting SAT scores. Use $\alpha = .05$.

Applying the Concepts—Advanced

12.27 Bordeaux wine sold at auction. The vineyards in the Bordeaux region of France are known for producing excellent red wines. However, the uncertainty of the weather during the growing season, the phenomenon that wine tastes better with age, and the fact that some Bordeaux vineyards produce better wines than others encourage speculation concerning the value of a case of wine produced by a certain vineyard during a certain year (or of a certain vintage). As a result, many wine experts attempt to predict the auction price of a case of Bordeaux wine. The publishers of a newsletter titled *Liquid Assets: The International Guide to Fine Wine* discussed a multiple-regression approach to predicting the London auction price of red Bordeaux wine in *Chance* (Fall 1995). The natural logarithm of the price y (in dollars) of a case containing a dozen bottles of red wine was modeled as a function of weather during the growing season and age of vintage. Data collected for the vintages of 1952 to 1980 were used. Three models were fit to the data. The results of the regressions are summarized in the accompanying table.

a. For each model, conduct a t-test for each of the β parameters in the model. Interpret the results.

b. When the natural logarithm of y is used as a dependent variable, the antilogarithm of a β coefficient minus 1 (i.e.,

$e^{\beta_i} - 1$) represents the percentage change in y for every one-unit increase in the associated x value.* Use this information to interpret the β estimates of each model.

c. On the basis of the values of R^2 and s shown, which of the three models would you use to predict red Bordeaux wine prices? Explain.

	Beta Estimates (Standard Errors)		
Independent Variables	Model 1	Model 2	Model 3
x_1 = Vintage year	.0354 (.0137)	.0238 (.00717)	.0240 (.00747)
x_2 = Average growing-season temperature (°C)	(not included)	.616 (.0952)	.608 (.116)
x_3 = Sept.–Aug. rainfall (cm)	(not included)	−.00386 (.00081)	−.00380 (.00095)
x_4 = Rainfall in months preceding vintage (cm)	(not included)	.0001173 (.000482)	.00115 (.000505)
x_5 = Average Sept. temperature (°C)	(not included)	(not included)	.00765 (.565)
	$R^2 = .212, s = .575$	$R^2 = .828, s = .287$	$R^2 = .828, s = .293$

Source: Ashenfelter, O., Ashmore, D., and LaLonde, R. "Bordeaux wine vintage quality and weather," *Chance,* Vol. 8, No. 4, Fall 1995, p. 116 (Table 2).

12.4 Using the Model for Estimation and Prediction

In Section 11.6, we discussed the use of the least squares line in estimating the mean value of y, $E(y)$, for some particular value of x, say, $x = x_p$. We also showed how to use the same fitted model to predict, when $x = x_p$, some new value of y to be observed in the future. Recall that the least squares line yielded the same value for both the estimate of $E(y)$ and the prediction of some future value of y. That is, both are the result of substituting x_p into the prediction equation $\hat{y} = \hat{\beta}_0 + \hat{\beta}_1 x$ and calculating $\hat{y}_p$. There the equivalence ends, however: The confidence interval for the mean $E(y)$ is narrower than the prediction interval for y because of the additional uncertainty attributable to the random error ε that arises in predicting some future value of y.

These same concepts carry over to the multiple-regression model. Consider a first-order model relating sale price (y) of a residential property to land value (x_1), improvements (x_2), and home size (x_3). Suppose we want to estimate the mean sale price for a given property with x_1 = \$15,000, x_2 = \$50,000, and x_3 = 1,800 square feet. Assuming that the first-order model represents the true relationship between the sale price and the three independent variables, we want to estimate

$$E(y) = \beta_0 + \beta_1 x_1 + \beta_2 x_2 + \beta_3 x_3$$
$$= \beta_0 + \beta_1(15{,}000) + \beta_2(50{,}000) + \beta_3(1{,}800)$$

After obtaining the least squares estimates, β_0, β_1, β_2, and β_3, we find the estimate of $E(y)$ to be

$$\hat{y} = \hat{\beta}_0 + \hat{\beta}_1(15{,}000) + \hat{\beta}_2(50{,}000) + \hat{\beta}_3(1{,}800)$$

To form a confidence interval for the mean (or for an individual value of y), we need to know the standard deviation of the sampling distribution for the estimator $\hat{y}$. For multiple-regression models, the form of this standard deviation is rather complicat-

---

*This result is derived by expressing the percentage change in price y as $(y_1 - y_0)/y_0$, where y_1 = the value of y when, say, $x = 1$ and y_0 = the value of y when $x = 0$. Now let $y^* = \ln(y)$, and assume that the model is $y^* = \beta_0 + \beta_1 x$. Then

$$y = e^{y^*} = e^{\beta_0}e^{\beta_1 x} = \begin{cases} e^{\beta_0} & \text{when } x = 0 \\ e^{\beta_0}e^{\beta_1} & \text{when } x = 1 \end{cases}$$

Substituting, we have

$$\frac{y_1 - y_0}{y_0} = \frac{e^{\beta_0}e^{\beta_1} - e^{\beta_0}}{e^{\beta_0}} = e^{\beta_1} - 1$$

ed. However, the regression routines of statistical software packages allow us to obtain the confidence intervals for mean values or individual values of y for any given combination of values of the independent variables. We illustrate with an example.

EXAMPLE 12.5
ESTIMATING $E(y)$ AND PREDICTING y: Auction Price Model

Problem Refer to Examples 12.1–12.4 and the first-order model $E(y) = \beta_0 + \beta_1 x_1 + \beta_2 x_2$, where y = auction price of a grandfather clock, x_1 = age of the clock, and x_2 = number of bidders.

a. Estimate the average auction price for all 150-year-old clocks sold at an auction with 10 bidders. Use a 95% confidence interval. Interpret the result.

b. Predict the auction price for a single 150-year-old clock sold at an auction with 10 bidders. Use a 95% prediction interval. Interpret the result.

c. Suppose you want to predict the auction price for one clock that is 50 years old and has 2 bidders. How should you proceed?

Solution

a. Here, the key words *average* and *for all* imply that we want to estimate the mean of y, $E(y)$. We want a 95% confidence interval for $E(y)$ when x_1 = 150 years and x_2 = 10 bidders. A MINITAB printout for this analysis is shown in Figure 12.7. The confidence interval (highlighted under "**95% CI**") is (1381.4, 1481.9). Thus, we are 95% confident that the mean auction price for all 150-year-old clocks sold at an auction with 10 bidders lies between $1,381.4 and $1,481.9.

b. The key words *predict* and *for a single* imply that we want a 95% prediction interval for y when x_1 = 150 years and x_2 = 10 bidders. This interval (highlighted under "**95% PI**" on the MINITAB printout shown in Figure 12.7) is (1154.1, 1709.3). We say, with 95% confidence, that the auction price for a single 150-year-old clock sold at an auction with 10 bidders falls between $1,154.1 and $1,709.3.

Regression Analysis: PRICE versus AGE, NUMBIDS

```
The regression equation is
PRICE = - 1339 + 12.7 AGE + 86.0 NUMBIDS


Predictor      Coef   SE Coef       T      P
Constant    -1339.0     173.8   -7.70  0.000
AGE         12.7406    0.9047   14.08  0.000
NUMBIDS      85.953     8.729    9.85  0.000


S = 133.485   R-Sq = 89.2%   R-Sq(adj) = 88.5%


Analysis of Variance


Source          DF        SS       MS       F      P
Regression       2   4283063  2141531  120.19  0.000
Residual Error  29    516727    17818
Total           31   4799790


Predicted Values for New Observations


New
Obs     Fit   SE Fit      95% CI             95% PI
  1  1431.7     24.6  (1381.4, 1481.9)   (1154.1, 1709.3)


Values of Predictors for New Observations


New
Obs   AGE   NUMBIDS
  1   150      10.0
```

FIGURE 12.7

MINITAB printout with 95% confidence intervals for grandfather clock model

c. Now we want to predict the auction price y for a single (*one*) grandfather clock when $x_1 = 50$ years and $x_2 = 2$ bidders. Consequently, we desire a 95% prediction interval for y. However, before we form this prediction interval, we should check to make sure that the selected values of the independent variables, $x_1 = 50$ and $x_2 = 2$, are both reasonable and within their respective sample ranges. If you examine the sample data shown in Table 12.2 (p. 632), you will see that the range for age is $108 \le x_1 \le 194$ and the range for number of bidders is $5 \le x_2 \le 15$. Thus, both selected values fall well *outside* their respective ranges. Recall the *Caution* box in Section 11.6 (p. 605) warning about the dangers of using the model to predict y for a value of an independent variable that is not within the range of the sample data. Doing so may lead to an unreliable prediction.

Look Back If we want to make the prediction requested in part **c**, we would need to collect additional data on clocks with the requested characteristics (i.e., $x_1 = 50$ years and $x_2 = 2$ bidders) and then refit the model.

Now Work Exercise 12.32

STATISTICS IN ACTION REVISITED

A First-Order Model for Condominium Sale Price

The developer of a Florida condominium complex wants to build a model for the sale price (y) of a condo unit (recorded in hundreds of dollars) and then use the model to predict the prices of future units sold. In addition to sale price, the **CONDO** file contains data on six potential predictor variables for a sample of 209 units sold. (See Table SIA12.1 on p. 627) These independent variables are defined as follows:

x_1 = floor location (i.e., floor height) of the unit $(1, 2, 3, \ldots,$ or 8$)$
x_2 = distance, in units, from the elevator $(1, 2, 3 \ldots,$ or 15$)$
x_3 = 1 if ocean view, 0 if non−ocean view
x_4 = 1 if end unit, 0 if not an end unit
x_5 = 1 if furnished unit, 0 if unfurnished
x_6 = 1 if sold at public auction, 0 if sold at developer's price

As our initial model, we consider the first-order regression model

$$E(y) = \beta_0 + \beta_1 x_1 + \beta_2 x_2 + \beta_3 x_3 + \beta_4 x_4 + \beta_5 x_5 + \beta_6 x_6$$

The MINITAB printout for the regression analysis is shown in Figure SIA12.2. The global F-statistic ($F = 49.99$) and associated p-value (.000) shown on the printout indicate that the overall model is statistically useful in predicting auction price. The value of the adjusted R^2, however, indicates that the model explains only about 59% of the sample variation in price, and the standard deviation of the model ($s = 21.8$) implies that the model can predict price to within about $2s = 43.6$ hundred dollars (i.e., $4,360). While the model appears to be "statistically" useful in predicting auction price, the moderate value of R_a^2 and relatively large $2s$ value indicate that the model may not yield accurate predictions.

[*Note:* Not all of the independent variables have statistically significant t-values. However, we caution against dropping the insignificant variables from the model at this stage. One reason (discussed in Section 12.3) is that performing a large number of t-tests will yield an inflated probability of at least one Type I error. In later sections of this chapter, we develop other reasons for why the multiple t-test approach is not a good strategy for determining which independent variables to keep in the model.]

The MINITAB printout shown in Figure SIA12.3 gives a 95% prediction interval for auction price and a 95% confidence interval for the mean price for the following x-values:

x_1 = 5 (i.e., unit on the fifth floor)
x_2 = 9 (i.e., distance of nine units from the elevator)
x_3 = 1 (i.e., ocean view)
x_4 = 0 (i.e., not an end unit)
x_5 = 0 (i.e., an unfurnished unit)
x_6 = 1 (i.e., a unit sold at public auction)

The 95% confidence interval of (204.05, 215.39) implies that, for all condo units with these x-values, the mean auction price falls between 204.05 and 215.39 hundred dollars, with 95% confidence. The 95% prediction interval of (166.33, 253.11) implies that, for an individual condo unit with these x-values, the auction price falls between 166.33 and 253.11 hundred dollars, with 95% confidence. Note the wide range of the prediction interval. This is due to the large magnitude of the model's standard deviation $s = 21.8$ hundred dollars. Again, although the model is deemed statistically useful in predicting auction price, it may not be "practically" useful. To reduce the magnitude of s, we will need to improve the model's predictive ability. (We consider such a model in the next Statistics in Action Revisited section.)

```
The regression equation is
PRICE100 = 187 - 1.16 FLOOR + 0.917 DISTANCE + 48.3 VIEW - 23.6 END
              + 6.95 FURNISH - 28.0 AUCTION


Predictor        Coef    SE Coef       T       P
Constant      186.990      4.693   39.84   0.000
FLOOR          -1.1599     0.7636  -1.52   0.130
DISTANCE        0.9168     0.3544   2.59   0.010
VIEW           48.250      3.281   14.70   0.000
END           -23.633      8.661   -2.73   0.007
FURNISH         6.945      3.243    2.14   0.033
AUCTION       -27.970      3.886   -7.20   0.000


S = 21.8163     R-Sq = 59.8%    R-Sq(adj) = 58.6%


Analysis of Variance

Source               DF       SS      MS       F       P
Regression            6   142750   23792   49.99   0.000
Residual Error      202    96142     476
Total               208   238893
```

FIGURE SIA12.2
MINITAB regression output for first-order model of condominium unit sale price

```
Predicted Values for New Observations

New
Obs      Fit    SE Fit        95% CI              95% PI
  1   209.72     2.87   (204.05, 215.39)   (166.33, 253.11)


Values of Predictors for New Observations

New
Obs   FLOOR   DISTANCE   VIEW        END      FURNISH   AUCTION
  1    5.00       9.00   1.00   0.000000     0.000000      1.00
```

FIGURE SIA12.3
MINITAB printout with 95% confidence and prediction intervals

Exercises 12.28–12.36

Understanding the Principles

12.28 Explain why we use $\hat{y}$ as an estimate of $E(y)$ and to predict y.

12.29 Which interval will be narrower, a 95% confidence interval for $E(y)$ or a 95% prediction interval for y? (Assume that the values of the x's are the same for both intervals.)

Applying the Concepts—Basic

SNOWGEESE

12.30 **Snow geese feeding trial.** Refer to the *Journal of Applied Ecology* study of the feeding habits of baby snow geese,

presented in Exercise 12.21 (p. 645). Recall that a first-order model was used to relate gosling weight change (y) to digestion efficiency (x_1) and acid-detergent fiber (x_2). The accompanying SAS printout shows a confidence interval for $E(y)$ for the first five feeding trials.

a. Interpret the confidence interval for $E(y)$ for trial 1.

b. Interpret the confidence interval for $E(y)$ for trial 2.

12.31 **Deep-space survey of quasars.** Refer to *The Astronomical Journal* study of quasars, presented in Exercise 12.22 (p. 645). Recall that a first-order model was used to relate a quasar's equivalent width (y) to its redshift (x_1), line flux (x_2), line luminosity (x_3), and $AB_{1450}(x_4)$. A portion of the SPSS spreadsheet showing 95% prediction intervals for y

SAS Output for Exercise 12.30

```
                  Dependent Variable: WTCHANGE

                         Output Statistics

                                  Dependent   Predicted      Std Error
                                                                 Mean Predict
Obs   DIET     DIGEFF   ADFIBER    Variable       Value      Mean Predict        95% CL Mean

  1   Plants        0     28.5     -6.0000     -0.8678         1.1392      -3.1722      1.4365
  2   Plants      2.5     27.5     -5.0000     -0.4763         1.1038      -2.7090      1.7563
  3   Plants        5     27.5     -4.5000     -0.5427         0.9964      -2.5580      1.4726
  4   Plants        0     32.5          0      -2.6992         0.9482      -4.6170     -0.7813
  5   Plants        0       32      2.0000     -2.4703         0.9592      -4.4104     -0.5301
```

SAS Output for Exercise 12.31

	REDSHIFT	LINEFLUX	LINELUM	AB1450	RFEWIDTH	LCL_95	UCL_95
1	2.81	-13.48	45.29	19.50	117	101.29	172.22
2	3.07	-13.73	45.13	19.65	82	59.62	125.89
3	3.45	-13.87	45.11	18.93	33	-35.09	37.04
4	3.19	-13.27	45.63	18.59	92	63.76	139.25
5	3.07	-13.56	45.30	19.59	114	90.69	158.57

for the first five observations in the data set is reproduced above. Interpret the interval corresponding to the fifth observation.

GASTURBINE

12.32 Cooling method for gas turbines. Refer to the *Journal of Engineering for Gas Turbines and Power* (Jan. 2005) study of a high-pressure inlet fogging method for a gas turbine engine, presented in Exercise 12.23 (p. 646). Recall that you fit a first-order model for heat rate (y) as a function of speed (x_1), inlet temperature (x_2), exhaust temperature (x_3), cycle pressure ratio (x_4), and air mass flow rate (x_5) to data saved in the **GASTURBINE** file. A MINITAB printout with both a 95% confidence interval for $E(y)$ and a prediction interval for y, for selected values of the x's, is shown here.

a. Interpret the 95% prediction interval for y in the words of the problem.

b. Interpret the 95% confidence interval for $E(y)$ in the words of the problem.

c. Will the confidence interval for $E(y)$ always be narrower than the prediction interval for y? Explain.

Applying the Concepts—Intermediate

DDT

12.33 Study of contaminated fish. Refer to Exercise 12.20 (p. 645) and the U.S. Army Corps of Engineers data on contaminated fish. You fit the first-order model $E(y) = \beta_0 + \beta_1 x_1 + \beta_2 x_2 + \beta_3 x_3$ to the data, where y = DDT level (parts per million), x_1 = number of miles upstream, x_2 = length (centimeters), and x_3 = weight (in grams). Predict, with 95% confidence, the DDT level of a fish caught 100 miles upstream with a length of 40 centimeters and a weight of 800 grams. Interpret the result.

12.34 California rain levels. An article published in *Geography* (July 1980) used multiple regression to predict annual rainfall levels in California. Data on the average annual precipitation (y), altitude (x_1), latitude (x_2), and distance from the Pacific coast (x_3) for 30 meteorological stations scattered throughout California are saved in the CALIRAIN file. (Selected observations are listed in the accompanying table.) Consider the first-order model $y = \beta_0 + \beta_1 x_1 + \beta_2 x_2 + \beta_3 x_3 + \varepsilon$.

MINITAB output for Exercise 12.32

```
Predicted Values for New Observations

New
Obs      Fit   SE Fit        95% CI                 95% PI
  1  12632.5   237.3  (12157.9, 13107.1)   (11599.6, 13665.5)


Values of Predictors for New Observations

New
Obs   RPM   INLET-TEMP   EXH-TEMP   CPRATIO   AIRFLOW
  1  7500         1000        525      13.5     10.0
```

CALIRAIN (Selected observations)

Station	Avg. Annual Precipitation y (inches)	Altitude x_1 (feet)	Latitude x_2 (degrees)	Distance from Coast x_3 (miles)
1. Eureka	39.57	43	40.8	1
2. Red Bluff	23.27	341	40.2	97
3. Thermal	18.20	4152	33.8	70
4. Fort Bragg	37.48	74	39.4	1
5. Soda Springs	49.26	6752	39.3	150
⋮	⋮	⋮	⋮	⋮
26. San Diego	9.94	19	32.7	5
27. Daggett	4.25	2105	34.1	85
28. Death Valley	1.66	−178	36.5	194
29. Crescent City	74.87	35	41.7	1
30. Colusa	15.95	60	39.2	91

Source: Taylor, P. J. "A pedagogic application of multiple regression analysis," *Geography*, July 1980, Vol. 65, pp. 203–212.

a. Fit the model to the data and give the least squares prediction equation.

b. Is there evidence that the first-order model is useful in predicting annual precipitation y? Test, using $\alpha = .05$.

c. Find a 95% prediction interval for y for the Giant Forest meteorological station (station 9). Interpret the interval.

ASWELLS

12.35 Arsenic in groundwater. Refer to the *Environmental Science & Technology* (Jan. 2005) study of the reliability of a commercial kit designed to test for arsenic in groundwater, presented in Exercise 12.19 (p. 644). Using the data in the **ASWELLS** file, you fit a first-order model for arsenic level (y) as a function of latitude, longitude, and depth. On the basis of the model statistics, the researchers concluded that the arsenic level is highest at a low latitude, high longitude, and low depth. Do you agree? If so, find a 95% prediction interval for arsenic level for the lowest latitude, highest longitude, and lowest depth that are within the range of the sample data. Interpret the result.

12.36 Boiler drum production. In a production facility, an accurate estimate of hours needed to complete a task is crucial to management in making such decisions as hiring the proper number of workers, quoting an accurate deadline for a client, or performing cost analyses regarding budgets. A manufacturer of boiler drums wants to use regression to predict the number of hours needed to erect the drums in future projects. To accomplish this task, data on 36 boilers were collected. In addition to hours (y), the variables measured were boiler capacity ($x_1 =$ lb/hr), boiler design pressure ($x_2 =$ pounds per square inch, or psi), boiler type ($x_3 = 1$ if industry field erected, 0 if utility field erected), and drum type ($x_4 = 1$ if steam, 0 if mud). The data are saved in the **BOILERS** file. (Selected observations are shown in the accompanying table.)

a. Fit the model $E(y) = \beta_0 + \beta_1 x_1 + \beta_2 x_2 + \beta_3 x_3 + \beta_4 x_4$ to the data and give the prediction equation.

b. Conduct a test for the global utility of the model. Use $\alpha = .01$.

c. Find a 95% confidence interval for $E(y)$ when $x_1 = 150,000$, $x_2 = 500$, $x_3 = 1$, and $x_4 = 0$. Interpret the result.

d. What type of interval would you use if you want to estimate the average number of hours required to erect all industrial mud boilers with a capacity of 150,000 lb/hr and a design pressure of 500 psi?

BOILERS (First and last five observations shown)

Hours y	Boiler Capacity x_1	Design Pressure x_2	Boiler Type x_3	Drum Type x_4
3,137	120,000	375	1	1
3,590	65,000	750	1	1
4,526	150,000	500	1	1
10,825	1,073,877	2,170	0	1
4,023	150,000	325	1	1
⋮	⋮	⋮	⋮	⋮
4,206	441,000	410	1	0
4,006	441,000	410	1	0
3,728	627,000	1,525	0	0
3,211	610,000	1,500	0	0
1,200	30,000	325	1	0

Source: Dr. Kelly Uscategui, University of Connecticut.

12.5 Model Building: Interaction Models

In Section 12.2, we demonstrated the relationship between $E(y)$ and the independent variables in a first-order model. When $E(y)$ is graphed against any one variable (say, x_1) for fixed values of the other variables, the result is a set of *parallel* straight lines. (See Figure 12.3, p. 634). When this situation occurs (as it always does for a first-order model), we say that the relationship between $E(y)$ and any one independent variable *does not depend* on the values of the other independent variables in the model.

However, if the relationship between $E(y)$ and x_1 does, in fact, depend on the values of the remaining x's held fixed, then the first-order model is not appropriate for predicting y. In this case, we need another model that will take into account this dependence. Such a model includes the *cross products* of two or more x's.

For example, suppose that the mean value $E(y)$ of a response y is related to two quantitative independent variables x_1 and x_2 by the model

$$E(y) = 1 + 2x_1 - x_2 + x_1 x_2$$

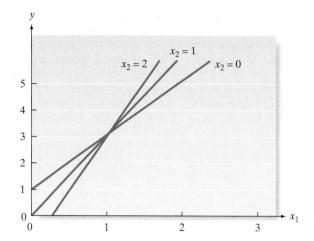

FIGURE 12.8

Graphs of
$1 + 2x_1 - x_2 + x_1x_2$
for $x_2 = 0, 1, 2$

A graph of the relationship between $E(y)$ and x_1 for $x_2 = 0$, 1, and 2 is displayed in Figure 12.8.

Note that the graph shows three nonparallel straight lines. You can verify that the slopes of the lines differ by substituting each of the values $x_2 = 0, 1$, and 2 into the equation. For $x_2 = 0$,

$$E(y) = 1 + 2x_1 - (0) + x_1(0) = 1 + 2x_1 \quad \text{(slope} = 2)$$

For $x_2 = 1$,

$$E(y) = 1 + 2x_1 - (1) + x_1(1) = 3x_1 \quad \text{(slope} = 3)$$

For $x_2 = 2$,

$$E(y) = 1 + 2x_1 - (2) + x_1(2) = -1 + 4x_1 \quad \text{(slope} = 4)$$

Note that the slope of each line is represented by $\beta_1 + \beta_3x_2 = 2 + x_2$. Thus, the effect on $E(y)$ of a change in x_1 (i.e., the slope) now *depends* on the value of x_2. When this situation occurs, we say that x_1 and x_2 **interact**. The cross-product term, x_1x_2, is called an **interaction term**, and the model $E(y) = \beta_0 + \beta_1x_1 + \beta_2x_2 + \beta_3x_1x_2$ is called an **interaction model** with two quantitative variables.

> **An Interaction Model Relating $E(y)$ to Two Quantitative Independent Variables**
>
> $$E(y) = \beta_0 + \beta_1x_1 + \beta_2x_2 + \beta_3x_1x_2$$
>
> where
>
> $(\beta_1 + \beta_3x_2)$ represents the change in $E(y)$ for every one-unit increase in x_1, holding x_2 fixed
>
> $(\beta_2 + \beta_3x_1)$ represents the change in $E(y)$ for every one-unit increase in x_2, holding x_1 fixed

A three-dimensional graph (generated by computer) of an interaction model in two quantitative x's is shown in Figure 12.9. The interaction model traces a ruled surface (twisted plane) in three-dimensional space—a surface unlike the flat planar surface displayed in Figure 12.4 (p. 634). If we slice the twisted plane at a fixed value of x_2, we obtain a straight line relating $E(y)$ to x_1; however, the slope of the line will change as we change the value of x_2.

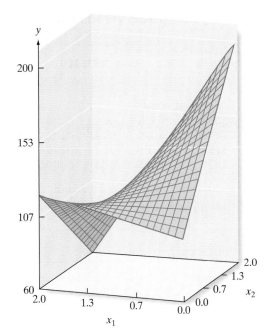

FIGURE 12.9

Computer-generated graph for a second-order interaction model

---

EXAMPLE 12.6

EVALUATING AN INTERACTION MODEL: Clock Auction Prices

Problem Refer to Examples 12.1–12.4. Suppose the collector of grandfather clocks, having observed many auctions, believes that the *rate of increase* in the auction price with age will be driven upward by a large number of bidders. Thus, instead of a relationship like that shown in Figure 12.10a, in which the rate of increase in price with age is the same for any number of bidders, the collector believes that the relationship is like that shown in Figure 12.10b. Note that as the number of bidders increases from 5 to 15, the slope of the price-versus-age line increases.

Consequently, the following interaction model is proposed:

$$y = \beta_0 + \beta_1 x_1 + \beta_2 x_2 + \beta_3 x_1 x_2 + \varepsilon$$

The 32 data points listed in Table 12.1 were used to fit the model with interaction. A portion of the MINITAB printout is shown in Figure 12.11.

a. Use the global *F*-test at $\alpha = .05$ to test the overall utility of the model.

b. Test the hypothesis (at $\alpha = .05$) that the price–age slope increases as the number of bidders increases—that is, that age and number of bidders, x_2, interact positively.

c. Estimate the change in auction price y of a 150-year-old grandfather clock for each additional bidder.

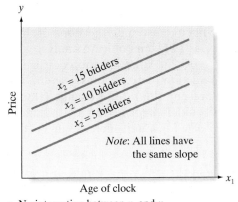

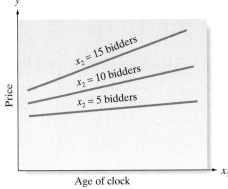

FIGURE 12.10

Examples of no-interaction and interaction models

a. No interaction between x_1 and x_2

b. Interaction between x_1 and x_2

Regression Analysis: PRICE versus AGE, NUMBIDS, AGEBID

```
The regression equation is
PRICE = 320 + 0.88 AGE - 93.3 NUMBIDS + 1.30 AGEBID


Predictor      Coef   SE Coef      T       P
Constant      320.5     295.1    1.09   0.287
AGE           0.878     2.032    0.43   0.669
NUMBIDS      -93.26     29.89   -3.12   0.004
AGEBID       1.2978    0.2123    6.11   0.000


S = 88.9145   R-Sq = 95.4%   R-Sq(adj) = 94.9%


Analysis of Variance
```

FIGURE 12.11

MINITAB printout of interaction model of auction price

```
Source          DF       SS       MS        F       P
Regression       3  4578427  1526142   193.04   0.000
Residual Error  28   221362     7906
Total           31  4799790
```

Solution

a. The global F-test is used to test the null hypothesis

$$H_0: \beta_1 = \beta_2 = \beta_3 = 0$$

The test statistic and p-value of the test (highlighted on the MINITAB printout) are $F = 193.04$ and $p = 0$, respectively. Since $\alpha = .05$ exceeds the p-value, there is sufficient evidence to conclude that the model fit is a statistically useful predictor of the auction price y.

b. The hypotheses of interest to the collector concern the interaction parameter β_3. Specifically,

$$H_0: \beta_3 = 0$$
$$H_a: \beta_3 > 0$$

Since we are testing an individual β parameter, a t-test is required. The test statistic and the two-tailed p-value (highlighted on the printout) are $t = 6.11$ and $p = 0$, respectively. The upper-tailed p-value, obtained by dividing the two-tailed p-value in half, is $0/2 = 0$. Since $\alpha = .05$ exceeds the p-value, the collector can reject H_0 and conclude that the rate of change of the mean price of the clocks with age increases as the number of bidders increases; that is, x_1 and x_2 interact positively. Thus, it appears that the interaction term should be included in the model.

c. To estimate the change in auction price y for every one-unit increase in number of bidders, x_2, we need to estimate the slope of the line relating y to x_2 when the age of the clock, x_1, is 150 years old. An analyst who is not careful may estimate this slope as $\hat{\beta}_2 = -93.26$. Although the coefficient of x_2 is negative, this does *not* imply that the auction price decreases as the number of bidders increases. Since interaction is present, the rate of change (slope) of the mean auction price with the number of bidders *depends* on x_1, the age of the clock. Thus, the estimated rate of change of y for a unit increase in x_2 (one new bidder) for a 150-year-old clock is

$$\text{Estimated } x_2 \text{ slope} = \hat{\beta}_2 + \hat{\beta}_3 x_1 = -93.26 + 1.30(150) = 101.74$$

In other words, we estimate that the auction price of a 150-year-old clock will *increase* by about \$101.74 for every additional bidder.

Look Back Although the rate of increase will vary as x_1 is changed, it will remain positive for the range of values of x_1 included in the sample. Extreme care is needed in interpreting the signs and sizes of coefficients in a multiple-regression model.

Now Work Exercise 12.42

Example 12.6 illustrates an important point about conducting t-tests on the β parameters in the interaction model. The "most important" β parameter in this model is the interaction β, β_3. [Note that this β is also the one associated with the highest-order term in the model, x_1x_2.*] Consequently, we will want to test H_0: $\beta_3 = 0$ after we have determined that the overall model is useful in predicting y. Once interaction is detected (as in Example 12.6), however, tests on the first-order terms x_1 and x_2 should *not* be conducted, since they are meaningless tests; the presence of interaction implies that both x's are important.

Caution

Once interaction has been deemed important in the model $E(y) = \beta_0 + \beta_1x_1 + \beta_2x_2 + \beta_3x_1x_2$, do not conduct t-tests on the β coefficients of the first-order terms x_1 and x_2. These terms should be kept in the model regardless of the magnitude of their associated p-values shown on the printout.

We close this section with a comment: You will probably never know *a priori* whether interaction exists between two independent variables; consequently, you will need to fit and test the interaction term to determine its importance.

Exercises 12.37–12.49

Understanding the Principles

12.37 Write an interaction model relating the mean value of y, $E(y)$, to
  a. two quantitative independent variables
  b. three quantitative independent variables [*Hint:* Include all possible two-way cross-product terms.]

12.38 If two variables x_1 and x_2 do not interact, how would you describe their effect on the mean response $E(y)$?

Learning the Mechanics

12.39 Suppose the true relationship between $E(y)$ and the quantitative independent variables x_1 and x_2 is

$$E(y) = 3 + x_1 + 2x_2 - x_1x_2$$

  a. Describe the corresponding three-dimensional response surface.
  b. Plot the linear relationship between y and x_2 for $x_2 = 0, 1, 2$, where $0 \le x_2 \le 5$.
  c. Explain why the lines you plotted in part **b** are not parallel.
  d. Use the lines you plotted in part **b** to explain how changes in the settings of x_1 and x_2 affect $E(y)$.
  e. Use your graph from part **b** to determine how much $E(y)$ changes when x_1 is changed from 2 to 0 and x_2 is simultaneously changed from 4 to 5.

12.40 Suppose you fit the interaction model

$$y = \beta_0 + \beta_1x_1 + \beta_2x_2 + \beta_3x_1x_2 + \varepsilon$$

to $n = 32$ data points and obtain the following results:

$$SS_{yy} = 479 \qquad SSE = 21 \qquad \hat{\beta}_3 = 10 \qquad s_{\hat{\beta}_3} = 4$$

  a. Find R^2 and interpret its value.
  b. Is the model adequate for predicting y? Test at $\alpha = .05$.
  c. Use a graph to explain the contribution of the x_1x_2 term to the model.
  d. Is there evidence that x_1 and x_2 interact? Test at $\alpha = .05$.

12.41 MINITAB was used to fit the model

$$y = \beta_0 + \beta_1x_1 + \beta_2x_2 + \beta_3x_1x_2 + \varepsilon$$

to $n = 15$ data points. The resulting printout is shown on p. 658.
  a. What is the prediction equation for the response surface?
  b. Describe the geometric form of the response surface of part **a**.
  c. Plot the prediction equation for the case when $x_2 = 1$. Do this twice more on the same graph for the cases when $x_2 = 3$ and $x_2 = 5$.
  d. Explain what it means to say that x_1 and x_2 interact. Explain why the graph you plotted in part **c** suggests that x_1 and x_2 interact.
  e. Specify the null and alternative hypotheses you would use to test whether x_1 and x_2 interact.
  f. Conduct the hypothesis test of part **e**, using $\alpha = .01$.

---

*The order of a term is equal to the sum of the exponents of the quantitative variables included in the term. Thus, when x_1 and x_2 are both quantitative variables, the cross product, x_1x_2, is a second-order term.

```
The regression equation is
Y = -2.55 + 3.82 X1 + 2.63 X2 -1.29 X1X2


Predictor     Coef   SE Coef      T      P
Constant    -2.550     1.142  -2.23  0.043
X1           3.815     0.529   7.22  0.000
X2           2.630     0.344   7.64  0.000
X1X2        -1.285     0.159  -8.06  0.000


S = 0.713      R-Sq = 85.6%    R-Sq(adj) = 81.6%


Analysis of Variance

Source          DF      SS      MS      F      P
Regression       3  33.149  11.050  21.75  0.000
Residual Error  11   5.587   0.508
Total           14  38.736
```

MINITAB output for
Exercise 12.41

Applying the Concepts—Basic

12.42 **Role of retailer interest in shopping behavior.** Retail inter-
NW est is defined by marketers as the level of interest a consumer has in a given retail store. Marketing professors at
the University of Tennessee at Chattanooga and the University of Alabama investigated the role of retailer interest
in consumers' shopping behavior. (*Journal of Retailing*,
Summer 2006.) Using survey data collected on $n = 375$
consumers, the professors developed an interaction model
for y = willingness of the consumer to shop at a retailer's
store in the future (called "repatronage intentions") as a
function of x_1 = consumer satisfaction and x_2 = retailer
interest. The regression results are shown below:
a. Is the overall model statistically useful in predicting y?
   Test, using $\alpha = .05$.
b. Conduct a test for interaction at $\alpha = .05$.
c. Use the β-estimates to sketch the estimated relationship between repatronage intentions (y) and satisfaction (x_1) when retailer interest is $x_2 = 1$ (a low value).
d. Repeat part **c** for the case when retailer interest is
   $x_2 = 7$ (a high value).
e. Put the two lines you sketched in parts **c** and **d** on the
   same graph to illustrate the nature of the interaction.

12.43 **Defects in nuclear missile housing parts.** The technique of
multivariable testing was discussed in *The Journal of the
Reliability Analysis Center* (First Quarter, 2004). Multivariable testing was shown to improve the quality of
carbon-foam rings used in nuclear missile housings. The
rings are produced via a casting process that involves mix-
ing ingredients, oven curing, and carving the finished part.
One type of defect analyzed was the number y of black
streaks in the manufactured ring. Two variables found to

affect the number of defects were turntable speed (revolutions per minute) x_1 and cutting blade position (inches
from center) x_2.
a. The researchers discovered "an interaction between
   blade position and turntable speed." Hypothesize a
   regression model for $E(y)$ that incorporates this
   interaction.
b. Interpret what it means practically to say that "blade
   position and turntable speed interact."
c. The researchers reported a positive linear relationship
   between number of defects (y) and turntable speed (x_1),
   but found that the slope of the relationship was much
   steeper for lower values of cutting blade position (x_2).
   What does this imply about the interaction term in the
   model you hypothesized in part **a**? Explain.

12.44 **Psychology of waiting in line.** While waiting in a long line
for service (e.g., to use an ATM or at the post office), at
some point you may decide to leave the line. The *Journal of
Consumer of Research* (Nov. 2003) published a study of consumer behavior while waiting in a line. College students
(sample size $n = 148$) were asked to imagine that they were
waiting in line at a post office to mail a package and that the
estimated waiting time was 10 minutes or less. After a 10-
minute wait, students were asked about their level of negative feelings (annoyed, anxious) on a scale of 1 (strongly
disagree) to 9 (strongly agree). Before answering, however,
the students were informed about how many people were
ahead of them and behind them in the line. The researchers
used regression to relate negative feelings score (y) to number ahead in line (x_1) and number behind in line (x_2).
a. The researchers fit an interaction model to the data.
   Write the hypothesized equation of this model.

Results for Exercise 12.42

Variable	Estimated β	t-value	p-value
Satisfaction (x_1)	.426	7.33	$< .01$
Retailer interest (x_2)	.044	0.85	$> .10$
Satisfaction $\times$ Retailer interest (x_1x_2)	$-.157$	-3.09	$< .01$

$R^2 = .65$, $F = 226.35$, p-value $< .001$

b. In the words of the problem, explain what it means to say that "x_1 and x_2 interact to affect y."

c. A t-test for the interaction β in the model resulted in a p-value greater than .25. Interpret this result.

d. From their analysis, the researchers concluded that "the greater the number of people ahead, the higher [is] the negative feeling score" and "the greater the number of people behind, the lower [is] the negative feeling score." Use this information to determine the signs of $\hat{\beta}_1$ and $\hat{\beta}_2$ in the model.

Applying the Concepts—Intermediate

12.45 Child abuse report. Licensed therapists are mandated by law to report child abuse by their clients. This law requires the therapist to breach confidentiality and possibly lose the client's trust. A national survey of licensed psychotherapists was conducted to investigate clients' reactions to legally mandated child-abuse reports. (*American Journal of Orthopsychiatry*, Jan. 1997.) The sample consisted of 303 therapists who had filed a child-abuse report against at least one of their clients. The researchers were interested in finding the best predictors of a client's reaction (y) to the report, where y is measured on a 30-point scale. (The higher the value, the more favorable was the client's response to the report.) The independent variables found to have the most predictive power are as follows:

x_1: Therapist's age (years)
x_2: Therapist's gender (1 if male, 0 if female)
x_3: Degree of therapist's role strain (25-point scale)
x_4: Strength of client–therapist relationship (40-point scale
x_5: Type of case (1 if family, 0 if not)
x_1x_2: Age × Gender interaction

a. Hypothesize a first-order model relating y to each of the five independent variables and the interaction term.

b. Give the null hypothesis for testing the contribution of x_4, strength of client–therapist relationship, to the model.

c. The test statistic for the test suggested in part **b** was $t = 4.408$, with an associated p-value of .001. Interpret this result.

d. The estimated β coefficient for the x_1x_2 interaction term was positive and highly significant ($p < .001$). According to the researchers, "This interaction suggests that … as the age of the therapist increased, … male therapists were less likely to get negative client reactions than were female therapists." Do you agree?

e. For the model presented here, $R^2 = .2946$. Interpret this value.

12.46 Unconscious self-esteem study. Psychologists define *implicit* self-esteem as unconscious evaluations of one's worth or value. In contrast, *explicit* self-esteem refers to the extent to which a person consciously considers oneself as valuable and worthy. An article published In *Journal of Articles in Support of the Null Hypothesis* (March 2006) investigated whether implicit self-esteem is really unconscious. A sample of 257 college undergraduate students completed a questionnaire designed to measure implicit self-esteem and explicit self-esteem. Thus, an implicit self-esteem score (x_1) and explicit self-esteem score (x_2) was obtained for each. (*Note*: Higher scores indicate higher levels of self-esteem.) Also, a second questionnaire was administered in order to obtain each subject's estimate of his or her level of implicit self-esteem. The score obtained from this questionnaire was called an estimated implicit self-esteem score (x_3). Finally, the researchers computed two measures of accuracy in estimating implicit self-esteem: $y_1 = (x_3 - x_1)$ and $y_2 = |x_3 - x_1|$.

a. The researchers fit the interaction model $E(y_1) = \beta_0 + \beta_1x_1 + \beta_2x_2 + \beta_3x_1x_2$. The t-test of the interaction term, β_3, was "nonsignificant," with a p-value $> .10$. However, both t-tests of β_1 and β_2 were statistically significant (p-value $< .001$). Interpret these results practically.

b. The researchers also fit the interaction model $E(y_2) = \beta_0 + \beta_1x_1 + \beta_2x_2 + \beta_3x_1x_2$. The t-test on the interaction term, β_3, was "significant," with a p-value $< .001$. Interpret this result practically.

12.47 Factors that affect an auditor's judgment. A study was conducted to determine the effects of linguistic delivery style and client credibility on auditors' judgments. (*Advances in Accounting and Behavioral Research*, 2003.) Each of 200 auditors from "Big 5" accounting firms were asked to assume that he or she was an audit team supervisor of a new manufacturing client and was performing an analytical review of the client's financial statement. The researchers gave the auditors different information on the client's credibility and the linguistic delivery style of the client's explanation. Each auditor then provided an assessment of the likelihood that the client's explanation accounts for the fluctuation in the financial statement. The three variables of interest—credibility (x_1), linguistic delivery style (x_2), and likelihood (y)—were all measured on a numerical scale. Regression analysis was used to fit the interaction model $y = \beta_0 + \beta_1x_1 + \beta_2x_2 + \beta_3x_1x_2 + \varepsilon$. The results are summarized in the table below.

a. Interpret the phrase "client credibility and linguistic delivery style interact" in the words of the problem.

b. Give the null and alternative hypotheses for testing the overall adequacy of the model.

c. Conduct the test suggested in part **b**, using the information in the table.

Results for Exercise 12.47

	Beta Estimate	Std Error	t-statistic	p-value
Constant	15.865	10.980	1.445	0.150
Client credibility (x_1)	0.037	0.339	0.110	0.913
Linguistic delivery Style (x_2)	−0.678	0.328	−2.064	0.040
Interaction (x_1x_2)	0.036	0.009	4.008	<0.005

$F = 55.35$ ($p < 0.0005$); Adjusted $R^2 = .450$

d. Give the null and alternative hypotheses for testing whether client credibility and linguistic delivery style interact.

e. Conduct the test suggested in part **d**, using the information in the table.

f. The researchers estimated the slope of the likelihood–linguistic delivery style line at a low level of client credibility ($x_1 = 22$). Obtain this estimate and interpret it in the words of the problem.

g. The researchers also estimated the slope of the likelihood–linguistic delivery style line at a high level of client credibility ($x_1 = 46$). Obtain this estimate and interpret it in the words of the problem.

ASWELLS

12.48 Arsenic in groundwater. Refer to the *Environmental Science & Technology* (Jan. 2005) study of the reliability of a commercial kit to test for arsenic in groundwater, presented in Exercise 12.19 (p. 644). Recall that you fit a first-order model for arsenic level (y) as a function of latitude (x_1), longitude (x_2), and depth (x_3) to data saved in the **ASWELLS** file.

a. Write a model for arsenic level (y) that includes first-order terms for latitude, longitude, and depth, as well as terms for interaction between latitude and depth and interaction between longitude and depth.

b. Use statistical software to fit the interaction model you wrote in part **a** to the data in the **ASWELLS** file. Give the least squares prediction equation.

c. Conduct a test (at $\alpha = .05$) to determine whether latitude and depth interact to affect arsenic level.

d. Conduct a test (at $\alpha = .05$) to determine whether longitude and depth interact to affect arsenic level.

e. Interpret practically the results of the tests you conducted in parts **c** and **d**.

GASTURBINE

12.49 Cooling method for gas turbines. Refer to the *Journal of Engineering for Gas Turbines and Power* (Jan. 2005) study of a high-pressure inlet fogging method for a gas turbine engine, presented in Exercise 12.23 (p. 646). Recall that you fit a first-order model for heat rate (y) as a function of speed (x_1), inlet temperature (x_2), exhaust temperature (x_3), cycle pressure ratio (x_4), and air mass flow rate (x_5) to data saved in the **GASTURBINE** file.

a. Researchers hypothesize that the linear relationship between heat rate (y) and temperature (both inlet and exhaust) depends on air mass flow rate. Write a model for heat rate that incorporates the researchers' theories.

b. Use statistical software to fit the interaction model you wrote in part **a** to the data in the **GASTURBINE** file. Give the least squares prediction equation.

c. Conduct a test (at $\alpha = .05$) to determine whether inlet temperature and air mass flow rate interact to affect heat rate.

d. Conduct a test (at $\alpha = .05$) to determine whether exhaust temperature and air mass flow rate interact to affect heat rate.

e. Interpret practically the results of the tests you conducted in parts **c** and **d**.

12.6 Model Building: Quadratic and Other Higher Order Models

All of the models discussed in the previous sections proposed straight-line relationships between $E(y)$ and each of the independent variables in the model. In this section, we consider models that allow for curvature in the relationships. Each of these models is a **second-order model**, because it includes an x^2-term.

First, we consider a model that includes only one independent variable x. The form of this model, called the **quadratic model**, is

$$y = \beta_0 + \beta_1 x + \beta_2 x^2 + \varepsilon$$

The term involving x^2, called a **quadratic term** (or **second-order term**), enables us to hypothesize curvature in the graph of the response model relating y to x. Graphs of the quadratic model for two different values of β_2 are shown in Figure 12.12. When the curve opens upward, the sign of β_2 is positive (see Figure 12.12a); when the curve opens downward, the sign of β_2 is negative (see Figure 12.12b).

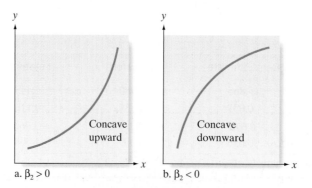

FIGURE 12.12

Graphs of two quadratic models

A Quadratic (Second-Order) Model in a Single Quantitative Independent Variable

$$E(y) = \beta_0 + \beta_1 x + \beta_2 x^2$$

where

β_0 is the y-intercept of the curve

β_1 is a shift parameter

β_2 is the rate of curvature

EXAMPLE 12.7
ANALYZING A QUADRATIC MODEL: Predicting Electrical Usage

Problem In all-electric homes, the amount of electricity expended is of interest to consumers, builders, and groups involved with energy conservation. Suppose we wish to investigate the monthly electrical usage y in all-electric homes and its relationship to the size x of the home. Moreover, suppose we think that monthly electrical usage in all-electric homes is related to the size of the home by the quadratic model

$$y = \beta_0 + \beta_1 x + \beta_2 x^2 + \varepsilon$$

To fit the model, the values of y and x are collected for 10 homes during a particular month. The data are shown in Table 12.3.

a. Construct a scatterplot of the data. Is there evidence to support the use of a quadratic model?

b. Use the method of least squares to estimate the unknown parameters β_0, β_1, and β_2 in the quadratic model.

c. Graph the prediction equation and assess how well the model fits the data, both visually and numerically.

d. Interpret the β estimates.

e. Is the overall model useful (at $\alpha = .01$) for predicting electrical usage y?

f. Is there sufficient evidence of concave-downward curvature in the electrical usage–home size relationship? Test, using $\alpha = .01$.

 ELECTRIC

TABLE 12.3 Home Size–Electrical Usage Data

Size of Home x (sq. ft)	Monthly Usage y (kilowatt-hours)
1,290	1,182
1,350	1,172
1,470	1,264
1,600	1,493
1,710	1,571
1,840	1,711
1,980	1,804
2,230	1,840
2,400	1,956
2,930	1,954

Solution

a. A scattergram of the data of Table 12.3, produced with MINITAB, is shown in Figure 12.13. The figure illustrates that the electrical usage appears to increase in a

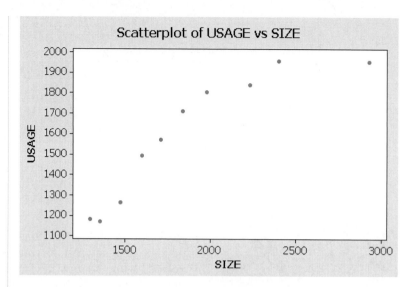

FIGURE 12.13

MINITAB scatterplot for electrical usage data

curvilinear manner with the size of the home. This relationship provides some support for the inclusion of the quadratic term x^2 in the model.

b. We used SAS to fit the model to the data in Table 12.3. Part of the SAS regression output is displayed in Figure 12.14. The least squares estimates of the β parameters (highlighted) are $\hat{\beta}_0 = -1,216.14$, $\hat{\beta}_1 = 2.39893$, and $\hat{\beta}_2 = -.00045$. Therefore, the equation that minimizes the SSE for the data is

$$\hat{y} = -1,216.14 + 2.3989x - .00045x^2$$

c. Figure 12.15 is a graph of the least squares prediction equation. Note that the graph provides a good fit to the data of Table 12.3. A numerical measure of fit is obtained with the adjusted coefficient of determination, R_a^2. From the SAS printout, $R_a^2 = .9767$. This implies that almost 98% of the sample variation in electrical usage (y) can be explained by the quadratic model (after adjusting for sample size and number of degrees of freedom).

d. The interpretation of the estimated coefficients in a quadratic model must be undertaken cautiously. First, the estimated y-intercept, $\hat{\beta}_0$, can be meaningfully interpreted

Dependent Variable: USAGE

Number of Observations Read		10
Number of Observations Used		10

Analysis of Variance

Source	DF	Sum of Squares	Mean Square	F Value	Pr > F
Model	2	831070	415535	189.71	<.0001
Error	7	15333	2190.36480		
Corrected Total	9	846402			

Root MSE	46.80133	R-Square	0.9819	
Dependent Mean	1594.70000	Adj R-Sq	0.9767	
Coeff Var	2.93480			

Parameter Estimates

Variable	DF	Parameter Estimate	Standard Error	t Value	Pr > |t|
Intercept	1	-1216.14389	242.80637	-5.01	0.0016
SIZE	1	2.39893	0.24584	9.76	<.0001
SIZESQ	1	-0.00045004	0.00005908	-7.62	0.0001

FIGURE 12.14

SAS regression output for electrical usage model

Fitted Line Plot
USAGE = - 1216 + 2.399 SIZE   - 0.000450 SIZE**2

FIGURE 12.15
MINITAB plot of least squares
model for electrical usage

only if the range of the independent variable includes zero—that is, if $x = 0$ is included in the sampled range of x. Although $\hat{\beta}_0 = -1{,}216.14$ seems to imply that the estimated electrical usage is negative when $x = 0$, this zero point is not in the range of the sample (the lowest value of x is 1,290 square feet), and the value is nonsensical (a home with 0 square feet); thus, the interpretation of $\hat{\beta}_0$ is not meaningful.

Quadratic Regression
Using the TI-84/TI-83 Graphing Calculator
I. Finding the quadratic regression equation

Step 1   *Enter the data.*

Press **STAT** and select **1:Edit**.
Note: If the list already contains data, clear the old data. Use the up arrow to highlight "**L1**" or "**L2**".
Press **CLEAR ENTER**.
Use the **ARROW** and **ENTER** keys to enter the data set into **L1** and **L2**.

Step 2   *Find the quadratic regression equation.*

Press **STAT** and highlight **CALC**.
Press **5** for **QuadReg**.
Press **ENTER**.
The screen will show the values for a, b, and c in the equation.
If the diagnostics are on, the screen will also give the value for r^2.
To turn the diagnostics feature on,
Press **2nd 0** for **CATALOG**.
Press the **ALPHA** key and x^{-1} for **D**.
Press the down **ARROW** until **DiagnosticsOn** is highlighted.
Press **ENTER** twice.

II. Graphing the quadratic curve with the scatterplot

Step 1   *Enter the data as shown in part I.*

Step 2   *Set up the data plot.*

Press **Y =** and **CLEAR** all functions from the Y registers.
Press **2nd Y =** for **STAT PLOT**.
Press **1** for **Plot**.
Set the cursor so that **ON** is flashing, and press **ENTER**.
For **Type**, use the **ARROW** and **ENTER** keys to highlight and select the scatterplot (first icon in the first row).

(continued)

For **Xlist**, choose the column containing the
x-data.
For **Freq**, choose the column containing the
y-data.

Step 3 *Find the regression equation and store the*
equation in Y1.

Press **STAT** and highlight **CALC**.
Press **5** for **Quad Reg** (*Note*: Don't press
ENTER here, because you want to store the
regression equation in Y1.)
Press **VARS**.
Use the right arrow to highlight **Y-VARS**.
Press **ENTER** to select **1:Function**.
Press **ENTER** to select **1:Y1**.
Press **ENTER**.

Step 4 *View the scatterplot and regression line.*

Press **ZOOM** and then press **9** to select
9:ZoomStat.

Example The figures at the right show a table of data
entered on the T1-84/T1-83, the quadratic
regression equation, and the graph obtained by
following the steps presented.

The estimated coefficient of *x* is $\hat{\beta}_1 = 2.3989$, but it no longer represents a slope
in the presence of the quadratic term x^2.* The estimated coefficient of the first-order
term *x* will not, in general, have a meaningful interpretation in the quadratic model.

The sign of the coefficient, $\hat{\beta}_2 = -.00045$, of the quadratic term, x^2, is the indicator of whether the curve is concave downward (mound shaped) or concave upward (bowl shaped). A negative $\hat{\beta}_2$ implies downward concavity, as in this example
(Figure 12.15), and a positive $\hat{\beta}_2$ implies upward concavity. Rather than interpreting
the numerical value of $\hat{\beta}_2$ itself, we utilize a graphical representation, as in Figure
12.16, to describe the model.

Note that Figure 12.15 implies that the estimated electrical usage levels off as
the home sizes increase beyond 2,500 square feet. In fact, the concavity of the model
would lead to decreasing usage estimates if we were to display the model out to 4,000
square feet and beyond. (See Figure 12.16.) However, model interpretations are not
meaningful outside the range of the independent variable, which has a maximum
value of 2,930 square feet in this example. Thus, although the model appears to support the hypothesis that the *rate of increase* per square foot *decreases* for home sizes
near the high end of the sampled values, the conclusion that usage will actually begin
to decrease for very large homes would be a *misuse* of the model, since no homes of
3,000 square feet or more were included in the sample.

e. To test whether the quadratic model is statistically useful, we conduct the global
F-test:

$$H_0: \beta_1 = \beta_2 = 0$$
$$H_a: \text{At least one of the preceding coefficients is nonzero}$$

From the SAS printout shown in Figure 12.14, the test statistic is $F = 189.71$, with an associated *p*-value near 0. Thus, for any reasonable α, we reject H_0 and conclude that the
overall model is a useful predictor of electrical usage *y*.

*For students with a knowledge of calculus, note that the slope of the quadratic model is the first derivative
$\partial y/\partial x = \beta_1 + 2\beta_2 x$. Thus, the slope varies as a function of *x*, unlike the constant slope associated with the
straight-line model.

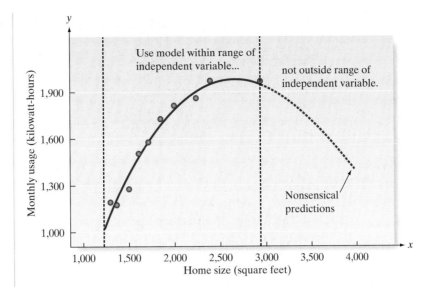

FIGURE 12.16

Potential misuse of quadratic model

f. Figure 12.15 shows concave-downward curvature in the relationship between the size of a home and electrical usage in the sample of 10 data points. To determine whether this type of curvature exists in the population, we want to test

$$H_0: \beta_2 = 0 \text{ (no curvature exists in the response curve)}$$
$$H_a: \beta_2 < 0 \text{ (downward concavity exists in the response curve)}$$

The test statistic for testing β_2, highlighted on the printout, is $t = -7.62$, and the associated two-tailed p-value is .0001. Since this is a one-tailed test, the appropriate p-value is $.0001/2 = .00005$. Now, $\alpha = .01$ exceeds this p-value. Thus, there is very strong evidence of downward curvature in the population; that is, electrical usage increases more slowly per square foot for large homes than for small homes.

Look Back Note that the SAS printout in Figure 12.14 also provides the t-test statistic and corresponding two-tailed p-values for the tests of $H_0: \beta_0 = 0$ and $H_0: \beta_1 = 0$. Since the interpretation of these parameters is not meaningful for this model, the tests are not of interest.

> **Now Work Exercise 12.60**

When two or more quantitative independent variables are included in a second-order model, we can incorporate squared terms for each x in the model, as well as the interaction between the two independent variables. A model that includes all possible second-order terms in two independent variables—called a **complete second-order model**—is given in the following box:

Complete Second-Order Model with Two Quantitative Independent Variables

$$E(y) = \beta_0 + \beta_1 x_1 + \beta_2 x_2 + \beta_3 x_1 x_2 + \beta_4 x_1^2 + \beta_5 x_2^2$$

Comments on the Parameters

β_0: y-intercept, the value of $E(y)$ when $x_1 = x_2 = 0$

β_1, β_2: Changing β_1 and β_2 causes the surface to shift along the x_1- and x_2-axes

β_3: Controls the rotation of the surface

β_4, β_5: Signs and values of these parameters control the type of surface and the rates of curvature.

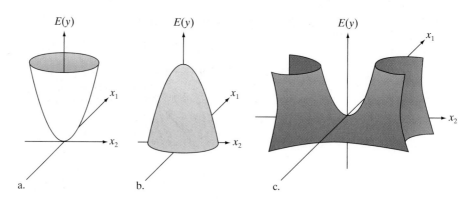

FIGURE 12.17
Graphs for three second-order surfaces

Three types of surfaces are produced by a second-order model:* a **paraboloid** that opens upward (Figure 12.17a), a paraboloid that opens downward (Figure 12.17b), and a **saddle-shaped surface** (Figure 12.17c).

A complete second-order model is the three-dimensional equivalent of a quadratic model in a single quantitative variable. Instead of tracing parabolas, however, it traces paraboloids and saddle-shaped surfaces. Since only a portion of the complete surface is used to fit the data, this model provides a very large variety of gently curving surfaces that can be used to fit data. It is a good choice for a model if you expect curvature in the response surface relating $E(y)$ to x_1 and x_2.

EXAMPLE 12.8

A MORE COMPLEX SECOND-ORDER MODEL: Predicting Hours Worked per Week

Problem A social scientist would like to relate the number of hours worked per week (outside the home) by a married woman to the number of years of formal education she has completed and the number of children in her family.

a. Identify the dependent variable and the independent variables.

b. Write the first-order model for this example.

c. Modify the model in part **b** so that it includes an interaction term.

d. Write a complete second-order model for $E(y)$.

Solution

a. The dependent variable is

$$y = \text{Number of hours worked per week by a married woman}$$

The two independent variables, both quantitative in nature, are

$$x_1 = \text{Number of years of formal education completed by the woman}$$
$$x_2 = \text{Number of children in the family}$$

b. The first-order model is

$$E(y) = \beta_0 + \beta_1 x_1 + \beta_2 x_2$$

This model would probably not be appropriate in the current situation because x_1 and x_2 may interact or curvature terms corresponding to x_1^2 and x_2^2 may be needed to obtain a good model for $E(y)$.

c. Adding the interaction term, we obtain

$$E(y) = \beta_0 + \beta_1 x_1 + \beta_2 x_2 + \beta_3 x_1 x_2$$

This model should be better than the model in part **b**, since we have now allowed for interaction between x_1 and x_2.

---

*The paraboloid opens upward (Figure 12.17a) when $\beta_4 + \beta_5 > 0$ and opens downward (Figure 12.17b) when $\beta_4 + \beta_5 < 0$; the saddle-shaped surface (Figure 12.17c) is produced when $\beta_3^2 > 4\beta_4\beta_5$.

d. The complete second-order model is

$$E(y) = \beta_0 + \beta_1 x_1 + \beta_2 x_2 + \beta_3 x_1 x_2 + \beta_4 x_1^2 + \beta_5 x_2^2$$

Since it would not be surprising to find curvature in the response surface, the complete second-order model would be preferred to the models in parts **b** and **c**. How can we tell whether the complete second-order model really does provide better predictions of hours worked than the models in parts **b** and **c**? The answers to these and similar questions are examined in Section 12.9.

Most relationships between $E(y)$ and two or more quantitative independent variables are second order and require the use of either the interactive or the complete second-order model to obtain a good fit to a data set. As in the case of a single quantitative independent variable, however, the curvature in the response surface may be very slight over the range of values of the variables in the data set. When this happens, a first-order model may provide a good fit to the data.

Exercises 12.50–12.66

Understanding the Principles

12.50 In the model $E(y) = \beta_0 + \beta_1 x + \beta_2 x^2$,
  a. Which β represents the y-intercept?
  b. Which β represents the shift?
  c. Which β represents the rate of curvature?

12.51 Write a second-order model relating the mean of y, $E(y)$, to
  a. one quantitative independent variable
  b. two quantitative independent variables
  c. three quantitative independent variables [*Hint:* Include all possible two-way cross-product terms and squared terms.]

Learning the Mechanics

12.52 Suppose you fit the quadratic model

$$E(y) = \beta_0 + \beta_1 x + \beta_2 x^2$$

to a set of $n = 20$ data points and find that $R^2 = .91$, $SS_{yy} = 29.94$, and $SSE = 2.63$.
  a. Is there sufficient evidence to indicate that the model contributes information relevant to predicting y? Test using $\alpha = .05$.
  b. What null and alternative hypotheses would you test to determine whether upward curvature exists?
  c. What null and alternative hypotheses would you test to determine whether downward curvature exists?

12.53 Suppose you fit the second-order model

$$y = \beta_0 + \beta_1 x + \beta_2 x^2 + \varepsilon$$

to $n = 25$ data points. Your estimate of β_2 is $\hat{\beta}_2 = .47$, and the estimated standard error of the estimate is .15.
  a. Test $H_0: \beta_2 = 0$ against $H_a: \beta_2 \neq 0$. Use $\alpha = .05$.
  b. Suppose you want to determine only whether the quadratic curve opens upward; that is, as x increases, the slope of the curve would increase. Give the test statistic and the rejection region for the test for $\alpha = .05$. Do the data support the theory that the slope of the curve increases as x increases? Explain.

12.54 MINITAB was used to fit the complete second-order model

$$E(y) = \beta_0 + \beta_1 x_1 + \beta_2 x_2 + \beta_3 x_1 x_2 + \beta_4 x_1^2 + \beta_5 x_2^2$$

to $n = 39$ data points. (See the MINITAB printout on p. 668.)
  a. Is there sufficient evidence to indicate that at least one of the parameters β_1, β_2, β_3, β_4, and β_5 is nonzero? Test, using $\alpha = .05$.
  b. Test $H_0: \beta_4 = 0$ against $H_a: \beta_4 \neq 0$. Use $\alpha = .01$.
  c. Test $H_0: \beta_5 = 0$ against $H_a: \beta_5 \neq 0$. Use $\alpha = .01$.
  d. Use graphs to explain the consequences of the tests in parts **b** and **c**.

12.55 Consider the following quadratic models:

$$(1)\; y = 1 - 2x + x^2$$
$$(2)\; y = 1 + 2x + x^2$$
$$(3)\; y = 1 + x^2$$
$$(4)\; y = 1 - x^2$$
$$(5)\; y = 1 + 3x^2$$

  a. Graph each of these quadratic models, side by side, on the same sheet of graph paper.
  b. What effect does the first-order term $(2x)$ have on the graph of the curve?
  c. What effect does the second-order term (x^2) have on the graph of the curve?

Applying the Concepts—Basic

12.56 Assertiveness and leadership. Management professors at Columbia University examined the relationship between assertiveness and leadership (*Journal of Personality and Social Psychology*, Feb. 2007). The sample comprised 388 people enrolled in a full-time master's in business administration (MBA) program. On the basis of answers to a questionnaire, the researchers measured two variables for each subject: assertiveness score (x) and leadership ability score (y). A quadratic regression model was fit to the data, with the following results:

Independent Variable	β Estimate	t-value	p-value
x	.57	2.55	.01
x^2	−.88	−3.97	< .01

Model $R^2 = .12$

```
The regression equation is
Y = -24.56 + 1.12 X1 + 27.99 X2 - 0.54 X1X2 - 0.004 X1SQ + 0.002 X2SQ


Predictor          Coef      SE Coef      T      P
Constant        -24.563        6.531  -3.76  0.001
X1               1.19848       0.1103  10.86  0.000
X2              27.988        79.489    0.35  0.727
X1X2            -0.5397        1.0338  -0.52  0.605
X1SQ            -0.0043        0.0004 -10.74  0.000
X2SQ             0.0020        0.0033   0.60  0.550


S = 2.762      R-Sq = 79.7%    R-Sq(adj) = 76.6%

Analysis of Variance

Source            DF       SS       MS       F      P
Regression         5   989.30   197.86   25.93  0.000
Residual Error    33   251.81     7.63
Total             38  1241.11
```

MINITAB output for
Exercise 12.54

a. Conduct a test of overall model utility. Use $\alpha = .05$.

b. The researchers hypothesized that leadership ability will increase at a decreasing rate with assertiveness. Set up the null and alternative hypotheses to test this theory.

c. Use the reported results to conduct the test you set up in part **b**. Give your conclusion (at $\alpha = .05$) in the words of the problem.

12.57 Testing tires for wear. Underinflated or overinflated tires can increase tire wear. A new tire was tested for wear at different pressures, with the results shown in the following table:

TIRES

Pressure x (pounds per square inch)	Mileage y (thousands)
30	29
31	32
32	36
33	38
34	37
35	33
36	26

a. Plot the data on a scattergram.

b. If you were given only the information for $x = 30, 31, 32$, and 33, what kind of model would you suggest? For $x = 33, 34, 35$, and 36? For all the data?

12.58 Catalytic converters in cars. A quadratic model was applied to motor vehicle toxic emissions data collected between 1984 and 1999 in Mexico City. (*Environmental Science & Engineering*, Sept. 1, 2000.) The following equation was used to predict the percentage (y) of motor vehicles without catalytic converters in the Mexico City fleet for a given year (x): $\hat{y} = 325{,}790 - 321.67x + 0.794x^2$.

a. Explain why the value $\hat{\beta}_0 = 325{,}790$ has no practical interpretation.

b. Explain why the value $\hat{\beta}_1 = -321.67$ should not be interpreted as a slope.

c. Examine the value of $\hat{\beta}_2$ to determine the nature of the curvature (upward or downward) in the sample data.

d. The researchers used the model to estimate "that just after the year 2021 the fleet of cars with catalytic converters will completely disappear." Comment on the danger of using the model to predict y in the year 2021.

12.59 Estimation of urban population by means of satellite images. Refer to the *Geographical Analysis* (Jan. 2007) study that demonstrated the use of satellite image maps for estimating urban population, presented in Exercise 12.14 (p. 643). A first-order model for census block population density (y) was fit as a function of the proportion of a block with low-density residential areas (x_1) and the proportion of a block with high-density residential areas (x_2). Now consider a complete second-order model for y.

a. Write the equation of the model.

b. Identify the terms in the model that allow for curvilinear relationships.

12.60 Violent behavior in children. Refer to the *Development Psychology* (Mar. 2003) study of the behavior of elementary school children, presented in Exercise 8.25 (p. 363). The researchers used a quadratic equation to model the level (y) of aggressive fantasies experienced by a child as a function of the child's age (x). [*Note:* Level y was measured as an average of responses to six questions (e.g., "Do you sometimes have daydreams about hitting or hurting someone you don't like?"). Responses were measured on a scale ranging from 1 (*never*) to 5 (*always*).]

a. Write the equation of the hypothesized model for $E(y)$.

b. Research psychologists theorized that a child's aggressive fantasies increase with age, but at a slower rate of acceleration in older children. Sketch the curve hypothesized by the researchers.

c. Set up H_0 and H_a for testing the researcher's theory.

d. The model was fit to data collected for over 11,000 elementary school children, with the following results:

$\hat{y} = 1.926 + .097x - .003x^2$, standard error of $\hat{\beta}_2 = .001$. Compute the test statistic for the test you set up in part **c**.

e. Use the result you found in part **d** to make the appropriate conclusion. Take $\alpha = .05$.

Applying the Concepts—Intermediate

12.61 Estimating change-point dosage. A standard method for studying toxic substances and their effects on humans is to observe the responses of rodents exposed to various doses of the substance over time. In the *Journal of Agricultural, Biological, and Environmental Statistics* (June 2005), researchers used least squares regression to estimate the "change-point" dosage, defined as the largest dose level that has no adverse effects. Data were obtained from a dose-response study of rats exposed to the toxic substance aconiazide. A sample of 50 rats was evenly divided into five dosage groups: 0, 100, 200, 500, and 750 milligrams per kilograms of body weight. The dependent variable y measured was the weight change (in grams) after a 2-week exposure. The researchers fit the quadratic model $E(y) = \beta_0 + \beta_1 x + \beta_2 x^2$, where x = dosage level, with the following results: $\hat{y} = 10.25 + .0053x - .0000266x^2$.

a. Construct a rough sketch of the least squares prediction equation. Describe the nature of the curvature in the estimated model.

b. Estimate the weight change (y) for a rat given a dosage of 500 mg/kg of aconiazide.

c. Estimate the weight change (y) for a rat given a dosage of 0 mg/kg of aconiazide. (This dosage is called the "control" dosage level.)

d. Of the five groups in the study, find the largest dosage level x which yields an estimated weight change that is closest to, but below, the estimated weight change for the control group. This value is the change-point dosage.

12.62 Revenues of popular movies. The *Internet Movie Database* (www.imdb.com) monitors the gross revenues of all major motion pictures. The accompanying table gives both the domestic (United States and Canada) and international gross revenues for a sample of 15 popular movies.

a. Write a first-order model for international gross revenues y as a function of domestic gross revenues x.

b. Write a second-order model for international gross revenues y as a function of domestic gross revenues x.

c. Construct a scatterplot of these data. Which of the models appears to be a better choice for explaining variation in international gross revenues?

d. Fit the model of part **b** to the data and investigate its usefulness. Is there evidence of a curvilinear relationship between international and domestic gross revenues? Test, using $\alpha = .05$.

e. On the basis of your analysis in part **d**, which of the two models better explains the variation in international gross revenues?

12.63 Genetics of a brain disease. Spinocerebellar ataxia type 1 (SCA1) is an inherited neurodegenerative disorder characterized by dysfunction of the brain. From a deoxyribonucleic acid (DNA) analysis of SCA1 chromosomes, researchers discovered the presence of repeat gene sequences. (*Cell Biology*, Feb. 1995.) In general, the more repeat sequences observed, the earlier was the onset of the disease (in years of the person's age). The scatterplot (p. 670) shows this relationship for data collected on 113 individuals diagnosed with SCA1.

a. Suppose you want to model the age y of onset of the disease as a function of number x of repeat gene sequences in SCA1 chromosomes. Propose a quadratic model for y.

b. Will the sign of β_2 in the model you proposed in part **a** be positive or negative? Base your decision on the results shown in the scatterplot.

c. The researchers reported a correlation of $r = -.815$ between age and number of repeats. Since $r^2 = (-.815)^2 = .664$, they concluded that about "66% of the variability in the age of onset can be accounted for by the number of repeats." Does this statement apply to the quadratic model $E(y) = \beta_0 + \beta_1 x + \beta_2 x^2$? If not, give the equation of the model for which it does apply.

12.64 Optimizing semiconductor material processing. Fluorocarbon plasmas are used in the production of semiconductor

IMDB

Movie Title (year)	Domestic Gross ($ millions)	International Gross ($ millions)
Titanic (1997)	600.7	1,234.6
E.T. (1982)	439.9	321.8
Pirates of the Caribbean: Dead Man's Chest (2006)	420.3	631.0
Jurassic Park (1993)	356.8	563.0
Lion King (1994)	328.4	455.0
Harry Potter and the Sorcerer's Stone (2001)	317.6	651.1
Sixth Sense (1999)	293.5	368.0
Jaws (1975)	260.0	210.6
Ghost (1990)	217.6	300.0
Saving Private Ryan (1998)	216.1	263.2
Gladiator (2000)	187.7	268.6
Dances with Wolves (1990)	184.2	240.0
The Exorcist (1973)	204.6	153.0
My Big Fat Greek Wedding (2002)	241.4	115.1
Rocky IV (1985)	127.9	172.6

Source: The *Internet Movie Database* (www.imdb.com).

Scatterplot for Exercise 12.63

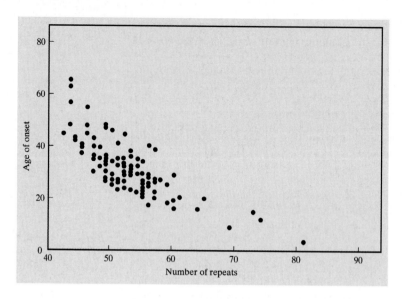

materials. In the *Journal of Applied Physics* (Dec. 1, 2000), electrical engineers at Nagoya University (Japan) studied the kinetics of fluorocarbon plasmas in order to optimize material processing. In one portion of the study, the surface production rate of fluorocarbon radicals emitted from the production process was measured at various points in time (in milliseconds) after the radio frequency power was turned off. The data are given in the accompanying table. Consider a model relating surface production rate (y) to time (x).

RADICALS

Rate	Time
1.00	0.1
0.80	0.3
0.40	0.5
0.20	0.7
0.05	0.9
0.00	1.1
−0.05	1.3
−0.02	1.5
0.00	1.7
−0.10	1.9
−0.15	2.1
−0.05	2.3
−0.13	2.5
−0.08	2.7
0.00	2.9

Source: Takizawa, K., et al. "Characteristics of C_3 radicals in high-density C_4F_8 plasmas studied by laser-induced fluorescence spectroscopy," *Journal of Applied Physics*, Vol. 88, No. 11, Dec. 1, 2000 (Figure 7).

a. Graph the data in a scattergram. What trend do you observe?

b. Fit a quadratic model to the data. Give the least squares prediction equation.

c. Is there sufficient evidence of upward curvature in the relationship between surface production rate and time after turnoff? Use $\alpha = .05$.

12.65 Public perceptions of health risks. In the *Journal of Experimental Psychology: Learning, Memory, and Cognition*

(July 2005), University of Basel (Switzerland) psychologists tested the ability of people to judge the risk of an infectious disease. The researchers asked German college students to estimate the number of people who are infected with a certain disease in a typical year. The median estimates, as well as the actual incidence of the disease for each in a sample of 24 infections, are listed in the table. Consider the quadratic model $E(y) = \beta_0 + \beta_1 x + \beta_2 x^2$, where y = actual incidence rate and x = estimated rate.

INFECTION

Infection	Actual Incidence	Estimate
Polio	0.25	300
Diphtheria	1	1,000
Trachoma	1.75	691
Rabbit Fever	2	200
Cholera	3	17.5
Leprosy	5	0.8
Tetanus	9	1,000
Hemorrhagic Fever	10	150
Trichinosis	22	326.5
Undulant Fever	23	146.5
Well's Disease	39	370
Gas Gangrene	98	400
Parrot Fever	119	225
Typhoid	152	200
Q Fever	179	200
Malaria	936	400
Syphilis	1,514	1,500
Dysentery	1,627	1,000
Gonorrhea	2,926	6,000
Meningitis	4,019	5,000
Tuberculosis	12,619	1,500
Hepatitis	14,889	10,000
Gastroenteritis	203,864	37,000
Botulism	15	37,500

Source: Hertwig, R., Pachur, T., & Kurzenhauser, S. "Judgments of risk frequencies: Tests of possible cognitive mechanisms," *Journal of Experimental Psychology: Learning, Memory, and Cognition*, Vol. 31, No. 4, July 2005 (Table 1).

a. Fit the quadratic model to the data, and then conduct a test to determine whether the actual incidence is curvilinearly related to the estimated incidence. (Use $\alpha = .05$.)

b. Construct a scatterplot of the data. Locate the data point for botulism on the graph. What do you observe?

c. Repeat part **a**, but omit the data point for botulism from the analysis. Has the fit of the model improved? Explain.

Applying the Concepts—Advanced

12.66 Tree frog study. The optomotor responses of tree frogs were studied in the *Journal of Experimental Zoology* (Sept. 1993). Microspectrophotometry was used to measure the threshold quantal flux (the light intensity at which the optomotor response was first observed) of tree frogs tested at different spectral wavelengths. The data revealed the relationship between the logarithm of quantal flux (y) and wavelength (x), shown in the following graph:

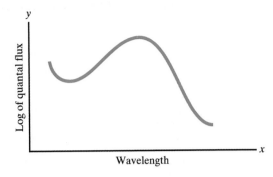

a. Explain why a first-order model would not be appropriate for modeling $E(y)$.

b. Explain why a second-order model would not be appropriate for modeling $E(y)$.

c. Demonstrate that the third-order model $E(y) = \beta_0 + \beta_1 x + \beta_2 x^2 + \beta_3 x^3$ may be the most appropriate model for $E(y)$.

12.7 Model Building: Qualitative (Dummy) Variable Models

Multiple-regression models can also be written to include **qualitative** (or **categorical**) independent variables. Qualitative variables, unlike quantitative variables, cannot be measured on a numerical scale. Therefore, we must code the values of the qualitative variable (called **levels**) as numbers before we can fit the model. These coded qualitative variables are called **dummy** (or **indicator**) **variables**, since the numbers assigned to the various levels are arbitrarily selected.

To illustrate, suppose a female executive at a certain company claims that male executives earn higher salaries, on average, than female executives with the same education, experience, and responsibilities. To support her claim, she wants to model the salary y of an executive, using a qualitative independent variable representing the gender of the executive (male or female).

A convenient method of coding the values of a qualitative variable at two levels involves assigning a value of 1 to one of the levels and a value of 0 to the other. For example, the **dummy variable** used to describe gender could be coded as follows:

$$x = \begin{cases} 1 & \text{if male} \\ 0 & \text{if female} \end{cases}$$

The choice of which level is assigned to 1 and which is assigned to 0 is arbitrary. The model then takes the following form:

$$E(y) = \beta_0 + \beta_1 x$$

The advantage of using a 0–1 coding scheme is that the β coefficients are easily interpreted. The foregoing model allows us to compare the mean executive salary $E(y)$ for males with the corresponding mean for females:

Males ($x = 1$): $\quad E(y) = \beta_0 + \beta_1(1) = \beta_0 + \beta_1$
Females ($x = 0$): $\quad E(y) = \beta_0 + \beta_1(0) = \beta_0$

These two means are illustrated in the bar graph in Figure 12.18.

First note that β_0 represents the mean salary for females (say, μ_F). When a 0–1 coding convention is used, β_0 will always represent the mean response associated with the level of the qualitative variable assigned the value 0 (called the **base level**). The difference between the mean salary for males and the mean salary for females, $\mu_M - \mu_F$, is represented by β_1; that is,

$$\mu_M - \mu_F = (\beta_0 + \beta_1) - (\beta_0) = \beta_1$$

This difference is shown in Figure 12.18.* With a 0–1 coding convention, β_1 will always represent the difference between the mean response for the level assigned the value 1 and the mean for the base level. Thus, for the executive salary model, we have

$$\beta_0 = \mu_F$$
$$\beta_1 = \mu_M - \mu_F$$

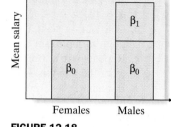

$E(y)$

Females   Males

FIGURE 12.18
Bar chart comparing $E(y)$ for males and females

Now carefully examine the model with a single qualitative independent variable at two levels, because we will use exactly the same pattern for any number of levels. Moreover, the interpretation of the parameters will always be the same.

One level (say, level A) is selected as the **base level**. Then, for the 0–1 coding† for the dummy variables,

$$\mu_A = \beta_0$$

The coding for all dummy variables is as follows: To represent the mean value of y for a particular level, let that dummy variable equal 1; otherwise, the dummy variable is set equal to 0. Using this system of coding, we obtain

$$\mu_B = \beta_0 + \beta_1$$
$$\mu_C = \beta_0 + \beta_2$$

and so on. Because $\mu_A = \beta_0$, any other model parameter will represent the difference between means for that level and the base level; that is,

$$\beta_1 = \mu_B - \mu_A$$
$$\beta_2 = \mu_C - \mu_A$$

and so on.

Procedure for Writing a Model with One Qualitative Independent Variable with k Levels

Always use a number of dummy variables that is one less than the number of levels of the qualitative variable. Thus, for a qualitative variable with k levels, use $k - 1$ dummy variables, as in

$$y = \beta_0 + \beta_1 x_1 + \beta_2 x_2 + \cdots + \beta_{k-1} x_{k-1} + \varepsilon$$

where x_i is the dummy variable for level $i + 1$ and

$$x_i = \begin{cases} 1 & \text{if } y \text{ is observed at level } i + 1 \\ 0 & \text{otherwise} \end{cases}$$

Then, for this system of coding,

$$\mu_A = \beta_0$$
$$\mu_B = \beta_0 + \beta_1 \qquad\qquad \text{and} \qquad\qquad \beta_1 = \mu_B - \mu_A$$
$$\mu_C = \beta_0 + \beta_2 \qquad\qquad\qquad\qquad\qquad\qquad \beta_2 = \mu_C - \mu_A$$
$$\mu_D = \beta_0 + \beta_3 \qquad\qquad\qquad\qquad\qquad\qquad \beta_3 = \mu_D - \mu_A$$
$$\vdots \qquad\qquad\qquad\qquad\qquad\qquad\qquad\qquad \vdots$$

---

*Note that β_1 could be negative. If β_1 were negative, the height of the bar corresponding to males would be reduced (rather than increased) from the height of the bar for females by the amount β_1. Figure 12.18 is constructed under the assumption that β_1 is a positive quantity.
†You do not have to use a 0–1 system of coding for the dummy variables. *Any* two-value system will work, but the interpretation given to the model parameters will depend on the code. Using the 0–1 system makes the model parameters easy to interpret.

EXAMPLE 12.9

A MODEL
WITH ONE
QUALITATIVE
INDEPENDENT
VARIABLE:

Golf Ball Driving
Distances

Problem Refer to Example 10.4 (p. 493). Recall that the USGA wants to compare the mean driving distances of four different golf ball brands (A, B, C, and D). Iron Byron, the USGA's robotic golfer, is used to hit a sample of 10 balls of each brand. The distance data are reproduced in Table 12.4.

a. Hypothesize a regression model for driving distance y, using Brand as an independent variable.

b. Interpret the β's in the model.

c. Use the model to determine whether the mean driving distances for the four brands are significantly different at $\alpha = .05$.

 GOLFCRD

TABLE 12.4 Driving Distances (in feet) for Four Golf Ball Brands

Brand A	Brand B	Brand C	Brand D
251.2	263.2	269.7	251.6
245.1	262.9	263.2	248.6
248.0	265.0	277.5	249.4
251.1	254.5	267.4	242.0
260.5	264.3	270.5	246.5
250.0	257.0	265.5	251.3
253.9	262.8	270.7	261.8
244.6	264.4	272.9	249.0
254.6	260.6	275.6	247.1
248.8	255.9	266.5	245.9

Solution

a. Note that golf ball brand (A, B, C, and D) is a qualitative variable (measured on a nominal scale). According to the previous box, for a four-level qualitative variable we require three dummy variables in the regression model. The model relating $E(y)$, where y is the distance the ball is driven by Iron Byron, to this single qualitative variable, golf ball Brand, is

$$E(y) = \beta_0 + \beta_1 x_1 + \beta_2 x_2 + \beta_3 x_3$$

where

$$x_1 = \begin{cases} 1 & \text{if Brand B} \\ 0 & \text{if not} \end{cases} \quad x_2 = \begin{cases} 1 & \text{if Brand C} \\ 0 & \text{if not} \end{cases} \quad x_3 = \begin{cases} 1 & \text{if Brand D} \\ 0 & \text{if not} \end{cases}$$

b. Since Brand A is the base level, β_0 represents the mean driving distance for Brand A (i.e., $\beta_0 = \mu_A$). The other β's are differences in means, namely,

$$\beta_1 = \mu_B - \mu_A$$
$$\beta_2 = \mu_C - \mu_A$$
$$\beta_3 = \mu_D - \mu_A$$

where μ_A, μ_B, μ_C, and μ_D are the mean distances for Brands A, B, C, and D, respectively.

c. Testing the null hypothesis that the means for the four brands are equal (i.e., $\mu_A = \mu_B = \mu_C = \mu_D$), is equivalent to testing

$$H_0: \beta_1 = \beta_2 = \beta_3 = 0$$

You can see this by observing that if $\beta_1 = \mu_B - \mu_A = 0$, then $\mu_A = \mu_B$. Similarly, $\beta_2 = \mu_C - \mu_A = 0$ implies that $\mu_A = \mu_C$, and $\beta_3 = \mu_D - \mu_A = 0$ implies that $\mu_A = \mu_D$. The alternative hypothesis is

$$H_a: \text{At least one of the parameters } \beta_1, \beta_2 \text{ and } \beta_3 \text{ differs from } 0$$

which implies that at least two of the four means (μ_A, μ_B, μ_C, and μ_D) differ.

Model Summary

Model	R	R Square	Adjusted R Square	Std. Error of the Estimate
1	.886[a]	.786	.768	4.60163

a. Predictors: (Constant), X3, X2, X1

ANOVA[b]

Model		Sum of Squares	df	Mean Square	F	Sig.
1	Regression	2794.389	3	931.463	43.989	.000[a]
	Residual	762.301	36	21.175		
	Total	3556.690	39			

a. Predictors: (Constant), X3, X2, X1
b. Dependent Variable: DISTANCE

Coefficients[a]

Model		Unstandardized Coefficients		Standardized Coefficients	t	Sig.
		B	Std. Error	Beta		
1	(Constant)	250.780	1.455		172.338	.000
	X1	10.280	2.058	.472	4.995	.000
	X2	19.170	2.058	.880	9.315	.000
	X3	-1.460	2.058	-.067	-.709	.483

a. Dependent Variable: DISTANCE

FIGURE 12.19
SPSS regression printout for dummy variable model

To test this hypothesis, we conduct the global F-test on the model. The SPSS printout for fitting the model

$$E(y) = \beta_0 + \beta_1 x_1 + \beta_2 x_2 + \beta_3 x_3$$

is shown in Figure 12.19. The value of the F statistic for testing the adequacy of the model, $F = 43.99$, and the observed significance level of the test, $p \approx .000$, are both highlighted. Since $\alpha = .05$ exceeds the p-value, we reject H_0 and conclude that at least one of the parameters differs from 0. Or, equivalently, we conclude that the data provide sufficient evidence to indicate that the mean driving distance does vary from one golf ball brand to another.

Look Back This global F-test is equivalent to the analysis-of-variance F-test in Chapter 10 for a completely randomized design.

Now Work Exercise 12.70

Caution

A common mistake by regression analysts is the use of a single dummy variable x for a qualitative variable at k levels, where $x = 1, 2, 3, \ldots, k$. Such a regression model will have unestimable β's and β's that are difficult to interpret. Remember, in modeling $E(y)$ with a single qualitative independent variable, the number of 0–1 dummy variables to include in the model will always be one less than the number of levels of the qualitative variable.

Exercises 12.67–12.82

Understanding the Principles

12.67 Write a regression model relating the mean value of y to a qualitative independent variable that can assume two levels. Interpret all the terms in the model.

12.68 Write a regression model relating $E(y)$ to a qualitative independent variable that can assume three levels. Interpret all the terms in the model.

Learning the Mechanics

12.69 The model $E(y) = \beta_0 + \beta_1 x_1 + \beta_2 x_2 + \beta_3 x_3$, where

$$x_1 = \begin{cases} 1 & \text{if level 2} \\ 0 & \text{if not} \end{cases}$$

$$x_2 = \begin{cases} 1 & \text{if level 3} \\ 0 & \text{if not} \end{cases}$$

$$x_3 = \begin{cases} 1 & \text{if level 4} \\ 0 & \text{if not} \end{cases}$$

was used to relate $E(y)$ to a single qualitative variable with four levels. This model was fit to $n = 30$ data points and the following result was obtained:

$$\hat{y} = 10.2 - 4x_1 + 12x_2 + 2x_3$$

a. Use the least squares prediction equation to find the estimate of $E(y)$ for each level of the qualitative independent variable.

b. Specify the null and alternative hypotheses you would use to test whether $E(y)$ is the same for all four levels of the independent variable.

12.70 MINITAB was used to fit the model

NW

$$y = \beta_0 + \beta_1 x_1 + \beta_2 x_2 + \varepsilon$$

where

$$x_1 = \begin{cases} 1 & \text{if level 2} \\ 0 & \text{if not} \end{cases}$$

$$x_2 = \begin{cases} 1 & \text{if level 3} \\ 0 & \text{if not} \end{cases}$$

to $n = 15$ data points. The results are shown in the accompanying MINITAB printout.

a. Report the least squares prediction equation.

b. Interpret the values of β_1 and β_2.

c. Interpret the following hypotheses in terms of μ_1, μ_2, and μ_3:

$$H_0: \beta_1 = \beta_2 = 0$$
$$H_a: \text{At least one of the parameters } \beta_1 \text{ and } \beta_2$$
$$\text{differs from 0}$$

d. Conduct the hypothesis test of part **c**.

Applying the Concepts—Basic

12.71 **Impact of race on football card values.** University of Colorado sociologists investigated the impact of race on the value of professional football players' "rookie" cards (*Electronic Journal of Sociology*, 2007). The sample consisted of 148 rookie cards of National Football League (NFL) players who were inducted into the Football Hall of Fame. The price of a card (in dollars) was modeled as a function of several qualitative independent variables: race of player (black or white), availability of the card (high or low), and position of the player (quarterback, running back, wide receiver, tight end, defensive lineman, linebacker, defensive back, or offensive lineman).

a. Create the appropriate dummy variables for each of the qualitative independent variables.

b. Write a model for price (y) as a function of race. Interpret the β's in the model.

c. Write a model for price (y) as a function of the availability of the card. Interpret the β's in the model.

d. Write a model for price (y) as a function of the player's position. Interpret the β's in the model.

12.72 **Chemical composition of rainwater.** Researchers at the University of Aberdeen (Scotland) developed a statistical model for estimating the chemical composition of water (*Journal of Agricultural, Biological, and Environmental Statistics*, March 2005). For one application, the nitrate concentration y (milligrams per liter) in a water sample collected after a heavy rainfall was modeled as a function of water source (groundwater, subsurface flow, or overground flow).

a. Write a model for $E(y)$ as a function of the qualitative independent variable.

```
The regression equation is
Y = 80.0 + 16.8 X1 + 40.4 X2


Predictor     Coef   SE Coef      T       P
Constant    80.000     4.082   19.60   0.000
X1          16.800     5.774    2.91   0.013
X2          40.400     5.774    7.00   0.000


S = 9.129     R-Sq = 80.5%    R-Sq(adj) = 77.2%


Analysis of Variance

Source            DF      SS       MS       F       P
Regression         2   4118.9   2059.5   24.72   0.000
Residual Error    12   1000.0     83.3
Total             14   5118.9
```

MINITAB output for
Exercise 12.70

b. Give an interpretation of each of the β parameters in the model you wrote in part **a**.

12.73 Detecting quantitative traits in genes. In gene therapy, it is important to know the location of a gene for a disease on the genome (genetic map). Although many genes yield a specific trait (e.g., disease or not), others cannot be categorized, since they are quantitative in nature (e.g., extent of disease). Researchers at the University of North Carolina at Wilmington developed statistical models that link quantitative genetic traits to locations on the genome. (*Chance*, Summer 2006.) The extent of a certain disease is determined by the absence (A) or presence (B) of a gene marker at each of two locations, L1 and L2, on the genome. For example, AA represents absence of the marker at both locations, while AB represents absence at location L1, but presence at location L2.

a. How many different gene marker combinations are possible at the two locations?

b. Using dummy variables, write a model for extent of the disease, y, as a function of gene marker combination.

c. Interpret the β-values in the model you wrote in part **b**.

d. Give the null hypothesis for testing whether the overall model from part **b** is statistically useful for predicting extent of the disease, y.

12.74 Improving SAT scores. Refer to the *Chance* (Winter 2001) study of students who paid a private tutor (or coach) to help them improve their SAT scores, presented in Exercise 2.101 (p. 74). Multiple regression was used to estimate the effect of coaching on SAT-Mathematics scores. Data on 3,492 students (573 of whom were coached) were used to fit the model $E(y) = \beta_0 + \beta_1 x_1 + \beta_2 x_2$, where $y =$ SAT-Math score, $x_1 =$ score on PSAT, and $x_2 = \{1$ if student was coached, 0 if not$\}$.

a. The fitted model had an adjusted R^2 value of .76. Interpret this result.

b. The estimate of β_2 in the model was 19, with a standard error of 3. Use this information to form a 95% confidence interval for β_2. Interpret the interval.

c. On the basis of the interval you found in part **b**, what can you say about the effect of coaching on SAT-Math scores?

12.75 Assassination risk. *New Scientist* (Apr. 3, 1993) published an article on strategies for foiling assassination attempts on politicians. The strategies are based on the findings of researchers at Middlesex University (United Kingdom) who used a multiple regression model for predicting the level y of assassination risk. One of the variables used in the model was the political status of a country (communist, democratic, or dictatorship).

a. Propose a model for $E(y)$ as a function of political status.

b. Interpret the β's in the model you proposed in part **a**.

Applying the Concepts Intermediate

TVADRECALL

12.76 Study of recall of TV commercials. Refer to the *Journal of Applied Psychology* (June 2002) study of recall of television commercials, presented in Exercise 10.28 (p. 501). Participants were assigned to watch one of three types of TV programs, with nine commercials embedded in each show. Group V watched a TV program (e.g., "Tour of Duty")

with a violent-content code rating, Group S viewed a show (e.g., "Strip Mall") with a sex-content code rating, and Group N watched a neutral TV program (e.g., "Candid Camera") with neither a V nor an S rating. The dependent variable measured for each participant was the score (y) on their recall of the brand names mentioned in the commercial messages, with scores ranging from 0 (no brands recalled) to 9 (all brands recalled). The data are saved in the **TVADRECALL** file.

a. Write a model for $E(y)$ as a function of viewer group.

b. Fit the model you wrote in part **a** to the data saved in the **TVADRECALL** file. Give the least squares prediction equation.

c. Conduct a test of overall model utility at $\alpha = .01$. Interpret the results. Show that the results agree with the analysis performed in Exercise 10.28?

d. The sample mean recall scores for the three groups were $\bar{y}_V = 2.08$, $\bar{y}_S = 1.71$, and $\bar{y}_N = 3.17$. Show how to find these sample means by using only the β-estimates obtained in part **b**.

12.77 Expert testimony in homicide trials of battered women. For over 20 years, courts have accepted evidence of "battered woman syndrome" as a defense in homicide cases. An article published In the *Duke Journal of Gender Law & Policy* (Summer 2003) examined the impact of expert testimony on the outcome of homicide trials that involve battered woman syndrome. On the basis of data collected on individual juror votes from past trials, the article reported that "when expert testimony was present, women jurors were more likely than men to change a verdict from not guilty to guilty after deliberations." Assume that when no expert testimony was present, male jurors were more likely than women to change a verdict from not guilty to guilty after deliberations. These results were obtained from a multiple-regression model for likelihood of changing a verdict from not guilty to guilty after deliberations, y, as a function of juror gender (male or female) and expert testimony (yes or no). Give the equation of a model for $E(y)$ that hypothesizes the relationships reported in the article. Illustrate the model with a sketch.

12.78 Comparing mosquito repellents. Which insect repellents protect best against mosquitoes? *Consumer Reports* (June 2000) tested 14 products that all claim to be an effective mosquito repellent. Each product was classified as either lotion/cream or aerosol/spray. The cost of the product (in dollars) was divided by the amount of the repellent needed to cover exposed areas of the skin (about 1/3 ounce) to obtain a cost-per-use value. Effectiveness was measured as the maximum number of hours of protection (in half-hour increments) provided when human testers exposed their arms to 200 mosquitoes. The data from the report are listed in the table on p. 677.

a. Suppose you want to use repellent type to model the cost per use (y). Create the appropriate number of dummy variables for repellent type, and write the model.

b. Fit the model you wrote in part **a** to the data.

c. Give the null hypothesis for testing whether repellent type is a useful predictor of cost per use (y).

d. Conduct the test suggested in part **c**, and give the appropriate conclusion. Use $\alpha = .10$.

e. Repeat parts **a**–**d** if the dependent variable is maximum number of hours of protection (y).

REPELLENT

Insect Repellent	Type	Cost/Use	Maximum Protection
Amway HourGuard 12	Lotion/Cream	$2.08	13.5 hours
Avon Skin-So-Soft	Aerosol/Spray	0.67	0.5
Avon BugGuard Plus	Lotion/Cream	1.00	2.0
Ben's Backyard Formula	Lotion/Cream	0.75	7.0
Bite Blocker	Lotion/Cream	0.46	3.0
BugOut	Aerosol/Spray	0.11	6.0
Cutter Skinsations	Aerosol/Spray	0.22	3.0
Cutter Unscented	Aerosol/Spray	0.19	5.5
Muskoll Ultra6Hours	Aerosol/Spray	0.24	6.5
Natrapel	Aerosol/Spray	0.27	1.0
Off! Deep Woods	Aerosol/Spray	1.77	14.0
Off! Skintastic	Lotion/Cream	0.67	3.0
Sawyer Deet Formula	Lotion/Cream	0.36	7.0
Repel Permanone	Aerosol/Spray	2.75	24.0

Source: "Buzz off," *Consumer Reports*, June 2000.

NZBIRDS

12.79 Extinct New Zealand birds. Refer to the *Evolutionary Ecology Research* (July 2003) study of the patterns of extinction in the New Zealand bird population, presented in Exercise 2.18 (p. 36). Recall that the **NZBIRDS** file contains qualitative data on flight capability (volant or flightless), habitat (aquatic, ground terrestrial, or aerial terrestrial), nesting site (ground, cavity within ground, tree, or cavity above ground), nest density (high or low), diet (fish, vertebrates, vegetables, or invertebrates), and extinct status (extinct, absent from island, present), and quantitative data on body mass (grams) and egg length (millimeters) for 132 bird species at the time of the Maori colonization of New Zealand.

a. Write a model for mean body mass as a function of flight capability.

b. Write a model for mean body mass as a function of diet.

c. Write a model for mean egg length as a function of nesting site.

d. Fit the model you wrote in part **a** to the data and interpret the estimates of the β's.

e. Conduct a test to determine whether the model from part **a** is statistically useful (at $\alpha = .01$) for estimating mean body mass.

f. Fit the model you wrote in part **b** to the data and interpret the estimates of the β's.

g. Conduct a test to determine whether the model from part **b** is statistically useful (at $\alpha = .01$) for estimating mean body mass.

h. Fit the model you wrote in part **c** to the data and interpret the estimates of the β's.

i. Conduct a test to determine whether the model from part **c** is statistically useful (at $\alpha = .01$) for estimating mean egg length.

12.80 Listen-and-look study. Where do you look when you are listening to someone speak? Researchers have discovered that listeners tend to gaze at the eyes or mouth of the speaker. In a study published in *Perception & Psychophysics* (Aug. 1998), subjects watched a videotape of a speaker giving a series of short monologues at a social gathering (e.g., a party). The level of background noise (multilingual voices and music) was varied during the listening sessions. Each subject wore a pair of clear plastic goggles on which an infrared corneal detection system was mounted, enabling the researchers to monitor the subject's eye movements. One response variable of interest was the proportion y of times the subject's eyes fixated on the speaker's mouth.

a. The researchers wanted to estimate $E(y)$ for four different noise levels: none, low, medium, and high. Hypothesize a model that will allow the researchers to obtain these estimates.

b. Interpret the β's in the model you hypothesized in part **a**.

c. Explain how to test the hypothesis of no differences in the mean proportions of mouth fixations for the four background noise levels.

12.81 Habitats of grizzly bears. Do grizzly bears segregate on the basis of sex? One hypothesis is that female grizzlies avoid male-occupied habitats because of competition for food and cannibalism. A competing theory is that females do not avoid males, but simply have different habitats available to them. These hypotheses were investigated in the *Journal of Wildlife Management* (July 1995). Grizzly bears were trapped, fitted with a radio collar, and released in the Highwood trapping zone (HTZ) in Alberta, Canada. The percentage of time, y, each bear used the HTZ as a habitat over a four-year period was recorded. The researchers modeled $E(y)$ as a function of reproductive class at five levels: estrous adult females, adult females with offspring, independent subadult females, adult males, and independent subadult males. One goal was to compare the mean percentage use of HTZ for the five classes of grizzly bears.

Grizzly Class	n	Mean Percentage of Use
Estrous adult females	5	38
Adult females with offspring	7	16
Independent subadult females	2	89
Adult males	7	43
Independent subadult males	8	58

Source: Wielgus, R. B., and Bunnell, F. L. "Tests of hypotheses for sexual segregation in grizzly bears," *Journal of Wildlife Management*, Vol. 59, No. 3, July 1995, p. 555 (Table 1).

a. Write a model for $E(y)$ that will enable the researchers to carry out the comparison.

b. The sample sizes and sample means for the five classes are shown in the table, p. 677. Use this information to find estimates of the β's in the model you wrote in part **a**.

c. Give the null hypothesis for a test to determine whether the mean percentage of use of HTZ differs among the grizzly bear classes.

d. The *p*-value for the test mentioned in part **c** was reported as .15. Interpret this result.

Applying the Concepts—Advanced

12.82 Heights of grade school repeaters. Refer to *The Archives of Disease in Childhood* (Apr. 2000) study of whether height influences a child's progression through elementary school, presented in Exercise 10.29 (p. 501). Recall that Australian schoolchildren were divided into equal thirds (tertiles) based on age (youngest third, middle third, and oldest third). The average heights of the three groups (for which all height measurements were standardized by using *z*-scores), by gender, are shown in the accompanying table.

a. Propose a regression model that will enable you to compare the average heights of the three age groups for boys.

b. Find the estimates of the β's in the model you proposed in part **a**.

c. Repeat parts **a** and **b** for girls.

	Sample Size	Youngest Tertile Mean Height	Middle Tertile Mean Height	Oldest Tertile Mean Height
Boys	1,439	0.33	0.33	0.16
Girls	1,409	0.27	0.18	0.21

Source: Wake, M., Coghlan, D., and Hesketh, K. "Does height influence progression through primary school grades?" *The Archives of Disease in Childhood*, Vol. 82, Apr. 2000 (Table 2).

12.8 Model Building: Models with Both Quantitative and Qualitative Variables (Optional)

Suppose you want to relate the mean monthly sales $E(y)$ of a company to the monthly advertising expenditure x for three different advertising media (say, newspaper, radio, and television) and you wish to use first-order (straight-line) models to model the responses for all three media. Graphs of these three relationships might appear as shown in Figure 12.20.

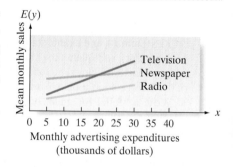

FIGURE 12.20

Graphs of the relationship between mean sales $E(y)$ and advertising expenditure x

Since the lines in Figure 12.20 are hypothetical, a number of practical questions arise. Is one advertising medium as effective as any other? That is, do the three mean sales lines differ for the three advertising media? Do the increases in mean sales per dollar input in advertising differ for the three advertising media? That is, do the *slopes* of the three lines differ? Note that the two practical questions have been rephrased into questions about the parameters that define the three lines of Figure 12.20. To answer these questions, we must write a single regression model that will characterize the three lines of the figure and that, by testing hypotheses about the lines, will answer the questions.

The response described previously, monthly sales, is a function of *two* independent variables, one quantitative (advertising expenditure x_1) and one qualitative (type of medium). We will proceed in stages to build a model relating $E(y)$ to these variables and will show graphically the interpretation we would give to the model at each stage. This approach will help you see the contributions of the various terms in the model.

1. The straight-line relationship between mean sales $E(y)$ and advertising expenditure is the same for all three media; that is, a single line will describe the relationship between $E(y)$ and advertising expenditure x_1 for all the media. (See Figure 12.21.) Thus,

$$E(y) = \beta_0 + \beta_1 x_1,$$

where

$$x_1 = \text{Advertising expenditure}$$

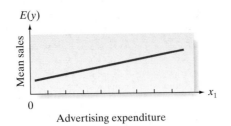

FIGURE 12.21

The relationship between $E(y)$ and x_1 is the same for all media

2. The straight lines relating mean sales $E(y)$ to advertising expenditure x_1 differ from one medium to another, but the rate of increase in mean sales per increase in dollar advertising expenditure x_1 is the same for all media; that is, the lines are parallel, but possess different y-intercepts. (See Figure 12.22). Hence,

$$E(y) = \beta_0 + \beta_1 x_1 + \beta_2 x_2 + \beta_3 x_3$$

where

$$x_1 = \text{Advertising expenditure}$$
$$x_2 = \begin{cases} 1 & \text{if radio medium} \\ 0 & \text{if not} \end{cases}$$
$$x_3 = \begin{cases} 1 & \text{if television medium} \\ 0 & \text{if not} \end{cases}$$

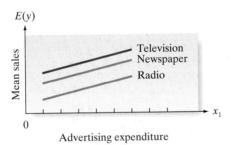

FIGURE 12.22

Parallel response lines for the three media

Notice that this model is essentially a combination of a first-order model with a single quantitative variable and a model with a single qualitative variable. That is,

First-order model with a single
quantitative variable: $\qquad E(y) = \beta_0 + \beta_1 x_1$

Model with single qualitative
variable at three levels: $\qquad E(y) = \beta_0 + \beta_2 x_2 + \beta_3 x_3$

where x_1, x_2, and x_3 are as just defined. The model described here implies no interaction between the two independent variables, which are advertising expenditure x_1 and the qualitative variable (type of advertising medium). The change in $E(y)$ for a one-unit increase in x_1 is identical (the slopes of the lines are equal) for all three advertising media. The terms corresponding to each of the independent variables are called **main-effect terms**, because they imply no interaction.

3. The straight lines relating mean sales $E(y)$ to advertising expenditure x_1 differ for the three advertising media; that is, both the line intercepts and the slopes differ. (See Figure 12.23.)

As you will see, this interaction model is obtained by adding terms involving the cross-product terms, one each from each of the two independent variables:

$$E(y) = \beta_0 + \overbrace{\beta_1 x_1}^{\substack{\text{Main effect,} \\ \text{advertising} \\ \text{expenditure}}} + \overbrace{\beta_2 x_2 + \beta_3 x_3}^{\substack{\text{Main effect,} \\ \text{type of} \\ \text{medium}}} + \overbrace{\beta_4 x_1 x_2 + \beta_5 x_1 x_3}^{\text{Interaction}}$$

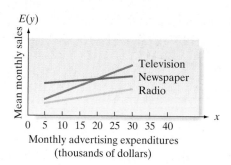

FIGURE 12.23
Different response lines for the
three media

Note that each of the preceding models is obtained by adding terms to model 1, the single first-order model used to model the responses for all three media. Model 2 is obtained by adding the main-effect terms for type of medium, the qualitative variable. Model 3 is obtained by adding the interaction terms to model 2.

EXAMPLE 12.10

INTERPRETING
THE β's IN A
MODEL WITH
MIXED
VARIABLES

Problem Substitute the appropriate values of the dummy variables in model 3 to obtain the equations of the three response lines in Figure 12.23.

Solution The complete model that characterizes the three lines in Figure 12.23 is

$$E(y) = \beta_0 + \beta_1 x_1 + \beta_2 x_2 + \beta_3 x_3 + \beta_4 x_1 x_2 + \beta_5 x_1 x_3$$

where

$$x_1 = \text{Advertising expenditure}$$

$$x_2 = \begin{cases} 1 & \text{if radio medium} \\ 0 & \text{if not} \end{cases}$$

$$x_3 = \begin{cases} 1 & \text{if television medium} \\ 0 & \text{if not} \end{cases}$$

Examining the coding, you can see that $x_2 = x_3 = 0$ when the advertising medium is newspaper. Substituting these values into the expression for $E(y)$, we obtain the newspaper medium line:

$$E(y) = \beta_0 + \beta_1 x_1 + \beta_2(0) + \beta_3(0) + \beta_4 x_1(0) + \beta_5 x_1(0) = \beta_0 + \beta_1 x_1$$

Similarly, we substitute the appropriate values of x_2 and x_3 into the expression for $E(y)$ to obtain the radio medium line ($x_2 = 1$, $x_3 = 0$),

$$E(y) = \beta_0 + \beta_1 x_1 + \beta_2(1) + \beta_3(0) + \beta_4 x_1(1) + \beta_5 x_1(0)$$
$$\underbrace{}_{\text{y-intercept}} \qquad \underbrace{}_{\text{Slope}}$$
$$= \overbrace{(\beta_0 + \beta_2)} + \overbrace{(\beta_1 + \beta_4)x_1}$$

and the television medium line ($x_2 = 0$, $x_3 = 1$),

$$E(y) = \beta_0 + \beta_1 x_1 + \beta_2(0) + \beta_3(1) + \beta_4 x_1(0) + \beta_5 x_1(1)$$
$$\underbrace{}_{\text{y-intercept}} \qquad \underbrace{}_{\text{Slope}}$$
$$= \overbrace{(\beta_0 + \beta_3)} + \overbrace{(\beta_1 + \beta_5)x_1}$$

Look Back If you were to fit model 3, obtain estimates of $\beta_0, \beta_1, \beta_2, \ldots, \beta_5$, and substitute them into the equations for the three media lines, you would obtain exactly the same prediction equations as you would if you were to fit three separate straight lines, one to each of the three sets of media data. You may ask why we would not fit the three lines separately. Why bother fitting a model that combines all three lines (model 3) into the same equation? The answer is that you need to use this procedure if you wish to use statistical tests to compare the three media lines. We need to be able to express a practical question about the lines in terms of a hypothesis that a set of parameters in the

a. What is the response line (equation) for $E(y)$ when $x_2 = x_3 = 0$? When $x_2 = 1$ and $x_3 = 0$? When $x_2 = 0$ and $x_3 = 1$?

b. What is the least squares prediction equation associated with level 1? Level 2? Level 3? Plot these on the same graph.

12.87 Consider the model

$$y = \beta_0 + \beta_1 x_1 + \beta_2 x_1^2 + \beta_3 x_2 + \beta_4 x_3 + \beta_5 x_1 x_2 +$$
$$\beta_6 x_1 x_3 + \beta_7 x_1^2 x_2 + \beta_8 x_1^2 x_3 + \varepsilon$$

where x_1 is a quantitative variable and

$$x_2 = \begin{cases} 1 & \text{if level 2} \\ 0 & \text{otherwise} \end{cases} \quad x_3 = \begin{cases} 1 & \text{if level 3} \\ 0 & \text{otherwise} \end{cases}$$

The resulting least squares prediction equation is

$$\hat{y} = 48.8 - 3.4x_1 + .07x_1^2$$
$$- 2.4x_2 - 7.5x_3 + 3.7x_1 x_2$$
$$+ 2.7x_1 x_3 - .02x_1^2 x_2$$
$$- .04x_1^2 x_3$$

a. What is the equation of the response curve for $E(y)$ when $x_2 = 0$ and $x_3 = 0$? When $x_2 = 1$ and $x_3 = 0$? When $x_2 = 0$ and $x_3 = 1$?

b. On the same graph, plot the least squares prediction equation associated with level 1, with level 2, and with level 3.

Applying the Concepts—Basic

12.88 Impact of race on football card values. Refer to the *Electronic Journal of Sociology* (2007) study of the impact of race on the value of professional football players' "rookie" cards, presented in Exercise 12.71 (p. 675). Recall that the sample consisted of 148 rookie cards of National Football League (NFL) players who were inducted into the Football Hall of Fame. The researchers modeled the natural logarithm of card price (y) as a function of the following independent variables:

Race: $x_1 = 1$ if black, 0 if white

Card availability: $x_2 = 1$ if high, 0 if low

Card vintage: $x_3 = $ year card printed

Finalist: $x_4 = $ natural logarithm of number of times player was on final Hall of Fame ballot

Position-QB: $x_5 = 1$ if quarterback, 0 if not

Position-RB: $x_7 = 1$ if running back, 0 if not

Position-WR: $x_8 = 1$ if wide receiver, 0 if not

Position-TE: $x_9 = 1$ if tight end, 0 if not

Position-DL: $x_{10} = 1$ if defensive lineman, 0 if not

Position-LB: $x_{11} = 1$ if linebacker, 0 if not

Position-DB: $x_{12} = 1$ if defensive back, 0 if not

[*Note:* For Position, offensive lineman is the base level]

a. The model $E(y) = \beta_0 + \beta_1 x_1 + \beta_2 x_2 + \beta_3 x_3 + \beta_4 x_4 + \beta_5 x_5 + \beta_6 x_6 + \beta_7 x_7 + \beta_8 x_8 + \beta_9 x_9 + \beta_{10} x_{10} + \beta_{11} x_{11} + \beta_{12} x_{12}$ was fit to the data, with the following results: $R^2 = .705$, adj-$R^2 = .681$, $F = 26.9$. Interpret the results practically. Make an inference about the overall adequacy of the model.

b. Refer to part **a**. Statistics for the race variable were reported as follows: $\hat{\beta}_1 = -147$, $s_{\hat{\beta}_1} = .145$, $t = -1.014$, p-value $= .312$. Use this information to make an in-

ference about the impact of race on the value of professional football players' rookie cards.

c. Refer to part **a**. Statistics for the card vintage variable were reported as follows: $\hat{\beta}_3 = -.074$, $s_{\hat{\beta}_3} = .007$, $t = -10.92$, p-value $= .000$. Use this information to make an inference about the impact of card vintage on the value of professional football players' rookie cards.

d. Write a first-order model for $E(y)$ as a function of card vintage (x_4) and position ($x_5 - x_{12}$) that allows for the relationship between price and vintage to vary with position.

12.89 Chemical composition of rainwater. Refer to the *Journal of Agricultural, Biological, and Environmental Statistics* (March 2005) study of the chemical composition of rainwater, presented in Exercise 12.72 (p. 675). Recall that the nitrate concentration y (milligrams per liter) in a sample of rainwater was modeled as a function of water source (groundwater, subsurface flow, or overground flow). Now consider adding a second independent variable, silica concentration (milligrams per liter), to the model.

a. Write a first-order model for $E(y)$ as a function of the independent variables. Assume that the rate of increase of nitrate concentration with silica concentration is the same for all three water sources. Sketch the relationships hypothesized by the model on a graph.

b. Write a first-order model for $E(y)$ as a function of the independent variables, but now assume that the rate of increase of nitrate concentration with silica concentration differs for the three water sources. Sketch the relationships hypothesized by the model on a graph.

12.90 Winning marathon times. Refer to the *Chance* (Winter 2000) study of men's and women's winning times in the Boston Marathon, presented in Exercise 11.20 (p. 574). Suppose the researchers want to build a model for predicting winning time (y) of the marathon as a function of year (x_1) in which race is run and gender of winning runner (x_2).

a. Set up the appropriate dummy variables (if necessary) for x_1 and x_2.

b. Write the equation of a model that proposes parallel straight-line relationships between winning time (y) and year (x_1), one line for each gender.

c. Write the equation of a model that proposes nonparallel straight-line relationships between winning time (y) and year (x_1), one line for each gender.

d. Which of the models do you think will provide the best predictions of winning time (y)? Base your answer on the graph displayed in Exercise 11.20.

12.91 Smoking and resting energy. The influence of cigarette smoking on resting energy expenditure (REE) in normal-weight and obese smokers was recently investigated. (*Health Psychology*, Mar. 1995.) The researchers hypothesized that the relationship between a smoker's REE and length of time since smoking differs for these two types of smokers. Consequently, they examined the interaction model

$$E(y) = \beta_0 + \beta_1 x_1 + \beta_2 x_2 + \beta_3 x_1 x_2$$

where

$y = $ REE, measured in kilocalories per day

$x_1 = $ Time, in minutes, after smoking, of metabolic energy reading (levels $= 10, 20,$ and 30 minutes)

$$x_2 = \begin{cases} 1 & \text{if normal weight} \\ 0 & \text{if obese} \end{cases}$$

a. Give the equation of the hypothesized line relating mean REE to time after smoking for obese smokers. What is the slope of the line?

b. Repeat part **a** for normal-weight smokers.

c. A test for interaction resulted in an observed significance level of .044. Interpret this value.

Applying the Concepts—Intermediate

12.92 RNA analysis of wheat genes. Engineers from the Department of Crop and Soil Sciences at Washington State University used regression to estimate the number of copies of a gene transcript in an aliquot of ribonucleic acid (RNA) extracted from a wheat plant. (*Electronic Journal of Biotechnology*, April 15, 2004.) The proportion (x_1) of RNA extracted from a wheat plant exposed to the cold was varied, and the transcript copy number $(y, in thousands)$ was measured for each of two cloned genes: Mn superoxide dismutase (MnSOD) and phospholipase D (PLD). The data are listed in the accompanying table.

a. Write a first-order model for number of copies (y) as a function of proportion (x_1) of RNA extracted and gene type (MnSOD or PLD). Assume that proportion of RNA and gene type interact to affect y.

b. Fit the model you wrote in part **a** to the data. Give the least squares prediction equation for y.

c. Conduct a test to determine whether, in fact, proportion of RNA and gene type interact. Test, using $\alpha = .01$.

d. Use the results from part **b** to estimate the rate of increase of number of copies (y) with proportion (x_1) of RNA extracted for the MnSOD gene type.

e. Repeat part **d** for the PLD gene type.

WHEATRNA

RNA Proportion (x_1)	Number of Copies $(y$, thousands)	
	MnSOD	PLD
0.00	401	80
0.00	336	83
0.00	337	75
0.33	711	132
0.33	637	148
0.33	602	115
0.50	985	147
0.50	650	142
0.50	747	146
0.67	904	146
0.67	1,007	150
0.67	1,047	184
0.80	1,151	173
0.80	1,098	201
0.80	1,061	181
1.00	1,261	193
1.00	1,272	187
1.00	1,256	199

Source: Baek K. H., and Skinner, D. Z. "Quantitative real-time PCR method to detect changes in specific transcript and total RNA amounts," *Electronic Journal of Biotechnology*, Vol. 7, No. 1, April 15, 2004 (adapted from Figure 2).

SNOWGEESE

12.93 Snowgeese feeding trial. Refer to the *Journal of Applied Ecology* study of feeding habits of baby snow geese, presented in Exercise 12.21 (p. 645).

a. Write a first-order model relating gosling weight change (y) to digestion efficiency (x_1) and diet (plants or duck chow) that allows for different slopes for each diet.

b. Fit the model you wrote in part **a** to the data saved in the **SNOWGEESE** trial. Give the least squares prediction equation.

c. Find the estimated slope of the line for goslings fed a diet of plants. Interpret its value.

d. Find the estimated slope of the line for goslings fed a diet of duck chow. Interpret its value.

e. Conduct a test to determine whether the slopes associated with the two diets are significantly different. Use $\alpha = .05$.

12.94 Lead levels in mountain moss. A study of the atmospheric pollution on the slopes of the Blue Ridge Mountains (in Tennessee) was conducted. The file **LEADMOSS** contains the levels of lead found in 70 fern moss specimens (in micrograms of lead per gram of moss tissue) collected from the mountain slopes, as well as the elevation of the moss specimen (in feet) and the direction (1 if east, 0 if west) of the slope face. The first five and last five observations of the data set are listed in the following table:

LEADMOSS (First and last five specimens shown.)

Specimen	Lead Level	Elevation	Slope Face
1	3.475	2,000	0
2	3.359	2,000	0
3	3.877	2,000	0
4	4.000	2,500	0
5	3.618	2,500	0
⋮	⋮	⋮	⋮
66	5.413	2,500	1
67	7.181	2,500	1
68	6.589	2,500	1
69	6.182	2,000	1
70	3.706	2,000	1

Source: Schilling, J. "Bioindication of atmospheric heavy metal deposition in the Blue Ridge using the moss, *Thuidium delicatulum*." master-of-science thesis, spring 2000.

a. Write the equation of a first-order model relating mean lead level $E(y)$ to elevation (x_1) and slope face (x_2). Include interaction between elevation and slope face in the model.

b. Graph the relationship between mean lead level and elevation for the different slope faces that is hypothesized by the model you wrote in part **a**.

c. In terms of the β's of the model from part **a**, give the change in lead level for every 1-foot increase in elevation for moss specimens on the east slope.

d. Fit the model from part **a** to the data, using an available statistical software package. Is the overall model statistically useful in predicting lead level? Test, using $\alpha = .10$.

12.95 "Sun safety" study. Excessive exposure to solar radiation is known to increase the risk of developing skin cancer, yet many people do not practice "sun safety." A group of University of Arizona researchers examined the feasibility of educating preschool (four- to five-year-old) children about sun safety. (*American Journal of Public Health*, July 1995.) A sample of 122 preschool children was divided into two groups: the control group and the intervention group. Children in the intervention group received a *Be Sun Safe* curriculum in preschool, while the control group did not. All children were tested for their knowledge, comprehension, and application of sun safety at two points in time: prior to the sun safety curriculum (pretest, x_1) and seven weeks following the curriculum (posttest, y).

a. Write a first-order model for mean posttest score $E(y)$ as a function of pretest score x_1 and group. Assume that no interaction exists between pretest score and group.

b. For the model you wrote in part **a**, show that the slope of the line relating posttest score to pretest score is the same for both groups of children.

c. Repeat part **a**, but assume that pretest score and group interact.

d. For the model of part **c**, show that the slope of the line relating posttest score to pretest score differs for the two groups of children.

Applying the Concepts—Advanced

12.96 Iron supplement for anemia. Many women suffer from anemia. A female physician who is also an avid jogger wanted to know if women who exercise regularly have a different mean red blood cell count than women who do not. She also wanted to know if the amount of a particular iron supplement a woman takes has any effect and whether the effect is the same for both groups. Write a model that will reflect the relationship between red blood cell count and the two independent variables just described, assuming that

a. the effect of the iron supplement on mean blood cell count is the same regardless of whether a woman exercises regularly.

b. the effect of the iron supplement on mean blood cell count depends on whether a woman exercises regularly.

12.9 Model Building: Comparing Nested Models (Optional)

To be successful model builders, we require a statistical method that will allow us to determine (with a high degree of confidence) which one among a set of candidate models best fits the data. In this section, we present such a technique for *nested models*.

> **Definition 12.3**
>
> Two models are **nested** if one model contains all the terms of the second model and at least one additional term. The more complex of the two models is called the **complete** model, and the simpler of the two is called the **reduced** model.

To illustrate the concept of nested models, consider the straight-line interaction model for the mean auction price $E(y)$ of a grandfather clock as a function of two quantitative variables: age of the clock (x_1) and number of bidders (x_2). The interaction model fit in Example 12.6 is

$$E(y) = \beta_0 + \beta_1 x_1 + \beta_2 x_2 + \beta_3 x_1 x_2$$

If we assume that the relationship between auction price (y), age (x_1), and bidders (x_2) is curvilinear, then the complete second-order model is more appropriate:

$$E(y) = \underbrace{\beta_0 + \beta_1 x_1 + \beta_2 x_2 + \beta_3 x_1 x_2}_{\text{Terms in interaction model}} + \underbrace{\beta_4 x_1^2 + \beta_5 x_2^2}_{\text{Quadratic terms}}$$

Note that the curvilinear model contains quadratic terms for x_1 and x_2, as well as the terms in the interaction model. Therefore, the models are nested models. In this case, the interaction model is nested within the more inclusive curvilinear model. Thus, the curvilinear model is the *complete* model and the interaction model is the *reduced* model.

Suppose we want to know whether the curvilinear model contributes more information relevant to the prediction of y than the straight-line interaction model does. This is equivalent to determining whether the quadratic betas β_4 and β_5 should be retained in the model. To test whether these terms should be retained, we set up the null and alternative hypotheses as follows:

H_0: $\beta_4 = \beta_5 = 0$ (i.e., quadratic terms are not important in predicting y).

H_a: At least one of the parameters β_4 and β_5 is nonzero (i.e., at least one of the quadratic terms is useful in predicting y).

Note that the terms being tested are those additional terms in the complete (curvilinear) model that are not in the reduced (straight-line interaction) model.

In Section 12.3, we presented the t-test for a single β coefficient and the global F-test for *all* the β parameters (except β_0) in the model. We now need a test for a *subset* of the β parameters in the complete model. The test procedure is intuitive. First, we use the method of least squares to fit the reduced model and calculate the corresponding sum of squares for error, SSE_R (the sum of squares of the deviations between the observed and the predicted y-values). Next, we fit the complete model and calculate its sum of squares for error, SSE_C. Then we compare SSE_R with SSE_C by calculating the difference, $SSE_R - SSE_C$. If the additional terms in the complete model are significant, then SSE_C should be much smaller than SSE_R, and the difference $SSE_R - SSE_C$ will be large.

Since SSE will always decrease when new terms are added to the model, the question is whether the difference $SSE_R - SSE_C$ is large enough to conclude that it is due to more than just an increase in the number of model terms and to chance. The formal statistical test utilizes an F-statistic, as shown in the following box:

F-Test for Comparing Nested Models

Reduced model: $E(y) = \beta_0 + \beta_1 x_1 + \cdots + \beta_g x_g$

Complete model: $E(y) = \beta_0 + \beta_1 x_1 + \cdots + \beta_g x_g + \beta_{g+1} x_{g+1} + \cdots + \beta_k x_k$

H_0: $\beta_{g+1} = \beta_{g+2} = \cdots = \beta_k = 0$

H_a: At least one of the β parameters specified in H_0 is nonzero.

Test statistic:
$$F = \frac{(SSE_R - SSE_C)/(k - g)}{SSE_C/[n - (k + 1)]}$$
$$= \frac{(SSE_R - SSE_C)/\#\ \beta\text{'s tested in } H_0}{MSE_C}$$

where

SSE_R = Sum of squared errors for the reduced model

SSE_C = Sum of squared errors for the complete model

MSE_C = Mean square error (s^2) for the complete model

$k - g$ = Number of β parameters specified in H_0 (i.e., number of β's tested)

$k + 1$ = Number of β parameters in the complete model (including β_0)

n = Total sample size

Rejection region: $F > F_\alpha$

where F is based on $\nu_1 = k - g$ numerator degrees of freedom and $\nu_2 = n - (k + 1)$ denominator degrees of freedom

---

When the assumptions listed in Section 12.1 about the random-error term are satisfied, this F-statistic has an F-distribution with ν_1 and ν_2 df. Note that ν_1 is the number of β parameters being tested and ν_2 is the number of degrees of freedom associated with s^2 in the complete model.

EXAMPLE 12.12
ANALYZING A COMPLETE SECOND-ORDER MODEL: Carnation Growth Data

Problem A botanist conducted an experiment to study the growth of carnations as a function of the temperature x_1 (°F) in a greenhouse and the amount of fertilizer x_2 [kilograms (kg) per plot] applied to the soil. Twenty-seven plots of equal size were treated with fertilizer in amounts varying between 50 and 60 kg per plot and were mechanically kept at constant temperatures between 80 and 100°F. Small carnation plants [approximately 15 centimeters (cm) in height] were planted in each plot, and their height y (cm) was measured after a six-week growing period. The resulting data are shown in Table 12.6.

a. Fit a complete second-order model to the data.

b. Sketch the fitted model in three dimensions.

c. Do the data provide sufficient evidence to indicate that the second-order terms β_3, β_4, and β_5 contribute information relevant to the prediction of y?

⊙ **CARNATIONS**

TABLE 12.6 Temperature (x_1), Amount of Fertilizer (x_2), and Height (y) of Carnations

x_1	x_2	y	x_1	x_2	y	x_1	x_2	y
80	50	50.8	90	50	63.4	100	50	46.6
80	50	50.7	90	50	61.6	100	50	49.1
80	50	49.4	90	50	63.4	100	50	46.4
80	55	93.7	90	55	93.8	100	55	69.8
80	55	90.9	90	55	92.1	100	55	72.5
80	55	90.9	90	55	97.4	100	55	73.2
80	60	74.5	90	60	70.9	100	60	38.7
80	60	73.0	90	60	68.8	100	60	42.5
80	60	71.2	90	60	71.3	100	60	41.4

Solution

a. The complete second-order model is

$$E(y) = \beta_0 + \beta_1 x_1 + \beta_2 x_2 + \beta_3 x_1 x_2 + \beta_4 x_1^2 + \beta_5 x_2^2$$

The data in Table 12.6 were used to fit this model, and a portion of the SAS output is shown in Figure 12.29.

The least squares prediction equation (rounded) is

$$\hat{y} = -5,127.90 + 31.10 x_1 + 139.75 x_2 - .146 x_1 x_2 - .133 x_1^2 - 1.14 x_2^2$$

b. A three-dimensional graph of this prediction model, called a **response surface**, is shown in Figure 12.30. Note that the height seems to be greatest for temperatures of

---

Dependent Variable: HEIGHT

Number of Observations Read   27
Number of Observations Used   27

Analysis of Variance

Source	DF	Sum of Squares	Mean Square	F Value	Pr > F
Model	5	8402.26454	1680.45291	596.32	<.0001
Error	21	59.17843	2.81802		
Corrected Total	26	8461.44296			

Root MSE	1.67870	R-Square	0.9930	
Dependent Mean	66.96296	Adj R-Sq	0.9913	
Coeff Var	2.50690			

Parameter Estimates

Variable	DF	Parameter Estimate	Standard Error	t Value	Pr > |t|
Intercept	1	-5127.89907	110.29601	-46.49	<.0001
TEMP	1	31.09639	1.34441	23.13	<.0001
FERT	1	139.74722	3.14005	44.50	<.0001
TEM_FERT	1	-0.14550	0.00969	-15.01	<.0001
TEMPSQ	1	-0.13339	0.00685	-19.46	<.0001
FERTSQ	1	-1.14422	0.02741	-41.74	<.0001

Test HIGHORD Results for Dependent Variable HEIGHT

Source	DF	Mean Square	F Value	Pr > F
Numerator	3	2204.11003	782.15	<.0001
Denominator	21	2.81802		

FIGURE 12.29

SAS printout of complete second-order model for height

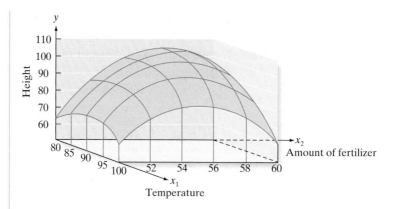

FIGURE 12.30

Plot of second-order least squares model for Example 12.12

about 85–90°F and for applications of about 55–57 kg of fertilizer per plot.* Further experimentation in these ranges might lead to a more precise determination of the optimal temperature–fertilizer combination.

c. To determine whether the data provide sufficient information to indicate that the second-order terms contribute information for the prediction of y, we wish to test

$$H_0: \beta_3 = \beta_4 = \beta_5 = 0$$

against the alternative hypothesis

H_a: At least one of the parameters β_3, β_4, and β_5 differs from 0.

The first step in conducting the test is to drop the second-order terms out of the complete (second-order) model and fit the reduced model

$$E(y) = \beta_0 + \beta_1 x_1 + \beta_2 x_2$$

to the data. The SAS printout for this model is shown in Figure 12.31.

The sums of squares for error, highlighted in Figures 12.29 and 12.31 for the complete and reduced models, respectively, are

$$SSE_C = 59.17843$$
$$SSE_R = 6{,}671.50852$$

Dependent Variable: HEIGHT

Number of Observations Read	27
Number of Observations Used	27

Analysis of Variance

Source	DF	Sum of Squares	Mean Square	F Value	Pr > F
Model	2	1789.93444	894.96722	3.22	0.0577
Error	24	6671.50852	277.97952		
Corrected Total	26	8461.44296			

Root MSE	16.67272	R-Square	0.2115
Dependent Mean	66.96296	Adj R-Sq	0.1458
Coeff Var	24.89842		

Parameter Estimates

Variable	DF	Parameter Estimate	Standard Error	t Value	Pr > |t|
Intercept	1	106.08519	55.94500	1.90	0.0700
TEMP	1	-0.91611	0.39298	-2.33	0.0285
FERT	1	0.78778	0.78596	1.00	0.3262

FIGURE 12.31

SAS printout of first-order model for height

*Students with a knowledge of calculus should note that we can solve for the exact temperature and amount of fertilizer that maximize height in the least squares model by solving $\partial \hat{y}/\partial x_1 = 0$ and $\partial \hat{y}/\partial x_2 = 0$ for x_1 and x_2. Sample estimates of these estimated optimal values are $x_1 = 86.25°F$ and $x_2 = 55.58$ kg per plot.

and s^2 for the complete model (highlighted on Figure 12.29) is

$$s^2 = \text{MSE}_C = 2.81802$$

Recall that $n = 27$, $k = 5$, and $g = 2$. Therefore, the calculated value of the F statistic, based on $\nu_1 = (k - g) = 3$ numerator df and $\nu_2 = [n - (k + 1)] = 21$ denominator df, is

$$F = \frac{(\text{SSE}_R - \text{SSE}_C)/(k - g)}{\text{SSE}_C/[n - (k + 1)]} = \frac{(\text{SSE}_R - \text{SSE}_C)/(k - g)}{\text{MSE}_C}$$

where $\nu_1 = (k - g)$ is equal to the number of parameters involved in H_0. Therefore,

$$\textit{Test statistic: } F = \frac{(6{,}671.50852 - 59.17843)/3}{2.81802} = 782.15$$

The final step in the test is to compare this computed value of F with the tabulated value based on $\nu_1 = 3$ and $\nu_2 = 21$ df. If we choose $\alpha = .05$, then $F_{.05} = 3.07$ and the rejection region is

$$\textit{Rejection region: } F > 3.07.$$

Since the computed value of F falls in the rejection region (i.e., it exceeds $F_{.05} = 3.07$), we reject H_0 and conclude that at least one of the second-order terms contributes information relevant to the prediction of y. Thus, the second-order model appears to provide better predictions of y than does a first-order model.

Look Back Using special commands, you can get SAS to perform the desired nested-model F-test. The test statistic and p-value for the preceding test are highlighted at the bottom of the SAS printout in Figure 12.29.

Now Work Exercise 12.100

The nested-model F-test can be used to determine whether *any* subset of terms should be included in a complete model by testing the null hypothesis that a particular set of β parameters simultaneously equals 0. For example, we may want to test whether a set of interaction terms for quantitative variables or a set of main-effect terms for a qualitative variable should be included in a model. If we reject H_0, the complete model is the better of the two nested models.

Suppose the F-test in Example 12.12 yielded a test statistic that did not fall into the rejection region. Although we must be cautious about accepting H_0, most practitioners of regression analysis adopt the principle of *parsimony*. That is, in situations where two competing models are found to have essentially the same predictive power (as in this case), the model with the lesser number of β's (i.e., the more parsimonious model) is selected. On the basis of this principle, we would drop the three second-order terms and select the straight-line (reduced) model over the second-order (complete) model.

Definition 12.4

A **parsimonious model** is a general linear model with a small number of β parameters. In situations where two competing models have essentially the same predictive power (as determined by an F-test), choose the more parsimonious of the two.

When the candidate models in model building are nested models, the F-test developed in this section is the appropriate procedure to apply to compare the models. However, if the models are not nested, this F-test is not applicable. In such a situation, the analyst must base the choice of the best model on statistics such as R_a^2 and s. It is important to remember that decisions based on these and other numerical descriptive measures of the adequacy of a model cannot be supported with a measure of reliability and are often highly subjective in nature.

STATISTICS IN ACTION REVISITED

Building a Model for Condominium Sale Price

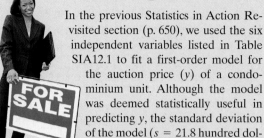

In the previous Statistics in Action Revisited section (p. 650), we used the six independent variables listed in Table SIA12.1 to fit a first-order model for the auction price (y) of a condominium unit. Although the model was deemed statistically useful in predicting y, the standard deviation of the model ($s = 21.8$ hundred dollars) was probably too large for the model to be "practically" useful. A more complicated model—one involving higher order terms (interactions and squared terms)—needs to be considered. We start with a second-order model involving only the two quantitative independent variables FLOOR (x_1) and DISTANCE (x_2). The model is given by the equation

$$E(y) = \beta_0 + \beta_1 x_1 + \beta_2 x_2 + \beta_3 x_1 x_2 + \beta_4(x_1)^2 + \beta_5(x_2)^2$$

The SAS printout for this model is shown in Figure SIA12.4. Note that the global F-test for the model is statistically significant (p-value < .0001).

Are the higher (second)-order terms in the model, namely, $\beta_3 x_1 x_2$, $\beta_4(x_1)^2$, and $\beta_5(x_2)^2$ necessary? If not, we can simplify the model by dropping these curvature terms. The hypothesis of interest is $H_0: \beta_3 = \beta_4 = \beta_5 = 0$. To test this subset of β's, we compare the second-order model with a model that lacks the interaction and curvilinear terms. The reduced model takes the form

$$E(y) = \beta_0 + \beta_1 x_1 + \beta_2 x_2$$

The results of this nested model (or partial) F-test are shown at the bottom of the SAS printout in Figure SIA12.4. The p-value of the test (highlighted) is less than .0001. Since this p-value is smaller than $\alpha = .01$, there is sufficient evidence to reject H_0. That is, there is evidence to indicate that at least one of the three higher order terms is a useful predictor of auction price.

To improve the model, we now add terms for the qualitative variables VIEW (x_3), END (x_4), FURNISH (x_5), and AUCTION (x_6). The developer theorizes that the impact of floor height and distance from the elevator on price will vary with the unit's view. Consequently, we also add interaction between floor and view and between distance and view. The complete model takes the form

```
                  Dependent Variable: PRICE100

            Number of Observations Read        209
            Number of Observations Used        209


                        Analysis of Variance

                                  Sum of         Mean
Source                  DF       Squares       Square    F Value    Pr > F

Model                    5         60858        12172      13.88    <.0001
Error                  203        178035    877.01813
Corrected Total        208        238893


            Root MSE              29.61449    R-Square    0.2548
            Dependent Mean       201.28708    Adj R-Sq    0.2364
            Coeff Var             14.71256


                        Parameter Estimates

                      Parameter    Standard
Variable      DF       Estimate       Error    t Value    Pr > |t|

Intercept      1      229.80506    13.17675      17.44     <.0001
FLOOR          1       -8.76315     4.49100      -1.95     0.0524
DISTANCE       1       -7.33316     2.31456      -3.17     0.0018
FLR_DIST       1       -0.17739     0.20153      -0.88     0.3798
FLOORSQ        1        0.76065     0.44691       1.70     0.0903
DISTSQ         1        0.66948     0.13221       5.06     <.0001


        Test HIORDER Results for Dependent Variable PRICE100

                                      Mean
        Source            DF        Square    F Value    Pr > F

        Numerator          3    8500.32594       9.69    <.0001
        Denominator      203     877.01813
```

FIGURE SIA12.4

SAS printout of the second-order model for condo sale price—quantitative variables only

$$E(y) = \beta_0 + \beta_1 x_1 + \beta_2 x_2 + \beta_3 x_1 x_2 + \beta_4 (x_1)^2$$
$$+ \beta_5 (x_2)^2 + \beta_6 x_3 + \beta_7 x_3 x_1 + \beta_8 x_3 x_2$$
$$+ \beta_9 x_3 x_1 x_2 + \beta_{10} x_3 (x_1)^2 + \beta_{11} x_3 (x_2)^2$$
$$+ \beta_{12} x_4 + \beta_{13} x_5 + \beta_{14} x_6$$

The SAS printout for this complete model is shown in Figure SIA12.5. The overall model is statistically useful (p-value <.0001 for global F-test), explaining about 68% (adjusted $R^2 = .6815$) of the sample variation in auction prices. The model standard deviation, $s = 19$, implies that we can predict price to within about 38 hundred dollars. Both the adjusted R^2 and $2s$ values are improvements over the corresponding values for the first-order model of the previous Statistics in Action Revisited (p. 650).

To test the developer's theory of how the view affects the sales price relationship, we conduct a

nested-model F-test of all the VIEW (x_3) interaction terms. The null hypothesis of interest is $H_0: \beta_7 = \beta_8 = \beta_9 = \beta_{10} = \beta_{11} = 0$, and the reduced model takes the form

$$E(y) = \beta_0 + \beta_1 x_1 + \beta_2 x_2 + \beta_3 x_1 x_2$$
$$+ \beta_4 (x_1)^2 + \beta_5 (x_2)^2 + \beta_6 x_3 + \beta_{12} x_4$$
$$+ \beta_{13} \beta_5 + \beta_{14} x_6$$

The p-value of the test (highlighted at the bottom of the SAS printout in Figure SIA12.5) is less than .0001. Since this p-value is smaller than $\alpha = .01$, there is sufficient evidence to conclude that at least one of the view interaction terms is useful in predicting the auction price. This implies, as theorized by the developer, that the price–floor and price–distance relationships depend on the unit's view (ocean view or not).

```
                     Dependent Variable: PRICE100

              Number of Observations Read        209
              Number of Observations Used        209


                         Analysis of Variance

                             Sum of          Mean
Source              DF      Squares        Square     F Value    Pr > F

Model               14       167924         11995       32.79    <.0001
Error              194        70968     365.81593
Corrected Total    208       238893


             Root MSE            19.12632    R-Square      0.7029
             Dependent Mean     201.28708    Adj R-Sq      0.6815
             Coeff Var            9.50201


                         Parameter Estimates

                        Parameter      Standard
Variable        DF       Estimate         Error    t Value    Pr > |t|

Intercept        1      188.72646      13.15224      14.35     <.0001
FLOOR            1       -4.61416       4.49901      -1.03     0.3064
DISTANCE         1       -2.35297       2.43410      -0.97     0.3349
FLR_DIST         1       -0.33458       0.20177      -1.66     0.0989
FLOORSQ          1        1.01858       0.42699       2.39     0.0180
DISTSQ           1        0.29095       0.14111       2.06     reduced
VIEW             1       74.33636      17.73275       4.19     <.0001
VU_FLOOR         1       -4.77034       5.90393      -0.81     0.4201
VU_DIST          1       -1.62826       3.17204      -0.51     0.6083
VU_FLR_DIST      1        0.07496       0.27422       0.27     0.7849
VU_FLRSQ         1       -0.26670       0.57992      -0.46     0.6461
VU_DISTSQ        1        0.13340       0.18392       0.73     0.4691
END              1      -16.27750       7.90038      -2.06     0.0407
FURNISH          1        7.96051       2.99043       2.66     0.0084
AUCTION          1      -25.59314       3.66294      -6.99     <.0001


        Test VUINT Results for Dependent Variable PRICE100

                             Mean
Source              DF      Square     F Value    Pr > F

Numerator            5    2565.21064      7.01    <.0001
Denominator        194     365.81593
```

FIGURE SIA12.5

SAS regression printout for the complete second-order model of condo sale price—qualitative variables added

Exercises 12.97–12.109

Understanding the Principles

12.97 Determine which pairs of models that follow are nested models. For each pair of nested models, identify the complete and reduced model.
   a. $E(y) = \beta_0 + \beta_1 x_1 + \beta_2 x_2$
   b. $E(y) = \beta_0 + \beta_1 x_1$
   c. $E(y) = \beta_0 + \beta_1 x_1 + \beta_2 x_1^2$
   d. $E(y) = \beta_0 + \beta_1 x_1 + \beta_2 x_2 + \beta_3 x_1 x_2$
   e. $E(y) = \beta_0 + \beta_1 x_1 + \beta_2 x_2 + \beta_3 x_1 x_2 + \beta_4 x_1^2 + \beta_5 x_2^2$

12.98 Explain why the F-test used to compare complete and reduced models is a one-tailed, upper-tailed test.

12.99 What is a parsimonious model?

Learning the Mechanics

12.100 Suppose you fit the regression model
   NW
$$y = \beta_0 + \beta_1 x_1 + \beta_2 x_2 + \beta_3 x_1 x_2 + \beta_4 x_1^2 + \beta_5 x_2^2 + \varepsilon$$

to $n = 30$ data points and you wish to test
$$H_0: \beta_3 = \beta_4 = \beta_5 = 0$$

   a. State the alternative hypothesis H_a.
   b. Give the reduced model appropriate for conducting the test.
   c. What are the numerator and denominator degrees of freedom associated with the F statistic?
   d. Suppose the SSE's for the complete and reduced models are $SSE_R = 1{,}250.2$ and $SSE_C = 1{,}125.2$, respectively. Conduct the hypothesis test and interpret the results. Use $\alpha = .05$.

12.101 The complete model
$$y = \beta_0 + \beta_1 x_1 + \beta_2 x_2 + \beta_3 x_3 + \beta_4 x_4 + \varepsilon$$

was fit to $n = 20$ data points, with $SSE = 152.66$. The independent variables x_3 and x_4 were dropped from the model, yielding $SSE = 160.44$.
   a. How many β parameters are in the complete model? The reduced model?
   b. Specify the null and alternative hypotheses you would use to investigate whether the complete model contributes more information relevant to the prediction of y than the reduced model does.
   c. Conduct the hypothesis test of part **b**. Use $\alpha = .05$.

Applying the Concepts—Basic

12.102 **Mental health of a community.** An article in the *Community Mental Health Journal* (Aug. 2000) used multiple-regression analysis to model the level of community adjustment of clients of the Department of Mental Health and Addiction Services in Connecticut. The dependent variable, community adjustment (y), was measured quantitatively on the basis of staff ratings of the clients. (Lower scores indicate better adjustment.) The complete model was a first-order model with 21 independent variables. The independent variables were categorized as demographic (four variables), diagnostic (seven variables), treatment (four variables), and community (six variables).
   a. Write the equation of $E(y)$ for the complete model.
   b. Give the null hypothesis for testing whether the seven diagnostic variables contribute information relevant to the prediction of y.

   c. Give the equation of the reduced model appropriate for the test suggested in part **b**.
   d. The test in part **b** was carried out and resulted in a test statistic of $F = 59.3$ and p-value $<.0001$. Interpret this result in the words of the problem.

12.103 **Students' ability in science.** Refer to the *American Educational Research Journal* (Fall 1998) study of students' perceptions of their science ability in hands-on classrooms, presented in Exercise 12.24 (p. 646). Recall that the first-order main-effects model that was used to predict perception of ability (y) included the following independent variables:

   Control Variables
   $x_1 =$ Prior science attitude score
   $x_2 =$ Science ability test score
   $x_3 = 1$ if boy, 0 if girl
   $x_4 = 1$ if classroom 1 student, 0 if not
   $x_5 = 1$ if classroom 3 student, 0 if not
   $x_6 = 1$ if classroom 4 student, 0 if not
   $x_7 = 1$ if classroom 5 student, 0 if not
   $x_8 = 1$ if classroom 6 student, 0 if not

   Performance Behaviors
   $x_9 =$ Active-leading behavior score
   $x_{10} =$ Passive-assisting behavior score
   $x_{11} =$ Active-manipulating behavior score

   a. Hypothesize the equation of the first-order main-effects model for $E(y)$.
   b. The researchers also considered a model that included all possible interactions between the control variables and the performance behavior variables. Write the equation for this model for $E(y)$.
   c. The researchers determined that the interaction terms in the model formulated in part **b** were not significant; therefore, they used the model from part **a** to make inferences. Explain the best way to conduct this test for interaction. Give the null hypothesis of the test.

◉ GASTURBINE

12.104 **Cooling method for gas turbines.** Refer to the *Journal of Engineering for Gas Turbines and Power* (Jan. 2005) study of a high-pressure inlet fogging method for a gas turbine engine, presented in Exercise 12.23 (p. 646). Consider a model for the heat rate (kilojoules per kilowatt per hour) produced by a gas turbine as a function of cycle speed (revolutions per minute) and cycle pressure ratio. The data are saved in the **GASTURBINE** file.
   a. Write a complete second-order model for heat rate (y).
   b. Give the null and alternative hypotheses for determining whether the curvature terms in the complete second-order model are statistically useful in predicting the heat rate (y).
   c. For the test in part **b**, identify the complete and reduced models.
   d. Portions of the MINITAB printouts for the two models are shown on p. 695. Find the values of SSE_R, SSE_C, and MSE_C on the printouts.
   e. Compute the value of the test statistics for the test of part **b**.

Complete Model

```
The regression equation is
HEATRATE = 15583 + 0.078 RPM - 523 CPRATIO + 0.00445 RPM_CPR - 0.000000 RPMSQ
          + 8.84 CPRSQ


S = 563.513    R-Sq = 88.5%    R-Sq(adj) = 87.5%


Analysis of Variance

Source            DF        SS        MS       F      P
Regression         5  148526859  29705372   93.55  0.000
Residual Error    61   19370350    317547
Total             66  167897208
```

Reduced Model

```
The regression equation is
HEATRATE = 12065 + 0.170 RPM - 146 CPRATIO - 0.00242 RPM_CPR


S = 633.842    R-Sq = 84.9%    R-Sq(adj) = 84.2%


Analysis of Variance

Source            DF        SS        MS       F      P
Regression         3  142586570  47528857  118.30  0.000
Residual Error    63   25310639    401756
Total             66  167897208
```

MINITAB output for Exercise 12.104

f. Find the rejection region for the test of part **b**. Use $\alpha = .10$.

g. State the conclusion of the test in the words of the problem.

12.105 Study of supervisor-targeted aggression. "Moonlighters" are workers who hold two jobs at the same time. What are the factors that affect the likelihood of a moonlighting worker becoming aggressive toward his or her supervisor? This was the research question of interest in the *Journal of Applied Psychology* (July 2005). Completed questionnaires were obtained from $n = 105$ moonlighters, and the data were used to fit several multiple-regression models for supervisor-targeted aggression score (y). Two of the models (with R^2 values in parentheses) are shown in the table below:

a. Interpret the R^2 values for the models.

b. Give the null and alternative hypotheses for comparing the fits of Models 1 and 2.

c. Are the two models nested? Explain.

d. The nested F-test for comparing the two models resulted in $F = 42.13$ and p-value $< .001$. What can you conclude from these results?

e. A third model was fit, one that hypothesizes all possible pairs of interactions between self-esteem, history of aggression, interactional injustice at primary job, and abusive supervisor at primary job. Give the equation of this model (Model 3).

f. A nested F-test to compare Models 2 and 3 resulted in p-value $> .10$. What can you conclude from this result?

Applying the Concepts—Intermediate

12.106 "Sun safety" study. Refer to the *American Journal of Public Health* study of preschool children's awareness of sun safety, presented in Exercise 12.95 (p. 686). Consider the first-order interaction model

$$E(y) = \beta_0 + \beta_1 x_1 + \beta_2 x_2 + \beta_3 x_1 x_2$$

where

y = sun safety posttest score

x_1 = sun safety pretest score

$x_2 = \begin{cases} 1 & \text{if in the } Be\ Sun\ Safe \text{ intervention group} \\ 0 & \text{if in the control group} \end{cases}$

Models for Exercise 12.105

Model 1: $E(y) = \beta_0 + \beta_1(\text{Age}) + \beta_2(\text{Gender})$

$+ \beta_3(\text{Interaction injustice at secondary job}) + \beta_4(\text{Abusive supervisor at secondary job})$

$(R^2 = .101)$

Model 2: $E(y) = \beta_0 + \beta_1(\text{Age}) + \beta_2(\text{Gender})$

$+ \beta_3(\text{Interactional injustice at secondary job}) + \beta_4(\text{Abusive supervisor at secondary job})$
$+ \beta_5(\text{Self-esteeem}) + \beta_6(\text{History of aggression})$
$+ \beta_7(\text{Interactional injustice at primary job})$
$+ \beta_8(\text{Abusive supervisor at primary job})$

$(R^2 = .555)$

---

a. Assuming that interaction exists, give the reduced model for testing whether the mean posttest scores differ for the intervention and control groups.

b. With sun safety knowledge as the dependent variable, the test presented in part **a** was carried out and resulted in a p-value of .03. Interpret this result.

c. With sun safety comprehension as the dependent variable, the test presented in part **a** was carried out and resulted in a p-value of .033. Interpret this result.

d. With sun safety application as the dependent variable, the test presented in part **a** was carried out and resulted in a p-value of .322. Interpret this result.

12.107 **Improving SAT scores.** Refer to the *Chance* (Winter 2001) study of students who paid a private tutor (or coach) to help them improve their SAT scores, presented in Exercise 12.74 (p. 676). Recall that the baseline model, $E(y) = \beta_0 + \beta_1 x_1 + \beta_2 x_2$, where $y = $ SAT-Math score, $x_1 = $ score on PSAT, and $x_2 = \{1$ if student was coached, 0 if not$\}$, had the following results: $R_a^2 = .76$, $\hat{\beta}_2 = 19$, and $s_{\hat{\beta}_2} = 3$. As an alternative model, the researcher added several "control" variables, including dummy variables for student ethnicity (x_3, x_4, and x_5), a socioeconomic status index variable (x_6), two variables that measured high school performance (x_7 and x_8), the number of math courses taken in high school (x_9), and the overall GPA for the math courses (x_{10}).

a. Write the hypothesized equation for $E(y)$ for the alternative model.

b. Give the null hypothesis for a nested-model F-test comparing the initial and alternative models.

c. The nested model F-test from part **b**, was statistically significant at $\alpha = .05$. Interpret this result practically.

d. The alternative model from part **a** resulted in $R_a^2 = .79$, $\hat{\beta}_2 = 14$, and $s_{\hat{\beta}_2} = 3$. Interpret the value of R_a^2.

e. Refer to part **d**. Find and interpret a 95% confidence interval for β_2.

f. The researcher concluded that "the estimated effect of SAT coaching decreases from the baseline model when control variables are added to the model." Do you agree? Justify your answer.

g. As a modification to the model of part **a**, the researcher added all possible interactions between the coaching variable (x_2) and the other independent variables in the model. Write the equation for $E(y)$ for this modified model.

h. Give the null hypothesis for comparing the models from parts **a** and **g**. How would you perform this test?

12.108 **Glass as a waste encapsulant.** Since glass is not subject to radiation damage, the encapsulation of waste in glass is considered to be one of the most promising solutions to the problem of low-level nuclear waste in the environment. However, chemical reactions may weaken the glass. This concern led to a study undertaken jointly by the Department of Materials Science and Engineering at the University of Florida and the U.S. Department of Energy to assess the utility of glass as a waste encapsulant.* Corrosive chemical solutions (called corrosion baths) were prepared and applied directly to glass samples containing one of three types of waste (TDS-3A, FE, and AL); the chemical reactions were observed over time. A few of the key variables measured were

$y = $ Amount of silicon (in parts per million) found in solution at end of experiment. (This is both a measure of the degree of breakdown in the glass and a proxy for the amount of radioactive species released into the environment.)

$x_1 = $ Temperature (°C) of the corrosion bath

$x_2 = 1$ if waste type TDS-3A, 0 if not

$x_3 = 1$ if waste type FE, 0 if not

(Waste type AL is the base level.) Suppose we want to model amount y of silicon as a function of temperature (x_1) and type of waste (x_2, x_3).

a. Write a model that proposes parallel straight-line relationships between amount of silicon and temperature, one line for each of the three types of waste.

b. Add terms for the interaction between temperature and waste type to the model from part **a**.

c. Refer to the model from part **b**. For each type of waste, give the slope of the line relating amount of silicon to temperature.

d. Explain how you could test for the presence of temperature–type-of-waste interaction.

Applying the Concepts—Advanced

12.109 **Emotional distress in firefighters.** The *Journal of Human Stress* (Summer 1987) reported on a study of the "psychological response of firefighters to chemical fire." It is thought that the complete second-order model

$$E(y) = \beta_0 + \beta_1 x_1 + \beta_2 x_1^2 + \beta_3 x_2 + \beta_4 x_1 x_2 + \beta_5 x_1^2 x_2$$

where

$$y = \text{Emotional distress}$$
$$x_1 = \text{Experience (years)}$$
$$x_2 = 1 \text{ if exposed to chemical fire, 0 if not}$$

will be adequate to describe the relationship between emotional distress and years of experience for two groups of firefighters: those exposed to a chemical fire and those not exposed.

a. How would you determine whether the *rate* of increase of emotional distress with experience is different for the two groups of firefighters?

b. How would you determine whether there are differences in mean emotional distress *levels* that are attributable to exposure group?

---

*The background information for this exercise was provided by Dr. David Clark, Department of Materials Science and Engineering, University of Florida.

12.10 Model Building: Stepwise Regression (Optional)

Consider the problem of predicting the salary y of an executive. Perhaps the biggest problem in building a model to describe executive salaries is choosing the important independent variables to be included. The list of potentially important independent variables is extremely long (e.g., age, experience, tenure, education level, etc.), and we need some objective method of screening out those which are not important.

The problem of deciding which of a large set of independent variables to include in a model is a common one. Trying to determine which variables influence the profit of a firm, affect the blood pressure of humans, or are related to a student's performance in college are only a few examples.

A systematic approach to building a model with a large number of independent variables is difficult because the interpretation of multivariable interactions and higher order terms is tedious. We therefore turn to a screening procedure, available in most statistical software packages, known as *stepwise regression*.

The most commonly used **stepwise regression** procedure works as follows: The user first identifies the response y and the set of potentially important independent variables $x_1, x_2, \ldots, x_k$, where k is generally large. [*Note:* This set of variables could include both first-order and higher order terms. However, we often include only the main effects of both quantitative variables (first-order terms) and qualitative variables (dummy variables), since the inclusion of second-order terms greatly increases the number of independent variables.] The response and independent variables are then entered into the computer software, and the stepwise procedure begins.

Step 1   The software program fits all possible one-variable models of the form

$$E(y) = \beta_0 + \beta_1 x_i$$

to the data, where x_i is the ith independent variable, $i = 1, 2, \ldots, k$. For each model, the t-test (or the equivalent F-test) for a single β parameter is conducted to test the null hypothesis

$$H_0\colon \beta_1 = 0$$

against the alternative hypothesis

$$H_a\colon \beta_1 \neq 0$$

The independent variable that produces the largest (absolute) t value is then declared the best one-variable predictor of y.* Call this independent variable x_1.

Step 2   The stepwise program now begins to search through the remaining $(k - 1)$ independent variables for the best two-variable model of the form

$$E(y) = \beta_0 + \beta_1 x_1 + \beta_2 x_i$$

This is done by fitting all two-variable models containing x_1 and each of the other $(k - 1)$ options for the second variable x_i. The t-values for the test $H_0\colon \beta_2 = 0$ are computed for each of the $(k - 1)$ models (corresponding to the remaining independent variables $x_i, i = 2, 3, \ldots, k$), and the variable having the largest t is retained. Call this variable x_2. At this point, some software packages diverge in methodology. The better packages now go back and check the t-value of $\hat{\beta}_1$ after $\hat{\beta}_2 x_2$ has been added to the model. If the t-value has become nonsignificant at some specified α level (say, $\alpha = .05$), the variable x_1 is removed and a search is made for the independent variable with a β parameter that will yield the most significant t-value in the presence of $\hat{\beta}_2 x_2$. Other packages do not recheck the significance of $\hat{\beta}_1$, but proceed directly to step 3.

---

*Note that the variable with the largest t value is also the one with the largest (absolute) Pearson product moment correlation r (Section 11.5) with y.

The reason the t-value for x_1 may change from step 1 to step 2 is that the meaning of the coefficient $\hat{\beta}_1$ changes. In step 2, we are approximating a complex response surface in two variables by a plane. The best-fitting plane may yield a different value for $\hat{\beta}_1$ than that obtained in step 1. Thus, both the value of $\hat{\beta}_1$ and its significance usually change from step 1 to step 2. For this reason, the software packages that recheck the t-values at each step are preferred.

Step 3 The stepwise procedure now checks for a third independent variable to include in the model with x_1 and x_2. That is, we seek the best model of the form

$$E(y) = \beta_0 + \beta_1 x_1 + \beta_2 x_2 + \beta_3 x_i$$

To do this, we fit all the $(k - 2)$ models using x_1, x_2, and each of the $(k - 2)$ remaining variables x_i as a possible x_3. The criterion is again to include the independent variable with the largest t-value. Call this best third variable x_3. The better programs now recheck the t-values corresponding to the x_1- and x_2-coefficients, replacing the variables that yield nonsignificant t-values. This procedure is continued until no further independent variables can be found that yield significant t-values (at the specified α level) in the presence of the variables already in the model.

The result of the stepwise procedure is a model containing only those terms with t-values that are significant at the specified α level. Thus, in most practical situations, only several of the large number of independent variables remain. However, it is very important *not* to jump to the conclusion that all the independent variables which are important in predicting y have been identified or that the unimportant independent variables have been eliminated. Remember, the stepwise procedure is using only *sample estimates* of the true model coefficients (β's) to select the important variables. An extremely large number of single β parameter t-tests have been conducted, and the probability is very high that one or more errors have been made in including or excluding variables. That is, we have very likely included some unimportant independent variables in the model (Type I errors) and eliminated some important ones (Type II errors).

There is a second reason we might not have arrived at a good model. When we choose the variables to be included in the stepwise regression, we often omit high-order terms (to keep the number of variables manageable). Consequently, we may have initially omitted several important terms from the model. Thus, we should recognize stepwise regression for what it is: an objective *variable-screening* procedure.

Successful model builders will now consider second-order terms (for quantitative variables) and other interactions among variables screened by the stepwise procedure. Indeed, it would be best to develop this response surface model with a second set of data independent of that used for the screening, so that the results of the stepwise procedure can be partially verified with new data. This is not always possible, however, because in many modeling situations only a small amount of data is available.

Do not be deceived by the impressive-looking t values that result from the stepwise procedure: it has retained only the independent variables with the largest t values. Also, be certain to consider second-order terms in systematically developing the prediction model. Finally, if you have used a first-order model for your stepwise procedure, remember that it may be greatly improved by the addition of higher order terms.

Caution

Be wary of using the results of stepwise regression to make inferences about the relationship between $E(y)$ and the independent variables in the resulting first-order model. First, an extremely large number of t-tests have been conducted, leading to a high probability of making one or more Type I or Type II errors. Second, the stepwise model does not include any higher order or interaction terms. Stepwise regression should be used only when necessary—that is, when you want to determine which of a large number of potentially important independent variables should be used in the model-building process.

EXAMPLE 12.13

STEPWISE REGRESSION:

Modeling Executive Salary

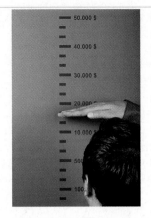

Problem An international management consulting company develops multiple-regression models for executive salaries of its client firms. The consulting company has found that models which use the natural logarithm of salary as the dependent variable have better predictive power than those using salary as the dependent variable.* A preliminary step in the construction of these models is the determination of the most important independent variables. For one firm, 10 potential independent variables (7 quantitative and 3 qualitative) were measured in a sample of 100 executives. The data, described in Table 12.7, are saved in the **EXECSAL** file. Since it would be very difficult to construct a complete second-order model with all of the 10 independent variables, use stepwise regression to decide which of the 10 variables should be included in the building of the final model for the logarithm of executive salaries.

 EXECSAL

TABLE 12.7 Independent Variables in the Executive Salary Example

Independent Variable	Description
x_1	Experience (years)—quantitative
x_2	Education (years)—quantitative
x_3	Bonus eligibility (1 if yes, 0 if no)—qualitative
x_4	Number of employees supervised—quantitative
x_5	Corporate assets (millions of dollars)—quantitative
x_6	Board member (1 if yes, 0 if no)—qualitative
x_7	Age (years)—quantitative
x_8	Company profits (past 12 months, millions of dollars)—quantitative
x_9	Has international responsibility (1 if yes, 0 if no)—qualitative
x_{10}	Company's total sales (past 12 months, millions of dollars)—quantitative

Solution We will use stepwise regression with the main effects of the 10 independent variables to identify the most important variables. The dependent variable y is the natural logarithm of the executive salaries. The MINITAB stepwise regression printout is shown in Figure 12.32.

Note that the first variable included in the model is x_1, years of experience. At the second step, x_3, a dummy variable for the qualitative variable bonus eligibility, is entered into the model. In steps 3, 4, and 5, the variables x_4 (number of employees supervised), x_2 (years of education), and x_5 (corporate assets), respectively, are selected for inclusion in the model. MINITAB stops after five steps, because no other independent variables met the criterion for admission into the model. As a default, MINITAB uses $\alpha = .15$ in the t-tests conducted. In other words, if the p-value associated with a β coefficient exceeds $\alpha = .15$, the variable is *not* included in the model.

The results of the stepwise regression suggest that we should concentrate on the preceding five independent variables. Models with second-order terms and interactions should be proposed and evaluated to determine the best model for predicting executive salaries.

Now Work Exercise 12.112

We conclude this section with some advice on the use of stepwise regression.

---

*This is probably because salaries tend to be incremented in *percentages* rather than dollar values. When a response variable undergoes percentage changes as the independent variables are varied, the logarithm of the response variable will be more suitable as a dependent variable.

```
                              Alpha-to-Enter: 0.15   Alpha-to-Remove: 0.15


                              Response is Y on 10 predictors, with N = 100


                              Step              1        2        3        4        5
                              Constant     11.091   10.968   10.783   10.278    9.962


                              X1           0.0278   0.0273   0.0273   0.0273   0.0273
                              T-Value       12.62    15.13    18.80    24.68    26.50
                              P-Value       0.000    0.000    0.000    0.000    0.000


                              X3                     0.197    0.233    0.232    0.225
                              T-Value                 7.10    10.17    13.30    13.74
                              P-Value                 0.000    0.000    0.000    0.000


                              X4                            0.00048  0.00055  0.00052
                              T-Value                          7.32    10.92    11.06
                              P-Value                          0.000    0.000    0.000


                              X2                                     0.0300   0.0291
                              T-Value                                   8.38     8.72
                              P-Value                                  0.000    0.000


                              X5                                              0.00196
                              T-Value                                            3.95
                              P-Value                                           0.000
```

FIGURE 12.32

MINITAB stepwise regression printout for executive salary data

```
                              S            0.161    0.131    0.106   0.0807   0.0751
                              R-Sq         61.90    74.92    83.91    90.75    92.06
                              R-Sq(adj)    61.51    74.40    83.41    90.36    91.64
                              Mallows C-p  343.9    195.5     93.8     16.8      3.6
```

Recommendation

Do *not* use the stepwise regression model as the final model for predicting y. Recall that the stepwise procedure tends to perform a large number of t-tests, inflating the overall probability of a Type I error, and does not automatically include higher order terms (e.g., interactions and squared terms) in the final model. Use stepwise regression as a variable-screening tool when there exists a large number of potentially important independent variables. Then begin building models for y, using the variables identified by stepwise regression.

Exercises 12.110–12.116

Understanding the Principles

12.110 Explain the difference between a stepwise model and a standard regression model.

12.111 Give two caveats associated with using the stepwise regression results as the final model for predicting y.

Learning the Mechanics

12.112 Suppose there are six independent variables $x_1, x_2, x_3, x_4, x_5,$ and x_6 that might be useful in predicting a response y. A total of $n = 50$ observations is available, and it is decided to employ stepwise regression to help in selecting the independent variables that appear to be useful. The computer fits all possible one-variable models of the form

$$E(y) = \beta_0 + \beta_1 x_i$$

where x_i is the ith independent variable, $i = 1, 2, \ldots, 6$. The information in the following table is provided from the computer printout:

Independent Variable	$\hat{\beta}_i$	$s_{\hat{\beta}_i}$
x_1	1.6	.42
x_2	−.9	.01
x_3	3.4	1.14
x_4	2.5	2.06
x_5	−4.4	.73
x_6	.3	.35

a. Which independent variable is declared the best one-variable predictor of y? Explain.

b. Would this variable be included in the model at this stage? Explain.

c. Describe the next phase that a stepwise procedure would execute.

Applying the Concepts—Basic

12.113 Entry-level job preferences. *Benefits Quarterly* (First Quarter, 1995) published a study of entry-level job preferences. A number of independent variables were used to model the job preferences (measured on a 10-point scale) of 164 business school graduates. Suppose stepwise regression is used to build a model for job preference score (y) as a function of the following independent variables:

$$x_1 = \begin{cases} 1 & \text{if flextime position} \\ 0 & \text{if not} \end{cases}$$

$$x_2 = \begin{cases} 1 & \text{if day care support required} \\ 0 & \text{if not} \end{cases}$$

$$x_3 = \begin{cases} 1 & \text{if spousal transfer support required} \\ 0 & \text{if not} \end{cases}$$

x_4 = Number of sick days allowed

$$x_5 = \begin{cases} 1 & \text{if applicant married} \\ 0 & \text{if not} \end{cases}$$

x_6 = Number of children of applicant

$$x_7 = \begin{cases} 1 & \text{if male applicant} \\ 0 & \text{if female applicant} \end{cases}$$

a. How many models are fit to the data in step 1? Give the general form of these models.

b. How many models are fit to the data in step 2? Give the general form of these models.

c. How many models are fit to the data in step 3? Give the general form of these models.

d. Explain how the procedure determines when to stop adding independent variables to the model.

e. Describe two major drawbacks to using the final stepwise model as the "best" model for job preference score (y).

12.114 Yield strength of steel alloy. Industrial engineers at the University of Florida used regression modeling as a tool to reduce the time and cost associated with developing new metallic alloys. (*Modelling and Simulation in Materials Science and Engineering*, Vol. 13, 2005.) To illustrate, the engineers build a regression model for the tensile yield strength (y) of a new steel alloy. The potential important predictors of yield strength are listed in the following table:

---

x_1 = Carbon amount (% weight)

x_2 = Manganese amount (% weight)

x_3 = Chromium amount (% weight)

x_4 = Nickel amount (% weight)

x_5 = Molybdenum amount (% weight)

x_6 = Copper amount (% weight)

x_7 = Nitrogen amount (% weight)

x_8 = Vanadium amount (% weight)

x_9 = Plate thickness (millimeters)

x_{10} = Solution treating (millimeters)

x_{11} = Ageing temperature (degrees Celsius)

---

a. The engineers used stepwise regression to search for a parsimonious set of predictor variables. Do you agree with this decision? Explain.

b. The stepwise regression selected the following independent variables: x_1 = Carbon, x_2 = Manganese, x_3 = Chromium, x_5 = Molybdenum, x_6 = Copper, x_8 = Vanadium, x_9 = Plate thickness, x_{10} = Solution treating, and x_{11} = Ageing temperature. On the basis of this information, determine the total number of first-order models that were fit in the stepwise routine.

c. Refer to part **b**. All the variables listed there were statistically significant in the stepwise model, with $R^2 = .94$. Consequently, the engineers used the estimated stepwise model to predict yield strength. Do you agree with this decision? Explain.

Applying the Concepts—Intermediate

12.115 Bus rapid-transit study. Bus rapid transit (BRT) is a rapidly growing trend in the provision of public transportation in America. The Center for Urban Transportation Research (CUTR) at the University of South Florida conducted a survey of BRT customers in Miami. (*Transportation Research Board* Annual Meeting, Jan. 2003.) Data on the following variables (all measured on a five-point scale, where 1 = "very unsatisfied" and 5 = "very satisfied") were collected for a sample of over 500 bus riders: overall satisfaction with BRT (y), safety on bus (x_1), seat availability (x_2), dependability (x_3), travel time (x_4), cost (x_5), information/maps (x_6), convenience of routes (x_7), traffic signals (x_8), safety at bus stops (x_9), hours of service (x_{10}), and frequency of service (x_{11}). CUTR analysts used stepwise regression to model overall satisfaction (y).

a. How many models are fit at Step 1 of the stepwise regression?

b. How many models are fit at Step 2 of the stepwise regression?

c. How many models are fit at Step 11 of the stepwise regression?

d. The stepwise regression selected the following eight variables to include in the model (in order of selection): $x_{11}, x_4, x_2, x_7, x_{10}, x_1, x_9,$ and x_3. Write the equation for $E(y)$ that results.

e. The model in part **d** was tested and resulted in $R^2 = .677$. Interpret this value.

f. Explain why the CUTR analysts should be cautious in concluding that the "best" model for $E(y)$ has been found.

12.116 Modeling species abundance. A marine biologist was hired by the EPA to determine whether the hot-water runoff from a particular power plant located near a large gulf is having an adverse effect on the marine life in the area. The biologist's goal is to acquire a prediction equation for the number of marine animals located at certain designated areas, or stations, in the gulf. On the basis of past experience, the EPA considered the following environmental factors as predictors for the number of animals at a particular station:

x_1 = Temperature of water (TEMP)

x_2 = Salinity of water (SAL)

x_3 = Dissolved oxygen content of water (DO)

Variables Entered/Removed[a]

Model	Variables Entered	Variables Removed	Method
1	ST_DEPTH		Stepwise (Criteria: Probability-of-F-to-enter <= .050, Probability-of-F-to-remove >= .100).
2	TGRSWT		Stepwise (Criteria: Probability-of-F-to-enter <= .050, Probability-of-F-to-remove >= .100).
3	TI		Stepwise (Criteria: Probability-of-F-to-enter <= .050, Probability-of-F-to-remove >= .100).

a. Dependent Variable: LOGNUM

Model Summary

Model	R	R Square	Adjusted R Square	Std. Error of the Estimate
1	.329[a]	.122	.121	.7615773
2	.427[b]	.182	.180	.7348470
3	.432[c]	.187	.184	.7348469

a. Predictors: (Constant), ST_DEPTH
b. Predictors: (Constant), ST_DEPTH, TGRSWT
c. Predictors: (Constant), ST_DEPTH, TGRSWT, TI

SPSS output for
Exercise 12.116

x_4 = Turbidity index, a measure of the turbidity of the water (TI)
x_5 = Depth of the water at the station (ST_DEPTH)
x_6 = Total weight of sea grasses in sampled area (TGRSWT)

As a preliminary step in the construction of this model, the biologist used a stepwise regression procedure to identify the most important of these six variables. A total of 716 samples was taken at different stations in the gulf, producing the SPSS printout shown above. (The response mea-sured was y, the logarithm of the number of marine animals found in the sampled area.)

a. According to the SPSS printout, which of the six independent variables should be used in the model?

b. Are we able to assume that the marine biologist has identified all the important independent variables for the prediction of y? Why?

c. Using the variables identified in part **a**, write the first-order model with interaction that may be used to predict y.

d. How would the marine biologist determine whether the model specified in part **c** is better than the first-order model?

e. Note the small value of R^2. What action might the biologist take to improve the model?

12.11 Residual Analysis: Checking the Regression Assumptions

When we apply regression analysis to a set of data, we never know for certain whether the assumptions of Section 12.1 are satisfied. How far can we deviate from the assumptions and still expect regression analysis to yield results that will have the reliability stated in this chapter? How can we detect departures (if they exist) from the assumptions, and what can we do about them? We provide some answers to these questions in this section.

Recall from Section 12.1 that, for any given set of values of $x_1, x_2, \ldots, x_k$, we assume that the random-error term ε has a normal probability distribution with mean equal to 0 and variance equal to σ^2. Also, we assume that the random errors are probabilistically independent. It is unlikely, however, that these assumptions are ever satisfied exactly in a practical application of regression analysis. Fortunately, experience has shown that least squares regression analysis produces reliable statistical tests, confidence intervals, and prediction intervals, as long as the departures from the assumptions are not too great. In this section, we present some methods for determining whether the data indicate significant departures from the assumptions.

Because the assumptions all concern the random-error component ε of the model, the first step is to estimate the random error. Since the actual random error associated with a particular value of y is the difference between the actual y value and its unknown mean, we estimate the error by the difference between the actual y value and the *estimated* mean. This estimated error is called the *regression residual*, or simply the **residual**, and is denoted by $\hat{\varepsilon}$. The actual error ε and residual $\hat{\varepsilon}$ are shown in Figure 12.33.

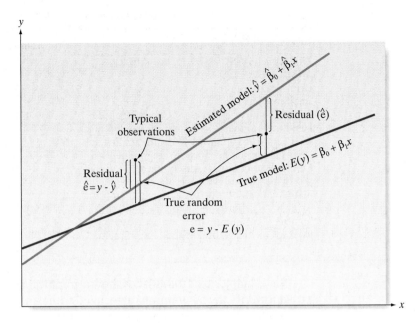

FIGURE 12.33

Actual random error ε and regression residual $\hat{\varepsilon}$

Definition 12.5

A **regression residual** $\hat{\varepsilon}$ is defined as the difference between an observed y-value and its corresponding predicted value:

$$\hat{\varepsilon} = (y - \hat{y}) = y - (\hat{\beta}_0 + \hat{\beta}_1 x_1 + \hat{\beta}_2 x_2 + \cdots + \hat{\beta}_k x_k)$$

Since the true mean of y (i.e., the true regression model) is not known, the actual random error cannot be calculated. However, because the residual is based on the estimated mean (the least squares regression model), it can be calculated and used to estimate the random error and to check the regression assumptions. Such checks are generally referred to as **residual analyses**. Two useful properties of residuals are given in the next box.

Properties of Regression Residuals

1. *The mean of the residuals is equal to 0.* This property follows from the fact that the sum of the differences between the observed y values and their least squares predicted $\hat{y}$ values is equal to 0:

$$\sum (\text{Residuals}) = \sum (y - \hat{y}) = 0$$

2. *The standard deviation of the residuals is equal to the standard deviations of the fitted regression model.* This property follows from the fact that the sum of the squared residuals is equal to SSE, which, when divided by the error degrees of freedom, is equal to the variance of the fitted regression model. The square root of the variance is both the standard deviation of the residuals and the standard deviation of the regression model:

$$\sum (\text{Residuals})^2 = \sum (y - \hat{y})^2 = \text{SSE}$$

$$s = \sqrt{\frac{\sum (\text{Residuals})^2}{n - (k + 1)}} = \sqrt{\frac{\text{SSE}}{n - (k + 1)}} = \sqrt{\text{MSE}}$$

Biography

**FRANCIS J. ANSCOMBE (1918–2001)—
ANSCOMBE'S DATA**

British citizen Frank Anscombe grew up in a small town near the English Channel. He attended Trinity College in Cambridge, England, on a merit scholarship, graduating with first-class honors in mathematics in 1939. He earned his master's degree in 1943. During World War II, Anscombe worked for the British Ministry of Supply, developing a mathematical solution for aiming antiaircraft rockets at German bombers and buzz bombs. Following the war, Anscombe worked at the Rothamsted Experimental

Station, applying statistics to agriculture. There, he formed his appreciation for solving problems with social relevance. During his career as a professor of statistics, Anscombe served on the faculty of Cambridge, Princeton, and Yale Universities. He was a pioneer in the application of computers to statistical analysis and was one of the original developers of residual analysis in regression. Anscombe is famous for a paper he wrote in 1973 in which he showed that one regression model could be fit by four very different data sets ("Anscombe's data"). Although Anscombe published 50 research articles on statistics, he also had serious interests in classical music, poetry, and art.

The examples that follow show how a graphical analysis of regression residuals can be used to verify the assumptions associated with a model and to support improvements to the model when the assumptions do not appear to be satisfied. Although the residuals can be calculated and plotted by hand, we rely on statistical software for these tasks in the examples and exercises.

First, we demonstrate how a residual plot can detect a model in which the hypothesized relationship between $E(y)$ and an independent variable x is misspecified. The assumption of mean error of 0 is violated in these types of models.*

EXAMPLE 12.14
ANALYZING RESIDUALS:
Electrical Usage Model

Problem Refer to the problem of modeling the relationship between home size (x) and electrical usage (y) in Example 12.7 (p. 661). The data for $n = 10$ homes are repeated in Table 12.8. MINITAB printouts for a straight-line model and a quadratic model fitted to the data are shown in Figures 12.34a and 12.34b, respectively. The residuals from these models are highlighted in the printouts. The residuals are then plotted on the vertical axis against the variable x, size of home, on the horizontal axis in Figures 12.35a and 12.35b.

 ELECTRIC

TABLE 12.8 Home Size–Electrical Usage Data

Size of Home x (sq. ft)	Monthly Usage y (kilowatt-hours)
1,290	1,182
1,350	1,172
1,470	1,264
1,600	1,493
1,710	1,571
1,840	1,711
1,980	1,804
2,230	1,840
2,400	1,956
2,930	1,954

a. Verify that each residual is equal to the difference between the observed y-value and the estimated mean value $\hat{y}$.

b. Analyze the plots of the residuals.

*For a misspecified model, the hypothesized mean of y, denoted by $E_h(y)$, will not equal the true mean of y, $E(y)$. Since $y = E_h(y) + \varepsilon$, then $\varepsilon = y - E_h(y)$ and $E(\varepsilon) = E\{y - E_h(y)\} = E(y) - E_h(y) \neq 0$.

```
The regression equation is
USAGE = 579 + 0.540 SIZE


Predictor      Coef   SE Coef      T      P
Constant      578.9     167.0   3.47  0.008
SIZE        0.54030   0.08593   6.29  0.000


S = 133.438    R-Sq = 83.2%   R-Sq(adj) = 81.1%


Analysis of Variance

Source          DF       SS       MS      F      P
Regression       1   703957   703957  39.54  0.000
Residual Error   8   142445    17806
Total            9   846402


Obs   SIZE   USAGE     Fit   SE Fit   Residual   St Resid
  1   1290  1182.0  1275.9    66.0      -93.9      -0.81
  2   1350  1172.0  1308.3    62.1     -136.3      -1.15
  3   1470  1264.0  1373.2    55.0     -109.2      -0.90
  4   1600  1493.0  1443.4    48.6       49.6       0.40
  5   1710  1571.0  1502.8    44.7       68.2       0.54
  6   1840  1711.0  1573.1    42.3      137.9       1.09
  7   1980  1804.0  1648.7    43.1      155.3       1.23
  8   2230  1840.0  1783.8    51.8       56.2       0.46
  9   2400  1956.0  1875.7    61.5       80.3       0.68
 10   2930  1954.0  2162.0    99.6     -208.0      -2.34R

R denotes an observation with a large standardized residual.
```

FIGURE 12.34a
MINITAB printout for straight-line model of electrical usage

```
The regression equation is
USAGE = - 1216 + 2.40 SIZE - 0.000450 SIZESQ


Predictor          Coef     SE Coef       T      P
Constant        -1216.1       242.8   -5.01  0.002
SIZE             2.3989      0.2458    9.76  0.000
SIZESQ      -0.00045004  0.00005908   -7.62  0.000


S = 46.8013    R-Sq = 98.2%   R-Sq(adj) = 97.7%


Analysis of Variance

Source          DF       SS       MS       F      P
Regression       2   831070   415535  189.71  0.000
Residual Error   7    15333     2190
Total            9   846402


Obs   SIZE   USAGE     Fit   SE Fit   Residual   St Resid
  1   1290  1182.0  1129.6    30.1       52.4       1.46
  2   1350  1172.0  1202.2    25.9      -30.2      -0.77
  3   1470  1264.0  1337.8    19.8      -73.8      -1.74
  4   1600  1493.0  1470.0    17.4       23.0       0.53
  5   1710  1571.0  1570.1    18.0        0.9       0.02
  6   1840  1711.0  1674.2    19.9       36.8       0.87
  7   1980  1804.0  1769.4    21.9       34.6       0.84
  8   2230  1840.0  1895.5    23.3      -55.5      -1.37
  9   2400  1956.0  1949.1    23.6        6.9       0.17
 10   2930  1954.0  1949.2    44.7        4.8       0.35 X

X denotes an observation whose X value gives it large influence.
```

FIGURE 12.34b
MINITAB printout for quadratic model of electrical usage

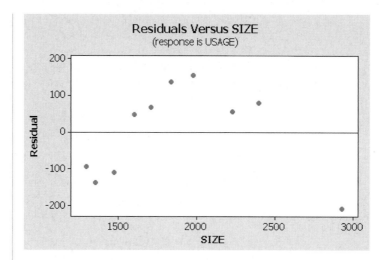

FIGURE 12.35a

MINITAB residual plot for straight-line model of electrical usage

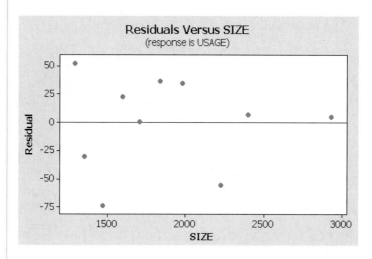

FIGURE 12.35b

MINITAB residual plot for quadratic model of electrical usage

Solution

a. Consider the first usage value in the data set, $y = 1,182$. For the straight-line model, the predicted value for this observation is $\hat{y} = 1,275.92$. Consequently, the residual is

$$\hat{\varepsilon} = (y - \hat{y}) = 1,182 - 1,275.9 = -93.9 \quad \text{(highlighted in Figure 12.34a)}$$

Similarly, the residual for the first y value from the quadratic model (Figure 12.34b) is

$$\hat{\varepsilon} = 1,182 - 1,129.6 = 52.4 \text{ (highlighted in Figure 12.34b)}$$

The two residuals agree (after rounding) with the first values given in the column labeled "**Residual**" in Figures 12.34a and 12.34b, respectively. Although the residuals both correspond to the same observed y value, 1,182, they differ because the predicted mean value changes, depending on whether the straight-line model or quadratic model is used. Similar calculations produce the remaining residuals.

b. The MINITAB plot of the residuals for the straight-line model (Figure 12.35a) reveals a nonrandom pattern. The residuals exhibit a curved shape, with the residuals for the small values of x below the horizontal 0 (mean of the residuals) line, the residuals corresponding to the middle values of x above the 0 line, and the residual for the largest value of x again below the 0 line. The indication is that the mean value of the random error *within* each of these ranges of x (small, medium, large) may not be equal to 0. Such a pattern usually indicates that curvature needs to be added to the model.

When the second-order term is added to the model, the nonrandom pattern disappears. In Figure 12.35b, the residuals appear to be randomly distributed around the 0 line, as expected. Also, the variation of the residuals around the 0 line appears to be much smaller for the quadratic model. The implication is that the quadratic model provides a considerably better model for predicting electrical usage.

Look Back The residual analysis verifies our conclusions from Example 12.7, where we found the quadratic term, $\beta_2 x^2$, to be statistically significant.

Residual analyses are also useful for detecting one or more observations that deviate significantly from the regression model. We expect approximately 95% of the residuals to fall within two standard deviations of the 0 line and all or almost all of them to lie within three standard deviations of their mean of 0. Residuals that are extremely far from the 0 line and disconnected from the bulk of the other residuals are called *outliers* and should receive special attention from the regression analyst.

> **Definition 12.6**
>
> A residual that is larger than $3s$ (in absolute value) is considered to be an **outlier**.

EXAMPLE 12.15

IDENTIFYING OUTLIERS: GrandFather Clock Price Model

Problem Refer to Example 12.6 (p. 655), in which we modeled the auction price y of a grandfather clock as a function of age x_1 and number of bidders, x_2. The data for this example are repeated in Table 12.9, with one important difference: The auction price of the clock at the top of the second column has been changed from $2,131 to $1,131 (highlighted in the table). The interaction model

$$E(y) = \beta_0 + \beta_1 x_1 + \beta_2 x_2 + \beta_3 x_1 x_2$$

is again fit to these (modified) data, with the MINITAB printout shown in Figure 12.36. The residuals are shown highlighted in the printout and then are plotted against the number of bidders, x_2, in Figure 12.37. Analyze the residual plot.

 CFCLOCKALT

TABLE 12.9 Altered Auction Price Data

Age x_1	Number of Bidders, x_2	Auction Price y	Age x_1	Number of Bidders, x_2	Auction Price y
127	13	$1,235	170	14	$1,131
115	12	1,080	182	8	1,550
127	7	845	162	11	1,884
150	9	1,522	184	10	2,041
156	6	1,047	143	6	845
182	11	1,979	159	9	1,483
156	12	1,822	108	14	1,055
132	10	1,253	175	8	1,545
137	9	1,297	108	6	729
113	9	946	179	9	1,792
137	15	1,713	111	15	1,175
117	11	1,024	187	8	1,593
137	8	1,147	111	7	785
153	6	1,092	115	7	744
117	13	1,152	194	5	1,356
126	10	1,336	168	7	1,262

Solution The residual plot dramatically reveals the one altered measurement. Note that one of the two residuals at $x_2 = 14$ bidders falls more than three standard deviations below 0. Note also that no other residual falls more than two standard deviations from 0.

What do we do with outliers once we identify them? First, we try to determine the cause. Were the data entered into the computer incorrectly? Was the observation recorded incorrectly when the data were collected? If so, we correct the observation and

```
The regression equation is
PRICE = - 513 + 8.17 AGE + 19.9 NUMBIDS + 0.320 AGE_BIDS


Predictor      Coef    SE Coef       T       P
Constant     -512.8      665.9   -0.77   0.448
AGE           8.165      4.585    1.78   0.086
NUMBIDS       19.89      67.44    0.29   0.770
AGE_BIDS     0.3196     0.4790    0.67   0.510


S = 200.598    R-Sq = 72.9%    R-Sq(adj) = 70.0%


Analysis of Variance

Source            DF        SS        MS       F       P
Regression         3   3033587   1011196   25.13   0.000
Residual Error    28   1126703     40239
Total             31   4160290


Obs  AGE    PRICE      Fit   SE Fit   Residual   St Resid
  1  127   1235.0   1310.4    59.3      -75.4      -0.39
  2  115   1080.0   1105.9    62.1      -25.9      -0.14
  3  127    845.0    947.5    61.1     -102.5      -0.54
  4  150   1522.0   1322.5    37.1      199.5       1.01
  5  156   1047.0   1179.5    60.3     -132.5      -0.69
  6  182   1979.0   1831.9    82.9      147.1       0.81
  7  156   1822.0   1598.0    61.9      224.0       1.17
  8  132   1253.0   1185.8    39.7       67.2       0.34
  9  137   1297.0   1178.9    39.0      118.1       0.60
 10  113    946.0    913.9    58.6       32.1       0.17
 11  137   1713.0   1561.0    78.4      152.0       0.82
 12  117   1024.0   1072.6    53.1      -48.6      -0.25
 13  137   1147.0   1115.2    44.3       31.8       0.16
 14  153   1092.0   1149.2    59.0      -57.2      -0.30
 15  117   1152.0   1187.2    69.7      -35.2      -0.19
 16  126   1336.0   1117.6    43.4      218.4       1.12
 17  170   1131.0   1914.4   116.7     -783.4      -4.80R
 18  182   1550.0   1597.7    62.8      -47.7      -0.25
 19  162   1884.0   1598.3    57.0      285.7       1.49
 20  184   2041.0   1776.6    70.7      264.4       1.41
 21  143    845.0   1048.4    58.9     -203.4      -1.06
 22  159   1483.0   1421.8    40.6       61.2       0.31
 23  108   1055.0   1130.7    97.9      -75.7      -0.43
 24  175   1545.0   1522.7    55.4       22.3       0.12
 25  108    729.0    695.5    99.6       33.5       0.19
 26  179   1792.0   1642.7    57.6      149.3       0.78
 27  111   1175.0   1224.0   107.2      -49.0      -0.29
 28  187   1593.0   1651.3    68.6      -58.3      -0.31
 29  111    785.0    781.1    80.9        3.9       0.02
 30  115    744.0    822.7    75.5      -78.7      -0.42
 31  194   1356.0   1480.7   133.6     -124.7      -0.83 X
 32  168   1262.0   1374.0    57.7     -112.0      -0.58
```

FIGURE 12.36

MINITAB regression printout for altered grandfather clock data

```
R denotes an observation with a large standardized residual.
X denotes an observation whose X value gives it large influence.
```

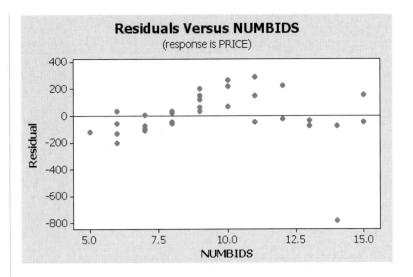

FIGURE 12.37

MINITAB residual plot of
altered grandfather clock data

FIGURE 12.38

MINITAB regression printout
when outlier is deleted

```
The regression equation is
PRICE = 474 - 0.46 AGE - 114 NUMBIDS + 1.48 AGE_BIDS


Predictor       Coef    SE Coef       T       P
Constant       474.0      298.2    1.59   0.124
AGE           -0.465      2.107   -0.22   0.827
NUMBIDS      -114.12      31.23   -3.65   0.001
AGE_BIDS      1.4781     0.2295    6.44   0.000


S = 85.8286    R-Sq = 95.2%    R-Sq(adj) = 94.7%


Analysis of Variance

Source           DF        SS        MS        F       P
Regression        3   3933417   1311139   177.99   0.000
Residual Error   27    198897      7367
Total            30   4132314
```

rerun the analysis. Another possibility is that the observation is not representative of the conditions we are trying to model. For example, in this case the low price may be attributable to extreme damage to the clock or to a clock of inferior quality compared with the others. In these cases, we probably would exclude the observation from the analysis. In many cases, you may not be able to determine the cause of the outlier. Even so, you may want to rerun the regression analysis excluding the outlier, in order to assess the effect of that observation on the results of the analysis.

Figure 12.38 shows the printout when the outlier observation is excluded from the grandfather clock analysis, and Figure 12.39 shows the new plot of the residuals against the number of bidders. Now only one of the residuals lies beyond two standard deviations from 0, and none lies beyond three standard deviations. Also, the statistics indicate a much better model without the outlier. Most notably, the standard deviation (s) has decreased from 200.6 to 85.83, indicating a model that will provide more precise estimates and predictions (narrower confidence and prediction intervals) for clocks that are similar to those in the reduced sample.

Look Back Remember that if the outlier is removed from the analysis when in fact it belongs to the same population as the rest of the sample, the resulting model may provide misleading estimates and predictions.

Now Work Exercise 12.129

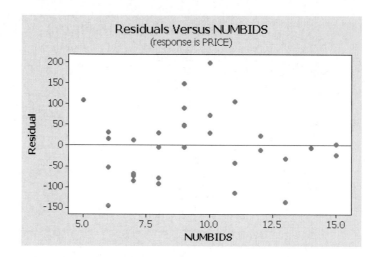

FIGURE 12.39

MINITAB residual plot when outlier is deleted

Outlier analysis is another example of testing the assumption that the expected (mean) value of the random error ε is 0, since this assumption is in doubt for the error terms corresponding to the outliers. The next example in this section checks the assumption of the normality of the random error component.

EXAMPLE 12.16

USING RESIDUALS TO CHECK FOR NORMAL ERRORS

Problem Refer to Example 12.15. Analyze the distribution of the residuals in the grandfather clock example both before and after the outlier residual is removed. Determine whether the assumption of a normally distributed error term is reasonable.

Solution A MINITAB histogram and normal probability plot for the two sets of residuals are shown in Figure 12.40 and Figure 12.41. Note that the outlier appears to skew the histogram in Figure 12.40a, whereas the histogram in Figure 12.41a appears to be

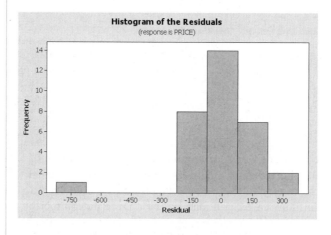

FIGURE 12.40a

MINITAB graphs of regression residuals for grandfather clock model (outlier included)

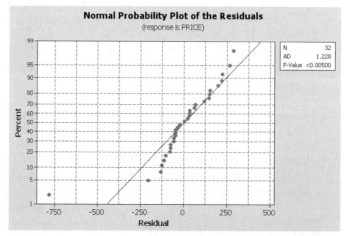

FIGURE 12.40b

(outlier included)

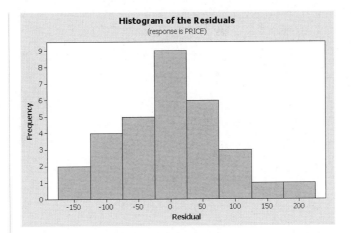

FIGURE 12.41a

MINITAB graphs of regression residuals for grandfather clock model (outlier deleted)

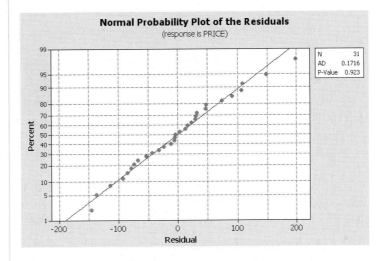

FIGURE 12.41b

(outlier deleted)

more mound shaped. Similarly, the pattern of the residuals in the normal probability plot in Figure 12.41b (with outlier deleted) is more nearly a straight line than the pattern in Figure 12.40b (with outlier included). Although the graphs do not provide formal statistical tests of normality, they do offer a descriptive display. In this example, the normality assumption appears to be more plausible after the outlier is removed. Consult the references for methods of conducting statistical tests of normality that use the residuals.

Now Work Exercise 12.124d

Of the four assumptions in Section 12.1, the assumption that the random error is normally distributed is the least restrictive when we apply regression analysis in practice. That is, moderate departures from a normal distribution have very little effect on the validity of the statistical tests, confidence intervals, and prediction intervals presented in this chapter. In that case, we say that regression analysis is **robust** with respect to nonnormal errors. However, great departures from normality cast doubt on any inferences derived from the regression analysis.

Residual plots can also be used to detect violations of the assumption of constant error variance. For example, a plot of the residuals versus the predicted value $\hat{y}$ may display one of the patterns shown in Figure 12.42. In these figures, the range in values of the residuals increases (or decreases) as $\hat{y}$ increases, thus indicating that the variance of the random error ε becomes larger or smaller as the estimate of $E(y)$ increases in value. Since $E(y)$ depends on the x-values in the model, this implies that the variance of ε is not constant for all settings of the x's.

In the final example of this section, we demonstrate how to use a plot of residuals to detect a nonconstant variance, and we suggest a useful remedy.

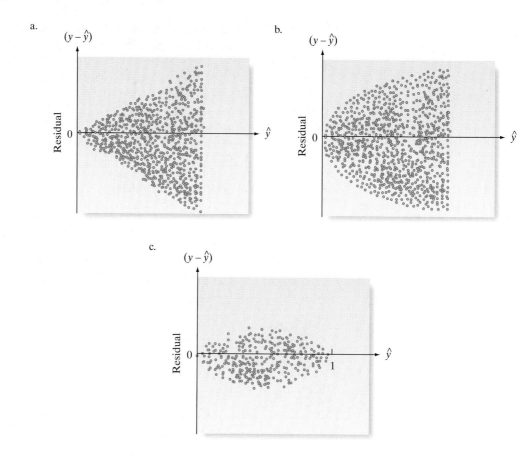

FIGURE 12.42
Residual plots showing
changes in the variance of ε

EXAMPLE 12.17
USING RESIDUALS TO CHECK FOR CONSTANT ERROR VARIANCE

Problem The data listed in Table 12.10 are the salaries y and years of experience, x, for a sample of 50 social workers. The first-order model $E(y) = \beta_0 + \beta_1 x$ was fit to the data by SPSS. The printout is shown in Figure 12.43, followed by a plot of the residuals versus $\hat{y}$ in Figure 12.44. Interpret the results. Make modifications to the model if necessary.

 **SOCWORK**

TABLE 12.10   Salary Data for Example 12.17

Years of Experience x	Salary y	Years of Experience x	Salary y	Years of Experience x	Salary y
7s	$26,075	21	$43,628	28	$99,139
28	79,370	4	16,105	23	52,624
23	65,726	24	65,644	17	50,594
18	41,983	20	63,022	25	53,272
19	62,308	20	47,780	26	65,343
15	41,154	15	38,853	19	46,216
24	53,610	25	66,537	16	54,288
13	33,697	25	67,447	3	20,844
2	22,444	28	64,785	12	32,586
8	32,562	26	61,581	23	71,235
20	43,076	27	70,678	20	36,530
21	56,000	20	51,301	19	52,745
18	58,667	18	39,346	27	67,282
7	22,210	1	24,833	25	80,931
2	20,521	26	65,929	12	32,303
18	49,727	20	41,721	11	38,371
11	33,233	26	82,641		

Solution The SPSS printout shown in Figure 12.43 suggests that the first-order model provides an adequate fit to the data. The R^2 value indicates that the model explains about 79% of the sample variation in salaries. The t value for testing β_1, 13.31, is highly significant (p-value ≈ 0) and indicates that the model contributes information relevant to the prediction of y. However, an examination of the residuals plotted against $\hat{y}$ (Figure 12.44) reveals a potential problem: Note the "cone" shape of the variability of the residuals; the size of the residuals increases as the estimated mean salary increases, implying that the constant-variance assumption is violated.

One way to stabilize the variance of ε is to refit the model, using a transformation on the dependent variable y. With economic data (e.g., salaries), a useful **variance-stabilizing transformation** is the natural logarithm of y, denoted $\ln(y)$.* We fit the model

$$\ln(y) = \beta_0 + \beta_1 x + \varepsilon$$

Model Summary[b]

Model	R	R Square	Adjusted R Square	Std. Error of the Estimate
1	.887[a]	.787	.782	8642.441

a. Predictors: (Constant), ESP

b. Dependent Variable: SALARY

ANOVA[b]

Model		Sum of Squares	df	Mean Square	F	Sig.
1	Regression	1.3E+10	1	1.324E+10	177.257	.000[a]
	Residual	3.6E+09	48	74691793.28		
	Total	1.7E+10	49			

a. Predictors: (Constant), ESP

b. Dependent Variable: SALARY

Coefficients[a]

Model		Unstandardized Coefficients B	Unstandardized Coefficients Std. Error	Standardized Coefficients Beta	t	Sig.
1	(Constant)	11368.72	3160.317		3.597	.001
	ESP	2141.381	160.839	.887	13.314	.000

a. Dependent Variable: SALARY

FIGURE 12.43

SPSS regression printout for first-order model of salary

Scatterplot

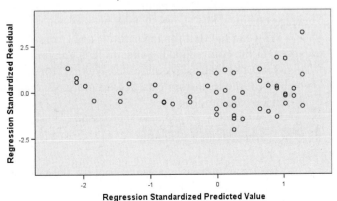

FIGURE 12.44

SPSS residual plot for first-order model of salary

*Other variance-stabilizing transformations that are used successfully in practice are $\sqrt{y}$ and $\sin^{-1}\sqrt{y}$. (Consult the references for more details on these transformations.)

Model Summary[b]

Model	R	R Square	Adjusted R Square	Std. Error of the Estimate
1	.929[a]	.864	.861	.1541127

a. Predictors: (Constant), ESP
b. Dependent Variable: LNSALARY

ANOVA[b]

Model		Sum of Squares	df	Mean Square	F	Sig.
1	Regression	7.212	1	7.212	303.660	.000[a]
	Residual	1.140	48	.024		
	Total	8.352	49			

a. Predictors: (Constant), ESP
b. Dependent Variable: LNSALARY

FIGURE 12.45

SPSS regression printout for model of logarithm of salary

Coefficients[a]

Model		Unstandardized Coefficients		Standardized Coefficients	t	Sig.
		B	Std. Error	Beta		
1	(Constant)	9.841	.056		174.631	.000
	ESP	.050	.003	.929	17.426	.000

a. Dependent Variable: LNSALARY

Scatterplot

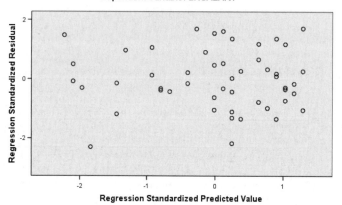

FIGURE 12.46

SPSS residual plot for model of logarithm of salary

to the data of Table 12.10. Figure 12.45 shows the regression analysis printout for the $n = 50$ measurements, while Figure 12.46 shows a plot of the residuals from the logarithmic model.

You can see that the logarithmic transformation has stabilized the error variances. Note that the cone shape is gone; there is no apparent tendency of the residual variance to increase as mean salary increases. We therefore are confident that inferences made on the basis of the logarithmic model are more reliable than those made on the basis of the untransformed model.

Now Work Exercise 12.124b

Residual analysis is a useful tool for the regression analyst, not only for checking assumptions, but also to provide information about how a model can be improved. A summary of the residual analysis presented in this section to check the assumption that the random error ε is normally distributed with mean 0 and constant variance is presented in the following box:

Steps in a Residual Analysis

1. Check for a misspecified model by plotting the residuals against each of the quantitative independent variables. Analyze each plot, looking for a curvilinear trend. This shape signals the need for a quadratic term in the model. Try a second-order term in the variable against which the residuals are plotted.

2. Examine the residual plots for outliers. Draw lines on the plots at two and three standard deviations below and above the 0 line. Examine residuals outside the three-standard-deviation lines as potential outliers, and check to see that approximately 5% of the residuals exceed the two-standard-deviation lines. Determine whether each outlier can be explained as an error in data collection or transcription, whether it corresponds to a member of a population different from that of the remainder of the sample, or whether it simply represents an unusual observation. If the observation is determined to be an error, fix it or remove it. Even if you can't determine the cause, you may want to rerun the regression analysis without the observation to determine its effect on the analysis.

3. Check for nonnormal errors by plotting a frequency distribution of the residuals, using a stem-and-leaf display, histogram, or normal probability plot. Check to see if obvious departures from normality exist. Extreme skewness of the frequency distribution may be due to outliers or could indicate the need for a transformation of the dependent variable. (Normalizing transformations are beyond the scope of this book, but you can find discussions of the procedure in the references.)

4. Check for unequal error variances by plotting the residuals against the predicted values $\hat{y}$. If you detect a cone-shaped pattern or some other pattern which indicates that the variance of ε is not constant, refit the model, using an appropriate variance-stabilizing transformation on y, such as $\ln(y)$. (Consult the references for other useful variance-stabilizing transformations.)

Residuals

Using the TI-84/TI-83 Graphing Calculator

Plotting Residuals

In computing a regression equation on the TI-84/TI-83, the residuals are automatically computed and saved to a list called **RESID**, which can be found under the **LIST menu (2nd STAT).**

Step 1   *Enter the data.*

> Press **STAT** and select **1:Edit**.
> *Note:* If the list already contains data, clear the old data. Use the up arrow to highlight "**L1**" or "**L2**"
> Press **CLEAR ENTER**.
> Use the **ARROW** and **ENTER** keys to enter the data set into **L1** and **L2**.

Step 2   *Compute the regression equation.*

> Press **STAT** and highlight **CALC**.
> Press **4** for **LinReg(ax + b)**.
> Press **ENTER**.

Step 3   *Set up the data plot.*

> Press **Y =** and **CLEAR** all functions from the Y registers.
> Press **2nd Y =** for **STATPLOT**.
> Press **1** for **Plot1**.
> Set the cursor so that **ON** is flashing, and press **ENTER**.

(continued)

For **Type**, use the **ARROW** and **ENTER** keys to highlight and select the scatterplot (first icon in the first row).
Move the cursor to **Xlist**, and choose the column containing the *x*-data.
Move the cursor to **Ylist**. Press **2nd STAT** for **LIST**. Use the down arrow to highlight the listname **RESID**, and press **ENTER**.

Step 4   *View the scatterplot of the residuals*

Press **ZOOM** 9 for **ZoomStat**

Example   The following figures show a table of data entered on the TI-84/TI-83 and the scatterplot of the residuals obtained by following the preceding steps:

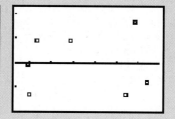

STATISTICS IN ACTION REVISITED

A Residual Analysis for the Condominium Sale Price Model

In the previous Statistics in Action Revisited section (p. 692), we found a second-order model to be both a statistically and practically useful model for predicting the auction price (*y*) of a condominium unit. Before using the model in practice, we need to examine the residuals to be sure that the standard regression assumptions are reasonably satisfied.

Figures SIA12.6 and SIA12.7 are MINITAB graphs of the residuals from the model. Except for a few outliers, the histogram shown in Figure SIA12.6 appears to be approximately normally distributed; consequently, the assumption of normal errors is reasonably satisfied. The scatterplot of the residuals against $\hat{y}$ shown in Figure SIA 12.7 reveals no distinct pattern; thus, the assumption of a constant error variance is reasonably satisfied.

To find the outliers, we used MINITAB to compute the residuals of the model. A list of the unusual residual

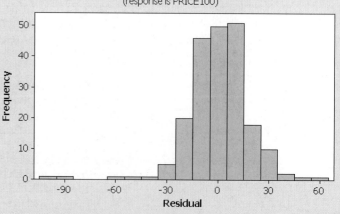

FIGURE SIA12.6
MINITAB histogram of residuals from second-order model of condo sale price

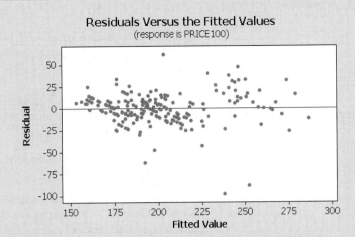

FIGURE SIA12.7

MINITAB plot of residuals versus predicted values from second-order model of condo sale price

values is shown in the MINITAB printout in Figure SIA12.8. Four condo units (numbers 111, 184, 185, and 188; the values of the residuals are highlighted on the printout) have residual values that are greater than 3 in absolute value. (Research reveals that all of these units are located on the fifth floor.) If we delete these observations from the data set and refit the model, we obtain the results shown in the MINITAB printout in Figure SIA12.9. You can see that the adjusted-R^2 value is now .793, an increase of about 9% from the previous value. Also, the standard deviation of the model is now $s = 15.1$, a reduction of about four hundred dollars from the previous value. Obviously, removing the outliers from the analysis yields a "better" prediction equation. If we can justify removing these four outliers (except for number 111, they were all undersold units), then we can use the model shown in Figure SIA12.9 to obtain more accurate predictions of future condo sale prices.

```
Unusual Observations

Obs   FLOOR   PRICE100      Fit   SE Fit   Residual   St Resid
 11    8.00    279.00    240.71    7.62      38.29       2.18R
 26    3.00    269.00    228.48    4.75      40.52       2.19R
 37    6.00    294.00    246.22    5.34      47.78       2.60R
111    5.00    265.00    202.98    3.69      62.02       3.30R
183    3.00    150.00    197.54    4.36     -47.54      -2.55R
184    5.00    140.00    238.04    6.02     -98.04      -5.40R
185    5.00    130.00    192.19    4.37     -62.19      -3.34R
186    6.00    182.00    224.70    5.17     -42.70      -2.32R
188    5.00    164.00    252.16    4.66     -88.16      -4.75R

R denotes an observation with a large standardized residual.
```

FIGURE SIA12.8

MINITAB list of outliers for the second-order model of condo sale price

```
The regression equation is
PRICE100 = 185 - 2.59 FLOOR - 1.98 DISTANCE - 0.387 FLR_DST + 0.912 FLOORSQ
           + 0.264 DISTSQ + 83.9 VIEW - 4.01 VU_FLR - 4.61 VU_DIST
           + 0.154 VU_FLR_DST - 0.426 VU_FLRSQ + 0.304 VU_DISTSQ - 13.1 END
           + 11.5 FURNISH - 31.8 AUCTION

Predictor      Coef   SE Coef       T       P
Constant     184.93     10.39   17.81   0.000
FLOOR        -2.591     3.570   -0.73   0.469
DISTANCE     -1.977     1.923   -1.03   0.305
FLR_DST     -0.3871    0.1593   -2.43   0.016
FLOORSQ      0.9120    0.3384    2.70   0.008
DISTSQ       0.2644    0.1115    2.37   0.019
VIEW          83.88     14.03    5.98   0.000
VU_FLR       -4.007     4.705   -0.85   0.396
VU_DIST      -4.608     2.529   -1.82   0.070
VU_FLR_DST   0.1535    0.2166    0.71   0.479
VU_FLRSQ    -0.4261    0.4624   -0.92   0.358
VU_DISTSQ    0.3041    0.1465    2.08   0.039
END         -13.142     6.244   -2.10   0.037
FURNISH      11.549     2.405    4.80   0.000
AUCTION     -31.816     2.954  -10.77   0.000


S = 15.0925   R-Sq = 80.7%   R-Sq(adj) = 79.3%

Analysis of Variance
```

FIGURE SIA12.9

MINITAB printout of second-order model of condo sale price with outliers deleted

```
Source            DF       SS      MS       F       P
Regression        14   181271   12948   56.84   0.000
Residual Error   190    43279     228
Total            204   224550
```

12.12 Some Pitfalls: Estimability, Multicollinearity, and Extrapolation

You should be aware of several potential problems when you construct a prediction model for some response y. A few of the most important ones are discussed in this final section.

Problem 1:
Parameter Estimability

Suppose you want to fit a model relating annual crop yield y to the total expenditure for fertilizer, x. We propose the first-order model

$$E(y) = \beta_0 + \beta_1 x$$

Now suppose we have three years of data and $1,000 is spent on fertilizer each year. The data are shown in Figure 12.47. You can see the problem: The parameters of the model cannot be estimated when all the data are concentrated at a single x value. Recall that it takes two points (x-values) to fit a straight line. Thus, the parameters are not estimable when only one x is observed.

A similar problem would occur if we attempted to fit the quadratic model

$$E(y) = \beta_0 + \beta_1 x + \beta_2 x^2$$

to a set of data for which only one or two different x-values were observed. (See Figure 12.48.) At least three different x-values must be observed before a quadratic model can be fit to a set of data (i.e., before all three parameters are estimable).

In general, the number of levels of observed x-values must be one more than the order of the polynomial in x that you want to fit.

For controlled experiments, the researcher can select experimental designs that will permit estimation of the model parameters. Even when the values of the independent variables cannot be controlled by the researcher, the independent variables are almost always observed at a sufficient number of levels to permit estimation of the model parameters. When the statistical software you use suddenly refuses to fit a model, however, the problem is probably inestimable parameters.

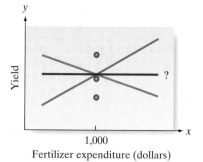

FIGURE 12.47

Yield and fertilizer expenditure data: three years

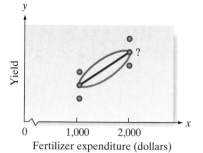

FIGURE 12.48

Only two x values observed: quadratic model is not estimable

Problem 2:
Multicollinearity

Often, two or more of the independent variables used in a regression model contribute redundant information. That is, the independent variables are correlated with each other. For example, suppose we want to construct a model to predict the gas mileage rating of a truck as a function of its load x_1 (in tons) and the horsepower x_2 (in foot-pounds per second) of its engine. We would expect heavy loads to require greater horsepower and to result in lower mileage ratings. Thus, although both x_1 and x_2 contribute information for the prediction of mileage rating y, some of the information is overlapping because x_1 and x_2 are correlated.

When the independent variables are correlated, we say *multicollinearity* exists. In practice, it is not uncommon to observe correlations among the independent variables. However, a few problems arise when serious multicollinearity is present in the regression variables.

Definition 12.7

Multicollinearity exists when two or more of the independent variables used in a regression are correlated.

First, high correlations among the independent variables increase the likelihood of rounding errors in the calculations of the β estimates, standard errors, and so forth. Second, and more important, the regression results may be confusing and misleading. Consider the model for gasoline mileage rating (y) of a truck,

$$E(y) = \beta_0 + \beta_1 x_1 + \beta_2 x_2$$

where x_1 = load and x_2 = horsepower. Fitting the model to a sample data set, we might find that the t-tests for testing β_1 and β_2 are both nonsignificant at the $\alpha = .05$ level, while the F-test for $H_0: \beta_1 = \beta_2 = 0$ is highly significant ($p = .001$). The tests may seem to be contradictory, but really they are not. One the one hand, the t-tests indicate that the contribution of one variable, say, x_1 = load, is not significant after the effect of x_2 = horsepower has been accounted for (because x_2 is also in the model). On the other hand, the significant F-test tells us that at least one of the two variables is making a contribution to the prediction of y (i.e., either β_1 or β_2 or both differ from 0). In fact, both are probably contributing, but the contribution of one overlaps with that of the other.

Multicollinearity can also have an effect on the signs of the parameter estimates. More specifically, a value of $\hat{\beta}_i$ may have the opposite sign from what is expected. In the truck gasoline mileage example, we expect heavy loads to result in lower mileage ratings and we expect higher horsepowers to result in lower mileage ratings; consequently, we expect the signs of both the parameter estimates to be negative. Yet, we may actually see a positive value of $\hat{\beta}_1$ and be tempted to claim that heavy loads result in *higher* mileage ratings. This is the danger of interpreting a β coefficient when the independent variables are correlated. Because the variables contribute redundant information, the effect of x_1 = load on y = mileage rating is measured only partially by β_1.

How can you avoid the problems of multicollinearity in regression analysis? One way is to conduct a designed experiment (Chapter 10), so that the levels of the x variables are uncorrelated. Unfortunately, time and cost constraints may prevent you from collecting data in this manner. Consequently, most data are collected observationally. Since observational data frequently consist of correlated independent variables, you will need to recognize when multicollinearity is present and, if necessary, make modifications in the regression analysis.

Several methods are available for detecting multicollinearity in regression. A simple technique is to calculate the coefficient of correlation, r, between each pair of independent variables in the model and use the procedure outlined in Section 11.5 to test for significantly correlated variables. If one or more of the r values is statistically different from 0, the variables in question are correlated and a multicollinearity problem may exist.* Other indications of the presence of multicollinearity include those just mentioned, namely, nonsignificant t-tests for the individual parameter estimates when the F-test for overall model adequacy is significant, and estimates with opposite signs from what is expected.[†]

Detecting Multicollinearity in the Regression Model

Multicollinearity may exist if there are

1. Significant correlations between pairs of independent variables

2. Nonsignificant t-tests for all (or nearly all) of the individual β parameters when the F-test for overall model adequacy is significant

3. Signs opposite from what is expected in the estimated β parameters

---

*Remember that r measures only the pairwise correlation between x values. Three variables, x_1, x_2, and x_3, may be highly correlated as a group, but may not exhibit large pairwise correlations. Thus, multicollinearity may be present even when all pairwise correlations are not significantly different from 0.

[†]More formal methods for detecting multicollinearity, such as variance-inflation factors (VIFs), are available. Independent variables with a VIF of 10 or above are usually considered to be highly correlated with one or more of the other independent variables in the model. Calculation of VIFs are beyond the scope of this introductory text. (Consult the chapter references for a discussion of VIFs and other formal methods of detecting multicollinearity.)

EXAMPLE 12.18

DETECTING MULTICOLLINEAR-ITY: Modeling Carbon Monoxide Content

Problem The Federal Trade Commission (FTC) annually ranks varieties of domestic cigarettes according to their tar, nicotine, and carbon monoxide content. The U.S. surgeon general considers each of these three substances hazardous to a smoker's health. Past studies have shown that increases in the tar and nicotine content of a cigarette are accompanied by an increase in the carbon monoxide emitted from the cigarette smoke. Table 12.11 presents data on tar, nicotine, and carbon monoxide content (in milligrams) and weight (in grams) for a sample of 25 (filter) brands tested in a recent year. Suppose we want to model carbon monoxide content y as a function of tar content x_1, nicotine content x_2, and weight x_3, using the model

$$E(y) = \beta_0 + \beta_1 x_1 + \beta_2 x_2 + \beta_3 x_3$$

The model is fit to the 25 data points in Table 12.11, and a portion of the SAS printout is shown in Figure 12.49. Examine the printout. Do you detect any signs of multicollinearity?

 FTC

TABLE 12.11   FTC Cigarette Data for Example 12.18

Tar (x_1)	Nicotine (x_2)	Weight (x_3)	Carbon Monoxide (y)
14.1	.86	.9853	13.6
16.0	1.06	1.0938	16.6
29.8	2.03	1.1650	23.5
8.0	.67	.9280	10.2
4.1	.40	.9462	5.4
15.0	1.04	.8885	15.0
8.8	.76	1.0267	9.0
12.4	.95	.9225	12.3
16.6	1.12	.9372	16.3
14.9	1.02	.8858	15.4
13.7	1.01	.9643	13.0
15.1	.90	.9316	14.4
7.8	.57	.9705	10.0
11.4	.78	1.1240	10.2
9.0	.74	.8517	9.5
1.0	.13	.7851	1.5
17.0	1.26	.9186	18.5
12.8	1.08	1.0395	12.6
15.8	.96	.9573	17.5
4.5	.42	.9106	4.9
14.5	1.01	1.0070	15.9
7.3	.61	.9806	8.5
8.6	.69	.9693	10.6
15.2	1.02	.9496	13.9
12.0	.82	1.1184	14.9

Source: Federal Trade Commission.

Solution First, note that the F-test for overall model utility is highly significant. The test statistic ($F = 78.98$) and the observed significance level (p-value $< .0001$) are highlighted on the SAS printout shown in Figure 12.49. Therefore, we can conclude at, say, $\alpha = .01$, that at least one of the parameters β_1, β_2, and β_3 in the model is nonzero. The t-tests for two of three individual β's, however, are nonsignificant. (The p-values for these tests are highlighted on the printout.) Unless tar (x_1) is the only one of the three variables that is useful in predicting carbon monoxide content, these results are the first indication of a potential multicollinearity problem.

The negative values for $\hat{\beta}_2$ and $\hat{\beta}_3$ (highlighted on the printout) are a second clue to the presence of multicollinearity. From past studies, the FTC expects carbon monoxide content (y) to increase when either nicotine content (x_2) or weight (x_3) increases;

Number of Observations Read   25
Number of Observations Used   25

Analysis of Variance

Source	DF	Sum of Squares	Mean Square	F Value	Pr > F
Model	3	495.25781	165.08594	78.98	<.0001
Error	21	43.89259	2.09012		
Corrected Total	24	539.15040			

Root MSE	1.44573	R-Square	0.9186
Dependent Mean	12.52800	Adj R-Sq	0.9070
Coeff Var	11.53996		

Parameter Estimates

Variable	DF	Parameter Estimate	Standard Error	t Value	Pr > |t|	Variance Inflation
Intercept	1	3.20219	3.46175	0.93	0.3655	0
TAR	1	0.96257	0.24224	3.97	0.0007	21.63071
NICOTINE	1	-2.63166	3.90056	-0.67	0.5072	21.89992
WEIGHT	1	-0.13048	3.88534	-0.03	0.9735	1.33386

Pearson Correlation Coefficients, N = 25
Prob > |r| under H0: Rho=0

	TAR	NICOTINE	WEIGHT
TAR	1.00000	0.97661 <.0001	0.49077 0.0127
NICOTINE	0.97661 <.0001	1.00000	0.50018 0.0109
WEIGHT	0.49077 0.0127	0.50018 0.0109	1.00000

FIGURE 12.49

SAS printout for model of CO content, Example 12.18

that is, the FTC expects *positive* relationships between y and x_2 and between y and x_3, not negative ones.

All signs indicate that a serious multicollinearity problem exists.*

Look Back To confirm our suspicions, we had SAS produce the coefficient of correlation, r, for each of the three pairs of independent variables in the model. The resulting output is shown (highlighted) at the bottom of Figure 12.49. You can see that tar (x_1) and nicotine (x_2) are highly correlated ($r = .9766$), while weight (x_3) is moderately correlated with the other two x's ($r \approx .5$). All three correlations have p-values less than .05; consequently, all three are significantly different from 0 at $\alpha = .05$.

Now Work Exercise 12.126

Once you have detected multicollinearity, you can choose from among several alternative measures available for solving the problem. Several of these are outlined in the next box. The appropriate measure to take depends on the severity of the multicollinearity and the ultimate goal of the regression analysis. Some researchers, when confronted with highly correlated independent variables, choose to include only one of the correlated variables in the final model. If you are interested only in using the model for estimation and prediction (step 6), you may decide not to drop any of the independent variables from the model. We have seen that it is dangerous to interpret the individual β parameters in the presence of multicollinearity. However, confidence intervals for $E(y)$ and prediction intervals for y generally remain unaffected *as long as the values of the x's used to predict y follow the same pattern of multicollinearity exhibited in the sample data.* That is, you must take strict care to ensure that the values of the x-variables fall within the range of the sample data.

*Note also that the variance-inflation factors (VIFs) for both tar and nicotine, given on the SAS printout, Figure 12.49, exceed 10.

Problem 3: Prediction Outside the Experimental Region

Many research economists have developed highly technical models to relate the state of the economy to various economic indexes and other independent variables. Many of these models are multiple-regression models, in which, for example, the dependent variable y might be next year's gross domestic product (GDP) and the independent variables might include this year's rate of inflation, this year's Consumer Price Index (CPI), etc. In other words, the model might be constructed to predict next year's economy using this year's knowledge.

Solutions to Some Problems Created by Multicollinearity in Regression*

1. Drop one or more of the correlated independent variables from the model. One way to decide which variables to keep in the model is to employ stepwise regression (Section 12.10).

2. If you decide to keep all the independent variables in the model,
  a. Avoid making inferences about the individual β parameters on the basis of the t-tests.
  b. Restrict inferences about $E(y)$ and future y values to values of the x's that fall within the range of the sample data.

Unfortunately, models such as these were almost all unsuccessful in predicting the recessions of the early 1970s and the late 1990s. What went wrong? One of the problems was that many of the regression models were used to **extrapolate** (i.e., predict y for values of the independent variables that were outside the region in which the model was developed). For example, the inflation rate in the late 1960s, when many of the models were developed, ranged from 6% to 8%. When the double-digit inflation of the early 1970s became a reality, some researchers attempted to use the same models to predict future growth in GDP. As you can see in Figure 12.50, the model may be highly accurate in predicting y when x is in the range of experimentation, but the use of the model outside that range is a dangerous practice.

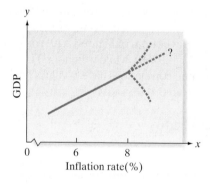

FIGURE 12.50

Using a regression model outside the experimental region

Problem 4: Correlated Errors

Another problem associated with using a regression model to predict a variable y on the basis of independent variables $x_1, x_2, \ldots, x_k$ arises from the fact that the data are frequently *time-series* data. That is, the values of both the dependent and independent variables are observed sequentially over a period of time. The observations then tend to be correlated over time, which in turn often causes the prediction errors of the regression model to be correlated. Thus, the assumption of independent errors is violated, and the model tests and prediction intervals are no longer valid. One solution to this problem is to construct a **time-series model**. (The interested reader should consult the references for details of time-series analysis.)

---

*Several other solutions are available. For example, in the case where higher order regression models are fit, the analyst may want to code the independent variables so that higher order terms (e.g., x^2) for a particular x-variable are not highly correlated with x. One transformation that works is $z = (x - \bar{x})/s$. Other, more sophisticated procedures for addressing multicollinearity (such as *ridge regression*) are beyond the scope of this text. (Consult the references at the end of the chapter.)

Exercises 12.117–12.135

Understanding the Principles

12.117 Define a regression residual.

12.118 Give two properties of the regression residuals from a model.

12.119 Define an outlier.

12.120 Define multicollinearity in regression.

12.121 Give three indicators of a multicollinearity problem.

12.122 Define extrapolation.

12.123 *True or False.* Regression models fit to time series data typically result in uncorrelated errors.

Learning the Mechanics

12.124 Identify the problem(s) in each of the residual plots shown
NW   at the bottom of the page.

12.125 Consider fitting the multiple regression model

$$E(y) = \beta_0 + \beta_1 x_1 + \beta_2 x_2 + \beta_3 x_3 + \beta_4 x_4 + \beta_5 x_5$$

A matrix of correlations for all pairs of independent variables is shown. Do you detect a multicollinearity problem? Explain.

	x_1	x_2	x_3	x_4	x_5
x_1	—	.17	.02	−.23	.19
x_2		—	.45	.93	.02
x_3			—	.22	−.01
x_4				—	.86
x_5					—

Applying the Concepts—Basic

12.126 **Factors identifying urban counties.** Refer to the
NW   *Professional Geographer* (Feb. 2000) study of urban and rural counties in the western United States, presented in Exercise 3.161 (p. 173). The researchers used six independent variables—total county population (x_1), population density (x_2), population concentration (x_3), population growth (x_4), proportion of county land in farms (x_5), and five-year change in agricultural land base (x_6)—to model the urban/rural rating (y) of a county on a scale of 1 (most rural) to 10 (most urban). Prior to running the multiple-regression analysis, the researchers were concerned about possible multicollinearity in the data. Following is a correlation matrix—that is, a table of correlations between all pairs of the independent variables:

Independent Variable	x_1	x_2	x_3	x_4	x_5
x_1 Total population					
x_2 Population density	.20				
x_3 Population concentration	.45	.43			
x_4 Population growth	−.05	−.14	−.01		
x_5 Farm land	−.16	−.15	−.07	−.20	
x_6 Agricultural change	−.12	−.12	−.22	−.06	−.06

Source: Berry, K. A., et al. "Interpreting what is rural and urban for western U.S. counties," *Professional Geographer*, Vol. 52, No. 1, Feb. 2000 (Table 2).

a. On the basis of the correlation matrix, is there any evidence of extreme multicollinearity?

b. The first-order model with all six independent variables was fit to the data. The multiple-regression results are shown in the accompanying table. On the basis of the reported tests, is there any evidence of extreme multicollinearity?

Independent Variable	β Estimate	p-value
x_1: Total population	0.110	0.045
x_2: Population density	0.065	0.230
x_3: Population concentration	0.540	0.000
x_4: Population growth	−0.009	0.860
x_5: Farm land	−0.150	0.003
x_6: Agricultural change	−0.027	0.58

Overall model: $R^2 = .44$ $R_a^2 = .43$ $F = 32.47$ p-value $<.001$

Source: Berry, K. A., et al. "Interpreting what is rural and urban for western U.S. counties," *Professional Geographer*, Vol. 52, No. 1, Feb. 2000 (Table 2).

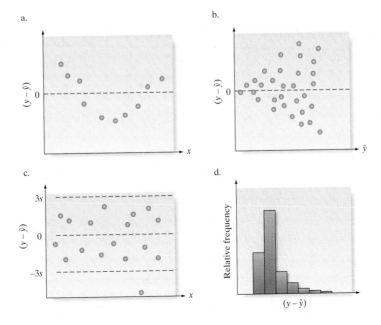

Residual plots for
Exercise 12.124

12.127 Personality and aggressive behavior. *Psychological Bulletin* (Vol. 132, 2006) reported on a study linking personality and aggressive behavior. Four of the variables measured in the study were aggressive behavior, irritability, trait anger, and narcissism. Pairwise correlations for these four variables are given in the following table:

Aggressive behavior–irritability: .77
Aggressive behavior–trait anger: .48
Aggressive behavior–narcissism: .50
Irritability–trait anger: .57
Irritability–narcissism: .16
Trait anger–narcissism: .13

a. Suppose aggressive behavior is the dependent variable in a regression model and the other variables are independent variables. Is there evidence of extreme multicollinearity? Explain.

b. Suppose narcissism is the dependent variable in a regression model and the other variables are independent variables. Is there evidence of extreme multicollinearity? Explain.

12.128 Yield strength of steel alloy. Refer to Exercise 12.114 (p. 701) and the *Modelling and Simulation in Materials Science and Engineering* (Vol. 13, 2005) study in which engineers built a regression model for the tensile yield strength (y) of a new steel alloy. The engineers discovered that the independent variable nickel (x_4) was highly correlated with the other 10 potential independent variables. Consequently, nickel was dropped from the model. Do you agree with this decision? Explain.

12.129 Passive exposure to smoke. Passive exposure to environmental tobacco smoke has been associated with suppression of growth and an increased frequency of respiratory tract infections in normal children. Is this association more pronounced in children with cystic fibrosis? To answer this question, 43 children (18 girls and 25 boys) attending a two-week summer camp for cystic fibrosis patients were studied. (*New England Journal of Medicine*, Sept. 20, 1990.) Researchers investigated the correlation between a child's weight percentile (y) and the number of cigarettes smoked per day in the child's home (x). The accompany-

ing table lists the data on the 25 boys. Using simple linear regression, the researchers predicted the weight percentile for the last observation ($x = 44$ cigarettes) to be $\hat{y} = 29.63$. Given that the standard deviation of the model is $s = 24.68$, is this observation an outlier? Explain.

12.130 Passive exposure to smoke (continued). Refer to Exercise 12.129. Two MINITAB residual plots for the simple linear regression model are shown on p. 725.

a. Which graph should be used to check for normal errors? Does the assumption of normality appear to be satisfied?

b. Which graph should be used to check for unequal error variances? Does the assumption of equal variances appear to be satisfied?

Applying the Concepts—Intermediate

12.131 Accuracy of software effort estimates. Periodically, software engineers provide estimates of their effort in developing new software. In the *Journal of Empirical Software Engineering* (Vol. 9, 2004), multiple regression was used to predict the accuracy of these estimates. The dependent variable, defined as the relative error in estimating effort, or

$$y = \frac{\text{Actual effort} - \text{Estimated effort}}{\text{Actual effort}}$$

was determined for each in a sample of $n = 49$ software development tasks. Eight independent variables were evaluated as potential predictors of relative error. Each of these was formulated as a dummy variable, as shown in the following table:

Company role of estimator: $x_1 = 1$ if developer, 0 if project leader
Task complexity: $x_2 = 1$ if low, 0 if medium/high
Contract type: $x_3 = 1$ if fixed price, 0 if hourly rate
Customer importance: $x_4 = 1$ if high, 0 if low/medium
Customer priority: $x_5 = 1$ if time of delivery, 0 if cost or quality
Level of knowledge: $x_6 = 1$ if high, 0 if low/medium
Participation: $x_7 = 1$ if estimator participates in work, 0 if not
Previous accuracy: $x_8 = 1$ if more than 20% accurate, 0 if less than 20% accurate

CFSMOKE

Weight Percentile y	No. of Cigarettes Smoked per Day x	Weight Percentile y	No. of Cigarettes Smoked per Day x
6	0	43	0
6	15	49	0
2	40	50	0
8	23	49	22
11	20	46	30
17	7	54	0
24	3	58	0
25	0	62	0
17	25	66	0
25	20	66	23
25	15	83	0
31	23	87	44
35	10		

Source: Rubin, B. K. "Exposure of children with cystic fibrosis to environmental tobacco smoke," *The New England Journal of Medicine*, Sept. 20, 1990. Vol. 323, No. 12, p. 85 (data extracted from Figure 3).

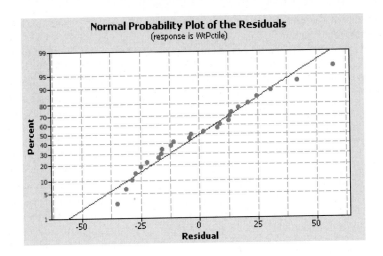

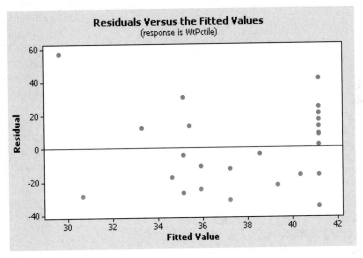

MINITAB output for
Exercise 12.130

a. The eight independent variables were entered into a stepwise regression, and the variables x_1 and x_8 were selected for entry into the model. Write the main-effects model for $E(y)$ as a function of these two variables.

b. The stepwise regression yielded the following prediction equation:

$$\hat{y} = .12 - .28x_1 + .27x_8$$

Give a practical interpretation of the β estimates multiplied by x_1 and x_8.

c. The researcher is concerned that the sign of $\hat{\beta}_1$ in the model is opposite from what is expected. (The researcher expects a project leader to have a smaller rel-

ative error of estimation than a developer.) Give at least one reason this phenomenon occurred.

12.132 Physical characteristics of boys. A physiologist wishes to investigate the relationship between the physical characteristics of preadolescent boys and their maximum oxygen uptake (measured in milliliters of oxygen per kilogram of body weight). The accompanying data were collected on a random sample of 10 preadolescent boys.

a. Fit the regression model
$$y = \beta_0 + \beta_1x_1 + \beta_2x_2 + \beta_3x_3 + \beta_4x_4 + \varepsilon$$
to the data, and give the least squares prediction equation.

BOYS10

Maximum Oxygen Uptake y	Age x_1 (years)	Height x_2 (centimeters)	Weight x_3 (kilograms)	Chest Depth x_4 (centimeters)
1.54	8.4	132.0	29.1	14.4
1.74	8.7	135.5	29.7	14.5
1.32	8.9	127.7	28.4	14.0
1.50	9.9	131.1	28.8	14.2
1.46	9.0	130.0	25.9	13.6
1.35	7.7	127.6	27.6	13.9
1.53	7.3	129.9	29.0	14.0
1.71	9.9	138.1	33.6	14.6
1.27	9.3	126.6	27.7	13.9
1.50	8.1	131.8	30.8	14.5

b. It seems reasonable to assume that the greater a child's weight, the greater should be the maximum oxygen uptake. Is $\hat{\beta}_3$, the estimated coefficient of weight x_3, positive as expected? Give an explanation for this result.

c. It would seem that the chest depth of a child should be positively correlated with lung volume and hence to maximum oxygen uptake. Is $\hat{\beta}_4$ significantly different from 0, as expected? If not, explain why.

d. Calculate the correlation coefficients between all pairs of the independent variables x_1–x_4. Do these correlations provide an explanation for the confusing signs and small t values associated with the estimated regression coefficients of the model?

DDT

12.133 Contamination of fish in the Tennessee River. Refer to the U.S. Army Corps of Engineers data on fish contaminated from the toxic discharges of a chemical plant located on the banks of the Tennessee River in Alabama, presented in Exercise 12.20 (p. 645). In that exercise, you fit the first-order model $E(y) = \beta_0 + \beta_1 x_1 + \beta_2 x_2 + \beta_3 x_3$, where y = DDT level in captured fish, x_1 = miles captured upstream, x_2 = fish length, and x_3 = fish weight. Conduct a complete residual analysis of the model. Do you recommend any modifications to be made to the model? Explain.

GASTURBINE

12.134 Cooling method for gas turbines. Refer to the *Journal of Engineering for Gas Turbines and Power* (Jan. 2005) study of a high-pressure inlet fogging method for a gas turbine engine, presented in Exercise 12.23 (p. 646). Now consider the interaction model $E(y) = \beta_0 + \beta_1 x_1 + \beta_2 x_2 + \beta_3 x_1 x_2$ for heat rate (y) of a gas turbine as a function of cycle speed (x_1) and cycle pressure ratio (x_2). Use the data saved in the **GASTURBINE** file to conduct a complete residual analysis of the model. Do you recommend making modifications to the model?

12.135 Socialization of graduate students. *Teaching Sociology* (July 1995) developed a model for the professional socialization of graduate students working toward a Ph.D. in sociology. One of the dependent variables modeled was professional confidence y, measured on a five-point scale. The model included over 20 independent variables and was fit to data collected on a sample of 309 sociology graduate students. One concern was whether multicollinearity existed in the data. A matrix of Pearson product moment correlations for 10 of the independent variables is shown below. [*Note:* Each entry in the table is the correlation coefficient r between the variable in the corresponding row and column.]

a. Examine the correlation matrix, and find the independent variables that are moderately or highly correlated.

b. What modeling problems may occur if the variables you found in part **a** are left in the model? Explain.

Matrix of correlations for Exercise 12.135

Independent Variable	(1)	(2)	(3)	(4)	(5)	(6)	(7)	(8)	(9)	(10)
(1) Father's occupation	1.000	.363	.099	−.110	−.047	−.053	−.111	.178	.078	.049
(2) Mother's education	.363	1.000	.228	−.139	−.216	.084	−.118	.192	.125	.068
(3) Race	.099	.228	1.000	.036	−.515	.014	−.120	.112	.117	.337
(4) Sex	−.110	−.139	.036	1.000	.165	−.256	.173	−.106	−.117	.073
(5) Foreign status	−.047	−.216	−.515	.165	1.000	−.041	.159	−.130	−.165	−.171
(6) Undergraduate GPA	−.053	.084	.014	−.256	−.041	1.000	.032	.028	−.034	.092
(7) Year GRE taken	−.111	−.118	−.120	.173	.159	.032	1.000	−.086	−.602	.016
(8) Verbal GRE score	.178	.192	.112	−.106	−.130	.028	−.086	1.000	.132	.087
(9) Years in graduate program	.078	.125	.117	−.117	−.165	−.034	−.602	.132	1.000	−.071
(10) First-year graduate GPA	.049	.068	.337	.073	−.171	.092	.016	.087	−.071	1.000

Source: Keith, B., and Moore, H. A. "Training sociologists: An assessment of professional socialization and the emergence of career aspirations," *Teaching Sociology*, Vol. 23, No. 3, July 1995, p. 205 (Table 1).

KEY TERMS

GUIDE TO MULTIPLE REGRESSION

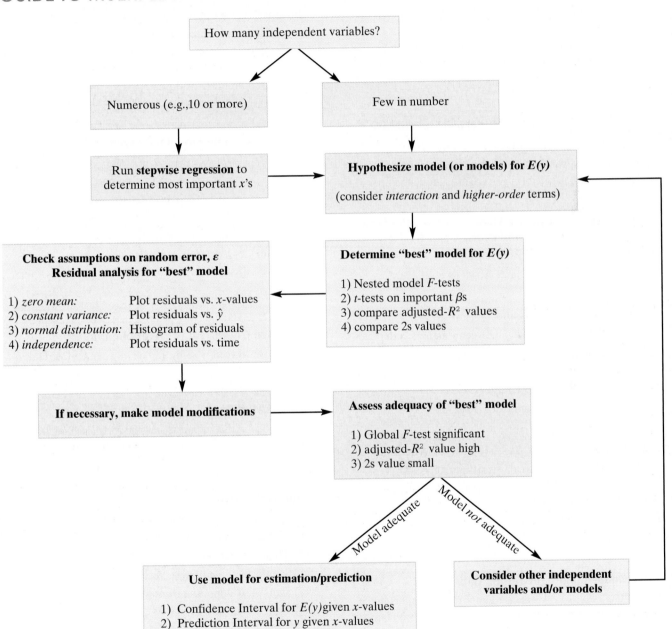

CHAPTER NOTES

Multiple-Regression Variables

y = **Dependent** variable (quantitative)

$x_1, x_2, \ldots, x_k$ are **independent** variables (quantitative or qualitative)

Quadratic Model in 1 Quantitative x

$$E(y) = \beta_0 + \beta_1 x + \beta_2 x^2$$

β_2 represents the rate of curvature of x.

($\beta_2 > 0$ implies *upward* curvature.)

($\beta_2 < 0$ implies *downward* curvature.)

Complete Second-Order Model in 2 Quantitative x's

$$E(y) = \beta_0 + \beta_1 x_1 + \beta_2 x_2 + \beta_3 x_1 x_2 + \beta_4 x_1^2 + \beta_5 x_2^2$$

β_4 represents the rate of curvature of x_1, holding x_2 fixed.

β_5 represents the rate of curvature of x_2, holding x_1 fixed.

Complete Second-Order Model in 1 Quantitative x and 1 Qualitative x (Two Levels, A and B)

$$E(y) = \beta_0 + \beta_1 x_1 + \beta_2 x_1^2 + \beta_3 x_2 + \beta_4 x_1 x_2 + \beta_5 x_1^2 x_2$$

$$x_2 = \{1 \text{ if level A, } 0 \text{ if level B}\}$$

Interaction between x_1 and x_2

Implies that the relationship between y and one x depends on the other x.

Parsimonious Model

A model with a small number of β parameters.

Recommendation for Assessing Model Adequacy

(1) Conduct global F-test; if significant, then

(2) Conduct t-tests on only the "most important" β's (*interaction* or *squared terms*).

(3) Interpret value of 2s.

(4) Interpret value of R_a^2.

Recommendation for Testing Individual β's

(1) If *curvature* (x^2) is deemed important, do not conduct test for first-order (x) term in the model.

(2) If *interaction* ($x_1 x_2$) is deemed important, do not conduct tests for first-order terms (x_1 and x_2) in the model.

Extrapolation

Occurs when you predict y for values of x's that are outside of range of sample data.

First-Order Model in k Quantitative x's

$$E(y) = \beta_0 + \beta_1 x_1 + \beta_2 x_2 + \ldots + \beta_k x_k$$

Each β_1 represents the change in y for every one-unit increase in x_1, holding all other x's fixed.

Interaction Model in 2 Quantitative x's

$$E(y) = \beta_0 + \beta_1 x_1 + \beta_2 x_2 + \beta_3 x_1 x_2.$$

($\beta_1 + \beta_3 x_2$) represents the change in y for every one-unit increase in x_1, for a fixed value of x_2.

($\beta_2 + \beta_3 x_1$) represents the change in y for every one-unit increase in x_2, for a fixed value of x_1.

Dummy Variable Model for 1 Qualitative x

$$E(y) = \beta_0 + \beta_1 x_1 + \beta_2 x_2 + \ldots + \beta_{k-1} x_{k-1}$$

$$x_1 = \{1 \text{ if level 1, } 0 \text{ if not}\}$$

$$x_2 = \{1 \text{ if level 2, } 0 \text{ if not}\}$$

$$\vdots$$

$$x_{k-1} = \{1 \text{ if level } k-1, 0 \text{ if not}\}$$

$\beta_0 = E(y)$ for level k (base level) $= \mu_k$

$\beta_1 = \mu_1 - \mu_k$

$\beta_2 = \mu_2 - \mu_k$

Adjusted Coefficient of Determination, R_a^2

Cannot be "forced" to 1 by adding independent variables to the model.

Nested Models

Are models such that one model (the *complete model*) contains all the terms of another model (the *reduced model*) plus at least one additional term.

Multicollinearity

Occurs when two or more x's are correlated.

Indicators of multicollinearity:

(1) Highly correlated x's

(2) Significant global F-test, but all t-tests nonsignificant

(3) Signs on β's opposite from what is expected

Problems with Using Stepwise Regression Model as the "Final" Model

(1) *Extremely large number of t-tests* inflate overall probability of at least one Type I error.

(2) *No higher order terms* (interactions or squared terms) are included in the model.

school. Two variables hypothesized to have an impact on achievement were track (college program of courses or not) and sector (Catholic school or public school). One of the models considered in the study was

$$E(y) = \beta_0 + \beta_1 x_1 + \beta_2 x_2 + \beta_3 x_1 x_2$$

where

$$y = \text{Verbal achievement score}$$
$$x_1 = 1 \text{ if college track, } 0 \text{ if not}$$
$$x_2 = 1 \text{ if Catholic school, } 0 \text{ if not}$$

a. How would you determine whether the impact of track (x_1) on verbal achievement score (y) depends on sector (x_2)? Set up the null and alternative hypotheses for the test.

b. In terms of the β's, give the mean verbal achievement score $E(y)$ for public school students not in a college program.

c. Repeat part b for public school students in a college program.

d. Subtract the result from part b from the result from part c to obtain the difference between the means of college-track and noncollege-track students in public schools.

e. In terms of the β's, give the mean verbal achievement score $E(y)$ for Catholic school students not in a college program.

f. Repeat part e for Catholic school students in a college program.

g. Subtract the result from part e from the result from part f to obtain the difference between the means of college-track and noncollege-track students in Catholic schools.

12.163 Sale prices of apartments. A Minneapolis, Minnesota, real-estate appraiser used regression analysis to explore the relationship between the sale prices of apartment buildings sold in Minneapolis and various characteristics of the properties. Twenty-five apartment buildings were randomly sampled from all apartment buildings that were sold during a recent year. The accompanying table lists the data collected by the appraiser. [*Note:* The physical condition of each apartment building is coded E (excellent), G (good), or F (fair).]

a. Write a model that describes the relationship between sale price and number of apartment units as three parallel lines, one for each level of physical condition. Be sure to specify the dummy-variable coding scheme you use.

b. Plot y against x_1 (number of apartment units) for all buildings in excellent condition. On the same graph, plot y against x_1 for all buildings in good condition. Do this again for all buildings in fair condition. Does it appear that the model you specified in part a is appropriate? Explain.

c. Fit the model from part a to the data. Report the least squares prediction equation for each of the three building condition levels.

d. Plot the three prediction equations of part c on a scattergram of the data.

e. Do the data provide sufficient evidence to conclude that the relationship between sale price and number

MNSALES

Code No.	Sale Price y ($\$$)	No. of Apartments, x_1	Age of Structure, x_2 (years)	Lot Size x_3 (sq. ft.)	No. of On-Site Parking Spaces, x_4	Gross Building Area x_5 (sq. ft.)	Condition of Apartment Building
0229	90,300	4	82	4,635	0	4,266	F
0094	384,000	20	13	17,798	0	14,391	G
0043	157,500	5	66	5,913	0	6,615	G
0079	676,200	26	64	7,750	6	34,144	E
0134	165,000	5	55	5,150	0	6,120	G
0179	300,000	10	65	12,506	0	14,552	G
0087	108,750	4	82	7,160	0	3,040	G
0120	276,538	11	23	5,120	0	7,881	G
0246	420,000	20	18	11,745	20	12,600	G
0025	950,000	62	71	21,000	3	39,448	G
0015	560,000	26	74	11,221	0	30,000	G
0131	268,000	13	56	7,818	13	8,088	F
0172	290,000	9	76	4,900	0	11,315	E
0095	173,200	6	21	5,424	6	4,461	G
0121	323,650	11	24	11,834	8	9,000	G
0077	162,500	5	19	5,246	5	3,828	G
0060	353,500	20	62	11,223	2	13,680	F
0174	134,400	4	70	5,834	0	4,680	E
0084	187,000	8	19	9,075	0	7,392	G
0031	155,700	4	57	5,280	0	6,030	E
0019	93,600	4	82	6,864	0	3,840	F
0074	110,000	4	50	4,510	0	3,092	G
0057	573,200	14	10	11,192	0	23,704	E
0104	79,300	4	82	7,425	0	3,876	F
0024	272,000	5	82	7,500	0	9,542	E

Source: Robinson Appraisal Co., Inc., Mankato, Minnesota.

of units varies with the physical condition of the apartments? Test, using $\alpha = .05$.

f. Check the data set for multicollinearity. How does your result affect your choice of independent variables to use in a model for sale price?

g. Consider the first-order model $E(y) = \beta_0 + \beta_1 x_1 + \cdots + \beta_5 x_5$. Conduct a complete residual analysis for the model to check the assumptions on ε.

12.164 Media coverage of a war. Does extensive media coverage of a military crisis influence public opinion on how to respond to the crisis? Political scientists at UCLA researched this question and reported their results in *Communication Research* (June 1993). The military crisis of interest was the 1990 Persian Gulf War, precipitated by Iraq's invasion of Kuwait. The researchers used multiple-regression analysis to model the level y of support Americans had for a military (rather than a diplomatic) response to the crisis. Values of y ranged from 0 (preference for a diplomatic response) to 4 (preference for a military response). The following independent variables were used in the model:

x_1 = Level of TV news exposure in a selected week (number of days)

x_2 = Knowledge of seven political figures (one point for each correct answer)

x_3 = Gender (1 if male, 0 if female)

x_4 = Race (1 if nonwhite, 0 if white)

x_5 = Partisanship (0–6 scale, where 0 = strong Democrat and 6 = strong Republican

x_6 = Defense spending attitude (1–7 scale, where 1 = greatly decrease spending and 7 = greatly increase spending

x_7 = Education level (1–7 scale, where 1 = less than eighth grade and 7 = college)

Data from a survey of 1,763 U.S. citizens were used to fit the model

$$E(y) = \beta_0 + \beta_1 x_1 + \beta_2 x_2 + \beta_3 x_3 + \beta_4 x_4 + \beta_5 x_5 + \beta_6 x_6 + \beta_7 x_7 + \beta_8 x_2 x_3 + \beta_9 x_2 x_4$$

The regression results are shown in the table below.

a. Interpret the β estimate for the variable x_1, TV news exposure.

b. Conduct a test to determine whether an increase in TV news exposure is associated with an increase in support for a military resolution of the crisis. Use $\alpha = .05$.

c. Is there sufficient evidence to indicate that the relationship between support for a military resolution (y) and gender (x_3) depends on political knowledge (x_2)? Test, using $\alpha = .05$.

d. Is there sufficient evidence to indicate that the relationship between support for a military resolution (y) and race (x_4) depends on political knowledge (x_2)? Test, using $\alpha = .05$.

e. The coefficient of determination for the model was $R^2 = .194$. Interpret this value.

f. Use the value of R^2, from part **e** to conduct a global test for model utility. Take $\alpha = .05$.

12.165 Extracting water from oil. In the oil industry, water that mixes with crude oil during production and transportation must be removed. Chemists have found that the oil can be extracted from the water–oil mix electrically. Researchers at the University of Bergen (Norway) conducted a series of experiments to study the factors that influence the voltage (y) required to separate the water from the oil. (*Journal of Colloid and Interface Science*, Aug. 1995.) The seven independent variables investigated in the study are listed in the accompanying table. (Each variable was measured at two levels: a "low" level and a "high" level.) Using different combinations of the independent variables, the researchers prepared 16 water–oil mixtures. Then each emulsion was exposed to a high electric field. In addition, three mixtures were tested when all independent variables were set to 0. The data for all 19 experiments are also given in the table, top p. 737.

a. Propose a first-order model for y as a function of all seven independent variables.

b. Use a statistical software package to fit the model to the data in the table.

c. Interpret the β estimates fully.

d. The researchers concluded that "in order to break a water–oil mixture with the lowest possible voltage, the volume fraction of the disperse phase (x_1) should be high, while the salinity (x_2) and the amount of surfactant (x_5) should be low." Use this information and the first-order model of part **b** to find a 95% prediction interval for this "low" voltage y. Interpret the interval.

12.166 Analysis of Tokyo urban air. Chemical engineers at Tokyo Metropolitan University analyzed urban air specimens for the presence of low-molecular-weight dicarboxylic acid. (*Environmental Science & Engineering*, Oct. 1993.) The dicarboxylic acid (as a percentage of total carbon) and oxidant concentrations for 19 air specimens collected

Variable	β Estimate	Standard Error	Two-Tailed p-Value
TV news exposure (x_1)	.02	.01	.03
Political knowledge (x_2)	.07	.03	.03
Gender (x_3)	.67	.11	< .001
Race (x_4)	−.76	.13	< .001
Partisanship (x_5)	.07	.01	< .001
Defense spending (x_6)	.20	.02	< .001
Education (x_7)	.07	.02	< .001
Knowledge × Gender ($x_2 x_3$)	−.09	.04	.02
Knowledge × Race ($x_2 x_4$)	.10	.06	.08

Source: Iyengar, S., and Simon, A. "News coverage of the Gulf Crisis and public opinion," *Communication Research*, Vol. 20, No. 3, June 1993, p. 380 (Table 2).

WATEROIL

Experiment Number	Voltage y (kw/cm)	Disperse Phase Volume x_1 (%)	Salinity x_2 (%)	Temperature x_3 (°C)	Time Delay x_4 (hours)	Surfactant Concentration x_5 (%)	Span: Triton x_6	Solid Particles x_7 (%)
1	.64	40	1	4	.25	2	.25	.5
2	.80	80	1	4	.25	4	.25	2
3	3.20	40	4	4	.25	4	.75	.5
4	.48	80	4	4	.25	2	.75	2
5	1.72	40	1	23	.25	4	.75	2
6	.32	80	1	23	.25	2	.75	.5
7	.64	40	4	23	.25	2	.25	2
8	.68	80	4	23	.25	4	.25	.5
9	.12	40	1	4	24	2	.75	2
10	.88	80	1	4	24	4	.75	.5
11	2.32	40	4	4	24	4	.25	2
12	.40	80	4	4	24	2	.25	.5
13	1.04	40	1	23	24	4	.25	.5
14	.12	80	1	23	24	2	.25	2
15	1.28	40	4	23	24	2	.75	.5
16	.72	80	4	23	24	4	.75	2
17	1.08	0	0	0	0	0	0	0
18	1.08	0	0	0	0	0	0	0
19	1.04	0	0	0	0	0	0	0

Source: Førdedal, H., et al. "A multivariate analysis of W/O emulsions in high external electric fields as studied by means of dielectric time domain spectroscopy," *Journal of Colloid and Interface Science*, Vol. 173, No. 2, Aug. 1995, p. 398 (Table 2).

from urban Tokyo are listed in the table below. Consider the straight-line model relating dicarboxylic acid percentage (y) to oxidant concentration (x). Conduct a complete residual analysis.

URBANAIR

Dicarboxylic Acid (%)	Oxidant (ppm)
.85	78
1.45	80
1.80	74
1.80	78
1.60	60
1.20	62
1.30	57
.20	49
.22	34
.40	36
.50	32
.38	28
.30	25
.70	45
.80	40
.90	45
1.22	41
1.00	34
1.00	25

Source: Kawamura, K., and Ikushima, K. "Seasonal changes in the distribution of dicarboxylic acids in the urban atmosphere," *Environmental Science & Technology*, Vol. 27. No. 10, Oct. 1993, p. 2232 (data extracted from Figure 4).

PONDICE

12.167 Characteristics of sea-ice melt ponds. Surface albedo is defined as the ratio of solar energy directed upward from a surface over energy incident upon the surface. Surface albedo is a critical climatological parameter of sea ice. The National Snow and Ice Data Center (NSIDC) collects data on the albedo, depth, and physical characteristics of ice-melt ponds in the Canadian Arctic. Data on 504 ice-melt ponds located in the Barrow Strait in the Canadian Arctic are saved in the **PONDICE** file. Environmental engineers want to examine the relationship between the broadband surface albedo level y of the ice and the pond depth x (in meters).

a. Construct a scattergram of the **PONDICE** data. On the basis of the scattergram, hypothesize a model for $E(y)$ as a function of x.

b. Fit the model you hypothesized in part **a** to the data in the **PONDICE** file. Give the least squares prediction equation.

c. Conduct a test of the overall adequacy of the model. Use $\alpha = .01$.

d. Conduct tests (at $\alpha = .01$) on any important β parameters in the model.

e. Find and interpret the values of adjusted-R^2 and s.

f. Do you detect any outliers in the data? Explain.

Applying the Concepts—Advanced

12.168 Abundance of bird species. Multiple-regression analysis was used to model the abundance y of an individual bird species in transects in the United Kingdom. (*Journal of Applied Ecology*, Vol. 32, 1995.) Three of the independent variables used in the model, all field boundary attributes, are

(1) Transect location (small pasture field, small arable field, or large arable field)

(2) Land use (pasture or arable) adjacent to the transect

(3) Total number of trees in the transect

a. Identify each of the independent variables as a quantitative or qualitative variable.

b. Write a first-order model for $E(y)$ as a function of the total number of trees.

c. Add main-effect terms for transect location to the model you wrote in part **b**. Graph the hypothesized relationships of the new model.

d. Add main-effect terms for land use to the model you came up with in part **c**. In terms of the β's of the new model, what is the slope of the relationship between $E(y)$ and number of trees for any combination of transect location and land use?

e. Add terms for interaction between transect location and land use to the model you arrived at in part **d**. Do these interaction terms affect the slope of the relationship between $E(y)$ and number of trees? Explain.

f. Add terms for interaction between number of trees and all coded dummy variables to the model you formulated in part **e**. In terms of the β's of the new model, give the slope of the relationship between $E(y)$ and number of trees for each combination of transect location and land use.

Critical Thinking Challenges

12.169 FLAG study of bid collusion. Road construction contracts in the state of Florida are awarded on the basis of competitive, sealed bids; the contractor who bids the lowest price wins the contract. During the 1980s, the Office of the Florida Attorney General (FLAG) suspected numerous contractors of practicing bid collusion (i.e., setting the winning bid price above the fair, or competitive, price in order to increase their own profit margin). By comparing the prices bid (and other important bid variables) of the fixed (i.e., rigged) contracts with the competitively bid contracts, FLAG was able to establish invaluable benchmarks for detecting future bid rigging. FLAG collected data on 279 road construction contracts. For each contract, the following variables were measured (the data are saved in the **FLAG** file):

🕑 **FLAG**

1. Price of contract ($) bid by lowest bidder
2. Department of Transportation (DOT) engineer's estimate of fair contract price ($)
3. Ratio of low (winning) bid price to DOT engineer's estimate of fair price
4. Status of contract (1 if fixed, 0 if competitive)
5. District (1, 2, 3, 4, or 5) in which construction project is located
6. Number of bidders on contract
7. Estimated number of days required to complete work
8. Length of road project (miles)
9. Percentage of costs allocated to liquid asphalt
10. Percentage of costs allocated to base material
11. Percentage of costs allocated to excavation
12. Percentage of costs allocated to mobilization
13. Percentage of costs allocated to structures
14. Percentage of costs allocated to traffic control
15. Subcontractor utilization (1 if yes, 0 if no)

Use the methodology of this chapter to build a model for low-bid contract price (y). Comment on how the status of the bid affects the price.

12.170 In Exercise 5.141 (p. 273), we introduced *The Bell Curve* (New York: Free Press, 1994) by Richard Herrnstein and Charles Murray (H&M), a controversial book about race, genes, IQ, and economic mobility. The book heavily employs statistics and statistical methodology in an attempt to support the authors' positions on the relationships among these variables and their social consequences. The main theme of *The Bell Curve* can be summarized as follows:

(1) Measured intelligence (IQ) is largely genetically inherited.

(2) IQ is correlated positively with a variety of socioeconomic status success measures, such as a prestigious job, a high annual income, and high educational attainment.

(3) From 1 and 2, it follows that socioeconomic successes are largely genetically caused and therefore resistant to educational and environmental interventions (such as affirmative action).

The statistical methodology (regression) employed by the authors and the inferences derived from the statistics were critiqued in *Chance* (Summer 1995) and *The Journal of the American Statistical Association* (Dec. 1995). The following are just a few of the problems with H&M's use of regression that have been identified:

Problem 1 H&M consistently use a trio of independent variables—IQ, socioeconomic status, and age—in a series of first-order models designed to predict dependent social outcome variables such as income and unemployment. (Only on a single occasion are interaction terms incorporated.) Consider, for example, the model

$$E(y) = \beta_0 + \beta_1 x_1 + \beta_2 x_2 + \beta_3 x_3$$

where y = income, x_1 = IQ, x_2 = socioeconomic status, and x_3 = age. H&M utilize t-tests on the individual β parameters to assess the importance of the independent variables. As with most of the models considered in *The Bell Curve*, the estimate of β_1 in the income model is positive and statistically significant at $\alpha = .05$, and the associated t-value is larger (in absolute value) than the t-values associated with the other independent variables. Consequently, *H&M claim that IQ is a better predictor of income than the other two independent variables*. No attempt was made to determine whether the model was properly specified or whether the model provides an adequate fit to the data.

Problem 2 In an appendix, the authors describe multiple regression as a "mathematical procedure that yields coefficients for each of [the independent variables], indicating how much of a change in [the dependent variable] can be anticipated for a given change in any particular [independent] variable, with all the others held constant." Armed with this information and the fact that the estimate of β_1 in the model just described is positive, *H&M infer that a high IQ necessarily implies (or causes) a high income, and a low IQ inevitably leads to a low income*. (Cause-and-effect inferences like this are made repeatedly throughout the book.)

Problem 3 The title of the book refers to the normal distribution and its well-known "bell-shaped" curve. There is a misconception among the general public that scores on intelligence tests (IQ) are normally distributed. In fact, most IQ scores have distributions that are decidedly skewed. Traditionally, psychologists and psychometricians have transformed these scores so that the resulting numbers have a precise normal distribution. H&M make a special point to do this. Consequently, *the measure of IQ used in all the regression models is normalized (i.e., transformed so that the resulting distribution is normal), despite the fact that regression methodology does not require predictor (independent) variables to be normally distributed.*

Problem 4 A variable that is not used as a predictor of social outcome in any of the models in *The Bell Curve* is level of education. H&M purposely omit education from the models, arguing that IQ causes education, not the other way around. Other researchers who have examined H&M's data report that *when education is included as an independent variable in the model, the effect of IQ on the dependent variable (say, income) is diminished.*

a. Comment on each of the problems identified. Why do these problems cast a shadow on the inferences made by the authors?

b. Using the variables specified in the model presented, describe how you would conduct the multiple-regression analysis. (Propose a more complicated model and describe the appropriate model tests, including a residual analysis.)

SUMMARY ACTIVITY: Collecting Data and Fitting a Multiple-Regression Model

Note: The use of statistical software is required for this project.

This is a continuation of the Summary Activity section in Chapter 11, in which you selected three independent variables as predictors of a dependent variable of your choice and obtained at least 10 data values. Now, by means of an available software package, fit the multiple-regression model

$$y = \beta_0 + \beta_1 x_1 + \beta_2 x_2 + \beta_3 x_3 + \varepsilon$$

where

$y = $ Dependent variable you chose

$x_1 = $ First independent variable you chose

$x_2 = $ Second independent variable you chose

$x_3 = $ Third independent variable you chose

a. Compare the coefficients $\hat{\beta}_1$, $\hat{\beta}_2$, and $\hat{\beta}_3$ with their corresponding slope coefficients in the Summary Activity of Chapter 11, where you fit three separate straight-line models. How do you account for the differences?

b. Calculate the coefficient of determination, R^2, and conduct the F-test of the null hypothesis $H_0: \beta_1 = \beta_2 = \beta_3 = 0$. What is your conclusion?

c. Check the data for multicollinearity. If multicollinearity exists, how should you proceed?

d. Now increase your list of 3 variables to include approximately 10 that you think would be useful in predicting the dependent variable. With the aid of statistical software, employ a stepwise regression program to choose the important variables among those you have listed. To test your intuition, list the variables in the order you think they will be selected before you conduct the analysis. How does your list compare with the stepwise regression results?

e. After the group of 10 variables has been narrowed to a smaller group of variables by the stepwise analysis, try to improve the model by including interactions and quadratic terms. Be sure to consider the meaning of each interaction or quadratic term before adding it to the model. (A quick sketch can be very helpful.) See if you can systematically construct a useful model for prediction. If you have a large data set, you might want to hold out the last observations to test the predictive ability of your model after it is constructed. (As noted in Section 12.10, using the same data to construct *and* to evaluate predictive ability can lead to invalid statistical tests and a false sense of security.)

REFERENCES

Barnett, V., and Lewis, T. *Outliers in Statistical Data.* New York: Wiley, 1978.

Belsley, D. A., Kuh, E., and Welsch, R. E. *Regression Diagnostics: Identifying Influential Data and Sources of Collinearity.* New York: Wiley, 1980.

Chatterjee, S., and Price, B. *Regression Analysis by Example,* 2d ed. New York: Wiley, 1991.

Draper, N., and Smith, H. *Applied Regression Analysis,* 2d ed. New York: Wiley, 1981.

Graybill, F. *Theory and Application of the Linear Model.* North Scituate, MA: Duxbury, 1976.

Kelting, H. "Investigation of Condominium sale prices in three market scenarios: Utility of stepwise, interactive, multiple regression analysis and implications for design and appraisal methodology." Unpublished paper, University of Florida, Gainesville, FL, 1979.

Mendenhall, W. *Introduction to Linear Models and the Design and Analysis of Experiments.* Belmont, CA: Wadsworth, 1968.

Mendenhall, W., and Sincich, T. *A Second Course in Statistics: Regression Analysis,* 6th ed. Upper Saddle River, NJ: Prentice Hall, 2003.

Mosteller, F., and Tukey, J. W. *Data Analysis and Regression: A Second Course in Statistics.* Reading, MA: Addison-Wesley, 1977.

Neter, J., Kutner, M., Nachtsheim, C., and Wasserman, W. *Applied Linear Statistical Models,* 4th ed. Homewood, IL: Richard Irwin, 1996.

Rousseeuw, P. J., and Leroy, A. M. *Robust Regression and Outlier Detection.* New York: Wiley, 1987.

Weisberg, S. *Applied Linear Regression,* 2d ed. New York: Wiley, 1985.

Using Technology

Multiple Regression with MINITAB

To conduct a multiple-regression analysis, first access the MINITAB worksheet file that contains the dependent and independent variables. Next, click on the "Stat" button on the MINITAB menu bar, and then click on "Regression" and "Regression" again, as shown in Figure 12.M.1.

The dialog box shown in Figure 12.M.2 then appears. Specify the dependent variable in the "Response" box and the independent variables in the "Predictors" box.

[*Note:* If your model includes interaction or squared terms, you must create and add these higher order variables to the MINITAB worksheet *prior to* running a regression analysis. You can do this by clicking the "Calc" button on the MINITAB main menu and selecting the "Calculator" option.]

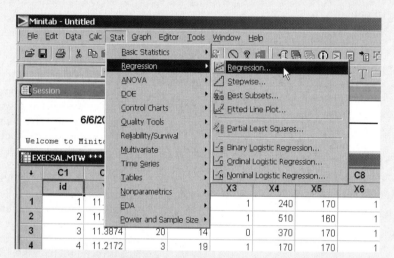

FIGURE 12.M.1
MINITAB menu options for regression

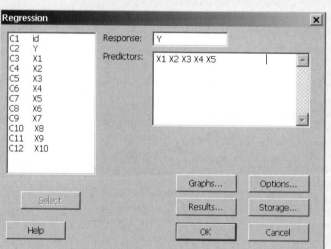

FIGURE 12.M.2
MINITAB regression dialog box

To produce prediction intervals for y and confidence intervals for $E(y)$, click the "Options" button and select the appropriate menu items in the resulting menu list. (See Figure 12.M.3.) Residual plots are obtained by clicking the "Graphs" button and making the appropriate selections on the resulting menu. (See Figure 12.M.4.) To return to the main Regression dialog box from any of these optional screens, click "OK. When you have made all your selections, click "OK" on the main Regression dialog box to produce the MINITAB multiple-regression printout.

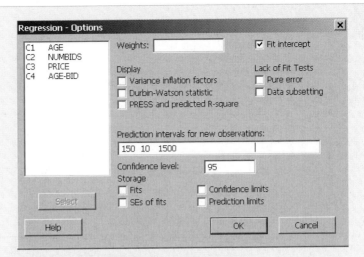

FIGURE 12.M.3
MINITAB options for
obtaining prediction intervals

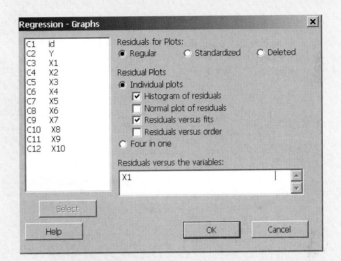

FIGURE 12.M.4
MINITAB options for
obtaining residual plots

To conduct a stepwise regression analysis, click on the "Stat" button on the main menu bar, then click on "Regression", and click on "Stepwise". (See Figure 12.M.1.) The dialog box shown in Figure 12.M.5 then appears. Specify the dependent variable in the "Response" box and the independent variables in the stepwise model in the "Predictors" box. As an option, you can select the click on the "Methods" button and specify the value of α to use in the analysis. (The default is $\alpha = .15$.) Click "OK" to view the stepwise regression results.

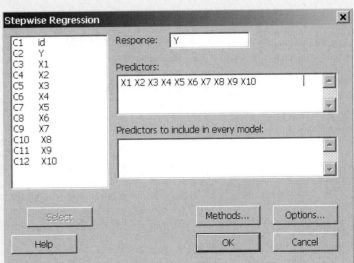

FIGURE 12.M.5
MINITAB stepwise regression
dialog box

Categorical Data Analysis

STATISTICS IN ACTION

College Students and Alcohol: Is Amount Consumed Related to Drinking Frequency?

USING TECHNOLOGY

Chi-Square Analyses with MINITAB

WHERE WE'VE BEEN

■ Presented methods for making inferences about the population proportion associated with a two-level qualitative variable (i.e., a binomial variable)

■ Presented methods for making inferences about the difference between two binomial proportions

WHERE WE'RE GOING

■ Discuss qualitative (i.e., categorical) data with more than two outcomes

■ Present a *chi-square* hypothesis test for comparing the category proportions associated with a single qualitative variable—called a *one-way analysis*

■ Present a chi-square hypothesis test for relating two qualitative variables—called a *two-way analysis*

STATISTICS IN ACTION

College Students and Alcohol: Is Amount Consumed Related to Drinking Frequency?

Traditionally, a common social activity on American college campuses is drinking alcohol. Despite laws on underage drinking, fraternities, sororities, and other campus groups often have alcohol available at their weekend parties. For some students, this activity leads to binge drinking and excessive alcohol use, often resulting in academic failure, physical violence, accidental injury, and even death. In fact, the Journal of Studies on Alcohol *(Vol. 63, 2002) recently reported that about 1,400 alcohol-related deaths occur each year on American college campuses.*

To gain insight into the alcohol consumption behavior of college students, professors Soyeon Shim (University of Arizona) and Jennifer Maggs (Pennsylvania State University) designed a study and reported their results in *Family and Consumer Sciences Research Journal* (Mar. 2005). Among the researchers' main objectives were (1) to segment college students on the basis of their rates of alcohol consumption and (2) to establish a statistical link between the frequency of drinking and the amount of alcohol consumed. They collected survey data from undergraduate students enrolled in a variety of courses at the University of Arizona, a large state university in the Southwest. To increase the likelihood of obtaining a representative sample, the researchers balanced the sample with both lower and upper division students, as well as students with majors in the social sciences, humanities, business, engineering, and the natural sciences. A total of 657 students completed usable surveys.

The survey consisted of a six-page booklet that took approximately 10 minutes to complete. Two of the many questions on the survey (and the subject of this *Statistics in Action*) pertained to the frequency with which the student drank alcohol (beer, wine, or liquor) during the previous one-month period and the average number of drinks the student consumed per occasion. From this information, the researchers categorized students according to Type of drinker. Responses for the three variables of interest were classified qualitatively as shown in Table SIA13.1. The data for the 657 students are saved in the **COLLDRINKS** file.

In an attempt to help the researcher's achieve their objectives, we apply the statistical methodology presented in this chapter to this data set in two *Statistics in Action Revisited* examples.

Statistics in Action Revisited

- Testing Category Proportions for Type of College Drinker (p. 749)

- Testing whether Frequency of Drinking Is Related to Amount of Alcohol Consumed (p. 762)

COLLDRINKS

TABLE SIA13.1 Qualitative Variables Measured in the Drinking Study

Variable Name	Levels (possible values)
AMOUNT	None, 1 drink, 2–3 drinks, 4–6 drinks, 7–9 drinks, 10 or more drinks
FREQUENCY	None, Once a month, Once or twice per week, More
TYPE	Non/Seldom, Social, Typical binge, Heavy binge

13.1 Categorical Data and the Multinomial Experiment

Recall from Section 1.4 (p. 11) that observations on a qualitative variable can only be categorized. For example, consider the highest level of education attained by a professional hockey player. Level of education is a qualitative variable with several categories, including some high school, high school diploma, some college, college undergraduate degree, and graduate degree. If we were to record education level for all professional hockey players, the result of the categorization would be a count of the numbers of players falling into the respective categories.

When the qualitative variable of interest results in one of two responses (e.g., yes or no, success or failure, favor or do not favor), the data—called *counts*—can be analyzed with the binomial probability distribution discussed in Section 4.4. However, qualitative variables, such as level of education, that allow for more than two categories for a response are much more common, and these must be analyzed by a different method.

Qualitative data with more than two levels often result from a **multinomial experiment**. The characteristics for a multinomial experiment with k outcomes are described in the next box. You can see that the binomial experiment of Chapter 4 is a multinomial experiment with $k = 2$.

Properties of the Multinomial Experiment

1. The experiment consists of n identical trials.

2. There are k possible outcomes to each trial. These outcomes are sometimes called **classes**, **categories**, or **cells**.

3. The probabilities of the k outcomes, denoted by $p_1, p_2, \ldots, p_k$, where $p_1 + p_2 + \cdots + p_k = 1$, remain the same from trial to trial.

4. The trials are independent.

5. The random variables of interest are the **cell counts** $n_1, n_2, \ldots, n_k$ of the number of observations that fall into each of the k categories.

EXAMPLE 13.1

IDENTIFYING A MULTINOMIAL EXPERIMENT

Problem Consider the problem of determining the highest level of education attained by each of a sample of $n = 40$ National Hockey League (NHL) players. Suppose we categorize level of education into one of five categories—some high school, high school diploma, some college, college undergraduate degree, and graduate degree—and count the number of the 40 players that fall into each category. Is this a multinomial experiment, to a reasonable degree of approximation?

Solution Checking the five properties of a multinomial experiment shown in the box, we have the following:

1. The experiment consists of $n = 40$ identical trials, each of which is undertaken to determine the education level of an NHL player.

2. There are $k = 5$ possible outcomes to each trial, corresponding to the five education-level responses.

3. The probabilities of the $k = 5$ outcomes p_1, p_2, p_3, p_4, and p_5, where p_i represents the true probability that an NHL player attains level-of-education category i, remain the same from trial to trial (to a reasonable degree of approximation).

4. The trials are independent; that is, the education level attained by one NHL player does not affect the level attained by any other player.

5. We are interested in the count of the number of hockey players who fall into each of the five education-level categories. These five cell counts are denoted n_1, n_2, n_3, n_4, and n_5.

Thus, the properties of a multinomial experiment are satisfied.

In this chapter, we are concerned with the analysis of categorical data—specifically, the data that represent the counts for each category of a multinomial experiment. In Section 13.2, we learn how to make inferences about the probabilities of categories for data classified according to a single qualitative (or categorical) variable. Then, in Section 13.3, we consider inferences about categorical probabilities for data classified according to two qualitative variables. The statistic used for these inferences is one that possesses, approximately, the familiar chi-square distribution.

13.2 Testing Categorical Probabilities: One-Way Table

In this section, we consider a multinomial experiment with k outcomes that correspond to the categories of a *single* qualitative variable. The results of such an experiment are summarized in a **one-way table.** The term *one-way* is used because only one variable is classified. Typically, we want to make inferences about the true percentages that occur in the k categories on the basis of the sample information in the one-way table.

To illustrate, suppose three political candidates are running for the same elective position. Prior to the election, we conduct a survey to determine the voting preferences of a random sample of 150 eligible voters. The qualitative variable of interest is *preferred candidate,* which has three possible outcomes: candidate 1, candidate 2, and candidate 3. Suppose the number of voters preferring each candidate is tabulated and the resulting count data appear as in Table 13.1.

TABLE 13.1 Results of Voter Preference Survey

Candidate		
1	**2**	**3**
61 votes	53 votes	36 votes

Note that our voter preference survey satisfies the properties of a multinomial experiment for the qualitative variable, preferred candidate. The experiment consists of randomly sampling $n = 150$ voters from a large population of voters containing an unknown proportion p_1 that favors candidate 1, a proportion p_2 that favors candidate 2, and a proportion p_3 that favors candidate 3. Each voter sampled represents a single trial that can result in one of three outcomes: The voter will favor candidate 1, 2, or 3 with probabilities p_1, p_2, and p_3, respectively. (Assume that all voters will have a preference.) The voting preference of any single voter in the sample does not affect the preference of any other; consequently, the trials are independent. Finally, you can see that the recorded data are the numbers of voters in each of the three preference categories. Thus, the voter preference survey satisfies the five properties of a multinomial experiment.

In this survey, and in most practical applications of the multinomial experiment, the k outcome probabilities $p_1, p_2, \ldots, p_k$ are unknown and we want to use the survey data to make inferences about their values. The unknown probabilities in the voter preference survey are

$$p_1 = \text{Proportion of all voters who favor candidate 1}$$
$$p_2 = \text{Proportion of all voters who favor candidate 2}$$
$$p_3 = \text{Proportion of all voters who favor candidate 3}$$

To decide whether the voters, in total, have a preference for any one of the candidates, we will test the null hypothesis that the candidates are equally preferred (i.e., $p_1 = p_2 = p_3 = \frac{1}{3}$) against the alternative hypothesis that one candidate is preferred (i.e., at least one of the probabilities p_1, p_2, and p_3 exceeds $\frac{1}{3}$). Thus, we want to test

H_0: $p_1 = p_2 = p_3 = \frac{1}{3}$ (no preference)

H_a: At least one of the proportions exceeds $\frac{1}{3}$ (a preference exists)

If the null hypothesis is true and $p_1 = p_2 = p_3 = \frac{1}{3}$, then the expected value (mean value) of the number of voters who prefer candidate 1 is given by

$$E_1 = np_1 = (n)\tfrac{1}{3} = (150)\tfrac{1}{3} = 50$$

Similarly, $E_2 = E_3 = 50$ if the null hypothesis is true and no preference exists.

The **chi-square test** measures the degree of disagreement between the data and the null hypothesis:

$$\chi^2 = \frac{[n_1 - E_1]^2}{E_1} + \frac{[n_2 - E_2]^2}{E_2} + \frac{[n_3 - E_3]^2}{E_3}$$
$$= \frac{(n_1 - 50)^2}{50} + \frac{(n_2 - 50)^2}{50} + \frac{(n_3 - 50)^2}{50}$$

Note that the farther the observed numbers n_1, n_2, and n_3 are from their expected value (50), the larger χ^2 will become. That is, large values of χ^2 imply that the null hypothesis is false.

Biography

KARL PEARSON
(1895–1980)—the Father of Statistics

While attending college, London-born Karl Pearson exhibited a wide range of interests, including mathematics, physics, religion, history, socialism, and Darwinism. After earning a law degree at Cambridge University and a Ph.D. in political science at the University of Heidelberg (Germany), Pearson became a professor of applied mathematics at University College in London. His 1892 book, *The Grammar of Science*, illustrated his convic-

tion that statistical data analysis lies at the foundation of all knowledge; consequently, many consider Pearson to be the "father of statistics." Among Pearson's many contributions to the field are introducing the term *standard deviation* and its associated symbol (σ); developing the distribution of the correlation coefficient; cofounding and editing the prestigious statistics journal *Biometrika*; and (what many consider his greatest achievement) creating the first chi-square "goodness-of-fit" test. Pearson inspired his students (including his son, Egon, and William Gossett) with his wonderful lectures and enthusiasm for statistics.

We have to know the distribution of χ^2 in repeated sampling before we can decide whether the data indicate that a preference exists. When H_0 is true, χ^2 can be shown to have (approximately) the familiar chi-square distribution of Section 8.7. For this one-way classification, the χ^2 distribution has $(k - 1)$ degrees of freedom.* The rejection region for the voter preference survey for $\alpha = .05$ and $k - 1 = 3 - 1 = 2$ df is

$$\text{Rejection region: } \chi^2 > \chi^2_{.05}$$

This value of $\chi^2_{.05}$ (found in Table VII) is 5.99147. (See Figure 13.1.) The computed value of the test statistic is

$$\chi^2 = \frac{(n_1 - 50)^2}{50} + \frac{(n_2 - 50)^2}{50} + \frac{(n_3 - 50)^2}{50}$$

$$= \frac{(61 - 50)^2}{50} + \frac{(53 - 50)^2}{50} + \frac{(36 - 50)^2}{50} = 6.52$$

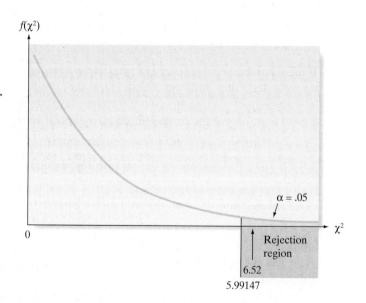

FIGURE 13.1

Rejection region for voter preference survey

*The derivation of the number of degrees of freedom for χ^2 involves the number of linear restrictions imposed on the count data. In the present case, the only constraint is that $\Sigma n_i = n$, where n (the sample size) is fixed in advance. Therefore, df $= k - 1$. For other cases, we will give the number of degrees of freedom for each usage of χ^2 and refer the interested reader to the references for more detail.

Since the computed $\chi^2 = 6.52$ exceeds the critical value of 5.99147, we conclude at the $\alpha = .05$ level of significance that there does exist a voter preference for one or more of the candidates.

Now that we have evidence to indicate that the proportions p_1, p_2, and p_3 are unequal, we can use the methods of Section 7.4 to make inferences concerning their individual values. [*Note:* We cannot use the methods of Section 9.4 to compare two proportions, because the cell counts are dependent random variables.] The general form for a test of hypothesis concerning multinomial probabilities is shown in the following box:

A Test of a Hypothesis about Multinomial Probabilities: One-Way Table

H_0: $p_1 = p_{1,0}$, $p_2 = p_{2,0}, \ldots, p_k = p_{k,0}$

where $p_{1,0}, p_{2,0}, \ldots, p_{k,0}$ represent the hypothesized values of the multinomial probabilities

H_a: At least one of the multinomial probabilities does not equal its hypothesized value

Test statistic: $\chi^2 = \sum \dfrac{[n_i - E_i]^2}{E_i}$

where $E_i = np_{i,0}$ is the **expected cell count**—that is, the expected number of outcomes of type i, assuming that H_0 is true. The total sample size is n.

Rejection region: $\chi^2 > \chi^2_\alpha$, where χ^2_α has $(k - 1)$ df

---

Conditions Required for a Valid χ^2 Test: One-Way Table

1. A multinomial experiment has been conducted. This is generally satisfied by taking a random sample from the population of interest.

2. The sample size n will be large enough so that, for every cell, the expected cell count $E(n_i)$ will be equal to 5 or more.*

EXAMPLE 13.2

A ONE-WAY χ^2 TEST—Effectiveness of a TV Program on Marijuana

Problem Suppose an educational television station has broadcast a series of programs on the physiological and psychological effects of smoking marijuana. Now that the series is finished, the station wants to see whether the citizens within the viewing area have changed their minds about how the possession of marijuana should be considered legally. Before the series was shown, it was determined that 7% of the citizens favored legalization, 18% favored decriminalization, 65% favored the existing law (an offender could be fined or imprisoned), and 10% had no opinion.

A summary of the opinions (after the series was shown) of a random sample of 500 people in the viewing area is given in Table 13.2. Test at the $\alpha = .01$ level to see whether these data indicate that the distribution of opinions differs significantly from the proportions that existed before the educational series was aired.

 MARIJUANA

TABLE 13.2 Distribution of Opinions about Marijuana Possession

Legalization	Decriminalization	Existing Laws	No Opinion
39	99	336	26

---

*The assumption that all expected cell counts are at least 5 is necessary in order to ensure that the χ^2 approximation is appropriate. Exact methods for conducting the test of hypothesis exist and may be used for small expected cell counts, but these methods are beyond the scope of this text.

Solution Define the proportions after the airing to be

$$p_1 = \text{Proportion of citizens favoring legalization}$$
$$p_2 = \text{Proportion of citizens favoring decriminalization}$$
$$p_3 = \text{Proportion of citizens favoring existing laws}$$
$$p_4 = \text{Proportion of citizens with no opinion}$$

Then the null hypothesis representing no change in the distribution of percentages is

$$H_0: p_1 = .07, \ p_2 = .18, \ p_3 = .65, \ p_4 = .10$$

and the alternative is

H_a: At least one of the proportions differs from its null hypothesized value

Thus, we have

$$\text{Test statistic: } \chi^2 = \sum \frac{[n_i - E_i]^2}{E_i}$$

where

$$E_1 = np_{1,0} = 500(.07) = 35$$
$$E_2 = np_{2,0} = 500(.18) = 90$$
$$E_3 = np_{3,0} = 500(.65) = 325$$
$$E_4 = np_{4,0} = 500(.10) = 50$$

Since all these values are larger than 5, the χ^2 approximation is appropriate. Also, if the citizens in the sample were randomly selected, then the properties of the multinomial probability distribution are satisfied.

Rejection region: For $\alpha = .01$ and df $= k - 1 = 3$, reject H_0 if $\chi^2 > \chi^2_{.01}$, where (from Table VII in Appendix A) $\chi^2_{.01} = 11.3449$.

We now calculate the test statistic:

$$\chi^2 = \frac{(39 - 35)^2}{35} + \frac{(99 - 90)^2}{90} + \frac{(336 - 325)^2}{325} + \frac{(26 - 50)^2}{50} = 13.249$$

Since this value exceeds the table value of χ^2 (11.3449), the data provide sufficient evidence ($\alpha = .01$) that the opinions on the legalization of marijuana have changed since the series was aired.

The χ^2 test can also be conducted with the use of an available statistical software package. Figure 13.2 is an SPSS printout of the analysis of the data in Table 13.2. The test statistic and p-value of the test are highlighted on the printout. Since $\alpha = .01$ exceeds $p = .004$, there is sufficient evidence to reject H_0.

OPINION

	Observed N	Expected N	Residual
LEGAL	39	35.0	4.0
DECRIM	99	90.0	9.0
EXISTLAW	336	325.0	11.0
NONE	26	50.0	-24.0
Total	500		

Test Statistics

	OPINION
Chi-Square[a]	13.249
df	3
Asymp. Sig.	.004

a. 0 cells (.0%) have expected frequencies less than 5. The minimum expected cell frequency is 35.0.

FIGURE 13.2
SPSS analysis of data in Table 13.2

Look Back If the conclusion for the χ^2 test is "fail to reject H_0," then there is insufficient evidence to conclude that the distribution of opinions differs from the proportions stated in H_0. Be careful not to "accept H_0" and conclude that $p_1 = .07$, $p_2 = .18$, $p_3 = .65$, and $p_4 = .10$. The probability (β) of a Type II error is unknown.

> **Now Work Exercise 13.9**

If we focus on one particular outcome of a multinomial experiment, we can use the methods developed in Section 7.4 for a binomial proportion to establish a confidence interval for any one of the multinomial probabilities.* For example, if we want a 95% confidence interval for the proportion of citizens in the viewing area who have no opinion about the issue, we calculate

$$\hat{p}_4 \pm 1.96\sigma_{\hat{p}_4}$$

where

$$\hat{p}_4 = \frac{n_4}{n} = \frac{26}{500} = .052 \quad \text{and} \quad \sigma_{\hat{p}_4} \approx \sqrt{\frac{\hat{p}_4(1 - \hat{p}_4)}{n}}$$

Thus, we get

$$.052 \pm 1.96\sqrt{\frac{(.052)(.948)}{500}} = .052 \pm .019$$

or (.033, .071). Consequently, we estimate that between 3.3% and 7.1% of the citizens now have no opinion on the issue of the legalization of marijuana. The series of programs may have helped citizens who formerly had no opinion on the issue to form an opinion, since it appears that the proportion of "no opinions" is now less than 10%.

ACTIVITY 13.1: Binomial versus Multinomial Experiments

In this activity, you will study the difference between binomial and multinomial experiments.

1. A television station has hired an independent research group to determine whether television viewers in the area prefer its local news program to the news programs of two other stations in the same city. Explain why a multinomial experiment would be appropriate, and design a poll that satisfies the five properties of a multinomial experiment. State the null and alternative hypotheses for the corresponding χ^2 test.

2. Suppose the television station believes that a majority of local viewers prefers its news program to those of its two competitors. Explain why a binomial experiment would be appropriate to support this claim, and design a poll that satisfies the five properties of a binomial experiment. State the null and alternative hypotheses for the corresponding test.

3. Generalize the situations in Exercises 1 and 2 in order to describe conditions under which a multinomial experiment can be rephrased as a binomial experiment. Is there any advantage in doing so? Explain.

STATISTICS IN ACTION REVISITED

Testing Category Proportions for Type of College Drinker

In the *Family and Consumer Sciences Research Journal* (Mar. 2005) study of college students and drinking (p. 743), one of the researchers' main objectives was to segment college students according to their rates of alcohol consumption. A segmentation was developed on the basis of the students' responses to the questions on frequency of drinking and average number of drinks per occasion. Four types, or groups, of college drinkers emerged: non/seldom drinkers, social drinkers, typical binge drinkers, and heavy binge drinkers. What are the proportions of students in each of these groups, and are these proportions statistically different?

(continued)

---

*Note that focusing on one outcome has the effect of lumping the other $(k - 1)$ outcomes into a single group. Thus, we obtain, in effect, two outcomes—or a binomial experiment.

FIGURE SIA13.1

SPSS descriptive statistics and graph for type of drinker

TYPE

		Frequency	Percent	Valid Percent	Cumulative Percent
Valid	Non/Seldom	118	18.0	18.0	18.0
	Social	282	42.9	42.9	60.9
	Typical Binge	163	24.8	24.8	85.7
	Heavy Binge	94	14.3	14.3	100.0
	Total	657	100.0	100.0	

TYPE

To answer these questions, we used SPSS to analyze the type-of-drinker variable in the **COLLDRINKS** file. Figure SIA13.1 shows summary statistics and a graph describing the four categories. From the summary table at the top of the printout, you can see that 118 (or 18%) of the students are non/seldom drinkers, 282 (or 43%) are social drinkers, 163 (or 25%) are typical binge drinkers, and 94 (or 14%) are heavy binge drinkers. These sample percentages are illustrated in the bar graph in Figure SIA13.1. In this sample of students, the largest percentage (43%) consists of social drinkers.

Is this sufficient evidence to indicate that the true proportions in the population of college students are different? Letting p_1, p_2, p_3, and p_4 represent the true proportions for non/seldom, social, typical binge, and heavy binge drinkers, respectively, we tested H_0: $p_1 = p_2 = p_3 = p_4 = .25$, using the chi-square test in SPSS. The printout is displayed in Figure SIA13.2. The cell frequencies and expected numbers are shown in the top table of the figure, while the chi-square test statistic (127.5) and p-value (.000) are shown in the bottom table. At any reasonably selected α-level (say, $\alpha = .01$), the small p-value indicates that there is sufficient evidence to reject the null hypothesis; thus, we conclude that the true proportions associated with the four type-of-drinker categories are indeed statistically different.

Chi-Square Test

Frequencies

TYPE

	Observed N	Expected N	Residual
Non/Seldom	118	164.3	-46.3
Social	282	164.3	117.8
Typical Binge	163	164.3	-1.3
Heavy Binge	94	164.3	-70.3
Total	657		

Test Statistics

	TYPE
Chi-Square[a]	127.493
df	3
Asymp. Sig.	.000

a. 0 cells (.0%) have expected frequencies less than 5. The minimum expected cell frequency is 164.3.

FIGURE SIA13.2

SPSS chi-square test for type-of-drinker categories

Exercises 13.1–13.18

Understanding the Principles

13.1 What are the characteristics of a multinomial experiment? Compare the characteristics with those of a binomial experiment.

13.2 What conditions must n satisfy to make the χ^2 test for a one-way table valid?

Learning the Mechanics

13.3 Use Table VII of Appendix A to find each of the following χ^2 values:
a. $\chi^2_{.05}$ for df $= 10$
b. $\chi^2_{.990}$ for df $= 50$
c. $\chi^2_{.10}$ for df $= 16$
d. $\chi^2_{.005}$ for df $= 50$

13.4 Use Table VII of Appendix A to find the following probabilities:
a. $P(\chi^2 \leq 1.063623)$ for df $= 4$
b. $P(\chi^2 > 30.5779)$ for df $= 15$
c. $P(\chi^2 \geq 82.3581)$ for df $= 100$
d. $P(\chi^2 < 18.4926)$ for df $= 30$

13.5 Find the rejection region for a one-dimensional χ^2-test of a null hypothesis concerning $p_1, p_2, \ldots, p_k$ if
a. $k = 3; \alpha = .05$
b. $k = 5; \alpha = .10$
c. $k = 4; \alpha = .01$

13.6 A multinomial experiment with $k = 3$ cells and $n = 320$ produced the data shown in the accompanying table. Do these data provide sufficient evidence to contradict the null hypothesis that $p_1 = .25, p_2 = .25$, and $p_3 = .50$? Test, using $\alpha = .05$.

	Cell		
	1	2	3
n_i	78	60	182

13.7 A multinomial experiment with $k = 4$ cells and $n = 205$ produced the data shown in the following table:

	Cell			
	1	2	3	4
n_i	43	56	59	47

a. Do these data provide sufficient evidence to conclude that the multinomial probabilities differ? Test, using $\alpha = .05$.
b. What are the Type I and Type II errors associated with the test of part **a**?
c. Construct a 95% confidence interval for the multinomial probability associated with cell 3.

13.8 A multinomial experiment with $k = 4$ cells and $n = 400$ produced the data shown in the accompanying table. Do these data provide sufficient evidence to contradict the null hypothesis that $p_1 = .2, p_2 = .4, p_3 = .1$, and $p_4 = .3$? Test, using $\alpha = .05$.

	Cell			
	1	2	3	4
n_i	70	196	46	88

Applying the Concepts—Basic

13.9 **Jaw dysfunction study.** A report on dental patients with
NW temporomandibular (jaw) joint dysfunction (TMD) was published in *General Dentistry* (Jan/Feb. 2004). A random sample of 60 patients was selected for an experimental treatment of TMD. Prior to treatment, the patients filled out a survey on two nonfunctional jaw habits—bruxism (teeth grinding) and teeth clenching—that have been linked to TMD. Of the 60 patients, 3 admitted to bruxism, 11 admitted to teeth clenching, 30 admitted to both habits, and 16 claimed they had neither habit.
a. Describe the qualitative variable of interest in the study. Give the levels (categories) associated with the variable.
b. Construct a one-way table for the sample data.
c. Give the null and alternative hypotheses for testing whether the percentages associated with the admitted habits are the same.
d. Calculate the expected numbers for each cell of the one-way table.
e. Calculate the appropriate test statistic.
f. Give the rejection region for the test at $\alpha = .05$.
g. Give the appropriate conclusion in the words of the problem.
h. Find and interpret a 95% confidence interval for the true proportion of dental patients who admit to both habits.

13.10 **Location of major sports venues.** There has been a recent trend for professional sports franchises in Major League Baseball (MLB), the National Football League (NFL), the National Basketball Association (NBA), and the National Hockey League (NHL) to build new stadiums and ballparks in urban, downtown venues. An article in *Professional Geographer* (Feb. 2000) investigated whether there has been a significant suburban-to-urban shift in the location of major sport facilities. In 1985, 40% of all major sport facilities were located downtown, 30% in central cities, and 30% in suburban areas. In contrast, of the 113 major sports franchises that existed in 1997, 58 were built downtown, 26 in central cities, and 29 in suburban areas.
a. Describe the qualitative variable of interest in the study. Give the levels (categories) associated with the variable.
b. Give the null hypothesis for a test to determine whether the proportions of major sports facilities in downtown, central city, and suburban areas in 1997 are the same as in 1985.
c. If the null hypothesis of part **b** is true, how many of the 113 sports facilities in 1997 would you expect to be located in downtown, central city, and suburban areas, respectively?
d. Find the value of the chi-square statistic for testing the null hypothesis of part **b**.

e. Find the (approximate) *p*-value of the test, and give the appropriate conclusion in the words of the problem. Assume that $\alpha = .05$.

13.11 Excavating ancient pottery. Refer to the *Chance* (Fall 2000) study of ancient Greek pottery, presented in Exercise 2.12 (p. 35). Recall that 837 pottery pieces were uncovered at the excavation site. The table describing the types of pottery found is reproduced here:

Pot Category	Number Found
Burnished	133
Monochrome	460
Painted	183
Other	61
Total	**837**

Source: Berg, I., and Bliedon, S. "The Pots of Phyiakopi: Applying statistical Techniques to Archaeology." *Chance,* Vol. 13, No. 4, Fall 2000.

a. Describe the qualitative variable of interest in the study. Give the levels (categories) associated with the variable.

b. Assume that the four types of pottery occur with equal probability at the excavation site. What are the values of $p_1, p_2, p_3,$ and p_4, the probabilities associated with the four pottery types?

c. Give the null and alternative hypotheses for testing whether one type of pottery is more likely to occur at the site than any of the other types.

d. Find the test statistic for testing the hypotheses stated in part **c**.

e. Find and interpret the *p*-value of the test. State the conclusion in the words of the problem if you use $\alpha = .10$.

13.12 "Made in the USA" survey. Refer to the *Journal of Global Business* (Spring 2002) study of what "Made in the USA" on product labels means to the typical consumer, presented in Exercise 2.13 (p. 36). Recall that 106 shoppers participated in the survey. Their responses, given as a percentage of U.S. labor and materials in four categories, are summarized in the accompanying table. Suppose a consumer advocate group claims that half of all consumers believe that "Made in the USA" means "100%" of labor and materials are produced in the United States, one-fourth believe that "75 to 99%" are produced in the United States, one-fifth believe that "50 to 74%" are produced in the United States, and 5 percent believe that "less than 50%" are produced in the United States.

Response to "Made in the USA"	Number of Shoppers
100%	64
75 to 99%	20
50 to 74%	18
Less than 50%	4

Source: "'Made in the USA': Consumer perceptions, deception and policy alternatives," *Journal of Global Business,* Vol. 13, No. 24, Spring 2002 (Table 3).

a. Describe the qualitative variable of interest in the study. Give the levels (categories) associated with the variable.

b. What are the values of $p_1, p_2, p_3,$ and p_4, the probabilities associated with the four response categories hypothesized by the consumer advocate group?

c. Give the null and alternative hypotheses for testing the consumer advocate group's claim.

d. Compute the test statistic for testing the hypotheses stated in part **c**.

e. Find the rejection region of the test at $\alpha = .10$.

f. State the conclusion in the words of the problem.

g. Find and interpret a 90% confidence interval for the true proportion of consumers who believe that "Made in the USA" means that "100%" of labor and materials are produced in the United States.

Applying the Concepts—Intermediate

13.13 Top Internet search engines. Nielsen/NetRatings is a global leader in Internet media and market research. In May 2006, the firm reported on the "search" shares (i.e., the percentage of all Internet searches) for the most popular search engines available on the Web. Google Search accounted for 50% of all searches, Yahoo! Search for 22%, MSN Search for 11%, and all other search engines for 17%. Suppose that, in a random sample of 1,000 recent Internet searches, 487 used Google Search, 245 used Yahoo! Search, 121 used MSN Search, and 147 used another search engine.

a. Do the sample data disagree with the percentages reported by Nielsen/NetRatings? Test, using $\alpha = .05$.

b. Find and interpret a 95% confidence interval for the percentage of all Internet searches that use the Google Search engine.

13.14 Sociology fieldwork methods. Refer to the *Teaching Sociology* (July 2006) study of the fieldwork methods used by qualitative sociologists, presented in Exercise 2.14 (p. 36). Recall that fieldwork methods can be categorized as follows: Interview, Observation plus Participation, Observation Only, and Grounded Theory. The accompanying table shows the number of papers published over the past seven years in each category. Suppose a sociologist claims that 70%, 15%, 10%, and 5% of the fieldwork methods involve interview, observation plus participation, observation only, and grounded theory, respectively. Do the data support or refute the claim? Explain.

⊙ FIELDWORK

Fieldwork Method	Number of Papers
Interview	5,079
Observation + Participation	1,042
Observation Only	848
Grounded Theory	537

Source: Hood, J.C. "Teaching against the Text: The Case of Qualitative Methods," *Teaching Sociology,* Vol. 34, July 2006 (Exhibit 2).

⊙ BIBLE

13.15 Do you believe in the Bible? Refer to the General Social Survey (GSS) and the question pertaining to a person's belief in the Bible, presented in Exercise 2.17 (p. 36). Recall that approximately 2,800 Americans selected from one of the following answers: (1) The Bible is the actual word of God and is to be taken literally; (2) the Bible is the inspired word of God, but not everything is to be taken literally; (3) the Bible is an ancient book of fables; or (4) the Bible has some other origin, but is recorded by men. The variable "Bible1" in the **BIBLE** file contains the responses.

a. Summarize the responses in a one-way table.

b. State the null and alternative hypotheses for testing whether the true proportions in each category are equal.

c. Find the expected number of responses in each answer category for the test mentioned in part **b**.

d. Compute the chi-square statistic for the test.

e. Give the appropriate conclusion for the test if $\alpha = .10$.

f. A more realistic null hypothesis is that 30% of Americans believe that the Bible is the actual word of God; 50% believe that it is inspired by God, but not to be taken literally; 15% believe that it is an ancient book of fables; and 5% believe that the Bible has some other origin. Repeat parts **b–e** for this hypothesis.

PONDICE

13.16 Characteristics of ice-melt ponds. Refer to the National Snow and Ice Data Center (NSIDC) collection of data on 504 ice-melt ponds in the Canadian Arctic, presented in Exercise 12.167 (p. 737). The data are saved in the **PONDICE** file. One variable of interest to environmental engineers studying the ponds is the type of ice observed in each. Ice type is classified as first-year ice, multiyear ice, or landfast ice. The SAS summary table for the types of ice of the 504 ice-melt ponds is reproduced at the bottom of the page.

a. Use a 90% confidence interval to estimate the proportion of ice-melt ponds in the Canadian Arctic that have first-year ice.

b. Suppose environmental engineers hypothesize that 15% of Canadian Arctic ice-melt ponds have first-year ice, 40% have landfast ice, and 45% have multiyear ice. Test the engineers' theory, using $\alpha = .01$.

Applying the Concepts—Advanced

13.17 Analysis of a Scrabble game. In the board game Scrabble™, a player initially draws a "hand" of seven tiles at random from 100 tiles. Each tile has a letter of the alphabet, and the player attempts to form a word from the letters in his or her hand. In *Chance* (Winter 2002), scientist C. J. Robinove investigated whether a handheld electronic version of the game, called ScrabbleExpress™, produces too few vowels in the 7-letter draws. For each of the 26 letters (and "blank" for any letter), the accompanying table gives the true relative frequency of the letter in the board game, as well as the frequency of occurrence of the letter

SCRABBLE

Letter	Relative Frequency in Board Game	Frequency in Electronic Game
A	.09	39
B	.02	18
C	.02	30
D	.04	30
E	.12	31
F	.02	21
G	.03	35
H	.02	21
I	.09	25
J	.01	17
K	.01	27
L	.04	18
M	.02	31
N	.06	36
O	.08	20
P	.02	27
Q	.01	13
R	.06	27
S	.04	29
T	.06	27
U	.04	21
V	.02	33
W	.02	29
X	.01	15
Y	.02	32
Z	.01	14
# (blank)	.02	34
Total		700

Source: Robinove, C. J. "Letter-frequency Bias in an Electronic Scrabble Game," *Chance,* Vol. 15, No. 1, Winter 2002, p. 31 (Table 3).

in a sample of 700 tiles (i.e., 100 "hands") randomly drawn in the electronic game.

a. Do the data support the scientist's contention that ScrabbleExpress™ "presents the player with unfair word selection opportunities" that are not the same as the Scrabble™ board game? Test, using $\alpha = .05$.

b. Use a 95% confidence interval to estimate the true proportion of letters drawn in the electronic game that are vowels. Compare the results with the true relative frequency of a vowel in the board game.

13.18 Political representation of religious groups. Do those elected to the U.S. House of Representatives really "represent" their constituents demographically? This was a

SAS output for Exercise 13.16

	The FREQ Procedure			
ICETYPE	Frequency	Percent	Cumulative Frequency	Cumulative Percent
First-year	88	17.46	88	17.46
Landfast	196	38.89	284	56.35
Multi-year	220	43.65	504	100.00

question of interest in *Chance* (Summer 2002). One of several demographics studied was religious affiliation. The accompanying table gives the proportion of the U.S. population for several religions, as well as the number of the 435 seats in the House of Representatives which are affiliated with that religion. Give your opinion on whether or not the members of the House of Representatives are statistically representative of the religious affiliation of their constituents in the United States.

USHOUSE

Religion	Proportion of U.S. Population	Number of Seats in House
Catholic	.28	117
Methodist	.04	61
Jewish	.02	30
Other	.66	227
TOTALS	1.00	435

13.3 Testing Categorical Probabilities: Two-Way (Contingency) Table

In Section 13.2, we introduced the multinomial probability distribution and considered data classified according to a single criterion. We now consider multinomial experiments in which the data are classified according to two criteria—that is, *classification with respect to two qualitative factors.*

Consider a study in the *Journal of Marketing* (Fall 1992) on the impact of using celebrities in television advertisements. The researchers investigated the relationship between the gender of a viewer and the viewer's brand awareness. Three hundred TV viewers were asked to identify products advertised by male celebrity spokespersons. The data are summarized in the **two-way table** shown in Table 13.3. This table, called a **contingency table**, presents multinomial count data classified on two scales, or **dimensions, of classification**: gender of viewer and brand awareness.

TABLE 13.3 Contingency Table for Marketing Example

		Gender		
		Male	Female	Totals
Brand Awareness	**Could Identify Product**	95	41	136
	Could Not Identify Product	55	109	164
	Totals	150	150	300

The symbols representing the cell counts for the multinomial experiment in Table 13.3 are shown in Table 13.4a, and the corresponding cell, row, and column probabilities are shown in Table 13.4b. Thus, n_{11} represents the number of viewers who are male and could identify the brand, and p_{11} represents the corresponding cell probability. Note the symbols for the row and column totals and also the symbols for the probability totals. The latter are called **marginal probabilities** for each row and column. The marginal probability p_{r1} is the probability that a TV viewer identifies the product; the marginal probability p_{c1} is the probability that a TV viewer is male. Thus,

$$p_{r1} = p_{11} + p_{12} \text{ and } p_{c1} = p_{11} + p_{21}$$

TABLE 13.4a Observed Counts for Contingency Table 13.3

		Gender		
		Male	Female	Totals
Brand Awareness	**Could Identify Product**	n_{11}	n_{12}	R_1
	Could Not Identify Product	n_{21}	n_{22}	R_2
	Totals	C_1	C_2	n

TABLE 13.4b Probabilities for Contingency Table 13.3

		Gender		
		Male	Female	Totals
Brand Awareness	**Could Identify Product**	p_{11}	p_{12}	p_{r1}
	Could Not Identify Product	p_{21}	p_{22}	p_{r2}
	Totals	p_{c1}	p_{c2}	1

We can see, then, that this really is a multinomial experiment with a total of 300 trials, $(2)(2) = 4$ cells or possible outcomes, and probabilities for each cell as shown in Table 13.4b. If the 300 TV viewers are randomly chosen, the trials are considered independent and the probabilities are viewed as remaining constant from trial to trial.

Suppose we want to know whether the two classifications of gender and brand awareness are dependent. That is, if we know the gender of the TV viewer, does that information give us a clue about the viewer's brand awareness? In a probabilistic sense, we know (Chapter 3) that the independence of events A and B implies that $P(AB) = P(A)P(B)$. Similarly, in the contingency table analysis, if the **two classifications are independent**, the probability that an item is classified into any particular cell of the table is the product of the corresponding marginal probabilities. Thus, under the hypothesis of independence, in Table 13.4b we must have

$$p_{11} = p_{r1}p_{c1} \quad p_{12} = p_{r1}p_{c2}$$
$$p_{21} = p_{r2}p_{c1} \quad p_{22} = p_{r2}p_{c2}$$

To test the hypothesis of independence, we use the same reasoning employed in the one-dimensional tests of Section 13.2. First, we calculate the *expected*, or *mean, count in each cell*, assuming that the null hypothesis of independence is true. We do this by noting that the expected count in a cell of the table is just the total number of multinomial trials, n, times the cell probability. Recall that n_{ij} represents the **observed count** in the cell located in the ith row and jth column. Then the expected cell count for the upper left-hand cell (first row, first column) is

$$E_{11} = np_{11}$$

or, when the null hypothesis (the classifications are independent) is true,

$$E_{11} = np_{r1}p_{c1}$$

Since these true probabilities are not known, we estimate p_{r1} and p_{c1} by the same proportions $\hat{p}_{r1} = R_1/n$ and $\hat{p}_{c1} = C_1/n$. Thus, the estimate of the expected value $E(n_{11})$ is

$$E_{11} = n\left(\frac{R_1}{n}\right)\left(\frac{C_1}{n}\right) = \frac{R_1C_1}{n}$$

Similarly, for each i, j,

$$E_{ij} = \frac{(\text{Row total})(\text{Column total})}{\text{Total sample size}}$$

Hence,

$$E_{12} = \frac{R_1C_2}{n}$$
$$E_{21} = \frac{R_2C_1}{n}$$
$$E_{22} = \frac{R_2C_2}{n}$$

Finding Expected Cell Counts for a Two-Way Contingency Table

The estimate of the expected number of observations falling into the cell in row i and column j is given by

$$E_{ij} = \frac{R_i C_j}{n}$$

where R_i = total for row i, C_j = total for column j, and n = sample size.

Using the data in Table 13.3, we find that

$$E_{11} = \frac{R_1 C_1}{n} = \frac{(136)(150)}{300} = 68$$

$$E_{12} = \frac{R_1 C_2}{n} = \frac{(136)(150)}{300} = 68$$

$$E_{21} = \frac{R_2 C_1}{n} = \frac{(164)(150)}{300} = 82$$

$$E_{22} = \frac{R_2 C_2}{n} = \frac{(164)(150)}{300} = 82$$

The observed data and the estimated expected values (in parentheses) are shown in Table 13.5.

We now use the χ^2 statistic to compare the observed and expected (estimated) counts in each cell of the contingency table:

$$\chi^2 = \frac{[n_{11} - E_{11}]^2}{E_{11}} + \frac{[n_{12} - E_{12}]^2}{E_{12}} + \frac{[n_{21} - E_{21}]^2}{E_{21}} + \frac{[n_{22} - E_{22}]^2}{E_{22}}$$

$$= \sum \frac{[n_{ij} - E_{ij}]^2}{E_{ij}}$$

(*Note:* The use of $\sum$ in the context of a contingency table analysis refers to a sum over all cells in the table.)

Substituting the data of Table 13.5 into this expression, we get

$$\chi^2 = \frac{(95 - 68)^2}{68} + \frac{(41 - 68)^2}{68} + \frac{(55 - 82)^2}{82} + \frac{(109 - 82)^2}{82} = 39.22$$

TABLE 13.5 Observed and Estimated Expected (in Parentheses) Counts

		Gender		
		Male	Female	Totals
	Could Identify Product	95	41	136
		(68)	(68)	
Brand Awareness	**Could Not Identify Product**	55	109	164
		(82)	(82)	
	Totals	150	150	300

Large values of χ^2 imply that the observed counts do not closely agree and hence that the hypothesis of independence is false. To determine how large χ^2 must be before it is too large to be attributed to chance, we make use of the fact that the sampling distribution of χ^2 is approximately a χ^2 probability distribution when the classifications are independent.

In testing the null hypothesis of independence in a two-way contingency table, the appropriate degrees of freedom will be $(r - 1)(c - 1)$, where r is the number of rows and c is the number of columns in the table.

For the brand awareness example, the number of degrees of freedom for χ^2 is $(r - 1)(c - 1) = (2 - 1)(2 - 1) = 1$. Then, for $\alpha = .05$, we reject the hypothesis of independence when

$$\chi^2 > \chi^2_{.05} = 3.84146$$

Since the computed $\chi^2 = 39.22$ exceeds the value 3.84146, we conclude that viewer gender and brand awareness are dependent events.

The pattern of **dependence** can be seen more clearly by expressing the data as percentages. We first select one of the two classifications to be used as the base variable. In the preceding example, suppose we select gender of the TV viewer as the classificatory variable to be the base. Next, we represent the responses for each level of the second categorical variable (brand awareness here) as a percentage of the subtotal for the base variable. For example, from Table 13.5, we convert the response for males who identify the brand (95) to a percentage of the total number of male viewers (150). That is,

$$(^{95}/_{150})100\% = 63.3\%$$

All of the entries in Table 13.5 are similarly converted, and the values are shown in Table 13.6. The value shown at the right of each row is the row's total, expressed as a percentage of the total number of responses in the entire table. Thus, the percentage of TV view-ers who identify the product is $(\frac{136}{300})100\% = 45.3\%$ (rounded to the nearest percent).

If the gender and brand awareness variables are independent, then the percentages in the cells of the table are expected to be approximately equal to the corresponding row percentages. Thus, we would expect the percentage of viewers who identify the brand for each gender to be approximately 45% if the two variables are independent. The extent to which each gender's percentage departs from this value determines the dependence of the two classifications, with greater variability of the row percentages meaning a greater degree of dependence. A plot of the percentages helps summarize the observed pattern. In the SPSS bar graph in Figure 13.3, we show the gender of the viewer (the base variable) on the horizontal axis and the percentage of TV viewers who identify the brand on the vertical axis. The "expected" percentage under the assumption of independence is shown as a dotted horizontal line.

Figure 13.3 clearly indicates the reason that the test resulted in the conclusion that the two classifications in the contingency table are dependent. The percentage of male TV viewers who identify the brand promoted by a male celebrity is more than twice as high as the percentage of female TV viewers who identify the brand. Statistical measures of the degree of dependence and procedures for making comparisons of pairs of levels for classifications are beyond the scope of this text, but can be found in the references. We will utilize descriptive summaries such as Figure 13.3 to examine the degree of dependence exhibited by the sample data.

The general form of a two-way contingency table containing r rows and c columns (called an $r \times c$ contingency table) is shown in Table 13.7. Note that the observed count

TABLE 13.6 Percentage of TV Viewers Who Identify Brand, by Gender

		Gender		
		Male	Female	Totals
	Could Identify Product	63.3	27.3	45.3
Brand Awareness	**Could Not Identify Product**	36.7	72.7	54.7
	Totals	100	100	100

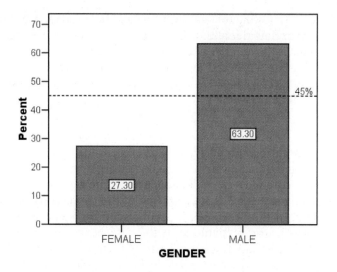

FIGURE 13.3

SPSS bar graph showing percentage of viewers who identified the TV product

in the ijth cell is denoted by n_{ij}, the ith row total is r_i, the jth column total is c_j, and the total sample size is n. Using this notation, we give the general form of the contingency table test for independent classifications in the following box:

General Form of a Two-way (Contingency) Table Analysis:
A Test for Independence

H_0: The two classifications are independent

H_a: The two classifications are dependent

Test statistic: $\chi^2 = \Sigma \dfrac{[n_{ij} - E_{ij}]^2}{\overline{E}_{ij}}$

where $E_{ij} = \dfrac{R_i C_j}{n}$

Rejection region: $\chi^2 > \chi^2_\alpha$, where χ^2_α has $(r - 1)(c - 1)$ df

---

Conditions Required for a Valid χ^2 Test: Contingency Tables

1. The n observed counts are a random sample from the population of interest. We may then consider this to be a multinomial experiment with $r \times c$ possible outcomes.

2. The sample size n will be large enough so that, for every cell, the expected count $E(n_{ij})$ will be equal to 5 or more.

TABLE 13.7 **General $r \times c$ Contingency Table**

		Column 1	Column 2	...	Column c	Row Totals
Row	1	n_{11}	n_{12}	...	n_{1c}	R_1
	2	n_{21}	n_{22}	...	n_{2c}	R_2
	$\vdots$	$\vdots$	$\vdots$		$\vdots$	$\vdots$
	r	n_{r1}	n_{r2}	...	n_{rc}	R_r
Column Totals		C_1	C_2	...	C_c	n

EXAMPLE 13.3

CONDUCTING A
TWO-WAY
ANALYSIS: Marital
Status and Religion

Problem A social scientist wants to determine whether the marital status (divorced or not divorced) of U.S. men is independent of their religious affiliation (or lack thereof). A sample of 500 U.S. men is surveyed, and the results are tabulated as shown in Table 13.8.

a. Test to see whether there is sufficient evidence to indicate that the marital status of men who have been or are currently married is dependent on religious affiliation. Take $\alpha = .01$.

b. Graph the data and describe the patterns revealed. Is the result of the test supported by the graph?

TABLE 13.8 Survey Results (Observed Counts), Example 13.3

		Religious Affiliation					
		A	B	C	D	None	Totals
Marital Status	**Divorced**	39	19	12	28	18	116
	Married, never divorced	172	61	44	70	37	384
	Totals	211	80	56	98	55	500

Solution

a. The first step is to calculate estimated expected cell frequencies under the assumption that the classifications are independent. Rather than compute these values by hand, we resort to a computer. The SAS printout of the analysis of Table 13.8 is displayed in Figure 13.4, each cell of which contains the observed (top) and expected (bottom) frequency in that cell. Note that E_{11}, the estimated expected count for the Divorced, A cell, is 48.952. Similarly, the estimated expected count for the Divorced, B cell, is $E_{12} = 18.56$. Since all the estimated expected cell frequencies are greater than 5, the χ^2 approximation for the test statistic is appropriate. Assuming that the men chosen were randomly selected from all married or previously married American men, the characteristics of the multinomial probability distribution are satisfied.

```
                      The FREQ Procedure

                 Table of MARITAL by RELIGION

  MARITAL      RELIGION

  Frequency|
  Expected |A        |B       |C       |D       |NONE    | Total

  DIVORCED |     39  |     19 |     12 |     28 |     18 |   116
           | 48.952 |  18.56 | 12.992 | 22.736 |  12.76 |

  NEVER    |    172  |     61 |     44 |     70 |     37 |   384
           | 162.05 |  61.44 | 43.008 | 75.264 |  42.24 |

  Total         211        80       56       98       55     500


            Statistics for Table of MARITAL by RELIGION

      Statistic                    DF       Value      Prob

      Chi-Square                    4       7.1355     0.1289
      Likelihood Ratio Chi-Square   4       6.9854     0.1367
      Mantel-Haenszel Chi-Square    1       6.4943     0.0108
      Phi Coefficient                       0.1195
      Contingency Coefficient               0.1186
      Cramer's V                            0.1195


                  Fisher's Exact Test

          Table Probability (P)     6.936E-06
              Pr <= P                  0.1251

             Sample Size = 500
```

FIGURE 13.4

SAS contingency table printout for Example 13.3

The null and alternative hypotheses we want to test are

H_0: The marital status of U.S. men and their religious affiliation are independent
H_a: The marital status of U.S. men and their religious affiliation are dependent

The test statistic, $\chi^2 = 7.135$, is highlighted at the bottom of the printout, as is the observed significance level (*p*-value) of the test. Since $\alpha = .01$ is less than $p = .129$, we fail to reject H_0; that is, we cannot conclude that the marital status of U.S. men depends on their religious affiliation. (Note that we could not reject H_0 even with $\alpha = .10$.)

b. The marital status frequencies can be expressed as percentages of the number of men in each religious affiliation category. The expected percentage of divorced men under the assumption of independence is $(^{116}/_{500})100\% = 23\%$. An SAS graph of the percentages is shown in Figure 13.5. Note that the percentages of divorced men (see the bars in the "DIVORCED" block of the SAS graph) deviate only slightly from that expected under the assumption of independence, supporting the result of the test in part **a**. That is, neither the descriptive bar graph nor the statistical test provides evidence that the male divorce rate depends on (varies with) religious affiliation.

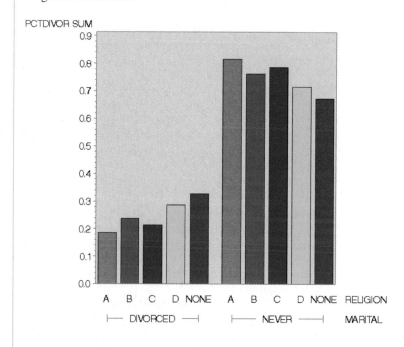

FIGURE 13.5

SAS side-by-side bar graphs showing percentage of divorced and never divorced males by religion

Now Work Exercise 13.27

ACTIVITY 13.2: **Contingency Tables**

In this Activity, you will revisit Activity 3.1, *Exit Polls* (p. 142). For convenience, the table shown in that activity is repeated here.

2004 Presidential Election, Vote by Gender

	Bush	Kerry	Other
Male (46%)	55%	44%	1%
Female (54%)	48%	51%	1%

Source: CNN.com

1. Determine whether this table and the similar tables that you found in the activity on page 142 are contingency tables. If not, do you have enough information to create a contingency

table for the data? If you need more information, state specifically what information you need.

2. Choose one of your examples from Activity 13.1 (p. 749) if it contains a contingency table or enough information to create one, or use the Internet or some other source to find a new example with a contingency table given. Determine whether the conditions for a valid χ^2 test are met. If not, choose a different example in which the conditions are met.

3. Perform a χ^2 test for independence for the example chosen in Exercise 2. Are the results what you would expect in the given situation? Explain.

Contingency Tables

Using the TI-84/TI-83 Graphing Calculator

Finding *p*-values for Contingency Tables

Step 1 *Access the Matrix menu to enter the observed values.*

Press **2nd x⁻¹** for **MATRX**. (*Note*: On the TI-83, press **MATRX**.)
Arrow right to **EDIT**.
Press **ENTER**.
Use the **ARROW** key to enter the row and column dimensions of your observed Matrix.
Use the **ARROW** key to enter your observed values into Matrix [A].

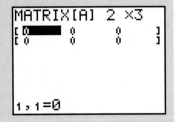

Step 2 *Access the Matrix menu to enter the expected values.*

Press **2nd x⁻¹** for **MATRX**. (*Note*: On the TI-83, press **MATRX**.)
Arrow right to **EDIT**.
Arrow down to **2:[B]**.
Press **ENTER**.
Use the **ARROW** key to enter the row and column dimensions of your expected matrix. (The dimensions will be the same as in Matrix A.)
Use the **ARROW** key to enter your expected values into Matrix [B].

```
MATRIX[B] 2 ×3
[ 0      0      0    ]
[ 0      0      0    ]



1,1=0
```

Step 3 *Access the Statistical Tests menu and perform the Chi-square test.*

Press **STAT**.
Arrow right to **TESTS**.
Arrow down to χ^2 **Test**.
Press **ENTER**.
Arrow down to **Calculate**.
Press **ENTER**.

```
X²-Test
 Observed:[A]
 Expected:[B]
 Calculate Draw
```

Step 4 *Reject H_0 if the p-value $< \alpha$*

Example

Our observed Matrix is [A] = 39   19   12   28   18
                              172 61   44   70   37

Our Expected Matrix is [B] = 48.952   18.56   12.992   22.736   12.76
                             162.05   61.44   43.008   75.264   42.24

Use $\alpha = .05$ to test the following hypotheses:

H_0: The Matrix entries represent independent events.
H_a: The Matrix entries represent events that **are not** independent.

The screens for this example are as follows:

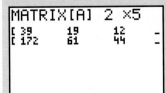

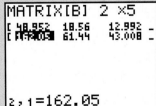

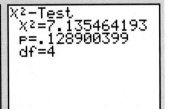

As you can see from the last screen, the *p*-value is 0.1289. Since the *p*-value is **greater** than $\alpha = .05$, we **do not** reject H_0.

STATISTICS IN ACTION REVISITED

Testing whether Frequency of Drinking Is Related to Amount of Alcohol Consumed

Refer again to the *Family and Consumer Sciences Research Journal* (Mar. 2005) study of college students and drinking (p. 743). A second objective of the researchers was to establish a statistical link between the frequency of drinking and the amount of alcohol consumed. That is, the researchers sought a link between frequency of drinking alcohol over the previous one-month period and average number of drinks consumed per occasion. Since both of these variables (FREQUENCY and AMOUNT) measured on the sample of 657 students in the **COLLDRINKS** file are qualitative, a contingency table analysis is appropriate.

Figure SIA13.3 shows the SPSS contingency table analyses relating frequency of drinking to average amount of alcohol consumed. The null hypothesis for the test is H_0: Frequency and Amount are independent.

The chi-square test statistic (756.6) and the *p*-value of the test (.000) are highlighted on the printout. If we conduct the test at $\alpha = .01$, there is sufficient evidence to reject H_0. That is, the data provide evidence indicating that, for college students, the average amount of alcohol consumed per occasion is associated with the frequency of drinking.

The row percentages highlighted in the contingency table of Figure SIA13.3 reveal the differences in drinking amounts for the different levels of drinking frequency. For frequency of drinking "None" and "Once a month", 0% drink heavily (7–9 or 10 or more drinks per occasion). However, for frequency of drinking "Twice a week" and "More," 12.7% and 17.1%, respectively, have 7–9 drinks per occasion, while 4.0% and 11.2%, respectively, have 10 or more drinks per occasion. These results led the researchers to report that "The frequent drinkers were more likely to consume more [alcohol] on each occasion, a tendency that clearly makes them heavy drinkers."

FREQNCY * AMOUNT Crosstabulation

			AMOUNT						
			None	1 drink	2-3 drinks	4-6 drinks	7-9 drinks	More	Total
FREQNCY	None	Count	118	0	0	0	0	0	118
		Expected Count	21.2	11.0	51.2	17.8	11.5	5.4	118.0
		% within FREQNCY	100.0%	.0%	.0%	.0%	.0%	.0%	100.0%
	OnceMonth	Count	0	30	43	20	0	0	93
		Expected Count	16.7	8.6	40.3	14.0	9.1	4.2	93.0
		% within FREQNCY	.0%	32.3%	46.2%	21.5%	.0%	.0%	100.0%
	TwiceWeek	Count	0	26	158	46	35	11	276
		Expected Count	49.6	25.6	119.7	41.6	26.9	12.6	276.0
		% within FREQNCY	.0%	9.4%	57.2%	16.7%	12.7%	4.0%	100.0%
	More	Count	0	5	84	33	29	19	170
		Expected Count	30.5	15.8	73.7	25.6	16.6	7.8	170.0
		% within FREQNCY	.0%	2.9%	49.4%	19.4%	17.1%	11.2%	100.0%
Total		Count	118	61	285	99	64	30	657
		Expected Count	118.0	61.0	285.0	99.0	64.0	30.0	657.0
		% within FREQNCY	18.0%	9.3%	43.4%	15.1%	9.7%	4.6%	100.0%

Chi-Square Tests

	Value	df	Asymp. Sig. (2-sided)
Pearson Chi-Square	756.606[a]	15	.000
Likelihood Ratio	706.412	15	.000
Linear-by-Linear Association	322.813	1	.000
N of Valid Cases	657		

a. 1 cells (4.2%) have expected count less than 5. The minimum expected count is 4.25.

FIGURE SIA13.3

SPSS contingency table analysis: frequency of drinking vs. average amount

Exercises 13.19–13.40

Understanding the Principles

13.19 What is a two-way (contingency) table?

13.20 *True* or *False*. One goal of a contingency table analysis is to determine whether the two classifications are dependent.

13.21 What conditions are required for a valid chi-square test of data from a contingency table?

Learning the Mechanics

13.22 Find the rejection region for a test of independence of two classifications for which the contingency table contains r rows and c columns and
a. $r = 5$, $c = 5$, $\alpha = .05$
b. $r = 3$, $c = 6$, $\alpha = .10$
c. $r = 2$, $c = 3$, $\alpha = .01$

13.23 Consider the following 2×3 (i.e., $r = 2$ and $c = 3$) contingency table:

			Column	
		1	2	3
Row	1	9	34	53
	2	16	30	25

a. Specify the null and alternative hypotheses that should be used in testing the independence of the row and column classifications.
b. Specify the test statistic and the rejection region that should be used in conducting the hypothesis test of part **a**. Use $\alpha = .01$.
c. Assuming that the row classification and the column classification are independent, find estimates for the expected cell counts.
d. Conduct the hypothesis test of part **a**. Interpret your result.

13.24 Refer to Exercise 13.23.
a. Convert the frequency responses to percentages by calculating the percentage of each column total falling in each row. Also, convert the row totals to percentages of the total number of responses. Display the percentages in a table.
b. Create a bar graph with row 1 percentage on the vertical axis and column number on the horizontal axis. Show the row 1 total percentage as a horizontal line on the graph.
c. What pattern do you expect to see if the rows and columns are independent? Does the plot support the result of the test of independence in Exercise 13.23?

13.25 Test the null hypothesis of independence of the two classifications A and B of the 3×3 contingency table shown here. Use $\alpha = .05$.

			B	
		B_1	B_2	B_3
	A_1	40	72	42
A	A_2	63	53	70
	A_3	31	38	30

13.26 Refer to Exercise 13.25. Convert the responses to percentages by calculating the percentage of each B class total falling into each A classification. Also, calculate the percentage of the total number of responses that constitute each of the A classification totals.
a. Create a bar graph with row A_1 percentage on the vertical axis and B classification on the horizontal axis. Does the graph support the result of the test of hypothesis in Exercise 13.25? Explain.
b. Repeat part **a** for the row A_2 percentages.
c. Repeat part **a** for the row A_3 percentages.

Applying the Concepts—Basic

13.27 **Children's perceptions of their neighborhood.** In *Health Education Research* (Feb. 2005), nutrition scientists at Deakin University (Australia) investigated children's perceptions of their environments. Each in a sample of 147 ten-year-old children drew maps of their home and neighborhood environment. The researchers examined the maps for certain themes (e.g., presence of a pet, television in the bedroom, opportunities for physical activity). The results, broken down by gender, for two themes (presence of a dog and TV in the bedroom) are shown in the tables below.
a. Find the sample proportion of boys who drew a dog on their maps.
b. Find the sample proportion of girls who drew a dog on their maps.
c. Compare the proportions you found in parts **a** and **b**. Does it appear that the likelihood of drawing a dog on the neighborhood map depends on gender?
d. Give the null hypothesis for testing whether the likelihood of a drawing a dog on the neighborhood map depends on gender.
e. Use the accompanying MINITAB printout (p. 764) to conduct the test mentioned in part **d** at $\alpha = .05$.
f. Conduct a test to determine whether the likelihood of drawing a TV in the bedroom is different for boys and girls. Use $\alpha = .05$.

⊙ **MAPDOG**

Presence of a Dog	Number of Boys	Number of Girls
Yes	6	11
No	71	59
TOTAL	77	70

⊙ **MAPTV**

Presence of TV in Bedroom	Number of Boys	Number of Girls
Yes	11	9
No	66	61
TOTAL	77	70

Source: Hume, C., Salmon, J., and Ball, K. "Children's perceptions of their home and neighborhood environments, and their association with objectively measured physical activity: A qualitative and quantitative study," *Health Education Research*, Vol. 20, No. 1, February 2005 (Table III).

Tabulated statistics: DOG, GENDER

```
Using frequencies in NUMBER


Rows: DOG    Columns: GENDER

           Boy    Girl     All

No          71      59     130
          68.10   61.90  130.00

Yes          6      11      17
           8.90    8.10   17.00

All         77      70     147
          77.00   70.00  147.00

Cell Contents:      Count
                    Expected count
```

MINITAB output for Exercise 13.27

```
Pearson Chi-Square = 2.250, DF = 1, P-Value = 0.134
Likelihood Ratio Chi-Square = 2.268, DF = 1, P-Value = 0.132
```

13.28 **Late-emerging reading disabilities.** Studies of children with reading disabilities typically focus on "early-emerging" difficulties identified prior to the fourth grade. Psychologists at Haskins Laboratories recently studied children with "late-emerging" reading difficulties (i.e., children who appeared to undergo a fourth-grade "slump" in reading achievement) and published their findings in the *Journal of Educational Psychology* (June 2003). A sample of 161 children was selected from fourth and fifth graders at elementary schools in Philadelphia. In addition to recording the grade level, the researchers determined whether each child had a previously undetected reading disability. Sixty-six children were diagnosed with a reading disability. Of these children, 32 were fourth graders and 34 were fifth graders. Similarly, of the 95 children with normal reading achievement, 55 were fourth graders and 40 were fifth graders.

a. Identify the two qualitative variables (and corresponding levels) measured in the study.

b. From the information provided, form a contingency table.

c. Assuming that the two variables are independent, calculate the expected cell counts.

d. Find the test statistic for determining whether the proportions of fourth and fifth graders with reading disabilities differs from the proportions of fourth and fifth graders with normal reading skills.

e. Find the rejection region for the test if $\alpha = .10$.

f. Is there a link between reading disability and grade level? Give the appropriate conclusion of the test.

13.29 **Masculinity and crime.** Refer to the *Journal of Sociology* (July 2003) study on the link between the level of masculinity and criminal behavior in men, presented in Exercise 9.25 (p. 428). The researcher identified events that a sample of newly incarcerated men were involved in and classified each event as "violent" (involving the use of a weapon, the throwing of objects, punching, choking, or kicking) or "avoided-violent" (involving pushing, shoving, grabbing, or threats of violence that did not escalate into a violent event). Each man (and corresponding event) was also classified as possessing "high-risk masculinity" (scored high on the Masculinity–Femininity Scale test and low on the Traditional Outlets of Masculinity Scale test) or "low-risk masculinity." The data on 1,507 events are summarized in the following table:

HRM

	Violent Events	Avoided-Violent Events	Totals
High-Risk Masculinity	236	143	379
Low-Risk Masculinity	801	327	1,128
Totals	1,037	470	1,507

Source: Krienert, J. L. "Masculinity and crime: A quantitative exploration of Messerschmidt's hypothesis," *Journal of Sociology,* Vol. 7, No. 2, July 2003 (Table 4).

a. Identify the two categorical variables measured (and their levels) in the study.

b. Identify the experimental units.

c. If the type of event (violent or avoided-violent) is independent of high- low-risk masculinity, how many of the 1,507 events would you expect to be violent and involve a high-risk-masculine man?

d. Repeat part **c** for the other combinations of event type and high- low-risk masculinity.

e. Calculate the χ^2 statistic for testing whether event type depends on high- low-risk masculinity.

f. Give the appropriate conclusion of the test mentioned in part **e**, using $\alpha = .05$.

13.30 **Healing heart patients with music, imagery, touch, and prayer.** "Frontier medicine" is a term used to describe medical therapies (e.g., energy healing, therapeutic prayer, spiritual healing) for which there is no plausible explanation. *The Lancet* (July 16, 2005) published the results of a study designed to test the effectiveness of two types of frontier medicine—music, imagery, and touch (MIT) therapy and therapeutic prayer—in healing cardiac care patients. Patients were randomly assigned to receive one of four types of treatment: (1) prayer, (2) MIT, (3) prayer and MIT, and (4) standard care (no prayer and no MIT). Six months after therapy, the patients were evaluated for a major adverse cardiovascular event (e.g., a heart attack). The results of the study are summarized in the accompanying table.

a. Identify the two qualitative variables (and associated levels) measured in the study.

b. State H_o and H_a for testing whether a major adverse cardiovascular event depends on type of therapy.

c. Use the MINITAB printout below to conduct the test mentioned in part **b** at $\alpha = .10$. On the basis of this test, what can the researchers infer about the effectiveness of music, imagery, and touch therapy and the effectiveness of healing prayer in heart patients?

HEALING

Therapy	Number of Patients with Major Cardiovascular Events	Number of Patients with No Events	TOTAL
Prayer	43	139	182
MIT	47	138	185
Prayer and MIT	39	150	189
Standard	50	142	192

Source: Krucoff, M. W., et al. "Music, imagery, touch, and prayer as adjuncts to interventional cardiac care: The Monitoring and Actualization of Noetic Trainings (MANTRA) II randomized study," *The Lancet*, Vol. 366, July 16, 2005 (Table 4).

Applying the Concepts—Intermediate

13.31 IQ and mental retardation. A person is diagnosed with mental retardation if, before the age of 18, his or her score on a standard IQ test is no higher than 70 (two standard deviations below the mean of 100). Researchers at Cornell and West Virginia Universities examined the impact of rising IQ scores on diagnoses of mental retardation (MR). (*American Psychologist*, October, 2003.) IQ data were collected from different school districts across the United States, and the students were tested with either the Wechsler Intelligence Scale for Children—Revised (WISC-R) or the Wechsler Intelligence Scale for Children—Third Revision (WISC-III) IQ tests. The researchers focused on those students with IQs just above the mental retardation cutoff (between 70 and 85), based on the original IQ test. These "borderline" MR students were then retested one year later with one of the IQ tests. The accompanying table gives the number of students diagnosed with mental retardation on the basis of the retest. Conduct a chi-square test for independence to determine whether the proportion of students diagnosed with MR depends on the IQ test/retest method. Use $\alpha = .01$.

MRIQ

Test/Retest	Diagnosed with MR	Above MR Cutoff IQ	TOTAL
WISC-R / WISC-R	25	167	192
WISC-R / WISC-III	54	103	157
WISC-III / WISC-III	36	141	177

Source: Kanaya, T., Scullin, M. H., and Ceci, S. J. "The Flynn effect and U.S. Policies," *American Psychologist*, Vol. 58, No. 10, Oct. 2003 (Figure 1).

Tabulated statistics: THERAPY, EVENT

```
Using frequencies in NUMBER


Rows: THERAPY    Columns: EVENT

                  No     Yes     All

MIT              138      47     185
               140.7    44.3   185.0


Prayer           139      43     182
               138.4    43.6   182.0


Prayer&MIT       150      39     189
               143.8    45.2   189.0


Standard         142      50     192
               146.1    45.9   192.0


All              569     179     748
               569.0   179.0   748.0


Cell Contents:        Count
                      Expected count
```

MINITAB output for Exercise 13.30

```
Pearson Chi-Square = 1.828, DF = 3, P-Value = 0.609
Likelihood Ratio Chi-Square = 1.855, DF = 3, P-Value = 0.603
```

13.32 Creating menus to influence others. Refer to the *Journal of Consumer Research* (Mar. 2003) study on influencing the choices of others by offering undesirable alternatives, presented in Exercise 8.149 (p. 403). In another experiment conducted by the researcher, 96 subjects were asked to imagine that they had just moved to an apartment with two others and that they were shopping for a new appliance (e.g., a television, a microwave oven). Each subject was asked to create a menu of three brand choices for his or her roommates; then subjects were randomly assigned (in equal numbers) to one of three different "goal" conditions: (1) Create the menu in order to influence roommates to buy a preselected brand, (2) create the menu in order to influence roommates to buy a brand of your choice, and (3) create the menu with no intent to influence roommates. The researcher theorized that the menus created to influence others would likely include undesirable alternative brands. Consequently, the number of menus in each goal condition that was consistent with the theory was determined. The data are summarized in the accompanying table. Analyze the data for the purpose of determining whether the proportion of subjects who select menus consistent with the theory depends on the goal condition. Use $\alpha = .01$.

MENU3

Goal Condition	Number Consistent with Theory	Number Not Consistent with Theory	Totals
Influence/preselected brand	15	17	32
Influence/own brand	14	18	32
No influence	3	29	32

Source: Hamilton, R. W. "Why do people suggest what they do not want? Using context effects to influence others' choices," *Journal of Consumer Research*, Vol. 29, March 2003 (Table 2).

13.33 Politics and religion. University of Maryland professor Ted R. Gurr examined the political strategies used by ethnic groups worldwide in their fight for minority rights. (*Political Science & Politics*, June 2000.) Each in a sample of 275 ethnic groups was classified according to world region and highest level of political action reported. The data are summarized in the contingency table below. Conduct a test at $\alpha = .10$ to determine whether political strategy of ethnic groups depends on world region. Support your answer with a graph.

13.34 Trapping grain moths. In an experiment described in the *Journal of Agricultural, Biological, and Environmental Statistics* (Dec. 2000), bins of corn were stocked with various parasites (e.g., grain moths) in late winter. In early summer (June), three bowl-shaped traps were placed on the surface of the grain in order to capture the moths. All three traps were baited with a sex pheromone lure; however, one trap used an unmarked sticky adhesive, one was marked with a fluorescent red powder, and one was marked with a fluorescent blue powder. The traps were set on a Wednesday, and the catch was collected the following Thursday and Friday. The accompanying table shows the number of moths captured in each trap on each day. Conduct a test (at $\alpha = .10$) to determine whether the percentages of moths caught by the three traps depends on the day of the week.

MOTHTRAP

	Adhesive, No Mark	Red Mark	Blue Mark
Thursday	136	41	17
Friday	101	50	18

Source: Wileyto, E. P. et al. "Self-marking recapture models for estimating closed insect populations," *Journal of Agricultural, Biological, and Environmental Statistics*, Vol. 5, No. 4, December 2000 (Table 5A).

13.35 Classifying air threats with heuristics. The *Journal of Behavioral Decision Making* (Jan. 2007) published a study on the use of heuristics to classify the threat level of approaching aircraft. Of special interest was the use of a fast and frugal heuristic—a computationally simple procedure for making judgments with limited information—named "Take-the-Best-for-Classification" (TTB-C). The subjects were 48 men and women, some from a Canadian Forces reserve unit, others university students. Each subject was presented with a radar screen on which simulated approaching aircraft were identified with asterisks. By using the computer mouse to click on the asterisk, one could receive further information about the aircraft. The goal was to identify the aircraft as "friend" or "foe" as fast as possible. Half the subjects were given cue-based instructions for determining the type of aircraft, while the other half were given pattern-based instructions. The researcher also classified the heuristic strategy used by the subject as TTB-C, Guess, or Other. Data on the two variables Instruction type and Strategy, measured for each of the 48 subjects, are saved in the **AIRTHREAT** file. (Data on the first and last five subjects are shown in the table on p. 767.) Do the data provide sufficient evidence at $\alpha = .05$

ETHNIC

		Political Strategy		
		No Political Action	Mobilization, Mass Action	Terrorism, Rebellion, Civil War
	Latin American	24	31	7
	Post-Communist	32	23	4
World Region	**South, Southeast, East Asia**	11	22	26
	Africa/Middle East	39	36	20

Source: Gurr, T. R. "Nonviolence in ethnopolitics: Strategies for the attainment of group rights and autonomy." *Political Science & Politics*, Vol. 33, No. 2, June 2000 (Table 1).

to indicate that choice of heuristic strategy depends on type of instruction provided? How about at $\alpha = .01$?

AIRTHREAT (Selected observations)

Instruction	Strategy
Pattern	Other
Pattern	Other
Pattern	Other
Cue	TTBC
Cue	TTBC
⋮	⋮
Pattern	TTBC
Cue	Guess
Cue	TTBC
Cue	Guess
Pattern	Guess

Source: Bryant, D. J. "Classifying simulated air threats with fast and frugal heuristics," *Journal of Behavioral Decision Making*, Vol. 20, January 2007 (Appendix C).

SEEDLING

13.36 Subarctic plant study. The traits of seed-bearing plants indigenous to subarctic Finland were studied in *Arctic, Antarctic, and Alpine Research* (May 2004). Plants were categorized according to *type* (dwarf shrub, herb, or grass), *abundance of seedlings* (no seedlings, rare seedlings, or abundant seedlings), *regenerative group* (no vegetative reproduction, vegetative reproduction possible, vegetative reproduction ineffective, or vegetative reproduction effective), *seed weight class* (0–.1, .1–.5, .5–1.0, 1.0–5.0, and > 5.0 milligrams), and *diaspore morphology* (no structure, pappus, wings, fleshy fruits, or awns/hooks). The data on a sample of 73 plants are saved in the **SEEDLING** file.

a. A contingency table for plant type and seedling abundance, produced by MINITAB, is shown in the next column. (*Note:* NS = no seedlings, SA = seedlings abundant, and SR = seedlings rare.) Suppose you want to perform a chi-square test of independence to determine whether seedling abundance depends on plant type. Find the expected cell counts for the contingency table. Are the assumptions required for the test satisfied?

b. Reformulate the contingency table by combining the NS and SR categories of seedling abundance. Find the expected cell counts for this new contingency table. Are the assumptions required for the test satisfied?

Tabulated statistics: Abundance, Type

```
Rows: Abundance    Columns: Type

          DwarfShrub   Grasses   Herbs   All

   NS              3         1       1     5
   SA              5        14      32    51
   SR              5         2      10    17
   All            13        17      43    73


   Cell Contents:        Count
```

MINITAB output for Exercise 13.36

c. Reformulate the contingency table of part **b** by combining the dwarf shrub and grasses categories of plant type. Find the expected cell counts for this contingency table. Are the assumptions required for the test satisfied?

d. Carry out the chi-square test for independence on the contingency table you came up with in part **c**, using $\alpha = .10$. What do you conclude?

13.37 Susceptibility to hypnosis. A standardized procedure for determining a person's susceptibility to hypnosis is the Stanford Hypnotic Susceptibility Scale, Form C (SHSS:C). Recently, a new method called the Computer-Assisted Hypnosis Scale (CAHS), which uses a computer as a facilitator of hypnosis, has been developed. Each scale classifies a person's hypnotic susceptibility as low, medium, high, or very high. Researchers at the University of Tennessee compared the two scales by administering both tests to each of 130 undergraduate volunteers. (*Psychological Assessment*, Mar. 1995.) The hypnotic classifications are summarized in the table below. A contingency table analysis will be performed to determine whether CAHS level and SHSS level are independent.

a. Check to see if the assumption of expected cell counts of 5 or more is satisfied. Should you proceed with the analysis? Explain.

b. One way to satisfy the assumption of part **a** is to combine the data for two or more categories (e.g., high and very high) in the contingency table. Form a new contingency table by combining the data for the high and very high categories in both the rows and the columns.

c. Calculate the expected cell counts in the new contingency table you formed in part **c**. Is the assumption now satisfied?

d. Perform the chi-square test on the new contingency table. Use $\alpha = .05$. Interpret the results.

HYPNOSIS

		CAHS Level				
		Low	Medium	High	Very High	Totals
SHSS: C Level	**Low**	32	14	2	0	48
	Medium	11	14	6	0	31
	High	6	14	19	3	42
	Very High	0	2	4	3	9
	Totals	49	44	31	6	130

Source: Grant, C. D., and Nash, M. R. "The Computer-Assisted Hypnosis Scale: Standardization and Norming of a Computer-administered Measure of Hypnotic Ability," *Psychological Assessment*, Vol. 7, No. 1, Mar. 1995, p. 53 (Table 4).

GANGS

Gang Classification Score	Homemade Weapon Carried	
	Yes	No
0 (Never joined a gang, no close friends in a gang)	255	2,551
1 (Never joined a gang, 1–4 close friends in a gang)	110	560
2 (Never joined a gang, 5 or more friends in a gang)	151	636
3 (Inactive gang member)	271	959
4 (Active gang member, no position of rank)	175	513
5 (Active gang member, holds position of rank)	476	831

Source: Knox, G. W., et al. "A gang classification system for corrections," *Journal of Gang Research,* Vol. 4, No. 2, Winter 1997, p. 54 (Table 4).

13.38 **Gangs and homemade weapons.** The National Gang Crime Research Center (NGCRC) has developed a six-level gang classification system for both adults and juveniles. The six categories are shown in the accompanying table. The classification system was developed as a potential predictor of a gang member's propensity for violence in prison, jail, or a correctional facility. To test the system, the NGCRC collected data on approximately 10,000 confined offenders and assigned each a score from the gang classification system. (*Journal of Gang Research,* Winter 1997.) One of several other variables measured by the NGCRC was whether or not the offender had ever carried a homemade weapon (e.g., knife) while in custody. The data on gang score and homemade weapon are summarized in the table above. Conduct a test to determine whether carrying a homemade weapon in custody depends on gang classification score. (Use $\alpha = .01$.) Support your conclusion with a graph.

Applying the Concepts—Advanced

13.39 **Efficacy of an HIV vaccine.** New, effective AIDS vaccines are now being developed through the process of "sieving"— that is, sifting out infections with some strains of HIV. Harvard School of Public Health statistician Peter Gilbert demonstrated how to test the efficacy of an HIV vaccine in *Chance* (Fall 2000). As an example, using the 2×2 table shown below, Gilbert reported the results of VaxGen's preliminary HIV vaccine trial. The vaccine was designed to eliminate a particular strain of the virus called the "MN strain." The trial consisted of 7 AIDS patients vaccinated with the new drug and 31 AIDS patients who were treated with a placebo (no vaccination). The table shows the number of patients who tested positive and negative for the MN strain in the trial follow-up period.

a. Conduct a test to determine whether the vaccine is effective in treating the MN strain of HIV. Use $\alpha = .05$.

HIVVAC1

Patient Group		MN Strain		Totals
		Positive	Negative	
	Unvaccinated	22	9	31
	Vaccinated	2	5	7
	Totals	24	14	38

Source: Gilbert, P. "Developing an AIDS vaccine by sieving," *Chance,* Vol. 13, No. 4, Fall 2000.

b. Are the assumptions for the test you carried out in part **a,** satisfied? What are the consequences if the assumptions are violated?

c. In the case of a 2×2 contingency table, R. A. Fisher (1935) developed a procedure for computing the exact *p*-value for the test (called *Fisher's exact test*). The method utilizes the hypergeometric probability distribution of Chapter 4 (p. 216). Consider the hypergeometric probability

$$\frac{\binom{7}{2}\binom{31}{22}}{\binom{38}{24}}$$

which represents the probability that 2 out of 7 vaccinated AIDS patients test positive and 22 out of 31 unvaccinated patients test positive—that is, the probability of the result shown in table, given that the null hypothesis of independence is true. Compute this probability (called the *probability of the contingency table*).

d. Refer to part **c.** Two contingency tables (with the same marginal totals as the original table) that are more unsupportive of the null hypothesis of independence than the observed table are shown below. First, explain why these tables provide more evidence to reject H_0 than the original table does. Then compute the probability of each table, using the hypergeometric formula.

e. The *p*-value of Fisher's exact test is the probability of observing a result at least as unsupportive of the null

HIVVAC2

Patient Group		MN Strain		Totals
		Positive	Negative	
	Unvaccinated	23	8	31
	Vaccinated	1	6	7
	Totals	24	14	38

HIVVAC3

Patient Group		MN Strain		Totals
		Positive	Negative	
	Unvaccinated	24	7	31
	Vaccinated	0	7	7
	Totals	24	14	38

The FREQ Procedure

Table of GROUP by MNSTRAIN

GROUP   MNSTRAIN

Frequency Expected	NEG	POS	Total
UN	9 11.421	22 19.579	31
V	5 2.5789	2 4.4211	7
Total	14	24	38

Statistics for Table of GROUP by MNSTRAIN

Statistic	DF	Value	Prob
Chi-Square	1	4.4112	0.0357
Likelihood Ratio Chi-Square	1	4.2893	0.0384
Continuity Adj. Chi-Square	1	2.7773	0.0956
Mantel-Haenszel Chi-Square	1	4.2952	0.0382
Phi Coefficient		-0.3407	
Contingency Coefficient		0.3225	
Cramer's V		-0.3407	

WARNING: 50% of the cells have expected counts less
than 5. Chi-Square may not be a valid test.

Fisher's Exact Test

Cell (1,1) Frequency (F)	9
Left-sided Pr <= F	0.0498
Right-sided Pr >= F	0.9940
Table Probability (P)	0.0438
Two-sided Pr <= P	0.0772

Sample Size = 38

SAS output for
Exercise 13.39

hypothesis as is the observed contingency table, given the same marginal totals. Sum the probabilities of parts **c** and **d** to obtain the *p*-value of Fisher's exact test. (To verify your calculations, check the *p*-value labeled **Left-sided Pr < = F**) at the bottom of the SAS printout shown above.) Interpret this value in the context of the vaccine trial.

13.40 Examining the "Monty Hall Dilemma." In Exercise 3.182 (p. 177) you solved the game show problem of whether or not to switch your choice of three doors, one of which hides a prize, after the host reveals what is behind a door that is not chosen. (Despite the natural inclination of many to keep one's first choice, the correct answer is that you should switch your choice of doors.) This problem is sometimes called the "Monty Hall Dilemma," named for Monty Hall, the host of the popular TV game show *Let's Make a Deal*. In *Thinking & Reasoning* (Oct. 2006), Wichita State University professors set up an experiment designed to influence subjects to switch their original choice of doors. Each subject participated in 23 trials. In trial 1, three (boxes) representing doors were presented on a computer screen; only one box hid a prize. In each subsequent trial, an additional box was presented, so that in trial 23, twenty-five boxes were presented. In each trial, after a box was selected, all of the remaining boxes except for one either (1) were shown to be empty (*Empty* condition), (2) disappeared (*Vanish* condition), (3) disappeared,

and the chosen box was enlarged (*Steroids* condition), or (4) disappeared, and the remaining box not chosen was enlarged (*Steroids2* condition). Twenty-seven subjects were assigned to each condition. The number of subjects who ultimately switched boxes is tallied, by condition, in the following table for both the first trial and the last trial:

MONTYHALL

	First Trial (1)		Last Trial (23)	
Condition	Switch Boxes	No Switch	Switch Boxes	No Switch
Empty	10	17	23	4
Vanish	3	24	12	15
Steroids	5	22	21	6
Steroids2	8	19	19	8

Source: Howard, J. N., Lambdin, C. G., and Datteri, D. L. "Let's Make a Deal: Quality and Availability of Second-stage Information as a Catalyst for Change," *Thinking & Reasoning,* October 2006 (Table 2).

a. For a selected trial, does the likelihood of switching boxes depend on condition?
b. For a given condition, does the likelihood of switching boxes depend on trial number?
c. On the basis of the results you obtained in parts **a** and **b**, what factors influence a subject to switch choices?

13.4 A Word of Caution about Chi-Square Tests

Because the χ^2 statistic for testing hypotheses about multinomial probabilities is one of the most widely applied statistical tools, it is also one of the most abused statistical procedures. Consequently, the user should always be certain that the experiment satisfies the assumptions underlying each procedure. Furthermore, the user should be certain that the sample is drawn from the correct population—that is, from the population about which the inference is to be made.

The use of the χ^2 probability distribution as an approximation to the sampling distribution for χ^2 should be avoided when the expected counts are very small. The approximation can become very poor when these expected counts are small; thus, the true α level may be quite different from the tabular value. As a rule of thumb, an expected cell count of at least 5 means that the χ^2 probability distribution can be used to determine an approximate critical value.

If the χ^2 value does not exceed the established critical value of χ^2, *do not accept the hypothesis of independence.* You would be risking a Type II error (accepting H_0 when it is false), and the probability β of committing such an error is unknown. The usual alternative hypothesis is that the classifications are dependent. Because the number of ways in which two classifications can be dependent is virtually infinite, it is difficult to calculate one or even several values of β to represent such a broad alternative hypothesis. Therefore, we avoid concluding that two classifications are independent, even when χ^2 is small.

Finally, if a contingency table χ^2 value does exceed the critical value, we must be careful to avoid inferring that a *causal* relationship exists between the classifications. Our alternative hypothesis states that the two classifications are statistically dependent—and a statistical dependence does not imply causality. Therefore, *the existence of a causal relationship cannot be established by a contingency table analysis.*

KEY TERMS

CATEGORICAL DATA ANALYSIS GUIDE

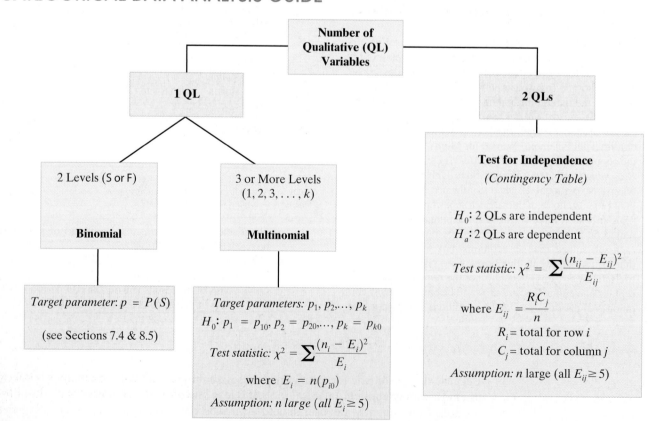

CHAPTER NOTES

Multinomial Data

Qualitative data that fall into more than two categories (or classes)

Properties of a Multinomial Experiment

(1) n identical trials

(2) k possible outcomes to each trial

(3) probabilities of the k outcomes $(p_1, p_2, \ldots, p_k)$ where $p_1 + p_2 + \ldots + p_k = 1$, remain the same from trial to trial

(4) trials are independent

(5) variables of interest: *cell counts* (i.e., number of observations falling into each outcome category), denoted $n_1, n_2, \ldots, n_k$

Key Symbols/Notation

$p_{i,0}$	Value of multinomial probability p_1 hypothesized in H_0
χ^2	Chi-square test statistic used in analysis of categorical data
n_i	Number of observed outcomes in cell i of a one-way table
E_i	Expected number of outcomes in cell i of a one-way table
p_{ij}	Probability of an outcome in row i and column j of a two-way table
n_{ij}	Number of observed outcomes in row i and column j of a two-way table
E_{ij}	Expected number of outcomes in row i and column j of a two-way table
R_i	Total number of outcomes in row i of a two-way table
C_j	Total number of outcomes in column j of a two-way table

One-Way Table

Summary table for a *single* qualitative variable

Two-Way (Contingency) Table

Summary table for *two* qualitative variables

Chi-Square (χ^2) Statistic

used to test category probabilities in one-way and two-way tables

Chi-square tests for independence

should **not** be used to *infer a causal relationship between two QLs*

Conditions Required for Valid χ^2 Tests

(1) multinomial experiment

(2) sample size n is large (expected cell counts are all greater than or equal to 5)

SUPPLEMENTARY EXERCISES 13.41–13.65

Understanding the Principles

13.41 *True or False*. Rejecting the null hypothesis in a chi-square test for independence implies that a causal relationship exists between the two categorical variables.

13.42 What is the difference between a one-way chi-square analysis and a two-way chi-square analysis?

Learning the Mechanics

13.43 A random sample of 250 observations was classified according to the row and column categories shown in the following table:

		Column		
		1	2	3
Row	**1**	20	20	10
	2	10	20	70
	3	20	50	30

a. Do the data provide sufficient evidence to conclude that the rows and columns are dependent? Test, using $\alpha = .05$.

b. Would the analysis change if the row totals were fixed before the data were collected?

c. Do the assumptions required for the analysis to be valid differ according to whether the row (or column) totals are fixed? Explain.

d. Convert the table entries to percentages by using each column total as a base and calculating each row response as a percentage of the corresponding column total. In addition, calculate the row totals and convert them to percentages of all 250 observations.

e. Create a bar graph with the percentages from row 1 on the vertical axis and the column number on the horizontal axis. Draw a horizontal line corresponding to the total percentage for row 1. Does the graph support the result of the test conducted in part **a**?

f. Repeat part **e** for the percentages from row 2.

g. Repeat part **e** for the percentages from row 3.

13.44 A random sample of 150 observations was classified into the categories shown in the following table:

	Category				
	1	2	3	4	5
n_i	28	35	33	25	29

a. Do the data provide sufficient evidence that the categories are not equally likely? Use $\alpha = .10$.

b. Form a 90% confidence interval for p_2, the probability that an observation will fall into category 2.

Applying the Concepts—Basic

13.45 Dosing errors at hospitals. Each year, approximately 1.3 million people in the United States suffer adverse drug effects (ADEs)—that is, unintended injuries caused by prescribed medication. A study in the *Journal of the American Medical Association* (July 5, 1995) identified the cause of 247 ADEs that occurred at two Boston hospitals. The researchers found that dosing errors (i.e., wrong dosage prescribed or dispensed) were the most common. The table summarizes the proximate cause of 95 ADEs that resulted from a dosing error. Conduct a test (at $\alpha = .10$) to determine whether the true percentages of ADEs in the five "cause" categories are different.

Cause of Wrong Dosage	Number of ADEs
(1) Lack of knowledge of drug	29
(2) Rule violation	17
(3) Faulty dose checking	13
(4) Slips	9
(5) Other	27

13.46 Scanning Internet messages. *Inc. Technology* (Mar. 18, 1997) reported the results of an Equifax/Harris Consumer Privacy Survey in which 328 Internet users indicated their level of agreement with the following statement: "The government needs to be able to scan Internet messages and user communications to prevent fraud and other crimes." The number of users in each response category is summarized as follows:

Agree Strongly	Agree Somewhat	Disagree Somewhat	Disagree Strongly
59	108	82	79

a. Specify the null and alternative hypotheses you would use to determine whether the opinions of Internet users are evenly divided among the four categories.

b. Conduct the test of part **a**, using $\alpha = .05$.

c. In the context of this exercise, what is a Type I error? A Type II error?

d. What assumptions must hold in order to ensure the validity of the test you conducted in part **b**?

13.47 Risk factor for lumbar disease. One of the most common musculoskeletal disorders is lumbar disk disease (LDD). Medical researchers reported finding a common genetic risk factor for LDD (*Journal of the American Medical Association*, Apr. 11, 2001). The study included 171 Finnish patients diagnosed with LDD (the patient group) and 321 without LDD (the control group). Of the 171 LDD patients, 21 were discovered to have the genetic trait. Of the 321 people in the control group, 15 had the genetic trait.

a. Consider the two categorical variables group and presence/absence of genetic trait. Form a 2 × 2 contingency table for these variables.

b. Conduct a test to determine whether the genetic trait occurs at a higher rate in LDD patients than in the controls. Use $\alpha = .01$.

c. Construct a bar graph that will visually support your conclusion in part **b**.

13.48 Seat-belt use study. The *American Journal of Public Health* (July 1995) reported on a population-based study of trauma in Hispanic children. One of the objectives of the study was to compare the use of protective devices in motor vehicles that transported Hispanic children and non-Hispanic white children. On the basis of data collected from the San Diego County Regionalized Trauma System, 792 children treated for injuries sustained in vehicular accidents were classified according to ethnic status (Hispanic or non-Hispanic white) and seat-belt usage (worn or not worn) during the accident. The data are summarized in the following table:

🔘 **TRAUMA**

	Hispanic	Non-Hispanic White	Totals
Seat belts worn	31	148	179
Seat belts not worn	283	330	613
Totals	314	478	792

Source: Matteneci, R. M., et al. "Trauma among Hispanic children: A population-based study in a regionalized system of trauma care," *American Journal of Public Health*, Vol. 85, No. 7, July 1995, p. 1007 (Table 2).

a. Calculate the sample proportion of injured Hispanic children who were not wearing seat belts during the accident.

b. Calculate the sample proportion of injured non-Hispanic white children who were not wearing seatbelts during the accident.

c. Compare the sample proportions from parts **a** and **b**. Do you think the true population proportions differ?

TUMORS

		Diet				
		High Fat/No Fiber	High Fat/Fiber	Low Fat/No Fiber	Low Fat/Fiber	Totals
Cancer Tumors	Yes	27	20	19	14	80
	No	3	10	11	16	40
	Totals	30	30	30	30	120

Source: Tampa Tribune, Apr. 3, 1991.

d. Conduct a test to determine whether seat-belt usage in motor vehicle accidents depends on ethnic status in the San Diego County Regionalized Trauma System. Use $\alpha = .01$.

e. Construct a 99% confidence interval for the difference between the proportions you found in parts **a** and **b**. Interpret the interval.

13.49 High-fiber food and cancer. According to research reported in the *Journal of the National Cancer Institute* (Apr. 1991), eating foods high in fiber may help protect against breast cancer. The researchers randomly divided 120 laboratory rats into four groups of 30 each. All of the rats were injected with a drug that causes breast cancer. Then each rat was fed a diet of fat and fiber for 15 weeks. However, the levels of fat and fiber varied from group to group. At the end of the feeding period, the number of rats with cancer tumors was determined for each group. The data are summarized in the table above.

a. Does the sampling appear to satisfy the assumptions for a multinomial experiment? (See Section 13.1.) Explain.

b. Calculate the expected cell counts for the contingency table.

c. Calculate the χ^2 statistic.

d. Is there evidence to indicate that diet and presence/absence of cancer are independent? Test, using $\alpha = 05$.

e. Compare the percentage of rats on a high-fat, no-fiber diet with cancer with the percentage of rats on a high-fat, fiber diet with cancer, using a 95% confidence interval. Interpret the result.

13.50 Travel habits of retirees. A study in the *Annals of Tourism Research* (Vol. 19, 1992) investigates the relationship of retirement status (pre- and postretirement) to various items related to the travel industry. One part of the study investigated the differences in the length of stay of a trip for pre- and postretirees. A sample of 703 travelers were asked how long they stayed on a typical trip. The results are shown in the accompanying table. Use the information in the table to determine whether the retirement status of a traveler and the duration of a typical trip are dependent. Test, using $\alpha = .05$.

TRAVEL

Number of Nights	Preretirement	Postretirement
4–7	247	172
8–13	82	67
14–21	35	52
22 or more	16	32
Total	380	323

13.51 Hearing impairment study. The *Journal of Intellectual Disability Research* (Feb. 1995) published a longitudinal study of hearing impairment in a group of elderly patients with intellectual disability. The hearing function of each patient was screened each year over a 10-year period. At the study's conclusion, the hearing loss of each patient was categorized as severe, moderate, mild, or none. The classifications of the 28 surviving patients are summarized in the table below.

HEARIMP

Hearing Loss	Number of Patients
None	7
Mild	7
Moderate	9
Severe	5
Total	28

a. Conduct a test to determine whether the true proportions of intellectually disabled elderly patients in each of the hearing-loss categories differ. Use $\alpha = .05$.

b. Use a 90% confidence interval to estimate the proportion of disabled elderly patients with severe hearing loss.

13.52 Butterfly hot spots. *Nature* (Sept. 1993) reported on a study of animal and plant species "hot spots" in Great Britain. A hot spot is defined as a 10-km² area that is species rich—that is, heavily populated by a species of interest. Analogously, a cold spot is a 10-km² area that is species poor. The accompanying table gives the number of butterfly hot spots and the number of butterfly cold spots in a sample of 2,588 10-km² areas. In theory, 5% of the areas should be butterfly hot spots and 5% should be butterfly cold spots, while the remaining areas (90%) are neutral. Test the theory, using $\alpha = .01$.

Butterfly hot spots	123
Butterfly cold spots	147
Neutral areas	2,318
Total	2,588

Source: Prendergast, J. R., et al. "Rare species, the coincidence of diversity hotspots and conservation strategies." Nature, Vol. 365, No. 6444, Sept. 23, 1993, p. 335 (Table 1).

Applying the Concepts—Intermediate

13.53 Iraq War survey. The Pew Internet & American Life Project commissioned Princeton Survey Research Associates to develop and carry out a survey of what Americans think about the recent War in Iraq. Some of the results of the March 2003 survey of over 1,400 American adults are saved in the **IRAQWAR** file. Responses to the following questions were recorded:

1. Do you support or oppose the Iraq War? (1 = Support, 2 = Oppose)
2. Do you ever go online to access the Internet or World Wide Web? (1 = Yes, 2 = No)
3. Do you consider yourself a Republican, Democrat, or Independent? (1 = Rep., 2 = Dem., 3 = Ind.)
4. Have you or anyone in your household served in the U.S. military? (1 = Yes, I have; 2 = Yes, other; 3 = Yes, both; 4 = No)
5. In general, would you describe your political views as very conservative, conservative, moderate, liberal, or very liberal? (1 = Very conservative, 2 = Conservative, 3 = Moderate, 4 = Liberal, 5 = Very liberal)
6. What is your race? (1 = White, 2 = African-American, 3 = Asian, 4 = Mixed, 5 = Native American, 6 = Other)
7. What is your income range? (1 = < 10K, 2 = 10–20K, 3 = 20–30K, 4 = 30–40K, 5 = 40–50K, 6 = 50–75K, 7 = 75–100K, 8 = > 100K)
8. Do you live in a suburban, rural, or urban community? (1 = urban, 2 = suburban, 3 = rural)

Conduct a series of contingency table analyses to determine whether support for the Iraq War depends on one or more of the other categorical variables measured in the March 2003 survey.

13.54 Pig farmer study. An article in *Sociological Methods & Research* (May 2001) analyzed the data presented in the accompanying table. A sample of 262 Kansas pig farmers were classified according to their education level (college or not) and size of their pig farm (number of pigs). Conduct a test to determine whether a pig farmer's education level has an impact on the size of the pig farm. Use $\alpha = .05$ and support your answer with a graph.

PIGFARM

| | | Education Level | | |
		No College	College	Totals
	<1,000 pigs	42	53	95
	1,000–2,000 pigs	27	42	69
Farm Size	**2,001–5,000 pigs**	22	20	42
	>5,000 pigs	27	29	56
	Totals	118	144	262

Source: Agresti, A., and Liu, I. "Strategies for modeling a categorical variable allowing multiple category choices." *Sociological Methods & Research,* Vol. 29, No. 4, May 2001 (Table I).

13.55 Multiple-sclerosis drug. Interferons are proteins produced naturally by the human body that help fight infections and regulate the immune system. A drug developed from interferons, called Avonex, is now available for treating patients with multiple sclerosis (MS). In a clinical study, 85 MS patients received weekly injections of Avonex over a two-year period. The number of exacerbations (i.e., flare-ups of symptoms) was recorded for each patient and is summarized in the accompanying table. For MS patients who take a placebo (no drug) over a similar two-year period, it is known from

previous studies that 26% will experience no exacerbations, 30% one exacerbation, 11% two exacerbations, 14% three exacerbations, and 19% four or more exacerbations.

Number of Exacerbations	Number of Patients
0	32
1	26
2	15
3	6
4 or more	6

Source: Biogen, Inc.

a. Conduct a test to determine whether the exacerbation distribution of MS patients who take Avonex differs from the percentages reported for placebo patients. Use $\alpha = .05$.
b. Find a 95% confidence interval for the true percentage of Avonex MS patients who remain free of exacerbations during a two-year period.
c. Refer to part **b**. Is there evidence that Avonex patients are more likely to have no exacerbations than placebo patients? Explain.

13.56 Flight response of geese to helicopter traffic. Offshore oil drilling near an Alaskan estuary has led to increased air traffic—mostly large helicopters—in the area. The U.S. Fish and Wildlife Service commissioned a study to investigate the impact these helicopters have on the flocks of Pacific brant geese that inhabit the estuary in the fall before migrating. (*Statistical Case Studies: A Collaboration between Academe and Industry,* 1998.) Two large helicopters were flown repeatedly over the estuary at different altitudes and lateral distances from the flock. The flight responses of the geese (recorded as "low" or "high"), the altitude (in hundreds of meters), and the lateral distance (also in hundreds of meters) for each of 464 helicopter overflights were recorded and are saved in the **PACGEESE** file. The data for the first 10 overflights are shown in the following table:

PACGEESE (First 10 observations shown)

Overflight	Altitude	Lateral Distance	Flight Response
1	0.91	4.99	HIGH
2	0.91	8.21	HIGH
3	0.91	3.38	HIGH
4	9.14	21.08	LOW
5	1.52	6.60	HIGH
6	0.91	3.38	HIGH
7	3.05	0.16	HIGH
8	6.10	3.38	HIGH
9	3.05	6.60	HIGH
10	12.19	6.60	HIGH

Source: Erickson, W., Nick, T., and Ward, D. "Investigating Flight Response of Pacific Brant to Helicopters at Izembek Lagoon, Alaska by Using Logistic Regression," *Statistical Case Studies: A Collaboration between Academe and Industry,* ASA-SIAM Series on Statistics and Applied Probability, 1998.

a. The researchers categorized altitude as follows: less than 300 meters, 300–600 meters, and 600 or more meters. Summarize the data in the **PACGEESE** file by creating a contingency table for altitude category and flight response.

DISRUPT

	Disruptive Behavior	Nondisruptive Behavior	Totals
With Developmental Delays	12	3	15
Without Developmental Delays	5	10	15
Total	17	13	30

Source: Kopp, C. B., Baker, B., and Brown, K. W. "Social skills and their correlates: Preschoolers with developmental delays," *American Journal on Mental Retardation*, Vol. 96, No. 4, Jan. 1992.

b. Conduct a test to determine whether flight response of the geese depends on altitude of the helicopter. Test, using $\alpha = .01$.

c. The researchers categorized lateral distance as follows: less than 1,000 meters, 1,000–2,000 meters, 2,000–3,000 meters, and 3,000 or more meters. Summarize the data in the **PACGEESE** file by creating a contingency table for lateral distance category and flight response.

d. Conduct a test to determine whether flight response of the geese depends on lateral distance of helicopter from the flock. Test, using $\alpha = .01$.

e. The current Federal Aviation Authority (FAA) minimum altitude standard for flying over the estuary is 2,000 feet (approximately 610 meters). On the basis of the results obtained in parts **a–d**, what changes to the FAA regulations do you recommend in order to minimize the effects to Pacific brant geese.

13.57 Birds feeding on gypsy moths. A field study was conducted to identify the natural predators of the gypsy moth. (*Environmental Entomology*, June 1995.) For one part of the study, 24 black-capped chickadees (common wintering birds) were captured in mist nets and individually caged. Each bird was offered a mass of gypsy moth eggs attached to a piece of bark. Half the birds were offered no other food (no choice), and half were offered a variety of other naturally occurring foods such as spruce and pine seeds (choice). The numbers of birds that did and did not feed on the gypsy moth egg mass are given in the accompanying

MOTH

	Fed on Egg Mass	
	Yes	No
Choice of foods	2	10
No choice	8	4

table. Analyze the data in the table to determine whether a relationship exists between food choice and feeding or not feeding on gypsy moth eggs. Use $\alpha = .10$.

13.58 Social play of children. The *American Journal on Mental Retardation* (Jan. 1992) published a study of the social interactions of two groups of children. Independent random samples of 15 children with and 15 children without developmental delays (i.e., mild mental retardation) comprised the subjects of the experiment. After observing the children during "free play," researchers recorded the number of children who exhibited disruptive behavior (e.g., ignoring or rejecting other children, taking toys from another child) for each group. The data are summarized in the two-way table shown above. Analyze the data and interpret the results.

13.59 Lifestyles of husbands and wives. The *Journal of Adlerian Theory, Research and Practice* (Mar. 1986) investigated the role lifestyles play in forming a marriage. Adlerian psychologists group people into one of the following five lifestyle types:

1. *Pleasing priority:* a strong desire to make others happy and win their approval

2. *Achieving priority:* industrious, responsible, orderly, with an active approach to life (particularly in the workplace)

3. *Outdoing priority:* a strong desire to be on top, in a position of superiority over others; likes to be considered the best at whatever he or she does

4. *Suppressing (control) priority:* maintains control over emotions; discloses very little of him or herself

5. *Avoiding priority:* is easily hurt; avoids any potentially painful (physical or emotional) situation.

Data on both wife's and husband's lifestyles were obtained for 202 married couples living in family housing at the University of Georgia. The results are summarized in the table below.

LIFESTYLE

		Wife's Lifestyle					
		Pleasing	Outdoing	Avoiding	Control	Achieving	Totals
	Pleasing	9	6	6	3	9	33
	Outdoing	7	11	12	11	5	46
Husband's Lifestyle	Avoiding	8	8	6	11	5	38
	Control	8	10	7	15	11	51
	Achieving	4	6	7	10	7	34
	Totals	36	41	38	50	37	202

Source: Evans, T. D., and Bozarth, J. "Pairing of personality profiles in marriage," *Journal of Adlerian Theory, Research and Practice*, Vol. 42, No. 1, March 1986, pp. 59–64.

a. The key question of the study is "Do the personality profiles contribute to marriage pairings?" In other words, is there a relationship between the personality priorities of the husband-and-wife pairs? Analyze the data for the researchers.

b. If no relationship between the personality priorities of the husband and wife pairs has been found in part **a**, then analyze the data for husbands and wives separately. Are there differences in the proportions of husbands who fall into the five personality priorities? Are there differences in the proportions of wives who fall into the five personality profiles?

13.60 **Orientation clue experiment.** *Human Factors* (Dec. 1988) published a study of color brightness as a body orientation clue. Ninety college students reclining on their backs in the dark were disoriented when positioned on a rotating platform under a slowly rotating disk that blocked their field of vision. The subjects were asked to say "Stop" when they felt as if they were right-side up. The position of the brightness pattern on the disk in relation to each student's body orientation was then recorded. Subjects selected only three disk brightness patterns as subjective vertical clues: (1) brighter side up, (2) darker side up, and (3) brighter and darker sides aligned on either side of the subjects' heads. The frequency counts for the experiment are given in the accompanying table. Conduct a test to compare the proportions of subjects who fall into the three disk-orientation categories. Assume that you want to determine whether the three proportions differ. Use $\alpha = .05$.

BODYCLUE

	Disk Orientation	
Brighter Side Up	Darker Side Up	Bright and Dark Sides Aligned
58	15	17

COUPONS

13.61 **Coupon usage study.** A hot topic in marketing research is the exploration of a technology-based self-service (TBSS) encounter, in which various technologies (e.g., ATMs, online banking, self-scanning at retail stores) allow the customer to perform all or part of the service. Marketing professor Dan Ladik of the University of Suffolk investigated whether there were differences in customer characteristics and customer satisfaction between users of discount coupons distributed through the mail (nontechnology users) and users of coupons distributed via the Internet (TBSS users). A questionnaire measured several qualitative variables (defined in the accompanying table) for each of 440 coupon users. The data are saved in the **COUPONS** file.

a. Consider the variable Coupon User Type. Conduct a test (at $\alpha = .05$) to determine whether the proportions of mail-only users, Internet-only users, and users of both media are statistically different. Illustrate the results with a graph.

b. The researcher wants to know whether there are differences in customer characteristics (i.e., Gender, Education, Work Status, and Coupon Satisfaction) among the three types of coupon users. For each characteristic, conduct a contingency table analysis (at $\alpha = .05$) to deter-

Variable Name	Levels (Possible Values)
Coupon User Type	Mail, Internet, or Both
Gender	Male or Female
Education	High School, Vo-Tech/College, 4-year College Degree, or Graduate School
Work Status	Full Time, Part Time, Not Working, Retired
Coupon Satisfaction	Satisfied, Unsatisfied, Indifferent

mine whether Coupon User Type is related to that characteristic. Illustrate your results with graphs.

13.62 **Battle simulation trials.** In order to evaluate their situational awareness, fighter aircraft pilots participate in battle simulations. At a random point in the trial, the simulator is frozen and data on situational awareness are immediately collected. The simulation is then continued until, ultimately, performance (e.g., number of kills) is measured. A study reported in *Human Factors* (Mar. 1995) investigated whether temporarily stopping the simulation results in any change in pilot performance. Trials were designed so that some simulations were stopped to collect situational awareness data while others were not. Each trial was then classified according to the number of kills made by the pilot. The data for 180 trials are summarized in the accompanying contingency table. Conduct a contingency table analysis and interpret the results fully.

SIMKILLS

	Number of Kills					
	0	1	2	3	4	Totals
Stops	32	33	19	5	2	91
No Stops	24	36	18	8	3	89
Totals	56	69	37	13	5	180

Applying the Concepts—Advanced

13.63 **Goodness-of-fit test.** A statistical analysis is to be done on a set of data consisting of 1,000 monthly salaries. The analysis requires the assumption that the sample was drawn from a normal distribution. A preliminary test, called the χ^2 *goodness-of-fit test*, can be used to help determine whether it is reasonable to assume that the sample is from a normal distribution. Suppose the mean and standard deviation of the 1,000 salaries are hypothesized to be $1,200 and $200, respectively. Using the standard normal table, we can approximate the probability of a salary being in the intervals listed in the table on p. 777. The third column represents the expected number of the 1,000 salaries to be found in each interval if the sample was drawn from a normal distribution with $\mu = 1,200$ and $\sigma = 200$. Suppose the last column contains the actual observed frequencies in the sample. Large differences between the observed and expected frequencies cast doubt on the normality assumption.

a. Compute the χ^2 statistic on the basis of the observed and expected frequencies.

b. Find the tabulated χ^2 value when $\alpha = .05$ and there are five degrees of freedom. (There are $k - 1 = 5$ df associated with this χ^2 statistic.)

Table for Exercise 13.63

Interval	Probability	Expected Frequency	Observed Frequency
Less than $800	.023	23	26
$800 < $1,000	.136	136	146
$1,000 < $1,200	.341	341	361
$1,200 < $1,400	.341	341	311
$1,400 < $1,600	.136	136	143
$1,600 or above	.023	23	13

c. On the basis of the χ^2 statistic and the tabulated χ^2 value, is there evidence that the salary distribution is nonnormal?

d. Find the approximate observed significance level for the test in part c.

13.64 **Testing normality.** Suppose a random variable is hypothesized to be normally distributed with a mean of 0 and a standard deviation of 1. A random sample of 200 observations of the variable yields frequencies in the intervals listed in the table shown below. Do the data provide sufficient evidence to contradict the hypothesis that x is normally distributed with $\mu = 0$ and $\sigma = 1$? Use the technique developed in Exercise 13.63.

Critical Thinking Challenge

13.65 **A "rigged" election?** *Chance* (Spring 2004) presented data from a recent election held to determine the board of directors of a local community. There were 27 candidates for the board, and each of 5,553 voters was allowed to choose 6 candidates. The claim was that "a fixed vote with fixed percentages [was] assigned to each and every candidate, making it impossible to participate in an honest election." Votes were tallied in six time slots: after 600 total votes were in, after 1200, after 2,444, after 3,444, after 4,444, and, finally, after 5,553 votes. The data on three of the candidates (Smith, Coppin, and Montes) are shown in the accompanying table. A residential organization believes that "there was nothing random about the count and tallies for each time slot, and specific unnatural or rigged percentages were being assigned to each and every candidate." Give your opinion. Is the probability of a candidate receiving votes independent of the time slot, and if so, does this imply a rigged election?

RIGVOTE

Time Slot	1	2	3	4	5	6
Votes for Smith	208	208	451	392	351	410
Votes for Coppin	55	51	109	98	88	104
Votes for Montes	133	117	255	211	186	227
Total Votes	600	600	1,244	1,000	1,000	1,109

Source: Gelman, A. "55,000 residents desperately need your help!" *Chance*, Vol. 17, No. 2, Spring 2004 (Figures 1 and 5).

Table for Exercise 13.64

Interval	$x < -2$	$-2 \leq x < -1$	$-1 \leq x < 0$	$0 \leq x < 1$	$1 \leq x < 2$	$x \geq 2$
Frequency	7	20	61	77	26	9

SUMMARY ACTIVITY: "Guesstimates" of Population Proportions

Many researchers rely on surveys to estimate the proportions of experimental units in populations that possess certain specified characteristics. A political scientist may want to estimate the proportion of an electorate in favor of a certain legislative bill. A social scientist may be interested in the proportions of people in a geographical region who fall into certain socioeconomic classifications. A psychologist might want to compare the proportions of patients who have different psychological disorders.

Choose a specific topic, similar to those described in the previous paragraph, that interests you. Define clearly the population of interest, identify data categories of specific interest, and identify the proportions associated with them. Now "*guesstimate*" the proportions of the population that you think fall into each of the categories. For example, you might guess that all the proportions are equal, or that the first proportion is twice as large as the second but equal to the third, etc.

You are now ready to collect the data by obtaining a random sample from your population of interest. Select a sample size so that all expected cell counts are at least 5 (preferably larger), and then collect the data.

Use the count data you have obtained to test the null hypothesis that the true proportions in the population are equal to your presampling guesstimates. Would failure to reject this null hypothesis imply that your guesstimates are correct?

REFERENCES

Agresti, A. *Categorical Data Analysis*. New York: Wiley, 1990.

Cochran, W. G. "The χ^2 test of goodness of fit." *Annals of Mathematical Statistics*, 1952, 23.

Conover, W. J. *Practical Nonparametric Statistics*, 2d ed. New York: Wiley, 1980.

Fisher, R. A. "The logic of inductive inference (with discussion)." *Journal of the Royal Statistical Society*, Vol. 98, 1935, pp. 39–82.

Hollander, M., and Wolfe, D. A. *Nonparametric Statistical Methods*. New York: Wiley, 1973.

Savage, I. R. "Bibliography of nonparametric statistics and related topics." *Journal of the American Statistical Association*, 1953, 48.

Using Technology

Chi-Square Analyses with MINITAB

MINITAB can conduct chi-square tests on both one-way and two-way (contingency) tables.

One-Way Table: To conduct a chi-square test on a one-way table, first access the MINITAB worksheet file that contains the sample data for the qualitative variable of interest. [*Note*: The data file can have actual values (levels) of the variable for each observation or, alternatively, two columns, one listing the levels of the qualitative variable and the other with the observed counts for each level.] Next, click on the "Stat" button on the MINITAB menu bar, and then click on "Tables" and "Chi-Square Goodness-of-Fit Test (One Variable)", as shown in Figure 13.M.1.

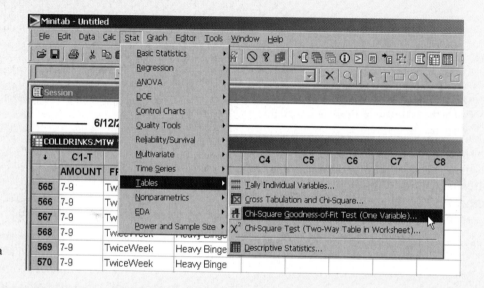

FIGURE 13.M.1

MINITAB menu options for a one-way chi-square analysis

The dialog box shown in Figure 13.M.2 then appears. If you have one column of data for your qualitative variable, select "Categorical data" and specify the variable name (or column) in the box. If, instead, you have summary information in two columns (see note in previous paragraph), select "Observed counts" and specify the column with the counts and the column with the variable names in the respective boxes. Select "Equal proportions" for a test of equal proportions, or select "Specific proportions" and enter the hypothesized proportion next to each level in the resulting box. Click "OK" to generate the MINITAB printout.

Two-way Table: To conduct a chi-square test for a two-way table, first access the MINITAB worksheet file that contains the sample data. The data file should contain two qualitative variables, with category values for each of the *n* observations in the data set. Alternatively, the worksheet can contain the cell counts for each of the categories of the two qualitative

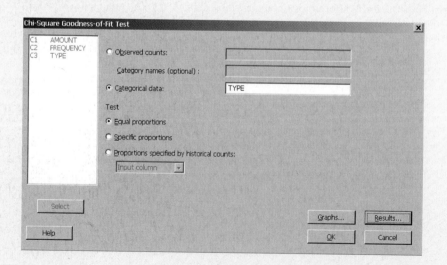

FIGURE 13.M.2

MINITAB one-way chi-square dialog box

variables. Next, click on the "Stat" button on the MINITAB menu bar, and then click on "Tables" and "Cross Tabulation and Chi-Square," as shown in Figure 13.M.3.

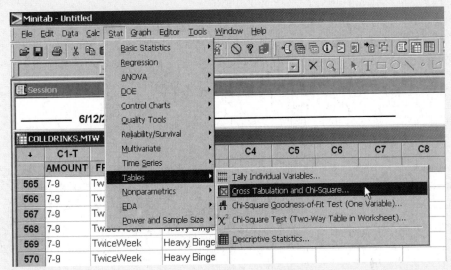

FIGURE 13.M.3
MINITAB menu options for a two-way chi-square analysis

The dialog box shown in Figure 13.M.4 then appears. Specify one qualitative variable in the "For rows" box and the other qualitative variable in the "For columns" box. [*Note:* If your worksheet contains cell counts for the categories, enter the variable with the cell counts in the "Frequencies are in" box.] Next, select the summary statistics (e.g., counts, percentages) you want to display in the contingency table. Then click the "Chi-square" button. The dialog box shown in Figure 13.M.5 then appears. Select "Chi-Square analysis" and "Expected cell counts" and click "OK." When you return to the "Cross Tabulation" menu screen, click "OK" to generate the MINITAB printout.

[*Note:* If your MINITAB worksheet contains only the cell counts for the contingency table in columns, click the "Chi-Square Test (Two-way Table in Worksheet)" menu option (see Figure 13.M.3) and specify the columns in the "Columns containing the table" box. Click "OK" to produce the MINITAB printout.]

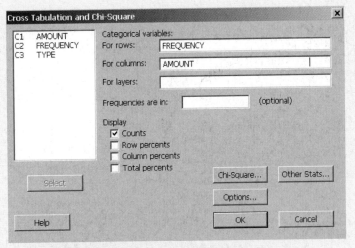

FIGURE 13.M.4
MINITAB cross-tabulation dialog box

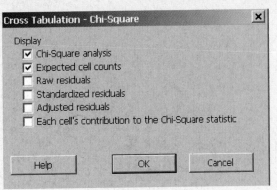

FIGURE 13.M.5
MINITAB cross-tabulation chi-square options

Chapter
14
Nonparametric Statistics

14

Nonparametric Statistics

STATISTICS IN ACTION

How Vunerable Are New Hampshire Wells to Groundwater Contamination?

USING TECHNOLOGY

Nonparametric Tests with MINITAB

WHERE WE'VE BEEN

■ Presented methods for making inferences about means (Chapters 7–10) and for making inferences about the correlation between two quantitative variables (Chapter 11)

■ These methods required that the data be normally distributed or that the sampling distributions of the relevant statistics be normally distributed.

WHERE WE'RE GOING

■ Develop the need for inferential techniques that require fewer or less stringent assumptions than the methods of Chapters 7–10 and 11

■ Introduce *nonparametric* tests that are based on ranks (i.e., on an ordering of the sample measurements according to their relative magnitudes)

STATISTICS IN ACTION

How Vulnerable Are New Hampshire Wells to Groundwater Contamination?

Methyl tert-butyl ether (commonly known as MTBE) is a volatile, flammable, colorless liquid manufactured by the chemical reaction of methanol and isobutylene. MTBE was first produced in the United States as a lead fuel additive (octane booster) in 1979 and then as an oxygenate in reformulated fuel in the 1990s. Unfortunately, MTBE was introduced into water-supply aquifers by leaking underground storage tanks at gasoline stations, thus contaminating the drinking water. Consequently, by late 2006 most (but not all) American gasoline retailers had ceased using MTBE as an oxygenate, and accordingly, U.S. production has declined. Despite the reduction in production, there is no federal standard for MTBE in public water supplies; therefore, the chemical remains a dangerous pollutant, especially in states like New Hampshire that mandate the use of reformulated gasoline.

A study published in *Environmental Science & Technology* (Jan. 2005) investigated the risk of exposure to MTBE through drinking water in New Hampshire. In particular, the study reported on the factors related to MTBE contamination in public and private New Hampshire wells. Data were collected on a sample of 223 wells. These data are saved in the **MTBE** file (part of which you analyzed in Exercise 2.19). One of the variables measured was MTBE level (micrograms per liter) in the well water. An MTBE value exceeding .2 microgram per liter on the measuring instrument is a detectable level of MTBE. Of the 223 wells, 70 had detectable levels of MTBE. (Although the other wells are below the detection limit of the measuring device, the MTBE values for these wells are recorded as .2 rather than 0.) The other variables on the data set are described in Table 14.1.

How contaminated are these New Hampshire wells? Is the level of MTBE contamination different for the two classes of wells? For the two types of aquifers? What environmental factors are related to the MTBE level of a groundwater well? These are just a few of the research questions addressed in the study.

The researchers applied several nonparametric methods to the data in order to answer the research questions. We demonstrate the use of this methodology in four *Statistics in Action Revisited* examples.

Statistics in Action Revisited

- Testing the Median MTBE Level of Groundwater Wells (p. 14-8)

- Comparing the MTBE Levels of Different Types of Groundwater Wells (p. 14-16)

- Comparing the MTBE Levels of Different Types of Groundwater Wells (continued) (p. 14-31)

- Testing the Correlation of MTBE Level with Other Environmental Factors (p. 14-46)

 MTBE

TABLE 14.1 Variables Measured in the MTBE Contamination Study

Variable Name	Type	Description	Units of Measurement, or Levels
CLASS	QL	Class of well	Public or Private
AQUIFER	QL	Type of aquifer	Bedrock or Unconsolidated
DETECTION	QL	MTBE detection status	Below limit or Detect
MTBE	QN	MTBE level	micrograms per liter
PH	QN	pH level	standard pH unit
DISSOXY	QN	Dissolved oxygen	milligrams per liter
DEPTH	QN	Well depth	meters
DISTANCE	QN	Distance to underground storage tank	meters
INDUSTRY	QN	Industries in proximity	Percent of industrial land within 500 meters of well

14.1 Introduction: Distribution-Free Tests

The confidence interval and testing procedures developed in Chapters 7–10 all involve making inferences about population parameters. Consequently, they are often referred to as **parametric statistical tests**. Many of these parametric methods (e.g., the small-sample *t*-test of Chapter 8 or the ANOVA *F*-test of Chapter 10) rely on the assumption that the data are sampled from a normally distributed population. When the data are normal, these tests are *most powerful*. That is, the use of such parametric tests maximizes power—the probability of the researcher correctly rejecting the null hypothesis.

Consider a population of data that is decidedly nonnormal. For example, the distribution might be flat, peaked, or strongly skewed to the right or left. (See Figure 14.1.) Applying the small-sample *t*-test to such a data set may lead to serious consequences. Since the normality assumption is clearly violated, the results of the *t*-test are unreliable. Specifically (1) the probability of a Type I error (i.e., rejecting H_0 when it is true) may be larger than the value of α selected, and (2) the power of the test, $1 - \beta$, is not maximized.

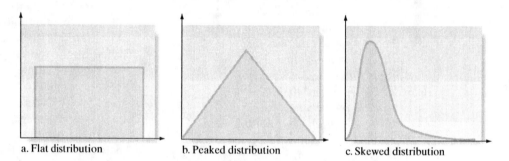

FIGURE 14.1
Some nonnormal distributions for which the *t*-statistic is invalid

a. Flat distribution   b. Peaked distribution   c. Skewed distribution

A number of *nonparametric* techniques are available for analyzing data that do not follow a normal distribution. Nonparametric tests do not depend on the distribution of the sampled population; thus, they are called *distribution-free tests*. Also, nonparametric methods focus on the location of the probability distribution of the population, rather than on specific parameters of the population, such as the mean (hence the name "nonparametric").

Definition 14.1

Distribution-free tests are statistical tests that do not rely on any underlying assumptions about the probability distribution of the sampled population.

Definition 14.2

The branch of inferential statistics devoted to distribution-free tests is called **nonparametrics**.

Nonparametric tests are also appropriate when the data are nonnumerical in nature, but can be ranked.* For example, when taste-testing foods or in other types of consumer product evaluations, we can say that we like product A better than product B, and B better than C, but we cannot obtain exact quantitative values for the respective measurements. Nonparametric tests based on the ranks of measurements are called *rank tests*.

Definition 14.3

Nonparametric statistics (or tests) based on the ranks of measurements are called **rank statistics** (or **rank tests**).

---

*Qualitative data that can be ranked in order of magnitude are called *ordinal* data.

In this chapter, we present several useful nonparametric methods. Keep in mind that these nonparametric tests are more powerful than their corresponding parametric counterparts in those situations where either the data are nonnormal or the data are ranked.

In Section 14.2, we develop a test for making inferences about the central tendency of a single population. In Sections 14.3 and 14.5, we present rank statistics for comparing two or more probability distributions using independent samples. In Sections 14.4 and 14.6, the matched-pairs and randomized block designs are used to make nonparametric comparisons of populations. Finally, in Section 14.7, we present a nonparametric measure of correlation between two variables.

14.2 Single-Population Inferences

In Chapter 8, we utilized the z- and t-statistics for testing hypotheses about a population mean. The z-statistic is appropriate for large random samples selected from "general" populations—that is, samples with few limitations on the probability distribution of the underlying population. The t-statistic was developed for small-sample tests in which the sample is selected at random from a *normal* distribution. The question is, How can we conduct a test of hypothesis when we have a small sample from a *nonnormal* distribution?

The **sign test** is a relatively simple nonparametric procedure for testing hypotheses about the central tendency of a nonnormal probability distribution. Note that we used the phrase *central tendency* rather than *population mean*. This is because the sign test, like many nonparametric procedures, provides inferences about the population *median* rather than the population mean μ. Denoting the population median by the Greek letter η, we know (Chapter 2) that η is the 50th percentile of the distribution (Figure 14.2) and, as such, is less affected by the skewness of the distribution and the presence of outliers (extreme observations). Since the nonparametric test must be suitable for all distributions, not just the normal, it is reasonable for nonparametric tests to focus on the more robust (less sensitive to extreme values) measure of central tendency; the median.

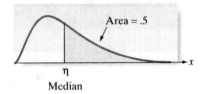

FIGURE 14.2
Location of the population median, η

For example, increasing numbers of both private and public agencies are requiring their employees to submit to tests for substance abuse. One laboratory that conducts such testing has developed a system with a normalized measurement scale in which values less than 1.00 indicate "normal" ranges and values equal to or greater than 1.00 are indicative of potential substance abuse. The lab reports a normal result as long as the median level for an individual is less than 1.00. Eight independent measurements of each individual's sample are made. One individual's results are shown in Table 14.1.

 SUBABUSE

TABLE 14.1 Substance Abuse Test Results

.78	.51	3.79	.23	.77	.98	.96	.89

If the objective is to determine whether the *population* median (i.e., the true median level if an infinitely large number of measurements were made on the same individual sample) is less than 1.00, we establish that as our alternative hypothesis and test

$$H_0: \eta = 1.00$$

$$H_a: \eta < 1.00$$

The one-tailed sign test is conducted by counting the number of sample measurements that "favor" the alternative hypothesis—in this case, the number that are less than 1.00. If the null hypothesis is true, we expect approximately half of the measurements to fall

on each side of the hypothesized median, and if the alternative is true, we expect significantly more than half to favor the alternative—that is, to be less than 1.00. Thus,

Test statistic: S = Number of measurements less than 1.00, the null
hypothesized median

If we wish to conduct the test at the $\alpha = .05$ level of significance, the rejection region can
be expressed in terms of the observed significance level, or p-value, of the test:

Rejection region: p − value $\leq .05$

In this example, $S = 7$ of the 8 measurements are less than 1.00. To determine the
observed significance level associated with that outcome, we note that the number of
measurements less than 1.00 is a binomial random variable (check the binomial characteristics presented in Chapter 4), and *if H_0 is true*, the binomial probability p that a measurement lies below (or above) the median 1.00 is equal to .5 (Figure 14.2). What is the
probability that a result is *as contrary to or more contrary to H_0* than the one observed?
That is, what is the probability that 7 *or more* of 8 binomial measurements will result in
Success (be less than 1.00) if the probability of Success is .5? Binomial Table II in
Appendix A (with $n = 8$ and $p = .5$) indicates that

$$P(x \geq 7) = 1 - P(x \leq 6) = 1 - .965 = .035$$

Thus, the probability that at least 7 of 8 measurements would be less than 1.00 *if the true
median were 1.00* is only .035. The p-value of the test is therefore .035.

This p-value can also be obtained from a statistical software package. The
MINITAB printout of the analysis is shown in Figure 14.3, with the p-value highlighted.
Since $p = .035$ is less than $\alpha = .05$, we conclude that this sample provides sufficient evidence to reject the null hypothesis. The implication of this rejection is that the laboratory can conclude at the $\alpha = .05$ level of significance that the true median level for the
individual tested is less than 1.00. However, we note that one of the measurements, with
a value of 3.79, greatly exceeds the others and deserves special attention. This large measurement is an outlier that would make the use of a t-test and its concomitant assumption of normality dubious. The only assumption necessary to ensure the validity of the
sign test is that the probability distribution of measurements is continuous.

Sign Test for Median: READING

```
Sign test of median =   1.000 versus < 1.000

              N   Below   Equal   Above        P   Median
READING   8       7       0       1   0.0352   0.8350
```

FIGURE 14.3
MINITAB printout of sign test

The use of the sign test for testing hypotheses about population medians is summarized in the following box:

Sign Test for a Population Median η

One-Tailed Test	**Two-Tailed Test**
H_0: $\eta = \eta_0$	H_0: $\eta = \eta_0$
H_a: $\eta > \eta_0$ [or H_a: $\eta < \eta_0$]	H_a: $\eta \neq \eta_0$
Test statistic:	*Test statistic:*
S = Number of sample measurements greater than η_0 [or S = number of measurements less than η_0]	S = Larger of S_1 and S_2, where S_1 is the number of measurements less than η_0 and S_2 is the number of measurements greater than η_0

[*Note:* Eliminate observations from the analysis that are exactly equal to the hypothesized median, η_0.]

(continued)

Observed significance level:

p-value $= P(x \geq S)$

Observed significance level:

p-value $= 2P(x \geq S)$

where x has a binomial distribution with parameters n and $p = .5$. (Use Table II, Appendix A.)

Rejection region: Reject H_0 if p-value $\leq \alpha$

Conditions Required for a Valid Application of the Sign Test

The sample is selected randomly from a continuous probability distribution.

[*Note:* No assumptions need to be made about the shape of the probability distribution.]

Recall that the normal probability distribution provides a good approximation of the binomial distribution when the sample size is large. For tests about the median of a distribution, the null hypothesis implies that $p = .5$, and the normal distribution provides a good approximation if $n \geq 10$. (Samples with $n \geq 10$ satisfy the condition that $np \pm 2\sqrt{npq}$ is contained in the interval from 0 to n.) Thus, we can use the standard normal z-distribution to conduct the sign test for large samples. The large-sample sign test is summarized in the next box.

Large-Sample Sign Test for a Population Median η

One-Tailed Test	**Two-Tailed Test**
$H_0: \eta = \eta_0$	$H_0: \eta = \eta_0$
$H_a: \eta > \eta_0$ [or $H_a: \eta < \eta_0$]	$H_a: \eta \neq \eta_0$

$$\text{Test statistic: } z = \frac{(S - .5) - .5n}{.5\sqrt{n}}$$

[*Note:* S is calculated as shown in the previous box. We subtract .5 from S as the "correction for continuity." The null-hypothesized mean value is $np = .5n$, and the standard deviation is

$$\sqrt{npq} = \sqrt{n(.5)(.5)} = .5\sqrt{n}$$

(See Chapter 5 for details on the normal approximation to the binomial distribution.)]

Rejection region: $z > z_\alpha$ *Rejection region:* $z > z_{\alpha/2}$

where tabulated z-values can be found in Table IV, Appendix A.

EXAMPLE 14.1

SIGN TEST
APPLICATION—
Failure Times
of CD Players

Problem A manufacturer of compact disc (CD) players has established that the median time to failure for its players is 5,250 hours of utilization. A sample of 20 CD players from a competitor is obtained, and the players are tested continuously until each fails. The 20 failure times range from 5 hours (a "defective" player) to 6,575 hours, and 14 of the 20 exceed 5,250 hours. Is there evidence that the median failure time of the competitor's product differs from 5,250 hours? Use $\alpha = .10$.

Solution The null and alternative hypotheses of interest are

$$H_0: \eta = 5{,}250 \text{ hours}$$
$$H_a: \eta \neq 5{,}250 \text{ hours}$$

Since $n \geq 10$, we use the standard normal z statistic:

$$\text{Test statistic: } z = \frac{(S - .5) - .5n}{.5\sqrt{n}}$$

Here, S is the maximum of S_1 (the number of measurements greater than 5,250) and S_2 (the number of measurements less than 5,250). Also,

$$\text{Rejection region:} \quad z > 1.645, \text{ where } z_{\alpha/2} = z_{.05} = 1.645$$

Assumptions: The probability distribution of the failure times is continuous (time is a continuous variable), but nothing is assumed about its shape.

Since the number of measurements exceeding 5,250 is $S_2 = 14$, it follows that the number of measurements less than 5,250 is $S_1 = 6$. Consequently, $S = 14$, the greater of S_1 and S_2. The calculated z statistic is therefore

$$z = \frac{(S - .5) - .5n}{.5\sqrt{n}} = \frac{13.5 - 10}{.5\sqrt{20}} = \frac{3.5}{2.236} = 1.565$$

The value of z is not in the rejection region, so we cannot reject the null hypothesis at the $\alpha = .10$ level of significance.

Look Back The manufacturer should not conclude, on the basis of this sample, that its competitor's CD players have a median failure time that differs from 5,250 hours. The manufacturer will not "accept H_0," however, since the probability of a Type II error is unknown.

Now Work Exercise 14.5

The one-sample nonparametric sign test for a median provides an alternative to the t-test for small samples from nonnormal distributions. However, if the distribution is approximately normal, the t-test provides a more powerful test about the central tendency of the distribution.

STATISTICS IN ACTION REVISITED

Testing the Median MTBE Level of Groundwater Wells

We return to the study of MTBE contamination of New Hampshire groundwater wells (p. 14-3). The Environmental Protection Agency (EPA) has not set a Federal standard for MTBE in public water supplies; however, several states have developed their own standards. New Hampshire has a standard of 13 micrograms per liter; that is, no groundwater well should have an MTBE level that exceeds 13 micrograms per liter. Also, only half the wells in the state should have MTBE levels that exceed .5 microgram per liter. This implies that the median MTBE level should be less than .5. Do the data collected by the researchers provide evidence to indicate that the median level of MTBE in New Hampshire groundwater wells is less than .5 microgram per liter? To answer this question, we applied the sign test to the data saved in the MTBE file. The MINITAB printout is shown in Figure SIA14.1

We want to test $H_0: \eta = .5$ versus $H_a: \eta < .5$. According to the printout, 180 of the 223 sampled groundwater wells had MTBE levels below .5. Consequently, the test statistic value is $S = 180$. The one-tailed p-value for the test (highlighted on the printout) is .0000. Thus, the sign test is significant at $\alpha = .01$. Therefore, the data do provide sufficient evidence to indicate that the median MTBE level of New Hampshire groundwater wells is less than .5 microgram per liter.

FIGURE SIA14.1

MINITAB sign test for MTBE data

Sign Test for Median: MTBE

Sign test of median = 0.5000 versus < 0.5000

	N	Below	Equal	Above	P	Median
MTBE	223	180	0	43	0.0000	0.2000

Exercises 14.1–14.15

Understanding the Principles

14.1 Under what circumstances is the sign test preferred to the *t*-test for making inferences about the central tendency of a population?

14.2 What is the probability that a randomly selected observation exceeds the
a. Mean of a normal distribution?
b. Median of a normal distribution?
c. Mean of a nonnormal distribution?
d. Median of a nonnormal distribution?

Learning the Mechanics

14.3 Use Table II of Appendix A to calculate the following binomial probabilities:
a. $P(x \geq 6)$ when $n = 7$ and $p = .5$
b. $P(x \geq 5)$ when $n = 9$ and $p = .5$
c. $P(x \geq 8)$ when $n = 8$ and $p = .5$
d. $P(x \geq 10)$ when $n = 15$ and $p = .5$. Also, use the normal approximation to calculate this probability, and then compare the approximation with the exact value.
e. $P(x \geq 15)$ when $n = 25$ and $p = .5$. Also, use the normal approximation to calculate this probability, and then compare the approximation with the exact value.

14.4 Consider the following sample of 10 measurements:

⚙ **LM14_4**

8.4	16.9	15.8	12.5	10.3	4.9	12.9	9.8	23.7	7.3

Use these data, the binomial tables (Table II, Appendix A), and $\alpha = .05$ to conduct each of the following sign tests:
a. $H_0: \eta = 9$ versus $H_a: \eta > 9$
b. $H_0: \eta = 9$ versus $H_a: \eta \neq 9$
c. $H_0: \eta = 20$ versus $H_a: \eta < 20$
d. $H_0: \eta = 20$ versus $H_a: \eta \neq 20$
e. Repeat each of the preceding tests, using the normal approximation to the binomial probabilities. Compare the results.
f. What assumptions are necessary to ensure the validity of each of the preceding tests?

14.5 Suppose you wish to conduct a test of the research hypothesis
NW that the median of a population is greater than 80. You randomly sample 25 measurements from the population and determine that 16 of them exceed 80. Set up and conduct the appropriate test of hypothesis at the .10 level of significance. Be sure to specify all necessary assumptions.

Applying the Concepts—Basic

14.6 Caffeine in Starbucks coffee. Scientists at the University of Florida College of Medicine investigated the level of caffeine in 16-ounce cups of Starbucks coffee. (*Journal of Analytical Toxicology*, Oct. 2003.) In one phase of the experiment, cups of Starbucks Breakfast Blend (a mix of Latin American coffees) were purchased on six consecutive days from a single specialty coffee shop. The amount of caffeine in each of the six cups (measured in milligrams) is provided in the following table:

⚙ **STARBUCKS**

564	498	259	303	300	307

a. Suppose the scientists are interested in determining whether the median amount of caffeine in Breakfast Blend coffee exceeds 300 milligrams. Set up the null and alternative hypotheses of interest.

b. How many of the cups in the sample have a caffeine content that exceeds 300 milligrams?
c. Assuming that $p = .5$, use the binomial table in Appendix A to find the probability that at least 4 of the 6 cups have caffeine amounts that exceed 300 milligrams.
d. On the basis of the probability you found in part **c**, what do you conclude about H_0 and H_a? (Use $\alpha = .05$.)

⚙ **LICHEN**

14.7 Radioactive lichen. Refer to the 2003 Lichen Radionuclide Baseline Research project to monitor the level of radioactivity in lichen, presented in Exercise 2.34 (p. 47). Recall that University of Alaska researchers collected 9 lichen specimens and measured the amount of the radioactive element cesium-137 (in microcuries per milliliter) in each specimen. (The natural logarithms of the data values, saved in the **LICHEN** file, are listed in the next table.) In Exercise 8.67 (p. 378), you used the *t*-statistic to test whether the mean cesium amount in lichen differs from $\mu = .003$ microcurie per milliliter. Use the MINITAB printout below to conduct an alternative nonparametric test at $\alpha = .10$. Does the result agree with that of the *t*-test from Exercise 8.67?

MINITAB output for Exercise 14.7

Sign Test for Median: CESIUM

```
Sign test of median = 0.00300 versus not = 0.00300

          N  Below  Equal  Above      P  Median
CESIUM    9      1      0      8  0.0391  0.00783
```

LICHEN

Location			
Bethel	−5.50	−5.00	
Eagle Summit	−4.15	−4.85	
Moose Pass	−6.05		
Turnagain Pass	−5.00		
Wickersham Dome	−4.10	−4.50	−4.60

Source: Lichen Radionuclide Baseline Research project, 2003.

14.8 Quality of white shrimp. In *The American Statistician* (May 2001), the nonparametric sign test was used to analyze data on the quality of white shrimp. One measure of shrimp quality is cohesiveness. Since freshly caught shrimp are usually stored on ice, there is concern that cohesiveness will deteriorate after storage. For a sample of 20 newly caught white shrimp, cohesiveness was measured both before and after storage on ice for two weeks. The difference in the cohesiveness measurements (before minus after) was obtained for each shrimp. If storage has no effect on cohesiveness, the population median of the differences will be 0. If cohesiveness deteriorates after storage, the population median of the differences will be positive.

a. Set up the null and alternative hypotheses to test whether cohesiveness will deteriorate after storage.

b. In the sample of 20 shrimp, there were 13 positive differences. Use this value to find the *p*-value of the test.

c. Make the appropriate conclusion (in the words of the problem) if $\alpha = .05$.

14.9 Ammonia in car exhaust. Refer to the *Environmental Science & Technology* (Sept. 1, 2000) study of ammonia levels near the exit ramp of a San Francisco highway tunnel, presented in Exercise 2.59 (p. 59). The daily ammonia concentrations (parts per million) on eight randomly selected days during afternoon drive time are reproduced in the accompanying table. Suppose you want to determine whether the median daily ammonia concentration for all afternoon drive-time days exceeds 1.5 ppm.

AMMONIA

1.53	1.50	1.37	1.51	1.55	1.42	1.41	1.48

a. Set up the null and alternative hypotheses for the test.

b. Find the value of the test statistic.

c. Find the *p*-value of the test.

d. Give the appropriate conclusion (in the words of the problem) if $\alpha = .05$.

14.10 Crab spiders hiding on flowers. Refer to the *Behavioral Ecology* (Jan. 2005) field study on the natural camouflage of crab spiders, presented in Exercise 2.36 (p. 48). Ecologists collected a sample of 10 adult female crab spiders, each sitting on the yellow central part of a daisy, and measured the chromatic contrast between each spider and the flower. The contrast values for the 10 crab spiders are reproduced in the next table. (*Note:* The lower the contrast, the more difficult it is for predators to see the crab spider on the flower.) Recall that a contrast of 70 or greater allows bird predators to see the spider. Consider a test to determine whether the population median chromatic contrast of spiders on flowers is less than 70.

SPIDER

57	75	116	37	96	61	56	2	43	32

Data adapted from Thery, M., et al. "Specific color sensitivities of prey and predator explain camouflage in different visual systems," *Behavioral Ecology*, Vol. 16, No. 1, Jan. 2005 (Table 1).

a. State the null and alternative hypotheses for the test of interest.

b. Calculate the value of the test statistic.

c. Find the *p*-value for the test.

d. At $\alpha = .10$, what is the appropriate conclusion? State your answer in the words of the problem.

Applying the Concepts—Intermediate

14.11 Biting rates of flies. The biting rate of a particular species of fly was investigated in a study reported in the *Journal of the American Mosquito Control Association* (Mar. 1995). Biting rate was defined as the number of flies biting a volunteer during 15 minutes of exposure. The species of fly being investigated was known to have a median biting rate of 5 bites per 15 minutes on Stanbury Island, Utah. However, it is theorized that the median biting rate is higher in bright, sunny weather. To test this theory, 122 volunteers were exposed to the flies during a sunny day on Stanbury Island. Of these volunteers, 95 experienced biting rates greater than 5.

a. Set up the null and alternative hypotheses for the test.

b. Calculate the approximate *p*-value of the test. [*Hint:* Use the normal approximation for a binomial probability.]

c. Make the appropriate conclusion at $\alpha = .01$.

14.12 Al Qaeda attacks on the United States. Refer to the *Studies in Conflict & Terrorism* (Vol. 29, 2006) analysis of recent incidents involving suicide terrorist attacks, presented in Exercise 2.30 (p. 46). The data in the accompanying table are the number of individual suicide bombings attacks for each in a sample of 21 recent incidents involving an attack against the United States by the Al Qaeda terrorist group. A counterterrorism expert claims that more than half of all Al Qaeda attacks against the United States involve two or fewer suicide bombings. Is there evidence to support this claim? Test at $\alpha = .05$.

ALQAEDA

1	1	2	1	2	4	1	1	1	1	2
3	4	5	1	1	1	2	2	2	1	

Source: Moghadam, A. "Suicide terrorism, occupation, and the globalization of martyrdom: A critique of *Dying to Win*," *Studies in Conflict & Terrorism*, Vol. 29, No. 8, 2006 (Table 3).

14.13 Freckling of superalloy ingots. Refer to the *Journal of Metallurgy* (Sep. 2004) study of freckling of superalloy ingots, presented in Exercise 2.179 (p. 105). Recall that freckles are defects that sometimes form during the solidification of the ingot. The freckle index for each of $n = 18$ superalloy ingots is shown in the next table. In the population of superalloy ingots, is there evidence to say that 50% of the ingots have a freckle index of 10 or higher? Test, using $\alpha = .01$.

⊚ **FRECKLE**

30.1	22.0	14.6	16.4	12.0	2.4	22.2	10.0	15.1
12.6	6.8	4.1	2.5	1.4	33.4	16.8	8.1	3.2

Source: Yang, W. H., et al. "A freckle criterion for the solidification of superalloys with a tilted solidification front," *Journal of Metallurgy*, Vol. 56, No. 9, Sep. 2004 (Table IV).

14.14 Study of guppy migration. In a study of the excessive transitory migration of guppy populations, 40 adult female guppies were placed in the left compartment of an experimental aquarium tank divided in half by a glass plate. After the plate was removed, the numbers of fish passing through the slit from the left compartment to the right one, and vice versa, were monitored every minute for 30 minutes. (*Zoological Science*, Vol. 6, 1989.) If an equilibrium is reached, the researchers would expect the median number of fish remaining in the left compartment to be 20. The data for the 30 observations (i.e., numbers of fish in the left compartment at the end of each 1-minute inter-

val) are shown in the accompanying table. Use the large-sample sign test to determine whether the median is less than 20. Test, using $\alpha = .05$.

14.15 Minimizing tractor skidding distance. Refer to the *Journal of Forest Engineering* (July 1999) study of minimizing tractor skidding distances along a new road in a European forest, presented in Exercise 8.69 (p. 379). The skidding distances (in meters) were measured at 20 randomly selected road sites. The data are repeated in the accompanying table. In Exercise 8.69, you conducted a test of hypothesis for the population mean skidding distance. Now conduct a test to determine whether the population median skidding distance is more than 400 meters. Use $\alpha = .10$.

⊚ **SKIDDING**

488	350	457	199	285	409	435	574	439	546
385	295	184	261	273	400	311	312	141	425

Source: Tujek, J. & Pacola, E. "Algorithms for skidding distance modeling on a raster Digital Terrain Model," *Journal of Forest Engineering*, Vol. 10, No. 1, July 1999 (Table 1).

⊚ **GUPPY**

16	11	12	15	14	16	18	15	13	15
14	14	16	13	17	17	14	22	18	19
17	17	20	23	18	19	21	17	21	17

Source: Terami, H., and Watanabe, M. "Excessive transitory migration of guppy populations. III. Analysis of perception of swimming space and a mirror effect," *Zoological Science*, Vol. 6, 1989, p. 977 (Figure 2).

14.3 Comparing Two Populations: Independent Samples

Suppose two independent random samples are to be used to compare two populations, but the *t*-test of Chapter 9 is inappropriate for making the comparison. We may be unwilling to make assumptions about the form of the underlying population probability distributions, or we may be unable to obtain exact values of the sample measurements. If the data can be ranked in order of magnitude in either of these cases, the **Wilcoxon rank sum test** (developed by Frank Wilcoxon) can be used to test the hypothesis that the probability distributions associated with the two populations are equivalent.

Biography

FRANK WILCOXON (1892–1965)—Wilcoxon Rank Tests

Frank Wilcoxon was born in Ireland, where his wealthy American parents were vacationing. He grew up in the family home in Catskill, New York, and then spent time working as an oil worker and tree surgeon in the back country of West Virginia. At age 25, Wilcoxon's parents sent him to Pennsylvania Military College, but he dropped out due to the death of his twin sister. Later, Wilcoxon earned degrees in chemistry from Rutgers (master's) and Cornell University (Ph.D.).

After receiving his doctorate, Wilcoxon began work as a chemical researcher at the Boyce Thompson Institute for Plant Research. There, he began studying R. A. Fisher's (p. 484) newly issued *Statistical Methods for Research Workers*. In a now-famous 1945 paper, Wilcoxon presented the idea of replacing the actual sample data in Fisher's tests by their ranks and called the tests the rank sum test and signed-rank test. These tests proved to be inspirational to the further development of nonparametrics. After retiring from industry, Wilcoxon accepted a Distinguished Lectureship position at the newly created Department of Statistics at Florida State University.

Suppose, for example, an experimental psychologist wants to compare reaction times for adult males under the influence of drug A with reaction times for those under the influence of drug B. Experience has shown that the populations of reaction-time

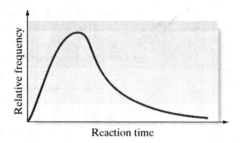

FIGURE 14.4

Typical probability distribution of reaction times

measurements often possess probability distributions that are skewed to the right, as shown in Figure 14.4. Consequently, a *t*-test should not be used to compare the mean reaction times for the two drugs, because the normality assumption that is required for the *t*-test may not be valid.

Suppose the psychologist randomly assigns seven subjects to each of two groups, one group to receive drug A and the other to receive drug B. The reaction time for each subject is measured at the completion of the experiment. These data (with the exception of the measurement for one subject in group A who was eliminated from the experiment for personal reasons) are shown in Table 14.2.

DRUGS

TABLE 14.2   Reaction Times of Subjects under the Influence of Drug A or B

Drug A		Drug B	
Reaction Time (seconds)	Rank	Reaction Time (seconds)	Rank
1.96	4	2.11	6
2.24	7	2.43	9
1.71	2	2.07	5
2.41	8	2.71	11
1.62	1	2.50	10
1.93	3	2.84	12
		2.88	13

The population of reaction times for either of the drugs—say, drug A—is that which could conceptually be obtained by giving drug A to all adult males. To compare the probability distributions for populations A and B, *we first rank the sample observations as though they were all drawn from the same population.* That is, we pool the measurements from both samples and then rank all the measurements from the smallest (a rank of 1) to the largest (a rank of 13). The results of this ranking process are also shown in Table 14.2.

If, on the one hand, the two populations were identical, we would expect the ranks to be *randomly mixed* between the two samples. If, on the other hand, one population tends to have longer reaction times than the other, we would expect the larger ranks to be mostly in one sample and the smaller ranks mostly in the other. Thus, the test statistic for the Wilcoxon test is based on the totals of the ranks for each of the two samples—that is, on the **rank sums**. When, for example, the sample sizes are equal, the greater the difference in the rank sums, the greater will be the weight of evidence indicating a difference between the probability distributions of the populations. In the reaction-times example, we denote the rank sum for drug A by T_1 and that for drug B by T_2. Then

$$T_1 = 4 + 7 + 2 + 8 + 1 + 3 = 25$$
$$T_2 = 6 + 9 + 5 + 11 + 10 + 12 + 13 = 66$$

The sum of T_1 and T_2 will always equal $n(n + 1)/2$, where $n = n_1 + n_2$. So, for this example, $n_1 = 6$, $n_2 = 7$, and

$$T_1 + T_2 = \frac{13(13 + 1)}{2} = 91$$

TABLE 14.3 Reproduction of Part of Table XII in Appendix A: Critical Values for the Wilcoxon Rank Sum Test

$\alpha = .025$ one-tailed; $\alpha = .05$ two-tailed

n_2 \ n_1	3		4		5		6		7		8		9		10	
	T_L	T_U	T_L	T_U	T_L	T_U	T_L	T_U	T_L	T_U	T_L	T_U	T_L	T_U	T_L	T_U
3	5	16	6	18	6	21	7	23	7	26	8	28	8	31	9	33
4	6	18	11	25	12	28	12	32	13	35	14	38	15	41	16	44
5	6	21	12	28	18	37	19	41	20	45	21	49	22	53	24	56
6	7	23	12	32	19	41	26	52	28	56	29	61	31	65	32	70
7	7	26	13	35	20	45	28	56	37	68	39	73	41	78	43	83
8	8	28	14	38	21	49	29	61	39	73	49	87	51	93	54	98
9	8	31	15	41	22	53	31	65	41	78	51	93	63	108	66	114
10	9	33	16	44	24	56	32	70	43	83	54	98	66	114	79	131

Since $T_1 + T_2$ is fixed, a small value for T_1 implies a large value for T_2 (and vice versa) and a large difference between T_1 and T_2. Therefore, the smaller the value of one of the rank sums, the greater is the evidence indicating that the samples were selected from different populations.

The test statistic for this test is the rank sum for the smaller sample; or, in the case where $n_1 = n_2$, either rank sum can be used. Values that locate the rejection region for this rank sum are given in Table XII of Appendix A, a partial reproduction of which is shown in Table 14.3. The columns of the table represent n_1, the first sample size, and the rows represent n_2, the second sample size. *The T_L and T_U entries in the table are the boundaries of the lower and upper regions, respectively, for the rank sum associated with the sample that has fewer measurements.* If the sample sizes n_1 and n_2 are the same, either rank sum may be used as the test statistic. To illustrate, suppose $n_1 = 8$ and $n_2 = 10$. For a two-tailed test with $\alpha = .05$, we consult the table and find that the null hypothesis will be rejected if the rank sum of sample 1 (the sample with fewer measurements), T, is less than or equal to $T_L = 54$ *or* greater than or equal to $T_U = 98$. The Wilcoxon rank sum test is summarized in the next two boxes.

Wilcoxon Rank Sum Test: Independent Samples*

Let D_1 and D_2 represent the probability distributions for populations 1 and 2, respectively.

One-Tailed Test

H_0: D_1 and D_2 are identical
H_a: D_1 is shifted to the right of D_2
[or H_a: D_1 is shifted to the left of D_2]

Test statistic:
T_1, if $n_1 < n_2$; T_2, if $n_2 < n_1$
(Either rank sum can be used if $n_1 = n_2$.)

Rejection region:
T_1: $T_1 \geq T_U$ [or $T_1 \leq T_L$]
T_2: $T_2 \leq T_L$ [or $T_2 \geq T_U$]

Two-Tailed Test

H_0: D_1 and D_2 are identical
H_a: D_1 is shifted either to the left or to the right of D_2

Test statistic:
T_1, if $n_1 < n_2$; T_2, if $n_2 < n_1$
(Either rank sum can be used if $n_1 = n_2$.)
We will denote this rank sum as T.

Rejection region:
$T \leq T_L$ or $T \geq T_U$

where T_L and T_U are obtained from Table XII of Appendix A.

Ties: Assign tied measurements the average of the ranks they would receive if they were unequal, but occurred in successive order. For example, if the third-ranked and fourth-ranked measurements are tied, assign each a rank of $(3 + 4)/2 = 3.5$.

---

*Another statistic used to compare two populations on the basis of independent random samples is the *Mann–Whitney U-statistic*, a simple function of the rank sums. It can be shown that the Wilcoxon rank sum test and the Mann–Whitney U-test are equivalent.

Conditions Required for a Valid Rank Sum Test:

1. The two samples are random and independent.

2. The two probability distributions from which the samples are drawn are continuous.

Note that the assumptions necessary for the validity of the Wilcoxon rank sum test do not specify the shape or type of probability distribution. However, the distributions are assumed to be continuous so that the probability of tied measurements is 0 (see Chapter 5) and each measurement can be assigned a unique rank. In practice, however, rounding of continuous measurements will sometimes produce ties. As long as the number of ties is small relative to the sample sizes, the Wilcoxon test procedure will still have an approximate significance level of α. The test is not recommended to compare discrete distributions, for which many ties are expected.

EXAMPLE 14.2

APPLYING THE RANK SUM TEST—Comparing Reaction Times of Two Drugs

Problem Do the data given in Table 14.2 provide sufficient evidence to indicate a shift in the probability distributions for drugs A and B—that is, that the probability distribution corresponding to drug A lies either to the right or to the left of the probability distribution corresponding to drug B? Test at the .05 level of significance.

Solution

H_0: The two populations of reaction times corresponding to drug A and drug B have the same probability distribution.

H_a: The probability distribution for drug A is shifted to the right or left of the probability distribution for drug B.*

Test statistic: Since drug A has fewer subjects than drug B, the test statistic is T_1, the rank sum of drug A's reaction times.

Rejection region: Since the test is two sided, we consult part a of Table XII for the rejection region corresponding to $\alpha = .05$. We will reject H_0 for $T_1 \leq T_L$ or $T_1 \geq T_U$. Thus, we will reject H_0 if $T_1 \leq 28$ or $T_1 \geq 56$.

Since T_1, the rank sum of drug A's reaction times in Table 14.2, is 25, it is in the rejection region. (See Figure 14.5.)[†] Therefore, there is sufficient evidence to reject H_0. This same conclusion can be reached with a statistical software package. The SAS printout of the

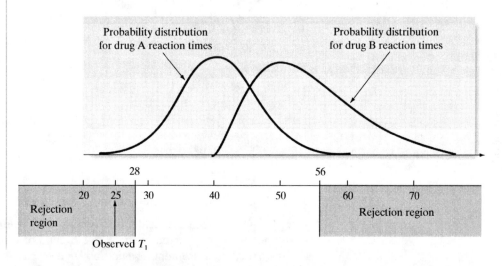

FIGURE 14.5
Alternative hypothesis and rejection region for Example 14.2.

*The alternative hypotheses in this chapter will be stated in terms of a difference in the *location* of the distributions. However, since the shapes of the distributions may also differ under H_a, some of the figures (e.g., Figure 14.5) depicting the alternative hypothesis will show probability distributions with different shapes.
[†]Figure 14.5 depicts only one side of the two-sided alternative hypothesis. The other would show the distribution for drug A shifted to the right of the distribution for drug B.

The NPAR1WAY Procedure

Wilcoxon Scores (Rank Sums) for Variable REACTIME
Classified by Variable DRUG

DRUG	N	Sum of Scores	Expected Under H0	Std Dev Under H0	Mean Score
A	6	25.0	42.0	7.0	4.166667
B	7	66.0	49.0	7.0	9.428571

Wilcoxon Two-Sample Test

Statistic (S)	25.0000

Normal Approximation

Z	-2.4286
One-Sided Pr < Z	0.0076
Two-Sided Pr > |Z|	0.0152

t Approximation

One-Sided Pr < Z	0.0159
Two-Sided Pr > |Z|	0.0318

Exact Test

One-Sided Pr <= S	0.0070
Two-Sided Pr >= |S - Mean|	0.0140

Kruskal-Wallis Test

Chi-Square	5.8980
DF	1
Pr > Chi-Square	0.0152

FIGURE 14.6

SAS printout for Example 14.2

analysis is shown in Figure 14.6. Both the test statistic ($T_1 = 25$) and one-tailed p-value ($p = .007$) are highlighted on the printout. The one-tailed p-value is less than $\alpha = .05$, leading us to reject H_0.

Look Back Our conclusion is that the probability distributions for drugs A and B are not identical. In fact, it appears that drug B tends to be associated with reaction times that are larger than those associated with drug A (because T_1 falls into the lower tail of the rejection region).

Now Work Exercise 14.20

ACTIVITY 14.1: *Keep the Change:* Nonparametric Statistics

In this activity, you will refer to your results from Activity 8.2: *Keep the Change: Tests of Hypotheses* and Activity 9.2: *Keep the Change: Inferences Based on Two Samples.*

1. Referring to Exercises 1 and 2 of Activity 8.2, explain why a sign test of the population median might be a better fit than the hypothesis test of the population mean, especially if the sample is small. Perform the corresponding sign test, assuming once again that your data set *Amounts Transferred* represents a random sample from all Bank of America customers' transfer amounts. Are your conclusions similar? Explain.

2. Referring to Exercises 4 and 5 of Activity 8.2, explain why a sign test of the population median might be a better fit than the hypothesis test of the population mean, especial-

ly if the sample is small. Perform the corresponding sign test, assuming once again that your data set *Bank Matching* represents a random sample from all Bank of America customers' bank matching. Are your conclusions similar? Explain.

3. Refer to Exercise 2 of Activity 9.2, in which you designed a study to compare the mean amounts for bank matching in California and bank matching in Florida. Design a Wilcoxon rank sum test to compare the corresponding probability distributions. Be specific about sample sizes, hypotheses, and how a conclusion will be reached. Under what conditions might the rank sum test provide more useful information than the mean comparison test?

Table XII in Appendix A gives values of T_L and T_U for values of n_1 and n_2 less than or equal to 10. When both sample sizes, n_1 and n_2, are 10 or larger, the sampling distribution of T_1 can be approximated by a normal distribution with mean

$$E(T_1) = \frac{n_1(n_1 + n_2 + 1)}{2}$$

and variance

$$\sigma_{T_1}^2 = \frac{n_1 n_2 (n_1 + n_2 + 1)}{12}$$

Therefore, for $n_1 \geq 10$ and $n_2 \geq 10$, we can conduct the Wilcoxon rank sum test using the familiar z-test of Chapters 8 and 9. The test is summarized in the following box:

The Wilcoxon Rank Sum Test for Large Samples ($n_1 \geq 10$ and $n_2 \geq 10$)

Let D_1 and D_2 represent the probability distributions for populations 1 and 2, respectively.

One-Tailed Test

H_0: D_1 and D_2 are identical
H_a: D_1 is shifted to the right of D_2
(or H_a: D_1 is shifted to the left of D_2)

Two-Tailed Test

H_0: D_1 and D_2 are identical
H_a: D_1 is shifted to the right or to the left of D_2

$$\text{Test statistic: } z = \frac{T_1 - \dfrac{n_1(n_1 + n_2 + 1)}{2}}{\sqrt{\dfrac{n_1 n_2 (n_1 + n_2 + 1)}{12}}}$$

Rejection region:

$z > z_\alpha$ (or $z < -z_\alpha$)

Rejection region:

$|z| > z_{\alpha/2}$

STATISTICS IN ACTION REVISITED

Comparing the MTBE Levels of Different Types of Groundwater Wells

Refer to the study of MTBE contamination of New Hampshire groundwater wells (p. 14-3). One of the objectives of the study was to determine whether the level of MTBE contamination is different for private and public wells and for bedrock and unconsolidated aquifers. For this objective, the researchers focused on only the 70 sampled wells that had detectable levels of MTBE. They wanted to determine whether the distribution of MTBE levels in public wells is shifted above or below the distribution of MTBE levels in private wells and whether the distribution of MTBE levels in bedrock aquifers is shifted above or below the distribution of MTBE levels in unconsolidated aquifers.

To answer these questions, the researchers applied the Wilcoxon rank sum test for two independent samples. In the first analysis, public and private wells were compared; in the second analysis, bedrock and unconsolidated aquifers were compared. The SAS printouts for these analyses are shown in

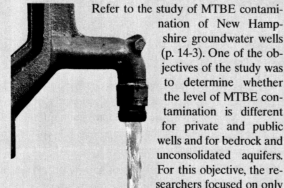

FIGURE SIA14.2

SAS rank sum test for comparing public and private wells

Figures SIA14.2 and SIA14.3, respectively. Both the test statistics and the two-tailed *p*-values are highlighted on the printouts.

For the comparison of public and private wells in Figure SIA14.2, *p*-value = .1108. Thus, at $\alpha = .05$, there is insufficient evidence to conclude that the distribution of MTBE levels differs for public and private New Hampshire groundwater wells. Although public wells tend to have higher MTBE values than private wells (note the rank sums in Figure SIA14.2), the difference is not statistically significant.

For the comparison of bedrock and unconsolidated aquifers in Figure SIA14.3, *p*-value = .0336. At $\alpha = .05$, there is sufficient evidence to conclude that the distribution of MTBE levels differs for bedrock and unconsolidated aquifers. Furthermore, the rank sums shown in Figure SIA14.3 indicate that bedrock aquifers have the higher MTBE levels.

[*Note*: Histograms of the MTBE levels for public wells, private wells, bedrock aquifers, and unconsolidated aquifers (not shown) reveal distributions that are highly skewed. Thus, application of the nonparametric rank sum test is appropriate.]

The NPAR1WAY Procedure

Wilcoxon Scores (Rank Sums) for Variable MTBE
Classified by Variable Aquifer

Aquifer	N	Sum of Scores	Expected Under H0	Std Dev Under H0	Mean Score
Bedrock	63	2345.50	2236.50	51.069646	37.230159
Unconsoli	7	139.50	248.50	51.069646	19.928571

Average scores were used for ties.

Wilcoxon Two-Sample Test

Statistic   139.5000

Normal Approximation
Z   -2.1245
One-Sided Pr < Z   0.0168
Two-Sided Pr > |Z| 0.0336

FIGURE SIA14.3

SAS rank sum test for comparing bedrock and unconsolidated aquifers

Exercises 14.16–14.33

Understanding the Principles

14.16 What is a rank sum?

14.17 *True or False.* If the rank sum for sample 1 is much larger than the rank sum for sample 2 when $n_1 = n_2$, then the distribution of population 1 is likely to be shifted to the right of the distribution of population 2.

14.18 What conditions are required for a valid application of the Wilcoxon rank sum test?

Learning the Mechanics

14.19 Specify the test statistic and the rejection region for the Wilcoxon rank sum test for independent samples in each of the following situations:
a. H_0: Two probability distributions, 1 and 2, are identical
H_a: The probability distribution for population 1 is shifted to the right or left of the probability distribution for population 2
$n_1 = 7, n_2 = 8, \alpha = .10$
b. H_0: Two probability distributions, 1 and 2, are identical
H_a: The probability distribution for population 1 is shifted to the right of the probability distribution for population 2
$n_1 = 6, n_2 = 6, \alpha = .05$
c. H_0: Two probability distributions, 1 and 2, are identical
H_a: The probability distribution for population 1 is shifted to the left of the probability distribution for population 2
$n_1 = 7, n_2 = 10, \alpha = .025$

d. H_0: Two probability distributions, 1 and 2, are identical
H_a: The probability distribution for population 1 is shifted to the right or left of the probability distribution for population 2
$n_1 = 20, n_2 = 20, \alpha = .05$

14.20 Suppose you want to compare two treatments, A and B. In particular, you wish to determine whether the distribution for population B is shifted to the right of the distribution for population A. You plan to use the Wilcoxon rank sum test.
a. Specify the null and alternative hypotheses you would test.
b. Suppose you obtained the following independent random samples of observations on experimental units subjected to the two treatments:

LM14_20

Sample A	37,	40,	33,	29,	42,	33,	35,	28,	34,
Sample B	65,	35,	47,	52					

Conduct a test of the hypotheses you specified in part **a**. Test, using $\alpha = .05$.

14.21 Suppose you wish to compare two treatments, A and B, on the basis of independent random samples of 15 observations selected from each of the two populations. If $T_1 = 173$, do the data provide sufficient evidence to indicate that distribution A is shifted to the left of distribution B? Test, using $\alpha = .05$.

14.22 Random samples of sizes $n_1 = 16$ and $n_2 = 12$ were drawn from populations 1 and 2, respectively. The measurements obtained are listed in the following table:

LM14_22

Sample 1				Sample 2		
9.0	15.6	25.6	31.1	10.1	11.1	13.5
21.1	26.9	24.6	20.0	12.0	18.2	10.3
24.8	16.5	26.0	25.1	9.2	7.0	14.2
17.2	30.1	18.7	26.1	15.8	13.6	13.2

a. Conduct a hypothesis test to determine whether the probability distribution for population 2 is shifted to the left of the probability distribution for population 1. Use $\alpha = .05$.

b. What is the approximate p-value of the test of part **a**?

14.23 Independent random samples are selected from two populations. The data are shown in the following table:

LM14_23

Sample 1		Sample 2		
15	16	5	9	5
10	13	12	8	10
12	8	9	4	

a. Use the Wilcoxon rank sum test to determine whether the data provide sufficient evidence to indicate a shift in the locations of the probability distributions of the sampled populations. Test, using $\alpha = .05$.

b. Do the data provide sufficient evidence to indicate that the probability distribution for population 1 is shifted to the right of the probability distribution for population 2? Use the Wilcoxon rank sum test with $\alpha = .05$.

Applying the Concepts—Basic

14.24 **Bursting strength of bottles.** Polyethylene terephthalate (PET) bottles are used for carbonated beverages. A critical property of PET bottles is their bursting strength (i.e., the pressure at which bottles filled with water burst when pressurized). In the *Journal of Data Science* (May 2003), researchers measured the bursting strength of PET bottles made from two different designs: an old design and a new design. The data (in pounds per square inch) for 10 bottles of each design are shown in the accompanying table. Suppose you want to compare the distributions of bursting strengths for the two designs.

PET

Old Design	210	212	211	211	190	213	212	211	164	209
New Design	216	217	162	137	219	216	179	153	152	217

a. Rank all 20 observed pressures from smallest to largest, and assign ranks from 1 to 20.

b. Sum the ranks of the observations from the old design.

c. Sum the ranks of the observations from the new design.

d. Compute the Wilcoxon rank sum statistic.

e. Carry out a nonparametric test (at $\alpha = .05$) to compare the distribution of bursting strengths for the two designs.

14.25 **Research on eating disorders.** The "fear of negative evaluation" (FNE) scores for 11 female students known to suffer from the eating disorder bulimia and 14 female students with normal eating habits, first presented in Exercise 2.38 (p. 48), are reproduced in the table at the bottom of the page. (Recall that the higher the score, the greater is the fear of a negative evaluation.) Suppose you want to determine whether the distribution of the FNE scores for bulimic female students is shifted above the corresponding distribution for female students with normal eating habits.

a. Specify H_0 and H_a for the test.

b. Rank all 25 FNE scores in the data set from smallest to largest.

c. Sum the ranks of the 11 FNE scores for bulimic students.

d. Sum the ranks of the 14 FNE scores for students with normal eating habits.

e. Give the rejection region for a nonparametric test of the data if $\alpha = .10$.

f. Conduct the test and give the conclusion in the words of the problem.

14.26 **Reading Japanese books.** Refer to the *Reading in a Foreign Language* (Apr. 2004) experiment to improve the Japanese reading comprehension levels of University of Hawaii students, presented in Exercise 9.15 (p. 426). Recall that 14 students participated in a 10-week extensive reading program in a second-semester Japanese course. The number of books read by each student and the student's course grade are repeated in the accompanying table. Consider a comparison of the distributions of number of books read by students who earn an "A" grade and those who earn a "B" or "C" grade.

JAPANESE

Number of Books	Course Grade	Number of Books	Course Grade
53	A	30	A
42	A	28	B
40	A	24	A
40	B	22	C
39	A	21	B
34	A	20	B
34	A	16	B

Source: Hitosugi, C. I., and Day, R. R. "Extensive reading in Japanese," *Reading in a Foreign Language*, Vol. 16, No. 1, Apr. 2004 (Table 4).

BULIMIA

Bulimic students	21	13	10	20	25	19	16	21	24	13	14			
Normal students	13	6	16	13	8	19	23	18	11	19	7	10	15	20

Source: Randles, R. H. "On neutral responses (zeros) in the sign test and ties in the Wilcoxon–Mann–Whitney test," *American Statistician*, Vol. 55, No. 2, May 2001 (Figure 3).

a. Rank all 14 observations from smallest to largest, and assign ranks from 1 to 14.

b. Sum the ranks of the observations for students with an "A" grade.

c. Sum the ranks of the observations for students with either a "B" or "C" grade.

d. Compute the Wilcoxon rank sum statistic.

e. Carry out a nonparametric test (at $\alpha = .10$) to compare the distribution of the number of books read by the two populations of students.

14.27 Visual acuity of children. In a comparison of the visual acuity of deaf and hearing children, eye movement rates are taken on 10 deaf and 10 hearing children. The data are shown in the accompanying table. A clinical psychologist believes that deaf children have greater visual acuity than hearing children. (The larger a child's eye movement rate, the more visual acuity the child possesses.)

EYEMOVE

Deaf Children		Hearing Children	
2.75	1.95	1.15	1.23
3.14	2.17	1.65	2.03
3.23	2.45	1.43	1.64
2.30	1.83	1.83	1.96
2.64	2.23	1.75	1.37

a. Use the Wilcoxon rank sum procedure to test the psychologist's claim at $\alpha = .05$.

b. Conduct the test by using the large-sample approximation for the Wilcoxon rank sum test. Compare the results with those found in part **a.**

14.28 Children's recall of TV ads. Refer to the *Journal of Advertising* (Spring 2006) study of children's recall of television advertisements, presented in Exercise 9.13 (p. 426). Two groups of children were shown a 60-second commercial for Sunkist Fun Fruit Rock-n-Roll Shapes. One group (the A/V group) was shown both the audio and video portions of the ad; the other group (the video-only group) was shown only the video portion of the commercial. The number out of 10 specific items from the ad recalled correctly by each child is shown in the accompanying table. Recall that the researchers theorized that children who receive an audiovisual presentation will have the same level of recall as those who receive only the visual aspects of the ad. Consider testing the researchers' theory, using the Wilcoxon rank sum test.

FUNFRUIT

A/V group: 0 4 6 6 1 2 2 6 6 4 1 2 6 1 3 0 2 5 4 5

Video-only group: 6 3 6 2 2 4 7 6 1 3 6 2 3 1 3 2 5 2 4 6

Source: Maher, J. K., Hu, M. Y., & Kolbe, R. H. "Children's recall of television ad elements," *Journal of Advertising*, Vol. 35, No. 1, Spring 2006 (simulated from summary information in Table 1).

a. Set up the appropriate null and alternative hypotheses for the test.

b. Find the value of the test statistic.

c. Give the rejection region for $\alpha = .10$.

d. Make the appropriate inference. What can you say about the researchers' theory?

Applying the Concepts—Intermediate

14.29 Computer-mediated communication study. Computer-mediated communication (CMC) is a form of interaction that heavily involves technology (e.g., instant messaging, e-mail). A study was conducted to compare relational intimacy in people interacting via CMC with people meeting face-to-face (FTF). (*Journal of Computer-Mediated Communication,* Apr. 2004.) Participants were 48 undergraduate students, of which half were randomly assigned to the CMC group and half to the FTF group. Each group was given a task that required communication among its group members. Those in the CMC group communicated via the "chat" mode of instant-messaging software; those in the FTF group met in a conference room. The variable of interest, relational intimacy score, was measured (on a seven-point scale) for each participant after each of three different meetings. Scores for the first meeting are given in the accompanying table. The researchers hypothesized that the relational intimacy scores for participants in the CMC group will tend to be lower than the relational intimacy scores for participants in the FTF group.

INTIMACY

CMC group:	4 3 3 4 3 3 3 3 4 4 3 4 3 3 2 4 2 4 5 4 4 4 5 3
FTF group:	5 4 4 4 3 3 3 4 3 3 3 3 4 4 4 4 4 3 3 3 4 4 2 4

Note: Data simulated from descriptive statistics provided in article.

a. Which nonparametric procedure should be used to test the researchers' hypothesis?

b. Specify the null and alternative hypotheses of the test.

c. Give the rejection region for the test, using $\alpha = .10$.

d. Conduct the test and give the appropriate conclusion in the context of the problem.

14.30 Rain in Colorado. The data in the accompanying table, extracted from *Technometrics* (Feb. 1986), represent daily accumulated streamflow and precipitation (in inches) for two U.S. Geological Survey stations in Colorado. Conduct a test to determine whether the distributions of daily accumulated streamflow and precipitation for the two stations differ with location. Use $\alpha = .10$. Why is a nonparametric test appropriate for these data?

COLORAIN

Station 1			Station 2		
127.96	108.91	100.85	114.79	85.54	280.55
210.07	178.21	85.89	109.11	117.64	145.11
203.24	285.37		330.33	302.74	95.36

Source: Gastwirth, J. L., and Mahmoud, H. "An efficient robust nonparametric test for scale change for data from a gamma distribution," *Technometrics,* Vol. 28, No. 1, Feb. 1986, p. 83 (Table 2).

14.31 Refer to the *Chance* (Fall 2002) study of a patent infringement case brought against Intel Corp., presented in Exercise 9.20 (p. 427). Recall that the case rested on whether a patent witness' signature was written on top of key text in a patent notebook or under the key text. Using an X-ray beam, zinc measurements were taken at several spots on the notebook page. The zinc measurements for three notebook locations—on a text line, on a witness line, and on the intersection of the witness and text lines—are reproduced in the following table:

PATENT

Text line:	.335	.374	.440			
Witness line:	.210	.262	.188	.329	.439	.397
Intersection:	.393	.353	.285	.295	.319	

a. Why might the Student's t-procedure you applied in Exercise 9.20 be inappropriate for analyzing these data?

b. Use a nonparametric test (at $\alpha = .05$) to compare the distribution of zinc measurements for the text line with the distribution for the intersection.

c. Use a nonparametric test (at $\alpha = .05$) to compare the distribution of zinc measurements for the witness line with the distribution for the intersection.

d. From the results you obtained in parts **b** and **c**, what can you infer about the mean zinc measurements at the three notebook locations?

14.32 Brood-parasitic birds. The term *brood-parasitic intruder* is used to describe a bird that searches for and lays eggs in a nest built by a bird of another species. For example, the brown-headed cowbird is known to be a brood parasite of the smaller willow flycatcher. Ornithologists theorize that those flycatchers which recognize, but do not vocally react to, cowbird calls are more apt to defend their nests and less likely to be found and parasitized. In a study published in *The Condor* (May 1995), each of 13 active flycatcher nests was categorized as parasitized (if at least one cowbird egg was present) or nonparasitized. Cowbird songs were taped and played back while the flycatcher pairs were sitting in the nest prior to incubation. The vo-

COWBIRD

Parasitized	Not Parasitized
2.00	1.00
1.25	1.00
8.50	0
1.10	3.25
1.25	1.00
3.75	.25
5.50	

Source: Uyehara, J. C., and Narins, P. M. "Nest defense by Willow Flycatchers to brood-parasitic intruders." *The Condor,* Vol. 97, No. 2, May 1995, p. 364 (Figure 1).

calization rate (number of calls per minute) of each flycatcher pair was recorded. The data for the two groups of flycatchers are given in the table. Do the data suggest (at $\alpha = .05$) that the vocalization rates of parasitized flycatchers are higher than those of nonparasitized flycatchers?

14.33 Family involvement in homework. Refer to the study of the impact of the interactive Teachers Involve Parents in Schoolwork (TIPS) program, presented in an earlier Statistics in Action (p. 409). Recall that 128 middle school students were assigned to complete TIPS homework assignments, while 98 students were assigned traditional, noninteractive homework assignments (ATIPS). At the end of the study, all students reported on the level of family involvement in their homework on a five-point scale (0 = Never, 1 = Rarely, 2 = Sometimes, 3 = Frequently, 4 = Always). The data for the science, math, and language arts homework are saved in the **HWSTUDY** file. (The first five and last five observations in the data set are reproduced in the accompanying table.)

a. Why might a nonparametric test be the most appropriate test to apply in order to compare the levels of family involvement in homework assignments of TIPS and ATIPS students?

b. Conduct a nonparametric analysis to compare the involvement in science homework assignments of TIPS and ATIPS students. Use $\alpha = .05$.

c. Repeat part **b** for mathematics homework assignments.

d. Repeat part **a** for language arts homework assignments.

HWSTUDY (selected observations)

Homework Condition	Science	Math	Language
ATIPS	1	0	0
ATIPS	0	1	1
ATIPS	0	1	0
ATIPS	1	2	0
ATIPS	1	1	2
⋮	⋮	⋮	⋮
TIPS	2	3	2
TIPS	1	4	2
TIPS	2	4	2
TIPS	4	0	3
TIPS	2	0	1

Source: Van Voorhis, F. L. "Teachers' use of interactive homework and its effects on family involvement and science achievement of middle grade students," paper presented at the annual meeting of the American Educational Research Association, Seattle, April 2001.

14.4 Comparing Two Populations: Paired Difference Experiment

Nonparametric techniques may also be employed to compare two probability distributions when a paired difference design is used. For example, consumer preferences for two competing products are often compared by having each of a sample of consumers rate both products. Thus, the ratings have been paired on each consumer. Following is an example of this type of experiment.

For some paper products, softness is an important consideration in determining consumer acceptance. One method of determining softness is to have judges give a sample of the products a softness rating. Suppose each of 10 judges is given a sample of two products that a company wants to compare. Each judge rates the softness of each product on a scale from 1 to 10, with higher ratings implying a softer product. The results of the experiment are shown in Table 14.4.

 SOFTPAPER

TABLE 14.4   Softness Ratings of Paper

Judge	Product A	B	Difference $(A - B)$	Absolute Value of Difference	Rank of $(A - B)$ Absolute Value
1	6	4	2	2	5
2	8	5	3	3	7.5
3	4	5	-1	1	2
4	9	8	1	1	2
5	4	1	3	3	7.5
6	7	9	-2	2	5
7	6	2	4	4	9
8	5	3	2	2	5
9	6	7	-1	1	2
10	8	2	6	6	10

$T_+ = $ Sum of positive ranks $ = 46$

$T_- = $ Sum of negative ranks $ = 9$

Since this is a paired difference experiment, we analyze the differences between the measurements. (See Section 9.3.) However, a nonparametric approach developed by Wilcoxon requires that we calculate the ranks of the absolute values of the differences between the measurements (i.e., the ranks of the differences after removing any minus signs). *Note that tied absolute differences are assigned the average of the ranks they would receive if they were unequal, but successive, measurements.* After the absolute differences are ranked, the sum of the ranks of the positive differences of the original measurements, T_+, and the sum of the ranks of the negative differences of the original measurements, T_-, are computed.

We are now prepared to test the nonparametric hypotheses:

H_0: The probability distributions of the ratings for products A and B are identical.

H_a: The probability distributions of the ratings differ (in location) for the two products. (Note that this is a two-sided alternative and that it implies a two-tailed test.)

Test statistic: $T = $ Smaller of the positive and negative rank sums T_+ and T_-

The smaller the value of T, the greater is the evidence indicating that the two probability distributions differ in location. The rejection region for T can be determined by consulting Table XIII in Appendix A, part of which is shown in Table 14.5. This table gives a value T_0 for both one-tailed and two-tailed tests for each value of n, the number of matched pairs. For a two-tailed test with $\alpha = .05$, we will reject H_0 if $T \le T_0$. You can see in Table 14.5 that the value of T_0 which locates the boundary of the rejection region for the judges' ratings for $\alpha = .05$ and $n = 10$ pairs of observations is 8. Thus, the rejection region for the test (see Figure 14.7) is

Rejection region: $T \le 8$ for $\alpha = .05$

Since the smaller rank sum for the paper data, $T_- = 9$, does not fall within the rejection region, the experiment has not provided sufficient evidence indicating that the two paper products differ with respect to their softness ratings at the $\alpha = .05$ level.

Note that if a significance level of $\alpha = .10$ had been used, the rejection region would have been $T \le 11$ and we would have rejected H_0. In other words, the samples do

TABLE 14.5   Reproduction of Part of Table XIII of Appendix A: Critical Values for the Wilcoxon Paired Difference Signed Rank Test

One-Tailed	Two-Tailed	$n = 5$	$n = 6$	$n = 7$	$n = 8$	$n = 9$	$n = 10$
$\alpha = .05$	$\alpha = .10$	1	2	4	6	8	11
$\alpha = .025$	$\alpha = .05$		1	2	4	6	8
$\alpha = .01$	$\alpha = .02$			0	2	3	5
$\alpha = .005$	$\alpha = .01$				0	2	3
		$n = 11$	$n = 12$	$n = 13$	$n = 14$	$n = 15$	$n = 16$
$\alpha = .05$	$\alpha = .10$	14	17	21	26	30	36
$\alpha = .025$	$\alpha = .05$	11	14	17	21	25	30
$\alpha = .01$	$\alpha = .02$	7	10	13	16	20	24
$\alpha = .005$	$\alpha = .01$	5	7	10	13	16	19
		$n = 17$	$n = 18$	$n = 19$	$n = 20$	$n = 21$	$n = 22$
$\alpha = .05$	$\alpha = .10$	41	47	54	60	68	75
$\alpha = .025$	$\alpha = .05$	35	40	46	52	59	66
$\alpha = .01$	$\alpha = .02$	28	33	38	43	49	56
$\alpha = .005$	$\alpha = .01$	23	28	32	37	43	49
		$n = 23$	$n = 24$	$n = 25$	$n = 26$	$n = 27$	$n = 28$
$\alpha = .05$	$\alpha = .10$	83	92	101	110	120	130
$\alpha = .025$	$\alpha = .05$	73	81	90	98	107	117
$\alpha = .01$	$\alpha = .02$	62	69	77	85	93	102
$\alpha = .005$	$\alpha = .01$	55	61	68	76	84	92

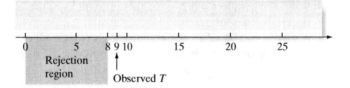

FIGURE 14.7

Rejection region for paired difference experiment

provide evidence that the probability distributions of the softness ratings differ at the $\alpha = .10$ significance level.

The **Wilcoxon signed rank test** is summarized in the next box. Note that the difference measurements are assumed to have a continuous probability distribution so that the absolute differences will have unique ranks. Although tied (absolute) differences can be assigned ranks by averaging, in order to ensure the validity of the test, the number of ties should be small relative to the number of observations.

Wilcoxon Signed Rank Test for a Paired Difference Experiment

Let D_1 and D_2 represent the probability distributions for populations 1 and 2, respectively.

One-Tailed Test

H_0: D_1 and D_2 are identical
H_a: D_1 is shifted to the right of D_2 [or
H_a: D_1 is shifted to the left of D_2]

Two-Tailed Test

H_0: D_1 and D_2 are identical
H_a: D_1 is shifted either to the left or
to the right of D_2

Calculate the difference within each of the n matched pairs of observations. Then rank the absolute value of the n differences from the smallest (rank 1) to the highest (rank n), and calculate the rank sum T_- of the negative differences and the rank sum T_+ of the

(continued)

positive differences. [*Note:* Differences equal to 0 are eliminated, and the number n of differences is reduced accordingly.]

Test statistic:	Test statistic:
T_-, the rank sum of the negative differences [or T_+, the rank sum of the positive differences]	T, the smaller of T_+ or T_-
Rejection region:	Rejection region:
$T_- \leq T_0$ [or $T_+ \leq T_0$]	$T \leq T_0$

where T_0 is given in Table XIII in Appendix A.

Ties: Assign tied absolute differences the average of the ranks they would receive if they were unequal, but occurred in successive order. For example, if the third-ranked and fourth-ranked differences are tied, assign both a rank of $(3 + 4)/2 = 3.5$.

Conditions Required for a Valid Signed Rank Test

1. The sample of differences is randomly selected from the population of differences.

2. The probability distribution from which the sample of paired differences is drawn is continuous.

EXAMPLE 14.3

APPLYING THE SIGNED RANK TEST—Comparing Two Crime Prevention Plans

Problem Suppose the police commissioner in a small community must choose between two plans for patrolling the town's streets. Plan A, the less expensive plan, uses voluntary citizen groups to patrol certain high-risk neighborhoods. In contrast, plan B would utilize police patrols. As an aid in reaching a decision, both plans are examined by 10 trained criminologists, each of whom is asked to rate the plans on a scale from 1 to 10. (High ratings imply a more effective crime prevention plan.) The city will adopt plan B (and hire extra police) only if the data provide sufficient evidence that criminologists tend to rate plan B more effective than plan A. The results of the survey are shown in Table 14.6. Do the data provide evidence at the $\alpha = .05$ level that the distribution of ratings for plan B lies above that for plan A?

 CRIMEPLAN

TABLE 14.6 Effectiveness Ratings by 10 Qualified Crime Prevention Experts

| Crime Prevention Expert | Plan | | Difference | Rank of Absolute Difference |
	A	B	(A − B)	
1	7	9	−2	4.5
2	4	5	−1	2
3	8	8	0	(Eliminated)
4	9	8	1	2
5	3	6	−3	6
6	6	10	−4	7.5
7	8	9	−1	2
8	10	8	2	4.5
9	9	4	5	9
10	5	9	−4	7.5

Positive rank sum = T_+ = 15.5

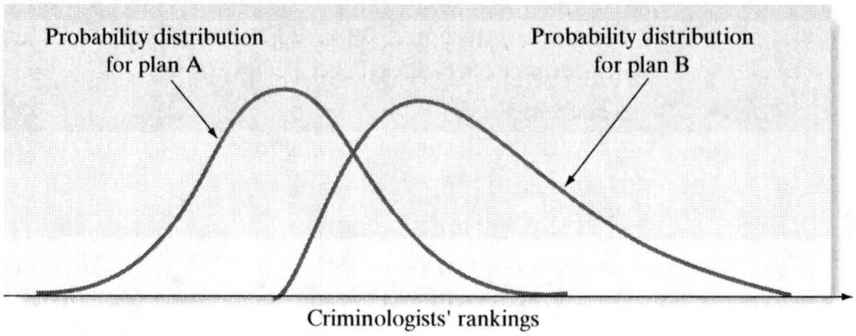

FIGURE 14.8
The alternative hypothesis for
Example 14.3

Solution The null and alternative hypotheses are as follows:

H_0: The two probability distributions of effectiveness ratings are identical

H_a: The effectiveness ratings of the more expensive plan (B) tend to exceed those of plan A

Observe that the alternative hypothesis is one sided (i.e., we only wish to detect a shift in the distribution of the B ratings to the right of the distribution of A ratings); therefore, it implies a one-tailed test of the null hypothesis. (See Figure 14.8.) If the alternative hypothesis is true, the B ratings will tend to be larger than the paired A ratings, more negative differences in pairs will occur, T_- will be large, and T_+ will be small. Because Table XIII is constructed to give lower-tail values of T_0, we will use T_+ as the test statistic and reject H_0 for $T_+ \leq T_0$.

The differences in ratings for the pairs (A − B) are shown in Table 14.6. Note that one of the differences equals 0. Consequently, we eliminate this pair from the ranking and reduce the number of pairs to $n = 9$. Looking in Table XIII, we have $T_0 = 8$ for a one-tailed test with $\alpha = .05$ and $n = 9$. Therefore, the test statistic and rejection region for the test are

$$Test\ statistic:\quad T_+, \text{ the positive rank sum}$$
$$Rejection\ region:\quad T_+ \leq 8$$

Summing the ranks of the positive differences from Table 14.6, we find that $T_+ = 15.5$. Since this value exceeds the critical value, $T_0 = 8$, we conclude that the sample provides

Wilcoxon Signed Ranks Test

Ranks

		N	Mean Rank	Sum of Ranks
A - B	Negative Ranks	6[a]	4.92	29.50
	Positive Ranks	3[b]	5.17	15.50
	Ties	1[c]		
	Total	10		

a. A < B

b. A > B

c. A = B

Test Statistics[b]

	A - B
Z	-.834[a]
Asymp. Sig. (2-tailed)	.404

a. Based on positive ranks.

b. Wilcoxon Signed Ranks Test

FIGURE 14.9
SPSS printout for Example 14.3

insufficient evidence at the $\alpha = .05$ level to support the alternative hypothesis. The commissioner *cannot* conclude that the plan utilizing police patrols tends to be rated higher than the plan using citizen volunteers. That is, on the basis of this study, extra police will not be hired.

An SPSS printout of the analysis, shown in Figure 14.9, confirms the preceding conclusion. Both the test statistic and two-tailed p-value are highlighted on the printout. Since the one-tailed p-value, $.404/2 = .202$, exceeds $\alpha = .05$, we fail to reject H_0.

Now Work Exercise 14.37

As is the case for the rank sum test for independent samples, the sampling distribution of the signed rank statistic can be approximated by a normal distribution when the number n of paired observations is large (say, $n \geq 25$). The large-sample z-test is summarized in the following box:

Wilcoxon Signed Rank Test for Large Samples ($n \geq 25$)

Let D_1 and D_2 represent the probability distributions for populations 1 and 2, respectively.

One-Tailed Test

H_0: D_1 and D_2 are identical

H_a: D_1 is shifted to the right of D_2 [or

H_a: D_1 is shifted to the left of D_2]

Two-Tailed Test

H_0: D_1 and D_2 are identical

H_a: D_1 is shifted either to the left or to the right of D_2

$$\text{Test statistic: } z = \frac{T_+ - [n(n+1)/4]}{\sqrt{[n(n+1)(2n+1)]/24}}$$

Rejection region:

$z > z_\alpha$ [or $z < -z_\alpha$]

Rejection region:

$|z| > z_{\alpha/2}$

Assumptions: The sample size n is greater than or equal to 25. Differences equal to 0 are eliminated and the number n of differences is reduced accordingly. Tied absolute differences receive ranks equal to the average of the ranks they would have received had they not been tied.

Exercises 14.34–14.49

Understanding the Principles

14.34 Explain the difference between the one- and two-tailed versions of the Wilcoxon signed rank test for the paired difference experiment.

14.35 In order to conduct the Wilcoxon signed rank test, why do we need to assume that the probability distribution of differences is continuous?

Learning the Mechanics

14.36 Specify the test statistic and the rejection region for the Wilcoxon signed rank test for the paired difference design in each of the following situations:

a. H_0: Two probability distributions, A and B, are identical

H_a: The probability distribution for population A is shifted to the right or left of the probability distribution for population B

$n = 20, \alpha = .10$

b. H_0: Two probability distributions, A and B, are identical

H_a: The probability distribution for population A is shifted to the right of the probability distribution for population B

$n = 39, \alpha = .05$

c. H_0: Two probability distributions, A and B, are identical

H_a: The probability distribution for population A is shifted to the left of the probability distribution for population B

$n = 7, \alpha = .005$

14.37 Suppose you want to test a hypothesis that two treatments, A and B, are equivalent against the alternative hypothesis that the responses for A tend to be larger than those for B. You plan to use a paired difference experiment and to analyze the resulting data with the Wilcoxon signed rank test.

a. Specify the null and alternative hypotheses you would test.

b. Suppose the paired difference experiment yielded the data in the accompanying table. Conduct the test, of part **a**. Test using $\alpha = .025$.

LM14_37

Pair	A	B	Pair	A	B
1	54	45	6	77	75
2	60	45	7	74	63
3	98	87	8	29	30
4	43	31	9	63	59
5	82	71	10	80	82

14.38 Suppose you wish to test a hypothesis that two treatments, A and B, are equivalent against the alternative that the responses for A tend to be larger than those for B.

   a. If the number of pairs equals 25, give the rejection region for the large-sample Wilcoxon signed rank test for $\alpha = .05$.

   b. Suppose that $T_+ = 273$. State your test conclusions.

   c. Find the p-value for the test and interpret it.

14.39 A paired difference experiment with $n = 30$ pairs yielded $T_+ = 354$.

   a. Specify the null and alternative hypotheses that should be used in conducting a hypothesis test to determine whether the probability distribution for population A is located to the right of that for population B.

   b. Conduct the test of part **a**, using $\alpha = .05$.

   c. What is the approximate p-value of the test of part **b**?

   d. What assumptions are necessary to ensure the validity of the test you performed in part **b**?

14.40 A random sample of nine pairs of measurements is shown in the following table:

⊚ **LM14_40**

Pair	Sample Data from Population 1	Sample Data from Population 2
1	8	7
2	10	1
3	6	4
4	10	10
5	7	4
6	8	3
7	4	6
8	9	2
9	8	4

   a. Use the Wilcoxon signed rank test to determine whether the data provide sufficient evidence to indicate that the probability distribution for population 1 is shifted to the right of the probability distribution for population 2. Test, using $\alpha = .05$.

   b. Use the Wilcoxon signed rank test to determine whether the data provide sufficient evidence to indicate that the probability distribution for population 1 is shifted either to the right or to the left of the probability distribution for population 2. Test, using $\alpha = .05$.

Applying the Concepts—Basic

14.41 **Treating psoriasis with the "Doctorfish of Kangal."** Refer to the *Evidence-Based Research in Complementary and Alternative Medicine* (Dec. 2006) study of treating psoriasis with ichthyotherapy, presented in Exercise 2.127 (p. 87). (Recall that the therapy is also known as the "Doctorfish of Kangal," since it uses fish from the hot pools of Kangal, Turkey, to feed on skin scales.) In the study, 67 patients diagnosed with psoriasis underwent three weeks of ichthyotherapy. The Psoriasis Area Severity Index (PASI) of each patient was measured both before and after treatment. (The lower the PASI score, the better is the skin condition.) Before and after-treatment PASI scores were compared with the use of the Wilcoxon signed rank test.

   a. Explain why the PASI scores should be analyzed with a test for paired differences.

   b. Refer to the box plots shown in Exercise 2.127. Give a reason that the researchers opted to use a nonparametric test to compare the PASI scores.

   c. The p-value for the Wilcoxon signed ranks test was reported as $p < .0001$. Interpret this result, and comment on the effectiveness of ichthyotherapy in treating psoriasis.

14.42 **Computer-mediated communication study.** Refer to the *Journal of Computer-Mediated Communication* (Apr. 2004) study comparing people who interact via computer-mediated communication (CMC) with those who meet face-to-face (FTF), presented in Exercise 14.29 (p. 14-19). Relational intimacy scores (measured on a seven-point scale) were obtained for each participant after each of three different meetings. The researchers hypothesized that relational intimacy scores for participants in the CMC group will tend to be higher at the third meeting than at the first meeting; however, they hypothesize that there are no differences in scores between the first and third meetings for the FTF group.

   a. Explain why a nonparametric Wilcoxon signed ranks test is appropriate for analyzing the data.

   b. For the CMC group comparison, give the null and alternative hypotheses of interest.

   c. Give the rejection region (at $\alpha = .05$) for conducting the test mentioned in part **b**. Recall that there were 14 participants assigned to the CMC group.

   d. For the FTF group comparison, give the null and alternative hypotheses of interest.

   e. Give the rejection region (at $\alpha = .05$) for conducting the test mentioned in part **d**. Recall that there were 14 participants assigned to the FTF group.

14.43 **Reading comprehension strategies of elementary school children.** An investigation of the reading comprehension strategies employed by good and average elementary school readers was the topic of research published in *The Reading Matrix* (April 2004). Both good and average readers were recruited on the basis of their scores on a midterm language test. Each group was evaluated on how often its members employed each of eight different reading strategies. The accompanying table gives the proportion of times the reading group used each strategy (called the Factor Specificity Index, or FSI score). The researchers conducted

⊚ **READSTRAT**

STRATEGY	FSI Scores Good Readers	FSI Scores Average Readers
Word meaning	.38	.32
Words in context	.29	.25
Literal comprehension	.42	.25
Draw inference from single string	.60	.26
Draw inference from multiple string	.45	.31
Interpretation of metaphor	.32	.14
Find salient or main idea	.21	.03
From judgment	.73	.80

Source: Ahmed, S., & Asraf, R.M. "Making sense of text: Strategies used by good and average readers," *The Reading Matrix*, Vol. 4, No. 1, April 2004 (Table 2).

a Wilcoxon signed rank test to compare the FSI score distributions of good and average readers.

a. State H_0 and H_a for the desired test of hypothesis.
b. For each strategy, compute the difference between the FSI scores of good and average readers.
c. Rank the absolute values of the differences.
d. Calculate the value of the signed rank test statistic.
e. Find the rejection region for the test, using $\alpha = .05$.
f. Make the appropriate inference in the words of the problem.

CRASH

14.44 **NHTSA new car crash tests.** Refer to the National Highway Traffic Safety Administration (NHTSA) new-car crash test data saved in the **CRASH** file. In Exercise 9.42 (p. 440), you compared the chest injury ratings of drivers and front-seat passengers by using the Student's t-procedure for matched pairs. Suppose you want to make the comparison for only those cars which have a driver's rating of five stars (the highest rating). The data for these 18 cars are listed in the accompanying table. Now consider analyzing the data by using the Wilcoxon signed rank test.

a. State the null and alternative hypotheses.
b. Use a statistical software package to find the signed rank test statistic.
c. Give the rejection region for the test, using $\alpha = .01$.

d. State the conclusion in practical terms. Report the p-value of the test.

CRASH

Chest Injury Rating			Chest Injury Rating		
Car	Driver	Passenger	Car	Driver	Passenger
1	42	35	10	36	37
2	42	35	11	36	37
3	34	45	12	43	58
4	34	45	13	40	42
5	45	45	14	43	58
6	40	42	15	37	41
7	42	46	16	37	41
8	43	58	17	44	57
9	45	43	18	42	42

Applying the Concepts—Intermediate

14.45 **Concrete-pavement response to temperature.** Civil engineers at West Virginia University have developed a three-dimensional model to predict the response of jointed concrete pavement to temperature variations. (*The International Journal of Pavement Engineering*, Sep. 2004.) To validate the model, its predictions were compared with field measurements of key concrete stress variables taken at a newly constructed highway. One variable measured was slab top transverse strain (i.e., change in length per unit length per unit time) at a distance of 1 meter from the longitudinal joint. The 5-hour changes (8:20 P.M. to 1:20 A.M.) in slab top transverse strain for six days are listed in the accompanying table. Analyze the data, using a nonparametric test. Is there a shift in the change in transverse strain distributions between field measurements and the model? Test, using $\alpha = .05$.

SLABSTRAIN

		Change in Transverse Strain	
Day	Change in Temperature (°C)	Field Measurement	3D Model
Oct. 24	−6.3	−58	−52
Dec. 3	13.2	69	59
Dec. 15	3.3	35	32
Feb. 2	−14.8	−32	−24
Mar. 25	1.7	−40	−39
May. 24	−.2	−83	−71

Source: Shoukry, S., William, G., and Riad, M. "Validation of 3DFE model of jointed concrete pavement response to temperature variations," *International Journal of Pavement Engineering*, Vol. 5, No. 3, Sep. 2004 (Table IV).

14.46 **Thematic atlas topics.** The regional atlas is an important educational resource that is updated on a periodic basis. One of the most critical aspects of a new atlas design is its thematic content. In a survey of atlas users (*Journal of Geography*, May/June 1995), a large sample of high school teachers in British Columbia ranked 12 thematic atlas topics for usefulness. The consensus rankings of the teachers (based on the percentage of teachers who responded that they "would definitely use" the topic) are given in the accompanying table. These teacher rankings were compared with the rankings a group of university geography alumni made three years earlier. Compare the distributions of theme rankings for the two groups with an appropriate nonparametric test. Use $\alpha = .05$. Interpret the results practically.

ATLAS

	Rankings	
Theme	High School Teachers	Geography Alumni
Tourism	10	2
Physical	2	1
Transportation	7	3
People	1	6
History	2	5
Climate	6	4
Forestry	5	8
Agriculture	7	10
Fishing	9	7
Energy	2	8
Mining	10	11
Manufacturing	12	12

Source: Keller, C. P., et al. "Planning the next generation of regional atlases: Input from educators," *Journal of Geography*, Vol. 94, No. 3, May/June 1995, p. 413 (Table 1).

14.47 **Treatment for tendon pain.** Refer to the *British Journal of Sports Medicine* (Feb. 1, 2004) study of chronic Achilles tendon pain, presented Exercise 10.64 (p. 523). Recall that each in a sample of 25 patients with chronic Achilles tendinosis was treated with heavy-load eccentric calf muscle training. Tendon thickness (in millimeters) was measured both before and following the treatment of each patient. The experimental data are reproduced in the next table. Use a nonparametric test to determine whether the treatment for tendonitis tends to reduce the thickness of tendons. Test, using $\alpha = .10$.

TENDON

Patient	Before Thickness (millimeters)	After Thickness (millimeters)
1	11.0	11.5
2	4.0	6.4
3	6.3	6.1
4	12.0	10.0
5	18.2	14.7
6	9.2	7.3
7	7.5	6.1
8	7.1	6.4
9	7.2	5.7
10	6.7	6.5
11	14.2	13.2
12	7.3	7.5
13	9.7	7.4
14	9.5	7.2
15	5.6	6.3
16	8.7	6.0
17	6.7	7.3
18	10.2	7.0
19	6.6	5.3
20	11.2	9.0
21	8.6	6.6
22	6.1	6.3
23	10.3	7.2
24	7.0	7.2
25	12.0	8.0

Source: Ohberg, L. et al. "Eccentric training in patients with chronic Achilles tendinosis: normalized tendon structure and decreased thickness at follow up." *British Journal of Sports Medicine*, Vol. 38, No. 1, Feb. 1, 2004 (Table 2).

14.48 Neurological impairment of POWs. Eleven prisoners of war during the war in Croatia were evaluated for neurological impairment after their release from a Serbian detention camp. (*Collegium Antropologicum*, June 1997.) All 11 experienced blows to the head and neck and/or loss of consciousness during imprisonment. Neurological impairment was assessed by measuring the amplitude of the visual evoked potential (VEP) in both eyes at two points in time: 157 days and 379 days after their release. (The higher the VEP value, the greater the neurological impairment.) The data on the 11 POWs are shown in the accompanying table. Determine whether the VEP measurements of POWs 379 days after their release tend to be greater than the VEP measurements of POWs 157 days after their release. Test, using $\alpha = .05$.

POWVEP

POW	157 Days after Release	379 Days after Release
1	2.46	3.73
2	4.11	5.46
3	3.93	7.04
4	4.51	4.73
5	4.96	4.71
6	4.42	6.19
7	1.02	1.42
8	4.30	8.70
9	7.56	7.37
10	7.07	8.46
11	8.00	7.16

Source: Vrca, A., et al. "The use of visual evoked potentials to follow-up prisoners of war after release from detention camps." *Collegium Antropologicum*, Vol. 21, No. 1, June 1997, p. 232. (Data simulated from information provided in Table 3.)

Applying the Concepts—Advanced

14.49 Bowlers' hot hand. Is the probability of a bowler rolling a strike higher after he has thrown four consecutive strikes? An investigation into the phenomenon of a "hot hand" in bowling was published in *The American Statistician* (Feb. 2004). Frame-by-frame results were collected on 43 professional bowlers from the 2002–2003 Professional Bowlers Association (PBA) season. For each bowler, the researchers calculated the proportion of strikes rolled after bowling four consecutive strikes and the proportion after bowling four consecutive nonstrikes. The data on 4 of the 43 bowlers, saved in the **HOTBOWLER** file, are shown in the following table:

a. Do the data on the sample of four bowlers provide support for the "hot hand" theory in bowling? Explain.

b. When the data on all 43 bowlers are used, the p-value for the hypothesis test is approximately 0. Interpret this result.

HOTBOWLER

Bowler	Proportion of Strikes After Four Strikes	Proportion of Strikes After Four Nonstrikes
Paul Fleming	.683	.432
Bryon Smith	.684	.400
Mike DeVaney	.632	.421
Dave D'Entremont	.610	.529

Source: Dorsey-Palmateer, R., & Smith, G. "Bowlers' Hot Hands," *American Statistician*, Vol. 58, No. 1, Feb. 2004 (Table 3).

14.5 Comparing Three or More Populations: Completely Randomized Design

In Chapter 10, we used an analysis of variance and the F-test to compare the means of k populations (treatments) on the basis of random sampling from populations that were normally distributed with a common variance σ^2. We now present a nonparametric technique for comparing the populations—the **Kruskal–Wallis H-test**—that requires no assumptions concerning the population probability distributions.

HOSPBEDS

TABLE 14.7   Number of Available Beds

Hospital 1		Hospital 2		Hospital 3	
Beds	Rank	Beds	Rank	Beds	Rank
6	5	34	25	13	9.5
38	27	28	19	35	26
3	2	42	30	19	15
17	13	13	9.5	4	3
11	8	40	29	29	20
30	21	31	22	0	1
15	11	9	7	7	6
16	12	32	23	33	24
25	17	39	28	18	14
5	4	27	18	24	16
$R_1 = 120$		$R_2 = 210.5$		$R_3 = 134.5$	

Suppose a health administrator wants to compare the unoccupied bed space for three hospitals located in the same city. She randomly selects 10 different days from the records of each hospital and lists the number of unoccupied beds for each day. (See Table 14.7.) Because the number of unoccupied beds per day may occasionally be quite large, it is conceivable that the population distributions of data may be skewed to the right and that this type of data may not satisfy the assumptions necessary for a parametric comparison of the population means. We therefore use a nonparametric analysis and base our comparison on the rank sums for the three sets of sample data. Just as with two independent samples (Section 14.3), the ranks are computed for each observation according to the relative magnitude of the measurements *when the data for all the samples are combined.* (See Table 14.7.) Ties are treated as they were for the Wilcoxon rank sum and signed rank tests, by assigning the average value of the ranks to each of the tied observations.

We test

H_0: The probability distributions of the number of unoccupied beds are the same for all three hospitals

H_a: At least two of the three hospitals have probability distributions of the number of unoccupied beds that differ in location

If we denote the three sample rank sums by R_1, R_2, and R_3, then the test statistic is given by

$$H = \frac{12}{n(n+1)} \sum \frac{R_j^2}{n_j} - 3(n+1)$$

where n_j is the number of measurements in the jth sample and n is the total sample size ($n = n_1 + n_2 + \ldots + n_k$). For the data in Table 14.7, we have $n_1 = n_2 = n_3 = 10$ and $n = 30$. The rank sums are $R_1 = 120$, $R_2 = 210.5$, and $R_3 = 134.5$. Thus,

$$H = \frac{12}{30(31)} \left[\frac{(120)^2}{10} + \frac{(210.5)^2}{10} + \frac{(134.5)^2}{10} \right] - 3(31)$$

$$= 99.097 - 93 = 6.097$$

The H statistic measures the extent to which the k samples differ with respect to their relative ranks. This is more easily seen by writing H in the alternative, but equivalent, form

$$H = \frac{12}{n(n+1)} \sum n_j (\bar{R}_j - \bar{R})^2$$

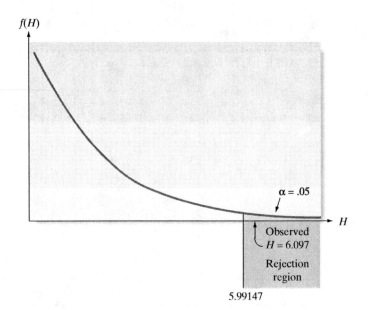

FIGURE 14.10

Rejection region for the comparison of three probability distributions

where $\bar{R}_j$ is the mean rank corresponding to sample j and $\bar{R}$ is the mean of all the ranks [i.e., $\bar{R} = \frac{1}{2}(n + 1)$]. Thus, the H statistic is 0 if all samples have the same mean rank and becomes increasingly large as the distance between the sample mean ranks grows.

If the null hypothesis is true, the distribution of H in repeated sampling is approximately a χ^2 (chi-square) distribution. This approximation of the sampling distribution of H is adequate as long as one of the k sample sizes exceeds 5. (See the references for more detail.) The degrees of freedom corresponding to the approximate sampling distribution of H will always be $(k - 1)$—one less than the number of probability distributions being compared. Because large values of H support the alternative hypothesis that the populations have different probability distributions, the rejection region for the test is located in the upper tail of the χ^2 distribution.

For the data of Table 14.7, the approximate distribution of the test statistic H is χ^2 with $(k - 1) = 2$ df. To determine how large H must be before we will reject the null hypothesis, we consult Table VII in Appendix A. For $\alpha = .05$ and df = 2, $\chi^2_{.05} = 5.99147$. Therefore, we can reject the null hypothesis that the three probability distributions are the same if

$$H > 5.99147$$

The rejection region is pictured in Figure 14.10. Since the calculated $H = 6.097$ exceeds the critical value of 5.99147, we conclude that at least one of the three hospitals tends to have a larger number of unoccupied beds than the others.

Now Work Exercise 14.52

The same conclusion can be reached from a computer printout of the analysis. The test statistic and the p-value of the nonparametric test are highlighted on the MINITAB printout in Figure 14.11. Since $\alpha = .05$ exceeds p-value = .047, there is sufficient evidence to reject H_0.

The Kruskal–Wallis H-test for comparing more than two probability distributions is summarized in the next box. Note that we can use the Wilcoxon rank sum test of Section 14.3 to compare a pair of populations (selected a priori) if the Kruskal–Wallis H-test supports the alternative hypothesis that at least two of the probability distributions differ.*

---

*A method similar to the multiple-comparison procedure of Chapter 10 can be used to rank the treatment medians. This nonparametric multiple comparisons of medians will control the experimentwise error rate selected by the analyst. [See Daniel (1990) and Dunn (1964) for details.]

Kruskal-Wallis Test: BEDS versus HOSPITAL

```
Kruskal-Wallis Test on BEDS

HOSPITAL   N  Median  Ave Rank     Z
1         10   15.50      12.0  -1.54
2         10   31.50      21.1   2.44
3         10   18.50      13.5  -0.90
Overall   30             15.5

H = 6.10  DF = 2  P = 0.047
H = 6.10  DF = 2  P = 0.047  (adjusted for ties)
```

FIGURE 14.11

MINITAB Kruskal–Wallis test comparing three hospitals

Kruskal–Wallis H-Test for Comparing k Probability Distributions

H_0: The k probability distributions are identical

H_a: At least two of the k probability distributions differ in location

Test statistic: $H = \dfrac{12}{n(n+1)} \sum \dfrac{R_j^2}{n_j} - 3(n+1)$

where

n_j = Number of measurements in sample j

R_j = Rank sum for sample j, where the rank of each measurement is computed according to its relative magnitude in the totality of data for the k samples

n = Total sample size = $n_1 + n_2 + \ldots + n_k$

Rejection region: $H > \chi_\alpha^2$ with $(k-1)$ degrees of freedom.

Ties: Assign tied measurements the average of the ranks they would receive if they were unequal, but occurred in successive order. For example, if the third-ranked and fourth-ranked measurements are tied, assign both a rank of $(3+4)/2 = 3.5$. The number of ties should be small relative to the total number of observations.

Conditions Required for the Valid Application of the Kruskal–Wallis Test

1. The k samples are random and independent.
2. There are five or more measurements in each sample.
3. The k probability distributions from which the samples are drawn are continuous.

STATISTICS IN ACTION REVISITED

Comparing the MTBE Levels of Different Types of Groundwater Wells (continued)

In the previous *Statistics in Action Revisited* (p. 14-16), we demonstrated the use of Wilcoxon rank sum tests to compare the MTBE distributions of public and private groundwater wells and of bedrock and unconsolidated aquifers. The environmental researchers also investigated how the combination of well class and aquifer affected the MTBE levels of the 70 wells in the **MTBE** file that had detectable levels of MTBE. Although there are four possible combinations of well class and aquifer, data were available for only three: Private/bedrock, Public/bedrock, and Public/unconsolidated.

The distributions of MTBE levels for these three groups of wells were compared with the use of the Kruskal–Wallis nonparametric test for independent samples. The SAS printout for the analysis is shown in Figure SIA14.4. The test statistic is $H = 9.12$ and the

(continued)

p-value is .0104 (highlighted). At $\alpha = .05$, there is sufficient evidence to indicate differences in the distributions of MTBE levels of the three class–aquifer types. (However, at $\alpha = .01$, no significant differences are found.) On the basis of the mean rank sum scores shown on the printout, it appears that public wells with bedrock aquifers have the highest levels of MTBE contamination.

FIGURE SIA14.4
SAS Kruskal–Wallis test for comparing MTBE levels of wells

The NPAR1WAY Procedure

Wilcoxon Scores (Rank Sums) for Variable MTBE
Classified by Variable wellaq

wellaq	N	Sum of Scores	Expected Under H0	Std Dev Under H0	Mean Score
Private/Bedro	22	654.50	781.00	79.027002	29.750000
Public/Uncon	7	139.50	248.50	51.069646	19.928571
Public/Bedroc	41	1691.00	1455.50	83.856064	41.243902

Average scores were used for ties.

Kruskal–Wallis Test

Chi-Square	9.1244
DF	2
Pr > Chi-Square	0.0104

Exercises 14.50–14.62

Understanding the Principles

14.50 Which of the following results would lead you to conclude that the treatments in a balanced completely randomized design have distributions that differ in location?
  a. The rank sums for all treatments are about equal.
  b. The rank sum for one treatment is much larger than the rank sum for all other treatments.

14.51 Under what circumstances does the χ^2 distribution provide an appropriate characterization of the sampling distribution of the Kruskal–Wallis H statistic?

Learning the Mechanics

14.52 Data were collected from three populations—A, B, and
NW C,—by means of a completely randomized design. The following describes the sample data:
$$n_A = n_B = n_C = 15$$
$$R_A = 235 \quad R_B = 439 \quad R_C = 361$$
  a. Specify the null and alternative hypotheses that should be used in conducting a test of hypothesis to determine whether the probability distributions of populations A, B, and C differ in location.
  b. Conduct the test of part **a**. Use $\alpha = .05$.
  c. What is the approximate p-value of the test of part **b**?
  d. Calculate the mean rank for each sample and compute H according to the formula that utilizes these means. Verify that this formula yields the same value of H that you obtained in part **b**.

14.53 Suppose you want to use the Kruskal–Wallis H-test to compare the probability distributions of three populations. The following are independent random samples selected from the three populations:

 LM14_53

I:	34 56 65 59 82 70 45
II:	24 18 27 41 34 42 33
III:	72 101 91 76 80 75

  a. What experimental design was used?
  b. Specify the null and alternative hypotheses you would test.
  c. Specify the rejection region you would use for your hypothesis test at $\alpha = .01$.
  d. Conduct the test at $\alpha = .01$.

Applying the Concepts—Basic

 TVADRECALL

14.54 **Study of recall of TV commercials.** Refer to the *Journal of Applied Psychology* (June 2002) study of the recall of the content television commercials, presented in Exercise 10.28 (p. 501). In a designed experiment, 324 adults were randomly assigned to one of three viewer groups: (1) Watch a TV program with a violent content code (V) rating, (2) watch a show with a sex content code (S) rating, and, (3) watch a neutral TV program. The number of brand names recalled in the commercial messages was recorded for each participant, and the data are saved in the **TVADRECALL** file.
  a. Give the null and alternative hypotheses for a Kruskal–Wallis test applied to the data.
  b. The results of the nonparametric test are shown in the MINITAB printout on p. 14-33. Locate the test statistic and p-value on the printout.
  c. Interpret the results of part **b**, using $\alpha = .01$. What can the researchers conclude about the three groups of TV ad viewers?

14.55 **Effect of scopolamine on memory.** Refer to the *Behavioral Neuroscience* (Feb. 2004) study of the drug scopolamine's effects on memory for word-pair association presented in Exercise 10.33 (p. 501). Recall that a completely randomized design with three groups was used: Group 1 subjects were injected with scopolamine,

---

Kruskal-Wallis Test: RECALL versus GROUP

```
Kruskal-Wallis Test on RECALL

GROUP       N   Median   Ave Rank      Z
N         108    3.000      205.1    5.79
S         108    1.000      131.2   -4.26
V         108    2.000      151.2   -1.53
Overall   324               162.5

H = 36.04   DF = 2   P = 0.000
H = 37.15   DF = 2   P = 0.000   (adjusted for ties)
```

MINITAB output for Exercise 14.54

group 2 subjects were injected with a placebo, and group 3 subjects were not given any drug. The response variable was number of word pairs recalled. The data on all 28 subjects are reproduced in the following table:

SCOPOLAMINE

Group 1 (Scopolamine):	5 8 8 6 6 6 6 8 6 4 5 6
Group 2 (Placebo):	8 10 12 10 9 7 9 10
Group 3 (No drug):	8 9 11 12 11 10 12 12

a. Rank the data for all 28 observations from smallest to largest.
b. Sum the ranks of the observations from group 1.
c. Sum the ranks of the observations from group 2.
d. Sum the ranks of the observations from group 3.
e. Use the rank sums from parts b–d to compute the Kruskal–Wallis H statistic.
f. Carry out the Kruskal–Wallis nonparametric test (at $\alpha = .05$) to compare the distributions of number of word pairs recalled for the three groups.
g. Recall from Exercise 10.33 that the researchers theorized that group 1 subjects would tend to recall the fewest number of words. Use the Wilcoxon rank sum test to compare the word recall distributions of group 1 and group 2. (Use $\alpha = .05$.)

14.56 Biting rates of flies. Refer to the *Journal of the American Mosquito Control Association* study of biting flies, presented in Exercise 14.11 (p. 14-10). The effect of wind speeds, in kilometers per hour (kph), on the biting rate of the fly on Stanbury Island, Utah, was investigated by exposing samples of volunteers to one of six wind-speed conditions. The distributions of the biting rates for the six wind speeds were compared by means of the Kruskal–Wallis test. The rank sums of the biting rates for the six conditions are shown in the accompanying table.

Wind Speed (kph)	Number of Volunteers (n_j)	Rank Sum of Biting Rates (R_j)
< 1	11	1,804
1–2.9	49	6,398
3–4.9	62	7,328
5–6.9	39	4,075
7–8.9	35	2,660
9–20	21	1,388
Total	**217**	**23,653**

Source: Strickman, D., et al. "Meteorological effects on the biting activity of *Leptoconops americanus* (Diptera: Ceratopogonidae)," *Journal of the American Mosquito Control Association*, Vol. II, No. 1, Mar. 1995, p. 17 (Table 1).

a. The researchers reported the test statistic as $H = 35.2$. Verify this value.
b. Find the rejection region for the test, using $\alpha = .01$.
c. Draw the proper conclusions.
d. The researchers reported that the p-value of the test is less than .01. Does this value support your inference in part **c**? Explain.

14.57 Social reinforcement of exercise. Two University of Georgia researchers studied the effect of social reinforcement on the duration of exercise in adolescents with moderate mental retardation. (*Clinical Kinesiology*, Spring 1995.) Eleven adolescents with IQs ranging from 32 to 61 were divided into two groups. All participated in a six-week exercise program. Group A (4 subjects) received verbal and social reinforcement during the program, while Group B (7 subjects) received verbal and social reinforcement and kept a self-record of individual performances. The researchers theorized that Group B subjects would exercise for longer periods than Group A. Upon completion of the exercise program, all 11 subjects participated in a run/walk "race" in which the goal was to complete as many laps as possible during a 15-minute period. The number of laps completed (to the nearest quarter lap) was used as a measure of the duration of exercise.
a. Specify the null and alternative hypotheses for a nonparametric analysis of the data.
b. The Kruskal–Wallis H-test was applied to the data. The researchers reported the test statistic as $H = 5.1429$ and the observed significance level of the test as p-value $= .0233$. Interpret these results.
c. Are the assumptions for the test carried out in part **b** satisfied? If not, propose an alternative nonparametric method for the analysis.

Applying the Concepts—Intermediate

14.58 Energy expenditure of laughter. Refer to the *International Journal of Obesity* (Jan. 2007) study of the physiological changes that accompany laughter, presented in Exercise 8.27 (p. 364). Recall that pairs of subjects watched film clips designed to evoke laughter. In addition to heart rate, the researchers measured the duration of laughter (seconds per minute) and the energy expenditure (kilojoules per minute) of each pair during the laughing period. The subject pairs were then divided into four groups (quartiles)—0–5, 6–10, 10–20, and more than 20 seconds per minute—on the basis of duration of laughter. The energy expenditure values for the 45 subject pairs in the study are shown in the next table. (The data are simulated on the basis of reported summary statistics.) The researchers compared the energy expenditure distributions across the four laughter duration groups by means of the Kruskal–Wallis test.

a. State H_0 and H_a for the desired test of hypothesis.
b. Find the rejection region for the test, using $\alpha = .10$.
c. Compute the value of the test statistic.
d. On the basis of the results from parts **b** and **c**, what is the appropriate conclusion?
e. Compare the 0–5 and > 20 quartile groups, using the Wilcoxon rank sum test. What do you infer about the relationship between energy expenditure and duration of laughter?
f. Demonstrate why the researchers employed a non-parametric test on the data.

LAUGHTER

0–5 sec/min	6–10 sec/min	10–20 sec/min	> 20 sec/min
0.10	0.43	0.11	0.88
0.94	0.46	0.62	0.52
0.44	1.01	0.11	0.70
0.07	1.11	1.71	2.50
0.10	0.13	0.60	1.12
0.08	0.02	0.08	0.70
0.06	0.36	0.24	1.20
0.05	0.18	0.58	0.56
0.01	0.40	0.19	0.36
0.13	0.09	1.09	0.22
0.04	1.29	2.09	0.50
	0.50		

Source: Buchowski, M. S., et al. "Energy expenditure of genuine laughter,"
International Journal of Obesity, Vol. 31, No. 1, January 2007 (adapted from Figure 4).

14.59 Restoring self-control when intoxicated. Refer to the *Experimental and Clinical Psychopharmacology* (February 2005) study of self-control when intoxicated, presented in Exercise 10.32 (p. 503). After memorizing two lists of words (20 words on a green list and 20 words on a red list), students were randomly assigned to one of four different treatment groups. Students in Group A received two alcoholic drinks. Students in Group AC had caffeine powder dissolved in their alcoholic drinks. Group AR also received two alcoholic drinks, but received a monetary award for correct responses. Students in Group P (the

DRINKERS

AR	AC	A	P
.51	.50	.16	.58
.58	.30	.10	.12
.52	.47	.20	.62
.47	.36	.29	.43
.61	.39	−.14	.26
.00	.22	.18	.50
.32	.20	−.35	.44
.53	.21	.31	.20
.50	.15	.16	.42
.46	.10	.04	.43
.34	.02	−.25	.40

Adapted from: Grattan-Miscio, K. E., and Vogel-Sprott, M. "Alcohol, intentional control, and inappropriate behavior: Regulation by caffeine or an incentive," *Experimental and Clinical Psychopharmacology*, Vol. 13, No. 1, February 2005 (Table 1).

placebo group) were told that they would receive alcohol, but instead received two drinks containing a carbonated beverage (with a few drops of alcohol on the surface to provide an alcoholic scent). After consuming their drinks and resting for 25 minutes, the students performed a word completion task. Their scores (simulated on the basis of summary information from the article) are reported in the accompanying table. (*Note*: A score represents the difference between the proportion of correct responses on the green list of words and the proportion of incorrect responses on the red list of words.) Compare the task score distributions of the four groups, using an appropriate non-parametric test at $\alpha = .05$. What can you infer about the four groups of students?

14.60 Estimating the age of glacial drifts. Refer to the *American Journal of Science* (Jan. 2005) study of the chemical make-up of buried tills (glacial drifts) in Wisconsin, presented in Exercise 10.35 (p. 504). Recall that till specimens were obtained from five different boreholes (labeled UMRB-1, UMRB-2, UMRB-3, SWRA, and SD), and the ratio of aluminum to beryllium was measured for each specimen. The data are reproduced in the accompanying table. Conduct a nonparametric analysis of variance of the data, using $\alpha = .10$. Interpret the results.

TILLRATIO

UMRB-1:	3.75	4.05	3.81	3.23	3.13	3.30	3.21
UMRB-2:	3.32	4.09	3.90	5.06	3.85	3.88	
UMRB-3:	4.06	4.56	3.60	3.27	4.09	3.38	3.37
SWRA:	2.73	2.95	2.25				
SD:	2.73	2.55	3.06				

Source: Adapted from *American Journal of Science*, Vol. 305, No. 1, Jan. 2005, p. 16 (Table 2).

14.61 The "name game." Refer to the *Journal of Experimental Psychology—Applied* (June 2000) study of different methods of learning names, presented in Exercise 10.34

NAMEGAME

Simple Name Game:

24	43	38	65	35	15	44	44	18	27	0	38	50	31
7	46	33	31	0	29	0	0	52	0	29	42	39	26
51	0	42	20	37	51	0	30	43	30	99	39	35	19
24	34	3	60	0	29	40	40						

Elaborate Name Game:

39	71	9	86	26	45	0	38	5	53	29	0	62	0
1	35	10	6	33	48	9	26	83	33	12	5	0	0
25	36	39	1	37	2	13	26	7	35	3	8	55	50

Pairwise Intro:

5	21	22	3	32	29	32	0	4	41	0	27	5	9
66	54	1	15	0	26	1	30	2	13	0	2	17	14
5	29	0	45	35	7	11	4	9	23	4	0	8	2
18	0	5	21	14									

Source: Morris, P. E., and Fritz, C. O. "The name game: Using retrieval practice to improve the learning of names." *Journal of Experimental Psychology—Applied*, Vol. 6, No. 2, June 2000 (data simulated from Figure 1).

(p. 503). Recall that three groups of students used different methods to learn the names of the other students in their group. Group 1 used the "simple name game," Group 2 used the "elaborate name game," and Group 3 used "pairwise introductions." The table at the bottom of p. 14-34 lists the percentage of names recalled (after one year) for each student respondent.

a. Consider an analysis-of-variance *F*-test to determine whether the mean percentages of names recalled differ for the three name-retrieval methods. Demonstrate that the ANOVA assumptions are likely to be violated.

b. Use an alternative nonparametric test to compare the distributions of the percentages of names recalled for the three name-retrieval methods. Take $\alpha = .05$.

14.62 Forums for tax litigation. In disagreements between the Internal Revenue Service (IRS) and taxpayers that end up in litigation, taxpayers are permitted by law to choose the court forum. Three trial courts are available: (1) U.S. Tax Court, (2) Federal District Court, and (3) U.S. Claims Court. Each court possesses different requirements and restrictions that make the choice an important one for the taxpayer. A study of taxpayers' choice of forum in litigat-

ing tax issues was published in the *Journal of Applied Business Research* (Fall 1996). In a random sample of 161 litigated tax disputes, the researchers measured the taxpayers' choice of forum (Tax, District, or Claims Court) and tax deficiency (i.e., the disputed amount, in dollars). One of the objectives of the study was to determine those factors taxpayers consider important in their choice of forum. If tax deficiency (called DEF by the researchers) is an important factor, then the mean DEF values for the three tax courts should be significantly different.

a. The researchers applied a nonparametric test rather than a parametric test to compare the DEF distributions of the three tax litigation forums. Give a plausible reason for their choice.

b. What nonparametric test is appropriate for this analysis? Explain.

c. The accompanying table summarizes the data analyzed by the researchers. Use the information in the table to compute the appropriate test statistic.

d. The observed significance level of the test was reported as *p*-value = .0037. Interpret this result fully.

Court Selected by Taxpayer	Sample Size	Sample Mean DEF	Rank Sum of DEF Values
Tax	67	$ 80,357	5,335
District	57	74,213	3,937
Claims	37	184,648	3,769

Source: Billings, B. A., Green, B. P., and Volz, W. H. "Selection of forum for litigated tax issues," *Journal of Applied Business Research*, Vol. 12, No. 4, Fall 1996, p. 38 (Table 2).

14.6 Comparing Three or More Populations: Randomized Block Design

In Section 10.4, we employed an analysis of variance to compare *p* population (treatment) means when the data were collected under a randomized block design. The Friedman F_r- *test* provides another method of testing for a shift in location of a set of *p* populations.* Like other nonparametric tests, it requires no assumptions concerning the nature of the populations other than the capability of individual observations to be ranked.

In Section 14.3, we gave an example in which a completely randomized design was used to compare the reaction times of subjects under the influence of one of two drugs. When the effect of a drug is short lived and when the drug effect varies greatly from person to person, it may be useful to employ a *randomized block design*. Using the subjects as blocks, we hope to eliminate the variability among subjects and thereby increase the amount of information gained in the experiment. Suppose that three drugs—A, B, and C—are to be compared under a randomized block design. Each of the three drugs is administered to the *same subject*, with suitable time lags between the three doses. The order in which the drugs are administered is randomly determined for each subject. Thus, one drug would be administered to a subject and its reaction time would be noted; then, after a sufficient length of time, the second drug would be administered; etc.

Suppose six subjects are chosen and that the reaction times for each drug are as shown in Table 14.8. To compare the three drugs, we rank the observations within each subject (block) and then compute the rank sums for each of the drugs (treatments). Tied observations within blocks are handled in the usual manner: by assigning the average value of the ranks to each of the tied observations.

---

*The Friedman F_r-test was developed by the Nobel Prize–winning economist Milton Friedman.

REACTION2

TABLE 14.8   Reaction Time for Three Drugs

Subject	Drug A	Rank	Drug B	Rank	Drug C	Rank
1	1.21	1	1.48	2	1.56	3
2	1.63	1	1.85	2	2.01	3
3	1.42	1	2.06	3	1.70	2
4	2.43	2	1.98	1	2.64	3
5	1.16	1	1.27	2	1.48	3
6	1.94	1	2.44	2	2.81	3
		$R_1 = 7$		$R_2 = 12$		$R_3 = 17$

The null and alternative hypotheses are

H_0: The populations of reaction times are identically distributed for all three drugs

H_a: At least two of the drugs have probability distributions of reaction times that differ in location

The **Friedman F_r-statistic,** which is based on the rank sums for each treatment, is

$$F_r = \frac{12}{bk(k + 1)} \sum R_j^2 - 3b(k + 1)$$

where b is the number of blocks, k is the number of treatments, and R_j is the jth rank sum. For the data in Table 14.8,

$$F_r = \frac{12}{(6)(3)(4)}[(7)^2 + (12)^2 + (17)^2] - 3(6)(4) = 80.33 - 72 = 8.33$$

The Friedman F_r-statistic measures the extent to which the p samples differ with respect to their relative ranks within the blocks. This is more easily seen by writing F_r in the alternative, but equivalent, form

$$F_r = \frac{12}{bk(k + 1)} \sum b(\overline{R}_j - \overline{R})^2$$

where $\overline{R}_j$ is the mean rank corresponding to treatment j and $\overline{R}$ is the mean of all the ranks (i.e., $\overline{R} = \frac{1}{2}(k + 1)$]. Thus, the F_r-statistic is 0 if all treatments have the same mean rank and becomes increasingly large as the distance between the sample mean ranks grows.

Like the Kruskal–Wallis H statistic, the Friedman F_r-statistic has approximately a χ^2 sampling distribution with $(k - 1)$ degrees of freedom. Empirical results show the approximation to be adequate if either b (the number of blocks) or k (the number of treatments) exceeds 5. The Friedman F_r-test for a randomized block design is summarized in the following box:

Friedman F_r-Test for a Randomized Block Design

H_0: The probability distributions for the p treatments are identical

H_a: At least two of the probability distributions differ in location

Test statistic: $F_r = \dfrac{12}{bk(k + 1)} \sum R_j^2 - 3b(k + 1)$

where

b = Number of blocks
k = Number of treatments

(continued)

R_j = Rank sum of the jth treatment, where the rank
of each measurement is computed relative to its position
within its own block

Rejection region: $F_r > \chi_\alpha^2$ with $(k - 1)$ degrees of freedom

Ties: Assign tied measurements within a block the average of the ranks they would receive if they were unequal, but occurred in successive order. For example, if the third-ranked and fourth-ranked measurements are tied, assign each a rank of $(3 + 4)/2 = 3.5$. The number of ties should be small relative to the total number of observations.

Conditions Required for a Valid Friedman F_r-Test

1. The treatments are randomly assigned to experimental units within the blocks.
2. The measurements can be ranked within blocks.
3. The p probability distributions from which the samples within each block are drawn are continuous.

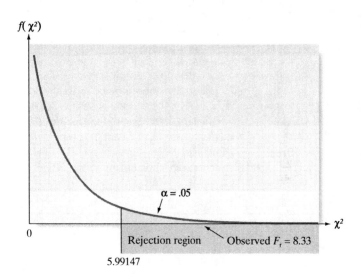

FIGURE 14.12
Rejection region for
reaction-time example

Friedman Test

Ranks

	Mean Rank
A	1.17
B	2.00
C	2.83

Test Statistics[a]

N	6
Chi-Square	8.333
df	2
Asymp. Sig.	.016

a. Friedman Test

FIGURE 14.13
SPSS Friedman test printout

For the drug example, we will use $\alpha = .05$ to form the rejection region

$$F_r > \chi_{.05}^2 = 5.99147 \text{ (see Figure 14.12)}$$

where $\chi_{.05}^2$ is based on $(k - 1) = 2$ degrees of freedom. Consequently, because the observed value $F_r = 8.33$ exceeds 5.99147, we conclude that at least two of the three drugs have probability distributions of reaction times that differ in location.

An SPSS printout of the nonparametric analysis, shown in Figure 14.13, confirms our inference. Both the test statistic and p-value are highlighted on the printout. Since p-value $= .016$ is less than our selected $\alpha = .05$, there is evidence to reject H_0.

Now Work Exercise 14.66

Clearly, the assumptions for this test—that the measurements are ranked within blocks and that the number of blocks (subjects) is greater than 5—are satisfied. However, we must be sure that the treatments are randomly assigned to blocks. For the procedure to be valid, we assume that the three drugs are administered in a random order to each subject. If this were not true, the difference in the reaction times for the three drugs might be due to the order in which the drugs were given.

Exercises 14.63–14.75

Understanding the Principles

14.63 Which of the following statements correctly describes how to rank the data in a randomized block design?
  a. For each treatment, rank the data across the blocks from smallest to largest.
  b. For each block, rank the data across the treatments from smallest to largest.

14.64 What conditions are required for a valid application of the Friedman F_r-test?

Learning the Mechanics

14.65 Data were collected under a randomized block design with four treatments (A, B, C, and D) and $b = 6$. The following rank sums were obtained:

$$R_A = 11 \quad R_B = 21 \quad R_C = 21 \quad R_D = 7$$

  a. How many blocks were used in the experimental design?
  b. Specify the null and alternative hypotheses that should be used in conducting a hypothesis test to determine whether the probability distributions for at least two of the treatments differ in location.
  c. Conduct the test of part **b**. Use $\alpha = .10$.
  d. What is the approximate p-value of the test of part **c**?
  e. Calculate the mean rank for each of the four treatments and compute the value of the F_r-test statistic according to the formula that utilizes those means. Verify that the test statistic is the same as the one you obtained in part **c**.

14.66 Suppose you have used a randomized block design to help
NW you compare the effectiveness of three different treatments: A, B, and C. You obtained the data given in the accompanying table and plan to conduct a Friedman F_r-test.

⊚ **LM14_66**

Block	Treatment		
	A	B	C
1	9	11	18
2	13	13	13
3	11	12	12
4	10	15	16
5	9	8	10
6	14	12	16
7	10	12	15

  a. Specify the null and alternative hypotheses you will test.
  b. Specify the rejection region for the test. Use $\alpha = .10$.
  c. Conduct the test and interpret the results.

14.67 An experiment was conducted under a randomized block design with four treatments and six blocks. The ranks of the measurements within each block are shown in the accompanying table. Use the Friedman F_r-test for a randomized block design to determine whether the data provide sufficient evidence to indicate that at least two of the treatment probability distributions differ in location. Test, using $\alpha = .05$.

⊚ **LM14_67**

Treatment	Block					
	1	2	3	4	5	6
1	3	3	2	3	2	3
2	1	1	1	2	1	1
3	4	4	3	4	4	4
4	2	2	4	1	3	2

Applying the Concepts—Basic

14.68 **Conditions impeding farm production.** A review of farmer involvement in agricultural research was presented in the *Journal of Agricultural, Biological, and Environmental Statistics* (Mar. 2001). In one study, each of six farmers ranked the level of farm production constraint imposed by five conditions: drought, pest damage, weed interference, farming costs, and labor shortage. The rankings, ranging from 1 (least severe) to 5 (most severe), and rank sums for the five conditions are listed in the table at the bottom of the page.
  a. Use the rank sums shown in the table to compute the Friedman F_r-statistic.
  b. At $\alpha = .05$, find the rejection region for a test to compare the farmer opinion distributions for the five conditions.
  c. Draw the proper conclusion in the words of the problem.

14.69 **Thematic atlas topics.** Refer to the *Journal of Geography*'s published rankings of regional atlas theme topics, presented in Exercise 14.46 (p. 14-27). In addition to high school teachers and university geography alumni, university geography students and representatives of the

⊚ **FARM6**

Farmer		Condition				
		Drought	Pest Damage	Weed Interference	Farming Costs	Labor Shortage
	1	5	4	3	2	1
	2	5	3	4	1	2
	3	3	5	4	2	1
	4	5	4	1	2	3
	5	4	5	3	2	1
	6	5	4	3	2	1
	Rank sum	27	25	18	11	9

Source: Riley, J., and Fielding, W. J. "An illustrated review of some farmer participatory research techniques," *Journal of Agricultural, Biological, and Environmental Statistics,* Vol. 6, No. 1, Mar. 2001 (Table 1).

MINITAB output for
Exercise 14.69

Friedman Test: RANK versus GROUP blocked by THEME

```
S = 0.93  DF = 3  P = 0.819
S = 1.08  DF = 3  P = 0.782 (adjusted for ties)

                          Sum
                           of
GROUP   N  Est Median   Ranks
  1    12      5.1250    27.0
  2    12      6.1250    32.5
  3    12      5.6250    29.0
  4    12      6.1250    31.5

Grand median = 5.7500
```

general public ranked the 12 thematic topics. The rankings of all four groups are shown in the table at the bottom of the page. A MINITAB analysis (above) compares the atlas theme-ranking distributions of the four groups.

a. Locate the rank sums on the printout.

b. Use the rank sums to find the Friedman F_r-statistic.

c. Locate the test statistic and the associated p-value on the printout.

d. Conduct the test and state the conclusion in the words of the problem.

14.70 Rotary oil rigs. Refer to Exercise 10.63 (p. 522) and the *World Oil* (Jan. 2002) study of rotary oil rigs. Three months were randomly selected, and the number of oil rigs running in each of three states—California, Utah, and Alaska—was recorded. The data for the randomized block design are reproduced in the accompanying table. Consider a nonparametric test to compare the distributions of rotary oil rigs running in the three states.

OILRIGS

Month	California	Utah	Alaska
1	27	17	11
2	34	20	14
3	36	15	14

a. State the null and alternative hypotheses for the test.

b. Rank the data within each month, and then sum the ranks for each state.

c. Use the rank sums from part b to find the value of the test statistic.

d. Give the rejection region of the test at $\alpha = .05$.

e. State the conclusion in the words of the problem. Does the conclusion agree with that produced by the ANOVA F-test conducted in Exercise 10.61?

14.71 Impact study of distractions while driving. The consequences of performing verbal and spatial-imagery tasks while driving were studied and the results published in the *Journal of Experimental Psychology—Applied* (Mar. 2000). Twelve drivers were recruited to drive on a highway in Madrid, Spain. During the drive, each subject was asked to perform three different tasks: a verbal task (repeating words that begin with a certain letter), a spatial-imagery task (imagining letters rotated a certain way), and no mental task. Since each driver performed all three tasks, the design is a randomized block with 12 blocks (drivers) and 3 treatments (tasks). Using a computerized head-free eye-tracking system, the researchers kept track of the eye fixations of each driver on three different objects—the interior mirror, the side mirror, and the speedometer—and determined the proportion of eye fixations on the object. The researchers used the Friedman nonparametric test to compare the distributions of the eye fixation proportions for the three tasks.

a. Using $\alpha = .01$, find the rejection region for the Friedman test.

b. For the response variable Proportion of eye fixations on the interior mirror, the researchers determined the Friedman test statistic to be $\chi^2 = 19.16$. Give the appropriate conclusion.

c. For the response variable Proportion of eye fixations on the side mirror, the researchers determined the

ATLAS2

Theme	Rankings			
	High School Teachers	Geography Alumni	Geography Students	General Public
Tourism	10	2	5	1
Physical	2	1	1	5
Transportation	7	3	7	2
People	1	6	2	3
History	2	5	9	4
Climate	6	4	4	8
Forestry	5	8	2	7
Agriculture	7	10	6	9
Fishing	9	7	10	6
Energy	2	8	7	10
Mining	10	11	11	11
Manufacturing	12	12	12	12

Source: Keller, C. P., et al. "Planning the next generation of regional atlases: Input from educators." *Journal of Geography*, Vol. 94, No. 3, May/June 1995, p. 413 (Table 1).

Friedman test statistic to be $\chi^2 = 7.80$. Give the appropriate conclusion.

d. For the response variable proportion of eye fixations on the speedometer, the researchers determined the Friedman test statistic to be $\chi^2 = 20.67$. Give the appropriate conclusion.

Applying the Concepts—Intermediate

14.72 Studies on treating Alzheimer's disease. Refer to the *eCAM* (November 2006) study of the quality of Alzheimer's research methodology, presented in Exercise 10.66 (p. 524). Recall that, for a sample of 13 research papers, the quality of the methodology on each of nine dimensions was measured with a summated Wong Scale. The data are reproduced in the table at the bottom of the page. (*Note:* The researchers labeled the nine dimensions as What-A, What-B, What-C, Who-A, Who-B, Who-C, How-A, How-B, and How-C.) Use the appropriate nonparametric test to compare the distributions of the Wong scores for the nine research methodology dimensions. Test, using $\alpha = .05$.

14.73 Effect of massage on boxers. Refer to the *British Journal of Sports Medicine* (Apr. 2000) experiment to investigate the effect of massage on boxing performance, presented in Exercise 10.68 (p. 525). Recall that the punching power (in newtons) of each of eight amateur boxers was measured after each of four rounds: (M1), round 1 following a pre-bout sports massage; (R1), round 1 following a pre-bout period of rest; (M5), round 5 following a sports massage between rounds; and (R5), round 5 following a period of rest between rounds. The data are reproduced in the next table. Use the appropriate nonparametric test to compare the punching power means of the four interventions. Compare the results with those of Exercise 10.66.

14.74 Plants and stress reduction. Refer to the Kansas State study designed to investigate the effects of plants on human stress levels, presented in Exercise 10.69 (p. 525). The data (at right) are given as finger temperatures for each of 10 students in a dimly lit room under three experimental conditions: presence of a live plant, presence of a plant photo, and absence of a plant (either live or photo). Analyze the data, using a nonparametric procedure. Do the students' finger temperatures depend on the experimental condition?

🔘 BOXING

		Intervention		
Boxer		M1	R1	M5	R5
	1	1243	1244	1291	1262
	2	1147	1053	1169	1177
	3	1247	1375	1309	1321
	4	1274	1235	1290	1285
	5	1177	1139	1233	1238
	6	1336	1313	1366	1362
	7	1238	1279	1275	1261
	8	1261	1152	1289	1266

Source: Hemmings, B., Smith, M., Graydon, J., and Dyson, R. "Effects of massage on physiological restoration, perceived recovery, and repeated sports performance," *British Journal of Sports Medicine*, Vol. 34, No. 2, Apr. 2000 (adapted from Table 3).

🔘 PLANTS

Student	Live Plant	Plant Photo	No Plant (control)
1	91.4	93.5	96.6
2	94.9	96.6	90.5
3	97.0	95.8	95.4
4	93.7	96.2	96.7
5	96.0	96.6	93.5
6	96.7	95.5	94.8
7	95.2	94.6	95.7
8	96.0	97.2	96.2
9	95.6	94.8	96.0
10	95.6	92.6	96.6

Source: Elizabeth Schreiber, Department of Statistics, Kansas State University, Manhattan, Kansas

🔘 TREATAD2

Paper	What-A	What-B	What-C	Who-A	Who-B	Who-C	How-A	How-B	How-C
1	3	3	2	2	2	3	2	2	3
2	3	3	2	1	3	2	3	2	2
3	2	2	3	1	2	2	1	2	3
4	2	3	3	2	1	3	2	1	2
5	2	3	2	2	2	3	1	3	2
6	2	3	2	1	1	1	2	2	1
7	2	3	2	2	1	3	2	2	2
8	2	2	2	1	2	3	3	2	3
9	1	2	2	2	2	3	1	1	1
10	2	3	2	1	2	2	2	3	3
11	2	2	1	1	1	2	3	2	3
12	2	3	3	2	1	3	1	2	3
13	3	3	2	2	1	3	2	2	3

Source: Chiappelli, F., et al. "Evidence-based research in complementary and alternative medicine III: Treatment of patients with Alzheimer's disease," *eCAM*, Vol. 3, No. 4, Nov. 2006 (Table 1).

14.75 **Absentee rates at a jeans plant.** Refer to Exercise 10.70 (p. 526) and the *New Technology, Work, and Employment* (July 2001) study of daily worker absentee rates at a jeans plant. Nine weeks were randomly selected and the absentee rate (percentage of workers absent) determined for each day (Monday through Friday) of the work week. The data are reproduced in the table. Conduct a nonparametric analysis of the data to compare the distributions of absentee rates for the five days of the work week.

⊚ **JEANS**

Week	Monday	Tuesday	Wednesday	Thursday	Friday
1	5.3	0.6	1.9	1.3	1.6
2	12.9	9.4	2.6	0.4	0.5
3	0.8	0.8	5.7	0.4	1.4
4	2.6	0.0	4.5	10.2	4.5
5	23.5	9.6	11.3	13.6	14.1
6	9.1	4.5	7.5	2.1	9.3
7	11.1	4.2	4.1	4.2	4.1
8	9.5	7.1	4.5	9.1	12.9
9	4.8	5.2	10.0	6.9	9.0

Source: Boggis, J. J. "The eradication of leisure." *New Technology, Work, and Employment*, Volume 16, Number 2, July 2001 (Table 3).

14.7 Rank Correlation

Suppose 10 new paintings are shown to two art critics and each critic ranks the paintings from 1 (best) to 10 (worst). We want to determine whether the critics' ranks are related. Does a correspondence exist between their ratings? If a painting is ranked high by critic 1, is it likely to be ranked high by critic 2? Or do high rankings by one critic correspond to low rankings by the other? That is, are the rankings of the critics *correlated*?

If the rankings are as shown in the "Perfect Agreement" columns of Table 14.9, we immediately notice that the critics agree on the rank of every painting. High ranks correspond to high ranks and low ranks to low ranks. This is an example of a *perfect positive correlation* between the ranks. In contrast, if the rankings appear as shown in the "Perfect Disagreement" columns of Table 14.9, then high ranks for one critic correspond to low ranks for the other. This is an example of *perfect negative correlation*.

In practice, you will rarely see perfect positive or perfect negative correlation between the ranks. In fact, it is quite possible for the critics' ranks to appear as shown in Table 14.10. Note that these rankings indicate some agreement between the critics, but not perfect agreement, thus pointing up a need for a measure of rank correlation.

Spearman's rank correlation coefficient, r_s, provides a measure of correlation between ranks. The formula for this measure of correlation is given in the next box. We also give a formula that is identical to r_s when there are no ties in rankings; this formula provides a good approximation to r_s when the number of ties is small relative to the number of pairs.

Note that if the ranks for the two critics are identical, as in the second and third columns of Table 14.9, the differences between the ranks will all be 0. Thus,

$$r_s = 1 - \frac{6\sum d^2}{n(n^2 - 1)} = 1 - \frac{6(0)}{10(99)} = 1$$

TABLE 14.9 Rankings of 10 Paintings by Two Critics

Painting	Perfect Agreement		Perfect Disagreement	
	Critic 1	Critic 2	Critic 1	Critic 2
1	4	4	9	2
2	1	1	3	8
3	7	7	5	6
4	5	5	1	10
5	2	2	2	9
6	6	6	10	1
7	8	8	6	5
8	3	3	4	7
9	10	10	8	3
10	9	9	7	4

TABLE 14.10 Rankings of Paintings: Less-than-perfect Agreement

	Critic		Difference between Rank 1 and Rank 2	
Painting	1	2	d	d^2
1	4	5	-1	1
2	1	2	-1	1
3	9	10	-1	1
4	5	6	-1	1
5	2	1	1	1
6	10	9	1	1
7	7	7	0	0
8	3	3	0	0
9	6	4	2	4
10	8	8	0	0
				$\Sigma d^2 = 10$

That is, *perfect positive correlation* between the pairs of ranks is characterized by a Spearman correlation coefficient of $r_s = 1$. When the ranks indicate perfect disagreement, as in the fourth and fifth columns of Table 14.9, $\Sigma d_i^2 = 330$ and

$$r_s = 1 - \frac{6(330)}{10(99)} = -1.$$

Thus, *perfect negative correlation* is indicated by $r_s = -1$.

Biography

**CHARLES E. SPEARMAN (1863–1945)—
Spearman's Correlation**

London-born Charles Spearman was educated at Leamington College before joining the British Army. After 20 years as a highly decorated officer, Spearman retired from the army and moved to Germany to begin his study of experimental psychology at the University of Liepzig. At the age of 41, he earned his Ph.D. and ultimately became one of the most influential figures in the field of psychology. Spearman was the originator of the classical theory of mental tests and developed the "two-factor" theory of intelligence. These theories were used to develop and support the "Plus-Elevens" tests in England: exams administered to British 11-year-olds that predict whether they should attend a university or a technical school. Spearman was greatly influenced by the works of Francis Galton (p. 561); consequently, he developed a strong statistical background. While conducting his research on intelligence, he proposed the rank-order correlation coefficient—now called "Spearman's correlation coefficient." During his career, Spearman spent time at various universities, including University College (London), Columbia University, Catholic University, and the University of Cairo (Egypt).

Spearman's Rank Correlation Coefficient

$$r_s = \frac{SS_{uv}}{\sqrt{SS_{uu}SS_{vv}}}$$

where

$$SS_{uv} = \sum (u_i - \bar{u})(v_i - \bar{v}) = \sum u_i v_i - \frac{\left(\sum u_i\right)\left(\sum v_i\right)}{n}$$

$$SS_{uu} = \sum (u_i - \bar{u})^2 = \sum u_i^2 - \frac{\left(\sum u_i\right)^2}{n}$$

$$SS_{vv} = \sum (v_i - \bar{v})^2 = \sum v_i^2 - \frac{\left(\sum v_i\right)^2}{n}$$

(continued)

u_i = Rank of the ith observation in sample 1

v_i = Rank of the ith observation in sample 2

n = Number of pairs of observations (number of observations in each sample)

**Shortcut Formula for r_s*

$$r_s = 1 - \frac{6\sum d_i^2}{n(n^2 - 1)}$$

where

$d_i = u_i - v_i$ (difference in the ranks of the ith observations for samples 1 and 2)

For the data of Table 14.10,

$$r_s = 1 - \frac{6\sum d^2}{n(n^2 - 1)} = 1 - \frac{6(10)}{10(99)} = 1 - \frac{6}{99} = .94$$

The fact that r_s is *close* to 1 indicates that the critics tend to agree, but the agreement is not perfect.

The value of r_s always falls between -1 and $+1$, with $+1$ indicating perfect positive correlation and -1 indicating a perfect negative correlation. The closer r_s falls to $+1$ or -1, the greater the correlation between the ranks. Conversely, the nearer r_s is to 0, the less is the correlation.

Note that the concept of correlation implies that two responses are obtained for each experimental unit. In the art critics example, each painting received two ranks (one from each critic) and the objective of the study was to determine the degree of positive correlation between the two rankings. Rank correlation methods can be used to measure the correlation between any pair of variables. If two variables are measured on each of n experimental units, we rank the measurements associated with each variable separately. Ties receive the average of the ranks of the tied observations. Then we calculate the value of r_s for the two rankings. This value measures the rank correlation between the two variables. We illustrate the procedure in Example 14.4.

EXAMPLE 14.4

SPEARMAN'S RANK CORRELATION—

Smoking Versus Babies' Weights

Problem A study is conducted to investigate the relationship between cigarette smoking during pregnancy and the weights of newborn infants. The 15 women smokers who make up the sample kept accurate records of the number of cigarettes smoked during their pregnancies, and the weights of their children were recorded at birth. The data are given in Table 14.11.

a. Calculate and interpret Spearman's rank correlation coefficient for the data.

b. Use a nonparametric test to determine whether level of cigarette smoking and weights of newborns are negatively correlated for all smoking mothers. Use $\alpha = .05$.

Solution

a. We first rank the number of cigarettes smoked per day, assigning a 1 to the smallest number (12) and a 15 to the largest (46). Note that the two ties receive the averages of their respective ranks. Similarly, we assign ranks to the 15 babies' weights. Since the number of ties is relatively small, we will use the shortcut formula to calculate r_s. The differences d between the ranks of the babies' weights and the ranks of the number of

---

*The shortcut formula is not exact when there are tied measurements, but it is a good approximation when the total number of ties is not large relative to n.

NEWBORN

TABLE 14.11 Data and Calculations for Example 14.4

Woman	Cigarettes per Day	Rank	Baby's Weight (pounds)	Rank	d	d^2
1	12	1	7.7	5	−4	16
2	15	2	8.1	9	−7	49
3	35	13	6.9	4	9	81
4	21	7	8.2	10	−3	9
5	20	5.5	8.6	13.5	−8	64
6	17	3	8.3	11.5	−8.5	72.25
7	19	4	9.4	15	−11	121
8	46	15	7.8	6	9	81
9	20	5.5	8.3	11.5	−6	36
10	25	8.5	5.2	1	7.5	56.25
11	39	14	6.4	3	11	121
12	25	8.5	7.9	7	1.5	2.25
13	30	12	8.0	8	4	16
14	27	10	6.1	2	8	64
15	29	11	8.6	13.5	−2.5	6.25
					Total =	795

cigarettes smoked per day are shown in Table 14.11. The squares of the differences, d^2, are also given. Thus,

$$r_s = 1 - \frac{6\sum d_i^2}{n(n^2 - 1)} = 1 - \frac{6(795)}{15(15^2 - 1)} = 1 - 1.42 = -.42$$

The value of r_s can also be obtained by computer. A SAS printout of the analysis is shown in Figure 14.14. The value of r_s, highlighted on the printout, agrees (except for rounding) with our hand-calculated value, $-.42$.

```
            The CORR Procedure

   2  Variables:    CIGARETTES WEIGHT


Spearman Correlation Coefficients, N = 15
        Prob > |r| under H0: Rho=0

                    CIGARETTES        WEIGHT

CIGARETTES            1.00000        -0.42473
                                      0.1145

WEIGHT               -0.42473         1.00000
                      0.1145
```

FIGURE 14.14
SAS Spearman correlation printout for Example 14.4

The negative correlation coefficient indicates that in this sample an increase in the number of cigarettes smoked per day is *associated with* (but is not necessarily the *cause of*) a decrease in the weight of the newborn infant.

b. If we define ρ as the **population rank correlation coefficient** [i.e., the rank correlation coefficient that could be calculated from all (x, y) values in the population], we can determine whether level of cigarette smoking and weights of newborns are negatively correlated by conducting the following test:

H_0: $\rho = 0$ (no population correlation between ranks)

H_a: $\rho < 0$ (negative population correlation between ranks)

Test statistic: r_s (the *sample* Spearman rank correlation coefficient)

To determine a rejection region, we consult Table XIV in Appendix A, which is partially reproduced in Table 14.12. Note that the left-hand column gives values of n, the number of pairs of observations. The entries in the table are values for an upper-

TABLE 14.12 Reproduction of Part of Table XIV in Appendix A: Critical Values of Spearman's Rank Correlation Coefficient

n	$\alpha = .05$	$\alpha = .025$	$\alpha = .01$	$\alpha = .005$
5	.900	—	—	—
6	.829	.886	.943	—
7	.714	.786	.893	—
8	.643	.738	.833	.881
9	.600	.683	.783	.833
10	.564	.648	.745	.794
11	.523	.623	.736	.818
12	.497	.591	.703	.780
13	.475	.566	.673	.745
14	.457	.545	.646	.716
15	.441	.525	.623	.689
16	.425	.507	.601	.666
17	.412	.490	.582	.645
18	.399	.476	.564	.625
19	.388	.462	.549	.608
20	.377	.450	.534	.591

tail rejection region, since only positive values are given. Thus, for $n = 15$ and $\alpha = .05$, the value .441 is the boundary of the upper-tailed rejection region, so $P(r_s > .441) = .05$ if $H_0: \rho = 0$ is true. Similarly, for negative values of r_s, we have $P(r_s < -.441) = .05$ if $\rho = 0$. That is, we expect to see $r_s < -.441$ only 5% of the time if there is really no relationship between the ranks of the variables.

The lower-tailed rejection region is therefore

$$\text{Rejection region } (\alpha = .05): \quad r_s < -.441$$

Since the calculated $r_s = -.42$ is not less than $-.441$, we cannot reject H_0 at the $\alpha = .05$ level of significance. That is, this sample of 15 smoking mothers provides insufficient evidence to conclude that a negative correlation exists between the number of cigarettes smoked and the weight of newborns for the populations of measurements corresponding to all smoking mothers. This does not, of course, mean that no relationship exists. A study using a larger sample of smokers and taking other factors into account (father's weight, sex of newborn child, etc.) would be more likely to reveal whether smoking and the weight of a newborn child are related.

Look Back The two-tailed p-value of the test (.1145) is highlighted on the SAS printout, shown in Figure 14.14. Since the lower-tailed p-value, $.1145/2 = .05725$, exceeds $\alpha = .05$, our conclusion is the same: Do not reject H_0.

Now Work Exercise 14.81

A summary of Spearman's nonparametric test for correlation is given in the following box:

Spearman's Nonparametric Test for Rank Correlation

One-Tailed Test	**Two-Tailed Test**
$H_0: \rho = 0$	$H_0: \rho = 0$
$H_a: \rho > 0 \, [\text{or } H_a: \rho < 0]$	$H_a: \rho \neq 0$

Test statistics: r_s, the sample rank correlation (see the formulas for calculating r_s)

Rejection region: $r_s > r_{s,\alpha}$	*Rejection region:* $|r_s| > r_{s,\alpha/2}$
$[\text{or } r_s < -r_{s,\alpha} \text{ when } H_a: \rho < 0]$	
where $r_{s,\alpha}$ is the value from Table XIV corresponding to the upper-tail area α and n pairs of observations	where $r_{s,\alpha/2}$ is the value from Table XIV corresponding to the upper-tail area $\alpha/2$ and n pairs of observations

(continued)

Ties: Assign tied measurements the average of the ranks they would receive if they were unequal, but occurred in successive order. For example, if the third-ranked and fourth-ranked measurements are tied, assign each a rank of $(3 + 4)/2 = 3.5$. The number of ties should be small relative to the total number of observations.

Conditions Required for a Valid Spearman's Test

1. The sample of experimental units on which the two variables are measured is randomly selected.
2. The probability distributions of the two variables are continuous.

STATISTICS IN ACTION REVISITED

Testing the Correlation of MTBE Level with Other Environmental Factors

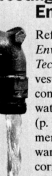

Refer again to the *Environmental Science & Technology* (Jan. 2005) investigation of the MTBE contamination of drinking water in New Hampshire (p. 14-3). The environmental researchers also wanted an estimate of the correlation between the MTBE level of a groundwater well and each of the other environmental variables listed in Table SIA14.1. Since the MTBE level is not normally distributed, they employed Spearman's rank correlation method. Also, because earlier analyses indicated that public and private wells have different MTBE distributions, the rank correlations were computed separately for each well class. SPSS printouts for this analysis are shown in Figures SIA14.5a–e. The values of r_s (and associated *p*-values) are highlighted on the printouts. Our interpretations follow:

MTBE vs. pH level (Figure SIA 15.4a). For private wells, $r_s = -.026$ (*p*-value $= .908$). Thus, there is a low negative association between MTBE level and

pH level for private wells—an association that is not significantly different from 0 (at $\alpha = .10$). For public wells, $r_s = .258$ (*p*-value $= .076$). Consequently, there is a low positive association (significant difference from 0 at $\alpha = .10$) for public wells between MTBE level and pH level.

MTBE vs. Dissolved oxygen (Figure SIA 15.4b). For private wells, $r_s = .086$ (*p*-value $= .702$). For public wells, $r_s = -.119$ (*p*-value $= .422$). Thus, there is a low positive association between MTBE level and dissolved oxygen for private wells, but a low negative association between MTBE level and dissolved oxygen for public wells. However, neither rank correlation is significantly different from 0 (at $\alpha = .10$).

MTBE vs. Industry percentage (Figure SIA 15.4c). For private wells, $r_s = -.123$ (*p*-value $= .586$). This low negative association between MTBE level and industry percentage for private wells is not significantly different from 0 (at $\alpha = .10$). For public wells, $r_s = .330$ (*p*-value $= .022$). Consequently, there is a low positive association (significantly different from 0 at $\alpha = .10$) for public wells between MTBE level and industry percentage.

FIGURE SIA14.5a

SPSS Spearman rank correlation test: MTBE and pH level

Correlations

CLASS					MTBE	PH
Private	Spearman's rho	MTBE	Correlation Coefficient		1.000	-.026
			Sig. (2-tailed)		.	.908
			N		22	22
		PH	Correlation Coefficient		-.026	1.000
			Sig. (2-tailed)		.908	.
			N		22	22
Public	Spearman's rho	MTBE	Correlation Coefficient		1.000	.258
			Sig. (2-tailed)		.	.076
			N		48	48
		PH	Correlation Coefficient		.258	1.000
			Sig. (2-tailed)		.076	.
			N		48	48

Correlations

CLASS					MTBE	DISSOXY
Private	Spearman's rho	MTBE	Correlation Coefficient		1.000	.086
			Sig. (2-tailed)		.	.702
			N		22	22
		DISSOXY	Correlation Coefficient		.086	1.000
			Sig. (2-tailed)		.702	.
			N		22	22
Public	Spearman's rho	MTBE	Correlation Coefficient		1.000	-.119
			Sig. (2-tailed)		.	.422
			N		48	48
		DISSOXY	Correlation Coefficient		-.119	1.000
			Sig. (2-tailed)		.422	.
			N		48	48

FIGURE SIA14.5b

SPSS Spearman rank correlation test: MTBE and dissolved oxygen

MTBE vs. Depth of well (Figure SIA 15.4d). For private wells, $r_s = -.410$ (p-value $= .103$). This low negative association between MTBE level and depth for private wells is not significantly different from 0 (at $\alpha = .10$). For public wells, $r_s = .444$ (p-value $= .002$). Consequently, there is a low positive association (significantly different from 0 at $\alpha = .10$) for public wells between MTBE level and depth.

MTBE vs. Distance from underground tank (Figure SIA 15.4e). For private wells,

$r_s = .136$ (p-value $= .547$). For public wells, $r_s = -.093$ (p-value $= .527$). Thus, there is a low positive association between MTBE level and distance for private wells, but a low negative association between MTBE level and distance for public wells. However, neither rank correlation is significantly different from 0 (at $\alpha = .10$).

In sum the only significant rank correlations were for public wells, where the researchers discovered low positive associations of MTBE level with pH level, industry percentage, and depth of the well.

Correlations

CLASS					MTBE	INDUSTRY
Private	Spearman's rho	MTBE	Correlation Coefficient		1.000	-.123
			Sig. (2-tailed)		.	.586
			N		22	22
		INDUSTRY	Correlation Coefficient		-.123	1.000
			Sig. (2-tailed)		.586	.
			N		22	22
Public	Spearman's rho	MTBE	Correlation Coefficient		1.000	.330*
			Sig. (2-tailed)		.	.022
			N		48	48
		INDUSTRY	Correlation Coefficient		.330*	1.000
			Sig. (2-tailed)		.022	.
			N		48	48

*. Correlation is significant at the 0.05 level (2-tailed).

FIGURE SIA14.5c

SPSS Spearman rank correlation test: MTBE and industry percentage

Correlations

CLASS					MTBE	DEPTH
Private	Spearman's rho	MTBE	Correlation Coefficient		1.000	-.410
			Sig. (2-tailed)		.	.103
			N		22	17
		DEPTH	Correlation Coefficient		-.410	1.000
			Sig. (2-tailed)		.103	.
			N		17	17
Public	Spearman's rho	MTBE	Correlation Coefficient		1.000	.444**
			Sig. (2-tailed)		.	.002
			N		48	46
		DEPTH	Correlation Coefficient		.444**	1.000
			Sig. (2-tailed)		.002	.
			N		46	46

**. Correlation is significant at the 0.01 level (2-tailed).

FIGURE SIA14.5d

SPSS Spearman rank correlation test: MTBE and depth

FIGURE SIA14.5e

SPSS Spearman rank correlation test: MTBE and distance

Correlations

CLASS					MTBE	DISTANCE
Private	Spearman's rho	MTBE	Correlation Coefficient		1.000	.136
			Sig. (2-tailed)		.	.547
			N		22	22
		DISTANCE	Correlation Coefficient		.136	1.000
			Sig. (2-tailed)		.547	.
			N		22	22
Public	Spearman's rho	MTBE	Correlation Coefficient		1.000	-.093
			Sig. (2-tailed)		.	.527
			N		48	48
		DISTANCE	Correlation Coefficient		-.093	1.000
			Sig. (2-tailed)		.527	.
			N		48	48

Exercises 14.76–14.92

Understanding the Principles

14.76 What is the value of r_s when there is perfect negative rank correlation between two variables? Perfect positive rank correlation?

14.77 What conditions are required for a valid Spearman's test?

Learning the Mechanics

14.78 Use Table XIV of Appendix A to find each of the following probabilities:
a. $P(r_s > .508)$ when $n = 22$
b. $P(r_s > .448)$ when $n = 28$
c. $P(r_s \le .648)$ when $n = 10$
d. $P(r_s < -.738$ or $r_s > .738)$ when $n = 8$

14.79 Specify the rejection region for Spearman's nonparametric test for rank correlation in each of the following situations:
a. $H_0: \rho = 0, H_a: \rho \neq 0, n = 10, \alpha = .05$
b. $H_0: \rho = 0, H_a: \rho > 0, n = 20, \alpha = .025$
c. $H_0: \rho = 0, H_a: \rho < 0, n = 30, \alpha = .01$

14.80 Compute Spearman's rank correlation coefficient for each of the following pairs of sample observations:

a.

x	33	61	20	19	40
y	26	36	65	25	35

b.

x	89	102	120	137	41
y	81	94	75	52	136

c.

x	2	15	4	10
y	11	2	15	21

d.

x	5	20	15	10	3
y	80	83	91	82	87

14.81 The following sample data were collected on variables x
NW and y:

LM14_81

x	0	3	0	-4	3	0	4
y	0	2	2	0	3	1	2

a. Specify the null and alternative hypotheses that should be used in conducting a hypothesis test to determine whether the variables x and y are correlated.
b. Conduct the test of part a, using $\alpha = .05$.
c. What is the approximate p-value of the test of part b?
d. What assumptions are necessary to ensure the validity of the test of part b?

Applying the Concepts—Basic

14.82 Mongolian desert ants. Refer to the *Journal of Biogeography* (Dec. 2003) study of ants in Mongolia, presented in Exercise 11.22 (p. 574). Data on annual rainfall, maximum daily temperature, and number of ant species recorded at each of 11 study sites are reproduced in the table below.
a. Consider the data for the five sites in the Dry Steppe region only. Rank the five annual rainfall amounts. Then rank the five maximum daily temperature values.
b. Use the ranks, from part a to find and interpret the rank correlation between annual rainfall (y) and maximum daily temperature (x).
c. Repeat parts a and b for the six sites in the Gobi Desert region.
d. Now consider the rank correlation between the number of ant species (y) and annual rainfall (x). Using all

GOBIANTS

Site	Region	Annual Rainfall (mm)	Max. Daily Temp. (°C)	Number of Ant Species
1	Dry Steppe	196	5.7	3
2	Dry Steppe	196	5.7	3
3	Dry Steppe	179	7.0	52
4	Dry Steppe	197	8.0	7
5	Dry Steppe	149	8.5	5
6	Gobi Desert	112	10.7	49
7	Gobi Desert	125	11.4	5
8	Gobi Desert	99	10.9	4
9	Gobi Desert	125	11.4	4
10	Gobi Desert	84	11.4	5
11	Gobi Desert	115	11.4	-4

Source: Pfeiffer, M., et al. "Community organization and species richness of ants in Mongolia along an ecological gradient from steppe to Gobi desert," *Journal of Biogeography*, Vol. 30, No. 12, Dec. 2003 (Tables 1 and 2).

the data, compute and interpret Spearman's rank correlation statistic.

14.83 Extending the life of an aluminum smelter pot. Refer to the *American Ceramic Society Bulletin* (Feb. 2005) study of the lifetime of an aluminum smelter pot, presented in Exercise 11.24 (pp. 575–576). Since the life of a smelter pot depends on the porosity of the brick lining, the researchers measured the apparent porosity and the mean pore diameter of each of six bricks. The data are reproduced in the following table:

SMELTPOT

Brick	Apparent Porosity (%)	Mean Pore Diameter (micrometers)
A	18.8	12.0
B	18.3	9.7
C	16.3	7.3
D	6.9	5.3
E	17.1	10.9
F	20.4	16.8

Source: Bonadia, P., et al. "Aluminosilicate refractories for aluminum cell linings," *American Ceramic Society Bulletin*, Vol. 84, No. 2, Feb. 2005 (Table II).

a. Rank the apparent porosity values for the six bricks. Then rank the six pore diameter values.
b. Use the ranks from part **a** to find the rank correlation between apparent porosity (y) and mean pore diameter (x). Interpret the result.
c. Conduct a test for positive rank correlation. Use $\alpha = .01$.

14.84 Organizational use of the Internet. Researchers from the United Kingdom and Germany attempted to develop a theoretically grounded measure of organizational Internet use (OIU) and published their results in *Internet Research* (Vol. 15, 2005). Using data collected from a sample of 77 websites, they investigated the link between OIU level (measured on a seven-point scale) and several observation-based indicators. Spearman's rank correlation coefficient (and associated p-values) for several indicators are shown in the following table:

Indicator	Correlation with OIU Level	
	r_s	p-value
Navigability	.179	.148
Transactions	.334	.023
Locatability	.590	.000
Information Richness	−.115	.252
Number of files	.114	.255

Source: Brock, J. K., and Zhou, Y. "Organizational use of the internet," *Internet Research*, Vol. 15, No. 1, 2005 (Table IV).

a. Interpret each of the values of r_s given in the table.
b. Interpret each of the p-values given in the table. (Use $\alpha = .10$ to conduct each test.)

14.85 Effect of massage on boxers. Refer to the *British Journal of Sports Medicine* (Apr. 2000) study of the effect of massaging boxers between rounds, presented in Exercise 11.60 (p. 589). Two variables measured on the boxers were blood lactate level (y) and the boxer's perceived recovery (x). The data for 16 five-round boxing performances are reproduced in the next table.

BOXING2

Blood Lactate Level	Perceived Recovery
3.8	7
4.2	7
4.8	11
4.1	12
5.0	12
5.3	12
4.2	13
2.4	17
3.7	17
5.3	17
5.8	18
6.0	18
5.9	21
6.3	21
5.5	20
6.5	24

Source: Hemmings, B., Smith, M., Graydon, J., and Dyson, R. "Effects of massage on physiological restoration, perceived recovery, and repeated sports performance," *British Journal of Sports Medicine*, Vol. 34, No. 2, Apr. 2000 (data adapted from Figure 3).

a. Rank the values of the 16 blood lactate levels.
b. Rank the values of the 16 perceived recovery values.
c. Use the ranks from parts **a** and **b** to compute Spearman's rank correlation coefficient. Give a practical interpretation of the result.
d. Find the rejection region for a test to determine whether y and x are rank correlated. Use $\alpha = .10$.
e. What is the conclusion of the test you conducted in part **d**? State your answer in the words of the problem.

14.86 Assessment of biometric recognition methods. Biometric technologies have been developed to detect or verify an individual's identity. These methods are based on physiological characteristics (called *biometric signatures*), such as facial features, the iris of the eye, fingerprints, the voice, the shape of the hand, and the gait. In *Chance* (Winter 2004), four biometric recognition algorithms were compared. All four were applied to 1,196 biometric signatures, and "match" scores were obtained. The Spearman correlation between match scores for each possible pair of algorithms was determined. The rank correlation matrix is as follows:

Method	I	II	III	IV
I	1	.189	.592	.340
II		1	.205	.324
III			1	.314
IV				1

a. Locate the largest rank correlation and interpret its value.
b. Locate the smallest rank correlation and interpret its value.

Applying the Concepts—Intermediate

14.87 Media coverage of the 9–11 attacks and public opinion. The terrorist attacks of September 11, 2001, and related events (e.g., the war in Iraq) have, and continue to receive, much media coverage. How has this coverage influenced the American public's concern about terrorism? This was the topic of research conducted by journalism professors at the University of Missouri (*International Journal of Public Opinion*, Winter 2004). Using random-digit dialing, they conducted a telephone survey of 235 Americans. Each person was asked to rate, on a scale of 1 to 5, his or her level of concern about each of eight topics: a long war, future terrorist attacks, the effect on the economy, the Israel–Palestine conflict, biological threats, air travel safety, war protests, and Afghan civilian deaths. The eight scores were summed to obtain a "public agenda" score. The respondents were also asked how many days per week they read the newspaper, watch the local television news, and watch national television news. The responses to these three questions were also summed to obtain a "media agenda" score. The researchers hypothesized that the public agenda score would be positively related to the media agenda score.

a. Spearman's rank correlation between the two scores was computed to be $r_s = .643$. Give a practical interpretation of this value.

b. The researchers removed the "length of war" question from the data and recomputed the "public agenda" score. Spearman's rank correlation between the public agenda and media agenda scores was then calculated as $r_s = .714$. Interpret this result.

c. Refer to part b. Conduct Spearman's test for positive rank correlation at $\alpha = .01$.

14.88 **The "name game"** Refer to the *Journal of Experimental Psychology—Applied* (June 2000) study in which the "name game" was used to help groups of students learn the names of other students in the group, presented in Exercise 11.30 (pp. 577–578). Recall that one goal of the study was to investigate the relationship between proportion y of names recalled by a student and position (order x), of the student during the game. The data for 144 students in the first eight positions are saved in the NAMEGAME2 file. (The first five and last five observations in the data set are listed in the next table.)

a. To properly apply the parametric test for correlation on the basis of the Pearson coefficient of correlation, r (Section 11.6), both the x and y variables must be normally distributed. Demonstrate that this assumption is violated for these data. What are the consequences of the violation?

SAS output for Exercise 14.88

The CORR Procedure

2 Variables: POSITION RECALL

Spearman Correlation Coefficients, N = 144
        Prob > |r| under H0: Rho=0

	POSITION	RECALL
POSITION	1.00000	0.20652 0.0130
RECALL	0.20652 0.0130	1.00000

NAMEGAME2 (selected observations)

Position	Recall
2	0.04
2	0.37
2	1.00
2	0.99
2	0.79
⋮	⋮
9	0.72
9	0.88
9	0.46
9	0.54
9	0.99

Source: Morris, P. E., and Fritz, C. O. "The name game: Using retrieval practice to improve the learning of names," *Journal of Experimental Psychology—Applied,* Vol. 6, No. 2, June 2000 (data simulated from Figure 2).

b. Find Spearman's rank correlation coefficient on the accompanying SAS printout and interpret its value.

c. Find the observed significance level for testing for zero rank correlation on the SAS printout, and interpret its value.

d. At $\alpha = .05$, is there sufficient evidence of rank correlation between proportion y of names recalled by a student and position (order x), of the student during the game?

FCAT

14.89 **FCAT scores and poverty.** Refer to the *Journal of Educational and Behavioral Statistics* (Spring 2004) analysis of the link between Florida Comprehensive Assessment Test (FCAT) scores and sociodemographic factors, presented in Exercise 11.26 (p. 576). Data on average math and reading FCAT scores of third graders, as well as the percentage of students below the poverty level, for a sample of 22 Florida elementary schools are saved in the **FCAT** file.

a. Compute and interpret Spearman's rank correlation between FCAT math score (y) and percentage (x) of students below the poverty level.

b. Compute and interpret Spearman's rank correlation between FCAT reading score (y) and percentage (x) of students below the poverty level.

c. Determine whether the value of r_s in part **a** would lead you to conclude that FCAT math score and percent below poverty level are negatively rank correlated in the population of all Florida elementary schools. Use $\alpha = .01$ to make your decision.

d. Determine whether the value of r_s in part **b** would lead you to conclude that FCAT reading score and percent below poverty level are negatively rank correlated in the population of all Florida elementary schools. Use $\alpha = .01$ to make your decision.

14.90 **Pain empathy and brain activity.** Refer to the *Science* (Feb. 20, 2004) study on the relationship between brain activity and pain-related empathy in persons who watch others in pain, presented in Exercise 11.62 (pp. 589–590). Recall that 16 female partners watched while painful stimulation was applied to the finger of their respective male partners. The two variables of interest were y = female's pain-related brain activity (measured on a scale ranging from -2 to 2) and x = female's score on the Empathic Concern Scale

(0 to 25 points). The data are reproduced in the accompanying table. Use Spearman's rank correlation test to answer the research question, "Do people scoring higher in empathy show higher pain-related brain activity?"

BRAINPAIN

Couple	Brain Activity (y)	Empathic Concern (x)
1	.05	12
2	−.03	13
3	.12	14
4	.20	16
5	.35	16
6	0	17
7	.26	17
8	.50	18
9	.20	18
10	.21	18
11	.45	19
12	.30	20
13	.20	21
14	.22	22
15	.76	23
16	.35	24

Source: Singer, T. et al. "Empathy for pain involves the affective but not sensory components of pain," *Science,* Vol. 303, Feb. 20, 2004. (Adapted from Figure 4.)

14.91 Study of child bipolar disorders. Psychiatric researchers at the University of Pittsburgh Medical Center have developed a new test for measuring manic symptoms in pediatric bipolar patients. (*Journal of Child and Adolescent Psychopharmacology*, Dec., 2003.) The new test is called the Kiddie Schedule for Affective Disorders and Schizophrenia-Mania Rating Scale (KSADS-MRS). The new test was compared with the standard test, the Clinical Global Impressions—

MANIA

Patient	Change in KSADS-MRS (%)	Improvement in CGI-BP
1	80	6
2	65	5
3	20	4
4	−15	4
5	−50	4
6	20	3
7	−30	3
8	−70	3
9	−10	2
10	−25	2
11	−35	2
12	−65	2
13	−65	2
14	−70	2
15	−80	2
16	−90	2
17	−95	2
18	−90	1

Source: Axelson, D. et al. "A preliminary study of the Kiddie Schedule for Affective Disorders and Schizophrenia for School-Age Children Mania Rating Scale for children and adolescents," *Journal of Child and Adolescent Psychopharmacology,* Vol. 13, No. 4, Dec. 2003 (adapted from Figure 2).

Bipolar Scale (CGI-BP). Both tests were administered to a sample of 18 pediatric patients before and after they were treated for manic symptoms. The changes in the test scores are recorded in the accompanying table.

a. The researchers used Spearman's statistic to measure the correlation between the changes in the two test scores. Compute the value of r_s.

b. Is there sufficient evidence (at $\alpha = .05$) of positive rank correlation between the two test score changes in the population of all pediatric patients with manic symptoms?

14.92 Public perceptions of health risks. Refer to the *Journal of Experimental Psychology: Learning, Memory, and Cognition* (July 2005) study of the ability of people to judge the risk of an infectious disease, presented in Exercise 12.65 (p. 670). Recall that the researchers asked German college students to estimate the number of people infected with a certain disease in a typical year. The median estimates, as well as the actual incidence for each in a sample of 24 infections, are reproduced in the accompanying table.

a. Use graphs to demonstrate that the variables actual incidence and estimated incidence are not normally distributed.

b. Recall that the researchers used regression to model the relationship between actual incidence and estimated incidence. How does the result you found in part **a** affect this analysis?

c. Find Spearman's correlation coefficient for the two variables. Interpret this value.

d. Refer to part **c.** At $\alpha = .01$, is there a positive association between actual incidence and estimated incidence?

INFECTION

Infection	Actual Incidence	Estimated Incidence
Polio	0.25	300
Diphtheria	1	1000
Trachoma	1.75	691
Rabbit Fever	2	200
Cholera	3	17.5
Leprosy	5	0.8
Tetanus	9	1000
Hemorrhagic Fever	10	150
Trichinosis	22	326.5
Undulant Fever	23	146.5
Well's Disease	39	370
Gas Gangrene	98	400
Parrot Fever	119	225
Typhoid	152	200
Q Fever	179	200
Malaria	936	400
Syphilis	1514	1500
Dysentery	1627	1000
Gonorrhea	2926	6000
Meningitis	4019	5000
Tuberculosis	12619	1500
Hepatitis	14889	1000
Gastroenteritis	203864	37000
Botulism	15	37500

Source: Hertwig, R., Pachur, T., & Kurzenhauser, S. "Judgments of risk frequencies: Tests of possible cognitive mechanisms," *Journal of Experimental Psychology: Learning, Memory, and Cognition,* Vol. 31, No. 4, July 2005 (Table 1).

KEY TERMS

GUIDE TO SELECTING A NONPARAMETRIC METHOD

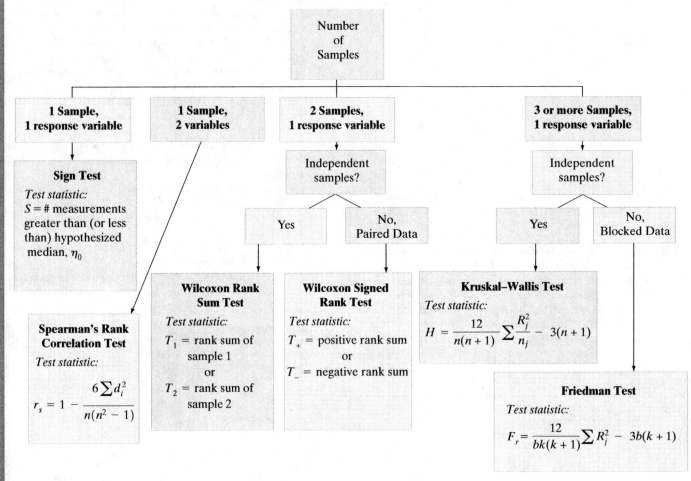

CHAPTER NOTES

Distribution-free Tests
Do not rely on assumptions about the probability distribution of the sampled population
One-sample nonparametric test for the population median **sign test**
Nonparametric test for *matched pairs:* **Wilcoxon signed rank test**
Nonparametric test for a *randomized block design:* **Friedman test**

Nonparametrics
Distribution-free tests that are based on **rank statistics**
Nonparametric test for *two independent samples:* **Wilcoxon rank sum test**
Nonparametric test for a *completely randomized design:* **Kruskal–Wallis test**
Nonparametric test for *rank correlation:* **Spearman's test**

Key Formulas

Sign test, large-sample test statistic:

$$z = \frac{(S - .5) - .5n}{.5\sqrt{n}}$$

Wilcoxon rank sum test, large-sample test statistic:

$$z = \frac{T_1 - \dfrac{n_1(n_1 + n_2 + 1)}{2}}{\dfrac{n_1 n_2(n_1 + n_2 + 1)}{12}}$$

Wilcoxon signed rank test, large-sample test statistic:

$$z = \frac{T_+ - \dfrac{n(n + 1)}{4}}{\dfrac{n(n + 1)(2n + 1)}{24}}$$

Key Symbols

η ... Population median
S ... Test statistic for sign test
T_1 ... Sum of ranks of observations in sample 1
T_2 ... Sum of ranks of observations in sample 2
T_L ... Critical lower Wilcoxon rank sum value
T_U ... Critical upper Wilcoxon rank sum value
T_+ ... Sum of ranks of positive differences of paired observations
T_- ... Sum of ranks of negative differences of paired observations
T_0 ... Critical value of Wilcoxon signed ranks test
R_j ... Rank sum of observations in sample j

H ... Test statistic for Kruskal–Wallis test
F_r ... Test statistic for Friedman test
r_s ... Spearman's rank correlation coefficient
p ... Population correlation coefficient

SUPPLEMENTARY EXERCISES 14.93–14.120

Understanding the Principles

14.93 When is it appropriate to use the t- and F-tests of Chapters 9 and 10 to compare two or more population means?

14.94 How does a nonparametric test differ from the parametric tests of Chapters 8–10?

14.95 For each of the following, give the appropriate nonparametric test to apply:
  a. Comparing two populations with independent samples
  b. Making an inference about a population median
  c. Comparing three or more populations with independent samples
  d. Making an inference about rank correlation
  e. Comparing two populations with matched pairs
  f. Comparing three or more populations with a block design

Learning the Mechanics

14.96 The data for three independent random samples are shown in the accompanying table. It is known that the sampled populations are not normally distributed. Use an appropriate test to determine whether the data provide sufficient evidence to indicate that at least two of the populations differ in location. Take $\alpha = .05$.

LM14_96

Sample 1		Sample 2		Sample 3	
18	15	12	34	87	50
32	63	33	18	53	64
43		10		65	77

14.97 A random sample of nine pairs of observations is recorded on two variables x and y. The data are shown in the following table:

LM14_97

Pair	x	y	Pair	x	y
1	19	12	6	29	10
2	27	19	7	16	16
3	15	7	8	22	10
4	35	25	9	16	18
5	13	11			

  a. Do the data provide sufficient evidence to indicate that ρ, the rank correlation between x and y, differs from 0? Test, using $\alpha = .05$.
  b. Do the data provide sufficient evidence to indicate that the probability distribution for x is shifted to the right of that for y? Test, using $\alpha = .05$.

14.98 Two independent random samples produced the measurements listed in the next table. Do the data provide sufficient evidence to conclude that there is a difference between the locations of the probability distributions for the sampled populations? Test, using $\alpha = .05$.

LM14_98

Sample 1		Sample 2	
1.2	1.0	1.5	1.9
1.9	1.8	1.3	2.7
.7	1.1	2.9	3.5
2.5			

14.99 An experiment was conducted using a randomized block design with five treatments and four blocks. The data are shown in the accompanying table. Do the data provide sufficient evidence to conclude that at least two of the treatment probability distributions differ in location? Test, using $\alpha = .05$.

LM14_99

Treatment	Block			
	1	2	3	4
1	75	77	70	80
2	65	69	63	69
3	74	78	69	80
4	80	80	75	86
5	69	72	63	77

Applying the Concepts—Basic

14.100 **Lunch at McDonald's.** According to the National Restaurant Association, hamburgers are the number-one selling fast-food item in the United States. An economist studying the fast-food buying habits of Americans paid graduate students to stand outside two suburban Boston McDonald's restaurants and ask departing customers whether they spent more than $2.25 on hamburger products for their lunch. Twenty answered yes, 50 said no, and 10 refused to answer the question. (*Newark Star-Ledger*, Mar. 17, 1997.)
  a. Apply the sign test to determine (at $\alpha = 05$); whether the median amount spent for hamburgers at lunch at McDonald's is less than $2.25.
  b. Does your conclusion apply to all Americans who eat lunch at McDonald's? Justify your answer. No
  c. What assumptions must hold to ensure the validity of your test in part **a**?

14.101 **Ordering exam questions.** An educational psychologist claims that the order in which test questions are asked affects a student's ability to answer correctly. To investigate this assertion, a professor randomly divides a class of 13 students into two groups: 7 in one group and 6 in the other. The professor prepares one set of test questions, but arranges the questions in two different orders. On test A, the questions are arranged in order of increasing difficulty (i.e., from easiest to most difficult); on test B, the order is reversed. One group of students is given test A, the other test B, and the test score is recorded for each student. The results are shown in the next table:

TESTORDER

Test A	90	71	83	82	75	91	65
Test B	66	78	50	68	80	60	

Use the Wilcoxon rank sum procedure to test for a difference (a shift in location) in the probability distributions of student scores on the two tests. Test using $\alpha = .05$.

14.102 Office rental growth rates. Real-estate market cycles are commonly divided into four phases that are based on the rate of change of the demand and supply of properties: Phase I, Recovery; Phase II, Expansion; Phase III, Hypersupply; and Phase IV, Recession. Glenn Mueller of Johns Hopkins University studied the office market cycles of U.S. real estate markets. (*Journal of Real Estate Research*, (Jul/Aug 1999.)) For each of the four market cycles, office rental growth rates (i.e., growth rates for asking rents) were measured for a sample of six different real-estate markets. The resulting data (in percentages) are presented in the accompanying table. A MINITAB printout of a Kruskal–Wallis analysis of the data is also provided (top, right).

MKTCYCLE

Phase I	Phase II	Phase III	Phase IV
2.7	10.5	6.1	−1.0
−1.0	11.5	1.2	6.2
1.1	9.4	11.4	−10.8
3.4	12.2	4.4	2.0
4.2	8.6	6.2	−1.1
3.5	10.9	7.6	−2.3

Source: Adapted from Mueller, G. R. "Real estate rental growth rates at different points in the physical market cycle." *Journal of Real Estate Research*, Vol. 18, No. 1 (Jul/Aug 1999), pp. 131–150.

a. Specify the null hypothesis of the Kruskal–Wallis test.
b. Find the mean rank for each market cycle phase on the printout. Multiply this value by the sample size, 6, to obtain the rank sum for each phase. Verify these rank sums by ranking the data.
c. Find the Kruskal–Wallis test statistic on the printout. Substitute the rank sums from part **a** into the appropriate formula to verify this value.
d. Give the rejection region for the test at $\alpha = .05$.

```
Kruskal-Wallis Test on GRWRATE

PHASE     N   Median   Ave Rank      Z
1         6    3.050       8.8   -1.50
2         6   10.700      20.8    3.33
3         6    6.150      14.8    0.90
4         6   -1.050       5.7   -2.73
Overall  24               12.5

H = 16.23   DF = 3   P = 0.001
H = 16.25   DF = 3   P = 0.001   (adjusted for ties)
```

e. Is there sufficient evidence to conclude that the distributions of office rental growth rates differ among the four market cycle phases?
f. Locate the *p*-value of the test on the printout and interpret this result.
g. What are the advantages and disadvantages of applying the Kruskal–Wallis *H*-test rather than the ANOVA *F*-test of Chapter 10?

14.103 Mosquito insecticide study. Refer to the *Journal of the American Mosquito Control Association* (Mar. 1995) study of the effectiveness of five different types of insecticides in controlling a species of Caribbean mosquito, presented in Exercise 10.118 (p. 552). The resistance ratios (i.e., the dosage of insecticide required to kill 50% of the larvae, divided by the known dosage for a susceptible mosquito strain) of the insecticides at each of seven Caribbean locations are reproduced in the table at the bottom of the page. Compare the resistance ratio distributions of the five insecticides using Friedman's nonparametric procedure. Are any of the insecticides more effective than any of the others?

14.104 Students' attitudes toward parents. Refer to the *Journal of Genetic Psychology* (March 1998) study of attitudes of male college students toward their parents, presented in Exercise 9.122 (p. 471). Recall that each of 13 students was asked to complete the following statement: My relationship with my father (mother) can best be described as (1) Awful, (2) Poor, (3) Average, (4) Good, or (5) Great. The study data are reproduced in the table on p. 14-56. The researchers want to compare male students' attitudes toward their fathers with their attitudes toward their mothers.

a. Why is a nonparametric test suitable for analyzing this data set?

MOSQUITO

		Insecticide				
		Temephos	Malathion	Fenitrothion	Fenthion	Chlorpyrifos
	Anguilla	4.6	1.2	1.5	1.8	1.5
	Antigua	9.2	2.9	2.0	7.0	2.0
	Dominica	7.8	1.4	2.4	4.2	4.1
Location	**Guyana**	1.7	1.9	2.2	1.5	1.8
	Jamaica	3.4	3.7	2.0	1.5	7.1
	St. Lucia	6.7	2.7	2.7	4.8	8.7
	Suriname	1.4	1.9	2.0	2.1	1.7

Source: Rawlins, S. C., and Oh Hing Wan, J. "Resistance in some Caribbean populations of *Aedes aegypti* to several insecticides," *Journal of the American Mosquito Control Association*, Vol. 11, No. 1, Mar. 1995 (Table 1).

FMATTITUDES

Student	Attitude toward Father	Attitude toward Mother
1	2	3
2	5	5
3	4	3
4	4	5
5	3	4
6	5	4
7	4	5
8	2	4
9	4	5
10	5	4
11	4	5
12	5	4
13	3	3

Source: Adapted from Vitulli, W. F., and Richardson, D. K. "College student's attitudes toward relationships with parents: A five-year comparative analysis." *Journal of Genetic Psychology*, Vol. 159, No. 1, (March 1998), pp. 45–52.

b. Specify H_0 and H_a for the test.
c. Compute and rank the differences between the students' attitudes toward their father and mother.
d. Sum the ranks of the positive and negative differences.

e. Find the rejection region for the test at $\alpha = .05$.
f. Give the conclusion of the test in the context of the problem. Compare your answer with the test results of Exercise 9.122b.

14.105 Feeding habits of fish. Refer to the *Brain and Behavior Evolution* (Apr. 2000) study of the feeding behavior of black-bream fish, presented in Exercise 2.142 (p. 92). Recall that the zoologists recorded the number of aggressive strikes of two blackbream feeding at the bottom of an aquarium in the 10-minute period following the addition of food. The following table lists the weekly number of strikes and age of the fish (in days):

BLACKBREAM

Week	Number of Strikes	Age of Fish (days)
1	85	120
2	63	136
3	34	150
4	39	155
5	58	162
6	35	169
7	57	178
8	12	184
9	15	190

Source: Shand, J., et al. "Variability in the location of the retinal ganglion cell area centralis is correlated with ontogenetic changes in feeding behavior in the Blackbream, *Acanthopagrus 'butcher'*." *Brain and Behavior*, Vol. 55, No. 4, Apr. 2000 (Figure H).

a. Find Spearman's correlation coefficient relating number of strikes (y) to age of fish (x).
b. Conduct a nonparametric test to determine whether number of strikes (y) and age (x) are negatively correlated. Test using $\alpha = .01$.

14.106 Assessing dementia. The Milan Overall Dementia Assessment (MODA) is a neuropsychologically oriented test that provides a measure of an individual's cognitive deterioration. MODA scores range from 0 to 100, with higher scores indicating a greater degree of deterioration. A team of psychologists and neurologists administered the MODA to a sample of 30 patients with Alzheimer's disease. (*Neuropsychologia*, June 1995.) In addition, all patients were given a "face-matching" test in which they were requested to match photographs of unknown faces. Scores on this test were recorded as the number of matching errors, with a maximum score of 27.
a. The researchers reported Spearman's rank correlation between the MODA and face-matching scores as $r_s = .48$. Interpret this result.
b. Test the hypothesis of a positive correlation between MODA score and face-matching score in Alzheimer's patients. Use $\alpha = .05$.

Applying the Concepts—Intermediate

14.107 Agent Orange and Vietnam Vets. Agent Orange, the code name for a herbicide developed for the U.S. Armed Forces in the 1960s, was found to be extremely contaminated with TCDD, or dioxin. During the Vietnam War, an estimated 19 million gallons of Agent Orange was used to destroy the dense plant and tree cover of the Asian jungle. As a result of this exposure, many Vietnam veterans have dangerously high levels of TCDD in their blood and adipose (fatty) tissue. A study published in *Chemosphere* (Vol. 20, 1990) reported on the TCDD levels of 20 Massachusetts Vietnam vets who were possibly exposed to Agent Orange. The TCDD amounts (measured in parts per trillion) in both plasma and fat tissue of the 20 vets are listed in the accompanying table. The data are saved in the **TCDD** file.

TCDD

Vet	Fat	Plasma
1	4.9	2.5
2	6.9	3.5
3	10.0	6.8
4	4.4	4.7
5	4.6	4.6
6	1.1	1.8
7	2.3	2.5
8	5.9	3.1
9	7.0	3.1
10	5.5	3.0
11	7.0	6.9
12	1.4	1.6
13	11.0	20.0
14	2.5	4.1
15	4.4	2.1
16	4.2	1.8
17	41.0	36.0
18	2.9	3.3
19	7.7	7.2
20	2.5	2.0

Source: Schecter, A., et al. "Partitioning of 2,3,7,8-chlorinated dibenzo-*p*-dioxins and dibenzofurans between adipose tissue and plasma lipid of 20 Massachusetts Vietnam veterans," *Chemosphere*, Vol. 20, Nos. 7–9, 1990, pp. 954–955 (Tables I and II).

a. Medical researchers consider a TCDD level of 3 parts per trillion (ppt) to be dangerously high. Do the data provide evidence (at $\alpha = .05$) to indicate that the median level of TCDD in the fat tissue of Vietnam vets exceeds 3 ppt?

b. Repeat part **a** for plasma.

c. Medical researchers also are interested in comparing the TCDD levels in fat tissue and plasma for Vietnam veterans. Specifically, they want to determine whether the distribution of TCDD levels in fat is shifted above or below the distribution of TCDD levels in plasma. Conduct this analysis (at $\alpha = .05$) and make the appropriate inference.

d. Find the rank correlation between the TCDD level in fat tissue and the TCDD level in plasma. Is there sufficient evidence (at $\alpha = .05$) of a positive association between the two TCDD measures?

14.108 Comparison of disposable razors. A major razor blade manufacturer advertises that its twin-blade disposable razor will "get you more shaves" than any single-blade disposable razor on the market. A rival blade company that has been very successful in selling single-blade razors wishes to test this claim. Marketing managers in this company randomly sampled eight single-blade shavers and eight twin-blade shavers, and counted the number of shaves that each got before a change of blades was indicated. The results are shown in the following table.

RAZORS

Twin Blades		Single Blade	
8	15	10	13
17	10	6	14
9	6	3	5
11	12	7	7

a. Do the data support the twin-blade manufacturer's claim? Use $\alpha = .05$.

b. Do you think that this experiment was designed in the best possible way? If not, what design might have been better?

c. What assumptions are necessary for the test performed in part **a** to be valid? Do the assumptions seem reasonable for this application?

14.109 Spending on information systems technology. University of Queensland researchers sampled private-sector and public-sector organizations in Australia to study the planning undertaken by their information systems departments. (*Management Science*, July 1996.) As part of the process, they asked each sample organization how much it had spent on information systems and technology in the previous fiscal year, as a percentage of the organization's total revenues. The results are reported in the next table:

a. Do the two sampled populations have identical probability distributions, or is the distribution for public-sector organizations in Australia located to the right of the distribution for Australia's private-sector firms? Test using $\alpha = .05$.

b. Is the p-value for the test less than or greater than .05? Justify your answer.

c. What assumption must be met to ensure the validity of the test you conducted in part **a**?

INFOSYS

Private Sector	Public Sector
2.58%	5.40%
5.05	2.55
.05	9.00
2.10	10.55
4.30	1.02
2.25	5.11
2.50	24.42
1.94	1.67
2.33	3.33

Adapted from Hann, J., and Weber, R. "Information systems planning: A model and empirical tests." *Management Science*, Vol. 42, No. 2 July 1996, pp. 1043–1064.

14.110 Hematology tests on workers. The accompanying table lists the lymphocyte count results from hematology tests administered to a sample of 50 West Indian or African workers. Test (at $\alpha = .05$) the hypothesis that the median lymphocyte count of all West Indian or African workers exceeds 20.

LYMPHO

14	28	11
15	17	25
19	14	30
23	8	32
17	25	17
20	37	22
21	20	20
16	15	20
27	9	20
34	16	26
26	18	40
28	17	22
24	23	61
26	43	12
23	17	20
9	23	35
18	31	

Source: Royston, J. P. "Some techniques for assessing multivariate normality based on the Shapiro-Wilk W." *Applied Statistics*, Vol. 32, No. 2, pp. 121–133.

14.111 Preventing metal corrosion. Corrosion of different metals is a problem in many mechanical devices. Three sealers used to help retard the corrosion of metals were tested to see whether there were any differences among them. Samples of 10 different metal compositions were treated with each of the three sealers, and the amount of corrosion was

CORRODE

Metal	Sealer		
	1	2	3
1	4.6	4.2	4.9
2	7.2	6.4	7.0
3	3.4	3.5	3.4
4	6.2	5.3	5.9
5	8.4	6.8	7.8
6	5.6	4.8	5.7
7	3.7	3.7	4.1
8	6.1	6.2	6.4
9	4.9	4.1	4.2
10	5.2	5.0	5.1

measured after exposure to the same environmental conditions for one month. The data are given in the table at the bottom of p. 14-57. Is there any evidence of a difference in the probability distributions of the amounts of corrosion among the three types of sealer? Use $\alpha = .05$.

14.112 Aggressiveness of twins. Twelve sets of identical twins are given psychological tests to determine whether the firstborn of the twins tends to be more aggressive than the second born. The test scores are shown in the accompanying table, where the higher score indicates greater aggressiveness. Do the data provide sufficient evidence (at $\alpha = .05$) to indicate that the firstborn of a pair of twins is more aggressive than the other? $T_- = 24.5$;

AGGTWINS

Set	Firstborn	Secondborn
1	86	88
2	71	77
3	77	76
4	68	64
5	91	96
6	72	72
7	77	65
8	91	90
9	70	65
10	71	80
11	88	81
12	87	72

14.113 Word association study. Three lists of words, representing three levels of abstractness, are randomly assigned to 21 experimental subjects so that 7 subjects receive each list. The subjects are asked to respond to each word on their list with as many associated words as possible within a given period. A subject's score is the total number of word associations, summing over all words in the list. Scores for each list are given in the accompanying table. Do the data provide sufficient evidence to indicate a difference (shift in location) between at least two of the probability distributions of the numbers of word associations that subjects can name for the three lists? Use $\alpha = .05$.

WORDLIST

List 1	List 2	List 3
48	41	18
43	36	42
39	29	28
57	40	38
21	35	15
47	45	33
58	32	31

14.114 Eye pupil size and deception. An experiment was designed to study whether eye pupil size is related to a person's attempt at deception. Eight students were asked to respond verbally to a series of questions. Before the questioning began, the size of one of each student's pupils was noted and the students were instructed to answer some of the questions dishonestly. (The number of questions answered dishonestly was left to individual

choice.) During questioning, the percentage increase in pupil size was recorded. Each student was then given a deception score based on the proportion of questions answered dishonestly. (High scores indicate a large number of deceptive responses.) The results are shown in the accompanying table. Can you conclude that the percentage increase in eye pupil size is positively correlated with deception score? Use $\alpha = .05$.

DECEPEYE

Student	Deception Score	Percentage Increase in Pupil Size
1	87	10
2	63	6
3	95	11
4	50	7
5	43	0
6	89	15
7	33	4
8	55	5

14.115 Exercise in MS patients. The metabolic and cardiopulmonary responses during maximal-effort exercise in persons with multiple sclerosis (MS) were studied. (*Clinical Kinesiology*, Spring 1995.) The following variables were measured for each of 10 MS patients:
1. Expanded Disability Status Scale (EDSS)—Ratings range from 1 to 4.5
2. Peak oxygen uptake (liters per minute) during an arm-cranking exercise (ARM)
3. Peak oxygen uptake (liters per minute) during a leg-cycling exercise (LEG)
4. Peak oxygen uptake (liters per minute) during a combined leg-cycling and arm-cranking exercise (LEG/ARM)

Spearman's rank correlation was calculated for each pair of variables. The following table gives the correlation r_s between the variables in the corresponding rows and columns:

	EDSS	ARM	LEG/ARM	LEG
EDSS	1.000	−.439	−.655	−.512
ARM		1.000	.634	.722
LEG/ARM			1.000	.890
LEG				1.000

Source: Ponichtera-Mulcare, J. A., et al. "Maximal aerobic exercise of individuals with multiple sclerosis using three modes of energy." *Clinical Kinesiology,* Vol. 49, No. 1, Spring 1995, p. 10 (Table 2).

a. Explain why the table shows rank correlations of 1.000 in the diagonal.
b. Give a practical interpretation of each of the other rank correlations in the table.
c. Is there sufficient evidence (at $\alpha = .01$) to conclude that EDSS and peak oxygen uptake are negatively correlated? Perform the test for each of the three exercises.

14.116 Fluoride in drinking water. Many water treatment facilities supplement the natural fluoride concentration with hydrofluosilicic acid in order to reach a target concentration of fluoride in drinking water. Certain levels are thought to enhance dental health, but very high concentrations can be dangerous. Suppose that one such treatment plant targets .75 milligram per liter (mg/L) for its water. The plant tests 25 samples each day to determine whether the median level differs from the target.

a. Set up the null and alternative hypotheses.

b. Set up the test statistic and rejection region, using $\alpha = .10$.

c. Explain the implication of a Type I error in the context of this application. A Type II error.

d. Suppose that one day's samples result in 18 values that exceed .75 mg/L. Conduct the test and state the appropriate conclusion in the context of this application.

e. When it was suggested to the plant's supervisor that a t-test should be used to conduct the daily test, she replied that the probability distribution of the fluoride concentrations was "heavily skewed to the right." Show graphically what she meant by this, and explain why this is a reason to prefer the sign test to the t-test.

14.117 Identifying mental disturbances. An experiment was conducted to determine whether a test designed to identify a certain form of mental disturbance could be easily interpreted by a person with little psychological training. Thirty judges were selected to review the results of 100 tests, half of which were given to disturbed patients and half to nondisturbed people. Of the 30 judges chosen, 10 were staff members of a mental hospital, 10 were trainees at the hospital, and 10 were undergraduate psychology majors. The results in the accompanying table give the number of the 100 tests correctly classified by each judge. Do the data provide sufficient evidence (at $\alpha = .05$) of a difference in the probability distributions of the number of correct identifications among the three types of judges?

MENTALID

Staff		Trainees		Undergraduates	
78	76	80	69	65	74
79	86	75	81	70	80
85	88	72	76	74	73
93	84	68	72	78	75
90	81	75	76	68	73

14.118 Ranking wines. Two expert wine tasters were asked to rank six brands of wine. Their rankings are shown in the following table:

WINETASTE

Brand	Expert 1	Expert 2
A	6	5
B	5	6
C	1	2
D	3	1
E	2	4
F	4	3

Do the data indicate a positive correlation in the rankings of the two experts? Test, using $\alpha = .10$.

14.119 Controlling for corn mold. A serious drought-related problem for farmers is the spread of aflatoxin, a highly toxic substance generated by mold, which contaminates field corn. Three sprays—A, B, and C—have been developed to control aflatoxin in field corn. To determine whether differences exist among the sprays, 10 ears of corn are randomly chosen from a contaminated cornfield, and each is divided into three pieces of equal size. The sprays are then randomly assigned to the pieces for each ear of corn, thus setting up a randomized block design. The accompanying table gives the amount (in parts per billion) of aflatoxin present in the corn samples after spraying. Determine whether there is evidence that the distributions of the levels of aflatoxin in corn differ for at least two of the three sprays. Test at $\alpha = .05$.

AFLATOX

	Spray		
Ear	A	B	C
1	21	23	15
2	29	30	21
3	16	19	18
4	20	19	18
5	13	10	14
6	5	12	6
7	18	18	12
8	26	32	21
9	17	20	9
10	4	10	2

Critical Thinking Challenge

14.120 Self-managed work teams and family life. Refer to the *Quality Management Journal* (Summer 1995) study of self-managed work teams (SMWTs), presented in Exercise 9.139 (p. 475). Recall that the researchers investigated the connection between SMWT work characteristics and workers' perceptions of positive spillover into family life. (One group of workers reported positive spillover of work skills to family life, while another group did not report positive work spillover.) The data collected on 114 AT&T employees, saved in the **SPILLOVER** file, are described in the accompanying table. In Exercise 9.139, you compared the two groups of workers on each characteristic, using the parametric methods of Chapter 9. Reanalyze the data, this time using nonparametrics. Are the job-related characteristics most highly associated with positive work spillover the same as those identified in Exercise 9.139? Comment on the validity of the parametric and nonparametric results.

SPILLOVER

Variables Measured in the SMWT Survey

Characteristic	Variable
Information Flow	Use of creative ideas (seven-point scale)
Information Flow	Utilization of information (seven-point scale)
Decision Making	Participation in decisions regarding personnel matters (seven-point scale)
Job	Good use of skills (seven-point scale)
Job	Task identity (seven-point scale)
Demographic	Age (years)
Demographic	Education (years)
Demographic	Gender (male or female)

SUMMARY ACTIVITY: Comparing Supermarket Prices (continued)

In Chapters 10 and 14, we discussed two methods of analyzing a randomized block design. When the populations have normal probability distributions and their variances are equal, we can employ the analysis of variance described in Chapter 10. Otherwise, we can use the Friedman F_r-test.

In the Summary Activity of Chapter 10, we asked you to conduct a randomized block design to compare supermarket prices and to use an analysis of variance to interpret the data. Now use the Friedman F_r-test to compare the supermarket prices.

How do the results of the two analyses compare? Explain the similarity (or lack of similarity) between the two results.

REFERENCES

Agresti, A., and Agresti, B. F. *Statistical Methods for the Social Sciences*, 2d ed. San Francisco: Dellen, 1986.

Conover, W. J. *Practical Nonparametric Statistics*, 2d ed. New York: Wiley, 1980.

Daniel, W. W. *Applied Nonparametric Statistics*, 2d ed. Boston: PWS-Kent, 1990.

Dunn, O. J. "Multiple comparisons using rank sums." *Technometrics*, Vol. 6, 1964.

Friedman, M. "The use of ranks to avoid the assumption of normality implicit in the analysis of variance." *Journal of the American Statistical Association*, Vol. 32, 1937.

Gibbons, J. D. *Nonparametric Statistical Inference*, 2d ed. New York: McGraw-Hill, 1985.

Hollander, M., and Wolfe, D. A. *Nonparametric Statistical Methods*. New York: Wiley, 1973.

Kruskal, W. H., and Wallis, W. A. "Use of ranks in one-criterion variance analysis." *Journal of the American Statistical Association*, Vol. 47, 1952.

Lehmann, E. L. *Nonparametrics: Statistical Methods Based on Ranks*. San Francisco: Holden-Day, 1975.

Marascuilo, L. A., and McSweeney, M. *Nonparametric and Distribution-Free Methods for the Social Sciences*. Monterey, CA: Brooks/Cole, 1977.

Wilcoxon, F., and Wilcox, R. A. "Some rapid approximate statistical procedures." The American Cyanamid Co., 1964.

Using Technology

Nonparametric Tests with MINITAB

Sign Test

The MINITAB worksheet file with the sample data should contain a single quantitative variable. Click on the "Stat" button on the MINITAB menu bar, and then click on "Nonparametrics" and "1-Sample Sign", as shown in Figure 14.M.1.

The dialog box shown in Figure 14.M.2 then appears. Enter the quantitative variable to be analyzed in the "Variables" box. Select the "Test median" option, and specify the hypothesized value of the median and the form of the alternative hypothesis ("not equal", "less than", or "greater than"). Click "OK" to generate the MINITAB printout.

Rank Sum Test

The MINITAB worksheet file with the sample data should contain two quantitative variables—one for each of the two samples

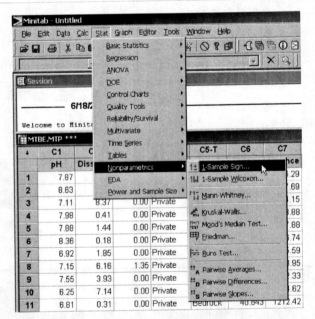

FIGURE 14.M.1

MINITAB nonparametric menu options

being compared. Click on the "Stat" button on the MINITAB menu bar, and then click on "Nonparametrics" and "Mann-Whitney". (See Figure 14.M.1.) The dialog box as shown in Figure 14.M.3 then appears.

Specify the variable for the first sample in the "First Sample" box and the variable for the second sample in the "Second Sample" box. Specify the form of the alternative hypothesis ("not equal", "less than", or "greater than"), and then click "OK" to generate the MINITAB printout.

Signed Rank Test

The MINITAB worksheet file with the matched-pairs data should contain two quantitative variables, one for each of the two groups being compared. You will need to compute the difference between these two variables and save it in a column on the worksheet. (Use the "Calc" button on the MINITAB menu bar.) Next, click on the "Stat" button on the MINITAB menu bar, then click on "Nonparametrics" and "1-Sample Wilcoxon". (See Figure 14.M.1.) The dialog box shown in Figure 14.M.4 then appears.

Enter the variable representing the paired differences in the "Variables" box. Select the "Test median" option and specify the hypothesized value of the median as "0". Select the form of the alternative hypothesis ("not equal", "less than", or "greater than"), and then click "OK" to generate the MINITAB printout.

Kruskal–Wallis Test

The MINITAB worksheet file that contains the completely randomized design data should contain one quantitative variable (the response, or dependent, variable) and one factor variable with at least two levels. Click on the "Stat" button on the MINITAB menu bar, and then click on "Nonparametrics" and "Kruskal–Wallis". (See Figure 14.M.1.) The dialog box shown in Figure 14.M.5 then appears. Specify the response variable in the "Response" box and the factor variable in the "Factor" box. Click "OK" to generate the MINITAB printout.

Friedman Test

The MINITAB spreadsheet file that contains the randomized block design data should contain one quantitative variable (the response, or dependent, variable), one factor variable, and one blocking variable. Click on the "Stat" button on the MINITAB menu bar, and then click on "Nonparametrics" and "Friedman". (See Figure 14.M.1.) The dialog box shown in

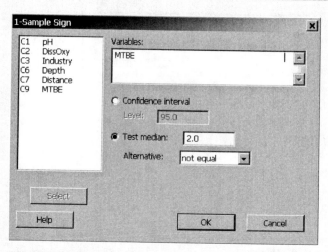

FIGURE 14.M.2
MINITAB 1-sample sign dialog box

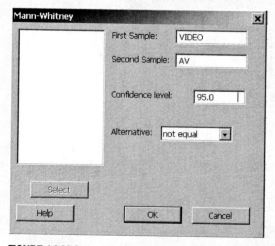

FIGURE 14.M.3
MINITAB Mann–Whitney (rank sum test) dialog box

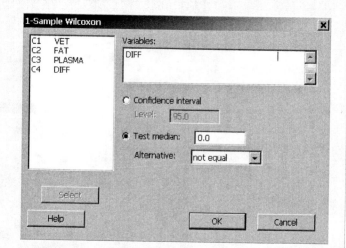

FIGURE 14.M.4
MINITAB 1-sample Wilcoxon dialog box

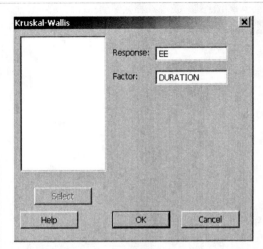

FIGURE 14.M.5
MINITAB Kruskal–Wallis dialog box

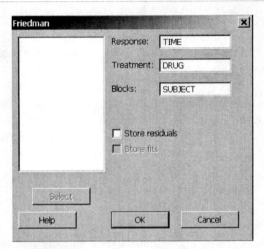

FIGURE 14.M.6
MINITAB Friedman dialog box

Figure 14.M.6 then appears. Specify the response, treatment, and blocking variables in the appropriate boxes, and then click "OK" to generate the MINITAB printout.

Rank Correlation

To obtain Spearman's rank correlation coefficient in MINITAB, you must first rank the values of the two quantitative variables of interest. Click the "Calc" button on the MINITAB menu bar, and create two additional columns; one for the ranks of the x-variable and one for the ranks of the y-variable. (Use the "Rank" function on the MINITAB calculator, as shown in Figure 14.M.7.) Next, click on the "Stat" button on the main menu bar, and then click on "Basic Statistics" and "Correlation." The dialog box shown in Figure 14.M.8 then appears. Enter the ranked variables in the "Variables" box and unselect the "Display p-values" option. Click "OK" to obtain the MINITAB printout. (You will need to look up the critical value of Spearman's rank correlation to conduct the test.)

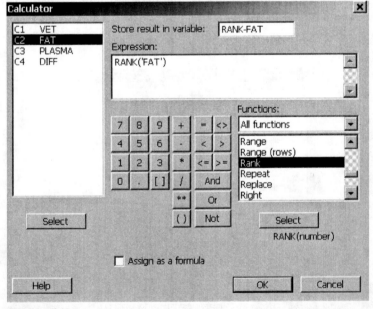

FIGURE 14.M.7
MINITAB calculator options for creating ranks

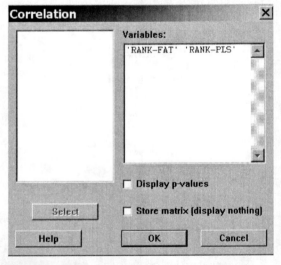

FIGURE 14.M.8
MINITAB correlation dialog box

Tables

TABLE I Random Numbers

Row \ Column	1	2	3	4	5	6	7	8	9	10	11	12	13	14
1	10480	15011	01536	02011	81647	91646	69179	14194	62590	36207	20969	99570	91291	90700
2	22368	46573	25595	85393	30995	89198	27982	53402	93965	34095	52666	19174	39615	99505
3	24130	48360	22527	97265	76393	64809	15179	24830	49340	32081	30680	19655	63348	58629
4	42167	93093	06243	61680	07856	16376	39440	53537	71341	57004	00849	74917	97758	16379
5	37570	39975	81837	16656	06121	91782	60468	81305	49684	60672	14110	06927	01263	54613
6	77921	06907	11008	42751	27756	53498	18602	70659	90655	15053	21916	81825	44394	42880
7	99562	72905	56420	69994	98872	31016	71194	18738	44013	48840	63213	21069	10634	12952
8	96301	91977	05463	07972	18876	20922	94595	56869	69014	60045	18425	84903	42508	32307
9	89579	14342	63661	10281	17453	18103	57740	84378	25331	12566	58678	44947	05585	56941
10	85475	36857	53342	53988	53060	59533	38867	62300	08158	17983	16439	11458	18593	64952
11	28918	69578	88231	33276	70997	79936	56865	05859	90106	31595	01547	85590	91610	78188
12	63553	40961	48235	03427	49626	69445	18663	72695	52180	20847	12234	90511	33703	90322
13	09429	93969	52636	92737	88974	33488	36320	17617	30015	08272	84115	27156	30613	74952
14	10365	61129	87529	85689	48237	52267	67689	93394	01511	26358	85104	20285	29975	89868
15	07119	97336	71048	08178	77233	13916	47564	81056	97735	85977	29372	74461	28551	90707
16	51085	12765	51821	51259	77452	16308	60756	92144	49442	53900	70960	63990	75601	40719
17	02368	21382	52404	60268	89368	19885	55322	44819	01188	65255	64835	44919	05944	55157
18	01011	54092	33362	94904	31273	04146	18594	29852	71585	85030	51132	01915	92747	64951
19	52162	53916	46369	58586	23216	14513	83149	98736	23495	64350	94738	17752	35156	35749
20	07056	97628	33787	09998	42698	06691	76988	13602	51851	46104	88916	19509	25625	58104
21	48663	91245	85828	14346	09172	30168	90229	04734	59193	22178	30421	61666	99904	32812
22	54164	58492	22421	74103	47070	25306	76468	26384	58151	06646	21524	15227	96909	44592
23	32639	32363	05597	24200	13363	38005	94342	28728	35806	06912	17012	64161	18296	22851
24	29334	27001	87637	87308	58731	00256	45834	15398	46557	41135	10367	07684	36188	18510
25	02488	33062	28834	07351	19731	92420	60952	61280	50001	67658	32586	86679	50720	94953
26	81525	72295	04839	96423	24878	82651	66566	14778	76797	14780	13300	87074	79666	95725
27	29676	20591	68086	26432	46901	20849	89768	81536	86645	12659	92259	57102	80428	25280
28	00742	57392	39064	66432	84673	40027	32832	61362	98947	96067	64760	64584	96096	98253
29	05366	04213	25669	26422	44407	44048	37937	63904	45766	66134	75470	66520	34693	90449
30	91921	26418	64117	94305	26766	25940	39972	22209	71500	64568	91402	42416	07844	69618
31	00582	04711	87917	77341	42206	35126	74087	99547	81817	42607	43808	76655	62028	76630
32	00725	69884	62797	56170	86324	88072	76222	36086	84637	93161	76038	65855	77919	88006
33	69011	65795	95876	55293	18988	27354	26575	08625	40801	59920	29841	80150	12777	48501
34	25976	57948	29888	88604	67917	48708	18912	82271	65424	69774	33611	54262	85963	03547
35	09763	83473	73577	12908	30883	18317	28290	35797	05998	41688	34952	37888	38917	88050

(continued)

TABLE I Continued

Row	1	2	3	4	5	6	7	8	9	10	11	12	13	14
36	91576	42595	27958	30134	04024	86385	29880	99730	55536	84855	29080	09250	79656	73211
37	17955	56349	90999	49127	20044	59931	06115	20542	18059	02008	73708	83517	36103	42791
38	46503	18584	18845	49618	02304	51038	20655	58727	28168	15475	56942	53389	20562	87338
39	92157	89634	94824	78171	84610	82834	09922	25417	44137	48413	25555	21246	35509	20468
40	14577	62765	35605	81263	39667	47358	56873	56307	61607	49518	89656	20103	77490	18062
41	98427	07523	33362	64270	01638	92477	66969	98420	04880	45585	46565	04102	46880	45709
42	34914	63976	88720	82765	34476	17032	87589	40836	32427	70002	70663	88863	77775	69348
43	70060	28277	39475	46473	23219	53416	94970	25832	69975	94884	19661	72828	00102	66794
44	53976	54914	06990	67245	68350	82948	11398	42878	80287	88267	47363	46634	06541	97809
45	76072	29515	40980	07391	58745	25774	22987	80059	39911	96189	41151	14222	60697	59583
46	90725	52210	83974	29992	65831	38857	50490	83765	55657	14361	31720	57375	56228	41546
47	64364	67412	33339	31926	14883	24413	59744	92351	97473	89286	35931	04110	23726	51900
48	08962	00358	31662	25388	61642	34072	81249	35648	56891	69352	48373	45578	78547	81788
49	95012	68379	93526	70765	10592	04542	76463	54328	02349	17247	28865	14777	62730	92277
50	15664	10493	20492	38391	91132	21999	59516	81652	27195	48223	46751	22923	32261	85653
51	16408	81899	04153	53381	79401	21438	83035	92350	36693	31238	59649	91754	72772	02338
52	18629	81953	05520	91962	04739	13092	97662	24822	94730	06496	35090	04822	86774	98289
53	73115	35101	47498	87637	99016	71060	88824	71013	18735	20286	23153	72924	35165	43040
54	57491	16703	23167	49323	45021	33132	12544	41035	80780	45393	44812	12512	98931	91202
55	30405	83946	23792	14422	15059	45799	22716	19792	09983	74353	68668	30429	70735	25499
56	16631	35006	85900	98275	32388	52390	16815	69290	82732	38480	73817	32523	41961	44437
57	96773	20206	42559	78985	05300	22164	24369	54224	35083	19687	11052	91491	60383	19746
58	38935	64202	14349	82674	66523	44133	00697	35552	35970	19124	63318	29686	03387	59846
59	31624	76384	17403	53363	44167	64486	64758	75366	76554	31601	12614	33072	60332	92325
60	78919	19474	23632	27889	47914	02584	37680	20801	72152	39339	34806	08930	85001	87820
61	03931	33309	57047	74211	63445	17361	62825	39908	05607	91284	68833	25570	38818	46920
62	74426	33278	43972	10110	89917	15665	52872	73823	73144	88662	88970	74492	51805	99378
63	09066	00903	20795	95452	92648	45454	09552	88815	16553	51125	79375	97596	16296	66092
64	42238	12426	87025	14267	20979	04508	64535	31355	86064	29472	47689	05974	52468	16834
65	16153	08002	26504	41744	81959	65642	74240	56302	00033	67107	77510	70625	28725	34191
66	21457	40742	29820	96783	29400	21840	15035	34537	33310	06116	95240	15957	16572	06004
67	21581	57802	02050	89728	17937	37621	47075	42080	97403	48626	68995	43805	33386	21597
68	55612	78095	83197	33732	05810	24813	86902	60397	16489	03264	88525	42786	05269	92532
69	44657	66999	99324	51281	84463	60563	79312	93454	68876	25471	93911	25650	12682	73572
70	91340	84979	46949	81973	37949	61023	43997	15263	80644	43942	89203	71795	99533	50501

(continued)

TABLE I   Continued

Column / Row	1	2	3	4	5	6	7	8	9	10	11	12	13	14
71	91227	21199	31935	27022	84067	05462	35216	14486	29891	68607	41867	14951	91696	85065
72	50001	38140	66321	19924	72163	09538	12151	06878	91903	18749	34405	56087	82790	70925
73	65390	05224	72958	28609	81406	39147	25549	48542	42627	45233	57202	94617	23772	07896
74	27504	96131	83944	41575	10573	08619	64482	73923	36152	05184	94142	25299	84387	34925
75	37169	94851	39117	89632	00959	16487	65536	49071	39782	17095	02330	74301	00275	48280
76	11508	70225	51111	38351	19444	66499	71945	05422	13442	78675	84081	66938	93654	59894
77	37449	30362	06694	54690	04052	53115	62757	95348	78662	11163	81651	50245	34971	52924
78	46515	70331	85922	38329	57015	15765	97161	17869	45349	61796	66345	81073	49106	79860
79	30986	81223	42416	58353	21532	30502	32305	86482	05174	07901	54339	58861	74818	46942
80	63798	64995	46583	09785	44160	78128	83991	42865	92520	83531	80377	35909	81250	54238
81	82486	84846	99254	67632	43218	50076	21361	64816	51202	88124	41870	52689	51275	83556
82	21885	32906	92431	09060	64297	51674	64126	62570	26123	05155	59194	52799	28225	85762
83	60336	98782	07408	53458	13564	59089	26445	29789	85205	41001	12535	12133	14645	23541
84	43937	46891	24010	25560	86355	33941	25786	54990	71899	15475	95434	98227	21824	19585
85	97656	63175	89303	16275	07100	92063	21942	18611	47348	20203	18534	03862	78095	50136
86	03299	01221	05418	38982	55758	92237	26759	86367	21216	98442	08303	56613	91511	75928
87	79626	06486	03574	17668	07785	76020	79924	25651	83325	88428	85076	72811	22717	50585
88	85636	68335	47539	03129	65651	11977	02510	26113	99447	68645	34327	15152	55230	93448
89	18039	14367	64337	06177	12143	46609	32989	74014	64708	00533	35398	58408	13261	47908
90	08362	15656	60627	36478	65648	16764	53412	09013	07832	41574	17639	82163	60859	75567
91	79556	29068	04142	16268	15387	12856	66227	38358	22478	73373	88732	09443	82558	05250
92	92608	82674	27072	32534	17075	27698	98204	63863	11951	34648	88022	56148	34925	57031
93	23982	25835	40055	67006	12293	02753	14827	23235	35071	99704	37543	11601	35503	85171
94	09915	96306	05908	97901	28395	14186	00821	80703	70426	75647	76310	88717	37890	40129
95	59037	33300	26695	62247	69927	76123	50842	43834	86654	70959	79725	93872	28117	19233
96	42488	78077	69882	61657	34136	79180	97526	43092	04098	73571	80799	76536	71255	64239
97	46764	86273	63003	93017	31204	36692	40202	35275	57306	55543	53203	18098	47625	88684
98	03237	45430	55417	63282	90816	17349	88298	90183	36600	78406	06216	95787	42579	90730
99	86591	81482	52667	61582	14972	90053	89534	76036	49199	43716	97548	04379	46370	28672
100	38534	01715	94964	87288	65680	43772	39560	12918	86537	62738	19636	51132	25739	56947

Source: Abridged from W. H. Beyer (ed.), CRC Standard Mathematical Tables, 24th edition. (Cleveland: The Chemical Rubber Company), 1976. Reproduced by permission of the publisher.

TABLE II   Binomial Probabilities

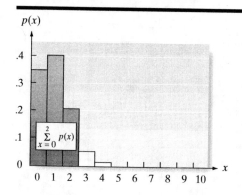

Tabulated values are $\sum_{x=0}^{k} p(x)$. *(Computations are rounded at the third decimal place.)*

a. $n = 5$

k \ p	.01	.05	.10	.20	.30	.40	.50	.60	.70	.80	.90	.95	.99
0	.951	.774	.590	.328	.168	.078	.031	.010	.002	.000	.000	.000	.000
1	.999	.977	.919	.737	.528	.337	.188	.087	.031	.007	.000	.000	.000
2	1.000	.999	.991	.942	.837	.683	.500	.317	.163	.058	.009	.001	.000
3	1.000	1.000	1.000	.993	.969	.913	.812	.663	.472	.263	.081	.023	.001
4	1.000	1.000	1.000	1.000	.998	.990	.969	.922	.832	.672	.410	.226	.049

b. $n = 6$

k \ p	.01	.05	.10	.20	.30	.40	.50	.60	.70	.80	.90	.95	.99
0	.941	.735	.531	.262	.118	.047	.016	.004	.001	.000	.000	.000	.000
1	.999	.967	.886	.655	.420	.233	.109	.041	.011	.002	.000	.000	.000
2	1.000	.998	.984	.901	.744	.544	.344	.179	.070	.017	.001	.000	.000
3	1.000	1.000	.999	.983	.930	.821	.656	.456	.256	.099	.016	.002	.000
4	1.000	1.000	1.000	.998	.989	.959	.891	.767	.580	.345	.114	.033	.001
5	1.000	1.000	1.000	1.000	.999	.996	.984	.953	.882	.738	.469	.265	.059

c. $n = 7$

k \ p	.01	.05	.10	.20	.30	.40	.50	.60	.70	.80	.90	.95	.99
0	.932	.698	.478	.210	.082	.028	.008	.002	.000	.000	.000	.000	.000
1	.998	.956	.850	.577	.329	.159	.063	.019	.004	.000	.000	.000	.000
2	1.000	.996	.974	.852	.647	.420	.227	.096	.029	.005	.000	.000	.000
3	1.000	1.000	.997	.967	.874	.710	.500	.290	.126	.033	.003	.000	.000
4	1.000	1.000	1.000	.995	.971	.904	.773	.580	.353	.148	.026	.004	.000
5	1.000	1.000	1.000	1.000	.996	.981	.937	.841	.671	.423	.150	.044	.002
6	1.000	1.000	1.000	1.000	1.000	.998	.992	.972	.918	.790	.522	.302	.068

(continued)

TABLE II   Continued

d. n = 8

k \ p	.01	.05	.10	.20	.30	.40	.50	.60	.70	.80	.90	.95	.99
0	.923	.663	.430	.168	.058	.017	.004	.001	.000	.000	.000	.000	.000
1	.997	.943	.813	.503	.255	.106	.035	.009	.001	.000	.000	.000	.000
2	1.000	.994	.962	.797	.552	.315	.145	.050	.011	.001	.000	.000	.000
3	1.000	1.000	.995	.944	.806	.594	.363	.174	.058	.010	.000	.000	.000
4	1.000	1.000	1.000	.990	.942	.826	.637	.406	.194	.056	.005	.000	.000
5	1.000	1.000	1.000	.999	.989	.950	.855	.685	.448	.203	.038	.006	.000
6	1.000	1.000	1.000	1.000	.999	.991	.965	.894	.745	.497	.187	.057	.003
7	1.000	1.000	1.000	1.000	1.000	.999	.996	.983	.942	.832	.570	.337	.077

e. n = 9

k \ p	.01	.05	.10	.20	.30	.40	.50	.60	.70	.80	.90	.95	.99
0	.914	.630	.387	.134	.040	.010	.002	.000	.000	.000	.000	.000	.000
1	.997	.929	.775	.436	.196	.071	.020	.004	.000	.000	.000	.000	.000
2	1.000	.992	.947	.738	.463	.232	.090	.025	.004	.000	.000	.000	.000
3	1.000	.999	.992	.914	.730	.483	.254	.099	.025	.003	.000	.000	.000
4	1.000	1.000	.999	.980	.901	.733	.500	.267	.099	.020	.001	.000	.000
5	1.000	1.000	1.000	.997	.975	.901	.746	.517	.270	.086	.008	.001	.000
6	1.000	1.000	1.000	1.000	.996	.975	.910	.768	.537	.262	.053	.008	.000
7	1.000	1.000	1.000	1.000	1.000	.996	.980	.929	.804	.564	.225	.071	.003
8	1.000	1.000	1.000	1.000	1.000	1.000	.998	.990	.960	.866	.613	.370	.086

f. n = 10

k \ p	.01	.05	.10	.20	.30	.40	.50	.60	.70	.80	.90	.95	.99
0	.904	.599	.349	.107	.028	.006	.001	.000	.000	.000	.000	.000	.000
1	.996	.914	.736	.376	.149	.046	.011	.002	.000	.000	.000	.000	.000
2	1.000	.988	.930	.678	.383	.167	.055	.012	.002	.000	.000	.000	.000
3	1.000	.999	.987	.879	.650	.382	.172	.055	.011	.001	.000	.000	.000
4	1.000	1.000	.998	.967	.850	.633	.377	.166	.047	.006	.000	.000	.000
5	1.000	1.000	1.000	.994	.953	.834	.623	.367	.150	.033	.002	.000	.000
6	1.000	1.000	1.000	.999	.989	.945	.828	.618	.350	.121	.013	.001	.000
7	1.000	1.000	1.000	1.000	.998	.988	.945	.833	.617	.322	.070	.012	.000
8	1.000	1.000	1.000	1.000	1.000	.998	.989	.954	.851	.624	.264	.086	.004
9	1.000	1.000	1.000	1.000	1.000	1.000	.999	.994	.972	.893	.651	.401	.096

(continued)

TABLE II Continued

g. *n* = 15

k \ p	.01	.05	.10	.20	.30	.40	.50	.60	.70	.80	.90	.95	.99
0	.860	.463	.206	.035	.005	.000	.000	.000	.000	.000	.000	.000	.000
1	.990	.829	.549	.167	.035	.005	.000	.000	.000	.000	.000	.000	.000
2	1.000	.964	.816	.398	.127	.027	.004	.000	.000	.000	.000	.000	.000
3	1.000	.995	.944	.648	.297	.091	.018	.002	.000	.000	.000	.000	.000
4	1.000	.999	.987	.838	.515	.217	.059	.009	.001	.000	.000	.000	.000
5	1.000	1.000	.998	.939	.722	.403	.151	.034	.004	.000	.000	.000	.000
6	1.000	1.000	1.000	.982	.869	.610	.304	.095	.015	.001	.000	.000	.000
7	1.000	1.000	1.000	.996	.950	.787	.500	.213	.050	.004	.000	.000	.000
8	1.000	1.000	1.000	.999	.985	.905	.696	.390	.131	.018	.000	.000	.000
9	1.000	1.000	1.000	1.000	.996	.966	.849	.597	.278	.061	.002	.000	.000
10	1.000	1.000	1.000	1.000	.999	.991	.941	.783	.485	.164	.013	.001	.000
11	1.000	1.000	1.000	1.000	1.000	.998	.982	.909	.703	.352	.056	.005	.000
12	1.000	1.000	1.000	1.000	1.000	1.000	.996	.973	.873	.602	.184	.036	.000
13	1.000	1.000	1.000	1.000	1.000	1.000	1.000	.995	.965	.833	.451	.171	.010
14	1.000	1.000	1.000	1.000	1.000	1.000	1.000	1.000	.995	.965	.794	.537	.140

h. *n* = 20

k \ p	.01	.05	.10	.20	.30	.40	.50	.60	.70	.80	.90	.95	.99
0	.818	.358	.122	.012	.001	.000	.000	.000	.000	.000	.000	.000	.000
1	.983	.736	.392	.069	.008	.001	.000	.000	.000	.000	.000	.000	.000
2	.999	.925	.677	.206	.035	.004	.000	.000	.000	.000	.000	.000	.000
3	1.000	.984	.867	.411	.107	.016	.001	.000	.000	.000	.000	.000	.000
4	1.000	.997	.957	.630	.238	.051	.006	.000	.000	.000	.000	.000	.000
5	1.000	1.000	.989	.804	.416	.126	.021	.002	.000	.000	.000	.000	.000
6	1.000	1.000	.998	.913	.608	.250	.058	.006	.000	.000	.000	.000	.000
7	1.000	1.000	1.000	.968	.772	.416	.132	.021	.001	.000	.000	.000	.000
8	1.000	1.000	1.000	.990	.887	.596	.252	.057	.005	.000	.000	.000	.000
9	1.000	1.000	1.000	.997	.952	.755	.412	.128	.017	.001	.000	.000	.000
10	1.000	1.000	1.000	.999	.983	.872	.588	.245	.048	.003	.000	.000	.000
11	1.000	1.000	1.000	1.000	.995	.943	.748	.404	.113	.010	.000	.000	.000
12	1.000	1.000	1.000	1.000	.999	.979	.868	.584	.228	.032	.000	.000	.000
13	1.000	1.000	1.000	1.000	1.000	.994	.942	.750	.392	.087	.002	.000	.000
14	1.000	1.000	1.000	1.000	1.000	.998	.979	.874	.584	.196	.011	.000	.000
15	1.000	1.000	1.000	1.000	1.000	1.000	.994	.949	.762	.370	.043	.003	.000
16	1.000	1.000	1.000	1.000	1.000	1.000	.999	.984	.893	.589	.133	.016	.000
17	1.000	1.000	1.000	1.000	1.000	1.000	1.000	.996	.965	.794	.323	.075	.001
18	1.000	1.000	1.000	1.000	1.000	1.000	1.000	.999	.992	.931	.608	.264	.017
19	1.000	1.000	1.000	1.000	1.000	1.000	1.000	1.000	.999	.988	.878	.642	.182

(continued)

TABLE II   Continued

i. $n = 25$

k \ p	.01	.05	.10	.20	.30	.40	.50	.60	.70	.80	.90	.95	.99
0	.778	.277	.072	.004	.000	.000	.000	.000	.000	.000	.000	.000	.000
1	.974	.642	.271	.027	.002	.000	.000	.000	.000	.000	.000	.000	.000
2	.998	.873	.537	.098	.009	.000	.000	.000	.000	.000	.000	.000	.000
3	1.000	.966	.764	.234	.033	.002	.000	.000	.000	.000	.000	.000	.000
4	1.000	.993	.902	.421	.090	.009	.000	.000	.000	.000	.000	.000	.000
5	1.000	.999	.967	.617	.193	.029	.002	.000	.000	.000	.000	.000	.000
6	1.000	1.000	.991	.780	.341	.074	.007	.000	.000	.000	.000	.000	.000
7	1.000	1.000	.998	.891	.512	.154	.022	.001	.000	.000	.000	.000	.000
8	1.000	1.000	1.000	.953	.677	.274	.054	.004	.000	.000	.000	.000	.000
9	1.000	1.000	1.000	.983	.811	.425	.115	.013	.000	.000	.000	.000	.000
10	1.000	1.000	1.000	.994	.902	.586	.212	.034	.002	.000	.000	.000	.000
11	1.000	1.000	1.000	.998	.956	.732	.345	.078	.006	.000	.000	.000	.000
12	1.000	1.000	1.000	1.000	.983	.846	.500	.154	.017	.000	.000	.000	.000
13	1.000	1.000	1.000	1.000	.994	.922	.655	.268	.044	.002	.000	.000	.000
14	1.000	1.000	1.000	1.000	.998	.966	.788	.414	.098	.006	.000	.000	.000
15	1.000	1.000	1.000	1.000	1.000	.987	.885	.575	.189	.017	.000	.000	.000
16	1.000	1.000	1.000	1.000	1.000	.996	.946	.726	.323	.047	.000	.000	.000
17	1.000	1.000	1.000	1.000	1.000	.999	.978	.846	.488	.109	.002	.000	.000
18	1.000	1.000	1.000	1.000	1.000	1.000	.993	.926	.659	.220	.009	.000	.000
19	1.000	1.000	1.000	1.000	1.000	1.000	.998	.971	.807	.383	.033	.001	.000
20	1.000	1.000	1.000	1.000	1.000	1.000	1.000	.991	.910	.579	.098	.007	.000
21	1.000	1.000	1.000	1.000	1.000	1.000	1.000	.998	.967	.766	.236	.034	.000
22	1.000	1.000	1.000	1.000	1.000	1.000	1.000	1.000	.991	.902	.463	.127	.002
23	1.000	1.000	1.000	1.000	1.000	1.000	1.000	1.000	.998	.973	.729	.358	.026
24	1.000	1.000	1.000	1.000	1.000	1.000	1.000	1.000	1.000	.996	.928	.723	.222

TABLE III   Poisson Probabilities

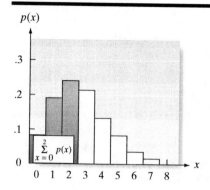

Tabulated values are $\sum_{x=0}^{k} p(x)$. *(Computations are rounded at the third decimal place.)*

λ \ k	0	1	2	3	4	5	6	7	8	9
.02	.980	1.000								
.04	.961	.999	1.000							
.06	.942	.998	1.000							
.08	.923	.997	1.000							
.10	.905	.995	1.000							
.15	.861	.990	.999	1.000						
.20	.819	.982	.999	1.000						
.25	.779	.974	.998	1.000						
.30	.741	.963	.996	1.000						
.35	.705	.951	.994	1.000						
.40	.670	.938	.992	.999	1.000					
.45	.638	.925	.989	.999	1.000					
.50	.607	.910	.986	.998	1.000					
.55	.577	.894	.982	.998	1.000					
.60	.549	.878	.977	.997	1.000					
.65	.522	.861	.972	.996	.999	1.000				
.70	.497	.844	.966	.994	.999	1.000				
.75	.472	.827	.959	.993	.999	1.000				
.80	.449	.809	.953	.991	.999	1.000				
.85	.427	.791	.945	.989	.998	1.000				
.90	.407	.772	.937	.987	.998	1.000				
.95	.387	.754	.929	.981	.997	1.000				
1.00	.368	.736	.920	.981	.996	.999	1.000			
1.1	.333	.699	.900	.974	.995	.999	1.000			
1.2	.301	.663	.879	.966	.992	.998	1.000			
1.3	.273	.627	.857	.957	.989	.998	1.000			
1.4	.247	.592	.833	.946	.986	.997	.999	1.000		
1.5	.223	.558	.809	.934	.981	.996	.999	1.000		

(continued)

TABLE III   Continued

λ \ k	0	1	2	3	4	5	6	7	8	9
1.6	.202	.525	.783	.921	.976	.994	.999	1.000		
1.7	.183	.493	.757	.907	.970	.992	.998	1.000		
1.8	.165	.463	.731	.891	.964	.990	.997	.999	1.000	
1.9	.150	.434	.704	.875	.956	.987	.997	.999	1.000	
2.0	.135	.406	.677	.857	.947	.983	.995	.999	1.000	
2.2	.111	.355	.623	.819	.928	.975	.993	.998	1.000	
2.4	.091	.308	.570	.779	.904	.964	.988	.997	.999	1.000
2.6	.074	.267	.518	.736	.877	.951	.983	.995	.999	1.000
2.8	.061	.231	.469	.692	.848	.935	.976	.992	.998	.999
3.0	.050	.199	.423	.647	.815	.916	.966	.988	.996	.999
3.2	.041	.171	.380	.603	.781	.895	.955	.983	.994	.998
3.4	.033	.147	.340	.558	.744	.871	.942	.977	.992	.997
3.6	.027	.126	.303	.515	.706	.844	.927	.969	.988	.996
3.8	.022	.107	.269	.473	.668	.816	.909	.960	.984	.994
4.0	.018	.092	.238	.433	.629	.785	.889	.949	.979	.992
4.2	.015	.078	.210	.395	.590	.753	.867	.936	.972	.989
4.4	.012	.066	.185	.359	.551	.720	.844	.921	.964	.985
4.6	.010	.056	.163	.326	.513	.686	.818	.905	.955	.980
4.8	.008	.048	.143	.294	.476	.651	.791	.887	.944	.975
5.0	.007	.040	.125	.265	.440	.616	.762	.867	.932	.968
5.2	.006	.034	.109	.238	.406	.581	.732	.845	.918	.960
5.4	.005	.029	.095	.213	.373	.546	.702	.822	.903	.951
5.6	.004	.024	.082	.191	.342	.512	.670	.797	.886	.941
5.8	.003	.021	.072	.170	.313	.478	.638	.771	.867	.929
6.0	.002	.017	.062	.151	.285	.446	.606	.744	.847	.916

λ \ k	10	11	12	13	14	15	16
2.8	1.000						
3.0	1.000						
3.2	1.000						
3.4	.999	1.000					
3.6	.999	1.000					
3.8	.998	.999	1.000				
4.0	.997	.999	1.000				
4.2	.996	.999	1.000				
4.4	.994	.998	.999	1.000			
4.6	.992	.997	.999	1.000			
4.8	.990	.996	.999	1.000			
5.0	.986	.995	.998	.999	1.000		
5.2	.982	.993	.997	.999	1.000		
5.4	.977	.990	.996	.999	1.000		
5.6	.972	.988	.995	.998	.999	1.000	
5.8	.965	.984	.993	.997	.999	1.000	
6.0	.957	.980	.991	.996	.999	.999	1.000

(continued)

TABLE III   Continued

λ \ k	0	1	2	3	4	5	6	7	8	9
6.2	.002	.015	.054	.134	.259	.414	.574	.716	.826	.902
6.4	.002	.012	.046	.119	.235	.384	.542	.687	.803	.886
6.6	.001	.010	.040	.105	.213	.355	.511	.658	.780	.869
6.8	.001	.009	.034	.093	.192	.327	.480	.628	.755	.850
7.0	.001	.007	.030	.082	.173	.301	.450	.599	.729	.830
7.2	.001	.006	.025	.072	.156	.276	.420	.569	.703	.810
7.4	.001	.005	.022	.063	.140	.253	.392	.539	.676	.788
7.6	.001	.004	.019	.055	.125	.231	.365	.510	.648	.765
7.8	.000	.004	.016	.048	.112	.210	.338	.481	.620	.741
8.0	.000	.003	.014	.042	.100	.191	.313	.453	.593	.717
8.5	.000	.002	.009	.030	.074	.150	.256	.386	.523	.653
9.0	.000	.001	.006	.021	.055	.116	.207	.324	.456	.587
9.5	.000	.001	.004	.015	.040	.089	.165	.269	.392	.522
10.0	.000	.000	.003	.010	.029	.067	.130	.220	.333	.458

λ	10	11	12	13	14	15	16	17	18	19
6.2	.949	.975	.989	.995	.998	.999	1.000			
6.4	.939	.969	.986	.994	.997	.999	1.000			
6.6	.927	.963	.982	.992	.997	.999	.999	1.000		
6.8	.915	.955	.978	.990	.996	.998	.999	1.000		
7.0	.901	.947	.973	.987	.994	.998	.999	1.000		
7.2	.887	.937	.967	.984	.993	.997	.999	.999	1.000	
7.4	.871	.926	.961	.980	.991	.996	.998	.999	1.000	
7.6	.854	.915	.954	.976	.989	.995	.998	.999	1.000	
7.8	.835	.902	.945	.971	.986	.993	.997	.999	1.000	
8.0	.816	.888	.936	.966	.983	.992	.996	.998	.999	1.000
8.5	.763	.849	.909	.949	.973	.986	.993	.997	.999	.999
9.0	.706	.803	.876	.926	.959	.978	.989	.995	.998	.999
9.5	.645	.752	.836	.898	.940	.967	.982	.991	.996	.998
10.0	.583	.697	.792	.864	.917	.951	.973	.986	.993	.997

λ	20	21	22
8.5	1.000		
9.0	1.000		
9.5	.999	1.000	
10.0	.998	.999	1.000

(continued)

TABLE III   Continued

λ \ k	0	1	2	3	4	5	6	7	8	9
10.5	.000	.000	.002	.007	.021	.050	.102	.179	.279	.397
11.0	.000	.000	.001	.005	.015	.038	.079	.143	.232	.341
11.5	.000	.000	.001	.003	.011	.028	.060	.114	.191	.289
12.0	.000	.000	.001	.002	.008	.020	.046	.090	.155	.242
12.5	.000	.000	.000	.002	.005	.015	.035	.070	.125	.201
13.0	.000	.000	.000	.001	.004	.011	.026	.054	.100	.166
13.5	.000	.000	.000	.001	.003	.008	.019	.041	.079	.135
14.0	.000	.000	.000	.000	.002	.006	.014	.032	.062	.109
14.5	.000	.000	.000	.000	.001	.004	.010	.024	.048	.088
15.0	.000	.000	.000	.000	.001	.003	.008	.018	.037	.070

λ \ k	10	11	12	13	14	15	16	17	18	19
10.5	.521	.639	.742	.825	.888	.932	.960	.978	.988	.994
11.0	.460	.579	.689	.781	.854	.907	.944	.968	.982	.991
11.5	.402	.520	.633	.733	.815	.878	.924	.954	.974	.986
12.0	.347	.462	.576	.682	.772	.844	.899	.937	.963	.979
12.5	.297	.406	.519	.628	.725	.806	.869	.916	.948	.969
13.0	.252	.353	.463	.573	.675	.764	.835	.890	.930	.957
13.5	.211	.304	.409	.518	.623	.718	.798	.861	.908	.942
14.0	.176	.260	.358	.464	.570	.669	.756	.827	.883	.923
14.5	.145	.220	.311	.413	.518	.619	.711	.790	.853	.901
15.0	.118	.185	.268	.363	.466	.568	.664	.749	.819	.875

λ \ k	20	21	22	23	24	25	26	27	28	29
10.5	.997	.999	.999	1.000						
11.0	.995	.998	.999	1.000						
11.5	.992	.996	.998	.999	1.000					
12.0	.988	.994	.987	.999	.999	1.000				
12.5	.983	.991	.995	.998	.999	.999	1.000			
13.0	.975	.986	.992	.996	.998	.999	1.000			
13.5	.965	.980	.989	.994	.997	.998	.999	1.000		
14.0	.952	.971	.983	.991	.995	.997	.999	.999	1.000	
14.5	.936	.960	.976	.986	.992	.996	.998	.999	.999	1.000
15.0	.917	.947	.967	.981	.989	.994	.997	.998	.999	1.000

(continued)

TABLE III Continued

λ \ k	4	5	6	7	8	9	10	11	12	13
16	.000	.001	.004	.010	.022	.043	.077	.127	.193	.275
17	.000	.001	.002	.005	.013	.026	.049	.085	.135	.201
18	.000	.000	.001	.003	.007	.015	.030	.055	.092	.143
19	.000	.000	.001	.002	.004	.009	.018	.035	.061	.098
20	.000	.000	.000	.001	.002	.005	.011	.021	.039	.066
21	.000	.000	.000	.000	.001	.003	.006	.013	.025	.043
22	.000	.000	.000	.000	.001	.002	.004	.008	.015	.028
23	.000	.000	.000	.000	.000	.001	.002	.004	.009	.017
24	.000	.000	.000	.000	.000	.000	.001	.003	.005	.011
25	.000	.000	.000	.000	.000	.000	.001	.001	.003	.006

λ \ k	14	15	16	17	18	19	20	21	22	23
16	.368	.467	.566	.659	.742	.812	.868	.911	.942	.963
17	.281	.371	.468	.564	.655	.736	.805	.861	.905	.937
18	.208	.287	.375	.469	.562	.651	.731	.799	.855	.899
19	.150	.215	.292	.378	.469	.561	.647	.725	.793	.849
20	.105	.157	.221	.297	.381	.470	.559	.644	.721	.787
21	.072	.111	.163	.227	.302	.384	.471	.558	.640	.716
22	.048	.077	.117	.169	.232	.306	.387	.472	.556	.637
23	.031	.052	.082	.123	.175	.238	.310	.389	.472	.555
24	.020	.034	.056	.087	.128	.180	.243	.314	.392	.473
25	.012	.022	.038	.060	.092	.134	.185	.247	.318	.394

λ \ k	24	25	26	27	28	29	30	31	32	33
16	.978	.987	.993	.996	.998	.999	.999	1.000		
17	.959	.975	.985	.991	.995	.997	.999	.999	1.000	
18	.932	.955	.972	.983	.990	.994	.997	.998	.999	1.000
19	.893	.927	.951	.969	.980	.988	.993	.996	.998	.999
20	.843	.888	.922	.948	.966	.978	.987	.992	.995	.997
21	.782	.838	.883	.917	.944	.963	.976	.985	.991	.994
22	.712	.777	.832	.877	.913	.940	.959	.973	.983	.989
23	.635	.708	.772	.827	.873	.908	.936	.956	.971	.981
24	.554	.632	.704	.768	.823	.868	.904	.932	.953	.969
25	.473	.553	.629	.700	.763	.818	.863	.900	.929	.950

λ \ k	34	35	36	37	38	39	40	41	42	43
19	.999	1.000								
20	.999	.999	1.000							
21	.997	.998	.999	.999	1.000					
22	.994	.996	.998	.999	.999	1.000				
23	.988	.993	.996	.997	.999	.999	1.000			
24	.979	.987	.992	.995	.997	.998	.999	.999	1.000	
25	.966	.978	.985	.991	.991	.997	.998	.999	.999	1.000

TABLE IV   Normal Curve Areas

z	.00	.01	.02	.03	.04	.05	.06	.07	.08	.09
.0	.0000	.0040	.0080	.0120	.0160	.0199	.0239	.0279	.0319	.0359
.1	.0398	.0438	.0478	.0517	.0557	.0596	.0636	.0675	.0714	.0753
.2	.0793	.0832	.0871	.0910	.0948	.0987	.1026	.1064	.1103	.1141
.3	.1179	.1217	.1255	.1293	.1331	.1368	.1406	.1443	.1480	.1517
.4	.1554	.1591	.1628	.1664	.1700	.1736	.1772	.1808	.1844	.1879
.5	.1915	.1950	.1985	.2019	.2054	.2088	.2123	.2157	.2190	.2224
.6	.2257	.2291	.2324	.2357	.2389	.2422	.2454	.2486	.2517	.2549
.7	.2580	.2611	.2642	.2673	.2704	.2734	.2764	.2794	.2823	.2852
.8	.2881	.2910	.2939	.2967	.2995	.3023	.3051	.3078	.3106	.3133
.9	.3159	.3186	.3212	.3238	.3264	.3289	.3315	.3340	.3365	.3389
1.0	.3413	.3438	.3461	.3485	.3508	.3531	.3554	.3577	.3599	.3621
1.1	.3643	.3665	.3686	.3708	.3729	.3749	.3770	.3790	.3810	.3830
1.2	.3849	.3869	.3888	.3907	.3925	.3944	.3962	.3980	.3997	.4015
1.3	.4032	.4049	.4066	.4082	.4099	.4115	.4131	.4147	.4162	.4177
1.4	.4192	.4207	.4222	.4236	.4251	.4265	.4279	.4292	.4306	.4319
1.5	.4332	.4345	.4357	.4370	.4382	.4394	.4406	.4418	.4429	.4441
1.6	.4452	.4463	.4474	.4484	.4495	.4505	.4515	.4525	.4535	.4545
1.7	.4554	.4564	.4573	.4582	.4591	.4599	.4608	.4616	.4625	.4633
1.8	.4641	.4649	.4656	.4664	.4671	.4678	.4686	.4693	.4699	.4706
1.9	.4713	.4719	.4726	.4732	.4738	.4744	.4750	.4756	.4761	.4767
2.0	.4772	.4778	.4783	.4788	.4793	.4798	.4803	.4808	.4812	.4817
2.1	.4821	.4826	.4830	.4834	.4838	.4842	.4846	.4850	.4854	.4857
2.2	.4861	.4864	.4868	.4871	.4875	.4878	.4881	.4884	.4887	.4890
2.3	.4893	.4896	.4898	.4901	.4904	.4906	.4909	.4911	.4913	.4916
2.4	.4918	.4920	.4922	.4925	.4927	.4929	.4931	.4932	.4934	.4936
2.5	.4938	.4940	.4941	.4943	.4945	.4946	.4948	.4949	.4951	.4952
2.6	.4953	.4955	.4956	.4957	.4959	.4960	.4961	.4962	.4963	.4964
2.7	.4965	.4966	.4967	.4968	.4969	.4970	.4971	.4972	.4973	.4974
2.8	.4974	.4975	.4976	.4977	.4977	.4978	.4979	.4979	.4980	.4981
2.9	.4981	.4982	.4982	.4983	.4984	.4984	.4985	.4985	.4986	.4986
3.0	.4987	.4987	.4987	.4988	.4988	.4989	.4989	.4989	.4990	.4990

Source: Abridged from Table I of A. Hald, *Statistical Tables and Formulas* (New York: Wiley), 1952. Reproduced by permission of A. Hald.

TABLE V Exponentials

λ	$e^{-\lambda}$	λ	$e^{-\lambda}$	λ	$e^{-\lambda}$	λ	$e^{-\lambda}$	λ	$e^{-\lambda}$
.00	1.000000	2.05	.128735	4.05	.017422	6.05	.002358	8.05	.000319
.05	.951229	2.10	.122456	4.10	.016573	6.10	.002243	8.10	.000304
.10	.904837	2.15	.116484	4.15	.015764	6.15	.002133	8.15	.000289
.15	.860708	2.20	.110803	4.20	.014996	6.20	.002029	8.20	.000275
.20	.818731	2.25	.105399	4.25	.014264	6.25	.001930	8.25	.000261
.25	.778801	2.30	.100259	4.30	.013569	6.30	.001836	8.30	.000249
.30	.740818	2.35	.095369	4.35	.012907	6.35	.001747	8.35	.000236
.35	.704688	2.40	.090718	4.40	.012277	6.40	.001661	8.40	.000225
.40	.670320	2.45	.086294	4.45	.011679	6.45	.001581	8.45	.000214
.45	.637628	2.50	.082085	4.50	.011109	6.50	.001503	8.50	.000204
.50	.606531	2.55	.078082	4.55	.010567	6.55	.001430	8.55	.000194
.55	.576950	2.60	.074274	4.60	.010052	6.60	.001360	8.60	.000184
.60	.548812	2.65	.070651	4.65	.009562	6.65	.001294	8.65	.000175
.65	.522046	2.70	.067206	4.70	.009095	6.70	.001231	8.70	.000167
.70	.496585	2.75	.063928	4.75	.008652	6.75	.001171	8.75	.000158
.75	.472367	2.80	.060810	4.80	.008230	6.80	.001114	8.80	.000151
.80	.449329	2.85	.057844	4.85	.007828	6.85	.001059	8.85	.000143
.85	.427415	2.90	.055023	4.90	.007447	6.90	.001008	8.90	.000136
.90	.406570	2.95	.052340	4.95	.007083	6.95	.000959	8.95	.000130
.95	.386741	3.00	.049787	5.00	.006738	7.00	.000912	9.00	.000123
1.00	.367879	3.05	.047359	5.05	.006409	7.05	.000867	9.05	.000117
1.05	.349938	3.10	.045049	5.10	.006097	7.10	.000825	9.10	.000112
1.10	.332871	3.15	.042852	5.15	.005799	7.15	.000785	9.15	.000106
1.15	.316637	3.20	.040762	5.20	.005517	7.20	.000747	9.20	.000101
1.20	.301194	3.25	.038774	5.25	.005248	7.25	.000710	9.25	.000096
1.25	.286505	3.30	.036883	5.30	.004992	7.30	.000676	9.30	.000091
1.30	.272532	3.35	.035084	5.35	.004748	7.35	.000643	9.35	.000087
1.35	.259240	3.40	.033373	5.40	.004517	7.40	.000611	9.40	.000083
1.40	.246597	3.45	.031746	5.45	.004296	7.45	.000581	9.45	.000079
1.45	.234570	3.50	.030197	5.50	.004087	7.50	.000553	9.50	.000075
1.50	.223130	3.55	.028725	5.55	.003887	7.55	.000526	9.55	.000071
1.55	.212248	3.60	.027324	5.60	.003698	7.60	.000501	9.60	.000068
1.60	.201897	3.65	.025991	5.65	.003518	7.65	.000476	9.65	.000064
1.65	.192050	3.70	.024724	5.70	.003346	7.70	.000453	9.70	.000061
1.70	.182684	3.75	.023518	5.75	.003183	7.75	.000431	9.75	.000058
1.75	.173774	3.80	.022371	5.80	.003028	7.80	.000410	9.80	.000056
1.80	.165299	3.85	.021280	5.85	.002880	7.85	.000390	9.85	.000053
1.85	.157237	3.90	.020242	5.90	.002739	7.90	.000371	9.90	.000050
1.90	.149569	3.95	.019255	5.95	.002606	7.95	.000353	9.95	.000048
1.95	.142274	4.00	.018316	6.00	.002479	8.00	.000336	10.00	.000045
2.00	.135335								

TABLE VI Critical Values of *t*

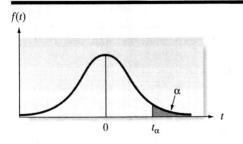

Degrees of Freedom	$t_{.100}$	$t_{.050}$	$t_{.025}$	$t_{.010}$	$t_{.005}$	$t_{.001}$	$t_{.0005}$
1	3.078	6.314	12.706	31.821	63.657	318.31	636.62
2	1.886	2.920	4.303	6.965	9.925	22.326	31.598
3	1.638	2.353	3.182	4.541	5.841	10.213	12.924
4	1.533	2.132	−2.776	3.747	4.604	7.173	8.610
5	1.476	2.015	2.571	3.365	4.032	5.893	6.869
6	1.440	1.943	2.447	3.143	3.707	5.208	5.959
7	1.415	1.895	2.365	2.998	3.499	4.785	5.408
8	1.397	1.860	2.306	2.896	3.355	4.501	5.041
9	1.383	1.833	2.262	2.821	3.250	4.297	4.781
10	1.372	1.812	2.228	2.764	3.169	4.144	4.587
11	1.363	1.796	2.201	2.718	3.106	4.025	4.437
12	1.356	1.782	2.179	2.681	3.055	3.930	4.318
13	1.350	1.771	2.160	2.650	3.012	3.852	4.221
14	1.345	1.761	2.145	2.624	2.977	3.787	4.140
15	1.341	1.753	2.131	2.602	2.947	3.733	4.073
16	1.337	1.746	2.120	2.583	2.921	3.686	4.015
17	1.333	1.740	2.110	2.567	2.898	3.646	3.965
18	1.330	1.734	2.101	2.552	2.878	3.610	3.922
19	1.328	1.729	2.093	2.539	2.861	3.579	3.883
20	1.325	1.725	2.086	2.528	2.845	3.552	3.850
21	1.323	1.721	2.080	2.518	2.831	3.527	3.819
22	1.321	1.717	2.074	2.508	2.819	3.505	3.792
23	1.319	1.714	2.069	2.500	2.807	3.485	3.767
24	1.318	1.711	2.064	2.492	2.797	3.467	3.745
25	1.316	1.708	2.060	2.485	2.787	3.450	3.725
26	1.315	1.706	2.056	2.479	2.779	3.435	3.707
27	1.314	1.703	2.052	2.473	2.771	3.421	3.690
28	1.313	1.701	2.048	2.467	2.763	3.408	3.674
29	1.311	1.699	2.045	2.462	2.756	3.396	3.659
30	1.310	1.697	2.042	2.457	2.750	3.385	3.646
40	1.303	1.684	2.021	2.423	2.704	3.307	3.551
60	1.296	1.671	2.000	2.390	2.660	3.232	3.460
120	1.289	1.658	1.980	2.358	2.617	3.160	3.373
∞	1.282	1.645	1.960	2.326	2.576	3.090	3.291

TABLE VII   Critical Values of χ^2

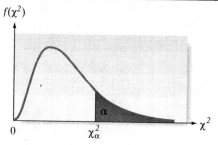

$f(\chi^2)$

0 χ^2_α χ^2

α

Degrees of Freedom	$\chi^2_{.995}$	$\chi^2_{.990}$	$\chi^2_{.975}$	$\chi^2_{.950}$	$\chi^2_{.900}$
1	.0000393	.0001571	.0009821	.0039321	.0157908
2	.0100251	.0201007	.0506356	.102587	.210720
3	.0717212	.114832	.215795	.351846	.584375
4	.206990	.297110	.484419	.710721	1.063623
5	.411740	.554300	.831211	1.145476	1.61031
6	.675727	.872085	1.237347	1.63539	2.20413
7	.989265	1.239043	1.68987	2.16735	2.83311
8	1.344419	1.646482	2.17973	2.73264	3.48954
9	1.734926	2.087912	2.70039	3.32511	4.16816
10	2.15585	2.55821	3.24697	3.94030	4.86518
11	2.60321	3.05347	3.81575	4.57481	5.57779
12	3.07382	3.57056	4.40379	5.22603	6.30380
13	3.56503	4.10691	5.00874	5.89186	7.04150
14	4.07468	4.66043	5.62872	6.57063	7.78953
15	4.60094	5.22935	6.26214	7.26094	8.54675
16	5.14224	5.81221	6.90766	7.96164	9.31223
17	5.69724	6.40776	7.56418	8.67176	10.0852
18	6.26481	7.01491	8.23075	9.39046	10.8649
19	6.84398	7.63273	8.90655	10.1170	11.6509
20	7.43386	8.26040	9.59083	10.8508	12.4426
21	8.03366	8.89720	10.28293	11.5913	13.2396
22	8.64272	9.54249	10.9823	12.3380	14.0415
23	9.26042	10.19567	11.6885	13.0905	14.8479
24	9.88623	10.8564	12.4011	13.8484	15.6587
25	10.5197	11.5240	13.1197	14.6114	16.4734
26	11.1603	12.1981	13.8439	15.3791	17.2919
27	11.8076	12.8786	14.5733	16.1513	18.1138
28	12.4613	13.5648	15.3079	16.9279	18.9392
29	13.1211	14.2565	16.0471	17.7083	19.7677
30	13.7867	14.9535	16.7908	18.4926	20.5992
40	20.7065	22.1643	24.4331	26.5093	29.0505
50	27.9907	29.7067	32.3574	34.7642	37.6886
60	35.5346	37.4848	40.4817	43.1879	46.4589
70	43.2752	45.4418	48.7576	51.7393	55.3290
80	51.1720	53.5400	57.1532	60.3915	64.2778
90	59.1963	61.7541	65.6466	69.1260	73.2912
100	67.3276	70.0648	74.2219	77.9295	82.3581

Source: From C. M. Thompson, "Tables of the Percentage Points of the χ^2-*Distribution*," *Biometrika*, 1941, 32, 188–189. Reproduced by permission of the *Biometrika* Trustees.

(continued)

TABLE VII   Continued

Degrees of Freedom	$\chi^2_{.100}$	$\chi^2_{.050}$	$\chi^2_{.025}$	$\chi^2_{.010}$	$\chi^2_{.005}$
1	2.70554	3.84146	5.02389	6.63490	7.87944
2	4.60517	5.99147	7.37776	9.21034	10.5966
3	6.25139	7.81473	9.34840	11.3449	12.8381
4	7.77944	9.48773	11.1433	13.2767	14.8602
5	9.23635	11.0705	12.8325	15.0863	16.7496
6	10.6446	12.5916	14.4494	16.8119	18.5476
7	12.0170	14.0671	16.0128	18.4753	20.2777
8	13.3616	15.5073	17.5346	20.0902	21.9550
9	14.6837	16.9190	19.0228	21.6660	23.5893
10	15.9871	18.3070	20.4831	23.2093	25.1882
11	17.2750	19.6751	21.9200	24.7250	26.7569
12	18.5494	21.0261	23.3367	26.2170	28.2995
13	19.8119	22.3621	24.7356	27.6883	29.8194
14	21.0642	23.6848	26.1190	29.1413	31.3193
15	22.3072	24.9958	27.4884	30.5779	32.8013
16	23.5418	26.2962	28.8454	31.9999	34.2672
17	24.7690	27.5871	30.1910	33.4087	35.7185
18	25.9894	28.8693	31.5264	34.8053	37.1564
19	27.2036	30.1435	32.8523	36.1908	38.5822
20	28.4120	31.4104	34.1696	37.5662	39.9968
21	29.6151	32.6705	35.4789	38.9321	41.4010
22	30.8133	33.9244	36.7807	40.2894	42.7956
23	32.0069	35.1725	38.0757	41.6384	44.1813
24	33.1963	36.4151	39.3641	42.9798	45.5585
25	34.3816	37.6525	40.6465	44.3141	46.9278
26	35.5631	38.8852	41.9232	45.6417	48.2899
27	36.7412	40.1133	43.1944	46.9630	49.6449
28	37.9159	41.3372	44.4607	48.2782	50.9933
29	39.0875	42.5569	45.7222	49.5879	52.3356
30	40.2560	43.7729	46.9792	50.8922	53.6720
40	51.8050	55.7585	59.3417	63.6907	66.7659
50	63.1671	67.5048	71.4202	76.1539	79.4900
60	74.3970	79.0819	83.2976	88.3794	91.9517
70	85.5271	90.5312	95.0231	100.425	104.215
80	96.5782	101.879	106.629	112.329	116.321
90	107.565	113.145	118.136	124.116	128.299
100	118.498	124.342	129.561	135.807	140.169

TABLE VIII   Percentage Points of the F-distribution, $\alpha = .10$

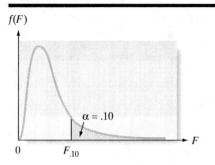

v_1				NUMERATOR DEGREES OF FREEDOM					
v_2	1	2	3	4	5	6	7	8	9
1	39.86	49.50	53.59	55.83	57.24	58.20	58.91	59.44	59.86
2	8.53	9.00	9.16	9.24	9.29	9.33	9.35	9.37	9.38
3	5.54	5.46	5.39	5.34	5.31	5.28	5.27	5.25	5.24
4	4.54	4.32	4.19	4.11	4.05	4.01	3.98	3.95	3.94
5	4.06	3.78	3.62	3.52	3.45	3.40	3.37	3.34	3.32
6	3.78	3.46	3.29	3.18	3.11	3.05	3.01	2.98	2.96
7	3.59	3.26	3.07	2.96	2.88	2.83	2.78	2.75	2.72
8	3.46	3.11	2.92	2.81	2.73	2.67	2.62	2.59	2.56
9	3.36	3.01	2.81	2.69	2.61	2.55	2.51	2.47	2.44
10	3.29	2.92	2.73	2.61	2.52	2.46	2.41	2.38	2.35
11	3.23	2.86	2.66	2.54	2.45	2.39	2.34	2.30	2.27
12	3.18	2.81	2.61	2.48	2.39	2.33	2.28	2.24	2.21
13	3.14	2.76	2.56	2.43	2.35	2.28	2.23	2.20	2.16
14	3.10	2.73	2.52	2.39	2.31	2.24	2.19	2.15	2.12
15	3.07	2.70	2.49	2.36	2.27	2.21	2.16	2.12	2.09
16	3.05	2.67	2.46	2.33	2.24	2.18	2.13	2.09	2.06
17	3.03	2.64	2.44	2.31	2.22	2.15	2.10	2.06	2.03
18	3.01	2.62	2.42	2.29	2.20	2.13	2.08	2.04	2.00
19	2.99	2.61	2.40	2.27	2.18	2.11	2.06	2.02	1.98
20	2.97	2.59	2.38	2.25	2.16	2.09	2.04	2.00	1.96
21	2.96	2.57	2.36	2.23	2.14	2.08	2.02	1.98	1.95
22	2.95	2.56	2.35	2.22	2.13	2.06	2.01	1.97	1.93
23	2.94	2.55	2.34	2.21	2.11	2.05	1.99	1.95	1.92
24	2.93	2.54	2.33	2.19	2.10	2.04	1.98	1.94	1.91
25	2.92	2.53	2.32	2.18	2.09	2.02	1.97	1.93	1.89
26	2.91	2.52	2.31	2.17	2.08	2.01	1.96	1.92	1.88
27	2.90	2.51	2.30	2.17	2.07	2.00	1.95	1.91	1.87
28	2.89	2.50	2.29	2.16	2.06	2.00	1.94	1.90	1.87
29	2.89	2.50	2.28	2.15	2.06	1.99	1.93	1.89	1.86
30	2.88	2.49	2.28	2.14	2.05	1.98	1.93	1.88	1.85
40	2.84	2.44	2.23	2.09	2.00	1.93	1.87	1.83	1.79
60	2.79	2.39	2.18	2.04	1.95	1.87	1.82	1.77	1.74
120	2.75	2.35	2.13	1.99	1.90	1.82	1.77	1.72	1.68
∞	2.71	2.30	2.08	1.94	1.85	1.77	1.72	1.67	1.63

DENOMINATOR DEGREES OF FREEDOM

Source: From M. Merrington and C. M. Thompson, "Tables of Percentage Points of the Inverted Beta (F)-Distribution," *Biometrika*, 1943, 33, 73–88.

(continued)

TABLE VIII   Continued

ν_2 \ ν_1	NUMERATOR DEGREES OF FREEDOM									
	10	12	15	20	24	30	40	60	120	∞
1	60.19	60.71	61.22	61.74	62.00	62.26	62.53	62.79	63.06	63.33
2	9.39	9.41	9.42	9.44	9.45	9.46	9.47	9.47	9.48	9.49
3	5.23	5.22	5.20	5.18	5.18	5.17	5.16	5.15	5.14	5.13
4	3.92	3.90	3.87	3.84	3.83	3.82	3.80	3.79	3.78	3.76
5	3.30	3.27	3.24	3.21	3.19	3.17	3.16	3.14	3.12	3.10
6	2.94	2.90	2.87	2.84	2.82	2.80	2.78	2.76	2.74	2.72
7	2.70	2.67	2.63	2.59	2.58	2.56	2.54	2.51	2.49	2.47
8	2.54	2.50	2.46	2.42	2.40	2.38	2.36	2.34	2.32	2.29
9	2.42	2.38	2.34	2.30	2.28	2.25	2.23	2.21	2.18	2.16
10	2.32	2.28	2.24	2.20	2.18	2.16	2.13	2.11	2.08	2.06
11	2.25	2.21	2.17	2.12	2.10	2.08	2.05	2.03	2.00	1.97
12	2.19	2.15	2.10	2.06	2.04	2.01	1.99	1.96	1.93	1.90
13	2.14	2.10	2.05	2.01	1.98	1.96	1.93	1.90	1.88	1.85
14	2.10	2.05	2.01	1.96	1.94	1.91	1.89	1.86	1.83	1.80
15	2.06	2.02	1.97	1.92	1.90	1.87	1.85	1.82	1.79	1.76
16	2.03	1.99	1.94	1.89	1.87	1.84	1.81	1.78	1.75	1.72
17	2.00	1.96	1.91	1.86	1.84	1.81	1.78	1.75	1.72	1.69
18	1.98	1.93	1.89	1.84	1.81	1.78	1.75	1.72	1.69	1.66
19	1.96	1.91	1.86	1.81	1.79	1.76	1.73	1.70	1.67	1.63
20	1.94	1.89	1.84	1.79	1.77	1.74	1.71	1.68	1.64	1.61
21	1.92	1.87	1.83	1.78	1.75	1.72	1.69	1.66	1.62	1.59
22	1.90	1.86	1.81	1.76	1.73	1.70	1.67	1.64	1.60	1.57
23	1.89	1.84	1.80	1.74	1.72	1.69	1.66	1.62	1.59	1.55
24	1.88	1.83	1.78	1.73	1.70	1.67	1.64	1.61	1.57	1.53
25	1.87	1.82	1.77	1.72	1.69	1.66	1.63	1.59	1.56	1.52
26	1.86	1.81	1.76	1.71	1.68	1.65	1.61	1.58	1.54	1.50
27	1.85	1.80	1.75	1.70	1.67	1.64	1.60	1.57	1.53	1.49
28	1.84	1.79	1.74	1.69	1.66	1.63	1.59	1.56	1.52	1.48
29	1.83	1.78	1.73	1.68	1.65	1.62	1.58	1.55	1.51	1.47
30	1.82	1.77	1.72	1.67	1.64	1.61	1.57	1.54	1.50	1.46
40	1.76	1.71	1.66	1.61	1.57	1.54	1.51	1.47	1.42	1.38
60	1.71	1.66	1.60	1.54	1.51	1.48	1.44	1.40	1.35	1.29
120	1.65	1.60	1.55	1.48	1.45	1.41	1.37	1.32	1.26	1.19
∞	1.60	1.55	1.49	1.42	1.38	1.34	1.30	1.24	1.17	1.00

DENOMINATOR DEGREES OF FREEDOM

TABLE IX   Percentage Points of the F-distribution, $\alpha = .05$

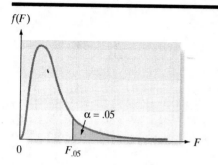

ν_2 \ ν_1	NUMERATOR DEGREES OF FREEDOM								
	1	**2**	**3**	**4**	**5**	**6**	**7**	**8**	**9**
1	161.4	199.5	215.7	224.6	230.2	234.0	236.8	238.9	240.5
2	18.51	19.00	19.16	19.25	19.30	19.33	19.35	19.37	19.38
3	10.13	9.55	9.28	9.12	9.01	8.94	8.89	8.85	8.81
4	7.71	6.94	6.59	6.39	6.26	6.16	6.09	6.04	6.00
5	6.61	5.79	5.41	5.19	5.05	4.95	4.88	4.82	4.77
6	5.99	5.14	4.76	4.53	4.39	4.28	4.21	4.15	4.10
7	5.59	4.74	4.35	4.12	3.97	3.87	3.79	3.73	3.68
8	5.32	4.46	4.07	3.84	3.69	3.58	3.50	3.44	3.39
9	5.12	4.26	3.86	3.63	3.48	3.37	3.29	3.23	3.18
10	4.96	4.10	3.71	3.48	3.33	3.22	3.14	3.07	3.02
11	4.84	3.98	3.59	3.36	3.20	3.09	3.01	2.95	2.90
12	4.75	3.89	3.49	3.26	3.11	3.00	2.91	2.85	2.80
13	4.67	3.81	3.41	3.18	3.03	2.92	2.83	2.77	2.71
14	4.60	3.74	3.34	3.11	2.96	2.85	2.76	2.70	2.65
15	4.54	3.68	3.29	3.06	2.90	2.79	2.71	2.64	2.59
16	4.49	3.63	3.24	3.01	2.85	2.74	2.66	2.59	2.54
17	4.45	3.59	3.20	2.96	2.81	2.70	2.61	2.55	2.49
18	4.41	3.55	3.16	2.93	2.77	2.66	2.58	2.51	2.46
19	4.38	3.52	3.13	2.90	2.74	2.63	2.54	2.48	2.42
20	4.35	3.49	3.10	2.87	2.71	2.60	2.51	2.45	2.39
21	4.32	3.47	3.07	2.84	2.68	2.57	2.49	2.42	2.37
22	4.30	3.44	3.05	2.82	2.66	2.55	2.46	2.40	2.34
23	4.28	3.42	3.03	2.80	2.64	2.53	2.44	2.37	2.32
24	4.26	3.40	3.01	2.78	2.62	2.51	2.42	2.36	2.30
25	4.24	3.39	2.99	2.76	2.60	2.49	2.40	2.34	2.28
26	4.23	3.37	2.98	2.74	2.59	2.47	2.39	2.32	2.27
27	4.21	3.35	2.96	2.73	2.57	2.46	2.37	2.31	2.25
28	4.20	3.34	2.95	2.71	2.56	2.45	2.36	2.29	2.24
29	4.18	3.33	2.93	2.70	2.55	2.43	2.35	2.28	2.22
30	4.17	3.32	2.92	2.69	2.53	2.42	2.33	2.27	2.21
40	4.08	3.23	2.84	2.61	2.45	2.34	2.25	2.18	2.12
60	4.00	3.15	2.76	2.53	2.37	2.25	2.17	2.10	2.04
120	3.92	3.07	2.68	2.45	2.29	2.17	2.09	2.02	1.96
∞	3.84	3.00	2.60	2.37	2.21	2.10	2.01	1.94	1.88

DENOMINATOR DEGREES OF FREEDOM

Source: From M. Merrington and C. M. Thompson, "Tables of Percentage Points of the Inverted Beta (F)-Distribution," *Biometrika,* 1943, 33, 73–88.

(continued)

TABLE IX   Continued

ν_1 ν_2	NUMERATOR DEGREES OF FREEDOM									
	10	12	15	20	24	30	40	60	120	∞
1	241.9	243.9	245.9	248.0	249.1	250.1	251.1	252.2	253.3	254.3
2	19.40	19.41	19.43	19.45	19.45	19.46	19.47	19.48	19.49	19.50
3	8.79	8.74	8.70	8.66	8.64	8.62	8.59	8.57	8.55	8.53
4	5.96	5.91	5.86	5.80	5.77	5.75	5.72	5.69	5.66	5.63
5	4.74	4.68	4.62	4.56	4.53	4.50	4.46	4.43	4.40	4.36
6	4.06	4.00	3.94	3.87	3.84	3.81	3.77	3.74	3.70	3.67
7	3.64	3.57	3.51	3.44	3.41	3.38	3.34	3.30	3.27	3.23
8	3.35	3.28	3.22	3.15	3.12	3.08	3.04	3.01	2.97	2.93
9	3.14	3.07	3.01	2.94	2.90	2.86	2.83	2.79	2.75	2.71
10	2.98	2.91	2.85	2.77	2.74	2.70	2.66	2.62	2.58	2.54
11	2.85	2.79	2.72	2.65	2.61	2.57	2.53	2.49	2.45	2.40
12	2.75	2.69	2.62	2.54	2.51	2.47	2.43	2.38	2.34	2.30
13	2.67	2.60	2.53	2.46	2.42	2.38	2.34	2.30	2.25	2.21
14	2.60	2.53	2.46	2.39	2.35	2.31	2.27	2.22	2.18	2.13
15	2.54	2.48	2.40	2.33	2.29	2.25	2.20	2.16	2.11	2.07
16	2.49	2.42	2.35	2.28	2.24	2.19	2.15	2.11	2.06	2.01
17	2.45	2.38	2.31	2.23	2.19	2.15	2.10	2.06	2.01	1.96
18	2.41	2.34	2.27	2.19	2.15	2.11	2.06	2.02	1.97	1.92
19	2.38	2.31	2.23	2.16	2.11	2.07	2.03	1.98	1.93	1.88
20	2.35	2.28	2.20	2.12	2.08	2.04	1.99	1.95	1.90	1.84
21	2.32	2.25	2.18	2.10	2.05	2.01	1.96	1.92	1.87	1.81
22	2.30	2.23	2.15	2.07	2.03	1.98	1.94	1.89	1.84	1.78
23	2.27	2.20	2.13	2.05	2.01	1.96	1.91	1.86	1.81	1.76
24	2.25	2.18	2.11	2.03	1.98	1.94	1.89	1.84	1.79	1.73
25	2.24	2.16	2.09	2.01	1.96	1.92	1.87	1.82	1.77	1.71
26	2.22	2.15	2.07	1.99	1.95	1.90	1.85	1.80	1.75	1.69
27	2.20	2.13	2.06	1.97	1.93	1.88	1.84	1.79	1.73	1.67
28	2.19	2.12	2.04	1.96	1.91	1.87	1.82	1.77	1.71	1.65
29	2.18	2.10	2.03	1.94	1.90	1.85	1.81	1.75	1.70	1.64
30	2.16	2.09	2.01	1.93	1.89	1.84	1.79	1.74	1.68	1.62
40	2.08	2.00	1.92	1.84	1.79	1.74	1.69	1.64	1.58	1.51
60	1.99	1.92	1.84	1.75	1.70	1.65	1.59	1.53	1.47	1.39
120	1.91	1.83	1.75	1.66	1.61	1.55	1.50	1.43	1.35	1.25
∞	1.83	1.75	1.67	1.57	1.52	1.46	1.39	1.32	1.22	1.00

DENOMINATOR DEGREES OF FREEDOM

TABLE X Percentage Points of the *F*-distribution, $\alpha = .025$

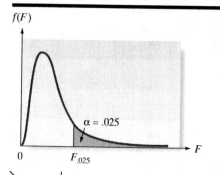

		NUMERATOR DEGREES OF FREEDOM							
ν_2	1	2	3	4	5	6	7	8	9
1	647.8	799.5	864.2	899.6	921.8	937.1	948.2	956.7	963.3
2	38.51	39.00	39.17	39.25	39.30	39.33	39.36	39.37	39.39
3	17.44	16.04	15.44	15.10	14.88	14.73	14.62	14.54	14.47
4	12.22	10.65	9.98	9.60	9.36	9.20	9.07	8.98	8.90
5	10.01	8.43	7.76	7.39	7.15	6.98	6.85	6.76	6.68
6	8.81	7.26	6.60	6.23	5.99	5.82	5.70	5.60	5.52
7	8.07	6.54	5.89	5.52	5.29	5.12	4.99	4.90	4.82
8	7.57	6.06	5.42	5.05	4.82	4.65	4.53	4.43	4.36
9	7.21	5.71	5.08	4.72	4.48	4.32	4.20	4.10	4.03
10	6.94	5.46	4.83	4.47	4.24	4.07	3.95	3.85	3.78
11	6.72	5.26	4.63	4.28	4.04	3.88	3.76	3.66	3.59
12	6.55	5.10	4.47	4.12	3.89	3.73	3.61	3.51	3.44
13	6.41	4.97	4.35	4.00	3.77	3.60	3.48	3.39	3.31
14	6.30	4.86	4.24	3.89	3.66	3.50	3.38	3.29	3.21
15	6.20	4.77	4.15	3.80	3.58	3.41	3.29	3.20	3.12
16	6.12	4.69	4.08	3.73	3.50	3.34	3.22	3.12	3.05
17	6.04	4.62	4.01	3.66	3.44	3.28	3.16	3.06	2.98
18	5.98	4.56	3.95	3.61	3.38	3.22	3.10	3.01	2.93
19	5.92	4.51	3.90	3.56	3.33	3.17	3.05	2.96	2.88
20	5.87	4.46	3.86	3.51	3.29	3.13	3.01	2.91	2.84
21	5.83	4.42	3.82	3.48	3.25	3.09	2.97	2.87	2.80
22	5.79	4.38	3.78	3.44	3.22	3.05	2.93	2.84	2.76
23	5.75	4.35	3.75	3.41	3.18	3.02	2.90	2.81	2.73
24	5.72	4.32	3.72	3.38	3.15	2.99	2.87	2.78	2.70
25	5.69	4.29	3.69	3.35	3.13	2.97	2.85	2.75	2.68
26	5.66	4.27	3.67	3.33	3.10	2.94	2.82	2.73	2.65
27	5.63	4.24	3.65	3.31	3.08	2.92	2.80	2.71	2.63
28	5.61	4.22	3.63	3.29	3.06	2.90	2.78	2.69	2.61
29	5.59	4.20	3.61	3.27	3.04	2.88	2.76	2.67	2.59
30	5.57	4.18	3.59	3.25	3.03	2.87	2.75	2.65	2.57
40	5.42	4.05	3.46	3.13	2.90	2.74	2.62	2.53	2.45
60	5.29	3.93	3.34	3.01	2.79	2.63	2.51	2.41	2.33
120	5.15	3.80	3.23	2.89	2.67	2.52	2.39	2.30	2.22
∞	5.02	3.69	3.12	2.79	2.57	2.41	2.29	2.19	2.11

DENOMINATOR DEGREES OF FREEDOM

Source: From M. Merrington and C. M. Thompson, "Tables of Percentage Points of the Inverted Beta (*F*)-Distribution," *Biometrika,* 1943, 33, 73–88.

(continued)

TABLE X   Continued

ν_1	NUMERATOR DEGREES OF FREEDOM									
ν_2	10	12	15	20	24	30	40	60	120	∞
1	968.6	976.7	984.9	993.1	997.2	1,001	1,006	1,010	1,014	1,018
2	39.40	39.41	39.43	39.45	39.46	39.46	39.47	39.48	39.49	39.50
3	14.42	14.34	14.25	14.17	14.12	14.08	14.04	13.99	13.95	13.90
4	8.84	8.75	8.66	8.56	8.51	8.46	8.41	8.36	8.31	8.26
5	6.62	6.52	6.43	6.33	6.28	6.23	6.18	6.12	6.07	6.02
6	5.46	5.37	5.27	5.17	5.12	5.07	5.01	4.96	4.90	4.85
7	4.76	4.67	4.57	4.47	4.42	4.36	4.31	4.25	4.20	4.14
8	4.30	4.20	4.10	4.00	3.95	3.89	3.84	3.78	3.73	3.67
9	3.96	3.87	3.77	3.67	3.61	3.56	3.51	3.45	3.39	3.33
10	3.72	3.62	3.52	3.42	3.37	3.31	3.26	3.20	3.14	3.08
11	3.53	3.43	3.33	3.23	3.17	3.12	3.06	3.00	2.94	2.88
12	3.37	3.28	3.18	3.07	3.02	2.96	2.91	2.85	2.79	2.72
13	3.25	3.15	3.05	2.95	2.89	2.84	2.78	2.72	2.66	2.60
14	3.15	3.05	2.95	2.84	2.79	2.73	2.67	2.61	2.55	2.49
15	3.06	2.96	2.86	2.76	2.70	2.64	2.59	2.52	2.46	2.40
16	2.99	2.89	2.79	2.68	2.63	2.57	2.51	2.45	2.38	2.32
17	2.92	2.82	2.72	2.62	2.56	2.50	2.44	2.38	2.32	2.25
18	2.87	2.77	2.67	2.56	2.50	2.44	2.38	2.32	2.26	2.19
19	2.82	2.72	2.62	2.51	2.45	2.39	2.33	2.27	2.20	2.13
20	2.77	2.68	2.57	2.46	2.41	2.35	2.29	2.22	2.16	2.09
21	2.73	2.64	2.53	2.42	2.37	2.31	2.25	2.18	2.11	2.04
22	2.70	2.60	2.50	2.39	2.33	2.27	2.21	2.14	2.08	2.00
23	2.67	2.57	2.47	2.36	2.30	2.24	2.18	2.11	2.04	1.97
24	2.64	2.54	2.44	2.33	2.27	2.21	2.15	2.08	2.01	1.94
25	2.61	2.51	2.41	2.30	2.24	2.18	2.12	2.05	1.98	1.91
26	2.59	2.49	2.39	2.28	2.22	2.16	2.09	2.03	1.95	1.88
27	2.57	2.47	2.36	2.25	2.19	2.13	2.07	2.00	1.93	1.85
28	2.55	2.45	2.34	2.23	2.17	2.11	2.05	1.98	1.91	1.83
29	2.53	2.43	2.32	2.21	2.15	2.09	2.03	1.96	1.89	1.81
30	2.51	2.41	2.31	2.20	2.14	2.07	2.01	1.94	1.87	1.79
40	2.39	2.29	2.18	2.07	2.01	1.94	1.88	1.80	1.72	1.64
60	2.27	2.17	2.06	1.94	1.88	1.82	1.74	1.67	1.58	1.48
120	2.16	2.05	1.94	1.82	1.76	1.69	1.61	1.53	1.43	1.31
∞	2.05	1.94	1.83	1.71	1.64	1.57	1.48	1.39	1.27	1.00

DENOMINATOR DEGREES OF FREEDOM

TABLE XI Percentage Points of the *F*-distribution, $\alpha = .01$

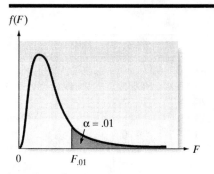

$f(F)$

$\alpha = .01$

$F_{.01}$

F

0

ν_1	NUMERATOR DEGREES OF FREEDOM								
ν_2	1	2	3	4	5	6	7	8	9
1	4,052	4,999.5	5,403	5,625	5,764	5,859	5,928	5,982	6,022
2	98.50	99.00	99.17	99.25	99.30	99.33	99.36	99.37	99.39
3	34.12	30.82	29.46	28.71	28.24	27.91	27.67	27.49	27.35
4	21.20	18.00	16.69	15.98	15.52	15.21	14.98	14.80	14.66
5	16.26	13.27	12.06	11.39	10.97	10.67	10.46	10.29	10.16
6	13.75	10.92	9.78	9.15	8.75	8.47	8.26	8.10	7.98
7	12.25	9.55	8.45	7.85	7.46	7.19	6.99	6.84	6.72
8	11.26	8.65	7.59	7.01	6.63	6.37	6.18	6.03	5.91
9	10.56	8.02	6.99	6.42	6.06	5.80	5.61	5.47	5.35
10	10.04	7.56	6.55	5.99	5.64	5.39	5.20	5.06	4.94
11	9.65	7.21	6.22	5.67	5.32	5.07	4.89	4.74	4.63
12	9.33	6.93	5.95	5.41	5.06	4.82	4.64	4.50	4.39
13	9.07	6.70	5.74	5.21	4.86	4.62	4.44	4.30	4.19
14	8.86	6.51	5.56	5.04	4.69	4.46	4.28	4.14	4.03
15	8.68	6.36	5.42	4.89	4.56	4.32	4.14	4.00	3.89
16	8.53	6.23	5.29	4.77	4.44	4.20	4.03	3.89	3.78
17	8.40	6.11	5.18	4.67	4.34	4.10	3.93	3.79	3.68
18	8.29	6.01	5.09	4.58	4.25	4.01	3.84	3.71	3.60
19	8.18	5.93	5.01	4.50	4.17	3.94	3.77	3.63	3.52
20	8.10	5.85	4.94	4.43	4.10	3.87	3.70	3.56	3.46
21	8.02	5.78	4.87	4.37	4.04	3.81	3.64	3.51	3.40
22	7.95	5.72	4.82	4.31	3.99	3.76	3.59	3.45	3.35
23	7.88	5.66	4.76	4.26	3.94	3.71	3.54	3.41	3.30
24	7.82	5.61	4.72	4.22	3.90	3.67	3.50	3.36	3.26
25	7.77	5.57	4.68	4.18	3.85	3.63	3.46	3.32	3.22
26	7.72	5.53	4.64	4.14	3.82	3.59	3.42	3.29	3.18
27	7.68	5.49	4.60	4.11	3.78	3.56	3.39	3.26	3.15
28	7.64	5.45	4.57	4.07	3.75	3.53	3.36	3.23	3.12
29	7.60	5.42	4.54	4.04	3.73	3.50	3.33	3.20	3.09
30	7.56	5.39	4.51	4.02	3.70	3.47	3.30	3.17	3.07
40	7.31	5.18	4.31	3.83	3.51	3.29	3.12	2.99	2.89
60	7.08	4.98	4.13	3.65	3.34	3.12	2.95	2.82	2.72
120	6.85	4.79	3.95	3.48	3.17	2.96	2.79	2.66	2.56
∞	6.63	4.61	3.78	3.32	3.02	2.80	2.64	2.51	2.41

DENOMINATOR DEGREES OF FREEDOM

Source: From M. Merrington and C. M. Thompson, "Tables of Percentage Points of the Inverted Beta (*F*)-Distribution," *Biometrika,* 1943, 33, 73–88.

(continued)

TABLE XI   Continued

ν_1 / ν_2	NUMERATOR DEGREES OF FREEDOM									
	10	12	15	20	24	30	40	60	120	∞
1	6,056	6,106	6,157	6,209	6,235	6,261	6,287	6,313	6,339	6,366
2	99.40	99.42	99.43	99.45	99.46	99.47	99.47	99.48	99.49	99.50
3	27.23	27.05	26.87	26.69	26.60	26.50	26.41	26.32	26.22	26.13
4	14.55	14.37	14.20	14.02	13.93	13.84	13.75	13.65	13.56	13.46
5	10.05	9.89	9.72	9.55	9.47	9.38	9.29	9.20	9.11	9.02
6	7.87	7.72	7.56	7.40	7.31	7.23	7.14	7.06	6.97	6.88
7	6.62	6.47	6.31	6.16	6.07	5.99	5.91	5.82	5.74	5.65
8	5.81	5.67	5.52	5.36	5.28	5.20	5.12	5.03	4.95	4.86
9	5.26	5.11	4.96	4.81	4.73	4.65	4.57	4.48	4.40	4.31
10	4.85	4.71	4.56	4.41	4.33	4.25	4.17	4.08	4.00	3.91
11	4.54	4.40	4.25	4.10	4.02	3.94	3.86	3.78	3.69	3.60
12	4.30	4.16	4.01	3.86	3.78	3.70	3.62	3.54	3.45	3.36
13	4.10	3.96	3.82	3.66	3.59	3.51	3.43	3.34	3.25	3.17
14	3.94	3.80	3.66	3.51	3.43	3.35	3.27	3.18	3.09	3.00
15	3.80	3.67	3.52	3.37	3.29	3.21	3.13	3.05	2.96	2.87
16	3.69	3.55	3.41	3.26	3.18	3.10	3.02	2.93	2.84	2.75
17	3.59	3.46	3.31	3.16	3.08	3.00	2.92	2.83	2.75	2.65
18	3.51	3.37	3.23	3.08	3.00	2.92	2.84	2.75	2.66	2.57
19	3.43	3.30	3.15	3.00	2.92	2.84	2.76	2.67	2.58	2.49
20	3.37	3.23	3.09	2.94	2.86	2.78	2.69	2.61	2.52	2.42
21	3.31	3.17	3.03	2.88	2.80	2.72	2.64	2.55	2.46	2.36
22	3.26	3.12	2.98	2.83	2.75	2.67	2.58	2.50	2.40	2.31
23	3.21	3.07	2.93	2.78	2.70	2.62	2.54	2.45	2.35	2.26
24	3.17	3.03	2.89	2.74	2.66	2.58	2.49	2.40	2.31	2.21
25	3.13	2.99	2.85	2.70	2.62	2.54	2.45	2.36	2.27	2.17
26	3.09	2.96	2.81	2.66	2.58	2.50	2.42	2.33	2.23	2.13
27	3.06	2.93	2.78	2.63	2.55	2.47	2.38	2.29	2.20	2.10
28	3.03	2.90	2.75	2.60	2.52	2.44	2.35	2.26	2.17	2.06
29	3.00	2.87	2.73	2.57	2.49	2.41	2.33	2.23	2.14	2.03
30	2.98	2.84	2.70	2.55	2.47	2.39	2.30	2.21	2.11	2.01
40	2.80	2.66	2.52	2.37	2.29	2.20	2.11	2.02	1.92	1.80
60	2.63	2.50	2.35	2.20	2.12	2.03	1.94	1.84	1.73	1.60
120	2.47	2.34	2.19	2.03	1.95	1.86	1.76	1.66	1.53	1.38
∞	2.32	2.18	2.04	1.88	1.79	1.70	1.59	1.47	1.32	1.00

DENOMINATOR DEGREES OF FREEDOM

TABLE XII   Critical Values of T_L and T_U for the Wilcoxon Rank Sum Test: Independent Samples

Test statistic is the rank sum associated with the smaller sample (if equal sample sizes, either rank sum can be used).

a. $\alpha = .025$ one-tailed; $\alpha = .05$ two-tailed

n_2 \ n_1	3 T_L	3 T_U	4 T_L	4 T_U	5 T_L	5 T_U	6 T_L	6 T_U	7 T_L	7 T_U	8 T_L	8 T_U	9 T_L	9 T_U	10 T_L	10 T_U
3	5	16	6	18	6	21	7	23	7	26	8	28	8	31	9	33
4	6	18	11	25	12	28	12	32	13	35	14	38	15	41	16	44
5	6	21	12	28	18	37	19	41	20	45	21	49	22	53	24	56
6	7	23	12	32	19	41	26	52	28	56	29	61	31	65	32	70
7	7	26	13	35	20	45	28	56	37	68	39	73	41	78	43	83
8	8	28	14	38	21	49	29	61	39	73	49	87	51	93	54	98
9	8	31	15	41	22	53	31	65	41	78	51	93	63	108	66	114
10	9	33	16	44	24	56	32	70	43	83	54	98	66	114	79	131

b. $\alpha = .05$ one-tailed; $\alpha = .10$ two-tailed

n_2 \ n_1	3 T_L	3 T_U	4 T_L	4 T_U	5 T_L	5 T_U	6 T_L	6 T_U	7 T_L	7 T_U	8 T_L	8 T_U	9 T_L	9 T_U	10 T_L	10 T_U
3	6	15	7	17	7	20	8	22	9	24	9	27	10	29	11	31
4	7	17	12	24	13	27	14	30	15	33	16	36	17	39	18	42
5	7	20	13	27	19	36	20	40	22	43	24	46	25	50	26	54
6	8	22	14	30	20	40	28	50	30	54	32	58	33	63	35	67
7	9	24	15	33	22	43	30	54	39	66	41	71	43	76	46	80
8	9	27	16	36	24	46	32	58	41	71	52	84	54	90	57	95
9	10	29	17	39	25	50	33	63	43	76	54	90	66	105	69	111
10	11	31	18	42	26	54	35	67	46	80	57	95	69	111	83	127

Source: From F. Wilcoxon and R. A. Wilcox, "Some Rapid Approximate Statistical Procedures," 1964, 20–23.

TABLE XIII   Critical Values of T_0 in the Wilcoxon Paired Difference Signed Rank Test

One-Tailed	Two-Tailed	$n = 5$	$n = 6$	$n = 7$	$n = 8$	$n = 9$	$n = 10$
$\alpha = .05$	$\alpha = .10$	1	2	4	6	8	11
$\alpha = .025$	$\alpha = .05$		1	2	4	6	8
$\alpha = .01$	$\alpha = .02$			0	2	3	5
$\alpha = .005$	$\alpha = .01$				0	2	3
		$n = 11$	$n = 12$	$n = 13$	$n = 14$	$n = 15$	$n = 16$
$\alpha = .05$	$\alpha = .10$	14	17	21	26	30	36
$\alpha = .025$	$\alpha = .05$	11	14	17	21	25	30
$\alpha = .01$	$\alpha = .02$	7	10	13	16	20	24
$\alpha = .005$	$\alpha = .01$	5	7	10	13	16	19
		$n = 17$	$n = 18$	$n = 19$	$n = 20$	$n = 21$	$n = 22$
$\alpha = .05$	$\alpha = .10$	41	47	54	60	68	75
$\alpha = .025$	$\alpha = .05$	35	40	46	52	59	66
$\alpha = .01$	$\alpha = .02$	28	33	38	43	49	56
$\alpha = .005$	$\alpha = .01$	23	28	32	37	43	49
		$n = 23$	$n = 24$	$n = 25$	$n = 26$	$n = 27$	$n = 28$
$\alpha = .05$	$\alpha = .10$	83	92	101	110	120	130
$\alpha = .025$	$\alpha = .05$	73	81	90	98	107	117
$\alpha = .01$	$\alpha = .02$	62	69	77	85	93	102
$\alpha = .005$	$\alpha = .01$	55	61	68	76	84	92
		$n = 29$	$n = 30$	$n = 31$	$n = 32$	$n = 33$	$n = 34$
$\alpha = .05$	$\alpha = .10$	141	152	163	175	188	201
$\alpha = .025$	$\alpha = .05$	127	137	148	159	171	183
$\alpha = .01$	$\alpha = .02$	111	120	130	141	151	162
$\alpha = .005$	$\alpha = .01$	100	109	118	128	138	149
		$n = 35$	$n = 36$	$n = 37$	$n = 38$	$n = 39$	
$\alpha = .05$	$\alpha = .10$	214	228	242	256	271	
$\alpha = .025$	$\alpha = .05$	195	208	222	235	250	
$\alpha = .01$	$\alpha = .02$	174	186	198	211	224	
$\alpha = .005$	$\alpha = .01$	160	171	183	195	208	
		$n = 40$	$n = 41$	$n = 42$	$n = 43$	$n = 44$	$n = 45$
$\alpha = .05$	$\alpha = .10$	287	303	319	336	353	371
$\alpha = .025$	$\alpha = .05$	264	279	295	311	327	344
$\alpha = .01$	$\alpha = .02$	238	252	267	281	297	313
$\alpha = .005$	$\alpha = .01$	221	234	248	262	277	292
		$n = 46$	$n = 47$	$n = 48$	$n = 49$	$n = 50$	
$\alpha = .05$	$\alpha = .10$	389	408	427	446	466	
$\alpha = .025$	$\alpha = .05$	361	379	397	415	434	
$\alpha = .01$	$\alpha = .02$	329	345	362	380	398	
$\alpha = .005$	$\alpha = .01$	307	323	339	356	373	

Source: From F. Wilcoxon and R. A. Wilcox, "Some Rapid Approximate Statistical Procedures," 1964, p. 28.

TABLE XIV   Critical Values of Spearman's Rank Correlation Coefficient

The α values correspond to a one-tailed test of $H_0: \rho = 0$. The value should be doubled for two-tailed tests.

n	$\alpha = .05$	$\alpha = .025$	$\alpha = .01$	$\alpha = .005$	n	$\alpha = .05$	$\alpha = .025$	$\alpha = .01$	$\alpha = .005$
5	.900	—	—	—	18	.399	.476	.564	.625
6	.829	.886	.943	—	19	.388	.462	.549	.608
7	.714	.786	.893	—	20	.377	.450	.534	.591
8	.643	.738	.833	.881	21	.368	.438	.521	.576
9	.600	.683	.783	.833	22	.359	.428	.508	.562
10	.564	.648	.745	.794	23	.351	.418	.496	.549
11	.523	.623	.736	.818	24	.343	.409	.485	.537
12	.497	.591	.703	.780	25	.336	.400	.475	.526
13	.475	.566	.673	.745	26	.329	.392	.465	.515
14	.457	.545	.646	.716	27	.323	.385	.456	.505
15	.441	.525	.623	.689	28	.317	.377	.448	.496
16	.425	.507	.601	.666	29	.311	.370	.440	.487
17	.412	.490	.582	.645	30	.305	.364	.432	.478

Source: From E. G. Olds, "Distribution of Sums of Squares of Rank Differences for Small Samples," *Annals of Mathematical Statistics,* 1938, 9.

TABLE XV   Critical Values of the Studentized Range, $\alpha = .05$

k ν	2	3	4	5	6	7	8	9	10	11
1	17.97	26.98	32.82	37.08	40.41	43.12	45.40	47.36	49.07	50.59
2	6.08	8.33	9.80	10.88	11.74	12.44	13.03	13.54	13.99	14.39
3	4.50	5.91	6.82	7.50	8.04	8.48	8.85	9.18	9.46	9.72
4	3.93	5.04	5.76	6.29	6.71	7.05	7.35	7.60	7.83	8.03
5	3.64	4.60	5.22	5.67	6.03	6.33	6.58	6.80	6.99	7.17
6	3.46	4.34	4.90	5.30	5.63	5.90	6.12	6.32	6.49	6.65
7	3.34	4.16	4.68	5.06	5.36	5.61	5.82	6.00	6.16	6.30
8	3.26	4.04	4.53	4.89	5.17	5.40	5.60	5.77	5.92	6.05
9	3.20	3.95	4.41	4.76	5.02	5.24	5.43	5.59	5.74	5.87
10	3.15	3.88	4.33	4.65	4.91	5.12	5.30	5.46	5.60	5.72
11	3.11	3.82	4.26	4.57	4.82	5.03	5.20	5.35	5.49	5.61
12	3.08	3.77	4.20	4.51	4.75	4.95	5.12	5.27	5.39	5.51
13	3.06	3.73	4.15	4.45	4.69	4.88	5.05	5.19	5.32	5.43
14	3.03	3.70	4.11	4.41	4.64	4.83	4.99	5.13	5.25	5.36
15	3.01	3.67	4.08	4.37	4.60	4.78	4.94	5.08	5.20	5.31
16	3.00	3.65	4.05	4.33	4.56	4.74	4.90	5.03	5.15	5.26
17	2.98	3.63	4.02	4.30	4.52	4.70	4.86	4.99	5.11	5.21
18	2.97	3.61	4.00	4.28	4.49	4.67	4.82	4.96	5.07	5.17
19	2.96	3.59	3.98	4.25	4.47	4.65	4.79	4.92	5.04	5.14
20	2.95	3.58	3.96	4.23	4.45	4.62	4.77	4.90	5.01	5.11
24	2.92	3.53	3.90	4.17	4.37	4.54	4.68	4.81	4.92	5.01
30	2.89	3.49	3.85	4.10	4.30	4.46	4.60	4.72	4.82	4.92
40	2.86	3.44	3.79	4.04	4.23	4.39	4.52	4.63	4.73	4.82
60	2.83	3.40	3.74	3.98	4.16	4.31	4.44	4.55	4.65	4.73
120	2.80	3.36	3.68	3.92	4.10	4.24	4.36	4.47	4.56	4.64
∞	2.77	3.31	3.63	3.86	4.03	4.17	4.29	4.39	4.47	4.55

(continued)

TABLE XV   Continued

k ν	12	13	14	15	16	17	18	19	20
1	51.96	53.20	54.33	55.36	56.32	57.22	58.04	58.83	59.56
2	14.75	15.08	15.38	15.65	15.91	16.14	16.37	16.57	16.77
3	9.95	10.15	10.35	10.52	10.69	10.84	10.98	11.11	11.24
4	8.21	8.37	8.52	8.66	8.79	8.91	9.03	9.13	9.23
5	7.32	7.47	7.60	7.72	7.83	7.93	8.03	8.12	8.21
6	6.79	6.92	7.03	7.14	7.24	7.34	7.43	7.51	7.59
7	6.43	6.55	6.66	6.76	6.85	6.94	7.02	7.10	7.17
8	6.18	6.29	6.39	6.48	6.57	6.65	6.73	6.80	6.87
9	5.98	6.09	6.19	6.28	6.36	6.44	6.51	6.58	6.64
10	5.83	5.93	6.03	6.11	6.19	6.27	6.34	6.40	6.47
11	5.71	5.81	5.90	5.98	6.06	6.13	6.20	6.27	6.33
12	5.61	5.71	5.80	5.88	5.95	6.02	6.09	6.15	6.21
13	5.53	5.63	5.71	5.79	5.86	5.93	5.99	6.05	6.11
14	5.46	5.55	5.64	5.71	5.79	5.85	5.91	5.97	6.03
15	5.40	5.49	5.57	5.65	5.72	5.78	5.85	5.90	5.96
16	5.35	5.44	5.52	5.59	5.66	5.73	5.79	5.84	5.90
17	5.31	5.39	5.47	5.54	5.61	5.67	5.73	5.79	5.84
18	5.27	5.35	5.43	5.50	5.57	5.63	5.69	5.74	5.79
19	5.23	5.31	5.39	5.46	5.53	5.59	5.65	5.70	5.75
20	5.20	5.28	5.36	5.43	5.49	5.55	5.61	5.66	5.71
24	5.10	5.18	5.25	5.32	5.38	5.44	5.49	5.55	5.59
30	5.00	5.08	5.15	5.21	5.27	5.33	5.38	5.43	5.47
40	4.90	4.98	5.04	5.11	5.16	5.22	5.27	5.31	5.36
60	4.81	4.88	4.94	5.00	5.06	5.11	5.15	5.20	5.24
120	4.71	4.78	4.84	4.90	4.95	5.00	5.04	5.09	5.13
∞	4.62	4.68	4.74	4.80	4.85	4.89	4.93	4.97	5.01

TABLE XVI   Critical Values of the Studentized Range, $\alpha = .01$

ν \ k	2	3	4	5	6	7	8	9	10	11
1	90.03	135.0	164.3	185.6	202.2	215.8	227.2	237.0	245.6	253.2
2	14.04	19.02	22.29	24.72	26.63	28.20	29.53	30.68	31.69	32.59
3	8.26	10.62	12.17	13.33	14.24	15.00	15.64	16.20	16.69	17.13
4	6.51	8.12	9.17	9.96	10.58	11.10	11.55	11.93	12.27	12.57
5	5.70	6.98	7.80	8.42	8.91	9.32	9.67	9.97	10.24	10.48
6	5.24	6.33	7.03	7.56	7.97	8.32	8.61	8.87	9.10	9.30
7	4.95	5.92	6.54	7.01	7.37	7.68	7.94	8.17	8.37	8.55
8	4.75	5.64	6.20	6.62	6.96	7.24	7.47	7.68	7.86	8.03
9	4.60	5.43	5.96	6.35	6.66	6.91	7.13	7.33	7.49	7.65
10	4.48	5.27	5.77	6.14	6.43	6.67	6.87	7.05	7.21	7.36
11	4.39	5.15	5.62	5.97	6.25	6.48	6.67	6.84	6.99	7.13
12	4.32	5.05	5.50	5.84	6.10	6.32	6.51	6.67	6.81	6.94
13	4.26	4.96	5.40	5.73	5.98	6.19	6.37	6.53	6.67	6.79
14	4.21	4.89	5.32	5.63	5.88	6.08	6.26	6.41	6.54	6.66
15	4.17	4.84	5.25	5.56	5.80	5.99	6.16	6.31	6.44	6.55
16	4.13	4.79	5.19	5.49	5.72	5.92	6.08	6.22	6.35	6.46
17	4.10	4.74	5.14	5.43	5.66	5.85	6.01	6.15	6.27	6.38
18	4.07	4.70	5.09	5.38	5.60	5.79	5.94	6.08	6.20	6.31
19	4.05	4.67	5.05	5.33	5.55	5.73	5.89	6.02	6.14	6.25
20	4.02	4.64	5.02	5.29	5.51	5.69	5.84	5.97	6.09	6.19
24	3.96	4.55	4.91	5.17	5.37	5.54	5.69	5.81	5.92	6.02
30	3.89	4.45	4.80	5.05	5.24	5.40	5.54	5.65	5.76	5.85
40	3.82	4.37	4.70	4.93	5.11	5.26	5.39	5.50	5.60	5.69
60	3.76	4.28	4.59	4.82	4.99	5.13	5.25	5.36	5.45	5.53
120	3.70	4.20	4.50	4.71	4.87	5.01	5.12	5.21	5.30	5.37
∞	3.64	4.12	4.40	4.60	4.76	4.88	4.99	5.08	5.16	5.23

(continued)

TABLE XVI   Continued

ν \ k	12	13	14	15	16	17	18	19	20
1	260.0	266.2	271.8	277.0	281.8	286.3	290.0	294.3	298.0
2	33.40	34.13	34.81	35.43	36.00	36.53	37.03	37.50	37.95
3	17.53	17.89	18.22	18.52	18.81	19.07	19.32	19.55	19.77
4	12.84	13.09	13.32	13.53	13.73	13.91	14.08	14.24	14.40
5	10.70	10.89	11.08	11.24	11.40	11.55	11.68	11.81	11.93
6	9.48	9.65	9.81	9.95	10.08	10.21	10.32	10.43	10.54
7	8.71	8.86	9.00	9.12	9.24	9.35	9.46	9.55	9.65
8	8.18	8.31	8.44	8.55	8.66	8.76	8.85	8.94	9.03
9	7.78	7.91	8.03	8.13	8.23	8.33	8.41	8.49	8.57
10	7.49	7.60	7.71	7.81	7.91	7.99	8.08	8.15	8.23
11	7.25	7.36	7.46	7.56	7.65	7.73	7.81	7.88	7.95
12	7.06	7.17	7.26	7.36	7.44	7.52	7.59	7.66	7.73
13	6.90	7.01	7.10	7.19	7.27	7.35	7.42	7.48	7.55
14	6.77	6.87	6.96	7.05	7.13	7.20	7.27	7.33	7.39
15	6.66	6.76	6.84	6.93	7.00	7.07	7.14	7.20	7.26
16	6.56	6.66	6.74	6.82	6.90	6.97	7.03	7.09	7.15
17	6.48	6.57	6.66	6.73	6.81	6.87	6.94	7.00	7.05
18	6.41	6.50	6.58	6.65	6.72	6.79	6.85	6.91	6.97
19	6.34	6.43	6.51	6.58	6.65	6.72	6.78	6.84	6.89
20	6.28	6.37	6.45	6.52	6.59	6.65	6.71	6.77	6.82
24	6.11	6.19	6.26	6.33	6.39	6.45	6.51	6.56	6.61
30	5.93	6.01	6.08	6.14	6.20	6.26	6.31	6.36	6.41
40	5.76	5.83	5.90	5.96	6.02	6.07	6.12	6.16	6.21
60	5.60	5.67	5.73	5.78	5.84	5.89	5.93	5.97	6.01
120	5.44	5.50	5.56	5.61	5.66	5.71	5.75	5.79	5.83
∞	5.29	5.35	5.40	5.45	5.49	5.54	5.57	5.61	5.65

Source: Biometrika Tables for Statisticians, Vol. 1, 3rd ed., edited by E. S. Pearson and H. O. Hartley (Cambridge University Press, 1966). Reproduced by permission of Professor E. S. Pearson and the *Biometrika* Trustees.

B

Calculation Formulas for Analysis of Variance

B.1   FORMULAS FOR THE CALCULATIONS IN THE COMPLETELY RANDOMIZED DESIGN

$$CM = \text{Correction for mean}$$

$$= \frac{(\text{Total of all observations})^2}{\text{Total number of observations}} = \frac{(\Sigma y_i)^2}{n}$$

$$SS(\text{Total}) = \text{Total sum of squares}$$

$$= (\text{Sum of squares of all observations}) - CM = \Sigma y_i^2 - CM$$

$$SST = \text{Sum of squares for treatments}$$

$$= \left(\begin{array}{c} \text{Sum of squares of treatments totals with} \\ \text{each square divided by the number of} \\ \text{observations for that treatment} \end{array} \right) - CM$$

$$= \frac{T_1^2}{n_1} + \frac{T_2^2}{n_2} + \dots + \frac{T_k^2}{n_k} - CM$$

$$SSE = \text{Sum of squares for error} = SS(\text{Total}) - SST$$

$$MST = \text{Mean square for treatments} = \frac{SST}{k - 1}$$

$$MSE = \text{Mean square for error} = \frac{SSE}{n - k}$$

$$F = \text{Test statistic} = \frac{MST}{MSE}$$

where

$$n = \text{Total number of observations}$$
$$k = \text{Number of treatments}$$
$$T_i = \text{Total for treatment } i \ (i = 1, 2, \dots, k)$$

B.2   FORMULAS FOR THE CALCULATIONS IN THE RANDOMIZED BLOCK DESIGN

$$CM = \text{Correction for mean}$$

$$= \frac{(\text{Total of all observations})^2}{\text{Total number of observations}} = \frac{(\Sigma y_i)^2}{n}$$

$$SS(\text{Total}) = \text{Total sum of squares}$$

$$= (\text{Sum of squares of all observations}) - CM = \Sigma y_i^2 - CM$$

$$SST = \text{Sum of squares for treatments}$$

$$= \left(\begin{array}{c} \text{Sum of squares of treatment totals with} \\ \text{each square divided by } b, \text{ the number of} \\ \text{observations for that treatment} \end{array} \right) - CM$$

$$= \frac{T_1^2}{b} + \frac{T_2^2}{b} + \dots + \frac{T_k^2}{b} - CM$$

$$SST = \text{Sum of squares for blocks}$$

$$= \left(\begin{array}{c} \text{Sum of squares of block totals with} \\ \text{each square divided by } p, \text{ the number} \\ \text{of observations in that block} \end{array} \right) - CM$$

$$= \frac{B_1^2}{k} + \frac{B_2^2}{k} + \dots + \frac{B_b^2}{k} - CM$$

$$SSE = \text{Sum of squares for error} = SS(\text{Total}) - SST - SSB$$

$$MST = \text{Mean square for treatments} = \frac{SST}{k-1}$$

$$MSB = \text{Mean square for blocks} = \frac{SSB}{b-1}$$

$$MSE = \text{Mean square for error} = \frac{SSE}{n-k-b+1}$$

$$F = \text{Test statistic} = \frac{MST}{MSE}$$

where

$$n = \text{Total number of observations}$$
$$b = \text{Number of blocks}$$
$$k = \text{Number of treatments}$$
$$T_i = \text{Total for treatment } i \ (i = 1, 2, \dots, k)$$
$$B_i = \text{Total for block } i \ (i = 1, 2, \dots, b)$$

B.3   FORMULAS FOR THE CALCULATIONS FOR A TWO-FACTOR FACTORIAL EXPERIMENT

$$CM = \text{Correction for mean}$$

$$= \frac{(\text{Total of all } n \text{ measurements})^2}{n} = \frac{\left(\sum_{i=1}^{n} y_i \right)^2}{n}$$

$$SS(\text{Total}) = \text{Total sum of squares}$$

$$= (\text{Sum of squares of all } n \text{ measurements}) - \text{CM} = \sum_{i=1}^{n} y_i^2 - \text{CM}$$

$$\text{SS}(A) = \text{Sum of squares for main effects, factor } A$$

$$= \begin{pmatrix} \text{Sum of squares of the totals } A_1, A_2, \dots, A_a \\ \text{divided by the number of measurements} \\ \text{in a single total, namely } br \end{pmatrix} - \text{CM}$$

$$= \frac{\sum_{i=1}^{a} A_i^2}{br} - \text{CM}$$

$$\text{SS}(B) = \text{Sum of squares for main effects, factor } B$$

$$= \begin{pmatrix} \text{Sum of squares of the totals } B_1, B_2, \dots, B_b \\ \text{divided by the number of measurements} \\ \text{in a single total, namely } ar \end{pmatrix} - \text{CM}$$

$$= \frac{\sum_{i=1}^{b} B_i^2}{ar} - \text{CM}$$

$$\text{SS}(AB) = \text{Sum of squares for } AB \text{ interaction}$$

$$= \begin{pmatrix} \text{Sum of squares of the cell totals} \\ AB_{11}, AB_{12}, \dots, AB_{ab} \text{ divided by} \\ \text{the number of measurements in} \\ \text{a single total, namely } r \end{pmatrix} - \text{SS}(A) - \text{SS}(B) - \text{CM}$$

$$= \frac{\sum_{j=1}^{b} \sum_{i=1}^{a} AB_{ij}^2}{r} - \text{SS}(A) - \text{SS}(B) - \text{CM}$$

where

$a = $ Number of levels of factor A

$b = $ Number of levels of factor B

$r = $ Number of replicates (observations per treatment)

$A_i = $ Total for level i of factor A ($i = 1, 2, \dots, a$)

$B_i = $ Total for level i of factor B ($i = 1, 2, \dots, b$)

$AB_{ij} = $ Total for treatment (ij), i.e., for ith level of factor A and ith level of factor B

B.4 TUKEY'S MULTIPLE COMPARISONS PROCEDURE. (EQUAL SAMPLE SIZES)

Step 1 Select the desired experimentwise error rate, α

Step 2 Calculate

$$\omega = q_\alpha(k, v) \frac{s}{\sqrt{n_t}}$$

where

$k = $ Number of sample means (i.e., number of treatments)

$s = \sqrt{\text{MSE}}$

$v = $ Number of degrees of freedom associated with MSE

$n_t = $ Number of observations in each of the k samples (i.e., number of observations per treatment)

$q_\alpha(k, v) = $ Critical value of the Studentized range (Tables XV and XVI of Appendix A)

Step 3   Calculate and rank the k sample means.

Step 4   Place a bar over those pairs of treatment means that differ by less than ω. A pair of treatments not connected by an overbar (i.e., differing by more than ω) implies a difference in the corresponding population means.

Note: The confidence level associated with all inferences drawn from the analysis is $(1 - \alpha)$.

B.5   BONFERRONI MULTIPLE COMPARISONS PROCEDURE (PAIRWISE COMPARISONS)

Step 1   Calculate for each treatment pair (i, j)

$$B_{ij} = t_{\alpha/(2c)} s \sqrt{\frac{1}{n_i} + \frac{1}{n_j}}$$

where

k = Number of sample (treatment) means in the experiment

c = Number of pairwise comparisons

[*Note:* If all pairwise comparisons are to be made, then $c = k(k - 1)/2$]

$s = \sqrt{\text{MSE}}$

v = Number of degrees of freedom associated with MSE

n_i = Number of observations in sample for treatment i

n_j = Number of observations in sample for treatment j

$t_{\alpha/(2c)}$ = Critical value of t distribution with v df and tail area $\alpha/(2c)$ (Table VI in Appendix A)

Step 2   Rank the sample means and place a bar over any treatment pair (i, j) whose sample means differ by less than B_{ij}. Any pair of means not connected by an overbar implies a difference in the corresponding population means.

Note: The level of confidence associated with all inferences drawn from the analysis is at least $(1 - \alpha)$.

B.6   SCHEFFÉ'S MULTIPLE COMPARISONS PROCEDURE (PAIRWISE COMPARISONS)

Step 1   Calculate Scheffé's critical difference for each pair of treatments (i, j):

$$S_{ij} = \sqrt{(k - 1)(F\alpha)(\text{MSE})\left(\frac{1}{n_1} + \frac{1}{n_j}\right)}$$

where

k = Number of sample (treatment) means

MSE = Mean squared error

n_i = Number of observations in sample for treatment i

n_j = Number of observations in sample for treatment j

F_α = Critical value of F distribution with $k - 1$ numerator df and v denominator df (Tables XIII, IX, X, and XI of Appendix A)

v = Number of degrees of freedom associated with MSE

Step 2   Rank the k sample means and place a bar over any treatment pair (i, j) that differs by less than S_{ij}. Any pair of sample means not connected by an overbar implies a difference in the corresponding population means.

Short Answers to Selected Odd Exercises

Chapter 1

1.3 population; variable(s); sample; inference; measure of reliability   **1.11** qualitative; qualitative   **1.13 a.** earthquake sites **b.** sample **c.** ground motion (qualitative); magnitude (quantitative); ground acceleration (quantitative)   **1.15 b.** qualitative **e.** survey data   **1.17 a.** sample **b.** industry (qualitative); compensation (quantitative); stock shares (quantitative); age (quantitative); efficiency rating (quantitative)   **1.19** Town, Type of water supply and presence of hydrogen sulphide are qualitative; all others are quantitative **1.21 a.** quantitative **b.** quantitative   **c.** qualitative   **d.** quantitative   **e.** qualitative   **f.** quantitative   **g.** qualitative   **1.23 a.** designed experiment   **b.** smokers   **c.** quantitative   **d.** population: all smokers in the U.S.; sample: 50,000 smokers in trial   **e.** the difference in mean age at which each of the scanning methods first detects a tumor.   **1.25 a.** designed experiment   **b.** amateur boxers   **c.** heart rate (quantitative); blood lactate level (quantitative)   **d.** no difference between the two groups of boxers   **e.** no   **1.27 a.** designed experiment   **b.** inferential statistics   **c.** all possible burn patients   **1.29 b.** number of headers per game and IQ   **c.** both quantitative   **1.31** ambiguous question

Chapter 2

2.5 a. X − 8, Y − 9, Z − 3   **b.** X − .40, Y − .45, Z − .15   **2.7 a.** 39/266 = .147   **b.** level 2 − .286, level 3 − .188, level 4 − .327, level 5 − .041, level 6 − .011   **e.** level 4   **2.9 a.** relative frequencies: Black − .203; White − .637; Sumatran − .017; Javan − .003; Indian − .140   **c.** .839; .161   **2.11 a.** .389   **b.** yes   **c.** multi-year ice is most common   **2.13 a.** survey   **b.** quantitative   **c.** about 60%   **2.15** 75% of sampled CEOs had advanced degrees   **2.17 a.** relative frequencies: 1 − .338; 2 − .470; 3 − .164; 4 − .017; 8 − .011   **2.25 a.** 23   **2.27** frequencies: 50, 75, 125, 100, 25, 50, 50, 25   **2.29 a.** 70%   **b.** 10%

2.31 a.

Stem	Leaf
1	6
2	0 1 2 4 8
3	0 4 4 9
4	0 0 2
5	3

b. A students tend to read the most books
2.35 a.

Stem	Leaf
1	0000000
2	0
3	00
4	000
5	
6	
7	
8	
9	0
10	0
11	0
12	00

b. Yes   **2.37** most of the PMI's range from 3 to 7.5
2.39 a.

Stem	Leaf
0	1 1 2 3 4 5 5 9
1	1 2 3
2	0 0
3	9
4	6
5	6
6	1 5
7	
8	
9	
10	0

c. eclipses **2.41 a.** Response rate of the familiarity group is higher. **b.** Familiarity group has highest rate; control group has lowest rate **2.43 a.** 33 **b.** 175 **c.** 20 **d.** 71 **e.** 1,089 **2.45 a.** 6 **b.** 50 **c.** 42.8 **2.47** mean, median, mode **2.49** sample size and variability of the data **2.51 a.** mean < median **b.** mean > median **c.** mean = median **2.53** mode = 15; mean = 14.545; median = 15 **2.55 a.** 8.5 **b.** 25 **c.** .78 **d.** 13.44 **2.57 a.** mean = 31.6; median = 32; mode = 34 and 40 **b.** little or no skewness **2.59 a.** 1.47 **b.** 1.49 **2.61 a.** mean = -4.86; median = -4.85; mode = -5.00 **2.63 b.** probably none **2.65 a.** qualitative, qualitative, quantitative, quantitative **c.** mean = 93.6; median = 91.5; mode = 86 **d.** mean = 95.3; median = 92; mode = 92 **e.** mean = 101.9; median = 103; mode = 113 **f.** three centers **g.** YND: mean = 46.88, median = 43.7, mode = 0; SLI: mean = 30.17, median = 32.5, mode = 0; OND: mean = 0, median = 0, mode = 0 **2.67 a.** mean = $-.15$; median = $-.11$; 4 modes **c.** mean = $-.12$; median = $-.105$; 4 modes **2.69** largest value minus smallest value **2.73** more variable **2.75 a.** 5, 3.7, 1.92 **b.** 99, 1949.25, 44.15 **c.** 98, 1307.84, 36.16 **2.77** data set 1: 1, 1, 2, 2, 3, 3, 4, 4, 5, 5; data set 2: 1, 1, 1, 1, 1, 5, 5, 5, 5, 5 **2.79 a.** 3, 1.3, 1.14 **b.** 3, 1.3, 1.14 **c.** 3, 1.3, 1.14 **2.81 a.** 29, 75.7, 8.70 **b.** 24, 72.7, 8.53 **c.** A students **2.83 a.** .18 **b.** .0041 **c.** .064 **d.** Morning **2.85 a.** 12, 9.37, 3.06 **b.** 8, 5.15, 2.27; data less variable **c.** 8, 5.06, 2.25; data less variable **2.87 a.** dollars; quantitative **b.** at least 3/4; at least 8/9; nothing; nothing **2.89 a.** $\approx 68\%$ **b.** $\approx 95\%$ **c.** $\approx$ all **2.91** range/6 = 104.17, range/4 = 156.25; no **2.93 a.** $\bar{x}$ = 94.91, s = 4.83 **b.** (90.08, 99.74); (85.25, 104.57); (80.42, 109.40) **c.** 81.1%, 97.6%, 98.2%; yes **2.95 a.** unknown **b.** $\approx 84\%$ **2.97 a.** (0, 300.5) **b.** (0, 546) **c.** handrubbing appears to be more effective **2.99 a.** at least 8/9 of the velocities will fall within $936 \pm 3(10)$ **b.** No **2.101 a.** 19 ± 195 **b.** 7 ± 147 **c.** SAT-Math **2.103 a.** 25%; 75% **b.** 50%; 50% **c.** 80%; 20% **d.** 16%; 84% **2.105** $\approx 95\%$ **2.107 a.** z = 2 **b.** z = -3 **c.** z = -2 **d.** z = 1.67 **2.109** 26th percentile **2.111 a.** z = -3.50 **b.** z = .64 **2.113 a.** 23 **b.** z = 3.28 **2.115 a.** -0.2 **b.** -0.06 **c.** z = -4.65 **2.117 a.** z = 2.0: 3.7; z = -1.0: 2.2; z = .5: 2.95; z = -2.5: 1.45 **b.** 1.9 **c.** z = 1.0 and 2.0; GPA = 3.2 and 3.7; mound-shaped, symmetric **2.123 a.** no, z = .73 **b.** yes, z = -3.27 **c.** no, z = 1.36 **d.** yes, z = 3.73 **2.125 a.** 4 **b.** $Q_U \approx 6$, $Q_L \approx 3$ **c.** 3 **d.** skewed right **e.** 50%; 75% **f.** 12, 13, and 16 **2.127 a.** 10, 15, 27.5 **b.** 3.5, 5, 7.5 **c.** effective **2.129 a.** -1.26 **b.** No **2.131 b.** medians: Familiar ≈ 45, Treatment ≈ 35.5, Control ≈ 29 **c.** IQR for Treatment is the largest **d.** yes **e.** no **2.133 a.** 62, 72, 78, and 84 **b.** 62, 72, and 78 **2.135 a.** z = -3 **b.** yes **c.** no **d.** z = -1.5; yes **2.139** slight positive linear trend **2.141** yes, positive linear trend **2.143 a.** nonlinear increasing **b.** nonlinear increasing **2.145 a.** no **b.** yes, slight positive **c.** reliability is suspect (only 5 data points) **2.147 a.** negative trend **b.** positive trend between plant coverage and diversity **2.149** Yes; accuracy decreases as driving distance increases **2.157 a.** $-1, 1, 2$ **b.** $-2, 2, 4$ **c.** 1, 3, 4 **d.** .1, .3, .4 **2.159 a.** 3.1234 **b.** 9.0233 **c.** 9.7857 **2.161 a.** $\bar{x}$ = 5.67, s^2 = 1.07, s = 1.03 **b.** $\bar{x}$ = $-\$1.5$, s^2 = 11.5, s = \$3.39 **c.** $\bar{x}$ = .413%, s^2 = .088, s = .297% **d.** 3; \$10; .7375% **2.163** yes, positive **2.165 a.** pie chart **b.** breast cancer **c.** 19% **2.167 b.** z = -1.06 **2.169** 5.4% **c.** average player rating is 1068 **2.171 a.** relative frequencies: violence $-$ .664; sympathetic $-$ .181; harm $-$ .126; comic $-$ .021; criticism $-$ .007 **2.173 a.** "favorable/recommended"; .635 **b.** yes **2.175 a.** current: 42.0%; retired: 58.0% **b.** Most (40 of 50) Beanie babies have values less than \$100. **c.** yes, positive **d.** unknown; at least 84%; at least 93.7% **e.** 44%; 100%; 100% **f.** 90%; 98%; 98% **2.177** Over half of the whistle types were "Type a" **2.179 a.** no outliers **2.181 a.** Seabirds $-$ quantitative; length $-$ quantitative; oil $-$ qualitative **b.** transect **c.** oiled: 38%; unoiled: 62% **e.** distributions are similar **f.** 3.27 ± 13.4 **g.** 3.495 ± 11.936 **h.** unoiled **2.183 b.** yes **c.** A1775A: $\bar{x}$ = 19,462.2, s = 532.29; A1775B: $\bar{x}$ = 22,838.5, s = 560.98 **d.** cluster A1775A **2.185** yes; z = -2.5 **2.187 a.** quantitative: days and year **b.** lesser crimes **c.** yes **d.** mean = 41.4 days; median = 15 days **e.** no; z = 2.38 **f.** no **2.189 a.** median **b.** mean **2.191** survey results biased, not reliable

Chapter 3

3.9 a. .5 **b.** .3 **c.** .6 **3.11** P(A) = .55; P(B) = .50; P(C) = .70 **3.13 a.** 10 **b.** 20 **c.** 15,504 **3.15 a.** $(R_1R_2), (R_1R_3), (R_2R_3),$ $(R_1B_1), (R_1B_2), (R_2B_1), (R_2B_2), (R_3B_1), (R_3B_2), (B_1B_2)$ **b.** 1/10 for each sample point **c.** P(A) = 1/10, P(B) = 6/10, P(C) = 3/10 **3.17** .05 **3.19 a.** .01 **b.** yes **3.21 a.** .261 **b.** Trunk $-$ .85, Leaves $-$ .10, Branch $-$ .05 **3.23 a.** Interview; Observation + Participation; Observation Only; Grounded Theory **c.** .677, .139, .113, .072 **d.** .748 **3.25 a.** 6 **b.** .282, .065, .339, .032, .008, .274 **c.** .686 **3.27 a.** 28 **b.** 1/28 **3.29** 693/1,686,366 = .000411 **3.31 a.** 15 **b.** 20 **c.** 15 **d.** 6 **3.41 b.** P(A) = 7/8, P(B) = 1/2, $P(A \cup B)$ = 7/8, $P(A^c)$ = 1/8, $P(A \cap B)$ = 1/2 **c.** 7/8 **d.** no **3.43 a.** $^3/_4$ **b.** 13/20 **c.** 1 **d.** 2/5 **e.** $^1/_4$ **f.** 7/20 **g.** 1 **h.** 1/4 **3.45 a.** .65 **b.** .72 **c.** .25 **d.** .08 **e.** .35 **f.** .72 **g.** .65 **g.** A and C, B and C, C and D **3.47 a.** School laboratory, In Transit, Chemical plant, Non-chemical plant, Other **b.** .06, .26, .21, .35, .12 **c.** .06 **d.** .56 **e.** .74 **3.49 b.** .43 **c.** .57 **3.51 a.** {11, 13, 15, 17, 29, 31, 33, 35} **b.** {2, 4, 6, 8, 10, 11, 13, 15, 17, 20, 22, 24, 26, 28, 29, 31, 33, 35, 1, 3, 5, 7, 9, 19, 21, 23, 25, 27} **c.** P(A) = 9/19, P(B) = 9/19, $P(A \cap B)$ = 4/19, $P(A \cup B)$ = 14/19, P(C) = 9/19 **d.** {11, 13, 15, 17} **e.** 14/19, no **f.** 2/19 **g.** {1, 2, 3, ..., 29, 31, 33, 35} **h.** 16/19 **3.53 b.** .156 **c.** .617 **d.** .210 **e.** .449 **f.** yes **3.55 a.** (PTW-R, Jury), (PTW-R, Judge), (PTW-A/D, Jury), (PTW-A/D, Judge), (DTW-R, Jury), (DTW-R, Judge), (DTW-A/D, Jury), (DTW-A/D, Judge) **b.** .684 **c.** .124 **d.** no **e.** .316 **f.** .717 **g.** .091 **3.57** P(9) = 25/216 is less than P(10) = 27/216 **3.59** $P(A \cap B) = P(A) \cdot P(B)$ **3.61** $P(A \cap B) = P(A) \cdot P(B|A)$ **3.63 a.** .5 **b.** .25 **c.** no **3.65 a.** .08 **b.** .40 **c.** .52 **3.67 a.** P(A) = .4; P(B) = .4; $P(A \cap B)$ = .3 **b.** $P(E_1|A)$ = .25, $P(E_2|A)$ = .25, $P(E_3|A)$ = .5 **c.** .75 **3.69** no **3.71** 1/3, 0, 1/14, 1/7, 1 **3.73** .40 **3.75 a.** .1 **b.** .522 **c.** The person is guessing **3.77 a.** .7 **b.** .5 **c.** .5 **3.79 a.** .23 **b.** .729 **3.81 a.** 38/132 = .2879 **b.** 29/123 = .236 **3.83 a.** P(A|I) = .9, P(B|I) = .95, P(A|N) = .2, P(B|N) = .1 **b.** .855 **c.** .02 **d.** .995 **3.85 a.** .333 **b.** .120 **c.** No **d.** probability of playing Center depends on race **3.87** $P(A|B) = 0$ **3.89 a.** (A defeats B, C defeats D, A defeats C), (A defeats B, C defeats D, C defeats A), (A defeats B, D defeats C, A defeats D), (A defeats B, D defeats C, D defeats A), (B defeats A, C defeats D, B defeats C), (B defeats A, C defeats D, C defeats B), (B defeats A, D defeats C, B defeats D), (B defeats A, D defeats C, D defeats B) **b.** P(A wins) = 2/8 = .25 **c.** .576 **3.91 a.** .553 **b.** P(W | CA) = 1; P(W | CB) = .873; P(W | CC) = .559; P(W | BA) = .741; P(W | BB) = .547; P(W | BC) = .342; P(W | AA) = .536; P(W | AB) = .216; P(W | AC) = .128 **c.** .856 **d.** .552 **3.93 b.** Worst $-$ .250, 2nd worst $-$ .200, 3rd worst $-$ .157, 4th worst $-$ .120, 5th worst $-$ .089, 6th worst $-$ .064, 7th worst $-$ .044, 8th worst $-$ .029, 9th worst $-$ .018, 10th worst $-$ .011, 11th worst $-$ .007, 12th worst $-$ .006, 13th worst $-$ .005 **c.** 250/800 = .313 **d.** .297 **e.** .288 **3.99 a.** 35,820,200 **b.** 1/35,820,200 **c.** highly unlikely **3.111 a.** 4 **b.** 8 **c.** 32 **d.** 2^n **3.113 a.** 35 **b.** 15 **c.** 435 **d.** 45 **e.** $\binom{q}{r} = \dfrac{q!}{r!(q-r!)}$

3.115 a. 56 **b.** 1,680 **c.** 6,720 **3.117 a.** 24 **b.** 12 **3.119 a.** 30 **b.** 1,050 **3.121 a.** 6 **b.** 1/3 **3.123 a.** 18 **b.** 4/18
3.125 a. 21/252 **b.** 21/252 **c.** 105/252 **3.127 a.** 2,598,960 **b.** .002 **c.** .00394 **d.** .0000154 **3.131 a.** .225 **b.** .125 **c.** .35
d. .643 **e.** .357 **3.133** .2 **3.135 a.** .5 **b.** .99 **c.** .847 **3.137 a.** .158 **b.** .316 **c.** .526 **d.** #3 **3.139** .966 **3.141 a.** $A \cup B$
b. B^c **c.** $A \cap B$ **d.** $A^c|B$ **3.143 a.** 0 **b.** no **3.145** .5 **3.147 c.** $P(A) = 1/4; P(B) = \frac{1}{2}$ **e.** $P(A^c) = 3/4; P(B^c) = 1/2;$
$P(A \cap B) = 1/4; P(A \cup B) = 1/2; P(A \mid B) = 1/2; P(B \mid A) = 1$ **f.** no, no **3.149 a.** no **b.** .3, .1 **c.** .37 **3.151 a.** 720 **b.** 10
c. 10 **d.** 30 **e.** 20 **f.** 1 **g.** 5,040 **h.** 2,450 **3.153 a.** false **b.** true **c.** true **d.** false **3.155** $A = \{$8th-grader scores above 655$\}$
$P(A^c) = .95$ **3.157 b.** .147 **c.** .85 **d.** .65 **e.** yes **f.** African Americans are stopped for speeding more often than expected
3.159 a. {Single, shore parallel; Other; Planar} **b.** .1/3, 1/3, 1/3 **c.** 2/3 **d.** {No dunes/flat; Bluff/scarp; Single dune; Not observed}
e. 1/3, 1/6, 1/3, 1/6 **f.** 2/3 **3.161 a.** Total population, Agricultural change, Presence of industry, Growth, Population concentration
b. .18, .05, .27, .05, .45 **c.** .63 **3.163 a.** .385 **b.** .378 **c.** .183 **3.165 a.** .64, .32, .04 **b.** .72, .22, .06 **c.** dependent **3.167 a.** .116
b. .728 **3.169 a.** .7127 **b.** .2873 **c.** .9639 **d.** .3078 **e.** .0361 **f.** at least 3 **3.171 a.** #4 **b.** #4 or #6 **3.173 a.** 1 to 2 **b.** .5
c. .4 **3.175 a.** .25 **b.** .0156 **c.** .4219 **d.** .000000001, .9970 **3.177** .993 **3.179** 4.4739×10^{-28} **3.181** Probabilities are the
same **3.183** yes

Chapter 4

4.3 a. discrete **b.** continuous **c.** continuous **d.** discrete **e.** continuous **f.** continuous **4.5 a.** continuous **b.** discrete
c. discrete **d.** discrete **e.** discrete **f.** continuous **4.7** 0, 1, 2, 3, …; discrete **4.9** gender; IQ score **4.11** allergy to penicillin;
blood pressure **4.13** table, graph, formula **4.15 a.** .25 **b.** .40 **c.** .75 **4.17 a.** .7 **b.** .3 **c.** 1 **d.** .2 **e.** .8 **4.19 b.** $P(0) = 1/8$,
$P(1) = 3/8$, $P(2) = 3/8, P(3) = 1/8$ **d.** 1/2 **4.21 a.** 1 **b.** .24 **c.** .39 **4.23 a.** $P(6) = .282, P(7) = .065, P(8) = .339$,
$P(9) = .032, P(10) = .008, P(11) = .274$ **b.** .274 **4.25 a.** .9985, .0015, 0, 0 **c.** 1 **4.27** $P(-3) = .1, P(-1) = .105, P(5) = .795$
4.29 7/8 **4.31 a.** 0, 1, 2 **b.** $P(0) = .625, P(1) = .250, P(2) = .125$ **4.33** no **4.35 a.** 3.8 **b.** 10.56 **c.** 3.2496 **e.** no **f.** yes
4.37 a. $\mu_x = 1, \mu_y = 1$ **b.** distribution of x **c.** $\mu_x = 1, \sigma^2 = .6; \mu_y = 1, \sigma^2 = .2$ **4.39 b.** 4.65 **4.41 a.** 1.8 **b.** .9899 **c.** .96 **4.43 a.**
MC, MS, MB, MO, ML, CS, CB, CO, CL, SB, SO, SL, BO, BL, OL **b.** equally likely, with p = 1/15 **d.** $P(0) = 6/15, P(1) = 8/15$,

$$P(2) = 1/15 \quad \textbf{e. } .667 \quad \textbf{4.45 } -\$0.263 \quad \textbf{4.47 } \$0.25 \quad \textbf{4.49 } p(x) = \binom{7}{x}.2^x.8^{7-x} \quad (x = 0,1,2,\dots,7) \quad \textbf{4.51 a. } 15 \quad \textbf{b. } 10 \quad \textbf{c. } 1 \quad \textbf{d. } 1$$

e. 4 **4.53 a.** .4096 **b.** .3456 **c.** .027 **d.** .0081 **e.** .3456 **f.** .027 **4.55 a.** $\mu = 12.5, \sigma^2 = 6.25, \sigma = 2.5$ **b.** $\mu = 16, \sigma^2 = 12.8$,
$\sigma = 3.578$ **c.** $\mu = 60, \sigma^2 = 24, \sigma = 4.899$ **d.** $\mu = 63, \sigma^2 = 6.3, \sigma = 2.510$ **e.** $\mu = 48, \sigma^2 = 9.6, \sigma = 3.098$ **f.** $\mu = 40, \sigma^2 = 38.4$,
$\sigma = 6.197$ **4.57 a.** 0 **b.** .998 **c.** .137 **4.59 a.** $p = .5$ **b.** $p < .5$ **c.** $p > .5$ **4.61 b.** $n = 20, p = .8$ **c.** .174 **d.** .804
e. 16 **4.63 a.** .001 **b.** .322 **c.** .994 **4.65 a.** .986 **b.** ≈ 0 **c.** 5 **4.67 a.** .7908 **b.** .0556 **4.69 a.** .1 **b.** .7 **c.** .4783 **d.** .0078
e. yes **4.71 b.** = 2.4, = 1.47 **c.** $p = .9, q = .1, n = 24$, = 21.6, = 1.47 **4.75** 3 **4.77 b.** = 3, = 1.7321 **4.79 a.** .934 **b.** .191
c. .125 **d.** .223 **e.** .777 **f.** .001 **4.81 b.** = 3, = 1.7321 **c.** .966 **4.83 a.** .368 **b.** .264 **c.** .920 **4.85 a.** .3012 **b.** .3614
c. $\mu = 1.2, \sigma = 1.0954$ **4.87 a.** .125 **b.** 5 **c.** no; $p(0) = .007$ **4.89 a.** $p(2) = .039, p(6) = .160, p(10) = .047$ **c.** $\mu = 6.2$,
$\sigma = 2.49$ **d.** very unlikely **4.91** yes, .96 **4.95 a.** .3 **b.** .119 **c.** .167 **d.** .167 **4.97 b.** $\mu = 4, \sigma = .853$ **d.** .939 **4.99 a.**
hypergeometric **b.** binomial **4.101 a.** .383 **b.** .0002 **4.103** .2693 **4.105 a.** .0883 **b.** .1585 **4.107** $P(x = 1) = .25$
4.109 a. $\mu = 113.24, \sigma = 4.19$ **b.** $z = 6.38$ **4.111 a.** Poisson **b.** binomial **c.** binomial **4.113 a.** .192 **b.** .228 **c.** .772 **d.** .987
e. .960 **f.** 14; 4.2; 2.05 **g.** .975 **4.115 a.** .243 **b.** .131 **c.** .36 **d.** .157 **e.** .128 **f.** .121 **4.117 a.** .180 **b.** .015 **c.** .076
4.119 b. .05 **c.** 10 **4.121 b.** 1/30 **c.** .1455 **d.** .1559 **4.123** binomial **4.125 a.** yes **b.** .051 **c.** .757 **d.** .192 **e.** 3.678
4.127 a. $\mu = 520, \sigma = 13.491$ **b.** no, $z = -8.895$ **4.129** .642 **4.131 a.** 2 **b.** no, $p = .003$ **4.133 a.** .006 **b.** insecticide is less
effective than claimed **4.135 a.** .001 **b.** yes **4.137** .109 **4.139** NASA: .0004; Air Force: .5155; Air Force

Chapter 5

5.3 b. $\mu = 20, \sigma = 5.774$ **c.** (8.452, 31.548) **5.5 b.** $\mu = 3, \sigma = .577$ **c.** .577 **d.** .61 **e.** .65 **f.** 0 **5.7 a.** 0 **b.** 1 **c.** 1 **5.9 a.** .8
b. .3 **5.11 a.** .1333, .5714 **b.** .2667, 0 **5.13** $\mu = .5, \sigma = .2887$, 10th percentile = .1, $Q_L = .25, Q_U = .75$ **5.15 a.** continuous
c. $\mu = 7, \sigma = .2887$ **d.** .5 **e.** 0 **f.** .75 **g.** .0002 **5.17** .4444 **5.19** symmetric, bell-shaped curve **5.21** normal with = 0 and $\sigma = 1$
5.23 a. .4772 **b.** .3413 **c.** .4545 **d.** .2190 **5.25 a.** 0 **b.** .8413 **c.** .8413 **d.** .1587 **e.** .6826 **f.** .9544 **g.** .6934 **h.** .6378 **5.27 a.** 1.645
b. 1.96 **c.** −1.96 **d.** 1.28 **e.** 1.28 **5.29 a.** 0 **b.** 1 **c.** 2.5 **d.** −3 **e.** 5 **f.** 1.4 **5.31 a.** .0456; .0026 **b.** .6826; .9544 **c.** 325.2; 261.6
5.33 a. 19.76 **b.** 36.72 **c.** 48.64 **5.35** 182 **5.37 a.** .1442 **b.** .2960 **c.** .0023 **d.** .9706 **5.39 a.** .8413 **b.** .7528 **5.41 a.** .4107
b. .1508 **c.** .9066 **d.** .0162 **e.** 841.8 **5.43 f.** (62.26, 65.74); (61.01, 66.99); (59.72, 68.28); (58.90, 69.10); (57.30, 70.70) **5.45 a.** .0735
b. .3651 **c.** 7.29 **5.47** $d = 56.24$ **5.49 a.** $z_L = -.675, z_U = .675$ **b.** −2.68, 2.68 **c.** −4.69, 4.69 **d.** .0074, 0 **5.53 a.** .68 **b.** .95
c. .997 **5.55** plot c **5.57 a.** not normal (skewed right) **b.** $Q_L = 37.5, Q_U = 152.8, s = 95.8$ **c.** IQR/s = 1.204 **5.59 a.** 6 **b.** 5.275
c. IQR/s = 1.14 **5.61** no; IQR/s = .82 **5.63 a.** histogram too peaked **b.** more than 95% **5.65** both distributions approx
normal **5.67** IQR/s = 1.3, histogram approx. normal **5.69** lowest score of 0 is less than one standard deviation below the
mean **5.73 a.** yes **b.** $\mu = 10, \sigma^2 = 6$ **c.** .726 **d.** .7291 **5.75 a.** .1788 **b.** .5236 **c.** .6950 **5.77 a.** 16.25 **b.** 3.49 **c.** 1.07
d. .1762 **5.79 a.** $\mu = 1,500, \sigma^2 = 1,275$ **b.** .0026 **c.** no **5.81** ≈ 0 **5.83 a.** no **b.** yes **c.** yes **5.85** ≈ 0 **5.87 a.** 300 **b.** 800
c. 1 **5.93 a.** .367879 **b.** .950213 **c.** .223130 **d.** .993262 **5.95** .950213 **5.97 a.** .449329 **b.** .864665 **5.99** .434598 **5.101 a.** .367879
b. .606531 **c.** .135335 **d.** .814046 **5.103 a.** 17 **b.** .5862 **5.107 a.** exponential **b.** uniform **c.** normal **5.109 a.** .9821 **b.** .0179
c. .9505 **d.** .3243 **e.** .9107 **f.** .0764 **5.111 a.** .6915 **b.** .0228 **c.** .5328 **d.** .3085 **e.** 0 **f.** .9938 **5.113 a.** .3821 **b.** .5389 **c.** 0
d. .1395 **e.** .0045 **f.** .4602 **5.115** .8315 **5.117 a.** .9406 **b.** .9406 **c.** .1140 **5.119 a.** 0 **b.** 1 **5.121 a.** .667 **b.** .333 **c.** 82.5°F
5.123 a. .3745 **b.** .7553 **5.125** .3125 **5.127** .0154; very unlikely **5.129** .4364 **5.131** approx. normal **5.133 a.** (i) .384, (ii) .49, (iii) .212,
(iv) .84 **b.** (i) .3849, (ii) .4938, (iii) .2119, (iv) .8413 **c.** (i) .0009, (ii) .0038, (iii) .0001, (iv) .0013 **5.135** 52 minutes **5.137** 5.068 **5.139** 0;
unlikely **5.141 a.** .05, .20, .50, .20, .05 **b.** z-scores **c.** identical

Chapter 6

6.3 c. $1/16$ **6.5 c.** $.05$ **d.** no **6.13** unbiased, minimum variance **6.15 a.** 5 **b.** $E(\bar{x}) = 5$ **c.** $E(M) = 4.778$ **d.** $\bar{x}$ **6.19 b.** 1.61 **c.** $E(s^2) = 1.61$ **e.** $E(s) = 1.004$ **6.21** mean and standard deviation of sampling distribution of $\bar{x}$ **6.23** smaller **6.27 a.** $\mu = 100, \sigma = 5$ **b.** $\mu = 100, \sigma = 2$ **c.** $\mu = 100, \sigma = 1$ **d.** $\mu = 100, \sigma = 1.414$ **e.** $\mu = 100, \sigma = .447$ **f.** $\mu = 100, \sigma = .316$ **6.29 a.** $\mu = 2.9, \sigma^2 = 3.29, \sigma = 1.814$ **c.** $\mu_{\bar{x}} = 2.9, \sigma_{\bar{x}} = 1.283$ **6.31 a.** $\mu_{\bar{x}} = 30, \sigma_{\bar{x}} = 1.6$ **b.** approx. normal **c.** $.8944$ **d.** $.0228$ **e.** $.1303$ **f.** $.9699$ **6.35 a.** $\mu_{\bar{x}} = 320, \sigma_{\bar{x}} = 10$, approx. normal **b.** $.1359$ **c.** 0 **6.37 a.** 79 **b.** 2.3 **c.** approx. normal **d.** $.43$ **e.** $.3336$ **6.39 a.** $.10; .0002$ **b.** Central Limit Theorem **c.** $.0170$ **6.41 a.** $\mu_{\bar{x}} = .53, \sigma_{\bar{x}} = .0273$, approx. normal **b.** $.0336$ **c.** after **6.43 a.** $.0034$ **b.** $\mu > 6$ **6.45** handrubbing: $P(\bar{x} < 30) = .2743$; handwashing: $P(\bar{x} < 30) = .0047$; sample used handrubbing **6.47** false **6.49** true **6.51 b.** $E(A) = \alpha$ **c.** choose estimator with smallest variance **6.53 a.** $.5$ **b.** $.0606$ **c.** $.0985$ **d.** $.8436$ **6.59 a.** $\mu_{\bar{x}} = 89.34, \sigma_{\bar{x}} = 1.3083$ **c.** $.8461$ **d.** $.0367$ **6.61 a.** $\mu_{\bar{x}} = 1.3, \sigma_{\bar{x}} = .240$ **b.** yes **c.** $.1056$ **d.** $.0062$ **6.63** $.9772$ **6.65 a.** $.008$ **b.** n large **6.67 a.** $.3264$ **b.** 1.881 **c.** valid **6.69** $.9332$ **6.71 a.** $.0031$ **b.** more likely if $\mu = 156$; less likely if $\mu = 158$ **c.** less likely if $\sigma = 2$; more likely if $\sigma = 6$

Chapter 7

7.5 yes **7.7 a.** 1.645 **b.** 2.58 **c.** 1.96 **d.** 1.28 **7.9 a.** $28 \pm .784$ **b.** $102 \pm .65$ **c.** $15 \pm .0588$ **d.** $4.05 \pm .163$ **e.** no **7.11 a.** 83.2 ± 1.25 **c.** 83.2 ± 1.65 **d.** increases **e.** yes **7.13 a.** 19.3 **b.** 19.3 ± 3.44 **d.** random sample, large n **7.15 a.** $.36 \pm .0099$ **c.** first-year: $.303 \pm .0305$; landfast: $.362 \pm .0177$; multi-year: $.381 \pm .0101$ **7.17 a.** μ **b.** no; apply Central Limit Theorem **c.** $(0.4786, 0.8167)$ **d.** yes **7.19 a.** $1.13 \pm .67$ **b.** yes **7.21 a.** 19 ± 7.826 **b.** 7 ± 5.90 **c.** SAT-Math **7.23 a.** males: 16.79 ± 2.35; females: 10.79 ± 1.67 **b.** $.0975$ **c.** males **7.25** Central Limit Theorem no longer applies; σ unknown **7.27 a.** large: normal; small: t-distribution **b.** large: normal; small: unknown **7.29 a.** 2.228 **b.** 2.567 **c.** -3.707 **d.** -1.771 **7.31 a.** 5 ± 1.876 **b.** 5 ± 2.394 **c.** 5 ± 3.754 **d.** (a) $5 \pm .780$, (b) $5 \pm .941$, (c) 5 ± 1.276; width decreases **7.33 a.** $\bar{x} = 1.86, s = 1.195$ **b.** skewed right **c.** $1.86 \pm .45$ **e.** 90% **7.35 a.** $.009$ **b.** 2.306 **c.** $.009 \pm .0037$ **7.37 a.** $1.07 \pm .24$ **c.** normal **7.39 a.** both untreated: 20.9 ± 1.06; male treated: 20.3 ± 1.25; female treated: 22.9 ± 1.79; both treated: $18.6 \pm .79$ **b.** female treated **7.41 a.** 7.3 ± 1.41 **c.** PMI values normally distributed **7.43 a.** 37.3 ± 7.70 **c.** One hour before: $\mu > 25.5$ **7.47 a.** yes **b.** $.64 \pm .067$ **7.49 a.** yes **b.** no **c.** no **d.** no **7.51 a.** set of all gun ownership status (yes/no) values for all U.S. adults **b.** true percentage of all adults who own a gun **c.** $.26$ **d.** $.26 \pm .02$ **7.53 a.** $.63 \pm .03$ **b.** yes **7.55** $.219 \pm .024$ **7.57 a.** $.338 \pm .025$ **7.59 a.** $.524 \pm .095$ **7.61** 95% confident that proportion of health care workers with latex allergy who suspect he/she has allergy is between $.327$ and $.541$ **7.63** true **7.65** 519 **7.67 a.** 482 **b.** 214 **7.69** 34 **7.71 a.** $n = 16$: $W = .98$; $n = 25$: $W = .784$; $n = 49$: $W = .56$; $n = 100$: $W = .392$; $n = 400$: $W = .196$ **7.73 a.** small sample **b.** 125 **7.75** 21 **7.77** 14,735 **7.79** 129 **7.81** 271 **7.83 a.** μ **b.** μ **c.** p **d.** p **e.** p **7.85 a.** $t = 2.086$ **b.** $z = 1.96$ **c.** $z = 1.96$ **d.** $z = 1.96$ **e.** neither t nor z **7.87 a.** $.57 \pm .049$ **b.** 2,358 **7.89** (1) p; (2) μ; (3) μ; (4) μ **7.91 a.** $.03$ **b.** $.03 \pm .010$ **7.93 a.** $.90$ **b.** $.05$ **c.** 259 **7.95** $1.37 \pm .76$ **7.97** 95% confident that true proportion of all adults who are homeless is between $.045$ and $.091$ **7.99 a.** $.660 \pm .029$ **b.** $.301 \pm .035$ **7.101 a.** $.044 \pm .162$ **b.** no evidence of species inbreeding **7.103 a.** $.81 \pm .41$ **b.** 140 **7.105 a.** $.378 \pm .156$ **b.** $.703 \pm .147$ **c.** 41.405 ± 21.493 **d.** $.378 \pm .156$ **7.107 a.** $.094$ **b.** yes **c.** $.094 \pm .037$ **7.109 a.** 49.3 ± 8.60 **c.** Population is normal. **d.** 60 **7.111 a.** 781 **7.113 a.** yes **b.** missing measure of reliability **c.** 95% CI for μ: $.932 \pm .037$

Chapter 8

8.1 null hypothesis **8.3** α **8.7** no **8.9** H_0: $p = .75$, H_a: $p \neq .75$ **8.11 a.** H_0: $p = .45$ **b.** H_0: $= 2.5$ **8.13** H_0: $p = .05$, H_a: $p < .05$ **8.15 a.** H_0: $\mu = 15$, H_a: $\mu < 15$ **b.** conclude mean mercury level is less than 15 ppm when mean equals 15 ppm **c.** conclude mean mercury level equals 15 ppm when mean is less than 15 ppm **8.17 a.** H_0: No intrusion occurs **b.** H_a: Intrusion occurs **c.** $\alpha = .001$, $\beta = .5$ **8.21 g.** (a) $.025$, (b) $.05$, (c) $\approx .005$, (d) $\approx .10$, (e) $.10$, (f) $\approx .01$ **8.23 a.** $z = 1.67$, reject H_0 **b.** $z = 1.67$, fail to reject H_0 **8.25 a.** Type I: conclude mean response for all New York City public school children is not 3 when mean equals 3; Type II: conclude mean response for all New York City public school children equals 3 when mean is not equal to 3 **b.** $z = -85.52$, reject H_0 **c.** $z = -85.52$, reject H_0 **8.27** yes, $z = 3.95$ **8.29 a.** H_0: $\mu = 16$, H_a: $\mu < 16$ **b.** $z = -4.31$, reject H_0 **8.31 a.** $z = 4.03$, reject H_0 **8.33 a.** no **b.** $z = .61$, do not reject H_0 **d.** no **e.** $z = -.83$, do not reject H_0 **8.35 a.** $z = -3.72$, reject H_0 **8.37** small p-values **8.39 a.** fail to reject H_0 **b.** reject H_0 **c.** reject H_0 **d.** fail to reject H_0 **e.** fail to reject H_0 **8.41** $.0150$ **8.43** p-value $= .9279$, fail to reject H_0 **8.45 a.** fail to reject H_0 **b.** fail to reject H_0 **c.** reject H_0 **d.** fail to reject H_0 **8.47 a.** $.3446$ **b.** do not reject H_0 **8.49** p-value $< .0001$; reject H_0 at $\alpha = .05$ **8.51 b.** reject H_0 at $\alpha = .05$ **c.** reject H_0 at $\alpha = .05$ **8.53 a.** $.1970$ **b.** $.0985$ **c.** $.3788$ **d.** (a) $.20$; (b) $.10$; (c) $.40$ **e.** $s \leq 3.95$ **8.55** small n, normal population **8.57** $.10$; $.05$; $.05$ **8.59 a.** $t = -2.064$; fail to reject H_0 **b.** $t = -2.064$; fail to reject H_0 **c.** (a) $.05 < p$-value $< .10$; (b) $.10 < p$-value $< .20$ **8.61 b.** reject H_0 at $\alpha = .05$ **c.** p-value $= .076$; do not reject H_0 at $\alpha = .05$ **8.63 a.** H_0: $\mu = 5.70$, H_a: $\mu < 5.70$ **b.** $t < -2.821$ **c.** $t = -4.33$ **d.** reject H_0 **8.65** $t = -.43$; fail to reject H_0 **8.67** $t = 3.725$, p-value $= .0058$, reject H_0 **8.69** yes, $t = -2.53$ **8.71** yes, $t = 1.95$ **8.73** qualitative **8.75 a.** yes **b.** no **c.** no **d.** no **e.** no **8.77 a.** $z = -2.00$ **c.** reject H_0 **d.** $.0228$ **8.79 a.** $z = 1.13$, fail to reject H_0 **b.** $.1292$ **8.81 a.** p **b.** H_0: $p = .02$, H_a: $p > .02$ **c.** $z = 14.23$; $z > 1.645$ **d.** reject H_0 **e.** large n; yes **8.83** yes, $z = 1.74$ **8.85** yes, $z = -2.71$ **8.87** no, $z = 1.52$ **8.89 a.** no, $z = 1.49$ **b.** p-value $\approx .07$ **8.91** $z = 33.47$, reject H_0: $p = .5$ **8.93** power $= 1 - \beta$ **8.95 b.** 1,032.9 **d.** $.7422$ **e.** $.2578$ **8.97 a.** approx. normal, $\mu_{\bar{x}} = 50$, $\sigma_{\bar{x}} = 2.5$ **b.** approx. normal, $\mu_{\bar{x}} = 45$, $\sigma_{\bar{x}} = 2.5$ **c.** $.2358$ **d.** $.7642$ **8.99 a.** approx. normal, $\mu_{\bar{x}} = 10$, $\sigma_{\bar{x}} = 0.1$ **b.** approx. normal, $\mu_{\bar{x}} = 9.9$, $\sigma_{\bar{x}} = 0.1$ **c.** $.8300$ **d.** $.8300$ **8.101** power increases **8.103** $.1814$ **8.107** false **8.109 a.** $\chi^2 < 6.26214$ or $\chi^2 > 27.4884$ **b.** $\chi^2 > 40.2894$ **c.** $\chi^2 > 21.0642$ **d.** $\chi^2 < 3.57056$ **e.** $\chi^2 < 1.63539$ or $\chi^2 > 12.5916$ **f.** $\chi^2 < 13.8484$ **8.111 a.** $\chi^2 = 182.16$, reject H_0 **8.113 a.** $\chi^2 < 20.7065$ or $\chi^2 > 66.7659$ **b.** $\chi^2 = 63.72$ **c.** do not reject H_0 **8.115** $\chi^2 = 12.61$, fail to reject H_0 **8.117** $\chi^2 = 187.90$, do not reject H_0: $\sigma^2 = 225$ **8.119** $\chi^2 = 2.16$, fail to reject H_0 **8.121 a.** no, $\chi^2 = 2.09$ **b.** population of CO_2 amounts are normal **8.123** alternative **8.125** H_0, H_a, α **8.127** null **8.129 a.** $z = -1.78$, reject H_0 **b.** $z = -1.78$, fail to reject H_0 **c.** $.29 \pm .063$ **d.** $.29 \pm .083$ **e.** 549 **8.131 a.** $\chi^2 = 63.48$, reject H_0 **b.** $\chi^2 = 63.48$, reject H_0 **8.133 a.** H_0: Drug is unsafe, H_a: Drug is safe   **c.** α **8.135 a.** $t = -3.46$, reject H_o **b.** normal population   **8.137 a.** H_o: $p = .5$, H_a: $p \neq .5$ **b.** $z = 5.99$ **c.** yes   **d.** reject H_o **8.139** yes, $z = 12.36$ **8.141 a.** $t = 1.44$, p-value $= .169$, fail to reject H_o **8.143 a.** $z = .70$, fail to reject H_o **b.** yes   **8.145 a.** no, $z = 1.41$ **b.** small α **8.147 a.** no   **b.** $\beta = .5910$, power $= .4090$ **c.** power increases   **8.149** $z = 15.46$, reject H_o: $p = .167$ **8.151 b.** .37, .24   **8.153 a.** yes, $z = -2.33$ **b.** .1075   **8.155 a.** no at $\alpha = .01$, $z = 1.85$ **b.** yes at $\alpha = .01$, $z = 3.09$

Chapter 9

9.1 normally distributed with mean $\mu_1 - \mu_2$ and standard deviation $\sqrt{\dfrac{\sigma_1^2}{n_1} + \dfrac{\sigma_2^2}{n_2}}$ **9.3 a.** no   **b.** no   **c.** no   **d.** yes   **e.** no   **9.5** b

9.7 a. 14; .4   **b.** 10; .3   **c.** 4; .5   **d.** yes   **9.9 a.** .5989   **b.** $t = -2.39$, reject H_o **c.** $-1.24 \pm .98$ **9.11 a.** fail to reject H_o at $\alpha = .10$ **b.** p-value $= .0575$, reject H_o at $\alpha = .10$ **9.13 a.** H_o: $\mu_1 = \mu_2$, H_a: $\mu_1 \neq \mu_2$ **b.** $t = .62$ **c.** $|t| > 1.684$ **d.** fail to reject H_o; supports theory   **9.15 a.** $\mu_1 - \mu_2$ **b.** 12.5 ± 10.2 **9.17 b.** $z = -2.64$, reject H_o **c.** $z = .27$, fail to reject H_o **9.19 a.** $(-.60, 7.96)$ **b.** independent random samples from normal populations with equal variances   **9.21** $t = 1.08$, fail to reject H_o **9.23** no, $t = .18$ **9.25 a.** $\mu_1 - \mu_2$ **b.** no   **c.** .2262   **d.** fail to reject H_o **9.27** $t = -.46$, fail to reject H_o **9.29 a.** no standard deviations reported   **b.** $s_1 = s_2 = 5$ **c.** $s_1 = s_2 = 6$ **9.31** before   **9.33 a.** $t > 1.833$ **b.** $t > 1.328$ **c.** $t > 2.776$ **d.** $t > 2.896$ **9.35 a.** $\bar{x}_d = 2$, $s_d^2 = 2$ **b.** $\mu_d = \mu_1 - \mu_2$ **c.** 2 ± 1.484 **d.** $t = 3.46$, reject H_o **9.37 a.** $z = 1.79$, fail to reject H_o **b.** .0734   **9.39** yes; $(7.43, 13.57)$ **9.41 a.** μ_d **b.** paired difference   **c.** H_o: $\mu_d = 0$, H_a: $\mu_d > 0$ **d.** $t = 2.19$ **e.** reject H_o **9.43 a.** H_o: $\mu_d = 0$, H_a: $\mu_d \neq 0$ **b.** $z = 2.08$, p-value $= .0376$ **c.** reject H_o **9.45 b.** 95% CI for μ_d: 1.95 ± 1.91; control group has larger mean   **9.47 a.** $t = -2.97$, fail to reject H_o **b.** $-.42$; no   **c.** $t = .57$, fail to reject H_o; $-.23$, no   **d.** $t = 3.23$, fail to reject H_o; .19, no   **9.49** 95% CI for μ_d: $-.000523 \pm .000400$; use alternative method   **9.51** large, independent samples   **9.53 a.** no   **b.** no   **c.** no   **d.** no   **e.** no   **9.55 a.** $.07 \pm .067$ **b.** $.06 \pm .086$ **c.** $-.15 \pm .131$ **9.57** $z = 1.16$, fail to reject H_o **9.59 a.** .55   **b.** .70   **c.** $-.15 \pm .03$ **d.** 90% confidence **e.** Dutch boys   **9.61 a.** .143   **b.** .049   **c.** $z = 2.27$, fail to reject H_o **d.** reject H_o **9.63 a.** $z = 94.35$, reject H_o **b.** $-.139 \pm .016$ **9.65** yes, $z = 11.05$ **9.67** yes; $z = 2.13$, reject H_o at $\alpha = .05$ **9.69** $.48 \pm .144$; proportion greater for those who slept   **9.71 a.** at least 18 **b.** sample may not be representative of the population   **9.75** $n_1 = n_2 = 24$ **9.77 a.** $n_1 = n_2 = 29,954$ **b.** $n_1 = n_2 = 2,165$ **c.** $n_1 = n_2 = 1,113$ **9.79** $n_1 = n_2 = 49$ **9.81** $n_1 = n_2 = 130$ **9.83** $n_1 = n_2 = 1,729$ **9.85** $n_1 = n_2 = 136$ **9.87** normal, independent populations   **9.89** false   **9.91 a.** .025   **b.** .90   **c.** .99   **d.** .05   **9.93 a.** $F > 2.36$ **b.** $F > 3.04$ **c.** $F > 3.84$ **d.** $F > 5.12$ **9.95 a.** $F = 3.43$, reject H_o **b.** p-value $< .02$, reject H_o **9.97 a.** H_o: $\sigma_M^2 = \sigma_F^2$, H_a: $\sigma_M^2 < \sigma_F^2$ **b.** $F = 1.06$ **c.** $F > 1.26$ **d.** p-value $> .10$ **e.** fail to reject H_o **9.99** $F = 1.05$, fail to reject H_o; assumption is valid   **9.101** $F = 1.20$, reject H_o **9.103 a.** no, $F = 2.27$ **b.** p-value $> .10$ **9.105 a.** $F = 8.29$, reject H_o **b.** no   **9.107 a.** $\mu_1 - \mu_2$ **b.** $\mu_1 - \mu_2$ **c.** $p_1 - p_2$ **d.** σ_1^2/σ_2^2 **e.** $p_1 - p_2$ **9.109 a.** $t = .78$, fail to reject H_o **b.** 2.5 ± 8.99 **c.** $n_1 = n_2 = 225$ **9.111 a.** $3.9 \pm .31$ **b.** $z = 20.60$, reject H_o **c.** $n_1 = n_2 = 346$ **9.113 a.** p-value $= .871$, fail to reject H_o: $\mu_{no} - \mu_{yes} = 0$ **9.115 a.** time needed   **b.** climbers   **c.** paired experiment   **9.117 a.** H_o: $\mu_d = 0$, H_a: $\mu_d > 0$ **b.** paired difference test   **d.** leadership: fail to reject H_o at $\alpha = .05$; popularity: reject H_o at $\alpha = .05$; intellectual self-confidence: reject H_o at $\alpha = .05$ **9.119 a.** .153   **b.** .215   **c.** $-.062 \pm .070$ **9.121 a.** H_o: $\mu_1 = \mu_2$, H_a: $\mu_1 < \mu_2$ **b.** fail to reject H_o **9.123 a.** 749.5 ± 278.1 **9.125 a.** t test   **b.** yes   **c.** no   **d.** fail to reject H_o **e.** reject H_o at $\alpha = .05$ **9.127** $t = 1.77$, fail to reject H_o at $\alpha = .01$ **9.129 a.** $z = -.21$, fail to reject H_o **b.** $-.078 \pm .076$ **9.131** $-.33 \pm .22$ **9.133 a.** yes, $F = 10$ **b.** both populations normal   **9.135** $z = 3.55$, reject H_o: $p_1 - p_2 = 0$ **9.137** yes, $t = -2.19$ **9.139** use of creative ideas ($z = 8.85$); good use of job skills ($z = 4.76$)

Chapter 10

10.1 A, B, C, D   **10.5 a.** observational **b.** designed **c.** designed **d.** observational **e.** observational **f.** observational   **10.7 a.** age when cancer is first detected **b.** smokers **c.** type of screening method **d.** CT scan, chest X-ray   **10.9 a.** cockatiel **b.** yes **c.** experimental group **d.** 1, 2, 3 **e.** 3 **f.** total consumption   **10.11 a.** Temperature (45, 48, 51, and 54°C); Type of yeast (Baker's, Brewer's) **b.** autolysis yield **c.** 8   **10.17 a.** 6.59 **b.** 16.69 **c.** 1.61 **d.** 3.87   **10.19 a.** plot b **b.** 9; 14 **c.** 75; 75 **d.** 20; 144 **e.** 95 (78.95%); 219 (34.25%) **f.** MST $= 75$, MSE $= 2$, $F = 37.5$; MST $= 75$, MSE $= 14.4$, $F = 5.21$ **g.** reject H_o; reject H_o **h.** both populations normal with equal variances
10.21 plot a:

Source	df	SS	MS	F
Treatment	1	75	75	37.5
Error	10	20	2	
Total	11	95		

plot b:

Source	df	SS	MS	F
Treatment	1	75	75	5.21
Error	10	144	14.4	
Total	11	219		

10.23 a. $F = 1.5625$; do not reject H_o **b.** $F = 6.25$; reject H_o **c.** $F = 25$; reject H_o **d.** increases   **10.25 a.** exp. units: coaches; dep. variable: 7-point rating; factor: division; treatments: I, II, III   **b.** H_o: $\mu_I = \mu_{II} = \mu_{III}$ **c.** reject H_o **10.27 a.** completely randomized

b. treatments: 3, 6, 9, 12 robots; dep. variable.: energy expanded   **c.** $H_0: \mu_3 = \mu_6 = \mu_9 = \mu_{12}$, H_a: At least 2 μ's differ   **d.** reject H_0
10.29 a. $H_0: \mu_{young} = \mu_{middle} = \mu_{old}$ **b.** reject H_0 **c.** $H_0: \mu_{young} = \mu_{middle} = \mu_{old}$; fail to reject H_0 **10.31** yes, $F = 3.90$
10.33 b. treatments: scopolamine, glycopyrrolate, no drug; response: number of pairs recalled   **c.** 6.17; 9.38; 10.6   **d.** $F = 27.07$, reject
H_0 **10.35** yes, $F = 7.25$ **10.39 a.** no significant difference   **b.** μ_2 **c.** μ_1 **10.41 a.** 3   **b.** 10   **c.** 6   **d.** 45   **10.43** $\mu_1 > \mu_2$, $\mu_1 >$
$\mu_3, \mu_4 > \mu_2, \mu_4 > \mu_3$ **10.45 a.** 6   **b.** sourdough; control & yeast   **10.47 a.** 6   **b.** μ_{12} is the largest mean; $\mu_3, \mu_6,$ and μ_9 are not
significantly different   **10.49 a.** reject H_0 **b.** Control and Slide not significantly different   **10.51 b.** 3   **d.** $(\mu_{30-60} - \mu_{over60})$
10.53 $\mu_{UMRB-2} > \mu_{SD}, \mu_{UMRB-2} > \mu_{SWRA}, \mu_{UMRB-3} > \mu_{SD}, \mu_{UMRB-3} > \mu_{SWRA}, \mu_{UMRB-1} > \mu_{SWRA}$ **10.55** $\mu_T > \mu_V, \mu_T > \mu_C$
10.59 a. 3 blocks; 5 treatments   **b.** 15   **c.** $H_0: \mu_1 = \mu_2 = \mu_3 = \mu_4 = \mu_5$ **d.** $F = 9.109$ **e.** $F > 7.01$ **f.** reject H_0 **10.61 a.**

Source	df	SS	MS	F
Treatment	2	12.032	6.016	50.96
Block	3	71.749	23.916	202.59
Error	6	.708	.118	
Total	11	84.489		

b. yes, p-value $= .000$ **c.** yes, p-value $= .000$ **d.** $\mu_C < \mu_A < \mu_B$ **10.63 b.** California, Utah, Alaska   **c.** Months 1, 2, 3
d. $H_0: \mu_{Cal} = \mu_{Utah} = \mu_{Alas}$ **e.** $F = 38.07$, p-value $= .002$; reject H_0 **f.** $\mu_{Cal} > \mu_{Utah}, \mu_{Cal} > \mu_{Alas}$ **10.65 a.** randomized block
design **c.** reject H_0 at $\alpha > .009$ **d.** $\mu_{control} < \mu_{burning}$
10.67 b.

Source	df	SS	MS	F
Prompt	4	1185.00	296.25	39.87
Week	5	386.40	77.28	10.40
Error	20	148.60	7.43	
Total	29	1720.00		

c. yes, $F = 39.87$ **d.** $\mu_{Control} < (\mu_{Inf-Low}, \mu_{Inf-Hi}) < (\mu_{Freq-Low}, \mu_{Freq-Hi})$ **10.69** do not reject H_0, $F = .02$ **10.71 b.** $H_0: \mu_{Full-Dark} =$
$\mu_{TR-Light} = \mu_{TR-Dark}$ **c.** $F = 5.33$, reject H_0 **d.** $\mu_{Full-Dark} > (\mu_{TR-Light}, \mu_{TR-Dark})$ **10.77 a.** 2   **b.** no   **c.** yes; 3 and 5   **d.** 15
e. df(Error) $= 0$; replication   **10.79 a.**

Source	df	SS	MS	F
B	2	.8	.4000	2.00
B	3	5.3	1.7667	8.83
AB	6	9.6	1.6000	8.00
Error	12	2.4	.2000	
Total	23	18.1		

b. $SSA, SSB, SSAB$; yes, $F = 7.14$ **c.** yes   **d.** effects of one factor on the dependent variable are not the same at different levels of the
second factor **e.** $F = 8.00$, reject H_0 **f.** no   **10.81 a.** $F(AB) = .75$; $F(A) = 3$; $F(B) = 1.5$ **b.** $F(AB) = 7.5$; $F(A) = 3$; $F(B) = 3$
c. $F(AB) = 3$; $F(A) = 12$; $F(B) = 3$ **d.** $F(AB) = 4.5$; $F(A) = 36$; $F(B) = 36$ **10.83 a.** 6×6 factorial   **b.** Coagulant (5, 10, 20, 50,
100, 200); pH (4, 5, 6, 7, 8, 9); 36 treatments   **10.85 a.** event (3 wash-ups), strata (coarse, medium, fine, hydroid)   **b.** 12   **c.** 2
d. 24   **e.** Mussel density   **f.** interaction; fail to reject H_0 **g.** F(Event) $= .35$, fail to reject H_0; F(Strata) $= 217.33$, reject H_0
h. $\mu_{hydroid} > \mu_{fine} > (\mu_{medium}, \mu_{course})$ **10.87 a.** 2×2 factorial; Color (blue, red), question (difficult, simple)   **b.** sufficient evidence of
interaction at $\alpha = .05$ **10.89 b.** sufficient evidence of interaction at $\alpha = .01$ **c.** no   **10.91 a.** 2; 2; 4; 99 **b.** 9 **c.** sufficient evidence of
interaction **d.** no **e.** 18 months: $\mu_{control} < \mu_{photos}$; 24 months: $\mu_{control} < \mu_{drawings}, \mu_{control} < \mu_{photos}$; 30 months: $\mu_{control} < \mu_{drawings}$,
$\mu_{control} < \mu_{photos}$ **10.93 a.**

Source	df	SS	MS	F	P
Diet (D)	1	0.0124	0.0124	0.22	.645
Size (S)	1	8.0679	8.0679	141.18	.000
DxS	1	0.0364	0.0364	0.64	0.432
Error	24	1.3715	0.0571		
Total	27	9.4883			

b. Diet-Size interaction: fail to reject H_0; main effect Diet: fail to reject H_0; main effect Size: reject H_0 **10.95 a.** Low/Ambig: 450;
Low/Common:195; High/Ambig:152.5; High/Common:157.5   **b.** 9,120.25   **c.** SS(Load) $= 1,122.25$, SS(Name) $=$
625, SS(Load $\times$ Name) $= 676$ **d.** Low/Ambig: 225, 5400; Low/Common: 90.25, 2166; High/Ambig:90.25, 2166; High/Common:100,
2400   **e.** 12,132   **f.** 14,555.25

g.

Source	df	SS	MSE	F
Load	1	1,122.25	1,122.25	8.88
Name	1	625	625	4.95
Load $\times$ Name	1	676	676	5.35
Error	96	12,132	126.375	
Total	99	14,555.25		

h. yes   **i.** Significant interaction
10.101 a.

Source	df	SS	MS	F
Treatment	3	11.332	3.777	157.38
Block	4	10.688	2.672	111.33
Error	12	.288	.024	
Total	19	22.308		

b. yes, reject H_o **c.** yes; 6   **d.** yes, reject H_o **10.103 b.** yes   **c.** yes   **10.105 a.** ethical behavior   **b.** job (high tech, low tech); task (new, maintenance)   **c.** high/new, high/maintenance, low/new, low/maintenance   **d.** college students   **10.107** $F = 8.295$, reject H_o; $\mu_{OND} < (\mu_{SLI}, \mu_{YND})$ **10.109 a.** yes, $F = 39.1$ **b.** no   **c.** $(\mu_{NFP}, \mu_{FP}) < (\mu_{CSH}, \mu_{CSFB})$ **10.111 a.** $F = .53$, do not reject H_o
b. not appropriate   **10.113 a.**

Source	df	F	p-value
Time Period	3	11.25	.0001
Station	9		
Error	27		
Total	39		

b. reject H_o, $F = 11.25$ **c.** largest: either 7/9-7/23 or 7/24-8/8; smallest: 8/24-8/31   **10.115 a.** $F = 3.96$; reject H_o
b. $\mu_{Sad} < \mu_{Happy}$, $\mu_{Sad} < \mu_{Angry}$ **10.117 b.** yes, $F = 1,336.85$ **c.** yes; reject H_o, $F = 258.07$ **d.** no   **e.** 9 treatment means
10.119 a. df(Period) = 1, df(Gender) = 1, df(P $\times$ G) = 1, df(Error) = 120, df(Total) = 123   **10.121 a.** 2×2 factorial
b. factors: tent type and location; treatments: (treated, inside), (treated, outside), (untreated, inside), (untreated, outside)
c. number of mosquito bites   **d.** effect of tent type on mean number of bites depends on location   **10.123** yes, $F = 34.12$;
System 1 or System 4

Chapter 11
11.7 $\beta_1 = 1/3$, $\beta_0 = 14/3$, $y = 14/3 + (1/3)x$ **11.11** difference between the observed and predicted   **11.13** true
11.15 b. $\hat{y} = 7.10 - .78x$ **11.17 c.** $\hat{\beta}_1 = .918$, $\hat{\beta}_0 = .020$ **e.** -1 to 7   **11.19 c.** hoop pine   **11.21 a.** $y = \beta_0 + \beta_1 x + \epsilon$
b. $\hat{y} = 2.522 + 7.261x$ **11.23 a.** positive   **11.25 a.** $y = \beta_0 + \beta_1 x + \epsilon$ **b.** $\hat{y} = 250.14 - .6274x$ **e.** slope   **11.27 a.** $y = \beta_0 + \beta_1 x + \epsilon$ **b.** $\hat{y} = -.607 + 1.062x$ **c.** positive   **e.** $\hat{y} = -.148 + 1.022x$ **11.29 a.** $\hat{y} = 560.1 + 63.3x$ **b.** $\hat{y} = 326.5 + 1.48x$
c. $\hat{y} = 338.9 + 197.21x$ **11.31** yes, $\hat{y} = 5.2207 - .11402x$; decrease by .114 pound   **11.35 a.** 57.5; 3.19444   **b.** 257.5; 6.7763
c. 9.288; 1.1610   **11.37** 11.14: SSE = 1.22, $s^2 = .244$, $s = .494$; 11.17: SSE = 5.134, $s^2 = 1.03$, $s = 1.01$ **11.39** women's   **11.41 a.** SSE = 2760, $s^2 = 306.6$, and s = 17.51   **11.43 a.** 6.36   **b.** 3.42   **c.** reading score   **11.45 a.** \$908.50   **b.** \$736.66   **c.** \$846.73   **11.47** 0
11.49 divide the value in half   **11.51 a.** 95%: .31 $\pm$ 1.13; 90%: .31 $\pm$ .92   **b.** 95%: 64 $\pm$ 4.28; 90%: 64 $\pm$ 3.53   **c.** 95%: $-8.4 \pm .67$; 90%: $-8.4 \pm .55$ **11.53 b.** $\hat{y} = 2.554 + .246x$ **d.** $t = .627$ **e.** fail to reject H_o **f.** .246 $\pm$ 1.81   **11.55 a.** $H_o: \beta_1 = 0$, $H_a: \beta_1 < 0$
b. $t = -13.23$, p-value = .000   **c.** reject H_o **11.57 a.** $t = 10.05$, reject H_o **b.** 1.022 $\pm$ .180   **11.59** $-.0023 \pm .0016$
11.61 a. $y = \beta_0 + \beta_1 x + \epsilon$ **b.** $\hat{y} = -8.524 + 1.665x$ **d.** yes, $t = 7.25$ **e.** 1.67 $\pm$ .46   **11.63 a.** $t = 6.286$, reject H_o **b.** .88 $\pm$ .236
c. no evidence that slope differs from 1   **11.65 a.** $\hat{\beta}_0 = .515$, $\hat{\beta}_1 = .000021$ **b.** yes   **c.** very influential   **d.** $\hat{\beta}_0 = .515$, $\hat{\beta}_1 = .000021$
p-value = .332, fail to reject H_o **11.67** true   **11.69 a.** perfect positive linear   **b.** perfect negative linear   **c.** no linear   **d.** strong
positive linear **e.** weak positive linear   **f.** strong negative linear   **11.71** .877   **11.73 a.** moderate positive linear relationship; not
significantly different from 0 at $\alpha = .05$ **c.** weak negative linear relationship; not significantly different from 0 at $\alpha = .10$
11.75 b. .185   **11.77 b.** both positive   **c.** .706   **11.79 a.** moderately strong negative linear relationship between the number of
online courses taken and weekly quiz grade   **b.** yes, $t = -4.95$ **11.81 b.** piano: $r^2 = .1998$; bench: $r^2 = .0032$; motorbike: $r^2 = .3832$,
armchair: $r^2 = .0864$; teapot: $r^2 = .9006$ **c.** Reject H_o for all objects except bench and armchair   **11.83 a.** $y = \beta_0 + \beta_1 x + \epsilon$
b. $\beta_1 > 0$ **d.** no, $t = -3.12$ **11.85** $r = .570$, $r^2 = .325$ **11.89** true   **11.91 a.** $\hat{y} = 1.375 + .875x$ **c.** 1.5   **d.** .1875   **e.** 3.56 $\pm$ .33
f. 4.88 $\pm$ 1.06   **11.93 c.** 4.65 $\pm$ 1.12   **d.** 2.28 $\pm$ .63; $-.414 \pm 1.717$ **11.95 a.** prediction interval for y when x = 50   **b.** confidence
interval for E(y) when x = 70   **11.97** (92.298, 125.104)   **11.99 a.** $y = \beta_0 + \beta_1 x + \epsilon$ **b.** $\hat{y} = 155.912 - 1.086x$ **c.** no, $t = -2.05$
d. $(-21.56, 279.09)$ **11.101 a.** (2.955, 4.066)   **b.** (1.020, 6.000) **c.** prediction interval; yes   **11.103 a.** Brand A: 3.349 $\pm$ .587; Brand B:
4.464 $\pm$ .296   **b.** Brand A: 3.349 $\pm$ 2.224; Brand B: 4.464 $\pm$ 1.120   **c.** $-.65 \pm 3.606$ **11.105** E(y) = $\beta_0 + \beta_1 x$ **11.107** true

11.109 b. $\hat{y} = x$; $\hat{y} = 3$ **c.** $\hat{y} = x$ **d.** least squares line has the smallest SSE **11.111 a.** $y = \beta_0 + \beta_1 x + \epsilon$; negative **b.** yes **c.** no **11.113 a.** positive **b.** yes **c.** $\hat{y} = -85.68 + 614.04x$ **f.** $t = 1.82$, p-value $= .0936$, fail to reject H_o **g.** .2165 **i.** 89.32 **j.** $(63.26, 115.37)$ **11.115 a.** $y = \beta_0 + \beta_1 x + \epsilon$ **b.** $\hat{y} = 175.7033 - .8195x$ **e.** $t = -3.43$, reject H_o **11.117 b.** reject H_o **c.** .49 **11.119** $\hat{y} = -92.458 + 8.347x$; $t = 3.248$, reject H_o; $r = .42$ **11.121 a.** yes **b.** $\hat{\beta}_0 = -3.05$, $\hat{\beta}_1 = .108$ **c.** $t = 4.00$, reject H_o **d.** $r = .756$, $r^2 = .572$ **e.** 1.09 **f.** yes **11.123 a.** $\hat{\beta}_0 = -13.49$, $\hat{\beta}_1 = -.0528$ **b.** $-.0528 \pm .0178$; yes **c.** $r^2 = .854$ **d.** (.5987, 1.2653) **11.125 a.** yes; positive **b.** $y = \beta_0 + \beta_1 x + \epsilon$ **c.** $\hat{\beta}_0 = 20.1275$, $\hat{\beta}_1 = .62442$ **11.127 a.** $\hat{y} = 46.4x$ **b.** $\hat{y} = 478.44 + 45.15x$ **d.** no, $t = .91$ **11.129 a.** no; $r^2 = .748$ **b.** yes, $18(\hat{\beta}_1) = -.98$

Chapter 12

12.1 a. $E(y) = \beta_0 + \beta_1 x_1 + \beta_2 x_2$ **b.** $E(y) = \beta_0 + \beta_1 x_1 + \beta_2 x_2 + \beta_3 x_3 + \beta_4 x_4$ **c.** $E(y) = \beta_0 + \beta_1 x_1 + \beta_2 x_2 + \beta_3 x_3 + \beta_4 x_4 + \beta_5 x_5$ **12.5** test the null hypothesis that all the beta parameters (except $_0$) are equal to 0 **12.7 a.** $t = 1.45$, do not reject H_o **b.** $t = 3.21$, reject H_o**12.9** df $= n - (k + 1)$ **12.11 a.** yes **b.** yes, $F = 55.2$ **12.13 a.** $\hat{y} = 1.81231 + .10875x_1 + .00017x_2$ **c.** $(.026, .192)$ **d.** $(.00009, .00025)$ **e.** $\hat{y} = 1.20785 + .06343x_1 + .00056x_2$; $(.016, .111)$; $(.00025, .00087)$ **12.15 a.** $\hat{y} = 3.70 + .34x_1 + .49x_2 + .72x_3 + 1.14x_4 + 1.51x_5 + .26x_6 - .14x_7 - .10x_8 - .10x_9$ **c.** $t = -1.00$, do not reject H_o **d.** $(1.412, 1.608)$ **12.17 a.** $E(y) = \beta_0 + \beta_1 x_1 + \beta_2 x_2 + \beta_3 x_3$ **c.** reject H_o: $\beta_1 = \beta_2 = \beta_3 = 0$ **d.** reject H_o **e.** fail to reject H_o **f.** fail to reject H_o **12.19 a.** $E(y) = \beta_0 + \beta_1 x_1 + \beta_2 x_2 + \beta_3 x_3$ **b.** $\hat{y} = -86,868 - 2,218.8x_1 + 1,542.2x_2 - .3496x_3$ **d.** 103.3 **e.** $R^2 = .128$, R^2adj $= .120$ **f.** $F = 15.80$, reject H_o **g.** no **12.21 a.** $\hat{y} = 12.1804 - .0265x_1 - .45783x_2$ **c.** $t = -.50$, do not reject H_o **d.** $-.4578 \pm .3469$ **e.** $R^2 = .529$, $R^2_{adj} = .505$; R^2_{adj} **f.** yes, $F = 21.88$ **12.23 a.** $E(y) = \beta_0 + \beta_1 x_1 + \beta_2 x_2 + \beta_3 x_3 + \beta_4 x_4 + \beta_5 x_5$ **b.** $\hat{y} = 13,614.5 + .089x_1 - 9.20x_2 + 14.39x_3 + .35x_4 - .85x_5$ **d.** 458.83 **e.** .917 **f.** yes, $F = 147.30$ **12.25 b.** $F = 5.11$, reject H_o **12.27 a.** model 1: $t = 2.58$, reject H_o: $\beta_1 = 0$; model 2: $t = 3.32$, reject H_o: $\beta_1 = 0$, $t = 6.47$, reject H_o: $\beta_2 = 0$, $t = -4.77$, reject H_o: $\beta_3 = 0$, $t = 0.24$, do not reject H_o: $\beta_4 = 0$; model 3: $t = 3.21$, reject H_o: $\beta_1 = 0$, $t = 5.24$, reject H_o: $\beta_2 = 0$, $t = -4.00$, reject H_o: $\beta_3 = 0$, $t = 2.28$, reject H_o: $\beta_4 = 0$, $t = .014$, do not H_o: $\beta_5 = 0$ **c.** Model 2 **12.29** 95% CI for $E(y)$ **12.31** $(90.69, 158.57)$ **12.33** $(-183.76, 207.25)$ **12.35** $(24.03, 440.64)$ **12.37 a.** $E(y) = \beta_0 + \beta_1 x_1 + \beta_2 x_2 + \beta_3 x_1 x_2$ **b.** $E(y) = \beta_0 + \beta_1 x_1 + \beta_2 x_2 + \beta_3 x_3 + \beta_4 x_1 x_2 + \beta_5 x_1 x_3 + \beta_6 x_2 x_3$ **12.39 c.** interaction is present **12.41 a.** $\hat{y} = -2.550 + 3.815x_1 + 2.630x_2 - 1.285x_1 x_2$ **e.** H_o: $\beta_3 = 0$, H_a: $\beta_3 \neq 0$ **f.** p-value $= .000$, reject H_o **12.43 a.** $E(y) = \beta_0 + \beta_1 x_1 + \beta_2 x_2 + \beta_3 x_1 x_2$ **c.** $\beta_3 < 0$ **12.45 a.** $E(y) = \beta_0 + \beta_1 x_1 + \beta_2 x_2 + \beta_3 x_3 + \beta_4 x_4 + \beta_5 x_5 + \beta_6 x_1 x_2$ **b.** H_o: $\beta_4 = 0$ **c.** reject H_o **d.** yes **12.47 a.** affect of client credibility on likelihood depends on the level of linguistic delivery style **b.** H_o: $\beta_1 = \beta_2 = \beta_3 = 0$ **c.** $F = 55.35$, reject H_o **d.** H_o: $\beta_3 = 0$ **e.** $t = 4.01$, reject H_o **f.** .114 **g.** .978 **12.49 a.** $E(y) = \beta_0 + \beta_1 x_1 + \beta_2 x_2 + \beta_3 x_3 + \beta_4 x_4 + \beta_5 x_5 + \beta_6 x_2 x_5 + \beta_7 x_3 x_5$ **b.** $\hat{y} = 13.646 + .046x_1 - 12.68x_2 + 23.00x_3 - 3.02x_4 + 1.29x_5 + .016x_2 x_5 - .04x_3 x_5$ **c.** $t = 4.40$, reject H_o **d.** $t = -3.77$, reject H_o **12.51 a.** $E(y) = \beta_0 + \beta_1 x + \beta_2 x^2$ **b.** $E(y) = \beta_0 + \beta_1 x_1 + \beta_2 x_2 + \beta_3 x_1 x_2 + \beta_4 (x_1)^2 + \beta_5 (x_2)^2$ **b.** $E(y) = \beta_0 + \beta_1 x_1 + \beta_2 x_2 + \beta_3 x_1 x_2 + \beta_4 (x_1)^2 + _5 (x_2)^2$ **c.** $E(y) = \beta_0 + \beta_1 x_1 + \beta_2 x_2 + \beta_3 x_3 + \beta_4 x_1 x_2 + \beta_5 x_1 x_3 + \beta_6 x_2 x_3 + \beta_7 (x_1)^2 + \beta_8 (x_2)^2 + \beta_9 (x_3)^2$ **12.53 a.** $t = 3.133$, reject H_o **b.** $t = 3.133$, $t > 1.717$, reject H_o **12.55 b.** moves graph to right or left **c.** controls whether graph opens up or down **12.57 b.** 1st-order model, $\beta_1 > 0$; 1st-order model, $\beta_1 < 0$; 2nd-order model **12.59 a.** $E(y) = \beta_0 + \beta_1 x_1 + \beta_2 x_2 + \beta_3 x_1 x_2 + \beta_4 (x_1)^2 + \beta_5 (x_2)^2$ **b.** β_4 and β_5 **12.61 b.** 6.25 **c.** 10.25 **d.** 200 **12.63 a.** $E(y) = \beta_0 + \beta_1 x + \beta_2 x^2$ **b.** positive **c.** no; $E(y) = \beta_0 + \beta_1 x$ **12.65 a.** $\hat{y} = -288 + 1.395x + .0000351x^2$; $t = .36$, fail to reject H_o **b.** outlier **c.** yes; $R^2_{adj} = .996$, model statistically useful (p-value $= .000$), evidence of curvature (p-value $= .000$) **12.67** $E(y) = \beta_0 + \beta_1 x$; $x = \{1$ if level 2, 0 if level 1$\}$ **12.69 a.** 10.2, 6.2, 22.2, 12.2 **b.** H_0: $\beta_1 = \beta_2 = \beta_3 = 0$ **12.71 a.** Race: $x_1 = \{1$ if black, 0 if white$\}$; Availability: $x_2 = \{1$ if high, 0 if low$\}$; Position: $x_3 = \{1$ if quarterback, 0 if not$\}$, $x_4 = \{1$ if running back, 0 if not$\}$, $x_5 = \{1$ if wide receiver, 0 if not$\}$, $x_6 = \{$if tight end, 0 if not$\}$, $x_7 = \{1$ if defensive lineman, 0 if not$\}$, $x_8 = \{1$ if linebacker, 0 if not$\}$, $x_9 = \{1$ if defensiveback, 0 if not$\}$ **b.** $E(y) = \beta_0 + \beta_1 x_1$ **c.** $E(y) = \beta_0 + \beta_1 x_2$ **d.** $E(y) = \beta_0 + \beta_1 x_3 + \beta_2 x_4 + \beta_3 x_5 + \beta_4 x_6 + \beta_5 x_7 + \beta_6 x_8 + \beta_7 x_9$ **12.73 a.** 4; AA, AB, BA, BB **b.** $E(y) = \beta_0 + \beta_1 x_1 + \beta_2 x_2 + \beta_3 x_3$, where $x_1 = \{1$ if AA, 0 if not$\}$, $x_2 = \{1$ if AB, 0 if not$\}$, $x_3 = \{1$ if BA, 0 if not$\}$, **d.** H_o: $\beta_1 = \beta_2 = \beta_3 = 0$ **12.75 a.** $E(y) = \beta_0 + \beta_1 x_1 + \beta_2 x_2$; $x_1 = \{1$ if democratic, 0 otherwise$\}$, $x_2 = \{1$ if dictatorship, 0 otherwise$\}$ **b.** $\beta_0 = $ mean risk level for communist $= \mu_{communist}$; $\beta_1 = \mu_{democrat} - \mu_{communist}$; $\beta_2 = \mu_{dictator} - \mu_{communist}$ **12.77** $E(y) = \beta_0 + \beta_1 x_1 + \beta_2 x_2 + \beta_3 x_1 x_2$ **12.79 a.** $E(y) = \beta_0 + \beta_1 x$, where $x = \{1$ if flightless, 0 otherwise$\}$ **b.** $E(y) = \beta_0 + \beta_1 x_1 + \beta_2 x_2 + \beta_3 x_3$, where $x_1 = \{1$ if vertabrates, 0 if not$\}$, $x_2 = \{1$ if vegetables, 0 if not$\}$, $x_3 = \{1$ if invertabrates, 0 if not$\}$ **c.** $E(y) = \beta_0 + \beta_1 x_1 + \beta_2 x_2 + \beta_3 x_3$, where $x_1 = \{1$ if cavity within ground, 0 if not$\}$, $x_2 = \{1$ if trees, 0 if not$\}$, $x_3 = \{1$ if cavity above ground, 0 if not$\}$ **d.** $\hat{y} = 641 + 30,647x$ **e.** $F = 33.05$, reject H_o **f.** $\hat{y} = 903 + 2,997x_1 + 26,206x_2 - 660x_3$ **g.** $F = 8.43$, reject H_o **h.** $\hat{y} = 73.732 - 9.132x_1 - 45.01x_2 - 39.51x_3$ **i.** $F = 8.07$, reject H_o **12.81 a.** $E(y) = \beta_0 + \beta_1 x_1 + \beta_2 x_2 + \beta_3 x_3 + \beta_4 x_4$, where $x_1 - x_4$ are dummy variables for the five reproductive classes **b.** $\hat{\beta}_0 = 38$, $\hat{\beta}_1 = -22$, $\hat{\beta}_2 = 51$, $\hat{\beta}_3 = 5$, $\hat{\beta}_4 = 20$ **c.** H_o: $\beta_1 = \beta_2 = \beta_3 = \beta_4 = 0$ **d.** do not reject H_o **12.83 a.** $E(y) = \beta_0 + \beta_1 x_1$ **b.** $E(y) = \beta_0 + \beta_1 x_1 + \beta_2 x_2 + \beta_3 x_3$; $x_2 = \{1$ if level 2, 0 otherwise$\}$, $x_3 = \{1$ if level 3, 0 otherwise$\}$ **c.** $E(y) = \beta_0 + \beta_1 x_1 + \beta_2 x_2 + \beta_3 x_3 + \beta_4 x_1 x_2 + \beta_5 x_1 x_3$ **d.** $\beta_4 = \beta_5 = 0$ **e.** $\beta_2 = \beta_3 = \beta_4 = \beta_5 = 0$ **12.85** $E(y) = \beta_0 + \beta_1 x_1 + \beta_2 x_1^2 + \beta_3 x_2 + \beta_4 x_3 + \beta_5 x_4$, where $x_2 - x_4$ are dummy variables **12.87 a.** $\hat{y} = 48.8 - 3.4x_1 + .07x_1^2$; $\hat{y} = 46.4 + .3x_1 + .05x_1^2$; $\hat{y} = 41.3 - .7x_1 + .03x_1^2$ **12.89 a.** $E(y) = \beta_0 + \beta_1 x_1 + \beta_2 x_2 + \beta_3 x_3$ **b.** $E(y) = \beta_0 + \beta_1 x_1 + \beta_2 x_2 + \beta_3 x_3 + \beta_4 x_1 x_3 + \beta_5 x_2 x_3$ **12.91 a.** $E(y) = \beta_0 + \beta_1 x_1$; β_1 **b.** $E(y) = (\beta_0 + \beta_2) + (\beta_1 + \beta_3) x_1$; $\beta_1 + \beta_3$ **c.** evidence of interaction at $\alpha = .05$ **12.93 a.** $E(y) = \beta_0 + \beta_1 x_1 + \beta_2 x_2 + \beta_3 x_1 x_2$, where $x_2 = \{1$ if plant, 0 if duck chow$\}$ **b.** $\hat{y} = 8.14 - .016x_1 - 10.4x_2 + 0.95x_1 x_2$ **c.** .079 **d.** $-.016$ **e.** $t = .67$, fail to reject H_o **12.95 a.** $E(y) = \beta_0 + \beta_1 x_1 + \beta_2 x_2$ **b.** β_1 for both **c.** $E(y) = \beta_0 + \beta_1 x_1 + \beta_2 x_2 + \beta_3 x_1 x_2$ **d.** β_1; $\beta_1 + \beta_3$ **12.97** (a and b); (a and d); (a and e); (b and c); (b and d); (b and e); (c and e); (d and e) **12.99** model with a small number of β parameters **12.101 a.** 5; 3 **b.** H_o: $\beta_3 = \beta_4 = 0$ **c.** $F = .38$, do not reject H_o **12.103 a.** $E(y) = \beta_0 + \beta_1 x_1 + \beta_2 x_2 + \beta_3 x_3 + \beta_4 x_4 + \beta_5 x_5 + \beta_6 x_6 + \beta_7 x_7 + \beta_8 x_8 + \beta_9 x_9 + \beta_{10} x_{10} + \beta_{11} x_{11}$ **b.** $E(y) = \beta_0 + \beta_1 x_1 + \beta_2 x_2 + \beta_3 x_3 + \beta_4 x_4 + \beta_5 x_5 + \beta_6 x_6 + \beta_7 x_7 + \beta_8 x_8 + \beta_9 x_9 + \beta_{10} x_{10} + \beta_{11} x_{11} + \beta_{12} x_1 x_9 + \beta_{13} x_1 x_{10} + \beta_{14} x_1 x_{11} + \beta_{15} x_2 x_9 + \beta_{16} x_2 x_{10} + \beta_{17} x_2 x_{11} + \beta_{18} x_3 x_9 + \beta_{19} x_3 x_{10} + \beta_{20} x_3 x_{11} + \beta_{21} x_4 x_9 + \beta_{22} x_4 x_{10} + \beta_{23} x_4 x_{11} + \beta_{24} x_5 x_9 + \beta_{25} x_5 x_{10} +$

$\beta_{26}x_5x_{11} + \beta_{27}x_6x_9 + \beta_{28}x_6x_{10} + \beta_{29}x_6x_{11} + \beta_{30}x_7x_9 + \beta_{30}x_7x_9 + \beta_{31}x_7x_{10} + \beta_{32}x_7x_{11} + \beta_{33}x_8x_9 + \beta_{34}x_8x_{10} + \beta_{35}x_8x_{11}$
c. H_o: $\beta_{12} = \beta_{13} = \dots = \beta_{35} = 0$ **12.105 b.** H_o: $\beta_3 = \beta_4 = \beta_6 = \beta_7 = \beta_8 = 0$ **c.** yes **d.** reject H_o; complete model better
e. $E(y) = \beta_0 + \beta_1x_1 + \beta_2x_2 + \beta_3x_3 + \beta_4x_4 + \beta_5x_5 + \beta_6x_6 + \beta_7x_7 + \beta_8x_8 + \beta_9x_5x_6 + \beta_{10}x_5x_7 + \beta_{11}x_5x_8 + \beta_{12}x_6x_7 + \beta_{13}x_6x_8 + \beta_{14}x_7x_8$ **f.** do not reject H_o; no evidence of interaction **12.107 a.** $E(y) = \beta_0 + \beta_1x_1 + \beta_2x_2 + \beta_3x_3 + \beta_4x_4 + \beta_5x_5 + \beta_6x_6 + \beta_7x_7 + \beta_8x_8 + \beta_9x_9 + \beta_{10}x_{10}$ **b.** H_o: $\beta_3 = \beta_4 = \dots = \beta_{10} = 0$ **c.** at least one of the additional variables is important **e.** (8.12, 19.88) **f.** yes **g.** $E(y) = \beta_0 + \beta_1x_1 + \beta_2x_2 + \beta_3x_3 + \beta_4x_4 + \beta_5x_5 + \beta_6x_6 + \beta_7x_7 + \beta_8x_8 + \beta_9x_9 + \beta_{10}x_{10} + \beta_{11}x_1x_2 + \beta_{12}x_2x_3 + \beta_{13}x_2x_4 + \beta_{14}x_2x_5 + \beta_{15}x_2x_6 + \beta_{16}x_2x_7 + \beta_{17}x_2x_8 + \beta_{18}x_2x_9 + \beta_{19}x_2x_{10}$ **h.** H_o: $\beta_{11} = \beta_{12} = \dots = \beta_{19} = 0$; nested model F-test **12.109 a.** H_o: $\beta_4 = \beta_5 = 0$ **b.** H_o: $\beta_3 = \beta_4 = \beta_5 = 0$ **12.111** large number of t-tests inflating the overall ; no higher-order or interaction terms **12.113 a.** 7 **b.** 6 **c.** 5 **12.115 a.** 11 **b.** 10 **c.** 1 **d.** $E(y) = \beta_0 + \beta_1x_{11} + \beta_2x_4 + \beta_3x_2 + \beta_4x_7 + \beta_5x_{10} + \beta_6x_1 + \beta_7x_9 + \beta_8x_3$ **12.117** $(y - \hat{y})$ **12.123** false **12.125** yes; x_4 is highly correlated with both x_2 and x_5
12.127 a. no **b.** yes **12.129 a.** yes, residual = 57.37 **c.** no other outliers **12.131 a.** $E(y) = \beta_0 + \beta_1x_1 + \beta_2x_8$ **c.** multicollinearity **12.133** outliers: #105 and #115; error variances unequal **12.135 a.** race and foreign status, year GRE taken and years in graduate program **12.137 a.** $E(y) = \beta_0 + \beta_1x_1 + \beta_2x_2 + \beta_3x_3$; $x_1 = \{1$ if level 2, 0 otherwise$\}$, $x_2 = 1$ {if level 3, 0 otherwise}, $x_3 = \{1$ if level 4, 0 otherwise$\}$ **12.139 a.** $E(y) = \beta_0 + \beta_1x_1 + \beta_2x_2 + \beta_3x_3$, where $x_1 =$ quantitative, $x_2 = \{1$ if level 2, 0 if not$\}$, $x_3 = \{1$ if level 3, 0 if not$\}$ **b.** $E(y) = \beta_0 + \beta_1x_1 + \beta_2x_1^2 + \beta_3x_2 + \beta_4x_3 + \beta_5x_1x_2 + \beta_6x_1x_3 + \beta_7x_1^2x_2 + \beta_8x_1^2x_3$ **12.141 a.** yes, $F = 24.21$ **b.** $t = -2.01$, reject H_o **c.** $t = .31$, do not reject H_o **d.** $t = 2.38$, do not reject H_o **12.143** yes; $x_1 = 60$, $x_2 = .4$, $x_3 = 900$ are outside range of sample data **12.145** df(Error) = 0 **12.147 b.** $F = 3.72$, reject H_o **c.** no **d.** H_o: $\beta_1 = 0$
e. $t = 2.52$, reject H_o **f.** x_4 is highly correlated with x_5 **12.149 a.** $E(y) = \beta_0 + \beta_1x_1 + \beta_2x_2 + \beta_3x_3 + \beta_4x_4 + \beta_5x_5$ **b.** model is statistically useful **c.** $E(y) = \beta_0 + \beta_1x_1 + \beta_2x_2 + \beta_3x_3 + \beta_4x_4 + \beta_5x_5 + \beta_6x_6 + \beta_7x_7$ **12.151 c.** yes, $F = 30.45$
12.153 a. $E(y) = \beta_0 + \beta_1x$, where $x = 1$ {if enriched pond, 0 if natural pond} **b.** $\beta_0 =$ mean larval density of natural pond = $\mu_{natural}$; $\beta_1 = \mu_{enriched} - \mu_{natural}$ **c.** H_o: $\beta_1 = 0$, H_a: $\beta_1 > 0$ **d.** reject H_o **12.155 b.** yes, reject H_o: $\beta_4 = 0$ in favor of H_a: $\beta_4 > 0$ **12.157 a.** $E(y) = \beta_0 + \beta_1x_1 + \beta_2x_2 + \beta_3x_3$ **c.** yes, $F = 56$ **d.** do not reject H_o **12.159 a.** negative **b.** no, $F = 1.60$ **c.** no, $F = 1.61$ **12.161 b.** $\hat{y} = 42.2 - .0114x + .00000061x^2$ **c.** no, $t = 1.66$ **12.163 a.** $E(y) = \beta_0 + \beta_1x_1 + \beta_2x_6 + \beta_3x_7$, where $x_6 = \{1$ if good, 0 if not$\}$, $x_7 = \{1$ if fair, 0 if not$\}$ **c.** excellent: $\hat{y} = 188,875 + 15,617x_1$; good: $\hat{y} = 85,829 + 15,617x_1$; fair: $\hat{y} = 36,388 + 15,617x_1$ **e.** yes, $F = 5.82$ **f.** x_1, x_3 and x_5 are highly correlated **g.** assumptions are satisfied
12.165 a. $E(y) = \beta_0 + \beta_1x_1 + \beta_2x_2 + \beta_3x_3 + \beta_4x_4 + \beta_5x_5 + \beta_6x_6 + \beta_7x_7$ **b.** $\hat{y} = .998 - .022x_1 + .156x_2 - .017x_3 - .0095x_4 + .421x_5 + .417x_6 - .155x_7$ **d.** (−1.233, 1.038) **12.167 a.** $E(y) = \beta_0 + \beta_1x + \beta_2x^2$ **b.** $\hat{y} = .334 - .810x + .941x^2$
c. $F = 62.17$, reject H_o **d.** $t = 8.36$, reject H_o: $\beta_2 = 0$ in favor of H_a: $\beta_2 > 0$ **e.** $R_{adj}^2 = 196$, s = .088 **f.** yes **12.169** model includes $x_1 =$ DOT estimate, either $x_2 =$ low bid ratio or $x_3 = \{1$ if fixed,,0 if competitive$\}$, and $x_5 =$ estimated days to complete

Chapter 13
13.3 a. 18.3070 **b.** 29.7067 **c.** 23.5418 **d.** 79.4900 **13.5 a.** $\chi^2 > 5.99147$ **b.** $\chi^2 > 7.77944$ **c.** $\chi^2 > 11.3449$ **13.7 a.** no, $\chi^2 > 3.293$ **13.9 a.** jaw habits; bruxism, clenching, bruxism and clenching, neither **c.** H_o: $p_1 = p_2 = p_3 = p_4 = .25$, H_a: At least one p_i differs from .25 **d.** 15 **e.** $\chi^2 = 25.73$ **f.** $\chi^2 > 7.81473$ **g.** reject H_o **h.** (.37, .63) **13.11 a.** Pottery type; burnished, monochrome, painted, other **b.** $p_1 = p_2 = p_3 = p_4 = .25$ **c.** H_o: $p_1 = p_2 = p_3 = p_4 = .25$ **d.** $\chi^2 = 436.59$
e. p-value ≈ 0, reject H_o **13.13 a.** no, $\chi^2 = 7.39$ **b.** (.456, .518)
13.15 a.

1	2	3	4
450	627	219	23

b. H_o: $p_1 = p_2 = p_3 = p_4 = .25$ **c.** 329.75 for each category **d.** 634.36 **e.** reject H_o **f.** $\chi^2 = 39.29$, reject H_o **13.17 a.** yes, $\chi^2 = 360.48$ **b.** (.165, .223) **13.23 a.** H_o: Row & Column are independent, H_a: Row & Column are dependent **b.** $\chi^2 > 9.201034$
c.

	Column 1	Column 2	Column 3
Row 1	14.37	36.79	44.84
Row 2	10.63	27.21	33.16

d. $\chi^2 = 8.71$, fail to reject H_o **13.25** $\chi^2 = 12.33$, reject H_o **13.27 a.** .078 **b.** .157 **c.** possibly **d.** H_o: Presence of Dog & Gender are independent **e.** $\chi^2 = 2.25$, fail to reject H_o **f.** $\chi^2 = .064$, fail to reject H_o **13.29 a.** masculinity risk (high and low); event (violent and avoided-violent) **b.** 1,507 newly incarcerated men **c.** 260.8 **d.** 118.2, 776.2, 351.8 **e.** $\chi^2 = 10.1$ **f.** reject H_o
13.31 $\chi^2 = 23.46$, reject H_o **13.33** $\chi^2 = 35.41$, reject H_o **13.35** yes, $\chi^2 = 7.38$, p-value = .025; no
13.37 a. no **b.**

	CAHS		
SHSS:C	Low	Medium	High
Low	32	14	2
Medium	11	14	6
High	6	16	29

c. yes **d.** $\chi^2 = 46.70$, reject H_0 **13.39 a.** $\chi^2 = 4.407$, reject H_0 **b.** no **c.** .0438 **d.** .0057; .0003 **e.** p-value $= .0498$, reject H_0
13.41 false **13.43 a.** yes, $\chi^2 = 54.14$ **b.** no **c.** yes
d.

	Col. 1	Col. 2	Col. 3	Totals
Row 1	.400	.222	.091	.200
Row 2	.200	.222	.636	.400
Row 3	.400	.556	.273	.400

13.45 $\chi^2 = 16$, reject H_0
13.47 a.

	LLD		
Genetic Trait	Yes	No	Total
Yes	21	15	36
No	150	306	456
Total	171	321	492

b. $\chi^2 = 9.52$, reject H_0 **13.49 a.** possibly not **c.** $\chi^2 = 12.9$ **d.** yes, reject H_0 **e.** $.233 \pm .200$ **13.51 a.** $\chi^2 = 1.14$, do not reject H_0
b. $.179 \pm .119$ **13.53** Internet: $\chi^2 = .512$, do not reject H_0; party: $\chi^2 = 164.76$, reject H_0; military: $\chi^2 = 8.3$, reject H_0; views:
$\chi^2 = 174.39$, reject H_0; race: $\chi^2 = 69.18$, reject H_0; income: $\chi^2 = 16.39$, reject H_0; community: $\chi^2 = 17.31$, reject H_0
13.55 a. $\chi^2 = 17.16$, reject H_0 **b.** $.376 \pm .103$ **c.** yes **13.57** $\chi^2 = 6.17$, reject H_0 **13.59 a.** no, $\chi^2 = 13.72$ **b.** wife: no, $\chi^2 = 3.20$;
husband: no, $\chi^2 = 6.07$ **13.61 a.** $\chi^2 = 164.90$, reject H_0 **b.** Gender: $\chi^2 = 6.80$, reject H_0; Education: $\chi^2 = 6.59$, fail to reject H_0;
Work: $\chi^2 = 11.69$, fail to reject H_0; Satisfaction: $\chi^2 = 30.42$, reject H_0 **13.63 a.** $\chi^2 = 9.65$ **b.** 11.0705 **c.** no **d.** $.05 < p$-value
$< .10$ **13.65** $\chi^2 = 2.28$; insufficient evidence to reject the null hypothesis of independence

Chapter 14

14.1 population not normal **14.3 a.** .063 **b.** .500 **c.** .004 **d.** .151; .1515 **e.** .212; .2119 **14.5** $S = 16$, p-value $= .115$, do not reject
H_0 **14.7** $S = 8$, p-value $= .0391$, reject H_0 **14.9 a.** $H_0: \eta = 1.5$, $H_a: \eta > 1.5$ **b.** 3 **c.** .773 **d.** do not reject H_0
14.11 a. $H_0: \eta = 5$ **b.** $z = 6.07$, p-value $= 0$ **c.** reject H_0 **14.13** no; $S = 10$, p-value $= .3145$ **14.15** $S = 8$, p-value $= .8204$,
do not reject H_0 **14.17** true **14.19 a.** $T_1 \le 41$, $T_1 \ge 71$ **b.** $T_1 \ge 50$ **c.** $T_1 \le 43$ **d.** $|z| > 1.96$ **14.21** yes, $z = -2.47$
14.23 a. $T_1 = 62.5$ reject H_0 **b.** yes, $T_1 = 62.5$ **14.25 a.** $H_0: D_{\text{bulimic}} = D_{\text{normal}}$, $H_a: D_{\text{bulimic}} > D_{\text{normal}}$ **c.** 174.5 **d.** 150.5
e. $z > 1.28$ **f.** $z = 1.72$, reject H_0 **14.27 a.** $T_1 = 150.5$, reject H_0 **b.** $z = 3.44$, reject H_0 **14.29 a.** rank sum test **b.** $H_0: D_{\text{CMC}} = D_{\text{FTF}}$, $H_a: D_{\text{CMC}} < D_{\text{FTF}}$ **c.** $z < -1.28$ **d.** $z = -.23$, fail to reject H_0 **14.31 a.** zinc measurements non-normal **b.** $T_1 = 18$,
do not reject H_0 **c.** $T_2 = 32$, do not reject H_0 **14.33 a.** data not normal **b.** $z = -6.47$, reject H_0 **c.** $z = -.39$, do not reject H_0
d. $z = -1.35$, do not reject H_0 **14.37 a.** $H_a: D_A > D_B$ **b.** $T_- = 3.5$, reject H_0 **14.39 a.** $H_a: D_A > D_B$ **b.** $z = 2.499$, reject H_0
c. .0062 **14.41 a.** before and after measurements not independent **b.** scores not normal **c.** reject H_0, ichthyotherapy is effective
14.43 a. $H_0: D_{\text{good}} = D_{\text{average}}$, $H_a: D_{\text{good}} \ne D_{\text{average}}$ **d.** $T = 3$ **e.** $T \le 4$ **f.** reject H_0 **14.45** no, $T = 7$ **14.47** yes, $T_- = 50.5$
14.49 a. no, $T_- = 0$ **b.** reject H_0; supports the "hot hand" theory **14.51** samples size for each distribution is more than 5
14.53 a. completely randomized design **b.** H_0: Three probability distributions are identical **c.** $H > 9.21034$ **d.** $H = 14.53$,
reject H_0 **14.55 b.** 84 **c.** 145 **d.** 177 **e.** $H = 18.4$ **f.** reject H_0 **g.** $z = -3.36$, reject H_0 **14.57 b.** reject H_0
14.59 $H = 19.03$, reject H_0 **14.61 a.** normality assumption violated **b.** $H = 13.66$, reject H_0 **14.63** ranking b **14.65 a.** 6
b. H_0: The probability distributions for the four treatments are identical **c.** $F_r = 15.2$, reject H_0 **d.** p-value $< .005$
14.67 $F_r = 13$, reject H_0 **14.69 c.** $S = 93$, p-value $= .819$, **d.** do not reject H_0 **14.71 a.** $F_r > 9.21034$ **b.** reject H_0
c. do not reject H_0 **d.** reject H_0 **14.73** $F_r = 11.10$, reject H_0 at $= .05$ **14.75** $F_r = 6.78$, fail to reject H_0 **14.79 a.** $|r_s| > .648$
b. $r_s > .450$ **c.** $r_s < -.432$ **14.81 b.** $r_s = .745$, do not reject H_0 **c.** $.05 < p$-value $< .10$ **14.83 b.** $r_s = .943$ **c.** reject H_0
14.85 c. .713 **d.** $|r_s| > .425$ **e.** reject H_0 **14.87 a.** moderate positive association between the two scores **c.** reject H_0
14.89 a. $-.877$ **b.** $-.907$ **c.** reject H_0 **d.** reject H_0 **14.91 a.** .714 **b.** reject H_0 **14.95 a.** rank sum test **b.** sign test
c. Kruskal-Wallis test **d.** Spearman's test **e.** signed rank test **f.** Friedman's test **14.97 a.** no, $r_s = .40$ **b.** yes, $T_- = 1.5$
14.99 yes, $F_r = 14.9$ **14.101** no, $T_2 = 29$ **14.103** no; $F_r = 2.09$, do not reject H_0 **14.105 a.** $-.733$ **b.** do not reject H_0
14.107 a. no, $S = 14$, p-value $= .058$ **b.** no, $S = 12$, p-value $= .180$ **c.** $T = 50$, do not reject H_0 **d.** $r_s = .774$, reject H_0
14.109 a. yes, $T_2 = 105$ **b.** less than **14.111** yes, $F_r = 6.35$ **14.113** yes, $H = 7.154$ **14.115 c.** Arm: no, $r_s = -.439$; Leg/Arm:
no, $r_s = -.655$; Leg: no, $r_s = -.512$ **14.117** yes, $H = 15.33$ **14.119** $F_r = 7.85$, reject H_0

Index

Photo Credits

SINGLE PC LICENSE AGREEMENT AND LIMITED WARRANTY

READ THIS LICENSE CAREFULLY BEFORE OPENING THIS PACKAGE. BY OPENING THIS PACKAGE, YOU ARE AGREEING TO THE TERMS AND CONDITIONS OF THIS LICENSE. IF YOU DO NOT AGREE, DO NOT OPEN THE PACKAGE. PROMPTLY RETURN THE UNOPENED PACKAGE AND ALL ACCOMPANYING ITEMS TO THE PLACE YOU OBTAINED THEM [[FOR A FULL REFUND OF ANY SUMS YOU HAVE PAID FOR THE SOFTWARE]]. *THESE TERMS APPLY TO ALL LICENSED SOFTWARE ON THE DISK EXCEPT THAT THE TERMS FOR USE OF ANY SHAREWARE OR FREEWARE ON THE DISKETTES ARE AS SET FORTH IN THE ELECTRONIC LICENSE LOCATED ON THE DISK:*

1. GRANT OF LICENSE and OWNERSHIP: The enclosed computer programs and data ("Software") are licensed, not sold, to you by Pearson Education, Inc. publishing as Prentice-Hall, Inc. ("We" or the "Company") in consideration of your purchase or adoption of the accompanying Company textbooks and/or other materials, and your agreement to these terms. We reserve any rights not granted to you. You own only the disk(s) but we and/or our licensors own the Software itself. This license allows individuals who have purchased the accompanying Company textbook to use and display their copy of the Software on a single computer (i.e., with a single CPU) at a single location for <u>academic</u> use only, so long as you comply with the terms of this Agreement. You may make one copy for back up, or transfer your copy to another CPU, provided that the Software is usable on only one computer.

2. RESTRICTIONS: You may <u>not</u> transfer or distribute the Software or documentation to anyone else. Except for backup, you may not copy the documentation or the Software. You may <u>not</u> network the Software or otherwise use it on more than one computer or computer terminal at the same time. You may <u>not</u> reverse engineer, disassemble, decompile, modify, adapt, translate, or create derivative works based on the Software or the Documentation. You may be held legally responsible for any copying or copyright infringement that is caused by your failure to abide by the terms of these restrictions.

3. TERMINATION: This license is effective until terminated. This license will terminate automatically without notice from the Company if you fail to comply with any provisions or limitations of this license. Upon termination, you shall destroy the Documentation and all copies of the Software. All provisions of this Agreement as to limitation and disclaimer of warranties, limitation of liability, remedies or damages, and our ownership rights shall survive termination.

4. LIMITED WARRANTY AND DISCLAIMER OF WARRANTY: Company warrants that for a period of 60 days from the date you purchase this SOFTWARE (or purchase or adopt the accompanying textbook), the Software, when properly installed and used in accordance with the Documentation, will operate in substantial conformity with the description of the Software set forth in the Documentation, and that for a period of 30 days the disk(s) on which the Software is delivered shall be free from defects in materials and workmanship under normal use. The Company does <u>not</u> warrant that the Software will meet your requirements or that the operation of the Software will be uninterrupted or error-free. Your only remedy and the Company's only obligation under these limited warranties is, at the Company's option, return of the disk for a refund of any amounts paid for it by you or replacement of the disk. THIS LIMITED WARRANTY IS THE ONLY WARRANTY PROVIDED BY THE COMPANY AND ITS LICENSORS, AND THE COMPANY AND ITS LICENSORS DISCLAIM ALL OTHER WARRANTIES, EXPRESS OR IMPLIED, INCLUDING WITHOUT LIMITATION, THE IMPLIED WARRANTIES OF MERCHANTABILITY AND FITNESS FOR A PARTICULAR PURPOSE. THE COMPANY DOES NOT WARRANT, GUARANTEE OR MAKE ANY REPRESENTATION REGARDING THE ACCURACY, RELIABILITY, CURRENTNESS, USE, OR RESULTS OF USE, OF THE SOFTWARE.

5. LIMITATION OF REMEDIES AND DAMAGES: IN NO EVENT, SHALL THE COMPANY OR ITS EMPLOYEES, AGENTS, LICENSORS, OR CONTRACTORS BE LIABLE FOR ANY INCIDENTAL, INDIRECT, SPECIAL, OR CONSEQUENTIAL DAMAGES ARISING OUT OF OR IN CONNECTION WITH THIS LICENSE OR THE SOFTWARE, INCLUDING FOR LOSS OF USE, LOSS OF DATA, LOSS OF INCOME OR PROFIT, OR OTHER LOSSES, SUSTAINED AS A RESULT OF INJURY TO ANY PERSON, OR LOSS OF OR DAMAGE TO PROPERTY, OR CLAIMS OF THIRD PARTIES, EVEN IF THE COMPANY OR AN AUTHORIZED REPRESENTATIVE OF THE COMPANY HAS BEEN ADVISED OF THE POSSIBILITY OF SUCH DAMAGES. IN NO EVENT SHALL THE LIABILITY OF THE COMPANY FOR DAMAGES WITH RESPECT TO THE SOFTWARE EXCEED THE AMOUNTS ACTUALLY PAID BY YOU, IF ANY, FOR THE SOFTWARE OR THE ACCOMPANYING TEXTBOOK. BECAUSE SOME JURISDICTIONS DO NOT ALLOW THE LIMITATION OF LIABILITY IN CERTAIN CIRCUMSTANCES, THE ABOVE LIMITATIONS MAY NOT ALWAYS APPLY TO YOU.

6. GENERAL: THIS AGREEMENT SHALL BE CONSTRUED IN ACCORDANCE WITH THE LAWS OF THE UNITED STATES OF AMERICA AND THE STATE OF NEW YORK, APPLICABLE TO CONTRACTS MADE IN NEW YORK, AND SHALL BENEFIT THE COMPANY, ITS AFFILIATES AND ASSIGNEES. HIS AGREEMENT IS THE COMPLETE AND EXCLUSIVE STATEMENT OF THE AGREEMENT BETWEEN YOU AND THE COMPANY AND SUPERSEDES ALL PROPOSALS OR PRIOR AGREEMENTS, ORAL, OR WRITTEN, AND ANY OTHER COMMUNICATIONS BETWEEN YOU AND THE COMPANY OR ANY REPRESENTATIVE OF THE COMPANY RELATING TO THE SUBJECT MATTER OF THIS AGREEMENT. If you are a U.S. Government user, this Software is licensed with "restricted rights" as set forth in subparagraphs (a)-(d) of the Commercial Computer-Restricted Rights clause at FAR 52.227-19 or in subparagraphs (c)(1)(ii) of the Rights in Technical Data and Computer Software clause at DFARS 252.227-7013, and similar clauses, as applicable.

Should you have any questions concerning this agreement or if you wish to contact the Company for any reason, please contact in writing:

Director, Media Production
Pearson Education
1 Lake Street
Upper Saddle River, NJ 07458

CHAPTER 11 (cont'd)

$$s^2 = \frac{SSE}{n - 2}$$

$$s = \sqrt{s^2}$$

$$r^2 = \frac{SS_{yy} - SSE}{SS_{yy}}$$

CI for β_1: $\hat{\beta}_1 \pm (t_{\alpha/2})s/\sqrt{SS_{xx}}$

Test for β_1: $t = \dfrac{\hat{\beta}_1 - 0}{s/\sqrt{SS_{xx}}}$

CI for $E(y)$ when $x = x_{\hat{p}}$: $\hat{y} \pm t_{\alpha/2}s\sqrt{\dfrac{1}{n} + \dfrac{(x_p - \bar{x})^2}{SS_{xx}}}$

CI for y when $x = x_{\hat{p}}$: $\hat{y} \pm t_{\alpha/2}s\sqrt{1 + \dfrac{1}{n} + \dfrac{(x_p - \bar{x})^2}{SS_{xx}}}$

CHAPTER 12

First-Order Model (QN x's):
$$E(y) = \beta_0 + \beta_1 x_1 + \beta_2 x_2 + \cdots + \beta_k x_k$$

Interaction Model (QN x's):
$$E(y) = \beta_0 + \beta_1 x_1 + \beta_2 x_2 + \beta_3 x_1 x_2$$

Quadratic Model (QN x):
$$E(y) = \beta_0 + \beta_1 x + \beta_2 x^2$$

Complete 2nd-Order Model (QN x's):
$$E(y) = \beta_0 + \beta_1 x_1 + \beta_2 x_2 + \beta_3 x_1 x_2 + \beta_4 x_1^2 + \beta_5 x_2^2$$

Dummy Variable Model (QL x):
$$E(y) = \beta_0 + \beta_1 x_1 + \beta_2 x_2$$
where $x_1 = \{1 \text{ if A}, 0 \text{ if not}\}$, $x_2 = \{1 \text{ if B}, 0 \text{ if not}\}$

$$MSE = s^2 = \frac{SSE}{n - (k + 1)}$$

$$R^2 = \frac{SS_{yy} - SSE}{SS_{yy}}$$

$$R_a^2 = 1 - \left[\frac{(n - 1)}{n - (k + 1)}\right](1 - R^2)$$

Test for overall model: $F = \dfrac{MS(\text{Model})}{MSE}$

Test for individual β: $t = \dfrac{\hat{\beta}_i - 0}{s_{\hat{\beta}_i}}$

CI for β_i: $\hat{\beta}_i \pm (t_{\alpha/2})s_{\hat{\beta}_i}$

Nested model F test: $F = \dfrac{(SSE_R - SSE_C)/\# \beta\text{'s tested}}{MSE_C}$

CHAPTER 13

Multinomial test: $\chi^2 = \sum \dfrac{(n_i - E_i)^2}{E_i}$

$$E_i = n(p_{i0})$$

Contingency table test: $\chi^2 = \sum \dfrac{(n_{ij} - E_{ij})^2}{E_{ij}}$

$$E_{ij} = \frac{R_i C_j}{n}$$